LIFE: AN INTRODUCTION TO BIOLOGY

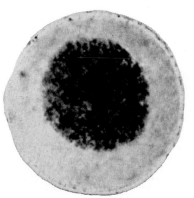
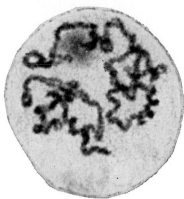
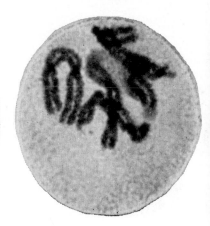

GEORGE GAYLORD SIMPSON

American Museum of Natural History
Columbia University

COLIN S. PITTENDRIGH

Princeton University

LEWIS H. TIFFANY

Northwestern University

Drawings by CARU Studios

Harcourt, Brace and Company   *New York*   *Burlingame*

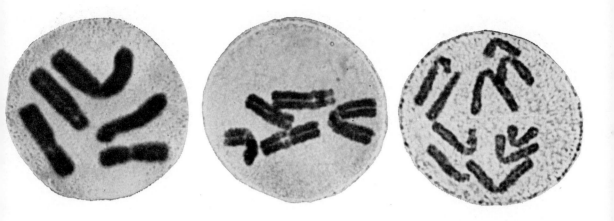

Life

An Introduction to Biology

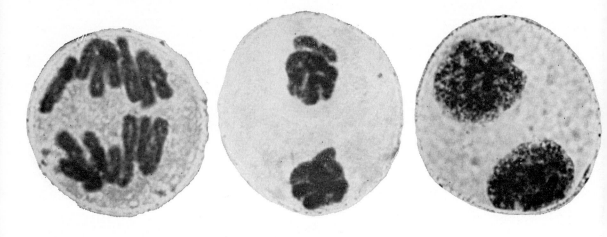

*Photographs of mitosis, above and on pages ii and iii, from
Dr. A. H. Sparrow, Brookhaven National Laboratory.*

PREFACE

This book is based on strong convictions. We believe that there is a unified science of life, a general biology that is distinct from a shotgun marriage of botany and zoology, or any others of the special life sciences. We believe that this science has a body of established and working principles. We believe that literally nothing on earth is more important to a rational living being than basic acquaintance with those principles.

This, then, is a "principles approach" to general biology. We have tried to give more than lip service to that aim, to keep principles always foremost in mind and to organize the whole text around them. We have tried to avoid the common error of presenting merely summary or introductory descriptions as principles. We recognize, however, that principles are meaningless unless they arise from concrete data and can be applied to particular problems. We have tried to underpin the principles with supporting facts and to show how the principles do arise from these facts.

We have discussed how scientists approach problems, which of course is all that is meant by the catchword "scientific method." Where appropriate and convenient we have introduced in sufficient detail a number of particular examples of important biological problems and their solutions, partial or complete. This has usually been done by an historical approach here and there in the text, additional and complementary to the more general historical summary in the last chapter.

We hope to discourage the idea that merely learning a specialized vocabulary is educational in a broader sense or has any useful relationship to wisdom. We have not hesitated to use carefully defined technical terms when these really contribute to the easier communication and comprehension of principles, but the technical vocabulary of the text is kept to a minimum. For selected examples we have introduced additional terminology in figures and their legends, where the user of the book may take it or leave it. These labeled drawings may also serve as a bridge between the text and the study of organisms in the laboratory, which is the place to learn such details of anatomy as may be useful or interesting to any particular reader.

General biology as here conceived is an exciting subject. It is another of our convictions that writing about it should not be flat, awkward, or didactic. We have not fully reached but we have striven toward the ideal that an introduction to biology should be interesting and should have literary quality.

The study of life is indeed a lively science. Along with a body of well-established knowledge, it includes uncertainties, speculations to be tested, places where knowledge now ends and where the seeking of new knowledge should therefore begin. We have not concealed these dynamic aspects of the search. On the contrary, in appropriate places we have stressed them.

Like other human activities, biological teaching and research have fads that change from place to place and from time to time. We have tried to avoid them and to give as well-rounded a treatment as we could manage. We have, for instance, treated systematics and biogeography on the same level and to the same depth as, say, biochemistry or genetics. One of the fads we have avoided is centering the treatment on man, writing a human biology or using man as a "typical animal" (a horrid expression). We thoroughly agree that the best reason for studying biology is the most human reason: Know thyself! But too narrow a striving toward that objective is self-defeating, because a true understanding of man can come only from placing him in perspective in the whole realm of life. Man is used as an example when he is a good example, and the human implications of, for instance, population growth or the evolution of behavior are specified. The subject, however, is always considered broader than our own species.

The most general principle of all in biology is evolution. Most treatments of the subject make such a statement, but many fail in conviction that it is really true. Some relegate evolution to a single chapter and treat all the rest of biology as if it really had nothing to do with evolution. Others, attempting to correct that fault, adopt what they call an "evolutionary approach" and equate biology with the description of organisms in a "phylogenetic sequence." The sequence is never in fact phylogenetic, and this approach rarely teaches much about the real principles of evolution. In this book we have tried to make evolution as pervasive as it really is in the world of life. Every topic has its evolutionary background and aspects.

Only those who have also tried to encompass our tremendous subject in one book know how difficult is the problem of organizing the material and how impossible is the achievement of a completely consistent and logical sequence. In general we have advanced by levels of inclusiveness: first the cell as the true unit in our subject (no lower level, such as the molecule, being in fact alive); then the organism in itself; then like organisms in their reproductive capacity; the further reproductive processes and interactions that lead to evolutionary changes; the diversity wrought by those changes; the aggregations of the diverse organisms into populations and communities; the spread of such aggregations in the dimensions of space; and finally the history that embraces all previous levels and dimensions plus that of time.

This book is written neither for the nonprofessional student of biology nor for the student who is beginning a professional career, but for both at once. It is still another of our convictions that grounding in the *principles* of *general* biology is equally useful to all. It is the most nearly indispensable (and the most interesting) view of the subject for the nonbiological student or the general public. It is at the same time the best basis from which to go on to specialization in botany, zoology, biochemistry, or any other of the life sciences.

In writing this book we have a full-year course in mind and have often given the student's interest and preparation the benefit of our doubt when deciding what to include. We have, however, attempted to organize the book's contents to serve the needs of shorter programs and of classes varying in their level of preparation. The individual teacher will easily detect those chapters or parts of chapters that are dispensable in his own program.

We have received much help during the long years of preparing this book. Some aid cannot well be specifically acknowledged, but we can acknowledge with gratitude that the whole manuscript has been read and criticized in detail by W. H. Camp, A. D. Chiquoine, Waldo H. Furgason, Albert S. Gordon, Ella Thea Smith, and Kenneth V. Thimann. Anne Roe has also read most of the manuscript and has more particularly helped with the psychological aspects of Chapter 10. Other friends read and criticized various chapters as follows: Chapter 5, Frank H. Johnson; Chapter 13, A. D. Hershey and A. E. Mirsky; Chapters 11 through 13, D. L. Lindsley; Chapter 14, J. T. Bonner.

We have thus had expert advice in the areas where we are least expert and also over the considerable range in which one or another of the three authors is reasonably competent. It is our own fault if we have erred by occasionally not following advice. A considerable part of the final draft was also given a trial run with a beginning college class to assure ourselves that it was teachable and to note ways to improve it.

It is a special pleasure to acknowledge our debt of thanks to Charles Halgren and his associates at the CARU Studios for their patience and skill in the execution of the figures. In illustrating our book we have, of course, drawn freely on earlier works. In all but a few instances, however, Mr. Halgren has redrawn the figure for our particular purpose. And he has done his work with a uniformity and clarity of style that we have greatly valued.

GEORGE GAYLORD SIMPSON
COLIN S. PITTENDRIGH
LEWIS H. TIFFANY

CONTENTS

PART 1

Introduction

INTRODUCTION TO PART 1

Our part opening is a spider's web, covered with dew and glistening in the morning light. It symbolizes many of those general features of life which form the subject matter of Part 1. The web, to be sure, is not alive, but it well reflects the complexity and organization of the animal that made it. A survey of the life in a forest and on a coral reef (Chapter 1) shows that such complexity and organization are characteristic of all living things. They are appropriately called *organisms*.

The spider's web is strong, sticky, and nearly invisible when the morning dew has evaporated. These features efficiently serve the end of feeding the spider. Like the behavior of spinning the web they are *adaptations* of the spider, part of its organization for the task of living. A sojourn in a forest and on a coral reef shows that the organization of all living things has this same adaptive characteristic, directed to the ends of food capture, survival, and reproduction.

The web and its function for the spider also signify that interdependence which typifies all living organisms. For the spider is utterly dependent on the flies and other insects it traps as food in its web. The fly in its turn had earlier been dependent on plants for food; and the plants themselves, although drawing energy directly from the sun, had been dependent on bacteria and earthworms for the maintenance of an adequate soil in which to grow. And so the web—now in a wholly metaphorical sense—symbolizes the interwoven and complex relationships that bind a great diversity of living organisms into one coherent *community*, whose central theme is the capture of food as fuel for the activities of life.

Chapter 2 sets the stage for a scientific study of life. It does so by tracing the broad nature of all science as a twofold search: a search for facts about the world, and a search for testable explanations of the facts. The chapter briefly sketches the birth and growth of modern science because an understanding of this serves to explain the rise and progress of biology, the science of life. It also reveals the central importance of Charles Darwin's book, *The Origin of Species* (1859). Darwin's theories of evolution and natural selection are given an introductory treatment at the outset of our book for two reasons: (1) their discovery first brought order into biology and unified the science of life with the physical sciences; and (2) they form the great unifying principles that run throughout the rest of this text.

Rabbits, a rich and perennial crop,
fall prey not only to hawks but also to coyotes,
weasels, and other hungry carnivores.
(Photo from U.S. Fish and Wildlife Service)

CHAPTER 1

The Living World

"KNOW THYSELF"

You are alive. That is the most important fact in the world. All around you are other living things. That fact is also important. It is, indeed, an aspect of the same fact. You would not yourself be alive if you were not part of the whole complex world of life. This is true not only in the sense that you depend on other forms of life for food, but also in other and larger senses. You live in a community, a community of other humans and also of many other living things in greater diversity and of greater impact on your own life than you may have realized as yet. You share with them many processes of living. The study of these processes in other animals and in plants is necessary for an understanding of your own life. Moreover, you are literally related to all the other living things, just as truly as you are related to your sisters and your cousins and

your aunts. You share a common ancestry with every other animal and every plant; you are a product of the same long, intricate history.

The real reason for studying biology is the old admonition: "Know thyself." The better you know yourself, the happier, healthier, more comprehending, and richer will be your life. You cannot, however, really know yourself if that is *all* you know. True understanding can come only from knowledge of life in general. The meaning of biology is its human meaning, its significance to you as a person, but that meaning can only be made clear if human biology is seen as a part of the biology of all life.

A Forest

ABUNDANCE AND DIVERSITY

Wherever you go with open eyes and mind, you will be impressed with the diversity, the abundance, and the interdependence of living things. Walk through a mountain forest, perhaps one of the beautiful forests (Fig. 1-1) of ponderosa pines in our Southwest. The stately old trees are 150 feet or more in height and 300 to 400 years old. One old-timer is known to have lived 660 years, but these pines are usually fully grown after about three centuries. They stand well apart, their long boughs not touching, as if they were intolerant of each other's shadows, as indeed they are.

1-1 A PONDEROSA PINE FOREST

The ponderosas stand well apart as if intolerant of each other's shadows. The stately trees are 150 feet or more in height and 300 to 400 years old.

Wild turkeys flock in the oak and piñon pines to gorge themselves on acorns and pine nuts.

Deer wander daintily, cropping leaves from the succulent vegetation.

Lower right, along the stream bank are different kinds of trees.

Below, insects are everywhere and make up in numbers what they lack in bulk. Here one beetle larva preys upon another.

All photos courtesy U.S. Forest Service except wild turkeys by Lanks from Monkmeyer

The seedlings share this intolerance. They do not spring up in the shade of their parents, but only in more open glades or where one of the old trees has died and fallen. The ponderosa pines require full sunlight. They have, like all plants, special needs as to soil, slope, drainage, temperature range, rainfall, and other conditions. We say they have their "preferences," although we should be cautious in applying such a word to organisms that make no conscious choices, growing unconsciously when seeds fall where their needs are met.

Along the bank of a stream running through the forest are different kinds of trees requiring moister soil than the ponderosas: alders, willows, and narrow-leaf cottonwoods. On exposed, rocky slopes are still others differing again in their needs: piñon pines, tree junipers locally called "cedars," and oak scrub (weeds to the mountain ranchers; what they call them will not be repeated here). The light that filters through the trees does not go unused. The forest floor is carpeted with herbaceous plants that make it green and flowery in summer. There are plants everywhere, from the cactus on an open, sandy southern slope to the iris on the marshy bank of a pool; each occurs in only a particular kind of place, a location that fulfills its particular needs.

On a calm summer day the trees and other plants are motionless as a still hush settles over the forest. The plants look as if they are in a state of suspended animation. The ceaseless activity we all associate with life seems gone, but this, in truth, is a mere illusion. Within the plants tremendous activity is afoot: water and chemicals are being drawn silently but steadily from the soil by the roots of the plants, and their leaves are drawing in all-important gases from the atmosphere. At the same time the leaves are capturing the energy in sunlight, energy generated by fierce atomic-nuclear reactions in the sun 93 million miles away. With this energy the plants compound special foods out of the raw materials they have silently taken from soil and air. This food manufacture, we shall shortly see, is the focal point of the whole forest's life.

Everywhere there are animals whose most obvious activity is the consumption of plants— and thereby of the foods the plants have compounded. Squirrels (handsome creatures with tufts on their ears) scamper up the ponderosa pines in search of cones, which they tear apart for the nutritious seeds. Deer wander daintily along, cropping leaves from the lower, more succulent vegetation. Wild turkeys flock in the oaks and piñon pines to gorge themselves on acorns and pine nuts. Pocket gophers burrow in the soil, eating bulbs and roots for their every meal.

But this pastoral stillness is only one mood of the forest. Overhead a hawk hovers and then swoops to earth with outstretched talons; the screech of death from the captured rabbit jars against the stillness. The deer are killed and eaten by mountain lions—or by men. Wildcats—or men, again—stalk the turkeys. Rabbits, a rich and perennial crop, fall prey not only to hawks but also to coyotes, weasels, and other hungry carnivores. The mood of the forest is different now, but the business is the same—the capture of energy and materials.

So far we have noticed only the largest living things. Insects all around us, minute compared with the mountain lion or the deer, make up in numbers what they lack in bulk. Some insects are all too obvious—a pest to the casual stroller—but a real search for them would reveal literally hundreds of other kinds, enough to occupy a whole congress of experts in their identification. Some insects, in the fashion of the squirrel and the gopher, busy themselves consuming plants directly, either sucking juices (bugs), chewing leaves (caterpillars), collecting pollen and honey (bees), or burrowing in the bark of trees (beetles). Others, like the wasp, have the more deadly aspect of the hawk and hover poised above another insect, ready to pounce and kill for the purpose of eating. A spider spins a web across the foliage of a bush and waits with patience for the unseeing fly to become trapped in its sticky meshwork.

Smaller still than even the smallest fly are the living things that fill every nook and cranny in the forest. A handful of soil may seem lifeless unless it happens to include a worm or some burrowing insect, but if it is taken into the laboratory and studied under a microscope it is sure to reveal an abundance of living things far below the limits of unaided vision. Here, for example, are mites and tiny worms. Cultures of soil in a test tube will bring to visibility growing colonies of microbes—bacteria and molds—and from these the lucky investigator may isolate a new antibiotic "miracle drug," as indeed some scientists already have! Even the clear mountain air we breathe in the forest is itself full of living things like mold spores, bacteria, and the pollen from nearby plants.

Each of the myriad forms of life that pack the forest has its own peculiarities. Each is different in size, shape, color, and other visible characteristics; and, more important, each has its own particular habitat in which it thrives. This pageant of detail is interesting and even quite entertaining, but in itself is inadequate to hold our attention for long.

When we stand and look at the forest, the endless array of detail falls into the perspective of a well-integrated drama being enacted before our eyes. This analogy of the forest life with the drama is both picturesque and useful. There are central themes in this drama that keep recurring everywhere, spelling out meaning in every detail. The characters—diverse in structure and personality—all play distinct and essential roles in a highly integrated scheme. Let us look at the most obvious of these major themes: *the traffic in energy.*

THE TRAFFIC IN ENERGY

Organization and the need for energy. The life of the forest revolves around individual living things—trees, rabbits, insects, and the rest. Individual living things have two major features which are related to each other and which give meaning to much of the forest community as a whole: (1) their complex organization and activity; and (2) their demand for an energy supply. The most complex and highly organized things in the world are living things, so much so, in fact, that the word *organism* has become synonymous with living thing. There is nothing helter-skelter or random, for instance, about the structure of a hawk. Its bones have a special construction combining strength with lightness: the lighter the animal, the easier it can fly. Every muscle in the hawk's body has a definite position in relation to the bones that must be

moved. Its eyesight is among the best in the animal world, capable of spotting from great heights that slightest stir on the ground that signifies rabbit = food. Its feet and its bill are constructed in such a way that the deadly task of seizing and killing is possible. The hawk in fact is like everything else alive, an *organized* system capable of autonomous movement; and as such it cannot exist and endure without a steady intake of energy. This need for energy is obvious enough insofar as the hawk does work we all recognize as such; flying, screeching, and seizing are all work. Like the work performed by man-made engines, it consists of an expenditure of energy, the consumption of some fuel. Energy is also required, however, in the life of the hawk for a less obvious but no less essential reason. All systems in the world, if unattended, tend steadily towards a state of disorder and disorganization, a fact that is distressingly familiar to the owner of a house, a filing system, or a factory. Unless work—the expenditure of energy—is put into them for maintenance, all organizations rapidly decay. Order and organization are achieved and maintained only at the price of payment in work, and this work, invisible directly to the human eye, is constantly being performed by the hawk, even when it is asleep, as well as by the ponderosa pine apparently lifeless in the stillness of the afternoon.

The acquisition of energy is therefore the primary and inescapable business of every living organism and precisely because it *is* an organism; it cannot maintain its organized state without an energy supply.

Plants—channel for energy. The sunlight that each day drenches the forest is the ultimate source of all the energy expended in the whole living community. The mountain lion in its leap, the deer browsing on the tree, and the iris opening its flower—all expend energy that is derived from sunlight. In the mountain lion and deer the energy has a complicated history, a history that is one of the major themes giving structure and meaning to the diversity in the forest community.

All living mechanisms, like the nonliving machines familiar in everyday life, are able to handle fuel of only a special type. Coal, in itself, is worthless in a human community that uses only electric engines. It becomes a useful energy supply only when special equipment—a generator in this case—is available to transform the energy locked in the coal into the electrical form usable by the engines on hand. Similarly, while all the energy used by living organisms is, in last analysis, sun energy, it is unusable until transformed into the form of fuel which living machinery can utilize. This fuel is a group of chemicals, principally sugars. Plants alone possess the ability to transform sun energy into usable sugar fuel, and thus the energy supply of the whole forest community is channeled through plants. The mountain lion eating the deer is using energy that came from the sun, but that energy was first compounded by plants into sugars that the deer ate and later yielded to the mountain lion that killed him.

The forest creatures are then very similar insofar as they all use the same sugar fuels. Their great diversity in structure and way of life is only diversity in how they all achieve the same end. This is really a familiar picture; it is like the human world of commerce, where there are so many ways of achieving the same end of making money. Competition in one field drives investment elsewhere, leading to a diversity of business that exploits every possible way of making a living. The diversity of feeding habits in the forest community reflects a similar underlying competition for resources.

The traffic in energy is only one of two major themes which impose meaning on the life of the forest. The other is the universal activity of reproduction. We will consider this in a visit to a coral reef.

A Coral Island

ABUNDANCE AGAIN, AND
A NEW DIVERSITY

Coral reefs (Fig. 1-2) do not occur everywhere in the world. Their distribution is limited to shallow and warm, clear and well-lit waters, conditions that are found only in the tropical and subtropical regions of the world.

Coral reefs are restricted in their distribution because they are produced—actually built— by a particular group of organisms, which, like all other living creatures, are adapted to thrive only under particular conditions.

The organisms which build up the reefs are principally a group of animals related to the jellyfishes and sea anemones familiar to any bather at the seaside. Unlike the jellyfishes, however, these organisms are sedentary. Like a plant, they sit in one place to make their living. The coral animals extract limelike substances from the sea water and then secrete them as a hard, compact external stony skeleton (Fig. 1-3). As the coral animal grows in size it divides into two parts, each like the original animal. The two new coral animals remain in contact, and continue to grow until each again divides. In this way there develops a whole colony of interconnected individuals each of which secretes its stony supporting skeleton.

At certain times of the year one colony of living coral initiates the growth of a wholly new colony. The coral animals shed minute eggs into the sea water. The eggs develop into tiny floating larvae that may eventually settle at a distance from the parent group and there grow into new coral animals initiating new colonies. After many years the individual colony dies. When this happens the living substance of the coral animals decays, but the nonliving stony skeleton remains. The accumulation of skeletons leads, in the passage of immense stretches of time, to the massive reef that we see today.

The world's greatest display of coral is the Great Barrier Reef which lies from 15 to 100 miles off the northeastern coast of Australia, running for nearly 1200 miles roughly north and south. Much of the reef is well below low tide; you may sail over it without even realizing it is there. In places, however, patches of reef, often elongated ovals in shape, have built up to the surface; a group of these is a "reefery." These patches make platforms that are barely awash at low tide. On some of them winds and waves pile up coral sand even above high-water mark so that an island is formed; and the island is soon invaded by pandanus palms and other vegetation. Here,

Between the clumps of living coral, brilliantly colored striped and spotted fishes dart along the channels.

1-2 THE GREAT BARRIER REEF

The world's greatest display of coral is the Great Barrier Reef, which lies from 15 to 100 miles off the northeastern coast of Australia, running for nearly 1200 miles roughly north and south.

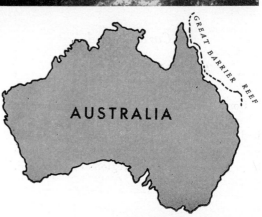

The coral *Tubipora*, which secretes a red skeleton. Note the expanded tentacles of the animals to the right.

The male (*left*) and female (*right*) of the crab *Hapalocarcinus*, which lives in the coral.

A sea cucumber (bêche-de-mer).

The turtles come ashore to lay their eggs.

A tern nesting on a coral island in the Great Barrier Reef.

All photos courtesy Australian News and Information Bureau, except coral detail from American Museum of Natural History

Much of the reef's life can be seen through a glass-bottomed boat.

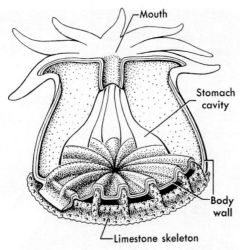

1-3 A coral animal and its limestone skeleton.

too, sea birds roost or burrow, and the turtles come ashore to lay their eggs.

At low tide the visitor may wade out onto the broad reef platform that surrounds the coral island. When he does he is confronted with one of the most spectacular displays of color the world of life can offer. Between the clumps of living coral, which reach just above the water at lowest tide, are crystal-clear channels floored with dazzling coral sand. Brilliantly colored striped and spotted fishes dart along the channels. On the channel floors are starfishes and many gray spotted or black rubbery tubelike objects, called sea cucumbers even though they are animals. Sea cucumbers cleaned and dried become "trepang" or "bêche-de-mer," which figures as local color in stories of the South Seas and from which the Chinese make soup.

At the very edge of the platform there may be a relatively barren zone of coral rock and boulders tossed up by the waves. If one of these boulders is turned over, a little world of hidden life is revealed. The bottom is coated with what looks, at first, like spots of vari-colored slime, white, yellow, pink, and red. Actually these are colonies of animals curiously varied and complex when studied with a lens. Here, too, under the rock are starfishes, red, white, and a particularly rich, velvety, midnight blue. An occasional "brittle star" contrasts sharply with its relatives, the slug-gish starfishes. When exposed, the brittle star lashes its slender arms so violently that some of them may break off. Clinging to the rocks are many living shellfish, among them glistening cowries of several colors and patterns.

Most colorful of all, however, are the clumps of coral themselves. They occur in dense forestlike growths in the larger pools on the reef, and on its outer slopes which descend into the deep water beyond. The coral is endlessly varied in shape and hue: spreading in fronds, intricately branching, or forming heavy, rounded heads; green, red, violet, yellow, and most of the other colors of the rainbow. There is one peculiarly fascinating fact about the colors of the coral: the coral animals themselves are really colorless. But in their stomachs and actually embedded in their flesh live myriads of colored microscopic plantlike organisms. This close association of coral animal and microscopic plant is evidently helpful to both parties. The little plants are believed to derive needed materials from the waste of the corals and in turn to produce oxygen needed by the corals. In any case, these particular microscopically small plants always live in the corals, and these particular corals never live without their colorful microscopic companions. One coral (called *Tubipora*) on the Great Barrier Reef secretes a red skeleton, but the skeletons of all the others are white, as many a person has found after collecting coral for its color. He finds that it fades when the animals and their colored plant companions die.

The coral clumps attract a host of other animals that form special communities rich in diversity. Conspicuous in this coral community are the giant clams. Three-quarters buried in the coral, these huge animals close their scalloped shells with a disconcerting squirt of water when a shadow falls on them. Here, too, on the coral clumps are worms living in self-made tubes, not such worms as occur in the garden, but gorgeous creatures with brilliantly colored tentacles. Soft corals (gruesomely styled "dead men's fingers"), sea anemones, many seaweeds, octopuses, sea hares (which do not look even remotely like hares!)—the list of the stony coral's associates seems almost endless if we include the myriads of microscopic plants and animals that swarm in the apparently clear water that surrounds them.

THE TRAFFIC IN ENERGY:
NEW VERSION

How very different the scene on the coral reef is from the pine forest of New Mexico! The two do not have a single kind of living organism in common, and hardly any that seem even remotely to resemble each other. Yet in broader view they have many similarities. In both places the basic operations of living things are the same; in both places the major theme of energy capture gives meaning to the relationships existing among the different organisms. Much that is strange and different on the coral reef relates to the peculiar form of its plant life and the way the animals feed on it.

In the forest, plant life is far more conspicuous than animal life. But you will have noticed in our description of the reef that we were mainly concerned with animals. To be sure, there are seaweeds, green, brown, and reddish on the reef, all of them compounding sugar fuels as a store of sun energy. Many of the reef animals, especially the sea snails, derive their food from these conspicuous forms of plant life. But by far the greatest source of food for the whole teeming animal community is the immense population of microscopically small plants in the surface waters washing the reef. These minute plants—absolutely invisible to the human eye without the help of a lens or microscope—are everywhere in the sea, absorbing minerals and capturing the sunlight as it passes through the clear water. Every drop of water on the reef contains some of these plants. It is for this reason that so many reef animals, unlike any of the forest, spend their whole lives in one spot. They sit and feed by filtering the minute plants from the sea water they continuously pass into their mouths or stomachs.

The pattern, then, is the same: the brisk commerce of life moves energy from sun to plant, from plant to the plant-eating (herbivorous) animal and from herbivore to animal-eating (carnivorous) animal. The rest is mostly detail of just how the business of living is carried out in the vastly different environments.

A SECOND THEME: REPRODUCTION

In our examination of the reef we noticed a second major theme: the reproduction of living organisms. Reproduction is a major theme running through the drama of the forest, and is just as important there as it is here on the reef. On the reef, however, we immediately noticed it as the cause of the very existence of the reef itself. As the coral animals continue to reproduce, each new generation adds its contribution of dead stony skeleton to the mass of the reef.

The growth and reproduction, the self-continuation, of living things are perhaps their most characteristic, defining properties. It is an established fact that nowadays no life, no living thing, comes into existence except as the offspring of another living thing. All living things reproduce themselves and do so with almost incredible accuracy, as attested by wells drilled in a reef. What kinds of coral animals lived in bygone eras? Some years ago two wells, one 378 and the other 506 feet deep, were drilled in the Great Barrier Reef. Under the thin film of living coral and other abundant life at the surface are hundreds of feet of reef rock. That thickness of what is now dead rock was deposited by once-living coral and other reef organisms. Through the ages, one generation built on top of the remains left by the last. In these particular borings, the oldest remains closely resemble the living organisms in spite of the fact that they lived *several thousands of years ago.*

In 1947 several wells were drilled at the famous Bikini Atoll (an atoll is a ringlike coral island) in the South Pacific. One of these borings brought up samples of coral skeleton laid down *20 to 25 million years ago.* The well reached the depth of 2556 feet and still had not come to the bottom of the reef rock. Reef corals cannot grow at any such depth in the sea today: they rarely live below a depth of about 200 feet and never below 250 feet. Moreover, we are confident for biological reasons that reef corals never could have lived at much greater depths. Yet here at Bikini their remains were found at a depth more than ten times their present deepest limit. Obviously something radical has happened here. Either the sea has risen or the sea bottom, the hard crust of the earth, has sunk, or both

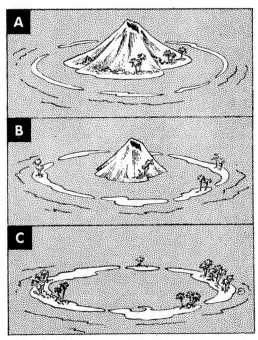

1-4 Darwin's theory of atoll formation. *A.* A coral reef fringes the coastline of an island. *B.* As the sea bottom (the earth's crust) sinks, the island slowly becomes submerged. The rate of sinking is slow enough for the growth of the coral reef to keep pace. *C.* Eventually the island is entirely submerged but the characteristically circular atoll remains.

(Fig. 1-4). That is an interesting point for the student of the earth's history. But another point is revealed, even more interesting to us as students of the history of life: the corals and other reef organisms at the bottom of this well are of different kinds from those living at the surface of Bikini now. Evidently life reproduces itself with remarkable fidelity, as the Great Barrier Reef wells attest (*thousands* of years); and yet in the very long run life changes, as the Bikini animals of *20 million* years ago prove. Twenty million years may seem an incredibly long time, but the history of life spans more than a billion years.

Life's Main Themes

IN THE COMMUNITY

To most readers a ponderosa pine forest in southwestern United States will seem remote. To all but a few readers the Great Barrier Reef will be even more remote. For everyone, a visit to the forest or the reef would be an adventure, and the more so the more one can see the underlying structure and meaning of the living community as a whole. This greater adventure into the realm of understanding can be had from a more modest excursion that is open to everyone. There is a character in a French play who is astonished to discover that he has been talking prose all his life. He had thought that prose was something exotic, remotely embodied in large tomes written by geniuses long since dead. The reef and the forest are remote and they are exotic; but they are not the only examples of living complex communities. Everyone is, and has been all his life, part of a complex living community; all around him is a diversity of smaller specialized living communities. Any familiar and accessible spot, while it may lack the scenic grandeur of the ponderosa forest and the coral reef, offers the opportunity for an adventure into the understanding of life—the structure and meaning of communities of living organisms.

In a field near your home, in a nearby park, in a stream, or even in your own backyard, the world of life reveals the same major themes we saw in the forest and on the reef. Here in the field energy flows into the whole world of life through the plants, which alone can fix solar energy into usable chemical form. The various animals secure energy from plants in their many characteristic ways. In the springtime and throughout the summer it is not only the young man's fancy that is agitated by the lengthening days and the warming sun. In the trees are nests of robins and of hawks, and under the ground the nests of the field mouse and the woodchuck—all of them astir with the business of a new family. From earliest spring, when crocuses first break the winter's drabness, to late fall, when the goldenrod is blooming, a long procession of flowers gives colorful notice of the plant world's reproduction. Wherever you go, whatever community you study, you will find the same two general themes in the life of that community: its pursuit of energy and materials for maintenance and growth; and the fact that it reproduces itself. The detail, which differs in each case, is related to the differing conditions of climate, soil, and water under which the community as a whole must thrive. The detail within each community is also related to the animal world's dependence on plants, and to that universal tendency among living things to diversify in specializations that exploit the resources of the environment to their limit.

IN THE INDIVIDUAL: ADAPTATION

It remains now to emphasize that the community's two great themes—reproduction, and the capture of materials and energy—are equally obvious in the life of its individual members. Indeed, a first understanding of the living individual comes from recognizing that its structure and behavior are organized in such a way that these two great ends are achieved. The individual organism is *adapted* (usefully organized) to survive and reproduce in its own particular environment. Like all great principles, this principle of adaptation is very simple in its essence. It states that any living thing is somehow fitted to live where it does in fact live. That seems almost too obvious to be worth saying. But the problems it raises are many and varied. Everyone knows that fishes swim in water and birds fly in air; that hawks feed on mice but bees feed on honey. Obviously they are all adapted in their different ways to do these things. But how? To say the hawk is *adapted to feed* on small terrestrial creatures implies more than simply, "It feeds on them." It implies that in the structure and behavior of the hawk there is a detailed organization which serves specifically this end; and the details of that organization, far from being obvious, require close study to be understood.

The phenomenon of life's adaptedness raises still other, greater problems. How did the hawk acquire its peculiar organization? How did it come by its swift flight and capacity to dive, its sharp beak and talons, and that unmatched vision which detects the mouse stirring so far below? These questions are among the profoundest in biology, and their answers certainly are not obvious.

Finally we must not let the more obvious adaptation to local conditions blind us to a wider adaptation. All living organisms have many characteristics in common. As a whole, life is adapted to the universe in which it occurs and to the planet on which, alone, we know it. In more detailed study of the life of the earth, this can and will be taken pretty much for granted. Nevertheless, it deserves some comment as introduction and background for that study.

Life's Home

THE VAST UNIVERSE

We live in an incredibly vast universe. Traveling at about 186,000 miles per second, light takes over 4 years to reach us from the nearest star. That works out at roughly 23,500,000,000,000 miles to the *nearest* star. It takes light about 200,000 years to travel across our particular cluster of stars. That is, our home galaxy is some 200,000 light-years in diameter. Out beyond this galaxy are innumerable other galaxies, millions of light-years distant and more. The most distant object visible with the naked eye—the spiral nebula in Andromeda—is about 900,000 light-years away, but modern telescopes reach far beyond that. As larger telescopes are built, the astronomers see (or, in practice, photograph) farther and farther, revealing more of the same and no signs of a limit. There are ingenious and interesting theories about limits to our universe, but the fact is that no one knows how large it is.

THE SOLAR SYSTEM

Until someone actually produces the "time drive," so common in science fiction and so entirely unknown to science, only one cozy little part of this awesomely immense universe has any direct interest to the biologist. Our solar system consists of nine planets and a variety of other objects (satellites of the planets, asteroids, comets, meteors) revolving around the sun. The sun is a rather commonplace or second-rate star, as stars go, about 860,000 miles in diameter and with a surface temperature of about 11,000° F.[1] With excep-

[1] This is the Fahrenheit temperature, which is the temperature scale most familiar to you. Technical work in science uses the centigrade scale, by which the sun's surface temperature is about 6000°. A temperature on the Fahrenheit scale can be converted to a temperature on the

1 Sun: ultimate energy source	2 Plant life	3 Coal	4 Fire and boiler	5 Steam turbine	6 Generator	7 Electric lamp

1-5   Energy conversions from sun to electric lamp.   *1.* The potential energy of atomic nuclear structure is released as kinetic energy (light). *2.* The kinetic energy of light is converted to kinetic energy of chemical reaction (photosynthesis) in plants and stored as potential chemical energy in large organic molecules. *3.* A buried tree becomes coal in which potential chemical energy is stored. *4.* Burning coal releases kinetic energy as heat that is converted into the kinetic energy of the steam jet's motion. *5.* The kinetic energy of the steam jet's motion is converted into the kinetic energy of the turbine's rotary motion. *6.* The kinetic energy of the turbine is converted into the kinetic energy of the generator's rotary motion; and this in turn is converted into the kinetic energy of an electric current. *7.* The kinetic energy of the electric current is converted into heat energy of the lamp's filament and the kinetic energy of the radiated light.

tions of no real importance, all the energy used by living things comes as radiation from the sun. This is true even of the energy used by human industry. For instance, the energy in your automobile is solar energy. It was radiated by the sun long ago, fixed in chemical form by living organisms, turned into petroleum by a series of other transformations, and finally made into gasoline at a refinery. Figure 1-5 illustrates another sequence of solar energy conversions. Atomic or, more strictly, nuclear energy does not come from solar radiation, but its extensive industrial use is not yet at hand.

THE PLANET EARTH: FITNESS
FOR LIFE

Our earth is an intermediate planet in position and size. It is the third from the sun, at an average distance of some 93,000,000 miles, and is about 8000 miles in diameter. It is the densest planet, 5½ times as dense as water.

centigrade scale using the following formula:
centigrade = 5 (Fahrenheit − 32)/9.

Its temperature at the surface varies greatly but generally averages between 50° and 60° F. throughout the year over the whole surface and only rarely and locally falls much below 30° F. or rises far above 100° F. It has a deep atmosphere, about ⅕ oxygen and ⅘ nitrogen, with considerable water vapor and carbon dioxide. It has a great deal of liquid water on and near the surface. It also has quantities of other chemical substances in various forms at and near the surface, where they are available for the use of living things.

Such facts about the nature of the earth, its climatic conditions, chemical composition, and so on could be greatly expanded. The reason for listing a few of them here is to point out that the earth is well fitted to the life that inhabits it. All the chemical elements necessary for all known expressions of life are here in available form and adequate amounts. And the physical characteristics of the earth are right: it has a suitable atmosphere; it is neither too close to the sun nor too far away.

Take the matter of temperature. In the universe, temperatures range from 460° below zero (Fahrenheit) to at least 35,000,000° above; 460° F. below is absolute zero—no heat at all—and 35,000,000° F. is approximately the temperature at the center of the sun. Higher temperatures doubtless exist. In all this tremendous scale, there is only a tiny range of 100° F. or so in which life normally operates. Living things become quiescent and eventually die with long-sustained temperatures much below the freezing point of water. Few of them can long survive above 100° or 150° F.; none can live near or above the boiling point of water. Just this insignificant part of the temperature scale of the universe includes the usual temperatures on earth.

Earth has other qualifications fitting it for life. For instance, water as a liquid is an absolutely indispensable part of all living matter. Water happens to be abundant on the earth. It also happens to be liquid from 32° to 212° F. (or a little below and a little above, depending on pressure and dissolved substances)—again neatly within usual earth temperatures. With a little study of chemistry, too, you will find that certain elements common on earth have special properties without which life as we know it would be quite impossible. This is particularly true for hydrogen, oxygen, and carbon, the three elements most abundant in all living things. It is true to a lesser degree of nitrogen, the next most abundant element in living matter.

All this shows that adaptation is a two-way proposition. It is not something that living things have or acquire. Adaptation is a relationship between living things and their environment. The environment has to fit them just as much as they fit the environment; otherwise—no life!

Why is the earth so well fitted to life? It seems peculiar, even downright providential, as our ancestors thought it literally was. As with so many knotty scientific problems, the answer is really simple if a little common sense is applied. Life, this particular state known to us as "life," is on earth precisely because it arose here and under these conditions. If the earth were not fit for living things, they would not be here but, if anywhere, on some other planet in some other solar system. If the earth had quite different conditions and something like life had nevertheless arisen, then that "life" would not be life as we know it but something quite different, perhaps not even recognized by us as truly alive.

LIFE ON OTHER WORLDS?

You would doubtless be a Venutian right now if Venus had, throughout its history, had the conditions that in fact have prevailed on earth, and earth had had Venus's history. Are there real Venutians waiting for us to land a spaceship? Trying to answer that question may not be very serious science, but it is certainly interesting. If we try to answer it scientifically, that is, by applying common sense and logic to what facts we actually know, the answer is disappointing for the fans of science fiction. From what was said above about the earth as a home for living things, it is evident that two different questions are really involved. First, are there other places where life as we know it could exist? Second, are there other possible sorts of living things that could exist under quite different conditions from those on earth?

Let us briefly consider the first question first. Life as we know it could exist only on a planet. The only planets we really know anything about are the nine of our own solar system. Of these, seven (including Venus) have conditions so different from those on earth that it is as certain as can be that life like that of earth does not exist on them. It is just conceivable that some particularly tough —and to us rudimentary and nonhuman— earthlike living things could exist on Mars. It is a far cry from saying that such a thing perhaps *could* live on Mars to saying that it *does*.

It is sometimes said that there are probably millions of planets much like earth elsewhere in the universe, even though there are no others in our own solar system. Among these millions, the argument runs, some must have developed living things like those on earth, and even what the science fiction writers call "humanoids." No planets at all like the earth are *known* to exist outside our solar system. The *chances* that earthlike planets exist elsewhere depend on theories as to how our own solar system originated. Was it a rare accident? In that case the chances are slim for other, similar systems. Or was it a fairly usual incident of stellar evolution? In that case chances would be relatively good.

There are still current half a dozen different theories about how our solar system originated. There are objections to all of them, and there is at present, anyway, no really decisive way to establish any one of them as correct. That life like ours *may* exist somewhere else, perhaps a million light-years distant, is an interesting speculation. That is all. It rests on no direct evidence, either one way or the other.

Then what about the second possibility, that life of a sort might exist under conditions quite different from those of earth? It is chemically possible, or perhaps we should say "conceivable," that ammonia, for instance, could play the role that water does here. Since pure ammonia boils at more than 90° below zero, other conditions of temperature, pressure, and so on would have to be very different from those of earth. This entails all sorts of other differences, such as those of energy exchange and other reactions at very low temperatures, high pressures, or both. In short, "organisms" on these planets would be so very different from ours that we would hardly recognize them as living in our usual sense of the word. That they could be recognizably "humanoid" is incredible. Beyond that, all is baseless speculation.

What Is Life?

So far we have talked quite a bit about life, but we still have not said just what life is. It is fundamental both to good writing and to good science to state exactly what you are talking about. We are talking about life, but it is unexpectedly difficult to frame or find a really good definition. At some time in school you have surely answered a question by saying, "Well, I know what it is, but I can't quite give a definition of it." That is the situation of biologists when they are being honest with themselves. They all know what life is, but none of them can give a completely satisfactory definition of it.

One way to define life is to tell what living things look like and what they do. That is what this whole book is about, so the whole book is perhaps as good a definition of life as we can offer. Not so much, therefore, by way of definition as by way of introduction to our book-long definition, we will briefly mention some of the usual characteristics of the various forms of life.

In the first place life is not to be thought of as a thing or substance. It is a *process*, or rather a series of interacting processes which are always associated with, and take place in, *a complex organization of materials*. Another way of looking at this is to recognize that only some very complex organizations of matter are capable of executing those processes which we recognize as life.

The living organization—the organism—maintains itself, *grows*, and *reproduces* its own likeness. In these activities it maintains a flow of energy and materials taken from its environment. This flow of materials and energy is called *metabolism*. Some of the materials taken in by the organism are incorporated directly into its own organization; others are first compounded into complex chemicals; from all these actions waste products accumulate and are discarded (excreted). The processes of metabolism involve work and demand a regular energy supply.

The most general and nearly definitive process of living organisms is their *reproduction*. The detailed ways of reproducing can be very different in various organisms, often but not always involving the added complication of sexuality. Nevertheless, all living things do reproduce their own likeness. They do so, moreover, with remarkable accuracy (as the Barrier Reef wells showed us); but this accuracy, great as it is, never attains perfection. All reproduction of organisms involves some *variation*. This has important consequences. If it were not so, there would be no diversity and no progress among living things.

Related to the property of reproduction and almost equally fundamental is the fact that living things exhibit *growth*. Some nonliving things grow, too, but in a different way. A growing crystal in a saturated solution or growing frost on a windowpane is only adding materials on the surface and along its edges. The growth of the living organism is not so simple, however; it involves internal expansion and copying of its own complex organization.

Another feature highly characteristic of life, although not confined to it, is *responsiveness*. This is extremely developed and obvious in higher animals, especially man. It occurs to some degree in all living things. An ameba reacts to the presence of particles or chemicals. Plants respond or react to changes in sunshine or other environmental conditions.

Still another characteristic universal in living things but not confined to them is movement that occurs within the organism or that results from internal changes, that is, *autonomous movement.* Many nonliving (inorganic) things have movement and even autonomous movement (an automobile does), but movement is always present during at least part of the life cycle of a living organism. Plants may seem motionless, but their growth is a slow movement, and there is considerable movement not only within their cells, but often from cell to cell.

Now we have stated some of the things that living things *do,* and we will state many more in later chapters. Does this add up to a statement of what life *is?* That is a very profound question, and one that has occupied scientists and philosophers from ancient times. It is still disputed, although most biologists now agree as to the essentials of an answer. Broadly speaking, there are two main possibilities. The first answer is "Yes. Life is a process occurring in a natural way in certain organizations of matter. It is, then, fully defined by the way in which living matter is organized and by the processes that occur in the organization." That is the answer of most biologists at the present time. The other answer is: "No. Life occurs in material organizations and is manifested in processes. But life itself is something additional and different, neither material process nor organized matter, something that cannot be isolated or examined in itself." That is the answer supported by some other biologists, many philosophers, and most theologians. We cannot tell you that either answer is *surely* correct. By the time you finish this book you will be in a position to decide for yourself which answer is more *probable.*

Chapter Summary

Life—a phenomenon of communities.

The diversity among individual organisms in the community—a diversity of ways of making a living.

Two major themes giving structure and meaning to the life of all communities:

(1) The traffic in energy and materials, in which plants play a key role.

(2) The universal presence of organic reproduction.

The concept of adaptation, a fundamental one in biology: the adaptation of the organism is the way it is organized to maintain and reproduce itself in the environment it inhabits.

The broad adaptation of all organisms to the conditions prevailing on the planet earth; the absence of such conditions elsewhere in our solar system; their occurrence, and that of life, in other solar systems a matter of speculation only.

Living systems as organizations of matter characterized by the processes of:

(1) Metabolism.

(2) Reproduction.

(3) Growth.

(4) Responsiveness.

The first glimmerings of modern evolutionary thought were those of Buffon, when he sought (1760) to explain similarities among vertebrate skeletons. (Courtesy American Museum of Natural History)

CHAPTER 2

Biological Principles

What Is Science?

The Great Barrier Reef revisited. The visitor to the Great Barrier Reef has many reactions. He is awed by its strangeness and its vastness. He is happy at its beauty. He is curious at all the detail he sees. These first reactions lead to others. His sense of awe, his humility, and his feeling of loneliness in a world of strange life may lead him on to religious emotions. His bounding joy may drive him, artist now, to spell out for others in words, painting, or music all the beauty as he sees it. Or perhaps his curiosity rules him. Why does the coral grow so freely only on the leeward side of the reef? Why is the living coral restricted to the well-lit waters near the surface? Why all the colors—what causes them? What is their meaning?

Awe, joy, curiosity—all these are reactions to the world we live in; similarly, religion, art, and science are human activities. All three may occur in one and the same man, but the temperament of a man is such a private and individual affair that he is likely to be more prone to one than another. All three activities have their own special value for mankind. All three contribute to the richness and diversity of human experience and culture. All three have their own goals and their methods of achieving those goals. We are concerned in this chapter with the activities of the curious man, who, following up his questions as to causes and meanings in the coral reef, becomes the "scientist."

What is science? Its sources, aims, and procedures. This is the first fact about science: it is a human activity. As such it is subject to all the frailties of human endeavor. Its history is a history of errors, slowly corrected; a history of effort, a search for a wider knowledge of facts and deeper, more embracing schemes for understanding and explaining them. Science is not a cold, infallible, impersonal machine; it is not just a collection of formulas and technical terms about abstruse questions remotely related to everyday life and thought. Science is ultimately refined common sense. It is the organized knowledge developed and possessed by men and women of the world they live in.

As a human endeavor, science is dependent on human motivation. The motivations for scientific endeavor are not hard to find. First, there is the ever-present need for knowledge that helps man master the environment he lives in, making it subservient to his needs. Our knowledge of astronomy began its growth impelled by the need of a calendar for the season-conscious Babylonian farmer. In our own day, the growth of knowledge of nuclear physics has been impelled in part by unhappier but no less practical considerations.

Secondly, and in the long run more important, there is an almost universal curiosity in men which seeks satisfaction in knowledge of the world for its own sake—knowledge not only of the facts themselves but of how they are related and how things are caused; in short, knowledge of how the world of fact can be explained and so understood. The simple and naïve questions of the small child when they recur in mature minds are the life's blood of science. "Who dug it?" as a question on first seeing the Grand Canyon is naïve only in phraseology; in the older man this child-question leads to our understanding of the cutting power of running water. Cats may be killed by curiosity, but science dies for the lack of it.

It is often said that the path which starts with curiosity and ends with scientific knowledge is a special one marked "scientific method." Certainly the path is not obvious at first sight. Curiosity is necessary for the attainment of scientific knowledge, but it is not in itself sufficient. The questions of children and of grown men have ended with the acceptance of magical answers too often for us to assume that there is nothing special in the methods of science. But ultimately these methods are what we call common sense, although we must add that common sense is for the most part a rare commodity. At any rate it is common sense to apply now and in the future those practices which in the past have led to sound knowledge, knowledge of practical value, knowledge that produces more knowledge. The methods of scientists in fact have become accepted largely because they have been found to work. They are those practices and methods that, out of many others, have been proven to yield enduring and sound explanations.

The aims of science are twofold: (1) the discovery of the facts about the universe in which we exist; and (2) the discovery of theoretical schemes that will explain the facts, schemes that will reduce the array of endless diversity in the world to a unity of relationships.

In practice, the discovery of fact and its explanation in theory are so interwoven that the two elements are hard to distinguish. The scientist may discover new facts that, within the framework of a theory, explain old facts, or he may discover new theories that explain old facts. If the theory is good, it will do more than this: it will point the way to the discovery of still more new facts. These relationships, however, must be clarified later. At this point we will consider separately our two aspects of scientific endeavor, discovery of fact and discovery of theory.

Facts as the starting point of science.

By isolating facts for discussion we can stress the real hallmark of science, the feature that distinguishes science from all other intellectual activities. The sciences are concerned with the structure of the world, and there is only one way we can find out about this, namely, by observing it. Facts are the stuff from which science starts, and, when men create theories to explain facts, the final judge of the worth of these theories is again the facts. This is common sense. But it was uncommon sense in the Middle Ages when men, and very intelligent men, regarded the writings of ancient Greece as a surer guide to the world than the simple observation of it.

The scientist then is first an observer and describer of the world. Observation of nature, however, itself reveals only facts, never theories or explanations. Theories are the products of men's minds, the tools they create to explain the facts. It is in the discovery of useful theories that the real adventure of the scientist resides. Here imagination and creative effort are needed. This picture of the scientist resembles, perhaps, that of the artist who creates his own view of the "meaning" and "truth" about the coral reef. Certainly both activities involve a creative effort, and both the artist and the scientist are entitled to speak of their own versions of truth and meaning. There is, however, an immense difference between the two activities, although this difference does not imply that one is better than the other. The artist's work cannot be evaluated by any public or factual standard; it is satisfying or not to the artist and his audience, according to whether it suits their esthetic taste. On the other hand, scientific theories, once created, are subject to scrutiny in the light of the facts. They can be publicly evaluated by a criterion—the facts—that everyone is forced to share in common. When theories do not conform with the facts, they are clearly inadequate. They must be modified to conform with the facts or, if this is impossible, discarded. The history of science is strewn with discarded theories.

What is a theory? There is widespread misunderstanding to the effect that theories are not only distinct from facts but in a sense the very opposite of them. This misunderstanding is suggested by common expressions like "such and such may be true in theory but not in fact," or "something is *only* theoretical." The subject of what a theory is demands whole books for full discussion, but, when all is said and done, theories are general statements that say how different observable facts are interrelated. We could say of science that its aim is the discovery of valid general statements—valid theories—which in brief and succinct form state the relationships observed between events and things.

This is simply illustrated by recalling the theory, familiar to most readers from elementary physics, that describes the relationships between the volume, the pressure, and the temperature of a gas. Gases like air, steam, bottled propane, and natural (petroleum) gas are commonplace in our everyday life; their behavior impinges on our welfare all the time. As a consequence of the improperly controlled behavior of gases, balloons, automobile tires, and gas storage tanks burst; controlled, their behavior serves us in innumerable ways like driving locomotives and automobiles. The brief general statement Pressure (P) × Volume (V) = Temperature (T) × the number (R) is, as a law or theoretical statement, of the highest importance and value for us. It has innumerable uses.

At a later stage in scientific training you may be interested in important distinctions made between natural laws and theories, but those distinctions are not crucial here. Both laws and theories have the same character; namely, they are *general statements of the relationships* between the things referred to in the law or theory. The general statement about gas behavior—$PV = RT$—summarizes the total past experience of all men who have observed how pressure and volume are affected by changes in temperature. Furthermore, insofar as we believe (with past experience to support us) that the laws describing the behavior of gases yesterday will apply tomorrow, it allows us to *predict* exactly what will happen to the volume of a gas at some future time if the pressure and temperature are changed in specified ways. On the other hand, the theory helps us *explain* why old automobile tires show an increased frequency of blowouts in high-speed desert driving. To be sure, here, as in most real situations, we need other theories for the full explanation, in this case one relating friction to heat; but this is beside the real point. The gas law not only *predicts* the outcome of future situations involving gas behavior, but *explains* past events involving gas behavior. Prediction and explanation are two sides of the same coin; they are of the essence of scientific endeavor and advancement, the reduction of the multitude of diverse particular things and events to special cases of a general invariant rule. *The individual case, thing, or process is explained scientifically when it is shown to be only a particular instance of a general regularity embodied in a theory.*

The discovery of theories: a creative activity. When one looks at a simple theoretical statement like $PV = RT$ he may wonder, at first sight, how it ever comes to involve the creative act. Were we right in saying that the imagination is involved in the discovery of the theories as distinct from facts? Is not $PV = RT$ only a shorthand statement summarizing all our observations? Is not the scientist, after all, a mere reporter of uncolored fact?

There is more than reporting involved in science. And we can here only outline for you a few ways in which the discovery and creation of a satisfactory general explanation is more than mere fact gathering. It is obvious that the unskilled watching of balloons, automobile tires, and gas tanks would never *automatically* result in the gas law. The unskilled observer would more than likely report his observations in terms of the size and color of balloons and the make and wall thickness of tires. These things he would observe directly. Would he observe *pressure* and *temperature?* What are they? They are ideas or concepts that a long line of observers and *thinkers* have created as useful tools to describe the behavior of gases. One important task for the scientist is this *creation of ideas* useful for the study of things. In biology, as in physics, you will encounter such ideas or concepts useful for the description and analysis of living organisms but not in themselves directly seen by an observer.

When you observe people you see boys and girls, men and women, not sex. Sex is an idea, the idea that there are two categories of people with respect to their roles in reproduction. This idea is of great use for laying the foundation of explanatory theories in biology. Once sex is perceived as a general idea we immediately notice that there are also two categories of chickens, one with a crest and one without. Are these two categories sex? Yes, they are categories of individual fowls that differ in their reproductive roles as do the categories of people. Could it be we are catching on to a general concept applying to all living things? Cats, in their external appearance, do not so readily reveal their two categories, but close observation of them shows that there are indeed the same two sexes. And so the increasing conviction that we are dealing with a generalization about living things leads us to new *directed observation* elsewhere. Shortly we recognize sex in flowering plants, in ferns and mushrooms, and indeed in virtually all organisms.

We have thus discovered an immense amount of new knowledge; and the knowledge is organized. It began not merely with observing men, boys, girls, and women; it really began with the discovery of the idea of sex. As we found this sexual differentiation in several kinds of living things, we guessed that probably all living things are sexually differentiated. *Guesses* do play a role in science, even if they are given the new name *induction*, which has a more respectable air about it, to say the least. But the process of induction—drawing the tentative conclusion that some individual things or events are only particular cases of a general rule—is an informed guess based on experience; and all it produces is a *hypothesis*. Now the distinction between hypothesis and theory is only one of degree, according to how well established is the generalization embodied in the theory or hypothesis. A generalization, about gas behavior or sex, is a hypothesis while it is only an intelligent guess or *induction* from limited experience; it becomes a theory, perhaps even without any change at all, once it has been tested thoroughly by renewed observation of facts.

It is in induction from limited experience that the creative element is involved in science. "Your guess is as good as mine" may be true for many situations, but not in science. Some men, as we discover sometimes a little sadly, can guess at the general rules in nature much better than others. But in the long run the element of uncertainty that inheres in any guess is taken out of science as a whole. The hypotheses produced by our informed guesses are discarded if they fail to pass the test of renewed and wider comparison with fact.

How we distinguish a good hypothesis from a bad one: testability. The scientist, unlike the magician, medicine man, and metaphysician, offers *hypotheses about nature that can be tested*. The progress he makes in explaining the world of fact is due to the rapidity with which bad hypotheses can be found out to be bad and be discarded. There are two senses in which we may describe a hypothesis as bad. The obvious one is where it turns out to be incorrect, does not stand up to repeated testing. But there is another sense in which it is bad—when it cannot be tested at all. The hypothesis that certain earthly events are due to small men hiding on the far side of the moon is certainly implausible for many reasons, but its worst feature is that it cannot be tested because these little men always keep the moon between themselves and us.

The same kind of untestable hypothesis often creeps into more serious efforts to explain nature, and it takes good common sense to see through the respectable garb it wears. Biology more than most sciences has been inflicted with a heavy share of such untestable, and therefore unscientific, hypotheses. The cause of evolution was once claimed by Bergson to be an *élan vital* (vital force). Now the *élan vital* has no dimensions; it cannot be seen, measured, or indeed recognized except by the evolution it has caused. This is no more a real explanation of evolution than an *élan locomotif* is the explanation of how a locomotive works. It tells us nothing new; and worst of all, it cannot be proved either right or wrong.

Not so with an acceptable hypothesis; it is testable, and through testing it repeatedly by both renewed observation and specially created experiment, mumbo-jumbo is kept at a minimum in science. Incidentally, let it be noticed here that there is no real difference in science between the direct observation of nature exemplified by the biologist who measures how many flies occur in a woodland at various hours of the day, and the observation that is involved in a laboratory experiment, no matter how elaborate it may be. The laboratory experiment is a short cut in which the observer creates the conditions he wishes to observe. The two approaches are complementary, especially in biology.

Theories as guides to new knowledge.

A good theory in science not only explains all it started out to explain but also predicts new facts to be looked for. There are two features of prediction from theory which need emphasizing. The first has already been treated briefly: a theory is tested most thoroughly in the light of its predictions; if it predicts well it is a good theory. But there is a second feature of paramount importance. Well-established theories, and even hypotheses, are the guideposts which take the scientist out into the bewildering array of detail in the world. Fact gathering in the hands of a scientist is a cultivated art; there is an infinity of facts in the world, and at any given time only a few of them are of vital importance to him.

Are you being a scientist when you count the sand grains on Coney Island beach? No. It is true you are gathering facts, perhaps carefully, but you are probably crazy. Scientists gather facts that are *relevant*. Relevant to what? To some theory to be tested or extended.

It is often misleadingly stated that one characteristic of a good scientist is that he approaches the world he wants to study—be it a world of gas pressures, chemical combinations, or animal behavior—with an open mind. This is at best a half-truth, and we must carefully distinguish what is true and false in it.

If in advocating the open-mind approach we are advocating the removal of all personal prejudice, we are on the side of common sense. If you really want to know what goes on in the world around you, you should let the facts, not your prejudices, inform you. Wishful thinking may be psychologically necessary for people in times of stress, but it never *determines* or *causes* what in fact goes on in reality—at least outside the wishfully thinking mind. If in fact death comes to all living things this will remain so independent of any wishing on our part that it were otherwise.

The open-mind policy is, however, often mistaken to imply more than the shedding of personal prejudice. It is nonsense when it is taken to imply that the scientist must approach his task with no preformed ideas of what he will find, or of what observations are worthwhile. Scientists have well-formed ideas of what is worth studying at any given time, and can make informed guesses as to what they will find. We know far too much about the general pattern of how things work to have no guesses at all as to the workings of a specific thing that interests us currently. All good observation and experiment is thus approached with a hypothesis in mind that suggests what is likely to be found. The scientist, aware he starts out with his own personal guess, safeguards himself against making only those observations that will conform with it by deliberately attempting to disprove it. This deliberate attempt at disproof means that he discards bad hypotheses as fast as he can and places the acceptable ones on the soundest possible basis.

The Rise of Modern Science, and the Physicist's Conceptual Scheme

THE RENAISSANCE IN SIXTEENTH-CENTURY EUROPE

Curiosity and the search for explanations are as old as man himself. What caused *that* to happen? How does *this* work? We have scientific answers to these questions today, but they were answered in other ways before the advent of science.

Something is "explained" when it is shown to be related to something else we already understand. Today we explain a new fact by relating it to an established law or theory But the thing primitive man understood best was human nature; accordingly, he explained facts and events in terms of human nature, in personified forces. One man was killed by a spear thrown by another man; a second man was mysteriously killed by disease—disease indeed was an "invisible" arrow. What would have been more plausible to primitive man than to attribute the causation of uncontrollable events to superhuman forces? The success of crops depended on rain which was a gift, given or withheld at the caprice of the rain god.

This primitive view of the world is wholly incompatible with science. If the causes of events are the personal whims of gods they cannot be explained through general, invariant rules. The very essence of science is the search for general rules which, when found, are summarized in laws and theories. For this reason the rise and growth of science depended on a radical change of attitude toward the universe. Man had first to see the universe as a vast and impersonal but rationally intelligible system. That is, he had first to believe in the existence of general laws before he could discover them.

We cannot point to a single place and time and say, "That is where and when science began." Like any phase of human culture, its beginnings are many and its evolution has been gradual. The beginnings of the scientific attitude and some substantial scientific achievement occurred in several ancient cultures, in Babylonia, Egypt, and Greece. But all these growths were abortive; they largely died with the culture of which they were a part. Greek science was lost in the Europe of the "Dark" Ages. Medieval scholars did, however, keep alive, and even cultivated, one ingredient essential to all later science. This was the rational outlook—the belief in a lawful universe. But this one ingredient is not the whole of science. The medieval scholars were content to create their own universal order by deducing it from theological dogmas and ancient written authority. The rational outlook must be wedded to the observation of nature and the process of induction before it becomes part of science.

Modern science emerged in sixteenth- and seventeenth-century Europe. Its birth was just one aspect of the great intellectual Renaissance of Europe. The Renaissance was in every way a period of renewed vigor. Its growing wealth and commerce fostered geographic exploration and new interests in the arts and sciences. Above all, the Renaissance was a time when the observation of nature, fresh and direct, replaced the medieval acceptance of dogma and authority. *Novum Organum* of Sir Francis Bacon (1561-1626)—a landmark in the rise of modern science—pled for the common-sense view that observation is the only true path to knowledge of the world.

The rebirth of science in the sixteenth century brought intellectual turmoil. Its premises clashed with tenets long established by custom and authority; and thus began a conflict which has never quite ended. The first significant eruption came when Copernicus (1543) said the earth circled around the sun. His theory was a blow at the cherished notion, inherited from the ancients, that man and his earthly home were the very center of the universe. This was the theory for which Giordano Bruno was later burned at the stake (1600). Under threat of excommunication, Galileo was forced publicly to retract the statement of his belief in the Copernican theory. The clash of Darwin's theory of evolution with human prejudice has hardly yet subsided in some places.

But the new science made a spectacular start in another and more important way. The work of Copernicus and Galileo was extended and developed by Newton, culminating in 1685 with a successful explanation of the movements of the planets. This was an accomplishment so brilliant and immense in scope that it influenced profoundly the growth of all later science, including biology. Let us see why.

NEWTON AND THE PHYSICIST'S CONCEPTUAL SCHEME

Science is founded on belief in a universal order in nature which men can discover. Its ultimate aim is to produce a unified, quantitatively exact, theory which reflects this universal order in nature and from which all the facts of our experience can be explained. A unified theory for all science is, however, a very distant goal. Even physics, more exact and unified than any other science, has still to be content in the meantime with an array of separate theories—theories about gases, theories about planets, theories about electricity. Nevertheless, as each branch of knowledge grows, its ideas and concepts do acquire a coherent relationship, even if they cannot all be fused into one exact and quantitative theory. They form a loosely organized conceptual scheme that gives the scientist a framework in terms of which he can discuss and think about his problems.

Such a conceptual scheme assumes one of the major functions of a theory for science in general: it directs observation and guides men in their search for new knowledge. And it sets a standard of acceptability for all partial explanations.

The physics of Newton's day owes its great importance not so much to the particular theories it evolved as to the general conceptual scheme it created for science as a whole. It formulated laws of motion and a theory of gravitation which together explained the motion of all matter. Everyone is familiar with the story of how Newton, watching an apple fall to the ground, conceived the notion of earth's gravitation. He realized that the apple did not *fall* to the earth: it was *pulled* to the earth as soon as it was freed. This concept of the earth's pull was what he needed to explain why the moon did not fly from its orbit around the earth off into space: the moon was continuously pulled by the same force that pulled the apple. Here was a hypothesis about truly universal order, and Newton could put it into exact and quantitative terms that permitted him to test it. If it were correct he could predict the speed of a falling apple, and he did so—correctly. These motions, so vastly different in magnitude—the fall of an apple, the circling of the moon around the earth, and the still greater circling of the earth around the sun—all of them came predictably within the scope of an exact theory.

It is easy to understand the influence of the Newtonian era on all later science. For it will always be as thrilling as it was in the seventeenth century to appreciate the precision of new-found scientific laws, and to sense the apparently boundless world of matter moving exactly and precisely, like a clockworks. Apple, moon, earth, and sun all move in obedience to a universal law. Universal order indeed existed, and men were discovering it with the new methods of induction from *observed* facts. The seventeenth century could not escape the feeling of assurance that comes with success. The scientists of this age faced the universe confident that in *matter* and its *impersonally determined motion* they had the conceptual scheme necessary to explain it all —"exactly and precisely like a clockworks." This analogy with a clockworks is not new with us; it was made many times in the Newtonian era, and, like a cartoon or caricature, it captures the essential flavor of the new conceptual scheme, which is the *impersonal determination of events*. The emergence in the seventeenth century of this physical conceptual scheme thus marked the end of animistic forces in nature as acceptable scientific causes.

The confidence of the seventeenth century was largely fulfilled. The material, deterministic view of the world grew throughout the eighteenth and nineteenth centuries because it continued to foster new discovery and insight. Eventually its power and authority as the grand road to scientific knowledge became beyond question. This success, however, was in large measure restricted to physics and chemistry, the sciences of the nonliving world.

During the late sixteenth and seventeenth centuries, biology also made a promising start. In Italy, where in large part the Renaissance began, Vesalius (1543) typified the new movement as one of the first students of anatomy to turn to the body itself rather than ancient authority as a source of anatomical knowledge. In England observation and experiment won a great victory in William Harvey's (1628) discovery of the circulation of the blood and the significance of the heart as a pump. In Holland, Anthony van Leeuwenhoek (1632-1723) applied newly developed lenses and microscope to the exploration of that world of previously invisible life in every pond and stream. And there were many others who added luster and promise to the new observation of living things in the seventeenth century.

Biology did not, however, make the giant strides that physics made. In part, at least, this was because many biological problems seemed intractable to the scheme of physical concepts which had come to dominate scientific thought in general. It is useful to think of a conceptual scheme as a *society of ideas*. It is like a society in that its constituent ideas are living things that influence each other. Like other things that must coexist, ideas must be compatible— they cannot constantly conflict. At any rate, a conceptual scheme exerts something like a social pressure for conformity both on the new ideas it admits and the problems it chooses to recognize. It is indeed common for scientists to be aware of problems but not to study them because they have no good guesses as to how to explain them in terms of the current scheme of thought. This was surely the fate of many biological problems during the seventeenth and eighteenth centuries. The conceptual scheme which the Newtonian era had given to science as a whole seemed quite inadequate for their discussion and ultimate explanation.

First there was the problem of human pride; man himself is a living being with a mind. Many people felt that the ideas of physics, focused on moving particles and the impersonal determination of events, had no relevance for understanding the mind and the world of thought. In any case it was vulgar to suggest it. If the Copernican theory had been a threat to human dignity, how much greater was this!

Second, human dignity aside, other living things presented apparently insurmountable difficulty for the physicist's conceptual scheme. For many people the exquisite way the structures of living organisms are evidently *designed* for the functions they serve could be explained in only one way: they had been created in their present form by an intelligent Designer. The full description of living organisms could not avoid use of phrases like "the purpose of legs is for running," "teeth are for the purpose of chewing." *Purpose* was seen everywhere in the world of life, but had no place in the physicists' world view of moving particles, which Tennyson summed up in his line "the stars, she whispers, *blindly* run."

Thus prior to 1859 the physicists' view did not offer a really complete formula for understanding all of the world man knew. Many people were content to leave the full explanation of life to natural theology rather than natural science. Those who were not content were faced with two alternatives: to invent vague concepts unacceptable in the society of physical ideas; or simply to shelve the problem as temporarily intractable. Thus, in the seventeenth, eighteenth, and early nineteenth centuries, biology was cluttered with "animal spirits" and "vital forces." But, for the most part, men who understood and valued the physicists' conceptual scheme preferred to wait for a new lead. This came in 1859, the year in which Darwin published *The Origin of Species*.

Foundations of Modern Biology

"THE ORIGIN OF SPECIES"

It was nearly 200 years after Newton and the birth of modern physics that Darwin's book was published, and equipped the biologist with an adequate conceptual scheme. *The Origin of Species* contained two theories about living things.

First, there is the *theory of evolution* in the strict sense. This states that all living organisms have evolved from common ancestors in a gradual historical process of change and diversification. The theory rejects the notion that all organisms were designed and created at the beginning of time. Its great implication is that we can fully understand living organisms in scientific terms only if we study the historical process by which they came into being.

Second, there is the *theory of natural selection* which Darwin advanced as an explanation of the *causes of evolution.* The theory of natural selection shows how, in the evolution of life, complexity, design and apparent purpose have been brought about by causes that are as automatic and materially deterministic as the fall of Newton's apple or the circling of the planets. Theological design and purpose are excluded.

In its fully developed modern form, the theory of evolution bridges the gap between biology and physics in another way. It regards the origin of life as only one aspect of the over-all evolution of the planet earth itself. Our planet is somewhere between two and five billion years old; during this immense stretch of time its form and physical condition have changed profoundly. Simple forms of life arose about two billion years ago as a natural consequence of changing conditions. And they arose as complex organizations of the same materials that make up the rest of our planet—the matter which the physicist studies. In their ultimate nature living organisms are thus at one with the rest of the universe, and the ideal of a unified science embracing the living and nonliving is, in principle, possible.

THE THEORY OF EVOLUTION

Glimmerings in the eighteenth century. Clear glimmerings of the evolutionary mode of thought can be found as far back as 1760, when the French naturalist Buffon was writing his *Natural History of Animals.* He, like other naturalists in the mid-eighteenth century, still believed that all living creatures were created at the beginning of time, independently of each other, to suit their special ways of life. But Buffon became uneasy with this explanation for reasons he spelled out when he discussed the structure of the

pig's foot. To appreciate his argument, we must compare, as Buffon did, the pig's foot with that of other four-footed animals like the horse and the dog (Fig. 2-1). What is it about these limbs that disturbed him? Two points.

First, if all these animals were created independently of one another, each for a special way of life, why do they show basic similarities in structure? They all have backbones and a skull; they all have four limbs, and each animal has a great deal of identical detail in the limbs. The bat that flies, the pig that walks, the mole that digs, the turtle that swims—the limbs of all these animals are only variations in which a common theme is detectable (Fig. 19-2). It looked in the mid-eighteenth century as if the creation of these animals had followed a generalized blueprint and had introduced only differences of detail in each. Now, if the blueprint is specially designed for walking, how can it also be the best for digging, for flying, for swimming? If these animals had been specially created, *independently* of each other, surely engineering ingenuity, with a free rein, would not have restricted itself to one blueprint.

Still more peculiar is another aspect of the pig's foot: it has *functionless* toes.[1] There are, of course, the two toes the animal walks on. But the closest scrutiny and thought fail to reveal any *purpose,* any meaning, to the two small side toes which never touch the ground. Clearly they cannot be accounted for in terms of the independent design and special creation of all creatures for their special way of life.

The old scheme of explanation was, thus, inadequate in the light of the facts. Facts are the final judge of the merit of theories, and in their light it was clear to Buffon that he needed a new way of explanation, a new theory. Again, it should be emphasized that no amount of new observation in itself will reveal the new theory we need. A new theory will come only if a man like Buffon creates it. Buffon did; and, as with all theories, it began as a sort of inspired guess.

Both the points disturbing Buffon could be

[1] The pig's foot is not unique in this respect. Functionless vestiges of toes can be seen in other animals like the horse (Fig. 2-1).

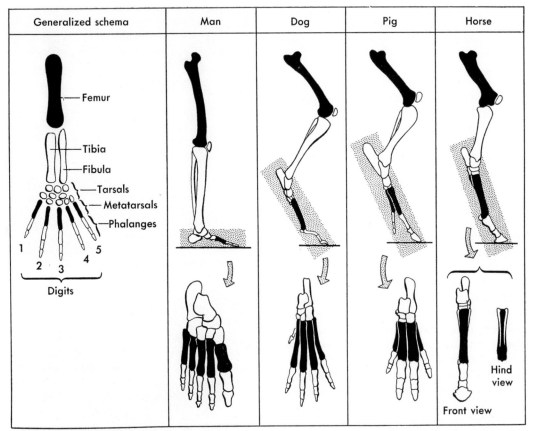

Generalized schema	Man	Dog	Pig	Horse

Femur

Tibia

Fibula

Tarsals

Metatarsals

Phalanges

1 5
2 3 4

Digits

Hind view

Front view

2-1 Vertebrate hindlimbs. The generalized schema shows the basic theme found in the hindlimbs of all vertebrates. Notice how the position of the foot differs in the four organisms illustrated.

explained, and thus no longer be "difficulties," if he viewed living things, not as an array of independently created organisms, but as descendants of common ancestors. He believed the pig had extra toes because it *inherited* them (modified to be sure) from an ancestor in which they were fully developed and functional. In Buffon's view these diverse animals —swimmers, runners, diggers, and fliers—all seemed to be making the most of one basic design because they were all descendants of a common ancestor from which they had inherited their similarities. Buffon regarded all these diverse animals as members of one ancient family, distant relatives scattered over the globe, each making his way in the conditions he found himself in—making the best, not necessarily of a *bad* job, but at any rate of limitations imposed by his inheritance.

The evolution of evolutionary thought.
Other naturalists before and after Buffon had similar glimmerings of the idea of evolution. Among them was Erasmus Darwin, Charles Darwin's grandfather, who had the evolutionary idea around 1790. During the later days of the French Revolution Buffon's student Lamarck wrote extensively about the evolutionary hypothesis. Still the idea, immensely useful as it would have been, did not catch on in the thought environment in which it then found itself. Not until 1859, a hundred years after Buffon, was the idea developed by Charles Darwin into a theory which transformed biological thought. This long delay is extremely interesting. It illustrates the living nature of science as a human activity, and how conservatism in thought—as in politics—is cautious about accepting

novelty too quickly. There were three main reasons for the delay. First, none of the pre-Darwinian thinkers had compiled sufficiently convincing evidence to substantiate their hypotheses. Second, no one had proposed a plausible and testable explanation of the causes of evolution. Third, the climate of thought had been that of belief in a static, nonevolving universe, created just about as it is now.

That medieval climate of thought had begun to change in early eighteenth century and continued steadily to do so until by 1859 the scientific world was at last prepared to accept a biological theory of historical change. In fact, the idea of biological evolution involved only a transfer and extension of evolutionary concepts already widely accepted in other fields. Geologists [2] had established that the earth had had a long history, that it had evolved through millions of years. Social and political philosophers had also generally concluded that human societies and institutions evolve. The French Revolution and the Industrial Revolution had provided examples of social evolution occurring before their very eyes. Thus on many sides an evolutionary climate of thought had grown up and had prepared the way for almost instant acceptance of Darwin's ideas. Like their bodily structure, the thought structure of living things evolves.

Proof of the theory of evolution. One of the many lines of evidence which Darwin marshaled in support of his theory of evolution concerned the fossil remains of animals preserved in the earth's rocks. This kind of evidence has been so greatly added to since Darwin's day that it now constitutes a virtual proof of the theory.

The structure of the earth itself has a wonderfully fascinating history. Its surface has been folded and crinkled by massive upheavals and settlings the durations of which are measured in millions of years. We know that the earth itself is at least two billion years old, probably much older. The crinklings of its

2 Darwin was strongly influenced by the great geologist Lyell, whose work marked final proof that the earth has evolved.

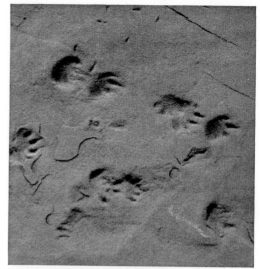

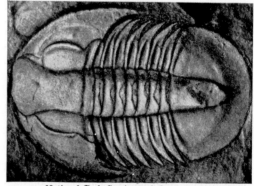

National Park Service and Smithsonian Institution

2-2 Fossils from the Grand Canyon. *Top,* footprints of a primitive amphibian or reptile. *Center,* part of an ancient seed fern (*Supaia*). *Bottom,* a primitive relative of our modern crabs and lobsters, belonging to a group called trilobites.

surface have given us mountain ranges now worn down by the abrasion of wind and water. Erosion going on every day, as now, again straddles almost unthinkably long stretches of time. For the curious and trained eye the story of these long-past events can be unraveled with considerable accuracy. For the geologist, as for the biologist, the explanation of present-day structures demands knowledge of *how they came to be* in an historical process of evolution—in this case an evolution of earth structure.

For the tale of earth's history, the most telling aspect is the way one class of rocks—*sedimentary rocks*—is laid down layer on layer as time passes. Rocks on the surface of the earth are constantly eroded in a diversity of ways, chemical and mechanical. An obvious form of erosion is caused by the buffeting of wind and water. Rock fragments worn away in this process are washed down into rivers as sand and silt. Eventually these sediments are deposited as *sedimentary* rocks, which often in

the course of time become compacted and hardened.

When living things die and fall into swamps and rivers or are washed down to sea or fall (as marine organisms do) to the ocean floor, they may become entombed in deposits of sediments. Encased in this way, they are sometimes protected from total decay: their entombed hard parts—bones, teeth, scales, or shells—are preserved as *fossils* in the sedimentary rocks (Fig. 2-2). As time passes, each new layer of rock is laid down *on top of* the earlier layer. When at a later time a river like the Colorado cuts through the many layers of sedimentary rocks, it exposes, as in the Grand Canyon (Fig. 2-3), a monumental document, not only of earth's history, but of the history of life. If you were to start at the bottom of the Grand Canyon and climb upwards to the rim, your journey would start not only 6000 feet below the rim; it would begin, in a sense, some two billion years ago. As you climbed upwards the layers of rocks you passed would

Union Pacific Railroad

2-3   The Grand Canyon of the Colorado River.

yield for you fossilized samples of the remains of the animals living in successive epochs.

The fossils found in the rocks prove conclusively that life has changed. We start near the bottom of the canyon with strange forms we have never seen before. Some ancient animals and plants, we find, were very durable: the history of a single kind may span many layers, many millions of years. By and large, however, the picture changes rapidly—rapidly for the climber of the canyon wall, who covers millions of years in hours of climbing. But the change is never chaotic: the new forms that appear are in most respects very much like "last year's model." As we approach the top of the sequence of rocks and fossils, the fossil creatures become more familiar, heralding the emergence of forms much like those alive today.

This vista is exciting for everyone, but there is a special thrill that comes with a little more biological information. The study of all the living vertebrate animals (animals which, like

fish, lizards, horses, and men, have backbones) shows they have many basic features in common. We emphasized that fact when we followed Buffon in his approach toward a theory of evolution (p. 26). Among the vertebrates there are also evidently many groups, each of which has its peculiarities. We can, for instance, readily distinguish such major groups as fishes, amphibians (frogs, salamanders), reptiles (snakes, lizards, turtles), birds, and mammals (dogs, horses, and men). They are all vertebrates, but each has special characteristics related to a way of life. When these groups are compared, keeping evolutionary ideas in mind, another highly significant fact becomes evident: there is a suggestion of a *sequence* among the groups. Mammals have many features in common with fishes (this is their common vertebrate inheritance), but even those basic features seem to be more highly elaborated in the mammals. For instance, both fishes and mammals have brains and there is much resemblance between them,

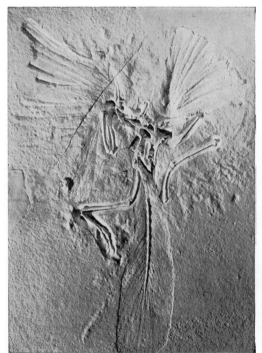 

American Museum of Natural History and British Museum (Natural History)

2.4 Archaeopteryx. *A.* A photograph of the actual fossil. *B.* A reconstruction of the animal. The feathers (birdlike feature) are clear in the fossil. The animal also possessed teeth and an incompletely specialized forelimb (reptile-like feature).

but the brains of mammals are more complex, somehow more *progressive* than those of fishes. Moreover, the mammals seem to have more things *added* to the basic vertebrate inheritance—such characteristics as retention of the egg in the mother's body and an elaborate mechanism for nourishing the developing young there.

Innumerable facts of this kind are explained by the hypothesis that these particular groups of vertebrates evolved one from another in this sequence: fish → amphibians → reptiles → mammals. Of course, no *recent* reptile can have given rise to the recent mammals. The hypothesis is that recent reptiles and recent mammals had a common ancestry and that the common ancestry was *more like* the recent reptiles than like the recent mammals. Or, the other way around, recent reptiles have not changed as much—evolved as far—as recent mammals. Similarly, recent amphibians have not evolved as far as recent reptiles, or recent fishes as far as recent amphibians.

This hypothesis is subject to a conclusive test. Although it is based on recent, now living animals, it *predicts* that fishes, amphibians, reptiles, and mammals will appear in the fossil record in that order. The fossils have been found and the facts are available; they agree precisely with the prediction and provide convincing proof that the hypothesis is true. In greater detail, the hypothesis also predicts that there were ancient animals *intermediate* between the main groups of vertebrates, although such intermediates no longer exist. That prediction is also completely fulfilled by fossils. Perhaps the most famous intermediate is that between reptiles and the birds (also derived from reptiles along a different line from that of reptile → mammal evolution): *Archaeopteryx* (Fig. 2-4). Fish-amphibian, amphibian-reptile, and reptile-mammal transitional forms are also now well known as fossils.

The information we get from fossils is not restricted to the great transitions from one major group to another. We have the detailed story of many individual case histories within larger groups. The history of the horse is a good example. Like the pig's foot, which originally stimulated Buffon to evolutionary ideas, the foot of the modern horse lacks some of the

five toes generally characteristic of vertebrates. Indeed, it has only one functional toe on each foot. The evolutionary history of the horse over the last 60 million years is well known. It shows that the horse's ancestor of 60 million years ago had not the one toe we see on each foot today, but four on the front and three on the hind. Furthermore, although the *exact* line of connection with still older ancestors is not yet established in detail, the fossils also clearly show that horses were derived from a primitive group (Condylarths) with *five* toes on each foot. In the evolution of the horse (Fig. 2-5) there has been a re-

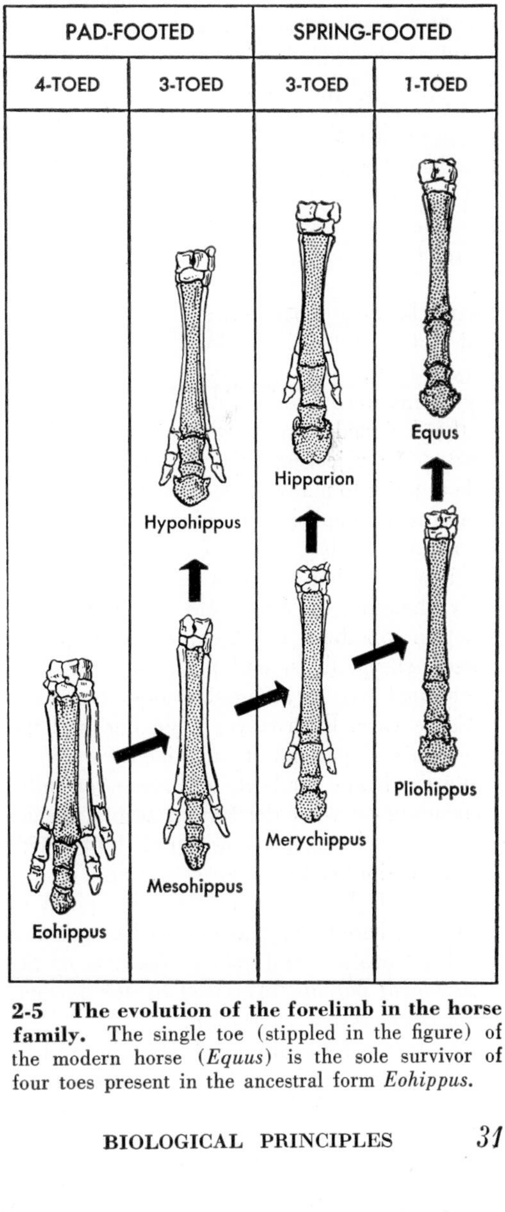

PAD-FOOTED		SPRING-FOOTED	
4-TOED	3-TOED	3-TOED	1-TOED

2-5 The evolution of the forelimb in the horse family. The single toe (stippled in the figure) of the modern horse (*Equus*) is the sole survivor of four toes present in the ancestral form *Eohippus*.

duction in number of toes that culminates in our modern horse, with only one toe that is functional, and bony slivers that are vestiges of two more.

THE THEORY OF NATURAL SELECTION

Darwin's first clue: selective breeding of farm animals. Darwin gave the name "natural selection" to the process which he regarded as the main cause of evolution. The name itself has caused confusion by suggesting to some people that evolutionary change is due to nature's undertaking a deliberate and conscious selection of organisms. This misunderstanding could not be greater, for, as we shall see, it misses the very point of genius which makes Darwin's theory of the causes of evolution superior to all others. The word "selection" occurred to Darwin because of his great interest in the practices of animal breeders. These practices form for us, as they did for Darwin, the best starting point for a brief outline of what natural selection is and means to biology as a whole.

In 1859 the evolutionary ideas of Buffon, Lamarck, and other early naturalists were still not accepted in biology. The orthodox view was still that all species (or kinds) of organisms were "immutable" (unchangeable) in the designed form in which they had been created. In rejecting this view, Darwin was able to point to many lines of evidence, among them the accomplishments of animal breeders. Ever since the beginning of recorded history, farmers and other breeders have been deliberately changing the form and hereditary constitution of their livestock, such as cows, horses, sheep, dogs, and pigeons. How does the animal breeder accomplish these changes?

Cattle vary. Even calves from one and the same pair of parents are not identical. Some cattle are better for beef, and some for milk. Depending on what the farmer wants, he deliberately selects the cows and bulls with which he builds the next generation of his herd. Slowly he improves—from his point of view—the hereditary make-up of his animals. His herd evolves, and *evolves because of the selection of parents*, exercised by the farmer, in each successive generation.

The force of all this struck Darwin, and he asked whether there could be *in nature* a force which in a blind mechanical fashion takes the place of the farmer who selects his animals. Could there be a process of *natural* (non-human) *selection* whereby animal and plant heredity is slowly changed from generation to generation, producing thereby the historical evolution so clearly seen in fossils and the living structures of "creatures"? [3]

The answer to Darwin's question is "yes"; and again the outlines of the answer were derived from an earlier writer. This time it was the famous minister-economist, the Reverend Thomas Malthus (1766-1834).

Darwin's second clue: what checks population growth. Malthus had been concerned about a simple piece of arithmetic involved in the reproduction of living things. Each generation arises from the preceding generation: the continuity of life hinges on the act of reproduction that bridges one generation to the next. Suppose, for a moment, that all offspring survive to reproduce in their turn. Then some trivial but important rules must be followed if the population is to remain stable in number. Each pair of parents must limit themselves to two children. Of course this is meant in terms of averages only. If one family produces four offspring and another produces none, then the average is two per family. And it is an average of precisely two per family that is needed to maintain the population at a stable number. One is not enough, and three is too many. Three offspring per pair of parents is a net gain of one, and represents a 50 per cent gain in population size each generation. The arithmetic may be trivial, but the consequences for living things is staggering.

Now the most cursory glance at nature reveals two facts that pose a major problem. First, in living things as a whole the number of offspring per pair of parents is much greater than two. If you have ever eaten caviar you will know that the female sturgeon

[3] This word "creature," which we all still use for living things, is itself a verbal fossil. It is preserved from that bygone epoch, ended with Darwin, when the conceptual scheme for life was one of special creation. Our language is full of such fossils testifying, like the petrified remains in the rocks, to an evolutionary process, in this case an evolution of thought, expression, and ways of explanation.

launches considerably more than two eggs into the world. As a ballad has it, "the female sturgeon is a very fine fish"; certainly the taste of her eggs is unique, but their abundance is not. It is vulgarly commonplace. Second, in spite of this profligacy, the sturgeon populations do not increase spectacularly, and this again is no distinction. It is the rule.

Populations in nature tend, in general, towards a stable population size, although temporary increases followed by compensatory declines are common. And even when—as in man since 1600—populations maintain sustained increases over long periods, the rate of increase is never as great as it would be if all the offspring in one generation succeeded in contributing to the next. Were this not so all living populations would increase at a fantastic rate that is never sustained in nature.

Clearly there is in each generation an excess of offspring that fail to attain reproductive status. What prevents the excess from reproducing are those everyday hazards which stand in the way of keeping alive long enough and healthy enough to mature, to find a mate, and—what is more—to be acceptable to that mate. To a large extent all life, plant and animal, has the aspect of a tragic process in the old Greek sense that the root of tragedy is the remorseless working of things. If life is not actually tragic, this is because life—apart from mankind—does not have *conscious* purposes whose thwarting by remorseless natural processes is tragedy itself. But all the external aspect of tragedy is there. Seeds fall on infertile ground; forests are devastated by disease and fire; young creatures, untutored in wariness, fall prey to hungry predators; and predators go with empty bellies because for the most part their prey is wary. Death comes to living things through accident, strife, or their own incompetence. And for the most part *death comes before they can reproduce*; this is why populations do not keep increasing. Malthus gave this picture, gloomy as it is, an even gloomier tinge. Some of the Malthusian gloom passed on into Darwin's writings, which probably laid too much stress on the bloody strife and combat in nature. But all the essentials of the correct answer are there, and Darwin saw their full significance.

Natural selection: solution of the riddle. There is a double significance to all the hazards of life. They not only (1) constitute the answer to Malthus' question of what checks population increases, but they also (2) constitute the natural substitute which Darwin sought for the animal husbandman who selectively breeds his livestock. In each generation in nature the small group of individuals which carries out the essential role of reproducing the next generation is truly a *select* group. The farmer selects on the basis of milk production, and slowly improves his herd in this respect. The *process of natural selection*, which is the sum total of life's hazards, *selects on the basis of competence to live, or rather competence to reproduce.*

Natural selection is like a gigantic and macabre game, a mixture of "blindman's buff" and "winner take all." Let us call it the target game. In this game the goal or purpose is to hit the target. The target is successful reproduction. The game is a very strange affair in all respects because the players do not know they are playing it. Accordingly they are quite unaware of the goal or the rules, of which, moreover, there are only two:

First, *every player that hits the target gets another turn, because the target is reproduction.* Every organism that reproduces leaves his offspring in the game; they, in turn, are potential reproducers. But the organisms that do not hit the target (i.e., do not reproduce) leave the game forever.

Second, *each player* (in the form of his offspring) *enters the next round with a stack of chips proportionate to his own success in the last round.* Thus the more offspring an organism produces, the greater are the chances that one of them will in his turn succeed in reproducing.

In spite of the scarcity of rules and the players' ignorance of them and of the goal, the game is a very orderly affair! The majority of players are highly skillful. How does this come about? In each round of the game (each generation) we start afresh with only those organisms whose parents successfully hit the target in the last round. The great biological fact of heredity makes all the difference. The chances of success in the next round are good or bad according to the player's inherited competence to leave offspring. Thus in each generation the proportions of more and less successful reproducers shift in favor of the more successful. The over-all performance of the players (the population of living organisms) improves with the long passage of time and untold numbers of generations.

Improvement in the performance of the target-game players is slow: organic evolution has spanned more than a billion years of earth's history. There are several reasons for this slowness. Many an unwary animal never meets a predator and, basically incompetent though he is, survives to hit the target of reproduction and thus leave incompetent offspring in the game's next round. But there is a more fundamental and important reason for the slowness of organic evolution than this inefficiency of natural selection. It is slow because organisms,[4] *not knowing* what their evolutionary target is, cannot deliberately improve. The progress of evolution is dependent entirely on chance variations in heredity over which the organism has no control. Most chance variations in hereditary constitution impair the ability of organisms to survive and reproduce, but a few constitute improvements. An all-important feature of the target game is that it automatically discriminates between the good and the bad hereditary changes and guarantees perpetuation, from generation to generation, of only the good innovations. Of course, "good" here simply means good in respect to survival and reproductive ability.

Here is the crucial point in the conceptual scheme which Darwin gave to biology. The apparently designed nature and purpose of living organisms are not the product of some personal purpose and intelligence. They are the outcome of a wholly material and deterministic process. Darwin's writings make us look more closely at the design and purpose—in a word, at the *adaptation*—of living organisms. We now perceive that all adaptation is precisely what we expect the target game (natural selection) to produce; it is all ultimately directed at survival in order to reproduce. Moreover, as we shall see in a later chapter (18), the adaptation of organisms has the makeshift

[4] Excepting man.

and opportunistic character that we would expect a blind and automatic process like natural selection to produce. It lacks—as Buffon noted for the pig's foot—what we would expect of an intelligent personal designer setting out to create organisms specifically for the tasks they must execute.

THE BIOLOGIST'S CONCEPTUAL SCHEME

The starlight we see has the same properties tonight when it strikes our eyes as it had when it set out on its long journey through space thousands of years ago. Had there been a human mind present seeking an explanation of light when it began its journey, the facts and their explanation would have been the same then as they are now. History does little but mark the passage of time in the physical world of nonliving matter.[5]

Not so with life. Here the passage of time is a pageant of change. It produces a sequence of unique and highly individualistic events that may alternately delight the historian of life because of their rich diversity, or vex him in their intractability to fit a simple formula. When you look at a living organism, as distinct from a grain of salt, you are looking at an "historical creature," something whose own individual form was molded by complex events in the long passage of time. To understand this creature you must understand its history—its evolution.

One cornerstone of evolutionary biology is that it regards living systems as having evolved, due to material causes, from nonliving systems. This is an event in life's history we know little about, for obvious reasons, although it is one we can make some very plausible inferences about. But as to the truth of the origin of life from nonliving matter, few biologists have any doubt.

Nonliving matter is the stuff that living things are made of, and the long line of discovery and understanding about matter, which the physicist and chemist have achieved, is like enormous capital in the biologist's bank account. It is there ready for use in his task of explaining how matter in its living state behaves, because all the laws that describe

[5] It is true there is such a thing as stellar evolution, but its products lack the complexity and apparent purpose characteristic of life.

the behavior of nonliving matter are fully valid when it becomes part of a living system.

Confronted with a living thing, the biologist will, therefore, certainly have to ask all the same questions that the chemist and physicist would ask: What is it made of? What does it do? How does it do it? What is the cause of this or that event in the organism? Pursuit of these questions leads to what is called the *causal* type of explanation in biology. Full answers to them would be given by a detailed account of the chemical composition and mechanical behavior of the living thing we were studying. Nevertheless, elaborate as these answers would be, they would still leave much to be explained. Why?

The historical nature of living things compels the biologist to ask two more questions unique to his science: "What function—what purpose—does this structure fulfill in the life of the organism?" and "How did it evolve?"

The horse's leg is not fully understood until we show how the detailed anatomy of bones, muscles, and ligaments serves the purpose of rapid locomotion; and how rapid locomotion serves the purpose of escape from swift predators; and, finally, how escape from predators keeps the horse in the target game—alive, that is, in order to reproduce. The question as to what purpose a living structure serves is now a perfectly valid and scientific question because it has been freed of the confusing personification of nature that it involved before we understood natural selection and its consequences. The question of purpose leads to what is called the *functional* mode of explanation in biology.

Causal and functional explanations still leave some features of the horse's leg unexplained. There are, for instance, those two slivers of bone in the horse's foot which we discussed earlier. No physical law explains them, and they serve no apparent purpose. It is only when we ask "How did the leg evolve?" that we find the explanation in the historical chain of events that derived today's horse, with its one-toed foot, from an ancestor with a many-toed foot. This is the *evolutionary* mode of explanation.

Living things are certainly different from the nonliving in requiring these special modes of explanation—functional and evolutionary.

But this does not imply that there is some special ingredient in living organisms—"life" or an *élan vital*—that is absent from nonliving things. We must emphasize that the word "life" can only be employed as a useful shorthand term referring collectively to the whole world of living things and the processes they undergo. It does not refer to a special something that exists independently of nonliving matter.

What, then, is the difference between matter, living and nonliving? It is the way the matter is organized or put together. The elements of matter that make up rocks, soil, air, and water are nitrogen, oxygen, hydrogen, carbon, potassium, sodium, and many others. These same elements are what we find when we analyze the living organism. Here, however, they are complexly combined and arranged in a fashion never encountered in the nonliving world. Put together in just the right way, these elements form a system—an *organism*—that possesses new capacities: growth and reproduction. The organism *grows* by feeding on nonliving materials [6] and incorporating them into its characteristic organization. Complex and fragile, the individual organism always dies, but before it does, it *reproduces*; it leaves a copy of itself. Remarkable as it is, the resemblance of offspring to parents is never perfect; *variation* is a universal feature of living things.

Variation and reproduction ultimately are responsible for the unique features of the world of life, the features that elicit the biologists' questions about function and evolution. Variation and reproduction thrust the whole world of life into the target game, guaranteeing perpetuation from generation to generation of only the most efficient reproducers. Once matter has become organized to reproduce, there is no escape from natural selection and the evolution it causes. What is evolved in this process are all those aspects of the living thing—*adaptations*—that serve the end of efficient reproduction, and that demand for their full understanding the unique biological questions about functional and historical ori-

6 Of course, nearly all animals appear to feed on living matter. But the lion's prey is dead and digested to a solution of molecules before it actually enters his body through the wall of his stomach and intestines (p. 79).

gin. Just what the organization of matter is that, once achieved, produces a living reproducing system remains unknown in all its detail; to learn this is an ultimate goal of the biological sciences.

A skeptic might be uneasy at the way the notion of "life" has evaporated, so to speak, into the "organization of matter." He would counter our view with two propositions. First, he would say that "life" does exist as something special and independent of matter—that "life" is Bergson's *élan vital*, a vital force. Second, he would charge that of course we do not detect "life" in our standard scientific analyses because, by its very nature, it cannot be pointed to or measured.

Our reply to these charges is as follows: The aim of science—as distinct from the arts, speculative philosophy, or religion—is to discover the facts of the world and the theoretical schemes that explain them. As scientists we demand that our theories, above all else, be of such a kind that we can know when they are wrong. Here, then, is our objection to the *élan vital*: it has no more respectable place in science than those little men who allegedly manipulate the stock market from an obscure spot on the other side of the moon. You cannot prove that *élan vital* exists; we cannot prove it does not. We can only bicker endlessly about it, and bickering never leads to knowledge. It is *as scientists* that we refrain from using the notion of an unknowable vital force in biological explanations. We do so because the whole history of science tells us that progress in the accumulation of knowledge and understanding has been dependent on the rejection of untestable hypotheses like yours, and on the provisional acceptance of hypotheses like mine. As scientists, however, we have no more right to deny the artistic or religious validity of your *belief* in a vital spirit than

you have the right to assert that such a spirit has a legitimate place in science.

Chapter Summary

Science as a human activity, motivated by our curiosity to understand the world we live in and by the practical need to master our environment.

Observed facts and their explanation by theories.

Theories as statements generalizing our experience; their discovery as a creative human process; the testability of all scientific theories.

The birth of modern science in the European Renaissance.

Its preoccupation with the physical problems of the nonliving world.

The development of the physicists' conceptual scheme: the idea of mechanism and the impersonal determination of events.

A conceptual scheme as a "society of ideas" influencing the growth and development of science.

Reason for the slow growth of biology: the adaptation of living organisms, perceived as "design" and "purpose," unexplainable in the physicists' conceptual scheme.

The impact of *The Origin of Species* on the growth of biology as a science: the theory of natural selection explains the evolution of adaptation as a natural process compatible with the physicists' way of thought.

Three modes of explanation in biology:
(1) Causal.
(2) Functional.
(3) Evolutionary.

The scientist's attitude toward "vital forces"; the difference between the living and the nonliving a difference only of complexity of organization.

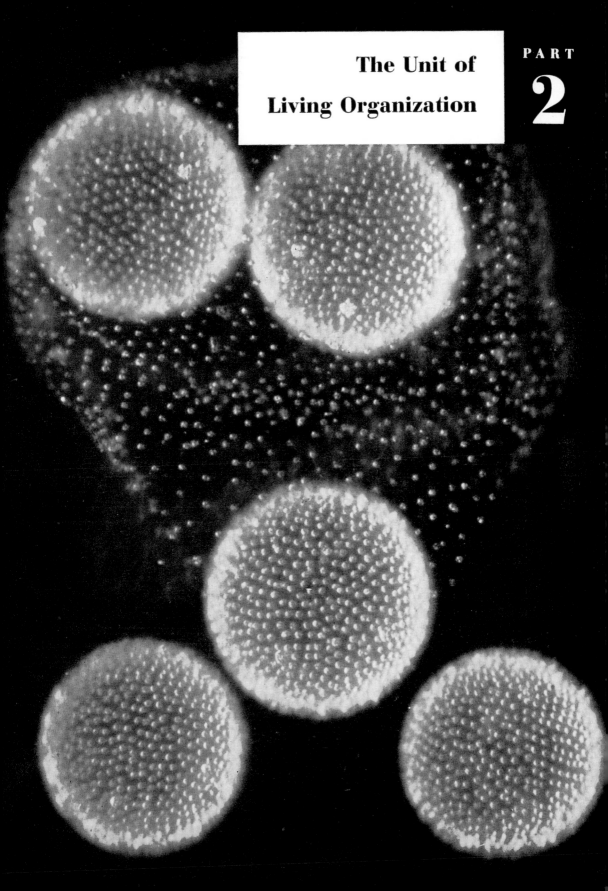

The Unit of
Living Organization

INTRODUCTION TO PART 2

The photograph introducing Part 2 illustrates a microscopically small organism called *Volvox*. It is breaking up and liberating five young *Volvox*. At the high magnification at which the photograph was taken, the structure of both parent and young resolves into hundreds of glistening round particles. These particles are cells; they are the basic structural units of all life and the subject matter of Part 2.

Organisms are composed of cells: plant or animal, large or small, *Volvox* or man—the generalization holds for *all* living things; they are either single cells or groups of cells. The discovery of this great truth, which is the heart of the cell theory, was one of the outstanding achievements of the nineteenth century and ranks with the theory of evolution as a cornerstone of modern biology.

Every cell is, so to speak, a world of life in miniature. Like the organism of which it is a part—or even the whole—the cell is complex and organized: it responds to stimuli and is capable of movement; it feeds and respires, expending energy to maintain its ordered state and execute other work such as secretion; and, like other larger living systems, it can reproduce itself. In large and structurally complex organisms like ourselves all special parts like bones, muscles, and nerves are composed of special cells: bone cells, muscle cells, and nerve cells.

As the significance of the cell theory became fully appreciated at the close of the nineteenth century, a great German biologist summed it up as follows:

> It is to the cell that the study of every bodily function sooner or later drives us. In the muscle cell lies the problem of the heartbeat and that of muscular contraction; in the gland cell reside the causes of secretion; in the epithelial cell, in the white blood cell, lies the problem of the absorption of food; and the secrets of the mind are hidden in the ganglion [nerve] cell. (Verworn, 1895)

With Verworn's fine sentences as our guide we turn in Part 2 from the gross features of life in the forest and on the coral reef to a study of the structure and activities of the cell as the basic unit of life.

Chapter 3 describes the form and visible organization of cells; it describes how they are differentiated in structure and are organized into tissues like bone, muscle, and nerve to fulfill diverse functions.

Chapter 4 answers the questions: What chemical substances are cells made of? What physical processes are involved in their living activities?

Chapter 5 then turns to the important questions: Where do cells get their materials and energy? How do they manipulate these resources in carrying on their organized life?

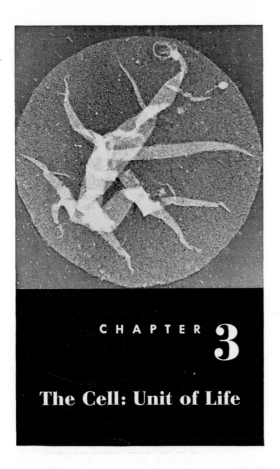

This delicate structure is the plasma membrane that was the living boundary of a human red blood cell. Cell contents have been removed and the membrane photographed ($\times 7000$) with an electron microscope. (Courtesy Dr. Joseph Hoffman, Princeton University)

CHAPTER 3

The Cell: Unit of Life

The Cell Theory

DEVELOPMENT OF THE CELL THEORY

"We have seen that all organisms are composed of essentially like parts, namely, of cells." (Schwann, 1839)

"Where a cell exists there must have been a pre-existing cell, just as the animal arises only from an animal and the plant only from a plant. The principle is thus established, even though the strict proof has not yet been produced for every detail, that throughout the whole series of living forms, whether entire animal or plant organisms, or their component parts, there rules an eternal law of continuous development [= continuous reproduction]." (Virchow, 1858)

These two statements, one in 1839 and the other in 1858, mark the emergence of the *cell theory* in its definite form. The cell theory is

one of the two great foundations of modern biology, the other being the theory of evolution (1859). The two theories have much in common: they reached their definitive form almost simultaneously, and both had been developing over a long period of time. In their modern form they merge almost inextricably.

A cell is the basic unit of life. It is the smallest unit of matter of which we can mean-

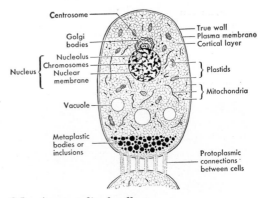

3-1 A generalized cell.

ingfully say, "This is alive." The vast majority of cells are small (Fig. 3-7). Most of them, indeed, are not visible as distinct units without the aid of a lens or microscope. On first inspection a cell appears as a simple sac of fluid material bounded by a membrane, containing a definite body called the nucleus.

It is impossible to be sure when living cells were first seen. Certainly it was long after the

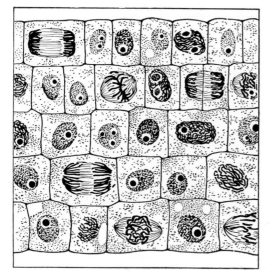
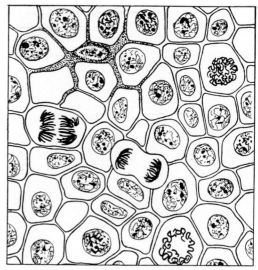

3-2 Cellular nature of plant and animal tissue. *A.* A section of part of the growing tip of an onion root. *B.* A piece of salamander skin. Nuclei and dividing cells can be seen in both tissues. In those cells which are dividing, the nucleus takes the form of threadlike bodies called chromosomes (p. 47).

necessary instruments were available. Simple lenses were known long before the Christian era began, and spectacles were commonly worn by the wealthy of the fourteenth century. But there is no record of optical instruments being put to biological use before the new curiosity of the Renaissance somehow sug-

3-3 Hooke's figures (1665) of cellular organization in cork.

Bettmann Archive

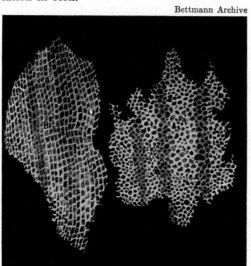

gested it. Two seventeenth-century biologists did see what we call cells today. Robert Hooke (1635-1703) observed with a lens that wood charcoal, cork, and other plant tissues are made up of small cavities separated by walls; in 1665 he described cellular organization in plants (Fig. 3-3). A few years later Anthony van Leeuwenhoek first saw minute single-celled organisms in a drop of pond water. But neither of these men, nor the many others who saw and drew cells throughout the eighteenth century, realized the significance of their observations.

It was not until 1839, when Schwann published the book quoted at the beginning of this chapter, that any *generalization* was made. Schwann clearly perceived that *all living organisms consist of cells: they are either single cells or groups of cells.* There is no life apart from the life of cells. Even in large and com-

3-4 A diversity of cells. All ×700 except *J*, which is ×1500. *A.* Human muscle cells. Note their elongate form. *B.* A fat storage cell from human connective tissue. The nucleus is a small body near the cell membrane. The whole of the (unstippled) central part of the cell is occupied by a large globule of fat. *C.* Human red blood cells. *D.* Human white blood cells. *E.* Three epithelial (p. 63) cells

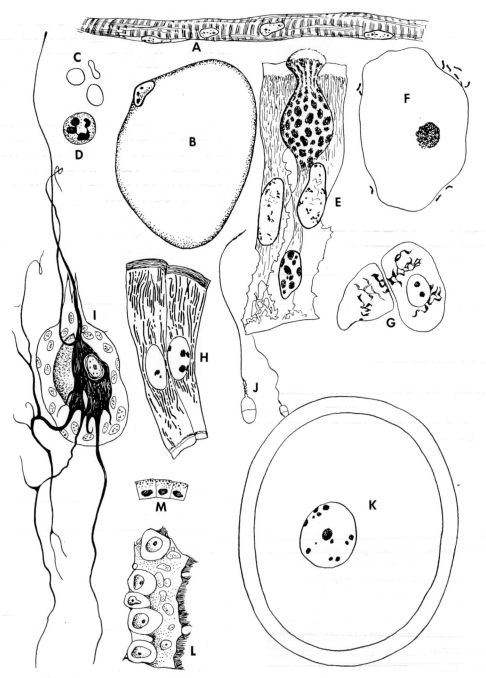

from the intestine of an axolotl, a larval salamander. The flask-shaped central cell secretes mucus which lubricates passage of food. *F*. An epithelial cell from the lining of the human vagina. Several bacteria lie beside it. *G*. Two cells from the liver of a mouse; the Golgi element (p. 48) can be seen in both of them. *H*. Two epithelial cells from the rat's in-intestine; they contain threadlike mitochondria (p. 48) lying above and below the nucleus. *I*. A human nerve cell. Note how it is drawn out into fiberlike processes. The nerve cell itself (black in the figure) is encased by a second cell containing many nuclei. *J*. Human sperm cell ($\times 1500$). *K*. Human egg cell, with a sperm entering it. *L*. Part of the human placenta (p. 389); five separate cells are overlaid by a syncytium that bears cilia (p. 225). A syncytium is a multinucleate mass of protoplasm that is not separated by membranes into distinct cells. *M*. Three cells from the human eye (retina) containing pigment granules.

plex organisms like man or a giant redwood tree the whole body proves to be an aggregation of some billions of cells. Every specialized part of such organisms—skin, bone, muscle, nerve, and even blood; wood, bark, flower, and root—proves to be composed of specialized cells.

It is a long way from merely observing cells to reaching the great inductive generalization that Schwann announced. A generalization as wide as Schwann's must surely indicate some underlying natural process of still greater consequence than the mere generalization itself. This underlying process is made clear in Virchow's later statement that all cells arise only from pre-existing cells. The full significance of this statement emerges when we consider how it relates the cell concept to two other major *generalizations* that appeared simultaneously with it. First, it conforms completely with the contemporary work of the French scientist Pasteur. Second, it merges with the theory of evolution that Darwin published in 1859, the year after Virchow's book.

Between 1859 and 1861 Pasteur proved as conclusively as science can that in the modern world no living thing arises except from other living things. Pasteur's work was immediately concerned with questions about the fermentation of wine and the putrefaction of other nutritious fluids. He had shown that the processes of fermentation and putrefaction were completely contingent on the presence of minute living organisms, "germs." He could kill the germs with heat and maintained what seemed at that time the preposterous assumption that the air was full of living germs. Thus he asserted that nutrient fluids, like broth, milk, or wine, must be exposed to the air before they will ferment or putrefy. His critics were still inclined to the view that the living germs responsible for fermentation did not come from the air but arose spontaneously from the nonliving materials in the wine or milk. Pasteur won his point with a wonderfully simple and conclusive experiment. He took two flasks that contained a nutrient broth infected with germs capable of causing putrefaction. One of these flasks was subjected to prolonged heating. The other flask was not heated; it putrefied immediately. The heated flask did not; it remained free of putrefaction for months until the neck of the flask was broken, exposing the broth to the direct fall of germs from the air. Once the neck was broken the broth putrefied immediately, and Pasteur showed that this was again due to germs. Pasteur's experiments marked the end of a line of similar work stretching back to Spallanzani in the eighteenth, and Redi in the seventeenth, century; it marked the end of belief in spontaneous generation and the establishment of the principle of *biogenesis*— "all life comes from life." Virchow's principle that "all cells come from cells" is just a more explicit form of this same truth, because all life takes the form of cells. Pasteur's minute "germs" were single-celled organisms, bacteria and yeasts.

The relationship of the cell theory to evolution follows from Virchow's sentence "The principle is thus established, . . . , that throughout the whole series of living forms, whether entire animal or plant organisms, or their component parts, there rules an eternal law of *continuous development*." Here Virchow is glimpsing, in his mind's eye, an unbroken continuity of cell generations stretching back almost endlessly in time, back to the beginning of life. It is only a step from this picture of all cells arising from other cells to the insight that all cells have a common ancestry. Schwann's perception "that all organisms are composed of essentially like parts, namely, of cells" recalls Buffon's perception that the structure of all vertebrate animals had much in common. Both insights are explained by the theory of evolution. Vertebrates, no matter how diverse, share a common structural plan because they share a common ancestry. In a similar fashion all living cells, no matter how diverse they may be (Figs. 3-2 and 3-4), show structural resemblances which are their common inheritance from still earlier forms of life. In cell and organism the novelty and diversity that have appeared in the course of evolution never obscure entirely those limitations imposed by an inheritance from ancient ancestors.

The transition from earlier observers like Hooke and Leeuwenhoek to Schwann is a transition from a simple observation of fact to an inductive *generalization* of great breadth. And

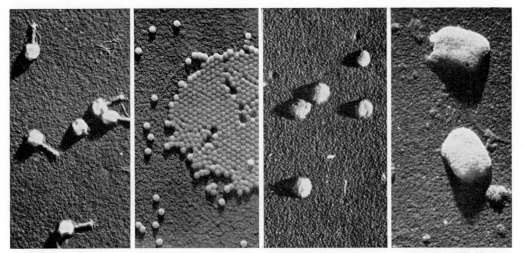

3-5 A variety of viruses. Photographed at the Virus Laboratory, University of California, Berkeley. From left to right: bacteriophage (by Dean Fraser and Robley C. Williams); poliomyelitis (by C. E. Schmerdt and Robley C. Williams); influenza (by Robley C. Williams); vaccinia (by Robley C. Williams). All ×50,000.

the transition from Schwann to Virchow is a transition from a simple generalization to a *theory* of major importance which explains the generalization. Before entering into a more detailed study of the cell, let us consider some implications of the cell theory; it will guide us in our study.

THE CELL—MINIMUM MATERIAL ORGANIZATION THAT IS ALIVE

There are some particles that are smaller than any cell and have been regarded by some biologists as alive. These are the _viruses_ (Fig. 3-5), familiar as the agents responsible for some human diseases like influenza and virus pneumonia. There are many different kinds of viruses in the world, all of them associated with and utterly dependent on living cells. When viruses enter the living cells or organisms as invaders, they are somehow multiplied or reproduced. The capacity of _self_-reproduction is certainly the most characteristic feature of living systems, and the fact that virus reproduction occurs has tempted some biologists to regard them as living. However, there exists the possibility—indeed the probability—that the virus is multiplied by the reproducing mechanism of the cell. No virus ever reproduces outside a living cell. Virus reproduction is as much dependent on the existence and organized abilities of the living cell as is the

cell's own reproduction. _The cell, in fact, is the minimum organization of matter that,_ in the modern world, _is capable of all those processes we collectively refer to as "life."_

In this generalization we included the qualification "in the modern world" because we are sure that, when life first arose from the nonliving world some billions of years ago, it did so in much simpler form than the cell as we know it now. For, simple as the cell appears in a figure like 3-6, it represents an enormous degree of complexity and organization, something much more than a single step away from nonliving matter. The fact that "precellular" living organizations no longer exist is understandable for several reasons. In the first place, life's environment has changed radically since it first arose; the conditions that made precellular life possible have long since passed. Secondly, the replacement of less by more efficiently reproducing systems is a universal aspect of organic evolution. The cell as we know it today represents a highly evolved organization of matter in which basic processes characteristic of life are performed with precision and assurance, indeed often with double assurance, as we shall see. The cell is a form of living organization that has long since replaced (probably for well over a billion years) the cruder precellular transitions between it and the nonliving world.

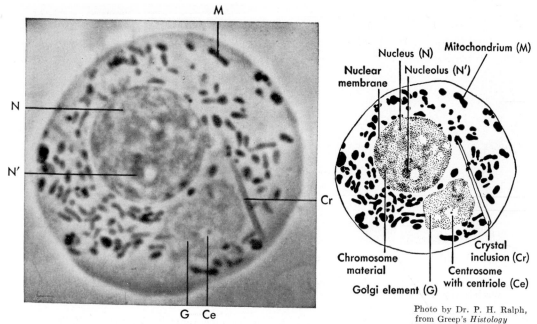

Nucleus (N) Mitochondrium (M)

Nuclear membrane Nucleolus (N′)

Cr

Chromosome material

Golgi element (G)

Centrosome with centriole (Ce)

Crystal inclusion (Cr)

Photo by Dr. P. H. Ralph, from Greep's *Histology*

3-6 A living cell. Young blood cell (human) (×3000).

The past existence of precellular life must not, however, blind us to the significance of our generalization about life today. The cell is life's minimum unit. In the cell and its relations with other cells we must seek the organization and mechanism that underlie all life's processes: the intake, storage, and release of energy; the intake of materials and their metabolism that lead to growth; the mechanism of sense perception and response to stimuli; the mechanism of movement; above all, the basis of life's most distinctive feature, reproduction.[1]

The Organization of the Cell

Our present purpose is not to pay much attention to the detailed differences between the great many different kinds of cells: we propose to focus attention on those features of structural organization that are common to all cells and that are clearly related to the fundamental activities of life as a whole.

SIZE AND SHAPE OF CELLS

The great majority of cells are very small (Fig. 3-7). While a few are visible to the naked eye, the vast majority are microscopic in size. In a large, multicellular animal, like man, the average diameter of the cell is about 10 microns, that is, 0.01 millimeter. Bacterial cells may be as small as 0.4 micron in diameter, which is near the limit of vision with ordinary microscopes. Some other cells are almost that small. There are, however, exceptions to the rule of small size; a single nerve cell in large animals may reach a length of several feet, although its diameter is relatively small. Eggs of animals are single cells before development begins, and they are commonly visible to the naked eye. Human eggs, which are unusually small as eggs go, can be seen without a lens but only as specks smaller than a period on this page. The eggs of an extinct bird (*Aepyornis* of Madagascar) had a capacity of more than two gallons and were, in volume, the largest known cells.[2]

[1] The German physiologist Verworn wrote in 1895, as the cell theory was fully maturing: "It is to the cell that the study of every bodily function sooner or later drives us. In the muscle cell lies the problem of the heartbeat and that of muscular contractions; in the gland cell reside the causes of secretion; in the epithelial cell, in the white blood cell, lies the problem of the absorption of food; and the secrets of the mind are hidden in the ganglion cell."

[2] Only the yolk of a bird's egg is a cell. It is usually greatly inflated with stored food ma-

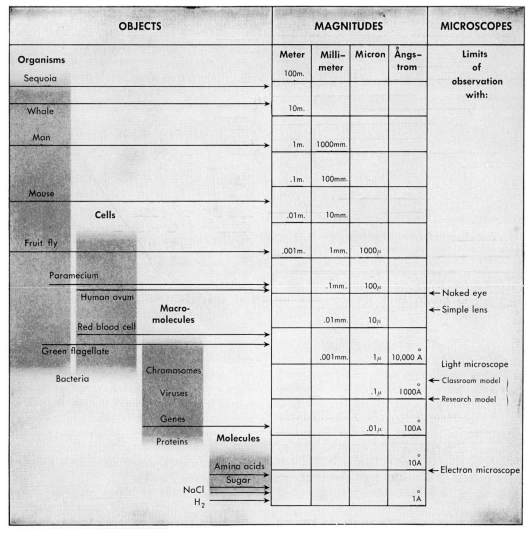

3-7 Objects, magnitudes, and appropriate microscopes.

It is almost impossible to generalize about the shape of cells. They assume a nearly endless variety of shapes, largely in relation to the special functions they serve in the organism as a whole. Human skin cells are flattened and platelike; nerve cells are enormously elongate in relation to their function of transmitting impulses over long distances; muscle cells are elongate; blood cells are biconcave and disclike. If there is any tendency to a general shape in cells it is spherical; but even cells that are relatively unspecialized in function

terial and surrounded by accessory materials familiar as the "white" and the shell of the egg.

and tend towards this shape are deformed by close packing to something like the polyhedral form seen in Fig. 3-8.

PROTOPLASM: A USEFUL BUT DANGEROUS WORD

It is usual to refer to all the constituents of the living cell collectively by the word *protoplasm*, which T. H. Huxley so aptly characterized as "the physical basis of life." Later biologists have given the special name *nucleoplasm* to the protoplasm in the nucleus, and distinguished the protoplasm outside the nucleus as *cytoplasm* (Fig. 3-1). All these terms

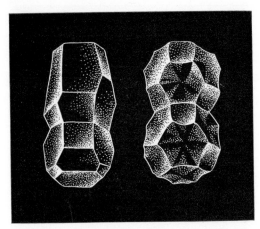

3-8 The shape of cells. They are usually poly-hedral because they are close-packed in a tissue.

are useful for convenient reference. They have the merit of brevity, with the drawback of obscuring underlying problems. Protoplasm is a dangerous word for living matter when it suggests a homogeneous something of which we can have, like water, a representative drop or piece. Protoplasm is a complexly organized system of heterogeneous parts, the smallest representative piece of which is the cell. Strictly speaking, it is no more accurate or meaningful to speak of a piece of a cell as composed of protoplasm than it is to refer to a radio as composed of radioplasm. How can there be a representative particle of radio-plasm when the whole radio is a complex and heterogeneous organization of tubes, con-densers, wires, and the like? It is only because we are still far from knowing all the organized constituents of the cell that we are driven, for convenience only, to refer to them collectively as protoplasm.

MEMBRANES AND WALLS

The principal chemical constituent of the cell is water, which sometimes accounts for over 90 per cent of the cell's weight. Accord-ingly, cells always have a more or less fluid character; the fact that they maintain any individuality and form is due to the universal presence of a *cell membrane*. The membrane retains the rest of the living system within it. The cell membrane, however, is not something outside the living system but an integral part of it. Indeed, the membrane plays a vital role

in regulating, to some extent, what passes into the cell from its environment, and what passes out. This membrane, sometimes called the plasma membrane, is extremely thin and deli-cate. Indeed it is often very difficult to recog-nize it as a distinct structure in the usual class-room preparations of cells. The illustration on p. 39 shows a picture, taken with the electron microscope, of the plasma membrane of a red blood cell after all the cell contents have been removed.

Nearly all organisms are faced with me-chanical problems in maintaining a definite form, because of the ultimately fluid nature of the living cellular system. Where the single cell lives its own independent life (see p. 52 below) the cell membrane itself may suffice. But this is not true of large multicellular or-ganisms, which would collapse under their own weight without support more rigid than the fluid protoplasm. In multicellular animals generally, this problem is met by the develop-ment of special *skeletons*, a familiar instance of which is our own bones. In plants, however, mechanical support is not derived exclusively from a wholly distinct skeletal system. Support comes from the *cell walls* that lie outside the membrane of *each* cell. Although, as we will see shortly, some cells specialize in producing extra thick and strong walls benefiting the whole organism, nevertheless each cell does have a wall (Fig. 3-9).

The cell walls of plants must be sharply distinguished from the cell membrane that lies within it. The wall is much thicker than the membrane. Moreover, unlike the membrane, the wall plays no active role in controlling the passage of materials in and out of the cell; its functional significance is entirely mechan-ical. In emphasizing the great functional dif-ferences between the walls and membranes of cells it is tempting to put it briefly by saying the membrane is a living structure and the wall is not. This temptation arises from the relative structural simplicity of the wall (it is generally composed mostly of cellulose and related molecules) and from its durability, which contrasts so sharply with the extremely complex and fragile nature of the membrane. This would, however, be a dangerous and mis-leading distinction to make. Indeed, it would be meaningless. For the whole cell, of which *both* walls and membranes are only parts, is the smallest unit of structural organization to which we can, with meaning,[3] apply the word "living."

THE NUCLEUS

Inside the membrane the most conspicuous and, usually, the largest distinct body is the *nucleus*. It is a roughly spherical, grayish body, denser than the cytoplasm in which it is embedded, and surrounded by a thin nuclear membrane. Its position is commonly central, and its role in the life of the cell is certainly central in the metaphoric sense. For the nucleus is the controlling headquarters of the cell. It contains within it a number of distinct linear or threadlike bodies, the *chromosomes*, which are the carriers of the cell's heredity (Figs. 3-2 and 3-12). It is the chromosomes in the nucleus that guide the development of organisms. They are the ultimate seat of the controls that maintain the order and organization of its entire living system. How this control is effected is a topic for later chapters. In essence it consists of manufacturing special chemical compounds that eventually enter the cytoplasm as the direct agents of control, regulating the chemical processes that go on there.

3 And the meaning we imply is that the structure is capable of its own independent growth and reproduction.

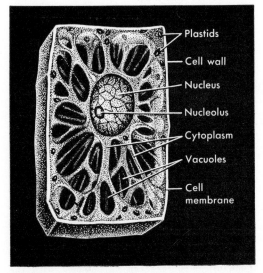

3-9 A mature plant cell. Note the characteristic vacuole (p. 48) and cell wall (p. 46).

In some cells the chromosomes can be recognized as distinct bodies at all times, but usually they are readily seen only when the cell and its nucleus are dividing. The chromosomes have a strong affinity for certain dyes, and it is this property from which they derive their name "chromosomes," from Greek *chroma* (color) and *soma* (body).

When the cell is not actively dividing and the chromosomes are not visible as distinct threads, they are nevertheless known to be still present in nonstainable form. When the nucleus is not dividing, a spherical body of uncertain function, the *nucleolus*, can be readily distinguished (Figs. 3-6 and 3-9). It disappears during nuclear division.

VISIBLE STRUCTURE OF THE CYTOPLASM

The cytoplasm, lying outside the nucleus, appears as a more or less transparent and somewhat viscous, or thick, fluid. It is never completely homogeneous, nor entirely *fluid*, even in its *visible* structure (cf. ultrastructure, p. 48). It always contains some of the following recognizably distinct constituents: centrosomes, plastids, mitochondria, Golgi element, and vacuoles.

The *centrosome* (Fig. 3-6) is a body lying just outside the nuclear membrane in animal cells. It is an essential part of the mechanism of nuclear division reviewed below (p. 51). It is rare in plants. It consists of a central small body (the centriole) from which a number of fine fiberlike structures radiate outwards.

In most plants and one-celled organisms, but not in the cells of higher animals, there are often special bodies in the cytoplasm called *plastids* (Fig. 3-9). They are usually associated with the formation, storage, or both, of particular substances important in the metabolism of the organisms. They might be thought of as specialized factories and warehouses. The green pigment, chlorophyll, of green plants nearly always occurs in plastids (chloroplasts) which are the sites of the fundamental process of photosynthesis (Chapter 5). There are other pigmented and unpigmented plastids in plants; in some of these starch and fats are formed and stored.

The cytoplasm of most cells contains granules, rods, or filaments known as *mitochondria* (Figs. 3-4*H* and 3-6). These particles are capable of moving about within the cytoplasm and of changing their shape to some extent. They are known to carry either on them or in them a group of enzymes (biological catalysts, p. 93) associated with energy release; and they tend to aggregate in that part of the cell which is most actively metabolizing at a given time.

Another group of cytoplasmic bodies are referred to as the *Golgi* element (Figs. 3-1 and 3-6). Their function remains unknown in spite of much attention and speculation.

Vacuoles are cavities in the cytoplasm bounded by a definite membrane. They contain water with various substances in solution. They are absent from young plant cells and most animal cells of any age, but in older plant cells (Fig. 3-9) one or more large vacuoles develop within the cytoplasm whose more viscous part, lying outside the vacuole membrane, becomes restricted to a thin layer just inside the cell membrane and wall. In such cells the nucleus always lies outside the vacuole in the viscous cytoplasm.

Large vacuoles rarely occur in animal cells, but smaller ones of various sorts may be present. In some cells the cell membrane forms a pouch around a food particle which later separates and becomes a temporary *food vacuole* (Fig. 3-13*A*). The food is broken down in the vacuole by juices secreted into it from the body of the cytoplasm. Another kind of vacuole is associated with the problem of maintaining a proper water balance in the cell. Water continually passes into some single-celled organisms for physical reasons over which the cell has no control (cf. osmosis, p. 82). These cells meet the problem by continually bailing out excess water, which is first concentrated into *contractile vacuoles* whose rhythmic contractions eject the water from the cell.

THE ULTRASTRUCTURE OF PROTOPLASM

The problem of invisible organization. A survey of the visible structure of the cell leaves one with a strong feeling that more of the living cell's organization is hidden from us than is revealed under the microscope.

TABLE 3-1

Chemical constituents of protoplasm

	Sea urchin	Man *
Water	77.3	66.0
Protein	15.2	16.0
Fats and lipoids †	4.8	13.0
Carbohydrates	1.4	0.6
Ash ‡	0.3	5.0

* Data for newborn child.
† Lipoids are fatlike compounds (see p. 77).
‡ Ash includes all other elements not included in the other categories (iron, potassium, and other metals).

Membrane, nucleus, plastids and a few other distinct bodies in the cytoplasm—it is not unduly complex. This, on reflection, is not surprising. For the life of the cell in one sense boils down to the organized chemical activity it undergoes, and we can no more *see* this chemical organization than we can *see* the chemical reaction proceed in a laboratory test tube. Our knowledge of atoms and the mechanism of chemical processes is extensive, but none of it is based on *direct* observation of either the atoms or their actions. Similarly, by indirect methods of analysis, we are beginning to understand numerous aspects of the ultrastructure [4] of protoplasm. The fact that it is not directly visible does not mean that it cannot be analyzed.

Table 3-1 gives the gross chemical analysis of protoplasm from two different sources, man and a sea urchin. The predominance of water we have noted before. The proteins are a special class of giant molecules that are uniquely associated with life. They form, as the table shows, the next largest group of protoplasmic constituents. Then follow carbohydrates and fats, molecules of very much smaller dimensions. Sugars and starches are familiar carbohydrates. The term "ash" includes a host of still smaller molecules, especially salts of var-

[4] In later chapters we will see how a knowledge of the nature of the cell's chemical reactions and the enzymes (p. 325) which catalyze them contributes towards the ultimate goal of unraveling the cell's fine-scale organization. The word "ultrastructure" is applied to this fine-scale organization which exists beyond the limits of the resolving power of the light microscope. Some ultrastructure can be detected with the electron microscope, but much remains beyond the limits of even this instrument.

ious kinds. We are sure, then, for a start, that protoplasm must be in large part an aqueous solution of many kinds of molecules, but observation of its behavior shows that there must be more to it than that. For instance, even in its most fluid condition, protoplasm is thicker, more viscous, than water or most solutions in water. Moreover, even within one and the same cell part, the viscosity varies; sometimes a piece of protoplasm flows freely, and at other times it acquires a thickly set jelly-like consistency. Experiment shows that these changes in viscosity are easily affected by acids and heat. These and other properties of protoplasm show that it cannot be exclusively regarded as a simple solution of chemicals in water: it must be, in part, what is called a *colloidal system*. This, in turn, tells us much that is suggestive of how a fine-scale structural organization may exist within it at the molecule level of size, far below the range of our direct vision. What are colloids?

Colloidal systems. Gases, liquids, and solids are the three most obvious states of matter. The same substance may exist in any of the three states. Water is a familiar example: it is a gas in clear air (or steam *before* the steam condenses and becomes visible), a liquid in a drink, a solid in an ice cube. A little thought will reveal that there are other states of matter. Suppose that a cube of sugar, a solid, is dissolved in water. It is no longer a solid, and yet it is not exactly a liquid, either. It is in *solution* in a liquid. Matter in a state of solution is characterized by the fact that its molecules separate from each other and each moves more or less independently through the medium in which it is dissolved.[5]

If instead of sugar you stir fine sand in a glass of water, the sand particles do not dissolve. For a time many of the unchanged, solid particles remain in *suspension* in the water. The system is not stable, however, and the particles eventually settle out of suspension and collect at the bottom of the glass. If extremely fine clay particles are stirred in the glass of water, some may settle out but many remain suspended indefinitely; that is, the system is *stable*. If the particles are small enough, they never do settle out unless something is done to change the system—unless, that is, it is disturbed by an influence from outside. *A stable suspension is a colloid.*

Colloids may also be formed by two liquids instead of a liquid and a solid (Fig. 3-10). If you stir kerosene into water, some small drops of kerosene remain suspended in the water for a while, but eventually they rise to the top. Such a system of one liquid dispersed in another is an *emulsion*. You will find it difficult or impossible to make drops of kerosene small enough to remain suspended in water indefinitely, forming a stable emulsion. Stable emulsions—colloids of liquid in liquid—do exist, however. Homogenized milk is one: a special procedure makes the liquid fat globules so small that they remain dispersed in the milk and do not rise to the top as cream.

The differences between true solutions, colloids, and unstable suspensions or emulsions hinge on the size of the particles involved; and colloids are also dependent on the electrical charge which the large particles carry. Consider the extreme cases first. Suspensions settle out eventually because of the pull of gravity on the large particles involved. Sugar molecules in water do not settle out because the pull of gravity is negligible on particles so small. All the molecules in a liquid and true solution are constantly in a random dancing movement in all directions. This random movement of the liquid (water) molecules is, in part, the reason why colloidal particles, of intermediate size, are not settled down by the slight pull of gravity on them. The colloid particles are constantly being bombarded and pushed in all directions, up as well as down, by the solvent molecules that surround them. They are also prevented from settling down because their electrical charges are all of the same sign (sometimes all positive and sometimes all negative); consequently they mutually repel each other, keeping the particles uniformly dispersed. When chemicals added to a colloid neutralize the charges in the particles, they no longer repel each other, and then they precipitate down.

---

[5] Those of you who have studied chemistry know that dissolved molecules often separate (dissociate) into smaller, electrically charged parts, ions. This phenomenon is extremely important in the study of chemical reactions, but its discussion is not essential for our present purposes.

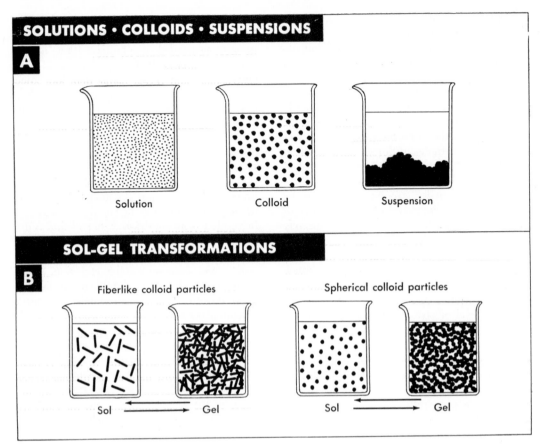

SOLUTIONS · COLLOIDS · SUSPENSIONS

A

Solution   Colloid   Suspension

SOL-GEL TRANSFORMATIONS

B

Fiberlike colloid particles   Spherical colloid particles

Sol   Gel   Sol   Gel

3-10   Solutions, colloids, and suspensions.

There is no hard and fast line between the sizes of particles that form solutions, colloids, or unstable suspensions. A substance is usually considered to be in true solution if it separates into individual molecules (or their ions) which are smaller than 0.001 micron. Aggregates of unseparated molecules are rarely as small as 0.001 micron and usually, therefore, form colloids. Larger aggregates form unstable suspensions or emulsions.

Proteins as colloids and fibers. Some single molecules are larger than 0.001 micron, and this happens to have an essential bearing on protoplasm. Extremely important constituents of protoplasm are proteins, *which are unusually large molecules,* including, indeed, the largest molecules known. Proteins usually dissolve in water and form solutions in the sense that their molecules do separate. Yet these molecules are often as large as the particles in colloids, and they do in fact form colloids in water. The result may be said to be simultaneously a solution and a colloid, or *chemically a solution* and *physically a colloid.*

Gelatin and albumen are proteins with very large molecules that form colloids in water. The white of an egg is a colloidal system of albumen in water, and the familiar Jello is also an aqueous colloid of gelatin. Jello, of course, can exist either as a freely flowing fluid (when the gelatin is dissolved in warm water) or as a thickly set jelly. This is a general property of colloids: they can assume either a *sol* or *gel* state and moreover can be transformed from one state to the other.[6]

6 Figure 3-10 illustrates what happens in sol-gel transformations. Basically, the change involves the withdrawal or addition of water in the system. In the sol state water is said to be the continuous phase. In the gel system when

The colloidal properties of protoplasm account for some of its known structural organization and behavior. Its capacity to form semisolid gels helps us understand how a system that is 90 per cent water can maintain any form whatsoever. The integrity of the cell membrane as a retaining boundary depends on this ability of the protoplasmic proteins to form gels. And the variations in viscosity that are observable in different parts of cells, and in the same part at different times, are reflections of reversible sol-gel changes.

The properties of protoplasm leave no doubt that it is simultaneously a complex solution and a colloid. That is, it consists of water in which small molecules (like sugars and salts) and their dissociated parts are dissolved, and in which there are also dispersed much larger molecules (proteins and fats) and molecular aggregates of colloidal size. This leads us part way towards an understanding of the invisible ultrastructure of protoplasm, but it still leaves us far from our goal.

What we ultimately must look for is some basis for maintaining order and organization within a semifluid system. It is difficult to imagine how organization can be maintained in true solutions the essence of which is the random movement and uniform distribution of its constituent molecules. Various hypotheses, all unproven as yet, have been advanced as to how spatial organization can be maintained. Most of them relate to the remarkably large size of proteins and the diversity of shapes, including fibers, which they can assume. The hypotheses envisage a semisolid framework of fibers and colloidal particles as the basis for maintaining spatial order and organization.

CELL REPRODUCTION

Any impression of structureless homogeneity that the cytoplasm may give is quickly dispelled once the cell commences its most remarkable visible activity, reproduction. We will be concerned in a later chapter with the

water is withdrawn the protein molecules compact into a spongelike network that is now the continuous phase; the water is the disperse phase. It is the spongelike network of the protein molecules, having various shapes including fibers, which gives the gel its semisolid consistency.

details of cell division as these bear on the mechanism of heredity. Here we note only its most obvious features. They illuminate the role and importance of the nucleus and the centrosome, and reveal better than any other process the elaborately organized behavior of which the cell is capable.

Cells multiply by dividing. This arithmetic oddity means that the number of cells increases by the splitting in two of single cells. This splitting of the cell is preceded by complex events involved in the division of the nucleus, a process called mitosis (Figs. 3-11 and 3-12).

When division of the nucleus commences, the chromosomes assume their stainable property and condense from initially very elongate threads to much more compact, sausagelike bodies. Each chromosome is composed of two equal strands. When the chromosomes have reached their maximum condensation, the nuclear membrane disappears. The nuclear membrane, like that on the outside of the cell, owes its firmness and individuality to what is basically its gel-colloid nature. Its disappearance and later reappearance is just one more example of the great importance of the capacity of colloids to shift from gel to sol and back to gel. The cell can build and tear down boundary membranes where and when it needs them and thus maintain order within its semifluid, semisolid state. By the time the nuclear membrane has disappeared, the centrosome has duplicated. Between the duplicate centrosomes there develops a most remarkable living structure. It is called the *spindle*. Its ultimate fine structure is actively studied by many biologists today, and it is still far from being fully understood.

The spindle consists of fibers which emanate from the two centrosomes to form the biconical spindle. The chromosomes now migrate onto the central or equatorial portion of the spindle; each becomes attached to spindle fibers. The two separate strands in each chromosome now move apart, as though drawn by the spindle fibers, toward the opposite poles of the spindle. In this way two groups of chromosomes, duplicates of each other, are collected at opposite ends of the cell. New nuclear membranes now develop in the protoplasm, enclosing each of the two new

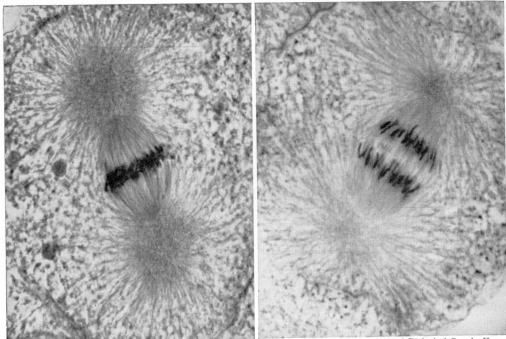

3-11 Mitosis in cells of the whitefish. The spindle lying between the two star-shaped centrosomes is very clear. The chromosomes lie on the central part, or equator, of the spindle. In the right-hand figure the two duplicate sets of chromosomes can be seen on their way to opposite ends of the spindle.

daughter nuclei. When this is done the cell constricts its wall between the nuclei and, splitting, gives rise to two cells from one. To the human observer this is an almost incredibly organized set of movements that dispels forever the notion of simplicity in the cell.

The other main significance of mitosis for us at this stage is simply that it is a mechanism for the *precise transmission* to each new nucleus of exactly equal sets of chromosomes. The demand for such precision lies in the fact that the chromosomes are the ultimate source of all the "instructions" which specify the cell's orderly behavior. As such, each new daughter cell cannot properly function without an exactly complete set of chromosomes. As Virchow stated, a living cell can only arise from another living cell; and this is so because its complex organization can neither be attained nor maintained without transmission from a parent cell of the specifications which the chromosomes carry.

Cells as Organisms

The plants and animals with which we are most familiar are composed of very large numbers of cells; their individual cells do not have a separate and independent life of their own. The cells are not organisms themselves

3-12 Mitosis in *Trillium*. The centrosome is missing in plant cells, and the spindle which is so clear in animal cells (Fig. 3-11) is not easily stained and seen, although it is present. In (1) the nucleus has not yet entered mitosis; the chromosomal material appears diffuse and structureless. In (2), (3), and (4) the chromosomes are progressively clearer as they shorten and thicken. There are five chromosomes, and each is present in duplicate. In (5) they are lying on the equator of the spindle, which is unstained and therefore invisible in this preparation. In (6) and (7) the duplicate sets of chromosomes move to opposite ends of the spindle. In (8) and (9) new nuclei are formed from the two sets of chromosomes, and the process of mitosis is completed. A wall eventually develops between the nuclei, and two new cells are thus established.

MITOSIS IN A PLANT *(Trillium)*

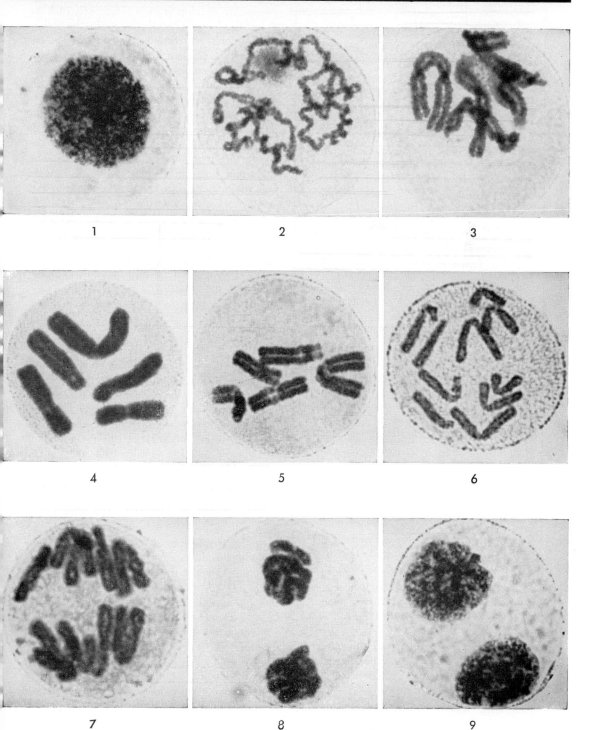

1

2

3

4

5

6

7

8

9

Dr. A. H. Sparrow, Brookhaven National Laboratory

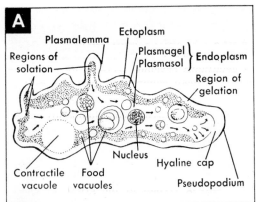

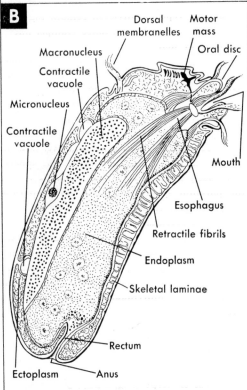

3-13 Cells as organisms: *A.* Ameba. *B. Epidinium.* Ameba shows very little visible specialization of parts, but in *Epidinium* such specialization is very extensive. All food enters through a mouth, whose location is fixed. The undigested remains of food are evacuated through a well-formed rectum and anus. The form of the animal is partly maintained by a definite skeletal structure. Retractile muscle-like fibers move the mouth and esophagus, and the movement of these fibers is controlled by nervelike fibers. Similar "neurofibrils" control the movement of elaborate membranelles, which are organs of locomotion. All the neurofibrils connect with a central "motor mass," which may be likened to a brain.

but are the parts of which organisms are constructed. However, even multicellular organisms do usually have a stage in their life history when they are single cells. That is, they commonly develop from a single cell such as a fertilized egg. Sometimes, as in the swimming spores of certain relatively lowly organisms, the single cell may lead an independent life for some time and behave like an active organism on its own, but this is still only a temporary stage in its life history.

There are, however, numerous small organisms, separate and distinct individuals, in which the body is never at any stage in the life history partitioned into separate cells. The body is a single mass of protoplasm, a single cell, divided only into the usual cytoplasm and nucleus. They are *unicellular organisms*, single cells living wholly independent lives. Some are commonly called "plants" and some "animals," according to their resemblances to the unquestionable, multicellular plants and animals. Among these unicellular organisms, however, the distinction is not really clear. In fact, one and the same organism may be classified sometimes as a plant and sometimes as an animal.

There is another point of view on this subject. In recent years many students have emphasized the fact that the terms "plant" and "animal" may be equivocal when applied to unicellular organisms and, further, that all unicellular organisms have much in common. They therefore propose to call them neither plants nor animals but Protista or protists. In a way this only doubles the difficulty of telling plants from animals, because some protists really are very like plants and almost surely closely related to them, and others really are similarly allied to animals. However, an additional factor is also involved. Many protists have quite complex anatomies, even including specialized cytoplasmic parts (organelles) analogous to the mouths, eyes, fins, and so on of multicellular animals (Fig. 3-13). Some also have several nuclei, even though there are no cell membranes or walls between the nuclei. It is therefore quite possible to argue that a protist is *not* equivalent to a single cell of a multicellular organism but is really analogous to the *whole* of such an organism. From this point of view the protists are not unicellular plants or animals but are _acellular organisms,_ that is, organisms not divided into separate cells. To sum up, the very same organisms, the protists, are considered unicellular when they are compared with single cells of higher organisms, and acellular when they are compared with the whole of a higher organism.

Note that there is no argument about the _facts._ The anatomical structures of the unicellular plants and animals or alternatively of the acellular protists are well known and not disputed. No one denies that some of them are plantlike in metabolism or physiology, others more animal-like, and others intermediate between the two or different from either. All that is involved is two different ways of looking at the same facts.

As a matter of convenience, we will call these organisms as a whole "protists" unless we are referring to some particular group of them.

Some protists, such as an ameba (Fig. 3-13) are quite simple, with little specialization of parts. Others have a high degree of differentiation into varying kinds of cytoplasm, corresponding to the tissues of multicellular organisms, and of structures correlated with special activities. Such structures are, in fact, organs just as much as are the organs with similar functions in multicellular organisms, although they are usually called "organelles" to distinguish them from organs composed of cells. Protists may have skeletons, excretory organs, light-sensitive organs (which may have lenses), conducting mechanisms analogous to nerves, contracting mechanisms analogous to muscles, explosive organs with which food is captured, mouths, anuses, a number of different sorts of organs of locomotion, and still other organs.

The Multicellular Organism

PROTISTAN COLONIES AND CELLULAR DIFFERENTIATION

When protists reproduce, they do so like any other single cell. The nucleus undergoes _mitosis_ and the cell mass constricts into two halves, each carrying a daughter nucleus. Sometimes, however, several or many organisms formed by division from what was originally one protist remain clumped together for a longer or shorter time. They may stick together at their outer surfaces or be caught in a gelatinous envelope secreted by the organisms. In these clumps each cell (or protist) continues to be essentially independent in form and in activity. The clumps are merely aggregates in space, with no particular biological interaction between their units.

Other protists carry the process of aggregation several steps farther. This is especially true among certain of the _green flagellates._ In some of these forms the individual cells formed by repeated division remain together, not incidentally and in chance clumps, but in _colonies_ of definite shape and of characteristic size when mature. A common arrangement is for the cells to be held in the outer part of a gelatinous envelope forming a hollow sphere. The number of cells, usually a power of two (why?), may vary from a few to about 50,000. Reproduction occurs when one or more cells start dividing and give rise to smaller daughter colonies inside the sphere. Eventually the daughter colonies break out of the parental sphere and grow into separate, new, mature colonies.

In some colonial forms (Fig. 3-14) the cells are not connected with each other and are all exactly alike. Each can give rise to a daughter colony (although they do not all necessarily do so). In such cases the cells are still essentially distinct individuals, protists that live together. In other forms, of which some species of _Volvox_ are examples, something more complex and of peculiar interest has occurred: the cells are connected to each other by strands of protoplasm running through the gelatinous envelope (Fig. 3-14). Thus the cells are no longer fully independent; happenings in one cell may affect its neighbors. Moreover, the cells are no longer quite alike. The number of cells may run into the thousands, but only four to twenty larger cells in the back part of the colony are capable of reproducing, giving rise to daughter colonies. The cells in the front part of a differentiated colony like this cannot reproduce. They are smaller and have relatively larger light-sensitive organelles. The latter feature influences the orientation and movement of the colony.

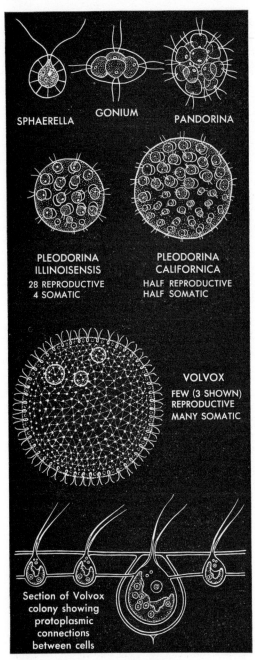

SPHAERELLA
GONIUM
PANDORINA

PLEODORINA
ILLINOISENSIS
28 REPRODUCTIVE
4 SOMATIC

PLEODORINA
CALIFORNICA
HALF REPRODUCTIVE
HALF SOMATIC

VOLVOX
FEW (3 SHOWN)
REPRODUCTIVE
MANY SOMATIC

Section of Volvox
colony showing
protoplasmic
connections
between cells

3-14 Colonial green flagellates.

Is this a colony of protists or is it a multicellular organism? On one hand, it is made up of similar cells and quite surely evolved from a unicellular or acellular protistan individual. On the other hand, the cells do have some differentiation of form and activity and slight co-ordination throughout the whole colony. The degree is far less than in unquestioned multicellular organisms, but the differentiation and co-ordination are suggestively similar in kind.

The colonies of *Volvox* and its relatives introduce a puzzling biological phenomenon that will appear repeatedly in our further study of living organisms. Like the cells of multicellular organisms, although to a much lesser degree, the cells of a *Volvox* colony differ in size, shape, potentialities, and other characteristics. In a word, they *differentiate* as they mature; each specializes in a division of the colony's total labor. And yet their heredity is exactly the same. They all arose from one cell, and at each mitosis the new nuclei were carefully endowed with identical sets of chromosomal controls. This puzzle of cellular differentiation, in spite of identical heredity, is one of biology's greatest problems and the subject of much further discussion in Chapter 14.

THE ORIGIN OF
MULTICELLULAR ORGANISMS

Biologists are universally agreed that present-day protists are, as their name implies,[7] persistent representatives of a group of organisms from which all multicellulars have evolved. The single-celled condition is the simpler one from which the multicellular must have derived. The existence today of forms like *Volvox* suggests one way that multicellulars may have evolved from protists, that is, by the remaining together and later differentiation of the separate protists produced by division. This is in fact the most widely accepted theory of the origin of multicellulars, but it is not necessarily true. Some protists exhibit a much greater structural differentiation *within their single cell* than occurs *between cells* in a *Volvox* colony. *Epidinium* (Fig. 3-13) is a case in point. Protists like *Epidinium* are really more like a multicellular organism in the extent of their visible differentiation than is the *Volvox* colony. They would, in fact, become rather advanced multicellular organisms simply by the development of dividing membranes between their various

7 From Greek "protos" (first).

parts. There is evidence that such a process can occur. For instance, there are organisms with several nuclei that are separated by membranes into distinct cells at some stages of the life history and not at others.

We will not pursue the matter further here, but it is of interest to know that there are at least these two distinct possibilities. It is also valuable to bear in mind that a series of transitional stages in organisms now living may but does not necessarily represent an evolutionary sequence that occurred hundreds of millions of years ago.[8] As to which theory is true, we do not know. It is possible that both are. Multicellular organisms probably evolved more than once. They may have arisen sometimes in one way and sometimes in another.

CELLULAR DIFFERENTIATION: CELLS, TISSUES, ORGANS, AND SYSTEMS

Examine a complex multicellular organism such as a tree or a man. It is plain, first of all, that the organism has its own individuality. It is a unit and acts as such. Yet the unit is made up of visibly different parts. The basic units, the cells, which we have been discussing in this chapter have many forms and functions within the individual. They are *differentiated*. A cell in a root tip is quite different from one in the surface of a leaf, and the leaf surface cell in turn differs from cells within the leaf. In your body a nerve cell, a muscle cell, and a blood cell are remarkably different.

Each kind of cell usually occurs with others similar to it, sharing in the same sorts of life processes. The whole leaf surface is covered with similar cells. A muscle is made up not of one cell but of thousands, all much the same in appearance and properties. Aggregations of similar cells are called *tissues*. Tissues of several or many different kinds often make up complex parts of organisms. Your hand, for instance, is a functionally distinct part of your body, an *organ*, composed of skin, bones, muscles, nerves, and other tissues. Leaves and flowers or eyes and ears are other organs that are complexes of different tissues. Organs may, in turn, be co-operating and interacting parts of a larger complex, an anatomical and physiological *system*. Your digestive system,

8 This important point is treated in Chapter 9 (p. 208) and especially in Chapter 22 (p. 539).

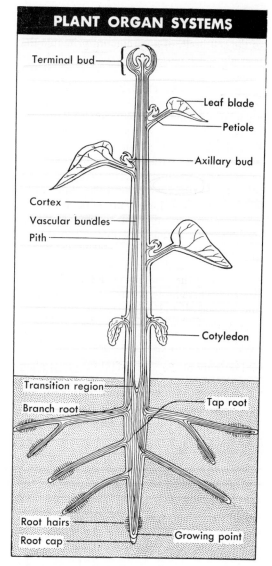

PLANT ORGAN SYSTEMS

Terminal bud — Leaf blade — Petiole — Axillary bud — Cortex — Vascular bundles — Pith — Cotyledon — Transition region — Branch root — Tap root — Root hairs — Root cap — Growing point

3-15 Plant organ systems.

for instance, is a sequence of organs from mouth through esophagus (the passageway from mouth to stomach) to stomach, small intestine, and large intestine to the anus. Each part or organ is different, but all interact one after the other in the processes of digestion. Each organ in the system is composed of tissues, and each tissue is composed of cells.

The striking differences that exist between tissues are related to the different functions they perform; the structure of muscle is related to its function of movement, the structure of nerve to its function of communication. This is in fact just one aspect, at the level of the cell itself, of a paramount principle that pervades all biology: *the structure of the living thing is related to the functions it performs.* Plants and animals are distinguished by great differences in their mode of life. The plant, nearly always sedentary, feeds directly on the materials of soil and air in a manner that demands the minimum of movement. This immobile existence is strongly reflected in its tissue organization. The animal, on the other hand, is dependent on living food which it must actively ingest in solid form and which, moreover, it must nearly always actively pursue. Its constant movements and its searching activity demand organs and tissues —sensory, muscular, nervous, and connective —for which the plant's way of life makes no demand. These basic differences between plant and animal should be borne in mind as we survey their characteristic tissues.

PLANT TISSUES

The body of the more highly evolved plants consists of two organ systems. The *root system* occurs below ground; and the *shoot system,* including stem and leaves, occurs above ground (Fig. 3-15). In these two organ systems four classes of tissue can be recognized.

Meristematic tissues. These tissues, called meristems for short, consist of thin-walled, unvacuolated, and unspecialized cells. In the spring and summer, when growth is active, cell divisions occur throughout the meristems. This produces new cells each of which subsequently differentiates into one of the three types of specialized (protective, fundamental, or conductive) tissue. Apical meristems occur at the tips of roots and shoots, and are responsible for the plant's growth in length. Meristematic tissue is also present elsewhere in the shoot and causes, as we will see later, its growth in thickness (Fig. 3-16).

Protective tissues. Protective tissues (epidermis and cork) comprise the outermost layers of cells which cover and protect underlying tissues in both organ systems.

Fundamental tissues. A variety of cell types are somewhat loosely classified collectively as *fundamental tissues.* Some of them (sclerenchyma and collenchyma) have heavily thickened walls, adding greatly to the mechanical strength of an organ—root, stem, or leaf. Others (parenchyma) are thin-walled, highly vacuolated cells, some of which contain the green chloroplasts which are the site of photosynthesis (Figs. 3-17 and 3-19).

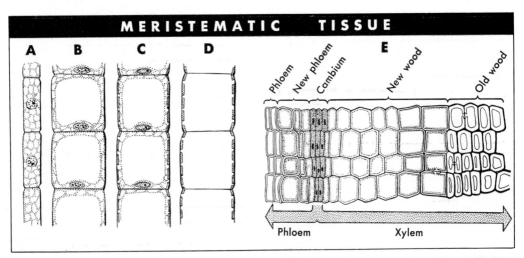

3-16 Meristematic tissue in plants. *A, B, C,* and *D* are successive stages in the differentiation of a xylem vessel (*D*) from a sheet of cambial cells (*A*). Note how the cells enlarge, vacuolate, acquire a thickened wall, and eventually lose their cytoplasm and nucleus. *E* is a cross section through part of a stem. Division of the cambial cells (stippled) produces new cells which on the right differentiate into xylem, and on the left differentiate into phloem.

A

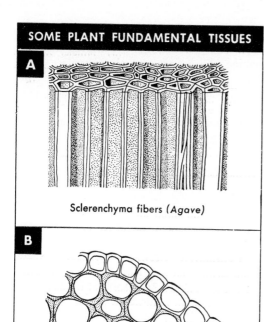

Sclerenchyma fibers (Agave)

B

Collenchyma fibers (Coleus)

3-17 Some plant fundamental tissues. Two types (sclerenchyma and collenchyma) of fundamental tissues are supportive. Their cell walls are specially thickened, conferring strength and rigidity on the whole tissue. In sclerenchyma the wall is uniformly and heavily thickened at all points. In collenchyma the thickening is heaviest at corners of the cell.

Conductive tissues. The conductive (or vascular) tissues are concerned with transport in the plant, as their name implies. There are two kinds of conductive tissue. The *xylem* transports water and dissolved minerals upwards from the roots, where they are absorbed from the soil, to all other parts of the plant. Xylem cells, like all other specialized types, begin their life as unspecialized cells, derived from a meristem. As they mature their walls become heavily thickened, often with conspicuous spiral bands. In more highly evolved

plants, adjacent xylem cells, one above the other, eventually lose their end walls and fuse with each other to form a continuously open vessel running up the axis of the plant. In mature form their cytoplasm and nuclei are lost, and, though they are dead, their function as conducting vessels is unimpaired. As we will see, each plant organ is supplied with an abundance of such xylem vessels.

The second type of conducting tissue is *phloem.* It transports the food materials manufactured in the leaves to all parts of the plant, both above and below the leaf. Mature phloem cells are elongate cylinders whose walls are not so heavily thickened as those of xylem cells. Nor do the end walls of the phloem cells break down. Instead, connection between phloem cells is effected through a series of

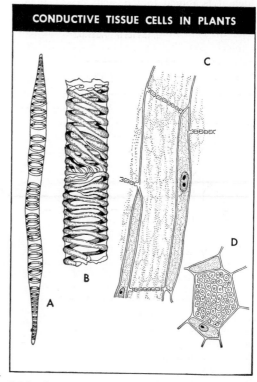

3-18 Conductive tissue cells in plants. *A* and *B* are xylem cells. Note the thickening of the cell walls. *C* and *D* are phloem cells. *C* shows one complete phloem cell whose end walls are sieve plates. The nucleated cell lying to the right of the phloem cell is called a companion cell and is a characteristic constituent of phloem tissue. *D* is an end view of a sieve plate; two companion cells lie beside it.

THE CELL: UNIT OF LIFE   59

pores in their end walls, which are appropriately called sieve plates. The nuclei of phloem cells disintegrate, but their cytoplasmic contents remain, fusing through the sieve-plate pores and forming a protoplasmic highway along which food is transported (Fig. 3-18).

Let us now see how these four types of tissue are organized in leaves, stems, and roots.

Tissue organization in the leaf. Each leaf bud arises in the late summer or fall from a small mound of meristematic tissue. In the following spring each opens, and, as the leaf grows to maturity, its constituent cells differentiate into specialized tissues. A simple leaf, as on a willow or lilac, has a flattened blade and a cylindrical piece (the petiole) by which it is joined to the stem of the plant. To examine the tissues a thin slice may be cut across the blade and viewed with a strong lens or microscope. These tissues are shown and labeled in Fig. 3-19.

Protective tissue is present in the form of a single layer of cells, tightly fitted together and looking like a jigsaw puzzle in surface view. This is the epidermis. Its cells, especially on the leaf's upper surface, are glossy and waterproof because of a heavy deposit of a fatlike substance (cutin). Between the upper and lower epidermis there are parenchyma cells containing chloroplasts. The parenchyma cells, which are pulled apart during the growth of the leaf, have open, gas-filled spaces between them. In the epidermis, especially on the lower side of the leaf, are numerous small openings (stomates) between two or more specialized cells which together form a mechanism that usually opens in light and closes in the dark. The stomata open into the spaces between parenchyma cells inside the leaf, and gases involved in photosynthesis and other reactions within these cells here diffuse from and to the outer air.

The conductive tissues in the leaf occur in the form of distinct veins, or *vascular bundles*, each of which contains both xylem and phloem

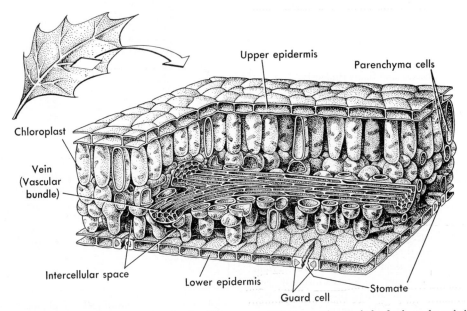

Upper epidermis

Parenchyma cells

Chloroplast

Vein (Vascular bundle)

Intercellular space

Lower epidermis

Guard cell

Stomate

3.19 Tissue organization of a leaf. The upper and lower surfaces of the leaf are bounded by an epidermis (protective tissue), which is one cell in thickness. Stomates are present on the lower epidermis. The bulk of the internal tissue is a parenchyma (fundamental tissue), whose cells contain chloroplasts. The parenchyma cells are loosely packed and are surrounded, therefore, by intercellular spaces which, via the stomates, are continuous with the external atmosphere. The mass of parenchyma is penetrated by veins (or vascular bundles) that consist mainly of conductive tissue (xylem and phloem) and some supportive fibers (fundamental tissue).

cells. The vascular bundles in the leaf blade are, of course, continuous with those in the petiole and, ultimately, with the conductive tissues throughout the main axis of root and shoot. The leaf is constantly supplied through the xylem with water and minerals. Through its phloem it, in turn, supplies to the rest of the plant the sugars it manufactures in its parenchyma cells.

Tissue organization in the stem. The word "stem" applies to all parts of the shoot system other than leaves—trunks and main branches as well as what are more commonly called "stems" in popular language. All these structures have similarities in their tissues and in their relationships to the life of the plant. In general, the differentiated stem tissues are involved in support, growth, and protection of the plant and in the movement of solutions. In addition some stems contain cells with *chloroplasts* and consequently manufacture sugars, but this is predominantly a leaf function. Stems also are often places of storage for food and water.

The tissues of the stem of a woody plant, such as ash or box elder (Fig. 3-20), are best studied in a section cut transversely across the stem. All the tissues are organized in a series of concentric cylinders surrounding a central mass of loose parenchyma cells, the pith. The first cylinder of tissue around the pith is the wood, composed of xylem cells. This is followed, in order, by cylinders of meristematic tissue (the cambium); phloem; parenchyma cells; a meristematic layer (the cork cambium); and, finally, the cork.

The two cylinders of meristematic tissue permit the stem to grow in width as it gets older. The protective tissue of the cork is composed of cells the walls of which are all impregnated with a waterproofing substance (suberin). This effectively protects underlying tissue against water loss but prevents the cork cells themselves from obtaining water, and consequently they die. As they are gradually sloughed off, they are replaced by new cells from the underlying cork cambium.

The principal layer of meristematic tissue is the cambium, between the xylem and phloem. In each growing season the new cells on its inner surface differentiate into new xylem, and those on its outer surface to new phloem. Thus in each growing season a new

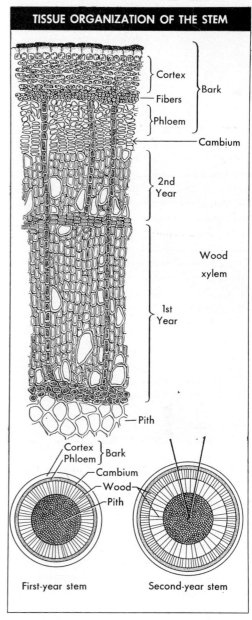

TISSUE ORGANIZATION OF THE STEM

Cortex
Bark
Fibers
Phloem
Cambium
2nd Year
Wood xylem
1st Year
Pith

Cortex
Phloem } Bark
Cambium
Wood
Pith

First-year stem   Second-year stem

3-20 Tissue organization of a woody stem (box elder). The two lower figures show diagrammatically how the tissues are organized as concentric cylinders. In the left-hand figure there is only one year's growth of wood; in the right-hand figure a second year's growth forms a distinct annual ring in the wood. The upper figure shows the cellular detail of the various tissue layers in a segment of a two-year-old stem. (See p. 62.)

THE CELL: UNIT OF LIFE   *61*

Carl Strüwe

3-21 Annual rings in the wood of pine (×23).

layer of xylem cells is added inside the cambium and a new layer of phloem is added on its outside. Moreover, the cells laid down during the most favorable part (spring) of each growing season are usually larger than the later cells, with the result that the phloem and especially the xylem show, in cross section, a well-marked series of annual growth rings (Fig. 3-21).[9] In climates without well-marked seasons, rings are faint or absent.

The great masses of xylem cells in the wood of a tree like the oak are of course dead

vessels. The oak, symbol of sturdy life, is in one sense therefore more dead than alive. However, the presence of the actively growing cambium between xylem and phloem guarantees a continual supply of living cells, whose number remains nearly constant throughout the life of the tree. Its increasing bulk with age is an increase of dead wood tissue, whose functional significance is its combination of conduction and mechanical support.

There is much less wood (xylem cells) in the stems of herbaceous plants, which usually have large amounts of pith. Their protective tissues commonly are green, containing chloroplasts and carrying on photosynthesis.

The organization of tissues we have outlined here applies generally to the plants in one (the dicotyledons) of two principal groups of plants. In the other group (the monocotyledons), which includes plants like the lily, bamboo, corn, and other grasses, the same kinds of tissues are present, but they are not organized in the series of concentric cylinders characteristic of the dicotyledons. The vascular bundles of xylem and phloem are scattered throughout the pith (Fig. 3-22). Nor is there a continuous cambium layer in the monocotyledons; consequently most of these plants cannot maintain a continuous growth in width. This is one reason why there are so few trees among monocotyledons (palms are an exception).

Tissue organization in the root.
Roots anchor plants, but their main role is the gathering in of water and dissolved salts from the soil. They may also store materials, especially starch, among other specialized activities. Their tissues are quite similar to those of stems, but they have no pith, and the vascular bundles are arranged in a somewhat different way. The surface cells just back of root tips usually have elongated extensions of their walls, forming root hairs (Fig. 3-23). The root hairs worm their way in between fine particles of soil. The development of these hairs is of functional significance to the root,

9 The formation of annual rings in the xylem allows us to determine the age of woody stems and to recognize, by their relative width, when good and bad growing seasons occur. The timbers of giant trees in western America are so old that their annual rings have revealed the history of climatic change over more than 1000 years. And the timbers in the abandoned cliff dwellings of the Mesa Verde in Colorado have permitted exact dating of their age.

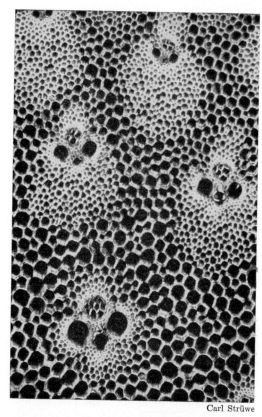

Carl Strüwe

3-22   Scattered vascular bundles in the stem of bamboo, a monocotyledonous plant (×75).

---

for it increases the surface through which water and dissolved minerals can be absorbed.

ANIMAL TISSUES

The higher animals have much more complex differentiation of organs than do any plants. The tissues and cells making up these organs are also more varied. Many tissues and tissue products are peculiar to certain groups of animals, for instance, bone to vertebrates or feathers to birds. There are, however, broad classes of tissues that occur in virtually all multicellular animals, differing only in detailed structure and origin. Among these broad classes are: surface tissue, muscle tissue, nervous tissue, connective tissue, and fluid tissue. As we review these classes now, bear in mind that their diversity and specialization are often related to the great mobility that characterizes animals.

Surface tissues: epithelia (Fig. 3-24). All organisms are enclosed. They have a boundary between themselves and the environment. In protists, this is simply the cell membrane and underlying, viscous cytoplasm. In multicellular forms, both plant and animal, it is one or more layers of cells—epithelia. Epithelia are tissues that cover surfaces, the external surface being only one of many in the animal as a whole. Some internal surfaces are actually continuous with the outside; for example, the surfaces of the mouth, throat, stomach, intestines, and lungs are covered with epithelia. Other internal surfaces, like the linings of blood vessels and body cavities,

3-23   Plant roots. Longitudinal section of a root, showing epidermal cells extending as *root hairs* into the soil between soil particles. The growing tip (*region of cell multiplication*) is protected by a root cap. The cells of the root cap are continuously abraded away by friction on the soil particles, as growth forces the tip downwards. It is continuously regenerated by cell divisions in the growing tip. Immediately behind the region of cell multiplication, new cells elongate under the pressure of osmosis (p. 82). The cells eventually mature (*region of maturation*) into specialized types such as xylem and phloem. The inset photograph shows root hairs on the young root of a radish plant germinating from its seed.

Photo by Hugh Spencer

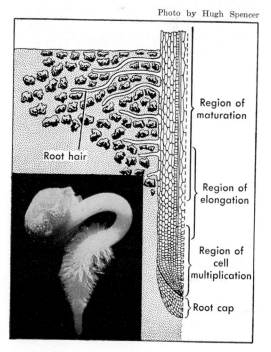

Root hair

Region of maturation

Region of elongation

Region of cell multiplication

Root cap

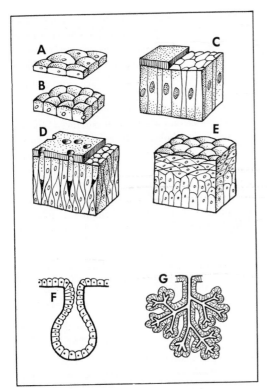

3-24 Animal epithelia. *A.* Simple squamous epithelium consists of flattened, tile-like cells; it lines cavities such as that of the mouth. *B.* Cuboidal epithelium occurs, for example, in kidney tubules (Fig. 7-15). *C.* Columnar epithelium occurs, for example, in the lining of the stomach. *D.* Ciliated columnar epithelium lines the breathing ducts (trachea, Fig. 6-13) of land vertebrates. *E.* Stratified epithelium occurs on surfaces subject to heavy wear, such as human skin. The lowest (germinative) layer of cells in the epithelium continually supplies, by mitosis, new cells to replace those worn away from the external layers. *F* and *G.* Diagrams of simple and more complex types of glands, consisting of epithelia specialized to produce and secrete some specific substance or substances.

have no connection with the outside but nevertheless, being surfaces, are covered with epithelia.

The functions of epithelia are a consequence of their surface position. They are *protective*, and subject to wear and tear. There is a continual death and replacement of epithelial cells. The epithelial cells are shed either cell by cell or—as in human skin—in small many-celled flakes,[10] so small that we are hardly

10 As in dandruff and the peeling that follows sunburn.

conscious of the fact that we are continuously shedding our skins. In some other animals— as in most snakes—the whole surface comes off in one piece from time to time.

As the organism's limiting boundary, epithelia also control what enters and leaves the body, just as its membrane controls traffic into and out of the individual cell. Thus the epithelia of the stomach and intestines *absorb* foodstuffs; oxygen enters the body through lung epithelia; urine is excreted by epithelia in the kidney, and so on. And all sense stimuli must enter the body via epithelia which, for this reason, are important constituents in sense organs like the eye and nose.

Skin is a word often synonymous with epithelium, but in man, as in many other animals, skin refers not to a single tissue but to a most complex organ. Human skin (Fig. 3-25) consists of many layers of cells only the outermost of which are epithelia. Below are muscle cells, blood vessels, nerves, and much of the loose fibrous connective tissue described later.

Muscle tissues. Probably the protoplasm of all types of cells is capable of contraction to some extent. In muscle cells this capacity is fully developed; the muscle cell is a specialist in this protoplasmic function. Multicellular animals as a whole and the parts within them are generally moved by muscular tissue. Muscles occur in all but the lowest animals, and muscular tissue is remarkably similar throughout the animal kingdom.

In higher vertebrates, like man, three different sorts of muscular tissue are distinguished: skeletal (or striated) muscle; smooth muscle; and heart muscle (Fig. 3-26). Muscle cells generally are elongate, their contraction occurring along the long axis of the cell. *Skeletal muscles,* which are conspicuously cross-banded when viewed under the microscope, are responsible for movement of the whole animal by moving its skeleton: legs move because their bones are moved by muscles. Muscle contraction is generally initiated by stimuli coming to them through nerves. Rapid transmission of nerve messages (impulses) and rapid response to them by muscle is the basis of the quick and beautifully co-ordinated movement of the higher animals. The response of skeletal muscle to

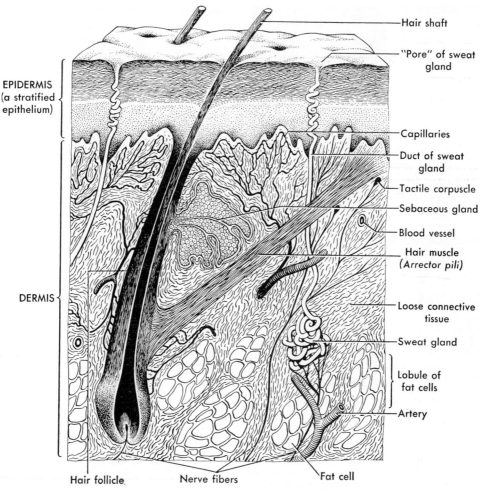

EPIDERMIS
(a stratified
epithelium)

DERMIS

Hair shaft

"Pore" of sweat
gland

Capillaries

Duct of sweat
gland

Tactile corpuscle

Sebaceous gland

Blood vessel

Hair muscle
(Arrector pili)

Loose connective
tissue

Sweat gland

Lobule of
fat cells

Artery

Hair follicle

Nerve fibers

Fat cell

3-25 Human skin is an organ consisting of many distinct tissues. On the outside is a many-layered epithelium, the outermost cells of which are continuously worn away. The tissue is maintained by the production of new cells from a generative layer (stippled in the figure) at the base of the epithelium. Below the epithelium lies the dermis, in which the following can be seen: capillary networks, arteries, and veins; nerve fibers and sense organs (tactile corpuscles); sweat glands; lobules of fat cells; hair follicles bearing hairs; muscles capable of raising the hairs; and loose connective tissue that serves to bind together the whole complex of other tissues.

stimulation is rapid; and so is its relaxation, readying it for new messages. *Smooth muscle,* unstriated, is responsible for much of the movement of internal organs such as the stomach and intestines. Smooth muscle is slow to contract and capable of more prolonged contraction than skeletal muscle. *Heart muscle* occurs only in the walls of the heart, as its name suggests. It is striated in much the same manner as skeletal tissue but is unique in other ways.

Skeletal muscle is often referred to as "voluntary muscle," in distinction to smooth and heart muscle, which are said to be "involuntary." This distinction arises from man's ability to exercise voluntary control over contraction of skeletal muscle and his lack of conscious control over the others. This distinction is, of course, difficult or impossible to use meaningfully in other animals.

Muscle tissue seems truly wonderful when thought of in its work of ceaseless contraction

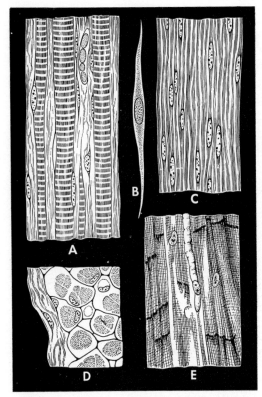

3-26 Muscle tissue. *A* and *D*. Skeletal (striped) muscle in longitudinal (*A*) and cross (*D*) section. The nuclei can be seen lying at the periphery of the muscle fibers. The individual muscle fibers are packed together in bundles embedded in loose connective tissue. *B*. An individual smooth muscle cell. *C*. A sheet of smooth muscle from the intestine of a cat. *E*. Heart, or cardiac, muscle.

in the heart, pumping decade after decade; in its power in a football player; in its rapid and precise response in a dancer; or in its boundless energy in a puppy. The lightning-fast yet almost incredibly intricate chemical process by which muscular energy is released seems still more wonderful (Chapter 6).

Nervous tissues. A small boy stubs his toe and gives a whoop. Unknown to him, he has demonstrated the action of one of the most complex and extraordinary of all the processes of life: the transmission of impulses by nervous tissue. This tissue is as widespread among animals as is muscular tissue.[11] The association is significant, for, among many other

11 Sponges are the only major group of multi-cellular animals in which nerves and muscles are absent.

things, nerves are involved in stimulation and co-ordination of muscular contraction.

In spite of the expected variety in details, nervous tissue is even more similar throughout the animal kingdom than is muscular tissue. Its basis is the nerve cell which, more than any other, illustrates the relation of cellular structure to function (Fig. 3-27). The function of the nerve cell is to transmit nerve impulses—or messages—often over long distances within the body. The nerve cell has a central cell body which contains the nucleus and is drawn out into two or more long protoplasmic processes termed nerve fibers. These fibers are an integral part of the cell (cf. fibers *outside* cells in connective tissue, p. 68). Some are simple, and others greatly branched; some end very near the cell body, while others extend for some distance. In large animals this may be a distance of 3 to 4 feet. The fibers of some nerve cells are surrounded by accessory cells forming a cellular sheath. A nerve is a group of fibers bound together by connective tissue (Fig. 3-27).

All the complexities of perception, behavior, and conscious thought that we find in ourselves and see, in varying degrees, in other animals are founded on a relatively simple basis. This is the nerve cell's capacity to transmit electrical impulses and join with other nerve cells in complexly organized association —the nervous system. The importance of this system for understanding ourselves and other living things is obvious. It will be discussed at some length later (Chapters 9 and 10).

Connective tissues. A wide variety of tissue types is included under the heading of connective tissues; and they are associated with a wide variety of functions (Fig. 3-28). All the tissues have one feature in common: the constituent cells lie in an extensive *matrix*, or bed, of extracellular material containing fibers. Both matrix and fibers are manufactured by the cells. The specialization of connective tissues is reflected in characteristic specialization of the intercellular matrix and fibers. We will distinguish two broad functional classes: supportive connective tissue, and binding connective tissue.

(1) *Supportive connective tissues.* Most kinds of animals are built around or within

3-27 Nerve tissue. A single neuron or nerve cell is diagramed at the left. Dendrites are incoming fibers that carry impulses to the cell body, in which the nucleus can be seen. The axon, which may branch, is the outgoing fiber along which the nerve impulse is transmitted. In some neurons the axon is surrounded by sheaths. In the neuron illustrated there is an inner sheath of the fatty substance myelin (black in the figure) and an outer sheath composed of a distinct cell, called a Schwann cell. In places the sheaths may be constricted, forming distinct nodes.

The lower right-hand figure is a partial cross section of a nerve. A nerve consists of many nerve fibers packed together by connective tissue (epineurium) into bundles. Blood vessels penetrate the nerve, supplying it with food and oxygen.

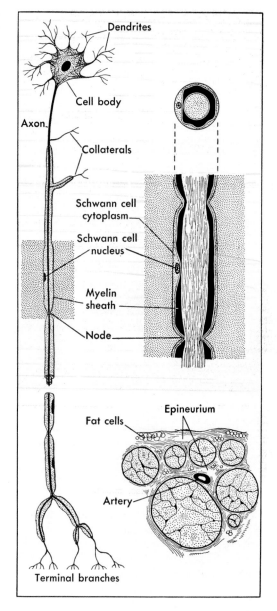

a hard supporting *skeleton* that not only helps to hold them together but also serves as a mechanical framework for locomotion. It may also protect against attack by other animals and assist in waterproofing, among other roles. In most animals without backbones, like the clam and insects, the skeleton is external to the body, secreted by—and lying on top of—an epithelial tissue. In vertebrates—animals with backbones—the skeleton consists of one or both of two supportive tissues, cartilage and bone, which we must treat more fully.

In *cartilage* (gristle) the intercellular matrix is extensive, consisting of organic compounds with a rubbery texture. This matrix gives the tissue an elasticity that resists compression. The fibers embedded in the matrix give cartilage added strength against pulling and stretching. Cartilage can be likened to the wall of a rubber tire; the rubber resists compression, and the internal nylon cords resist stretching. Most cartilages, like that in the nose and ear, are subject to stresses and pulls from all directions, and their fibers appropriately course in all directions within the matrix.

In some fishes (sharks and their relatives) cartilage forms the whole skeleton. In most vertebrates, however, the skeleton consists almost entirely of bone, cartilage being restricted largely to joints, where it forms resilient caps over the bone surfaces involved in the joint.

Bone, like other connective tissues, contains innumerable living cells. It owes its rigidity to the dense intercellular matrix secreted by

the bone cells. The rigidity, lacking in cartilage, is what makes bone such excellent supportive tissue for large and heavy [12] animals. Bone is rigid because the bone matrix is impregnated with mineral salts (mainly a complex phosphate of calcium) which commonly make up about two-thirds of the weight of

[12] Do you see any significance in the fact that the only large animals with wholly cartilaginous skeletons are aquatic? While on this line of thought, consider the fact that the largest animal alive (a whale) is aquatic.

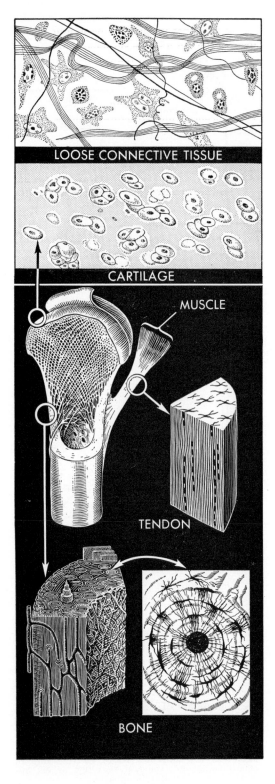

LOOSE CONNECTIVE TISSUE

CARTILAGE

MUSCLE

TENDON

BONE

fresh bone. The matrix is maintained in proper condition by the bone cells which lie within it. These, in turn, can remain alive only because the dense matrix is perforated by a system of canals carrying blood vessels which supply the cells with their needs.

(2) *Binding connective tissues.* The active movement characteristic of animals makes structural demands that are satisfied by many special tissues, including binding connective tissue. It includes tendons, ligaments, and loose connective tissue. In *tendons* and *ligaments* the intercellular matrix is packed with fibers which, unlike those of cartilage, are all oriented in one direction. Tendons bind muscles to bones and are subjected to a strong stress—always in one direction—when the muscle contracts and the bone is moved. Tendons are appropriately inelastic—were they not, some muscle contraction would be wasted on their stretch. On the other hand, ligaments, which envelop bones at a joint, are appropriately elastic. They have the same resilient "give" characteristic of the knee bandage sometimes used to supplement them in supporting a weak joint.

Loose connective tissue serves many functions. It binds constituent muscle cells together into the mass of the individual muscles (Fig. 3-26) and, similarly, nerve fibers into individual nerves. Indeed, it binds all kinds of organs together in loose but strong fashion that keeps them in proper place but allows them to move on each other as the organism moves. Again, between and within organs it serves as a loose elastic highway on which blood vessels and nerves are carried.

3-28 Connective and supportive tissues. The lower figure illustrates diagrammatically the structure and components of a long bone like the humerus (p. 226) of man. The head of the bone is capped by cartilage. Muscle is attached to the bone by a tendon whose cells (black in the figure) lie packed between inelastic fibers oriented along the axis of the tendon. The bone itself is essentially a cylinder. Within, the bone tissue has a spongy texture. A piece of the wall of the bone cylinder is shown at the lower left. It is perforated by blood vessels that supply food and oxygen to the living bone cells embedded in the hard ground substance. The bone (lower right) cells are organized in concentric cylinders at the center of which lies a blood vessel.

Fluid tissues. The internal fluids of animals generally contain living cells (Fig. 7-6). Since they are an essential and distinctive part of the biological system, they may well be considered as tissues. These fluids are the medium by which food, oxygen, and other materials reach the cells and by which products of cells are removed and taken elsewhere in the body. Lower animals generally have a single body fluid which seeps around between the cells and in body cavities. Higher animals, like man, usually have two body fluids, distinct in composition although they exchange materials. The lymph occurs in body cavities and between cells, although in many forms it also moves sluggishly through special vessels. The blood is pumped through a partly or completely closed system of vessels.

Chapter Summary

The cell theory and its relation to the theory of evolution—the foundations of modern biology.

The cell as the minimum organization of matter that is alive, the basic unit of life.

Protoplasm not a single substance, but a name loosely applied to the living organization of matter.

The visible structure of cells: walls, membranes, cytoplasm, and nucleus.

The concept of ultrastructure; colloids, fibers.

Cell reproduction; the nucleus.

Cells as complete organisms; protists; intracellular specialization.

Protistan colonies compared with multicellular organisms; the evolution of multi cellular organisms.

Tissues as aggregates of similar cells specialized in structure and function; organs as integrated aggregates of diverse tissues; systems as integrated aggregates of organs.

Plant tissues: their organization into leaf, stem, and root.

Animal tissues: their greater number and complexity; functional specializations related to the mobility of animals.

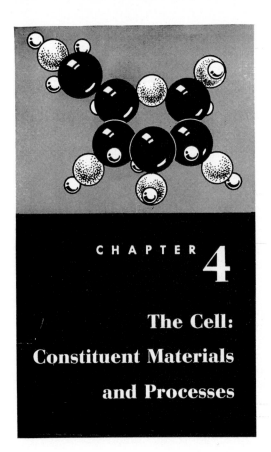

This is a model of the glucose molecule, a key constituent in the life of all cells. The largest, black atoms are carbon; the medium-sized, stippled ones are oxygen; and the smallest, white ones are hydrogen.

CHAPTER 4

The Cell:
Constituent Materials
and Processes

CELLULAR ENVIRONMENTS

Every cell, every group of cells, every organism is dependent upon and influenced by other cells, other groups of cells, other organisms. Every organism lives in an environment of which it is itself a part, along with others of its kind, organisms of other kinds, and many nonliving substances such as air, water, and soil. No organism lives alone, and no living thing is sufficient unto itself. To consider cell or organism apart from its environment is to consider the nonexistent, an abstraction that is not a real form of life. Relationships between life and environment are so pervasive a part of living that they are involved in all aspects of biology.

The fact that these relationships are so complex and that they do somehow affect every process of life makes it impossible to study them all at once or as a distinct and separate topic. It is necessary to take them up repeatedly, from different points of view and at different levels. In this part of the book we are concerned mostly with life in its most intimate aspects at its most basic level. Relationships to the environment here to be considered are thus mainly the exchanges and other interrelationships between cells and their environments: other cells and the various media (mainly fluids) in or on which cells live.

The degree of interdependence varies according to the properties of cells, their positions with respect to other cells, the kinds of organisms, and the surroundings of cells and organisms. One very essential sort of interdependence results from the fact that cells arise only from other cells. They are derived from one another in sequence through time. These aspects involve growth, reproduction, and heredity. Another sort of dependence is involved in the integration of cells in organisms. Some cells secrete hormones which modify the activities of other cells. Cells in organs and systems act to move or otherwise to affect the organism as a whole. Nerves (themselves cells) control and co-ordinate activities of other cells. These aspects, too, will be discussed later.

Perhaps the most fundamental interdependence of all is illustrated by the fact that all cells require certain sugars (and their derivatives) that are synthesized—or elaborated—in the first place only by the green cells of plants. Those green cells themselves are not independent. They require, at the least, supplies of raw materials from the environment and radiation from the distant sun. If they are parts of multicellular organisms they also require materials acquired or elaborated by other cells. In other words, every cell is dependent on sources outside itself for the materials of which it is composed and for the energy involved in its activities. Further, the rates of processes in the cell and also to some extent their nature depend largely on external influences such as light and heat. The present chapter will bear on these relationships: the sorts of materials and energy required by cells, the sources of these and how they get into the cell, and other effects of the environment.

The Materials of Life

One of the most fascinating things about life is the interplay of unity and diversity. From bacterium to sunflower and to man, all living things have much in common. Yet each sort of living thing is unique in its particular combinations of materials, processes, and relationships. All require just the same general sorts of materials. They require these in amounts and proportions which vary considerably, to be sure, but which vary within prescribed limits. Yet what they do with these materials is never precisely the same in any two sorts of organisms.

This unity-with-diversity can be strikingly illustrated by two exceptional cases. You would say—and, up to a point, quite correctly —that cellulose, the material of many plant cell walls and hence of wood, is a substance peculiar to plants as opposed to animals. Similarly, hemoglobin, the chemical that makes your blood red, seems completely characteristic of animals as opposed to plants. Yet cellulose occurs in a group of animals, the odd marine forms called tunicates (p. 538), and hemoglobin has been found in the root nodules of some leguminous plants.

These exceptions show that the diversity among organisms is, after all, based on still more fundamental similarities. Cellulose is a complex compound built up from sugar molecules. Similar processes of building up sugar molecules occur widely in animals producing, for instance, the glycogen (animal starch) in-

volved in muscular energy—and the point is further driven home by the fact that a few plants also make glycogen. Hemoglobin is a chemical combination of heme and globin. Compounds of the same general types are common in plants. For instance, chlorophyll, the green pigment of plants, is chemically very similar to heme. So the exceptional occurrence of cellulose in animals and of hemoglobin in plants illustrates a similarity in materials and in the way in which these are combined, even when the resulting combinations are different.

The material requirements of organisms are often summed up as food. Like many everyday words, "food" is an ambiguous word. No doubt bread and meat are food. But plain water is the largest material requirement of most organisms. Is water food? Vitamins are needed only in minute amounts. Are they food? Life requires relatively simple inorganic materials, such as water, used just so or as raw materials for more complex, organic compounds. The needed organic materials or foods are elaborated from raw materials by the organisms themselves, or are acquired by eating other organisms.

A LITTLE CHEMISTRY

It is necessary at this point to introduce some very simple chemistry, probably already familiar to you from general reading—and certainly less than you know if you have had an elementary course in chemistry or physical science. You surely know that the smallest particles in nature, electrons, protons, and the rest, are commonly organized into *atoms*. Atoms represent in most basic form the chemical *elements*, the building blocks for all larger chemical units. In view of the tremendous complexity of the matter composed of them, the number of elements is surprisingly small. Only 101 are known; several of them have been made artificially and may not occur in nature. About 35 are common in nature and important for life.

You also doubtless know that two or more atoms (up to thousands) can combine with each other, linked together by electrical forces, to form a *molecule*. If the molecule contains more than one kind of atom, it is a *compound*. Atoms and molecules or both can *react* with each other and produce different kinds of molecules. In ordinary chemical reactions, the number and kind of atoms are the same before and after the reaction. Only their combinations in molecules change.

Each element has a name and an abbreviation that stands for the name. The elements most important in biology are: hydrogen, abbreviation H; oxygen, O; carbon, C; and nitrogen, N. The simple (or empirical) formula for a molecule shows what atoms it contains. Water is H_2O, a formula which means that it has two atoms of hydrogen to one of oxygen. Reactions are written in terms of such formulas. The reaction for forming water from its elements is:

$$2H_2 + O_2 \rightarrow 2H_2O$$

That means that two molecules of hydrogen (each with two atoms) combined with one of oxygen (also with two atoms) and produced two molecules of water. There were four atoms of hydrogen and two of oxygen to begin with, and of course the same six atoms are there in the water after the reaction. One other point is that there is less energy in two molecules of water than in two of hydrogen and one of oxygen. In this reaction, energy is released from chemical form and appears in some other form such as heat. The most meaningful and complete formula for the reaction is therefore:

$$2H_2 + O_2 \rightarrow 2H_2O + Energy \text{ (heat)}$$

Some other simple chemical principles will be mentioned later, but this is all you need to know for the time being, and in fact this is the whole basis of chemistry. (It is true that things a bit more complicated are built upon this simple basis!)

INORGANIC MATERIALS

All the materials of life are *ultimately* derived from relatively simple inorganic [1] compounds and elements. Once they are assimilated by a living thing, these ultimate materials often become extremely elaborated and are passed on from one organism to an-

[1] "Organic" chemical compounds are complex molecules, all of which contain carbon and occur in nature only as the products of living organisms, or, nowadays, as the product of man's ingenuity in a chemical laboratory. Inorganic compounds occur in nature independently of the living organism.

other. Most of these elaborated chemicals are finally broken down into simple, inorganic forms again. There is, then, a cycle, with the inorganic materials at the beginning and end; it thus seems logical to begin consideration of life's materials with them. They include water, carbon dioxide, oxygen, nitrogen, and a great variety of what may be called, as a group, mineral salts.

Water. We have already noted that protoplasm is largely composed of water—plain water, H_2O. Higher plants and animals also contain much fluid that is not in the protoplasm but which bathes the cells or moves among them in vessels. This fluid, exemplified by the sap of trees or the blood of animals, is essentially water with a complex of inorganic and organic materials dissolved in it. The liquid part (plasma) of blood is about 90 per cent water; most active protoplasm contains about the same percentage of water. We are all familiar with the discomfort of animals (such as humans) and the wilting of plants when deprived of water. Some dormant structures, such as spores and seeds, can retain sufficient water to remain alive for months or even years without new supplies. Nevertheless, all organisms eventually die if their water supply continues to be inadequate.

Water plays three main roles in living things: (1) it is a medium in which other materials move from place to place; (2) it is the seat and facilitator of chemical reactions; (3) and it enters into reactions itself, and goes to make up some of the more complex materials of life. So many other substances dissolve in water that it is sometimes called a universal solvent. It is true that some of the materials necessary for life are scarcely or not at all soluble in water, but even these are commonly surrounded by water or suspended in it as colloids or emulsions. Water is probably involved in *all* the chemical reactions in cells, either as a solvent or as a reagent.

Some water used by life arises within the cells as a result of chemical reactions. For instance, the complete oxidation of fats produces large quantities of water. Some desert animals never drink liquid water, obtaining enough from metabolism of fats (also of carbohydrates). Generally, however, water as such must enter the organism from its environment, getting into individual cells from outside them. Water is also constantly lost from cells and organisms. The necessary balance between intake and outgo of water involves some of the most interesting processes and problems of life.

Water, as such, is thus a large and necessary part of all organisms. The role of water as a raw material for other compounds is no less essential. Practically all organic compounds contain hydrogen, the ultimate inorganic source of which is for the most part water, H_2O. Some other inorganic materials taken in by living things supply hydrogen in chemical combination, but this constitutes only a small fraction of what the organism uses. Hydrogen as an element, H_2, occurs in nature as a gas, but it is not abundant and is never utilized by living things. Water also supplies much of the oxygen in organic compounds. Oxygen, like hydrogen, occurs in nature as a gas; but unlike hydrogen, this elementary source is exploited by living things.

Carbon dioxide. It is the definition of *organic* compounds that they all contain carbon. Once it is incorporated in a living thing, a carbon atom may pass through hundreds or thousands of different combinations within one organism and then, commonly, within others and yet still others as the materials are passed on. The beginning and end of the cycle in the inorganic environment involve carbon in the simple compound CO_2, carbon dioxide. Under ordinary conditions this is a gas. (At temperatures lower than those in nature it solidifies; solid CO_2 is what we call dry ice.) The gas forms about 0.03 per cent of the atmosphere. This mere three-hundredths of one per cent is the main inorganic reservoir and source of carbon as a material for life.

The gas CO_2 does not usually enter directly into chemical reactions. However, it dissolves in water (as everyone knows who has ever opened a bottle of carbonated drink) and then reacts readily in various ways. This activity is due in part to the fact that CO_2 in solution reacts with water, itself, and forms a weak acid, carbonic acid, H_2CO_3, in accordance with the following equation:

$$CO_2 + H_2O \rightleftharpoons H_2CO_3$$

The double arrow, $\rightleftharpoons$, indicates that the equation, like a great many of those important in life processes, can readily go in either direction. Slight changes in pressure, heat, concentration, or presence of other chemicals can reverse the reaction:

$$CO_2 + H_2O \rightarrow H_2CO_3$$

and produce the opposite:

$$H_2CO_3 \rightarrow CO_2 + H_2O$$

The beginning of the incorporation of atmospheric CO_2 into the materials of life is a more complex series of reactions with water. In green plants these two raw materials are combined into simple sugars. This is an extremely important and basic synthesis for the whole world of life. It is discussed in the next chapter. From the simple sugars, the carbon is passed on into many other substances.

The end of carbon's participation in the chemistry of life usually involves its withdrawal from more complex compounds and its combination with oxygen. It thus forms CO_2 again, most of which finds its way more or less directly back into the atmosphere. Almost all organisms, both plants and animals, are constantly forming CO_2. The accumulation of this gas, or of H_2CO_3 readily formed from it, in cells or in fluids such as blood soon becomes harmful. Its elimination is therefore necessary.

Oxygen. The great majority of the compounds involved in the substances and processes of life contain carbon, hydrogen, and oxygen. Some contain no other elements. Others contain quantities, usually much smaller quantities, of various additional elements. The inorganic source of much oxygen in organic compounds is water. In addition to water and oxygen-containing organic foods, most organisms also require extra oxygen in the form of the element itself, O (or, as a molecule, O_2). Along with water and some salts (see p. 75), this is an inorganic material that can be utilized *directly* by animals as well as plants, in marked contrast to the carbon source, CO_2. (There are, however, some lowly organisms, mainly bacteria and parasites, that can live without oxygen and may even be killed by it.)

Oxygen is a gas, and its great inorganic reservoir is the atmosphere, which contains about 20 per cent (by volume) of elemental oxygen (that is, not combined with other elements). Oxygen dissolves readily in water, remaining in the form of the element, and so is also available to aquatic organisms. In fact, oxygen must be in solution in water to enter organisms living in air.

The principal role of elemental oxygen in cells is to combine with carbon and hydrogen, from the breakdown of organic compounds, producing carbon dioxide and water. The water so formed may be further utilized by the organism, but the carbon dioxide is almost entirely eliminated. The input of oxygen and output of carbon dioxide depend on the chemical activity of the cells and of the organism as a whole. Oxygen consumption is a fairly good measure of total metabolism in most organisms. If you have ever taken a basal metabolism test, this was the principle involved.

If carbon (for instance, charcoal) is burned in air, it combines in a simple way with oxygen and produces heat, which is, of course, one form of energy:

$$C + O_2 \rightarrow CO_2 + Energy$$

Because of this reaction, so familiar to everyone, and because the body's oxygen consumption and carbon dioxide elimination do tend to be proportional to total activity, it used to be supposed that some such reaction accounts for the body's heat and other energy. The notion is held by many people that "fuel" —organic compounds such as sugars or fats— is "burned"—combined directly with oxygen —in the body and that this is how we obtain energy. It is now known, however, that this is rarely if ever a significant source of useful organic energy. Most such energy is released by chemical reactions that do *not* use oxygen. As a rule, oxygen is used and CO_2 is formed only *after* the important energy release, in a sort of sweeping up of the debris of earlier reactions and setting up for their repetition, as will be explained in Chapter 5.

Animal metabolism utilizes but does not produce elemental oxygen. The process of combining CO_2 and H_2O to form sugars in green plants, however, involves release of O_2, and while this synthesis is going on it usually produces more oxygen than the plants need. Green plants in light thus usually give off oxygen to the surrounding water or air. In the dark, when the active phase of sugar production is not proceeding, plants produce no spare oxygen but continue to utilize oxygen and give off CO_2. This is why fish in a pond with green plants may be suffocated during the night. The dissolved oxygen in the water is being used up and none is being produced by the plants.

Nitrogen sources. After carbon, hydrogen, and oxygen, the most common element in protoplasm and in the materials of life is nitrogen, N (in molecules, N_2). It is, in particular, a constituent of all proteins, an extremely important class of organic compounds to be discussed later in this chapter.

There is a tremendous store of nitrogen in the atmosphere, which is (by volume) almost 80 per cent elemental nitrogen. Yet no animals and few plants can make direct use of this nitrogen. Most plants can utilize nitrogen from the environment only if it is in the form of various inorganic compounds: ammonia (NH_3) or its compounds; nitrates (salts containing NO_3); or nitrites (salts with NO_2). Animals need to take on nitrogen in the form of compounds, especially proteins, which they obtain from plants or from other animals. The withdrawal of nitrogen from the atmospheric reservoir and its incorporation into life thus depend on processes that make ammonia, nitrates, and nitrites. Some inorganic processes do this, especially lightning, but formation of these compounds is due more largely to a few kinds of organisms that are able to metabolize elemental nitrogen—to fix it, as it is said. Some bacteria, and simple plants (some algae, and fungi) can do this. Most noteworthy are bacteria that live in nodules in the roots of beans and related plants (legumes).

On the other hand, few organisms decompose compounds of nitrogen completely and produce the element nitrogen. Some denitrifying bacteria do this, but the end products of nitrogen metabolism in most organisms are still organic compounds, such as urea or uric acid in animals, or, at the simplest, ammonia. Since even ammonia can be utilized by some plants and is readily turned into nitrates and nitrites by certain bacteria, the nitrogen remains available to life for long periods of time and passage through many different organisms.

Mineral salts.[2] Besides C, H, O, and N, many other elements are required in smaller amounts by all forms of life. The inorganic sources of these are, in most cases, salts dissolved in water—water in the soil or in lakes, streams, and seas. Plants and, to some degree, aquatic animals usually acquire these salts directly from the water of the environment. Land animals also acquire and utilize salts directly to some extent, but obtain much of their mineral requirement more or less incidentally along with their organic food. This is one reason for emphasis on a balanced diet by physicians—we have not only the obvious requirements for building materials and energy in our food, but also the need for small amounts of many different minerals, not all of which are likely to be present in the required forms and quantities in any one food. In exceptional cases extra quantities of iron, calcium, iodine, or sodium may be needed and supplied medicinally, or reduction of mineral intake (for instance, of table salt) may be indicated.

Among the mineral elements, sulfur, phosphorus, potassium, sodium, calcium, magnesium, chlorine, iron, and copper are required by most or all organisms, although plants do not need sodium. Other elements are widely required, but perhaps not by all forms of life. For instance, in addition to those listed, iodine, manganese, zinc, and fluorine are elements essential in minute amounts to man and numerous other organisms. It has been found that elements present in such small quantities as to have escaped earlier detection may nevertheless be absolutely necessary to some organ-

isms. For example, the mysterious wasting away of sheep and cattle on some pastures was found to be due to a lack of cobalt. At present a great deal of research is being done on these "trace elements." The need for extremely small traces of a great many elements is turning out to be much more widespread than had been realized.

ORGANIC MATERIALS

Organisms vary greatly in their ability to build up the compounds needed for their lives. Plants generally can make all the organic materials they require, and animals generally cannot. This is a matter of nutritional needs and processes. Here we must note that various organic substances are essential *materials* for life and must somehow be acquired by all cells. This is true whether the cells make these materials for themselves, receive them from other cells of the same organism, or ultimately derive them from sources quite outside the organism. The materials to be discussed at this point fall into the very broad chemical groups of carbohydrates, fats, and proteins. There are other groups just as essential to life, notably the vitamins and hormones. They are, however, more clearly understood in connection with special processes considered later.

Carbohydrates, fats, and proteins include the principal building materials of cells; they are also the main sources of energy. These roles are not always, or even usually, clear-cut in the cell. It is quite common for the same material to act successively in building and in energy production. It may, indeed, do both at the same time. Proteins may be structural elements, sources of energy, and facilitators of reactions (catalysts) all at once. In the cell there is a constant, intricate, interweaving flow of materials and processes. The processes are not like building a house and then hauling in fuel and making a fire in the stove. The cell house is self-energizing; its materials are always in a state of flux; the general plan persists, but every brick or board is continuously being modified or torn out and replaced.

Carbohydrates. Carbohydrates have a particularly basic role as materials for life, for through them inorganic carbon is first incorporated into living things. Car-

2 Strictly speaking, the main inorganic nitrogen sources for life are actually mineral salts, and therefore belong under this heading, but they have such a special role that they have been briefly treated separately in the preceding section.

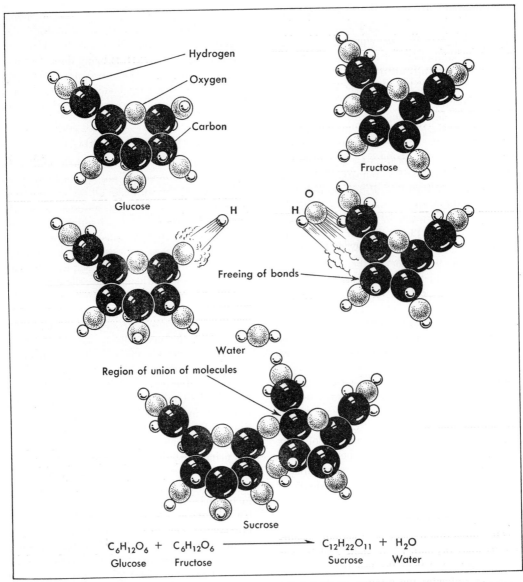

4-1 Carbohydrate molecules. Glucose, fructose, and their synthesis, by dehydration, into sucrose.

bohydrates also contribute to the formation of other sorts of organic compounds. Carbohydrates are important building materials, and they are especially involved in the chief energy-releasing processes in both plants and animals. They are composed entirely of carbon, hydrogen, and oxygen. Their molecules always contain just twice as many atoms of hydrogen as of oxygen—the same proportions as in water. Common examples of carbohydrates are sugar, starch, and cellulose.

Most carbohydrate molecules have a basic unit of six carbon atoms linked together in various ways, with hydrogen and oxygen atoms attached around them in different ways (Fig. 4-1). Because of the differences in attachments, two carbohydrates may contain the same numbers and kinds of atoms and still be quite different substances. Both fructose (fruit sugar) and glucose (a principal ingredient in corn syrup) have the formula $C_6H_{12}O_6$. This sort of formula, called *empirical*, shows the atoms present but not their arrangement. The arrangement in fructose and glucose differs in a way that makes them two distinct sorts of sugars, as we shall see.

By reactions commonly occurring in life processes, two or more groups of six carbon molecules of the simplest carbohydrates (simple sugars) can be bound together. When this happens between any two such molecules, two atoms of hydrogen and one of oxygen are dropped out of the compound. Those three atoms lose their places of attachment in the carbohydrate molecule and appear combined with each other, as water:

Glucose	Fructose	Sucrose (table sugar)	Water

$$C_6H_{12}O_6 + C_6H_{12}O_6 \rightarrow C_{12}H_{22}O_{11} + H_2O$$

(The process as it really goes forward is more complex. The equation only sums up what goes into the complex process and what comes out of it.)

Essentially the same process can link together large numbers of the six-carbon units and attached hydrogen and oxygen atoms, eliminating one molecule of water for each unit added:

n glucose molecules added together		Starch	n molecules of water

$$n\,(C_6H_{12}O_6) \xrightarrow[\text{or dehydration synthesis}]{\text{condensation}} (C_6H_{10}O_5)_n + n - 1\,H_2O$$

(Of course this process as it actually occurs in cells goes through many steps and is even more complicated than the last.)

Here n indicates the number of six-carbon units involved, a large number in this case. The result is a relatively large, complex, long molecule, called a *polysaccharide;* the term rather neatly sums up what has happened: it means "many sugars." This building up of a large molecule from simple sugar units is called *condensation;* it is a dehydration synthesis. It is one important way in which the materials of life are compounded. Like simple sugars, different polysaccharides may have the same empirical formula and yet be quite different because the atoms are arranged differ-

ently. For instance, cellulose and glycogen (an energy source in muscle, mentioned earlier) have the same general formula as starch:

$$(C_6H_{10}O_5)_n$$

Starch and glycogen are ready forms of storage of carbohydrates, starch usually in plants and glycogen usually in animals. They are not soluble in water and so can remain in cells unchanged until required. A potato is mainly a store of starch, and in animals glycogen is stored in the liver among other places. When the carbohydrate is utilized, it becomes soluble by the reverse of the summary equation given above:

Starch or glycogen	$n - 1$ molecules of water		n molecules of (soluble) glucose

$$(C_6H_{10}O_5)_n + n - 1\,H_2O \xrightarrow{\text{hydrolysis}} n\,(C_6H_{12}O_6)$$

You see that we could have written the equation $\rightleftharpoons$, showing that, like all other chemical processes in life, this can and does go both ways. This reverse of condensation is called *hydrolysis.* It is an essential part of the digestion of food, so much so that it is sometimes called "digestion." It is, however, also involved in processes not normally thought of as digestion, such as the release of blood sugar from the liver.[3]

Fats. Fats are also composed of carbon, hydrogen, and oxygen, but the ratio of hydrogen to oxygen is much greater than two to one, the ratio in carbohydrates. For instance, the empirical formula of stearin, a fat, is $C_{57}H_{110}O_6$. The way in which the molecules are put together is also characteristic. They resemble polysaccharides in being formed by the condensation of simpler units, but those units (fatty acids and glycerols in chemical terms) are markedly different from simple sugars. A fat can also be hydrolyzed back to its constituent units.

Fats are insoluble in water and are often stored in both plants and animals. They have other essential roles, but fats are a rich energy source. Their complete metabolism entails re-

[3] Since we have said that starch is insoluble, has it occurred to you to wonder why a starchy soda cracker dissolves if you chew it long enough or even just hold it in your mouth? The answer is that saliva contains a substance that hydrolyzes starch.

lease of over twice as much energy as for the same weight of carbohydrate. It also involves the formation of much more water, an important point for organisms in environments from which it is difficult to obtain sufficient water in a more direct way.

Proteins. The proteins are the stars of the biochemical opera. They include the largest and most complicated of all known molecules. In a sense, it is silly to say that one substance or another is more important when all are necessary. This is true of life's materials, from common water to the biggest protein. Yet proteins do have a very special importance. The complexity and diversity of life itself is largely dependent on the complexity and diversity of proteins. The proteins can, indeed, be said to direct the whole show in addition to starring in it, for the chromosomes, themselves partly protein, exert their control over the life of the cell through the agency of specific proteins (enzymes, p. 94) they manufacture. Thus proteins determine what will develop from a seed or an egg. From that point of view, we are what proteins made us. Even after development, proteins largely determine how the organism operates. Of course, they do so in conjunction with other materials, but theirs is the essential direction of most of the processes. They are also structural materials and sources of energy. Perhaps, after all, it is not out of line to say that proteins are among the two or three most important kinds of chemicals in the universe!

The large molecules of proteins are built up of smaller units in much the same way as are polysaccharides and fats. That is, the process is one of *condensation* (dehydration synthesis), with loss of a water molecule for each unit added. The units are, of course, quite different from those of polysaccharides and fats. In the case of proteins, the units are the *amino acids*, which have the general formula $CHR(NH_2)COOH$. In this formula C, H, N, and O stand for carbon, hydrogen, nitrogen, and oxygen in the usual way. R stands for other elements in the molecular structure. In the simplest amino acid, glycine, R is just a hydrogen atom, so that glycine is $CH_2(NH_2)$-COOH. In other cases R is more complex,

sometimes more complex than the central amino acid group to which it is bound.

The number of amino acids cannot be precisely stated at present. Twenty-four are reasonably established as distinct, of known formula, and present in the proteins of living organisms. All proteins contain many amino acid units. Ten thousand or so is a usual figure, and some proteins may contain a hundred thousand or more. The number of possible different arrangements of twenty-odd kinds of units in groups of ten to a hundred thousand is more than astronomical—it is completely inconceivable. It is much more than the total number of particles in the visible universe! There is, however, reason to think that not all the mathematically possible groupings are chemically or biologically possible. Certain sequences of amino acids apparently tend to recur in a fixed way in proteins. This reduces the possible number of different proteins, but still leaves an immensely large figure.

Only plants [4] can make *all* the amino acids they need and later fabricate them into complex proteins. Animals always depend on plants for some amino acids. Man, for instance, has to receive in his food nine of the twenty-four amino acids he eventually utilizes in protein synthesis; the other fifteen he manufactures from the basic nine. All organisms, without exception, manufacture proteins from amino acids, and it is not surprising that sensitive tests reveal that they all make some proteins peculiar to themselves. There must be, therefore, well over a million different kinds of proteins in the whole world of life, and the number may be much greater. Of these million or more proteins, only some five hundred have, however, been isolated and identified by biochemists.

We will later have something more to say about how proteins are formed and transformed in organic processes. Here we will add one other fact that will assume considerable importance as we go along. Besides the proteins, strictly speaking, there are *conjugated proteins*. These have, in addition to the amino acids, nonprotein groups chemically bound onto the molecule. The addition is called a *prosthetic group*. Two examples will

[4] Some fungi are probable exceptions.

give some idea of how important conjugated proteins and their prosthetic groups are. The directive activity of proteins in heredity, development, and other processes is particularly that of the nucleoproteins, conjugated proteins with a prosthetic group containing nucleic acid. Hemoglobin, on which our cells depend for oxygen, is a conjugated protein, globin, with a prosthetic group called heme.

The empirical formulas of proteins do not mean much; their amino acid composition is much more significant. Here are, however, the formulas of a few rather simple proteins, just to suggest how large the molecules are in comparison with most molecules: casein of milk, $C_{708}H_{1130}O_{224}N_{180}S_4P_4$; gliadin of wheat, $C_{685}H_{1068}O_{211}N_{196}S_5$; human hemoglobin, $C_{3032}H_{4816}O_{872}N_{780}S_8Fe_4$. (S is sulfur, P phosphorus, and Fe iron; you know the other symbols.)

Most proteins are soluble in water. Their molecules are, however, so large that a solution of proteins does not act like an ordinary solution of small molecules. It acts more as if the molecules were large clumps of molecules of more usual size. In other words, a protein solution is more like a colloid, as described in the preceding chapter.

The sizes of various molecules have a decided bearing on the different processes of life. A small molecule, for instance, may pass through a cell membrane readily when a large molecule cannot do so at all. This brings us to some consideration of how the materials of life are obtained, how they get to where they are needed, and how they move into and out of cells through the cell membranes.

How Cells Get Their Materials

In every living cell some particular compounds involved in its activities are made within the cell, and others come from outside. Cells vary enormously as to what compounds they make and what they take in, and also what they release. In multicellular organisms there is great diversity in this respect among the cells of one organism. Their cells are chemical specialists. There is also great diversity among different organisms. We have already seen that green plants can make sugars and most of the other essential foods, while animals cannot. These are matters of nutrition and of food chains among organisms in communities, above the level of cells. At this point, we are more concerned with the fact that each cell must obtain materials from outside itself, regardless of what compounds the cell itself makes or what it does with the materials taken in. The materials must also move within the cell.

Cells usually obtain their materials as molecules or parts of molecules (especially the ions of the chemists) from watery solutions. There are some real and some merely apparent exceptions to this generalization. Cells in direct contact with air may acquire and lose gases without there being an external liquid solution. (The gases are usually in solution when within the cell.) Even in cases apparently of this sort an external solution may really be involved. Your lungs do not extract oxygen directly from air, but from solution in a thin liquid film that covers the cells at the surface within the lungs. There are also cells that take in undissolved material from their surroundings, small bits of solid food, globules of fat, or the like. You may see an ameba surrounding a food particle and taking it whole into the cell. There are cells in your own body that do the same sort of thing. Among them are certain cells (phagocytes) in your blood that surround and digest bacteria, an important part of resistance to disease. This is more of an apparent exception than a real one. The particles taken in whole by an ameba or other cell are reduced to molecules in solution before they actually enter the protoplasm and take part in its chemical activities.

Thus even in these cases the rule holds that protoplasm usually obtains materials from a solution with which it is in contact. A cell, or rather a protist, living alone obtains its materials directly from the surrounding inorganic environment. The environment of such an organism is usually water and therefore a solution. Chemically pure water does not occur in nature, and no organisms can survive indefinitely in really pure water. All water in which life exists is a weaker or stronger solution. Cells in multicellular organisms are usually also in constant contact with solutions, solutions in adjacent cells or, commonly, in liquids moving outside but among the cells. These liquids, of which the sap of a tree or your blood plasma are special examples, are generally very elaborate solutions, intricately compounded and influenced by the chemistry of the whole organism.

The question of how cells get their materials thus reduces to the question of how molecules move about, sometimes in gases, but more often in the liquids in which the molecules are in solution.

HOW MOLECULES MOVE ABOUT

Some movements of molecules are sufficiently obvious to require little discussion. If a molecule is in solution in a liquid or is part of a gas, it is moved along by movements of the liquid or the gas. As usual, there are many complications and a long string of "why's" back of this fact, but the simple fact may suffice us here. It is a less obvious fact that molecules also move about under their own power, so to speak. This movement involves several principles, among which the most important for present purposes is that on an average more molecules move away from than toward a region where such molecules are especially numerous. This is the principle of *diffusion.* Molecules or atoms also move through a membrane. Principles here bear on the fact that some molecules of atoms move more easily than others through certain membranes and that some sorts of molecules or atoms under given conditions may move through a membrane in greater number in one direction than in the other. These are the principles of *semipermeability* and of *osmosis.*

The importance of principles involving membranes is evident from the fact that cells are enclosed in membranes. Materials have to pass through the cell membrane and therefore are subject to the principles of semipermeability and osmosis. These processes and also diffusion (closely related to them) are going on all the time throughout our bodies and in active parts of all other living organisms. They are so fundamental for the properties and activities of life that we must review them here.

Molecular movement. It is a physical property of matter, even of solids, that molecules are always moving. A simple demonstration of this is to uncork a bottle of perfume in a closed, still room. You may stand several feet from the bottle, but soon you will smell the perfume. Molecules have moved out from the bottle and through the air of the room. Your nose, which is capable of some of the most delicate chemical tests known, has detected the dispersed molecules.

Molecular movement in gases, such as that of the perfume molecules in air, is considerably faster than in liquids.[5] It is faster in liquids than in solids, although it also goes on among all the molecules of the densest solid. It is faster in hot than in cold substances; in fact, the movement of molecules *is* the phenomenon we call "heat."

Molecules are much too small to see. Consequently we cannot actually or directly see molecular motion, but there are simple ways to see it indirectly, by some of its visible results. Put a little face powder in a drop of water and look at it under the high power of an ordinary microscope. The particles of face powder (which are composed of many molecules) will be seen dancing about. They are being bombarded by the moving water molecules and are small enough to move when hit by a molecule.

Diffusion. In a drop of water millions of molecules move about virtually at random. The *average* result, the net effect of these movements in every direction, is nil. In spite of all this activity within it, the drop does not go anywhere, nor do the molecules become more concentrated in one part of the drop than in another. This is the usual situation when molecules are evenly distributed through the space or substance being studied, even where there is a uniform mixture of different kinds of molecules.

When you opened the perfume bottle, however, something else happened. There was a change in net effect; the perfume molecules

[5] The relatively great speed with which perfume molecules reach our nose is due only in part to the greater speed of diffusion in gas than liquid. In any normal room there are air currents that speed their passage. Currents or turbulence in water will also speed the movement of molecules in it.

did go somewhere. When the bottle was opened, there were no perfume molecules outside it. Soon there were such molecules at increasing distances away from the bottle. A short time later the molecules were still *highly concentrated* in the bottle, but also were highly concentrated near it. Concentration away from the bottle was progressively *lower*, or was zero before perfume reached a given part of the room. The motion of each molecule was random. Some even moved back into the bottle, but *more* moved out. The net effect, the average over millions of molecules, was that more molecules moved from regions of high to regions of low concentration.

This tendency for molecules to spread from regions of higher to those of lower concentration is quite general and is called *diffusion*. If it continues, the concentration eventually becomes the same everywhere. The perfume molecules become evenly distributed throughout the room. There is a state of *equilibrium*. What happens then? Does diffusion stop? Do the perfume molecules stop moving?

Diffusion of molecules in a gas, quite analogous to our example, takes place in some life processes. In many land plants, leaves have gas-filled spaces between the cells, spaces that have special openings to the outer air called "stomates." When the cells take up CO_2 from the air spaces, the concentration is lowered there and more CO_2 diffuses in through the stomates from the outside atmosphere. When the cells give up O_2 into the spaces, its concentration is there increased and O_2 diffuses out into the atmosphere.

Now consider another simple experiment (Fig. 4-2). If a crystal of copper sulfate (or any soluble, colored compound) is put in the bottom of a glass and the glass is filled with clear water, the water soon begins to turn colored around the crystal. The zone of colored water becomes larger from day to day. What is happening? At the surface of the crystal, copper sulfate is going, molecule by molecule, into *solution* in the water, the *solvent*. Naturally the dissolved molecules are more concentrated right at the surface of the crystal than elsewhere. They therefore diffuse into the surrounding water and so the colored zone spreads.

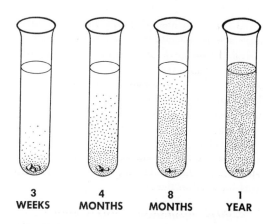

4-2 **Diffusion of copper sulfate in water.**

It spreads very slowly, however, much more slowly than the spread of perfume molecules in air. The perfume can be smelled three feet from the bottle within a few minutes, but it takes more than a year for copper sulfate to diffuse this far through water in recognizable amounts. If you have ever tried to run in a couple of feet of water, you know the reason for this difference in rate of diffusion. Water is a *denser* medium than air. Down at the level of the molecules, this means that in a gas the molecules are farther apart. Molecules are less likely to collide, and the diffusing molecules are less often slowed up or bounced back. In a liquid the molecules are much closer together and the diffusing molecules are slowed up much more. In either air or water, however, the molecules are very small in proportion to the space between them. There is plenty of room between them for the oncoming molecules of perfume or of copper sulfate, and the total volume of air or water is not increased by the diffusion.

In those examples, then, diffusion did not push the molecules of air or water farther apart. On the other hand, in a solid or a dense colloid the molecules are so close together that diffusion among them may force them apart. If a thin piece of dry gelatin is placed in water, it swells. Water has diffused into the gelatin and pushed its molecules apart. The resulting volume is greater than that of the dry gelatin alone but less than that of the dry gelatin plus the *original* volume of the water diffused into it. This particular sort of diffusion is called *imbibition*. The word simply means "drinking in," but is perhaps a more elegant way to put the matter.

Imbibition is a familiar part of daily life and of life processes. It makes wooden doors stick in rainy weather, and it makes bean seeds swell and burst their seed coats just before they sprout. The pressures caused by imbibition may be enormous. Imbibition in starch can develop pressures up to fifteen tons per square inch. Ships loaded with rice have been split apart when water got into the holds and was imbibed in the rice.

Semipermeability.   Now that we have discussed diffusion in general, we can take up diffusion through membranes, a special circumstance of peculiar importance in the life of cells. The first point is that some substances diffuse quite readily through some membranes. The membrane is no particular barrier to the given substance and is said to be *permeable* to it—a fairly obvious and clear special application of an everyday word. Of course if a substance cannot pass through a membrane, the membrane is impermeable to it. If a membrane is permeable to some substances and less permeable or impermeable to others, it is called *semipermeable* (or "differentially permeable," which may be more precise but is clumsier).

The point of this for our study of life is that cell membranes are semipermeable. They are generally permeable to water and impermeable to colloids. The membrane holds in the colloidal elements of the cytoplasm and yet permits water to move rather freely into and out of the cell, an essential feature of life processes at the level of cells. The cell membrane is also more or less permeable to various materials dissolved in water. Thus needed materials from outside can diffuse through the membrane. Once within the cell, they can be held in the colloidal mesh or in compounds to which the membrane is not permeable. Waste products can be converted into forms to which the membrane is permeable and so can leave the cell.

Actually the situation is more complicated than that, and in a very interesting way. Like other parts of cells, their membranes are in a continual state of flux. The degree of permeability to various substances is not con-

stant, varying quite markedly from time to time. Thus even without any change in its own state or composition, a substance may pass through the membrane at some time and be held back by it at others. The variation depends on many things, such as sugar content, acidity, electrical properties, or conditions of colloids within the cell, and, outside the cell, temperature, acidity, heat, light, concentrations of materials, and other factors. Alterations in membrane permeability greatly influence the kinds and amounts of materials diffusing into and out of cells. This is, therefore, one of the essential mechanisms in the regulation of basic life processes in the cell.

We have noted that cells need to obtain and to lose certain materials at various times. The membrane's permeability corresponds with these needs and is a mechanism that helps, when all goes normally, to ensure that the needs are met. You might be tempted to say that the membrane has these characteristics *because* of the cell's needs—and there you would part company with science. That sort of answer slips in a hidden metaphysical postulate that needs can *cause* their fulfillment; it is therefore to be rejected alike by science and by straightforward common sense. If you are at all inclined to balk at that conclusion consider facts of the following sort. Cell membranes may pass materials of no possible use to the cell (such as nitrogen into green plant cells); they may let out so much water that the cell dries up and dies; they may let in poisons that kill the cell.

Osmosis.   Try another experiment. Make a container of a membrane permeable to water: a pig's bladder or a frog skin is a natural membrane of this sort, or a collodion sack can be prepared. Fill it with water, close it tightly, and immerse it in water. Nothing noticeable will happen. Although the container is permeable to water, the concentration of water is the same inside as outside. Therefore as many molecules move out as move in, and equilibrium or the *status quo* is maintained. Now put a sugar solution in the container (preferably leaving it somewhat slack but without air inside) and immerse it in water (preferably distilled water) again. The container will swell up and become turgid (Fig. 4-3B).

What has happened? Evidently more water has moved in than out through the membranes. Why? What you already know of diffusion supplies the answer. Water molecules are less concentrated in the sugar solution than in pure water. Molecules move predominantly from the pure water into the solution (Fig. 4-3A). If the membrane were equally permeable to sugar and to water, sugar molecules would also move out of the container. But the membrane is semipermeable, being much more permeable to water than to sugar. So no (or very little) sugar moves out of the container, more water moves in than out, the amount of fluid in the container increases, and the container swells. That is the process of osmosis.

The influx of water into the container produces pressure, *osmotic pressure.* The flow through the membrane continues until the pressure inside forces water molecules out through the membrane as fast as osmosis brings them in. The pressure then ceases to rise, becoming steady. A state of equilibrium has been reached. The amount of osmotic pressure that can develop in a solution separated from distilled water by a semipermeable membrane depends on concentration of the solution, temperature, and other factors. Under given conditions, the pressure has a characteristic, constant value for any soluble substance. This possible pressure under standardized conditions is the *osmotic value* of the substance. Usually that value is not expressed directly in terms of pressure but by some correlated figure. You will often find it expressed in terms of a change, symbolized as Δ, in freezing point of a solution as compared with pure water. The relationship is rather complicated and we will not consider it in detail here (but see Fig. 4-4). But it may be convenient for you to know that Δ —1°, for instance, is a measure of osmotic value, that Δ —2° is a higher value, and so on.

In real life it would be unusual, indeed impossible, to find such a simple situation, with a solution of a single substance on one side of the membrane and pure water on the other side. There are always solutions of several or many different substances on both sides.

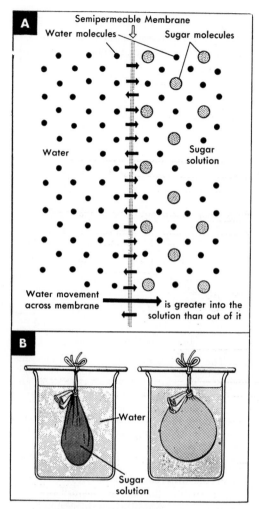

4.3 **Semipermeability.** *A.* the membrane; they are too big. Water molecules are less concentrated on the sugar-solution side of the membrane. The chance that water molecules will hit pores in the membrane, and thus cross it, is smaller on the sugar-solution side. More water therefore *enters* the solution than leaves it. *B.* The net movement of water into a sugar solution enclosed within a membrane-container creates a pressure (*osmotic pressure*) that causes the container to swell.

Then each solution has its own total osmotic value, Δ, resulting from the combination of all the things dissolved in it. What happens in such a case? If Δ is the same on both sides of the membrane, nothing happens. If it is higher on one side than the other, water will diffuse (predominantly) from the side of *lower* to that of *higher* Δ. In general, the

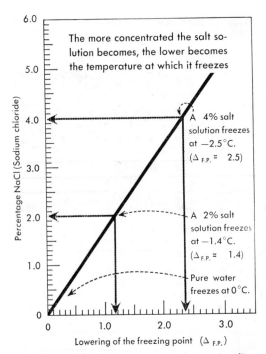

4-4 **The freezing point** of a solution of sodium chloride depends on its concentration. The higher the salt concentration, the lower is the freezing point of the solution. The freezing point depression ($\Delta_{F.P.}$) is therefore a convenient measure of the osmotic value of a solution because this, too, is dependent on the concentration of salts and other molecules.

greater the difference the faster the diffusion or, at any rate, the longer the diffusion will continue before equilibrium is reached.

Osmosis goes on, to some degree, all *Osmosis in Living Systems.* the time in most of the cells of any living thing. It is a constant and essential factor in the movement of materials into and out of cells. This continual osmosis usually goes on in a businesslike way, quietly and without any really striking results. Sometimes, however, effects of osmosis are clearly visible and even dramatic.

If a cell of almost any water plant—a filament of the little pond-scum alga *Spirogyra* will do nicely—is soaked in a 15 per cent solution of common sugar, the cell contents soon separate from the wall and form a mass in the center of the cell. The sugar solution soaked through the cell wall and

came in contact with the cell membrane. Remember that in plants the cell *wall* is different from the underlying *membrane*. The cell wall, unlike the membrane, is not semipermeable; the membrane is permeable to water, impermeable to sugar. The large vacuole in the center of the cell contains a dilute solution, with Δ definitely lower than that of the sugar solution. Osmosis therefore occurs: water diffuses out from the vacuole through the membrane into the space between membrane and wall. As the vacuole loses water and becomes smaller, that space enlarges. The membrane and its contained protoplasm are finally crowded into a ball at the center of the cell. This phenomenon is called *plasmolysis* (Fig. 4-5). Plasmolyzed cells ultimately die, but if you remove the cell from the sugar solution quickly enough and put it in pure water, it will recover and the protoplasm will return to its position near the wall. Why? (See also Fig. 4-6.)

Without seeing what actually goes on in the cells, you can demonstrate radical effects of osmosis even more simply in a kitchen. Put a leaf of lettuce in salt water. It will wilt, because the cells lose water by osmosis. Remove the leaf quickly and put it in pure water. It will recover its crispness. The process is the same as the wilting of a plant on a dry, sunny day and its recovery when the plant is

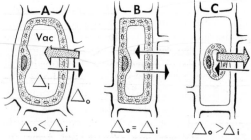

4-5 Plasmolysis of a plant cell. In *A* the osmotic pressure inside the cell (Δ_i) is greater than that outside (Δ_o). Consequently more water tends to move into the vacuole (*Vac*) than out of it. Increase of cell volume is resisted by the firm walls, and the cell thus becomes turgid. In *B* and *C* the osmotic pressures outside the cell (Δ_o) are experimentally increased. In *C*, because Δ_o is greater than Δ_i, more water leaves than enters the vacuole, which consequently shrinks away from the cell wall.

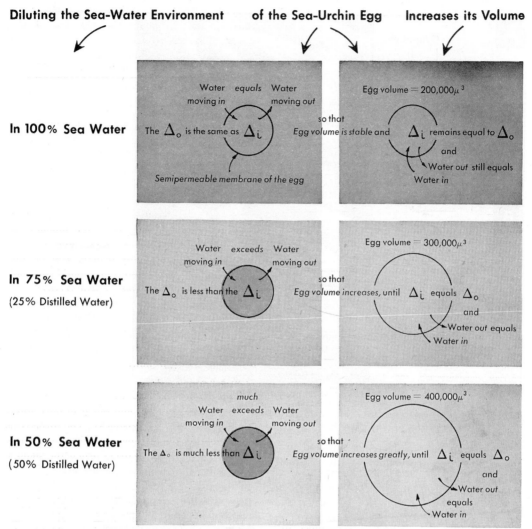

Diluting the Sea-Water Environment   of the Sea-Urchin Egg   Increases its Volume

In 100% Sea Water

Water *equals* Water
moving *in*   moving *out*

The Δ_o is the same as Δ_i

Semipermeable membrane of the egg

Egg volume $= 200,000 \mu^3$

so that
Egg volume *is stable and* Δ_i *remains equal to* Δ_o

and

Water out *still equals*
Water *in*

In 75% Sea Water

(25% Distilled Water)

Water *exceeds* Water
moving *in*   moving *out*

The Δ_o *is less than the* Δ_i

Egg volume $= 300,000 \mu^3$

so that
Egg volume *increases, until* Δ_i *equals* Δ_o

and

Water out *equals*
Water *in*

In 50% Sea Water

(50% Distilled Water)

much
Water *exceeds* Water
moving *in*   moving *out*

The Δ_o *is much less than* Δ_i

Egg volume $= 400,000 \mu^3$

so that
Egg volume *increases greatly, until* Δ_i *equals* Δ_o

and

Water out
equals
Water *in*

4-6   The sea-urchin egg as an osmometer.   Dilution of sea water surrounding the egg makes Δ_o (Δ outside the cell) less than Δ_i (Δ inside the cell). The osmotic pressure that develops is not resisted by a firm cell wall, as in a plant cell (cf. Fig. 4-5), and consequently the egg increases in volume until $\Delta_i = \Delta_o$.

watered—the same, that is, to the extent that both involve loss and recovery of water by the cells. The mechanism of water loss is different: it is osmosis between solutions in the lettuce and evaporation in the growing plant.

Another clear but more complex effect of osmosis can be seen in the outer layer (epidermis) of many leaves which have openings (stomates) with pairs of guard cells controlling their opening and closing (Fig. 4-7).

What happens is more or less as follows: Light falling on the guard cells starts a series of reactions that change insoluble starch to soluble sugar. Solution of the sugar lowers water-molecule concentration, and water comes in from adjacent cells by osmosis. The guard cells swell, and their structural relationships are such that this swelling pulls apart the walls of the stomate and opens it. In the dark the reactions are reversed and the stomate closes.

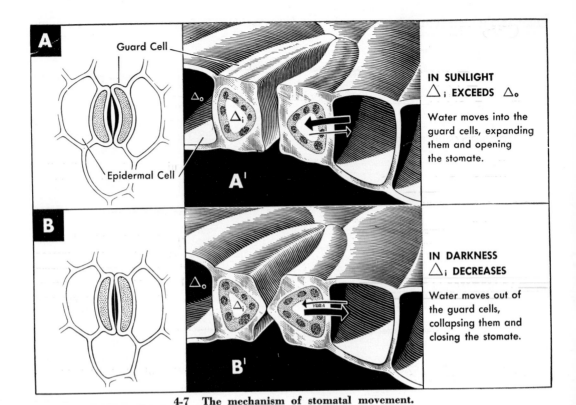

A — Guard Cell — Epidermal Cell — **A'**

Δ_o Δ_i

IN SUNLIGHT
Δ_i **EXCEEDS** Δ_o

Water moves into the guard cells, expanding them and opening the stomate.

B — **B'**

Δ_o Δ_i

IN DARKNESS
Δ_i **DECREASES**

Water moves out of the guard cells, collapsing them and closing the stomate.

4-7 **The mechanism of stomatal movement.**

WATER PROBLEMS

Here is an unusual fact that has had profound effects on the history of life: animals living in the sea may have great difficulty in keeping their cells from dying of thirst. It is a case of, "Water, water everywhere, nor any drop to drink." Simpler sea animals and most seaweeds have cells and internal fluids with Δ about as in sea water (where it is usually around $-2°$). They live in good water equilibrium. If their Δ falls, they lose water by osmosis to the sea water and Δ comes right back up to normal. If their Δ rises, they gain water and Δ drops to normal by dilution. But in many higher animals, including most fishes, Δ of the body fluids is well below that of sea water. Wherever there is a semipermeable membrane in contact with the sea water, in the gills, for instance, these fishes therefore tend to lose water continuously by osmosis. If there were no compensatory mechanisms, their cells would quickly lose so much water that they would die,

literally of thirst, although completely surrounded by water!

Obviously there are compensatory mechanisms, because fish do live quite successfully in the sea (Fig. 4-8). In most marine fishes these are the essentials: they drink sea water continually and in large quantities in replacement of osmotic water loss, and they secrete very little urine, avoiding loss of water in that way. But this results in enormous intake of salt, which would upset their metabolism (based on fluids with low Δ) if it were not quickly gotten rid of. It is rapidly and continuously excreted from the gills. That excretion goes *against* the direction of osmotic pressure, and it therefore requires work to be done in the cells. Much of the metabolic energy of marine fishes is used in getting rid of salt. Almost any engineer could design a simpler and more efficient system. In fact, sharks, although often considered "lower" types, do have a considerably more efficient osmotic mechanism. Organisms are not perfect or in some respects even particularly ef-

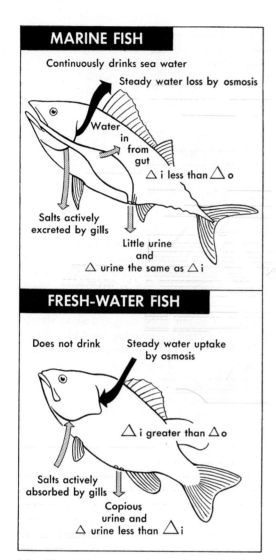

4-8 The maintenance of water balance in fish.

Within the figure:

MARINE FISH

Continuously drinks sea water

Steady water loss by osmosis

Water in from gut

$\triangle$ i less than $\triangle$ o

Salts actively excreted by gills

Little urine and $\triangle$ urine the same as $\triangle$ i

FRESH-WATER FISH

Does not drink

Steady water uptake by osmosis

$\triangle$ i greater than $\triangle$ o

Salts actively absorbed by gills

Copious urine and $\triangle$ urine less than $\triangle$ i

---

ficient mechanisms. They were not designed in a purposeful way. They are what a long, blind, unplanned history has made them.

Fresh-water fishes have just the opposite problem. Their internal $\triangle$ is considerably higher than that of fresh water. The osmotic tendency is therefore for water to flow into them, and this would soon cause death by swelling if not compensated. They drink little or no water and they continuously secrete great quantities of urine, getting rid of extra water acquired by osmosis. But this alone would tend to flush out the body salts, which would quickly kill the fish. Before the urine leaves the body the fish reabsorb much of its dissolved salt, and they also absorb salt through the gills. This, too, is work done against osmosis, and it takes a great deal of cell energy.

In most environments there are special difficulties in maintaining enough but not too much water in the cells. In the myriads of organisms there are many, often quite extraordinary, mechanisms that accomplish this in diverse ways and thus make life possible.

Light and Heat

In this summary of relationships between cells and their environments we have stressed the chemical needs of cells and the varied phenomena of diffusion. Most other relationships between life and environment are best considered in terms of organisms rather than of cells (Chapter 24). It must, however, be realized that any environmental factor may affect cells directly. This may be emphasized by brief consideration of effects of light and heat on cellular processes.

LIGHT

Life requires both materials and energy. Energy takes many forms, one of which is *chemical energy*. Such energy is bound up, stored quietly, so to speak, in chemical compounds. It can be released from such compounds by reactions and turned into other forms of energy, such as heat, movement, or light. Light is produced from chemical energy in an extraordinary array of living things— fireflies and some mushrooms, to mention only two examples. This is, however, a rather minor feature in the vast picture of life as a whole.

Although little of life's energy is turned back into light, practically all of it comes from light in the first place. The few exceptions are of no importance at this point. The process of turning light from the sun into chemical energy, available for all forms of life, is called *photosynthesis* and is a phenomenon of most plants and some protists. It is discussed in the next chapter.

Aside from this, which is by far the most basic effect of light on life, cells are always to some extent affected by light that falls on them. It does not fall on all; most cells of larger animals and plants are internal and in constant darkness. Some whole organisms also live in constant darkness or nearly so: in caves, in the deep sea, in the soil, inside larger plants and animals. Most fungi and bacteria grow best in the dark, and some are killed by much exposure to light.

Cells that do receive light are, at the least, slightly warmed thereby. Light also causes chemical changes, even in animal cells; this is evident from the apparent effects of light in tan and sunburn. Light also brings about the formation of vitamin D in human and some other animal cells. Bacteria may be killed by light, especially the shorter rays called "ultraviolet," which are the most active in most biochemical processes involving light.

That light is the means of vision has, clearly, tremendous importance. This will be discussed in connection with perception and behavior.

Intensity of light varies greatly, and these variations influence life. In green plants, diffuse light generally favors vegetative growth and, in some plants, bright light favors the formation of reproductive structures. Bright light retards growth in seedlings because of its influence on certain hormones necessary for growth. The daily alternation of light (day) and dark (night) also influences flowering in many plants, migration in animals, and other activities of organisms.

HEAT

All organisms require some heat in the environment in order to continue functioning. The range of temperatures in which life can exist was mentioned in Chapter 1, as well as the fact that this range is usual at the surface of the earth and in its waters. All cells produce some heat incidental to their activities, but as a rule this production is so small that cells are seldom far from the temperature of their environment. All cells also have a range of temperatures, their *optimum* temperature, often quite narrow, in which they do best. The optimum varies considerably in different cells and different organisms, which is a major factor in the distribution of plants and animals in climatic zones.

The reasons (at least the *proximate* reasons, answers to the first "why") for all these relationships lie mainly at the level of the cells. The physical properties of protoplasm, such as its fluidity or elasticity, are considerably affected by its temperature. The rates of biological processes in cells and often also the nature of these processes are also strongly influenced by temperature. Other things being equal, there is a tendency for average rates of these processes to double for every 10° C. rise in temperature. The approximation is quite rough, and there is great variation. There are also processes that reach a maximum rate at a certain temperature and become slower when this point is passed. Thus potato plants synthesize starch more rapidly at 20° than at 30° C., but utilize sugar much more rapidly at the latter temperature. The sugar that is not utilized is stored as starch. Other things being equal, the yield of potatoes is therefore higher at the lower temperature.

It is noteworthy that organic reactions proceed at what seem to the chemist very low temperatures. If you set fire to a lump of sugar in air, it burns with a hot flame. (Doubtless you know the trick of starting this reaction by putting a little cigarette ash on the lump before you touch a match to it.) But sugar is oxidized in us at our body temperature, and at considerably lower temperatures in some other organisms. Can you suggest a reason for this remarkable difference? It is one of the first topics for discussion in the next chapter.

Chapter Summary

Cellular environments, the source of needed materials and energy.

The similarity among cells in their constituent materials: "unity with diversity."

Atoms, molecules, energy, and chemical reactions.

Inorganic materials, derived from the nonliving world:

Water and its properties, especially as a solvent; as principal constituent of all living systems.

Carbon dioxide, the ultimate source of all life's carbon.

Oxygen and its role in respiration.

Nitrogen, a key constituent of proteins; the poor utilization of atmospheric N_2 by life; usual sources for plants and for animals.

Mineral salts, required in small amounts by all forms of life.

Organic materials, compounds that contain carbon and are synthesized only by living systems from inorganic raw materials. Three major groups:

Carbohydrates: sugars and polysaccharides; energy sources and structural materials.

Fats: their high content of hydrogen; high energy yield; function: principally storage.

Proteins: their large size and complexity; amino acids as their constituent building blocks; energy sources and the most important structural materials of the cell.

The cell's acquisition of materials, always from solutions.

Molecular movements in solutions; diffusion.

Cell membranes and their permeability to materials, a dominant role in the acquisition and retention of materials from the environment.

Semipermeability and osmosis: the movement (and its control) of water into and out of the living cell.

Light and heat, the cell's energy sources.

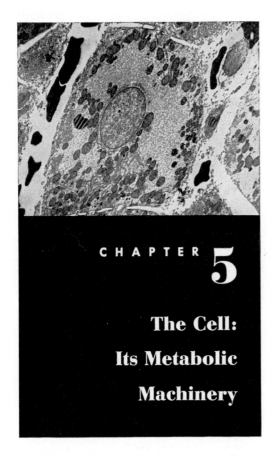

Liver cells photographed (×6500) with the electron microscope. Nucleus is the large oval body in center. Lying in the cytoplasm are mitochondria, which play a central role in the cell's energy metabolism. (Courtesy Dr. Don W. Fawcett, Cornell U. Med. College)

CHAPTER 5

The Cell: Its Metabolic Machinery

THE CELL THEORY: CHEMICAL VERSION

Some of the most important advances of biology since World War I have concerned the chemical nature and activities of the cell. The newer knowledge of cell biochemistry would have delighted the hearts of Darwin, Schwann, and Virchow because it is a wonderful extension down to chemical detail of the combined predictions of the evolution and cell theories. Evolution sees life as an evolved organization of materials that in themselves are not alive; the cell theory sees the cell as the unit of that living organization; and, together, cell and evolution theories predict a fundamental similarity in the material, or chemical constitution and organization of all living cells. It is this broad prediction that modern biochemistry has begun to realize.

The common ancestry of all cells—protists, plants, and animals—accounts for their marked similarity in constituent chemicals and processes. We glimpsed this similarity in Chapter 4. The life of all cells is founded on the chemistry of three major classes of molecules and their derivatives—carbohydrates, fats, and proteins.

Complexity characterizes the living organization at every level—the community, the individual organism, and the cell itself; and this complexity begins with life's constituent chemicals. Sugars, fats, and proteins are large complex molecules somehow essential for living processes. They are never encountered except as the product of living things.[1] Collectively they are called *organic* chemical compounds in distinction to the simpler *inorganic* molecules of the nonliving world.[2]

The cell synthesizes its large organic molecules from simpler inorganic molecules like carbon dioxide, water, and nitrates that are available in its physical environment. These syntheses and subsequent transformations of its characteristic molecules constitute the chemical life of the cell, its *metabolism*. Of the many questions we could ask to start our

[1] This fact was once thought to mean that a mysterious "life force" was necessary for their formation. Today organic molecules are readily made in the laboratory by the organic chemist. Enzyme catalysts, not a mysterious "life," are the keys to their synthesis in the cell. It is still true that they are dependent on living things for their creation, however—even if the living thing is an organic chemist working in his laboratory!

[2] See note 1, p. 72, Chapter 4.

study of cell metabolism we have selected one: "How does the cell manufacture its characteristic organic chemicals?" For this question leads us directly to the point that *the process of synthesizing complex molecules* from simpler ones *is chemical work,* and like other forms of work *it requires the expenditure of energy.* The key to understanding the pattern underlying the cell's metabolic framework lies in the concept of energy. What is it? What laws govern its transformations? How does the cell obtain its energy? How does the cell use energy to fabricate and organize its chemical constituents?

Energy and Work

ENERGY AND WORK IN GENERAL

Energy and work are well enough defined by our ordinary use of both words: work is something accomplished (ultimately, something moved); and energy is required to perform work. The physicist's definition of energy is only a difference in wording: *energy is the capacity to accomplish work.* This definition holds whether or not the work is done. A boulder at the top of a hill has *potential* energy while it is at rest—while not doing work; this energy becomes *kinetic* energy as the boulder does work in rolling down the hill. The work was performed at the expense of the boulder's potential energy inherent in its former position at the top of the hill.

Kinetic energy can always be thought of as the motion of matter, and work as movement accomplished. Kinetic energy may take many forms. The movement of the boulder was *mechanical* energy. *Light* is kinetic energy and may be thought of as the movement of minute particles, photons. An *electric* current is another form of kinetic energy, the movement of electrons from atom to atom in the wire through which the current is flowing. The *chemical* form of kinetic energy is the movement of atoms within or between molecules that takes place in a chemical reaction. And, finally, *heat* is the ceaseless, random motion of atoms in all directions within a gas, liquid, or solid. Hot and cold water differ in the speed at which their molecules are moving; in the hot water the motion is faster.

All these forms of energy are interconvertible to some extent, and the conversions of one to another are governed by two general laws called the First and Second Laws of Thermodynamics. The First Law is all that we need at the moment, and it states that energy is neither lost nor gained when it is converted from one form to another. We may transform the mechanical energy of a waterfall [3] into electricity by means of a turbine, but in doing so we will never get more energy out of the transformation than entered it. Nor will any be lost. [4]

CHEMICAL WORK

The chemical reaction. The form of energy with which the cell deals is principally chemical energy; its work is largely chemical work. Chemical work consists of the transformation of molecules that occur in a chemical reaction such as [5]

$$\text{Reactants} \quad \text{Products}$$
$$A + B \rightarrow C + D$$

The formula sums up the fact that the two molecules A and B (the reactants) react in such a way as to recombine their atomic parts, forming new molecules C and D (the products). Two groups of factors affect the reaction: (1) factors affecting collision and contact of the molecules; and (2) factors relating to energy expenditures in the performance of the chemical work.

Collision and contact. The molecules A and B are dispersed, undergoing continual random movements in all directions. Only when they collide and contact can A and B react with each other. Dependence of the reaction on collision explains several laws governing chemical reactions. All those factors that increase collision frequency increase the rate at which the reaction proceeds. Thus the

[3] Think out other forms of energy transformation commonly employed by man. How is the potential chemical energy in coal or oil eventually exploited in frying an egg on an electric stove? (Coal → Steam →Turbine → Electricity Heat)

[4] Some of the energy will, however, be transformed into a condition in which it can no longer be used or perform work.

[5] Other forms of chemical reaction are possible: thus one molecule may be broken into two ($A \rightarrow B + C$); or two may combine to form one ($A + B \rightarrow C$). And others are possible. What we say about $A + B \rightarrow C + D$ applies to all.

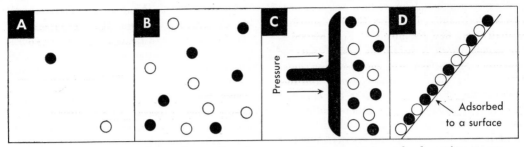

5-1 The effects on chemical reaction of concentration, pressure, and adsorption to a surface.

more *concentrated* the reactants are in the solution, the greater is their chance of contacting and the faster the reaction proceeds. Similarly, the reaction can be speeded up by subjecting the solution to *pressure* which effectively concentrates it, thus increasing collision frequency (Fig. 5-1). Increase in *temperature* speeds up the movement of the molecules and so raises the probability they will contact and react.

The contact necessary for a reaction between two molecules can be facilitated in another way. This is by *adsorbing* both re-

actants onto a surface where they are brought close together (Fig. 5-1). This is what happens in *surface catalysis*. Molecules of sulfur dioxide (SO_2) and oxygen (O_2) in air may contact each other so rarely that reaction between them is negligible. If, however, such air is passed over finely ground platinum, the SO_2 and O_2 molecules are adsorbed to the platinum surface; they contact and react. The platinum is said to be a *catalyst*; it *catalyzes* the reaction. The adsorption to the catalyst surface has an effect similar to that of raising the pressure or concentrating the

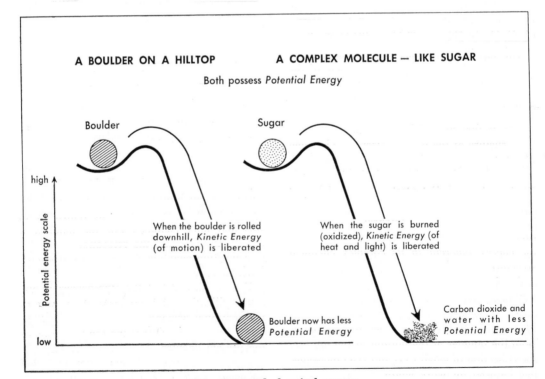

5-2 Potential chemical energy.

reactants. Usually, however, there is more to it than this; and the effect of the catalyst is far greater than it would be from either of the other ways. We will have a little more to say about catalysis later. It is a defining characteristic of a catalyst that it is never itself consumed in the course of reaction. When the reaction is complete, the catalyst's surface is freed to act again. A minute amount of catalyst can do a great deal of work.

The energy of chemical reactions. Contact between molecules is necessary if they are to react, but it is not sufficient. Energy considerations play a dominant role. Let us begin with the notion of the potential energy inherent in chemical structure.

The Potential Energy of Chemical Structure. It is a familiar fact that useful kinetic energy can be obtained from chemical compounds like sugar, coal, gas, or wood. When any of these compounds is burned, its complex molecular structure is destroyed and energy is liberated. In summary, the burning of sugar can be written as follows:

Sugar	Oxygen	Carbon dioxide	Water	Energy

$$C_6H_{12}O_6 \ + \ 6O_2 \ \rightarrow \ 6CO_2 + 6H_2O \ + \ E$$

The large sugar molecule is broken down by an *oxidation* process. The products of the reaction are the smaller, simpler molecules CO_2 and H_2O. The energy liberated takes the obvious form of light and heat. The important notion is that potential energy is inherent in the structure of the large molecules. *The complicated positions of their atoms might be compared to the position of the boulder at the top of a hill.* Potential energy is inherent in the boulder's position at the top of the hill. When sugar is disintegrated, by oxidation, into its simple constituents $CO_2 + H_2O$, the energy inherent in its complex chemical structure is freed, just as the boulder's energy is freed when it gives up its position on the hilltop. Figure 5-2 compares the two processes.

Work can be done with the kinetic energy liberated from both the boulder and the sugar. Both the boulder at the bottom of the hill and the collection of small CO_2 and H_2O molecules can be used for work again, but only if they are first restored to their former position.

ACTIVATION ENERGY AND REACTION ENERGY IN THE OXIDATION OF SUGAR

The sugar molecule must cross an energy barrier before it can react with oxygen

The heat motion of the sugar molecule causes it to "dance" in its energy valley; but extra *Activation Energy* must be supplied before the movements are big enough to cross the energy barrier. (The diagram exaggerates the size of the energy barrier.)

5-3 Activation and reaction energies.

The boulder must be pushed up the hill, and CO_2 and H_2O must be pushed up a "chemical hill." Both processes are work again, and both demand new energy resources. Notice that in repeatedly doing work the *same matter* can be used over and over. There may be a cycle of materials used; but there is *no cycle of energy*. It is a continual expenditure of capital funds. Where does all this capital lie? Ultimately all useful energy comes from the sun; this is a theme we will return to in this and later chapters. For the moment it suffices to note that the relocation of matter to a position enabling it to do work demands fresh energy.

Do you now detect the significance in the cell's utilization of large molecules? And of the continual demand for fresh energy (fresh food) in all life? This is the central theme of the present chapter.

Energy of Activation, and Enzymes. Let us return now to chemical reaction in general, keeping these energy ideas in mind. We must distinguish two kinds of energy function in the reaction. Once the boulder is started down the hill it liberates huge quantities of energy; once sugar is started on its oxidation it also liberates considerable energy. But both processes need a little expenditure to get them started. There is a little rise in front of the boulder which is, indeed, what keeps it in place. You must supply the activation energy to push it over this rise to start it on its downward path. And so it is in a chemical reaction. There is always a need for *activation energy* to get the process going.

All molecules are constantly jumping around; this is true of the molecule as a whole and of the atomic parts within it. In terms of Figure 5-3 this means that the sugar molecule is constantly dancing about inside the "energy valley" that keeps it from uniting with O_2 and then rolling downhill to CO_2 and H_2O. Sometimes—*very rarely*—a random dancing movement will take it over the energy barrier and the reaction

$$Sugar + O_2 \rightarrow CO_2 + H_2O + Energy$$

will proceed. But this is so extremely rare as to be utterly negligible. If left to themselves the sugar and oxygen reaction would effectively *never* take place. But the reaction can be speeded up by supplying just a *little* activation energy. The large kinetic energy liberated from the first full downhill roll activates the other molecules, and off they all go. The minute kinetic energy of a single spark can liberate untold amounts of energy once it is applied to a gasoline dump.

In the last section we noted that catalysts can have an effect similar to raising concentration or pressure. They bring molecules together by adsorbing them to a surface, but their effect is always greater than could be accounted for by this alone. Now we can go further. Catalysts speed up chemical reactions by in effect lowering the activation energy needed. How this is done is not clear. One might think of it picturesquely as tunneling through the activation-energy barrier.

A cell's possession of a special class of catalysts is one of its most outstanding properties and a key to the way it executes controlled chemical reactions rapidly. The catalysts in protoplasm are proteins called *enzymes,* pos-

sessing all the properties we have noted for catalysts in general. They speed up reactions that are otherwise so slow that they would virtually never occur; they are not consumed in the reaction and in small amounts execute much work. In addition, they have special properties we must note.

Being proteins, all enzymes are sensitive to heat; most enzymes are inactivated by temperatures considerably less than that of boiling water (100° C.). This property of enzymes, indeed of proteins in general, severely restricts the cell in its expediting of chemical reactions. In short, a cell cannot allow itself to be heated up as the laboratory chemist heats a test tube. Enzymes are also sensitive to conditions of acidity; some will not work in a cellular environment which is either too acid or too alkaline.

One of the most important properties of enzymes is their specificity. Enzymes differ in how specific they are in the reactions they catalyze, but all are specific to some extent. One of the least specific is the enzyme *lipase,* which catalyzes the breakdown of fats into their constitutents of glycerol and fatty acids. Lipase catalyzes the digestion (breakdown) of *all* fats. Apparently its specificity concerns a particular kind of chemical bond which all fats possess (p. 108). In an enzyme's name, as in *lipase,* the suffix *-ase* is appended to the name of the chemical upon which it acts— its *substrate.* Fats are called lipides by the chemist; hence *lipase* is an enzyme which acts on a lipide substrate. *Proteinases* act on proteins; *peroxidases* on peroxides; *maltase* on the sugar maltose; and so on.

Many enzymes are much more specific in their substrates than lipase. Later in this chapter we will review the many (over twenty-five) steps involved in the breakdown of sugar in the cell; each step is separately controlled by a highly specific enzyme.

As in inorganic catalysts like ground platinum mentioned earlier, the work of the enzyme is not completely understood. Part of its job is almost certainly bringing reactants together in proper contact (Fig. 5-4). It is much less clear how the activation energy for the reaction is in effect reduced, but it is thought to be connected with the fact that the enzyme does for the briefest of moments combine chemically with the reactants. Some theories of enzyme action envisage this as causing a slight deformation of the substrate molecules that facilitates their reaction. The fact that all enzymes are proteins may be important both to this interpretation of their action and to their specificity. Proteins are large molecules with complexly contoured surfaces. Specific complex surfaces may facilitate the contact and deformation of specific reactants. Very often some smaller nonprotein molecules form essential parts of enzyme complexes.

The Energy of the Reaction. Activation energy—and especially its effective annulment by the enzyme catalysts—is a key concept in understanding the chemical work of the cell. More fundamental still is the concept of energy released once the molecule is over its activation hump. The energy liberated is called the energy of the reaction (Fig. 5-3).

Reactions like the oxidation of sugar, in which the energy of reaction is given off or liberated, are called *exergonic* reactions. We have already noted that it is possible to restore CO_2 and H_2O to their former "position" as constituents of sugar, and that, like pushing the boulder up the hill, this requires energy. A reaction like this—the combination of carbon dioxide and water to form sugar—is called *endergonic* because energy must be paid into it. The amount of energy that must be paid in is exactly the same amount as was released when sugar was broken down.

The cell is continuously engaged in the business of manufacturing large and complex molecules from smaller ones. It is, in short, always executing (apparently) [6] endergonic reactions, and it must pay energy into them. How payment is made is something to be discussed later in this chapter. But we must emphasize one point here before leaving reaction energy. Enzymes do *not* in any way facilitate the cell's work by paying the requisite reaction energy into endergonic reactions; all

[6] We have had to qualify our statement with "apparently" because the cell, unable to use heat like a chemist, performs a subtle kind of magic in transforming ender- into exergonic reactions. Actually it conceals nothing up its sleeve when it performs this magic; it merely finds a way of paying without resorting to heat (p. 101).

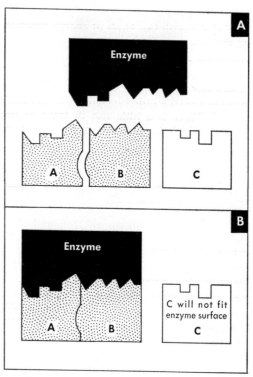

5-4 Enzyme catalysts bring reactants together in close contact and proper orientation for the reaction to proceed.

they do is to speed up, or lubricate, reactions which are otherwise possible energy-wise, but *slow*.

Oxidation-reduction: energy exchange.

The burning of sugar, coal, wood, and gasoline are all processes that consume oxygen and liberate energy. They are all special cases of a general process of *oxidation*, and all oxidations are energy-liberating chemical reactions. The reverse process is called a *reduction*, in which oxygen, instead of being consumed, is released. Energy, instead of being liberated, is bound into the chemical that is reduced. In the green leaves of plants, CO_2 and H_2O combine in a series of chemical reactions (photosynthesis) during which CO_2 is reduced—energy is bound—and oxygen is liberated.

The oxidation or reduction of a compound can be accomplished in another way besides addition or removal of oxygen—by removal or addition of hydrogen. Removal of hydrogen is an oxidation; its addition is a reduction. When these alternative ways of oxidizing and reducing are analyzed and compared, they are found to be special cases of a much more general process of energy exchange: the transfer of electrons from one atom to another. Energy is released by *removal of electrons; this is the general definition of oxidation.* Both addition of oxygen or removal of hydrogen effectively remove an electron from the oxidized compound and thus liberate energy. Similarly, the general definition of reduction is the *addition of electrons;* either removal of oxygen or addition of hydrogen to a compound effectively adds an electron and thus binds energy.

In terms of the model in Fig. 5-3, oxidation occurs as the molecule rolls downhill, liberating energy; and when molecules are reduced they are pushed uphill again. *Oxidations* are *exergonic,* and *reductions* are *endergonic.*

All these relations are summarized in Table 5-1. The reason for going into these matters here is because they are fundamental in the energy economy of the cell. Most of the cell's

energy transfers involve oxidation-reduction processes, and most of them are in practice accomplished by the removal of hydrogen (dehydrogenation) from the oxidized compound. Thus sugar is oxidized with release of energy in the cell by removing hydrogen from the sugar molecule, not by adding oxygen to it. The oxygen consumed in degrading sugar in living things acts as the hydrogen acceptor, not as an oxygen donor. (See Table 5-1. Oxygen acts as B, and sugar as AH, in equation 2.)

The Chemical Work of the Cell

BASIC ECONOMY: ENERGY
CAPTURE AND ENERGY RELEASE

Let us return now to the cell as a working economy and examine the main principles involved. The cell contains molecules of great structural complexity: carbohydrates, fats, and proteins. We can restate this as follows: *these molecules of the cell have high potential chemical energy.* There is a twofold significance in this fact.

First, it is by the chemical breakdown of large molecules that kinetic energy is released to power all the cell's and organism's many activities. You are expending kinetic energy when you run, when you merely move a finger, when your chest muscles move in breathing, or when your blood courses in your veins. And in every activity the energy derives from the potential chemical energy in your own constituent molecules as they are oxidized. You literally consume yourself when you do work. It is, then, small wonder that you must constantly feed—and feed, moreover, by taking in more large and complex molecules.

But there is a second significance. *Only living organisms possess these large molecules.* It is true that after you have partly burned yourself up on hard work you can repair the damage by refueling with some other form of life. But it too did work and fed; where did its food come from? If the supply were limited, life would have just so long to go before it stopped because its chemical fuel resources would have been expended. That life is not limited by a finite and expendable fuel source

TABLE 5-1

Oxidation-reduction processes

Oxidation	Reduction
The *oxidation* of a compound (A) may consist of	The *reduction* of a compound (A) may consist of
the addition of O	the removal of O
or	*or*
the removal of H	the addition of H
Both processes involve removing an electron from A (see equations below)	Both processes involve adding an electron to A
and	*and*
the release of energy from A	the binding of energy in A

Transfer of oxygen

(1) $A + BO \rightarrow AO + B$

oxidizing A is B is
agent; is an   oxidized   reduced
oxygen donor

Transfer of hydrogen

(2) $AH + B \rightarrow A + BH$

oxidizing A is B is
agent; is a   oxidized   reduced
hydrogen
acceptor

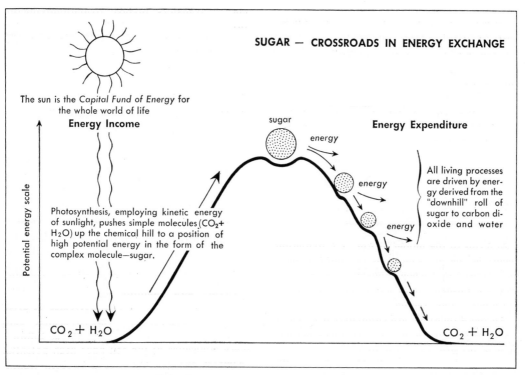

SUGAR — CROSSROADS IN ENERGY EXCHANGE

The sun is the *Capital Fund of Energy* for the whole world of life

Energy Income

sugar

energy

energy

energy

Energy Expenditure

All living processes are driven by energy derived from the "downhill" roll of sugar to carbon dioxide and water

Photosynthesis, employing kinetic energy of sunlight, pushes simple molecules (CO_2 + H_2O) up the chemical hill to a position of high potential energy in the form of the complex molecule—sugar.

Potential energy scale

$CO_2 + H_2O$

$CO_2 + H_2O$

5-5   Sugar: crossroads of metabolism.

is due entirely to the existence of *some* living cells which can *photosynthesize* sugars. These cells can use the energy of sunlight to push CO_2 and H_2O uphill again into sugar (a reduction process). The chemical machinery in green plants is a turbine for the whole world of life. Just as the hydroelectric turbine exploits the resources of a waterfall, transforming its energy into a form usable by other machines, so does the photosynthetic apparatus in the plant turn over the sun's energy to all other living things. It does so by transforming the kinetic energy of sunlight into the potential chemical form which living systems can exploit.

There are many ways of looking at the metabolism of living cells, and many details to fit together. But there is one feature that will always keep us oriented; like a major crossroads, it is the point to which we can always come back and find our way again. This feature is the central role of sugars in the economy of cells. In the balance sheet of life, all energy income leads to sugars, and all energy expenditures lead from them (Fig. 5-5).

The sugar fuels made by plants can be broken down in an oxidative process that releases energy. This is so both in the plant itself and in the animal that eats the plant. The oxidative release of energy is *respiration*, a process in one form or another co-extensive with life. In the vast majority of cases respiration involves the consumption of oxygen; like the burning of coal or wood, respiration stops when oxygen is withheld.

In over-all view we can sum up the chemical processes underlying life's energy economy as in Table 5-2.

Photosynthesis reduces carbon dioxide and binds energy with release of oxygen. Respiration is an oxidation of a carbon molecule (sugar); it releases energy and carbon dioxide. These two simple equations are unfortunately not all there is to it! They summarize end results but omit the numerous intermediate reactions. Furthermore, they make no reference to the chemical activities that use the energy released in respiration.

The great similarities in the chemistry of all cells derive largely from the fact that they

TABLE 5-2

(1) *Photosynthesis* in plants (endergonic) is an energy-binding *reduction.*

$$\underbrace{\overset{\text{Carbon dioxide}}{6CO_2} + \overset{\text{Water}}{6H_2O}}_{\text{low potential energy}} + \text{Kinetic energy} \xrightarrow{\text{enzymes}} \underbrace{\overset{\text{Sugar}}{C_6H_{12}O_6} + \overset{\text{Oxygen}}{6O_2}}_{\text{high potential energy}}$$

of sunlight

(2) *Respiration* in plants and animals (exergonic) is an energy-releasing *oxidation:*

$$\underbrace{\overset{\text{Sugar}}{C_6H_{12}O_6} + \overset{\text{Oxygen}}{6O_2}}_{\text{high potential energy}} \xrightarrow{\text{enzymes}} \underbrace{\overset{\text{Carbon dioxide}}{6CO_2} + \overset{\text{Water}}{6H_2O}}_{\text{low potential energy}} + \text{Kinetic energy}$$

of living processes

all have to start from the sugar crossroads. They resemble each other most markedly in how they break sugar down piecemeal, in how they trap and transfer the energy released, and in how they use it to compound their other constituents, the fats and proteins. Before we can go into these general patterns of energy expenditure and utilization shared by most cells, we must first examine the income side of the ledger. What facts about photosynthesis does equation 1 overlook?

ENERGY INCOME: PHOTOSYNTHESIS

In a way it is futile to discuss which of all life's many essential processes is the most fundamental; any essential process is, by definition, indispensable and therefore fundamental. But a special case could be made for photosynthesis. In a city dependent exclusively on uranium (U_{235}) for energy, there may be many different ways of doing an indispensable job once you have the energy, but you cannot dispense with the atomic reactor! Nor can you find a substitute. It seems precisely the same with photosynthesis; life as a whole has found no substitute for its primary energy transformer. There are some organisms (bacteria) that derive energy from the oxidation of small compounds, like nitrites to nitrates. But they are insignificant in the over-all view of life, and even in them the energy is incorporated in sugars.

Knowledge of the photosynthetic process was only slowly acquired through the seventeenth and eighteenth centuries. Van Helmont showed in the seventeenth century that a potted plant gained weight which could not be accounted for by withdrawal of food from the soil in the pot. Using a willow tree, he discovered that in five years it gained pounds while the soil lost only ounces. The gain in weight was evidently due to uptake either of gases from the atmosphere or of the water daily supplied to the pot or both. The fact that a plant takes up CO_2 from the air and releases O_2 was discovered by Priestley [7] in experiments which showed that plants and animals died when placed under bell jars separately, but survived when put in together, as shown in Fig. 5-6. The CO_2 given off by the respiring mouse supplies the plant with material for photosynthesis; the O_2 released by the plant's photosynthesis suffices for the respiration of both. It was not, however, until the nineteenth century that the facts were understood. The weight gain Van Helmont noted was due to manufacture of organic molecules from the CO_2 and H_2O. This manufacture was found to be dependent on light and on the green pigment chlorophyll in the leaf. Precisely *how* the sugar is manufactured in the green leaf is still something not fully resolved. We are still awaiting what the philosopher Kant called "the Newton of the green leaf," someone who will finally uncover its mystery. Perhaps this is no longer the proper way to look at it, however. It is doubtful now if a single "Newton" will be involved, for many able men have already solved parts of the problem. There is good reason to believe the remaining mystery will yield to the persistent study of the host of

7 Priestley (1733-1804) did not however know CO_2 and O_2 in the modern terms. He spoke of "fixed" and "good" air, respectively.

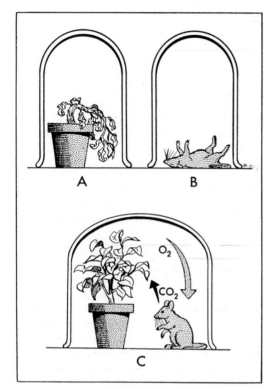

5-6 Priestley's experiments. In *A* the plant dies for lack of carbon dioxide; in *B* the mouse dies for lack of oxygen; in *C* both live.

blance to the hemoglobin of animals, in which heme, a compound closely related to chlorophyll but containing iron in place of magnesium, is attached to protein (Fig. 5-7). Other pigments, called carotenoids, are associated with chlorophyll in plants, where they may help to transfer energy to chlorophyll.

Protoheme

Chlorophyll

5.7 Chlorophyll and protoheme.

biochemists who are devoted to it. Our present knowledge largely concerns the role of chlorophyll, the origin of the O_2 liberated, the fact that many steps are involved, and that only one of them involves light.

Except in the blue-green algae and bacteria, chlorophyll occurs within the cells only in small bodies, plastids, which are designated *chloroplasts*. Within the chloroplasts the pigment is found in numerous still smaller bodies, the *grana*. A mature chloroplast of spinach, for instance, may contain forty to sixty grana. Chloroplast surfaces are the true photosynthetic surfaces of green plants.

Chlorophyll is generally a mixture of two different compounds: chlorophyll *a* ($C_{55}H_{72}O_5N_4Mg$) and chlorophyll *b* ($C_{55}H_{70}O_6N_4Mg$). All green plants have chlorophyll *a*; many algae and a few other green plants lack chlorophyll *b* and may have other, related compounds. In living cells, chlorophyll is attached to protein, which recalls the suggestive resem-

Light is generally necessary for the development of chlorophylls, that is, for their own synthesis. Iron and manganese are also necessary, although not present in chlorophylls themselves. Can you think of a possible reason for this requirement?

The color of any pigment is due to the fact that it absorbs some wave lengths of light more than others. Sunlight, as you doubtless recall, is a mixture of wave lengths ranging (as far as visible to our eyes) from long waves perceived by us as red to short waves perceived as violet. If part of the mixture is absorbed, we receive more of some lengths than of others and perceive the dominant lengths as color. Chlorophyll absorbs mostly red and violet and adjacent lengths from sunlight and so transmits or reflects mainly waves around the middle part of the visible spectrum, which we see as green. In many organic compounds the color seems to be a purely incidental result of molecular structure and not, in itself, related to a biological function. *In chlorophyll,* however, *the color is a manifestation of the fact that energy-rich radiation is being absorbed and used;* the red and violet ends of the spectrum consist of rays with the richest energy content. (What color would you guess the trees and fields would be had the middle portion of the spectrum been the most energy-rich?)

The entire process of photosynthesis consists of three successive phases, each of which probably involves several or many specific chemical reactions. The exact number and nature of all the steps within each phase are not yet known.

In the first phase the radiant energy trapped by chlorophyll is used to split water molecules:

$$2H_2O + \text{Energy transferred by chlorophyll} \rightarrow 4H + O_2$$

The oxygen, O_2, is liberated as a stable molecule. The hydrogen atoms, H, however, are is an unstable, highly reactive condition. They immediately combine (through a series of steps) with carbon dioxide, CO_2, to form a sugarlike compound with three carbon atoms in its molecule. That is the second phase of photosynthesis. The third phase, again involving a series of steps, is the transformation of the three-carbon compound into a simple sugar, glucose, with six carbon atoms in the molecule: $C_6H_{12}O_6$.

External energy comes into this sequence in the first phase only. That phase requires sunlight and chlorophyll. In later phases chlorophyll is not involved, and the energy originally trapped by it is passed along until it finally is incorporated in the stable, energy-rich basic food, glucose.

THE MECHANISM OF ENERGY RELEASE AND EXPENDITURE

Analogy with a business economy. The completion of photosynthesis brings us to the crossroads of metabolism. In the following sections we will outline the major features of the cell's energy expenditures, which are broadly similar in both plants and animals. It would be too much to expect that life, characteristically diverse in other aspects, would show no diversity in cell chemistry; and of course such diversity exists. But underlying it all is a hard core of basic processes that seem to form a framework for the metabolism of all cells. It is on the expenditure side of the budget that the common chemical basis of life is manifest—that the cell theory is manifest in chemical form.

It is useful to think about the cell's energy expenditure in terms of a broad analogy with a business community. Like such a community, the cell does work—movement, heat production, manufacture of new complex chemicals (fats, proteins), and, occasionally, even light production. Also, as in a business community, there is the over-all expensive task of maintaining order. For all this work, which includes both production and maintenance, payment must be made.

In a human community payment is made in the form of currency, but in the long run currency is only a token for energy of some kind. It is simply more convenient to pay a man a dollar for some goods or services than to pay him by spading his garden for an hour. It is also convenient to carry only small change in one's pocket for immediate use and to keep reserves either in the bank for quick withdrawal or more deeply stored in bonds or real estate.

In the cell's economy we detect a somewhat similar over-all pattern. The cell keeps some of its energy-wealth in deep storage (especially starches and fats); some is kept on quick call (glucose and compounds called phosphagens); and the cell makes immediate payments in what proves to be strictly small change (phosphate groups). In this analogy, payments are made by the cell directly in energy—energy in the form of a chemical structure.

Analogies are always dangerous when carried too far, but the present one, while no exception, does help us keep the details in perspective. Let us then look at this cellular economy, being careful to distinguish the following phases: (1) phosphate radicals as general currency; (2) methods of payment; (3) methods of currency (energy) conversion; (4) the nature of work done; (5) glucose and phosphagens as current accounts; (6) starches and fats as reserves.

A suitable energy currency: phosphate radicals. When the cell executes any of the thousands upon thousands of endergonic reactions necessary for its organized chemical life, it must supply energy for two separable purposes: (1) the energy of activation, and (2) the energy of reaction that pays for the complexity of structure that results. *In principle* the chemist in his laboratory can duplicate, separately, the reactions that occur in the cell. In executing some of these reactions, he would heat up the reactants both to activate them and to pay in the energy of reaction. But a cell would be killed were it heated above a certain temperature (less than 100° C.), a temperature that would be inadequate for the chemist's purpose. Most of the more complex molecules would be activated to roll downhill; they would be changed into less complex molecules. Specifically, the proteins, including enzymes, would be denatured (p. 94).

There is another reason of more general importance and implication why heat cannot be used by the cell to do its organized chemical work. Heat would be nonspecific in its effects; it would affect all reactions at once. The orderly life of the cell hinges on the performance of the proper reaction in the proper place at the proper time. Were you to punch all the keys on a calculating machine many times over, you would have included all the motions necessary for a calculation, but your energy expenditure would have brought chaos for you, not organized work. The cell faces a serious and general problem in how to pay for its endergonic reactions without resorting to the bludgeon of heat energy. It meets the problem in two ways.

First, it always employs enzymes to reduce the need for *activation energy*. Moreover, as we noted, its enzymes are very specific in the reactions they catalyze. You will now appreciate more fully the significance of enzyme specificity. It would not be very helpful to the cell's general order were a universal enzyme employed, simultaneously "lubricating" all reactions. The specificity of enzymes contributes largely to the cellular mechanism of *ordered chemical activity*.

Second, the cell pays its *reaction energy* debt for endergonic reactions by avoiding them! This surely sounds like double talk; it is the cell's magic referred to in our note on p. 95. The magic is really very simple. Let us uncover it in one generalized example. In this example we have assigned arbitrary energy contents to the molecules involved in order to clarify the nature of the basic trick.

Consider an endergonic or energy-binding reaction in which a chemist would use heat to supply the extra energy. The purpose is to form a complex, high-energy molecule D from simpler, low-energy molecules B and C as raw materials. Another product, E, incidentally results from the process.

Reagents: (Heat) $+ B + C \rightarrow D + E$

Their energy: 1 $+ 2 + 2 \rightarrow 3 + 2$

In the cell such a reaction uses a chemical source of energy in place of heat. This can be done in two steps. First, energy is transferred to one of the raw materials from some other energy-rich molecule, which may be symbolized as XR. If part of this molecule, R, combines with B, it transfers some of the energy from X to B. Characteristically, an enzyme activates the process.

$$B + XR \xrightarrow{\text{enzyme}} BR + X + \text{(Heat)}$$

$$2 + 6 \xrightarrow{\text{enzyme}} 5 + 2 + 1$$

Then the now energy-rich BR can combine with the other raw material, C, to form D and E:

$$BR + C \xrightarrow{\text{enzyme}} D + E + R + \text{(Heat)}$$

$$5 + 2 \longrightarrow 3 + 2 + 1 + 1$$

The oddity is that both of these reactions are energy-releasing, or exergonic, in spite of the fact that the products, D and E, together contain more energy than the raw materials, B and C. Nevertheless, there has been no cheating against the laws of thermodynamics. The extra energy came from XR, which had six energy units and was eventually split into X and R with a total of only three units. One of the three units thus freed went into the product D, and the other two were lost as heat. This principle of coupling exergonic reactions is the heart of the cell's mechanism for meeting its energy payments. One of the great unifying themes in the chemical life of the cell comes from the use of the molecule we have symbolized as XR, which is nearly always the same in such reactions. The composition of XR is now well-known: *adenosine triphosphate, or ATP for short*. It is a complex molecule, but we can ignore the details of its structure. Letting A stand for adenosine and P for phosphoric acid, we can write the structure of ATP as follows:

$$\text{A—P} \sim \text{P} \sim \text{P} = \text{ATP}$$

energy-rich
phosphate
groups

The ATP molecule has a high potential chemical-energy content which we can think of as largely concentrated in the two terminal phosphates and the bonds which attach them. This is indicated by the wavy bond symbol $\sim \text{P}$. Actual payment to "drive" the $B + C \to D + E$ exergonic reaction takes place as follows:

$$\text{exergonic: } B + \text{ATP} \xrightarrow{\text{enzyme}} B \sim \text{P} + \text{ADP}$$

The ATP has yielded one energy-rich phosphate, $\sim \text{P}$, to the molecule B. In doing so

ATP is degraded to the energy-poorer form, ADP, which is $A - \text{P} \sim \text{P}$. The coupled reaction can then follow:

$$\text{exergonic: } B \sim \text{P} + C \xrightarrow{\text{enzyme}} D + E + - \text{P}$$

The phosphate group $(- \text{P})$ that remains in the second reaction is no longer energy-rich. The energy debt to drive $B + C \to D + E$ was met by the downhill roll of $\text{ATP} \to \text{ADP} + - \text{P}$. You will notice that the two equations involving ATP, ADP, and $- \text{P}$ are identical with those given earlier using XR, X, and R. Clearly $\text{ATP} = \text{XR}$; $\text{ADP} = \text{X}$; and $- \text{P} = \text{R}$.

The over-all picture of ATP action is as follows: The cell pays out energy, in a currency of $\sim \text{P}$ radicals, to molecules unable to perform their required work exergonically. It is as though $\sim \text{P}$ were all the extra capital that was needed for a project to go ahead.

We can now work back toward a more general view of cellular economy by returning to our major crossroads, glucose. We began by noting that the oxidative breakdown of glucose (respiration) was the source of the cell's energy. How is the energy released by oxidizing sugar converted into the usable currency of ATP?

Respiration: release of sugar energy; coinage of phosphate currency. Figure 5-8 shows in outline form how energy liberated in the respiration of glucose is ultimately converted to phosphate currency. The oxidation of glucose proceeds stepwise, releasing small packets of energy adequate to regenerate ATP from ADP and $- \text{P}$. The reconstituted ATP then makes further payments by donating $\sim \text{P}$ to other compounds that require energy to proceed in the next step of their work.

There is a large number of individual steps, all enzyme-facilitated, involved in the respiratory degradation of sugar. It is unnecessary to consider them all in detail; we will distinguish four major stages as indicated in Fig. 5-9. The *first* stage consists of breaking down the glucose molecule (6-carbon skeleton) to two pyruvic acid molecules (3-carbon skeleton).

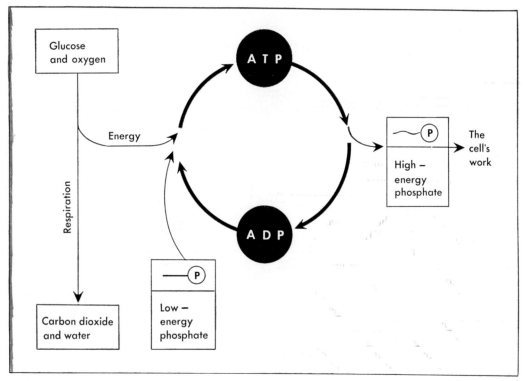

5-8   The ADP-ATP cycle.

This is done in six separate enzyme-facilitated steps, some of which involve adding phosphate groups to the sugar. The oxidative processes that are involved bind energy in the phosphate; —ⓅP becomes ~ⓅP. Two such ~ⓅP are then transferred to 2 ADP, making two new ATP molecules.

The second major stage consists of breaking down the pyruvic acid (3 carbons) molecules to acetic acid (2 carbons). This step again liberates energy as ~ⓅP, and also CO_2.

In the third step the 2-carbon fragments (acetic acid) are first combined with 4-carbon fragments to produce a new 6-carbon molecule (citric acid). The citric acid is then further degraded, first to a 5-carbon and then a 4-carbon molecule. Both these steps release CO_2 and much energy as ~ⓅP. The 4-carbon molecule now combines with more acetic acid (2-carbon), and the entire third stage starts over again. Indeed this third stage is an endless cyclic process, called "the Krebs citric acid cycle." We might think of it as a wheel onto which acetic acid from glucose is con-

tinually poured, only to be degraded ultimately to H, and CO_2, and energy.

The fourth major stage is a mopping-up operation. Each of the many individual energy-releasing oxidations involved in the first three major stages was a dehydrogenation. That is, hydrogen was stripped from the glucose fragments. In the fourth major step these hydrogens are carried by a series of enzymes (the flavoprotein and cytochrome system) to oxygen, which acts as the final hydrogen acceptor. Note, then, that the actual energy release, while surely an oxidation, consists of the removal of hydrogen, not the addition of oxygen.

By far the greatest amount of energy is liberated in the second and third (Krebs cycle) stages. The breakdown to pyruvic acid yields 2 new ATP molecules; the later stages yield 36 or 38 ATP molecules. We will see later that some organisms succeed in respiring (in the chemical sense of degrading sugar) either indefinitely or for short periods without using oxygen. This modified—anae-

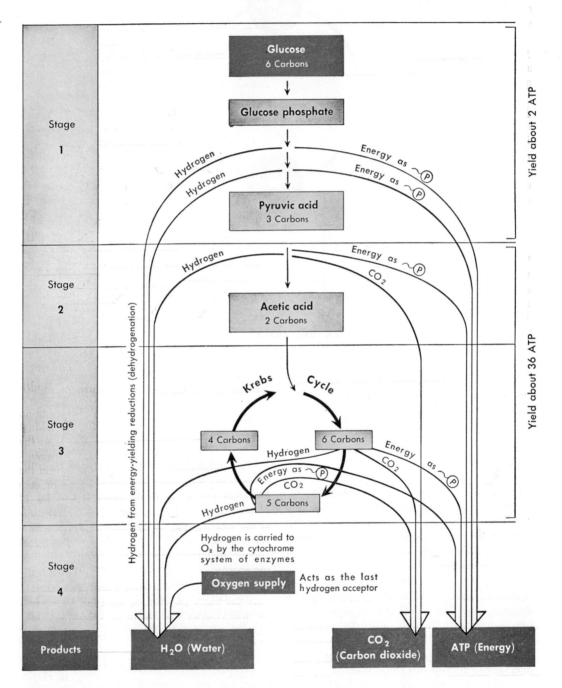

5-9 The respiration of glucose.

robic [8]—respiration is a modification of only the first stage we outlined. It proceeds only to pyruvic acid, which then has to act as its own hydrogen acceptor because no oxygen is present. It is essentially inefficient and yields *relatively* little energy.

The third and fourth stages of aerobic res- *with air* piration (the Krebs cycle energy releases and the mop-up of hydrogen by oxygen, forming water) are both effected by enzymes present as an organization in the mitochondria of the cell. You will recall that in discussing the structure of the cytoplasm, we noted that the mitochondria were major visible constituents, and that evidence exists indicating that they may congregate at focal points of cellular activity. It is not hard to imagine the significance of this. They are mobile payment trucks in the cell's active economy.

The significance of small-change currency. There are some striking and interesting features about the cell's phosphate currency. First is the fact—interesting especially to the evolutionary biologist—that *all* cells do their work with it. Second, phosphate currency is very "small change" in terms of cellular reserves or energy-capital. The energy released when glucose is burned amounts to 686,000 calories (per gram mole), but each $\sim$(P) in ATP is worth only about 12,000 calories (actually 11,500 by the time it is spent). The cell succeeds in capturing about 480,000 calories (yielding 40 $\sim$(P)) of the 686,000; that is, it succeeds in capturing about 70 per cent of the energy liberated by "burning" glucose in the particular way it does it.

The 70 per cent efficiency of the cell in capturing the freed energy from glucose oxidation is an astonishing figure. The majority of our own machines succeed in utilizing only about 30 per cent of the energy released to drive them. The remainder is lost as heat generated by the friction of moving parts, or analogous "leaks." Adaptation—the efficient organization of life to execute its essential processes—extends to the chemistry of the cell in clear fashion. How is this efficiency in

energy use effected? In essence it is achieved by not liberating more energy from glucose at any one time than a —(P) bond can pick up and store as $\sim$(P). In dispensing its wealth the cell does not shower its "bank teller" with more than he can handle at once.

Second, the stepwise breakdown of sugar yields "fragments" with 4-, 3-, and 2-carbon skeletons intermediate between the 6-carbon glucose and the 1-carbon CO_2. These intermediates play major roles in the rest of the cell's economy; they are useful raw materials for the manufacture of all fats and proteins. Let us turn now to this aspect of cellular work.

ENERGY UTILIZATION: SYNTHESIS FROM RAW MATERIALS

Principles. So far we have treated the cell's economy as though it were all a matter of energy—wealth and its expenditure. But an economy needs more than energy to do its work; it needs raw materials.[9] The Big Four basic constituents in the cell's raw materials are C, H, O, and N. The *ultimate* source of all the carbon is atmospheric CO_2, which is fixed (reduced) in photosynthesis (and probably to an almost insignificant extent in most cells by nonphotosynthetic methods). Oxygen enters the cell in gaseous form from the air and also in water. Hydrogen and nitrogen never enter as gases despite their abundance in the atmosphere. Hydrogen enters ultimately in water; nitrogen enters plants ultimately as nitrates (for example, potassium nitrate, KNO_3) absorbed from the soil by roots; and animals are ultimately dependent on plants for nitrogen. The point to be noted is that three of the Big Four (C, H, and O) enter the life of the cell by way of the glucose crossroads. We are back to the crossroads again in discussing materials, just as we were in discussing energy.

For our present purpose, which is to clarify only the basic skeleton of the cell's economy, we will restrict discussion of synthetic processes to essentials. These are as follows: (1) all synthetic steps are enzyme-controlled;

---

[8] Anaerobic, "without air"; cf. aerobic, "with air."

[9] We need not discuss here the question of raw material resources in any detail. You were introduced to the problem in the last chapter, and diversity in the over-all picture is taken up in Chapter 6, and again in Chapter 24.

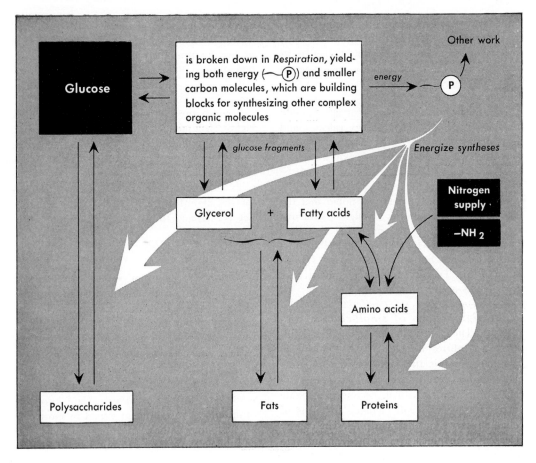

5-10   Synthetic pathways.

(2) all syntheses consume energy; (3) all cells tend to build complex molecules from relatively few intermediate building blocks; (4) all cells tend to link molecules together by a process of *dehydration* (the removal of water); (5) all cell syntheses obtain energy and materials (or both) from sugar metabolism (Fig. 5-10).

Polysaccharides. All the *polysaccharides* ("many sugars") are essentially compounded by linking together, through a chemical bond, sugars like glucose. These larger carbohydrate molecules such as starch (plants) or glycogen [10] (animals) are utilized for numerous purposes, the most generally important of which is the deep storage of energy reserves.

[10] Glycogen is sometimes called "animal starch."

The tubers of many plants like potatoes are composed of tissues given over almost entirely to starches as storage reserves. In plants, cellulose and related compounds are polysaccharide molecules used for mechanical purposes in cell walls.

The formation of polysaccharides from sugars is, like all organic syntheses, a complex series of reactions. Table 5-3 limits itself to the over-all net processes. In polysaccharides the synthesis is a *condensation,* or *dehydration synthesis.* Glucose molecules form a six-point ring, as our figure indicates. The skeleton of the ring consists of carbon atoms and one oxygen. Hydrogen and hydroxyl (—OH) groups are attached to the carbons. Two glucose molecules are bound by removing a complete hydroxyl (OH) group from one molecule and the hydrogen from a hydroxyl of another.

TABLE 5-3

Basic constituents and synthesis of polysaccharides

CONSTITUENTS

The glucose molecule is a polysaccharide building block. Its empirical formula is $C_6H_{12}O_6$. It has a ring structure shown more fully in (1) and simplified to a basic skeleton in (2).

SYNTHESIS

The synthesis of polysaccharides ("many sugars") from molecules like glucose involves many steps and the utilization of $\sim$ⓟ energy. These steps effectively summate to the linking of sugar molecules by *dehydration*, as follows:

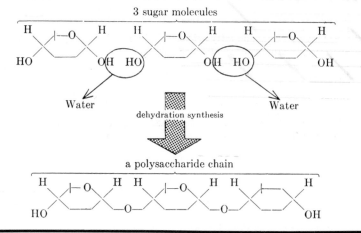

Thus water is formed, and the molecules are linked through the remaining oxygen. Notice that both ends of the sugar molecule can be linked to another. In fact, chains of nearly indefinite length can be created. Moreover, the chains, as in glycogen, can be branched so that the finished polysaccharide may be not only huge but very complex. For polysaccharide synthesis we can write a generalized equation covering all cases:

Simple sugar   Polysaccharide   Water

$$n\ (C_6H_{12}O_6) \xrightarrow{\text{enzymes}} (C_6H_{10}O_5)_n + n - 1\ H_2O$$

The symbol n designates the number of sugar molecules utilized, the number of $(C_6H_{10}O_5)$

units in the polysaccharide molecule; $n - 1$ is the number of water molecules produced. If $n = 6$, six simple sugars were utilized, one polysaccharide was formed with six $(C_6H_{10}O_5)$ units in it, and five water molecules were produced.

Fats. The synthesis of both fats and proteins also traces back to the sugar crossroad. Some of the intermediate products of the glucose breakdown eventually acquire an acidic group of atoms (—COOH), and are known as fatty acids. The simplest of these is acetic acid CH_3—COOH, which is on the main line of sugar degradation. The skeleton of the mol-

TABLE 5-4

Basic constituents and synthesis of fats

CONSTITUENTS

The constituents of fats are glycerol and fatty acids

Glycerol is a molecule with 3 carbons, each carrying an —OH group in addition to hydrogen:

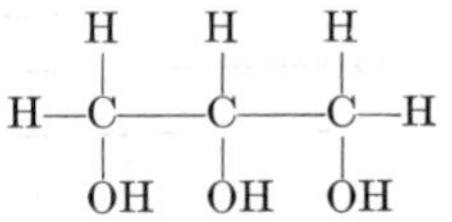

$$H-\overset{\overset{\displaystyle H}{|}}{C}-\overset{\overset{\displaystyle H}{|}}{\underset{\underset{\displaystyle OH}{|}}{C}}-\overset{\overset{\displaystyle H}{|}}{\underset{\underset{\displaystyle OH}{|}}{C}}-H$$

A *fatty acid* carries an acidic group (—COOH) in addition to the rest of the molecule, which may be varied and conveniently labeled as *R*. Thus all fatty acids can be written as in *1*; acetic acid (2) is an important example.

$$(1)\quad R-C\overset{\displaystyle O}{\underset{\displaystyle OH}{\diagup}} \qquad\qquad (2)\quad H-\overset{\overset{\displaystyle H}{|}}{\underset{\underset{\displaystyle H}{|}}{C}}-C\overset{\displaystyle O}{\underset{\displaystyle OH}{\diagup}} \quad \text{Acetic acid}$$

SYNTHESIS

Fats are synthesized from glycerol and fatty acids, again by a series of steps requiring energy. These steps link the fatty acids to the glycerol by *dehydration*, as follows:

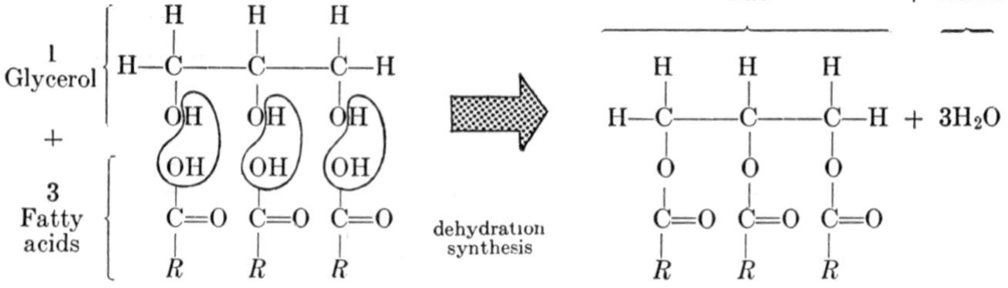

dehydration synthesis

Fat + Water

$$H-C-C-C-H + 3H_2O$$

---

ecule, apart from the COOH group, may become greatly added to and complicated. In acetic acid it is the simple CH_3— group. We will ignore the complexities that this skeleton may assume, and designate it all as *R*. This device permits us to generalize the structure of all fatty acids, acetic included, as *R—COOH* (Table 5-4).

The fatty acids are important building materials leading eventually to both fats and proteins. In fats they combine with glycerol, another derivative of sugar-breakdown products. The combination of fatty acids with glycerol is, in a summary view of many steps, again a dehydration synthesis. The great diversity in fats derives from the diversity of fatty acids that combine with the glycerol.

Fats in the human food and body are mostly derived from three fatty acids: oleic, palmitic, and stearic. The following equation suffices to indicate how large fat molecules can be:

Glycerol + Palmitic acid

$$C_3H_5(OH)_3 + 3C_{15}H_{31}COOH \underset{\text{enzyme}}{\overset{\text{lipase}}{\rightleftharpoons}}$$

Fat + Water

$$C_3H_5(C_{15}H_{31}COO)_3 + 3H_2O$$

Some fats occur in every cell of all living organisms; they are essential protoplasmic ingredients. In slightly modified form, associated with phosphorus, they play a major role in the structure and selective absorption properties of cell membranes. But deep storage is probably their main function. Their concen-

TABLE 5-5

Basic constituents and synthesis of proteins

CONSTITUENTS

The constituents of proteins are *amino acids*. These are synthesized from fatty acids by replacement of an H in the fatty acid by the —NH$_2$ group. Glycine, the simplest amino acid, is synthesized from acetic acid.

In general, amino acids can be written as:

where R may be very varied according to the fatty acid source.

SYNTHESIS

Proteins are complex molecules synthesized from amino acids as building blocks. The process, as usual, involves many steps and energy. The elementary process is illustrated in summary form here. It involves linking amino acids by dehydration synthesis into chains called polypeptide chains:

tration in some seeds and fruits of plants and in certain animal tissues generally represents storage for future metabolism. The concentration may, however, have other effects as well, such as insulation in warm-blooded animals.

Proteins. Fatty acids are also employed in synthesis of proteins, the most complex molecules of the cell. Here they go through a more elaborate processing. First they are transformed into *amino acids.* In this process one hydrogen in the fatty-acid molecule is replaced by an amino group —NH$_2$. Glycine,

the simplest amino acid, is obtained from acetic acid by such a substitution:

As with fatty acids, we can summarize all the complexities of the twenty-three known amino acids and generalize their structure as:

$$H_2N—R—COOH$$

or, more fully, as:

$$H \quad \quad O$$
$$| \quad \quad \quad ||$$
$$N-R-C-OH$$
$$|$$
$$H$$

In plants the amino group is prepared from nitrates ($-NO_3$), but animals, incapable of this work, are dependent on plants for their amino ($-NH_2$) groups. We will return to such differences in synthetic capacities, generally, in the next section of this chapter.

The next steps in protein synthesis consist basically of linking amino acids together into chains called polypeptides. Again, the over-all process is a dehydration, as shown in Table 5-5. A hydrogen from the amino group of one acid and the hydroxyl from the acidic group of another are removed to form water; the amino acids are then linked through the remains of one amino group and one acidic group, giving a highly characteristic peptide linkage:

$$H \quad \quad O \quad \quad \quad O$$
$$| \quad \quad \quad || \quad \quad \quad ||$$
$$N-R-C-N-R-C-OH$$
$$| \quad \quad \quad \quad | $$
$$H \quad \quad \quad H$$

a peptide linkage

Proteins are built up by the fabrication of polypeptide chains of enormous length and diversity in the sequence of their constituent amino acids. The polypeptide chains can be "tied" together by the formation of chemical bonds between members of the R part of the molecule. In this fashion proteins of almost unlimited size and diversity are formed.

The functional roles of proteins in the cell are many and diverse; there is no part of the cell that does not contain them. Membranes contain proteins; the cytoplasm is in large part an aqueous colloid of protein; mitochondria contain protein; chromosomes contain protein; and all enzymes are proteins. Proteins occur in many molecular shapes and sizes, one of which is fibrous. All important fibrous constituents of the cell are proteins. Collagen fibers that give strength to all connective tissues are protein, and the fibrous elements of muscle are protein. Muscle fibers

have a special and highly important property: they can contract. Contraction expends energy and is dependent on an ATP supply.

Other products. Organisms synthesize many other compounds that do not fall into the three major classes of molecules we have covered. Many of these other compounds—like pigments, alkaloids, essential oils, steroids—are of great importance, but we need not discuss them here in detail.

Interchangeability of resources. Fatty acids are involved at some stage in the synthesis of all three major kinds of molecules: carbohydrates, fats, and proteins. For this reason they constitute an important exchange station in the over-all economy of the cell. Considering the world of life as a whole, solar energy is first made available through the respiration of sugars. But much of the energy you expend today may derive more immediately from a beefsteak. Fats and proteins, initially synthesized at the expense of sugar energy (via ATP), may in their turn be broken down to release energy. Their breakdown products include fatty acids that may enter the Krebs cycle and be oxidized just as though they had been derived more directly from sugar. Thus all three major groups of molecules (carbohydrates, fats, and proteins) are interchangeable as energy resources, and also as raw material reservoirs. The carbon-chain skeleton of a fatty acid today may be part of a protein, fat, or carbohydrate tomorrow.

Synthesis, Nutrition, and Biochemical Systems

Syntheses and related transformations again illustrate the amazing unity and diversity of life. The same sorts of biochemical reactions, even in some cases the identical reactions, go on in an ameba, an alga, a man, or a redwood. These are, nevertheless, extremely different sorts of organisms. The difference cannot be ascribed to any single factor. It is, however, especially related to the autosynthesis of different proteins in these different organisms. All synthesize proteins from the same materials; a few fairly simple amino acids and prosthetic groups. All perform this synthesis in the same way, involving condensation and formation of a long polypeptide chain. Yet each sort of organism makes proteins peculiar to that sort, and even each individual has a different combination of proteins from every other individual.[11]

These basic distinctions do not arise from any differences in the powers of synthesis but only in the models that are followed. There are, however, great differences in the powers or sorts of syntheses among different organisms. The most general and striking difference of this sort is already becoming quite familiar to you: green plants can synthesize sugars from raw materials, and amino acids from sugars (or their derivatives) and a nitrogen source; animals, in general, cannot. The difference in ability to synthesize necessarily involves differences in intake of materials. As regards nutrition, green plants are called *autotrophic,* from the Greek words meaning "self-feeder," and animals are called *heterotrophic,* meaning "other-feeder," that is, feeding on others.

When put in such general terms, the difference between autotrophy and heterotrophy sounds clear-cut and absolute. So it is when we compare, say, a buttercup and a cow. If, however, we compare many different organisms, we find intergradations and great diversity in powers of synthesis. All organisms perform many syntheses, but none can synthesize all needed substances from their elements. From this point of view, all are partly autotrophic and partly heterotrophic unless we choose to define the words by some *one* sort of synthesis. This is, in fact, usually done, and "autotrophic" is generally restricted to organisms that perform chlorophyll photosynthesis of sugars (or related carbohydrates) is water. We have seen that even particular synthesis of sugars (or related carbohydrates) is not always performed in the same way. The reaction can be not only:

$$CO_2 + 2H_2O + Energy \rightarrow$$

$$(CH_2O) + H_2O + O_2$$

11 The only exceptions occur when two or more individuals arise from a single source individual, an event that does happen in a number of different ways, such as the development of identical twins in humans.

but also:

$$CO_2 + 2H_2S + Energy \rightarrow$$

$$(CH_2O) + H_2O + 2S$$

and the energy does not always come from light. Some simple organisms obtain energy by the oxidation of various inorganic compounds and utilize this energy in the basic organic synthesis of the type shown above. The source of energy may, for instance, be hydrogen sulfide, which may also be the reducing agent in the synthesis. The summary oxidation reaction is:

$$2H_2S + O_2 \rightarrow 2H_2O + 2S + Energy$$

Organisms that perform the basic synthesis in any other way than from carbon dioxide, water, and light energy are not particularly numerous or important in the general economy of nature at the present time. They are interesting because they illustrate a basic diversity of biochemical systems and may throw light on the origins of such systems.

Study of detailed nutritional requirements has revealed many differences in synthetic ability even between rather closely related forms. If an organism requires a particular compound (such as one of the vitamins) in its food in order to remain healthy, to grow, or to multiply, this is evidence that the organism cannot itself synthesize that compound. On the other hand, if a compound occurs and plays a vital role in an organism but is not necessary in its food, then the organism can and does synthesize it. Thus nutritional experiments reveal what syntheses are performed in each case. Humans require ascorbic acid (vitamin C) in their diet and cannot make this synthesis. Rats, although rather closely related to us and generally similar biochemically, can synthesize ascorbic acid. Most plants and animals can make this synthesis.

There are many such examples of lack of a specific synthesis in particular sorts of organisms. Some bacteria and other lowly, mostly acellular organisms are especially interesting. In step-by-step reactions of the sort now familiar to you, organisms may differ in which steps they can make. Take, for instance, a step-by-step sequence such as the following:

$$A \rightarrow B \rightarrow C \rightarrow D$$

Some organisms can make all the steps: they synthesize D with no dietary requirement except A. Related forms can make steps $B \to C \to D$ but not $A \to B$. They therefore require B in their diet. Still others may make the step $C \to D$ but not $A \to B$ or $B \to C$, and others cannot make any of these steps. What do these last two sorts of organisms require in the diet?

The same sort of effect may appear in complex reactions of the type:

$$\left. \begin{array}{c} A \to C \\ B \to D \end{array} \right\} C + D \to E$$

Some organisms carry through all three syntheses from the raw materials A and B. Others may require A and D or C and D or E in their diet. What syntheses are these organisms unable to perform? Do you know a specific synthesis of this type?

There is some evidence that the ancestry of all living organisms went through an autotrophic stage when they could make all necessary syntheses from elements and very simple inorganic compounds. The inability of recent organisms to make a specific synthesis may then usually be an evolutionary loss of a biochemical ability possessed by remote ancestors. New syntheses have certainly developed in some lines of evolution, but on the whole the loss of syntheses has probably been a ruling factor in the later evolution of biochemical systems. There can, for instance, be little doubt that ancestors of ours could synthesize ascorbic acid and that we need this in our food because the power was lost somewhere along the line.

In fact it is likely that other ancestors of ours, very remote ancestors indeed, had the power of photosynthesis and then lost it. Among the living acellular organisms called flagellates there are a number of pairs of forms that are almost exactly alike except that one has chlorophyll and performs photosynthesis and the other does not.[12] It is probable in each case that the nonphotosynthetic forms were directly derived from the photosynthetic

12 Here are the names of a few of the pairs in case you have opportunity to observe them: **Chlamydomonas-Polytoma, Cryptomonas-Chilomonas, Euglena-Astasia.** Among dinoflagellates there are several genera, such as **Gymnodinium,** in which some species are photosynthetic and others are not.

ones by loss of this synthesis. By experimental procedures it is possible to take some of the photosynthetic flagellates and to breed from them a strain that lacks chloroplasts and therefore cannot perform photosynthesis. (Why not?) This artificial strain lives and reproduces perfectly well as long as it is fed either the carbohydrates that it cannot synthesize or some other organic molecule as an energy source.

This experiment actually turns a plant into an animal as far as nutrition or the system of biochemical synthesis is concerned. Some such change was probably involved at that very distant time when plants and animals did become distinct and began to diverge along their separate paths of biochemical and bodily evolution. There is, indeed, reason to believe that the organisms among which the separation began may have been similar to the flagellates of today. The experiment may actually be repeating the beginning of that epochal event. As to whether the flagellates, themselves and as a group, are really animals or plants, there is no "really" about it. They are what you choose to call them. Among these organisms the distinction is purely arbitrary if not quite meaningless.

An organism that loses photosynthesis immediately becomes dependent for food on organisms retaining that synthesis. This is, of course, the basis of the dependence of the whole animal kingdom on the plant kingdom. Loss of any synthesis—and it has been mentioned that this is a frequent occurrence in the history of organisms—leads to greater dependence on other organisms. Such loss and increased dependence might be considered degeneration, and they have been so considered by some students of the subject. It is true that the real end of the trail (or is it only of one of the trails?) can hardly be considered other than degenerate. This end is seen in some parasites that retain almost no syntheses and depend on the plants or animals within which they live for nearly all compounds. (They always do retain at least one synthesis, however. Which one?) Yet the loss of syntheses is also associated with increased activity, greater anatomical complication, greater mobility, increased perception, and many other evolutionary changes that man, at least, is pleased to consider as progressive. Man himself, certainly the brightest if not in all respects the most advanced organism, has "degenerated" as much by loss of syntheses and is as dependent on other organisms for food as most parasites.

Here is another point you might think over, and one we are going to discuss later. Photosynthesis is a very complex process. Among other things, it depends on a number of compounds, such as chlorophyll and other enzymes, that have to be synthesized themselves. If photosynthesis arose in the course of evolution (and biologists agree that it did), there must have been organisms in existence before *any* of them were photosynthetic (p. 738).

Chapter Summary

The characteristic complexity of the cell's organic molecules; their synthesis one aspect of the cell's work.

The concepts of energy and work: energy as the capacity to accomplish work; the diverse forms of energy and their interchangeability; potential and kinetic energy.

Chemical reactions as a form of work involving the expenditure of energy.

Chemical energy, potential energy of chemical structure.

The energy of activation and the role of enzymes in facilitating chemical reactions.

The energy of reaction: exergonic and endergonic reactions.

Oxidation-reduction processes as transfers of electrons; transfers of energy.

The cell's energy exchanges likened to a business economy: sugar the focal point of the economy; energy income and expenditure; energy storage and transport; the use of phosphate radicals as a convenient form of energy currency.

Photosynthesis: energy income leading to the formation of sugars; the capture of light energy by chlorophyll; cleavage of water by energized chlorophyll, producing O_2 and 4H; the reduction of CO_2 by the 4H; the synthesis of reduced carbon dioxide to sugar.

Respiration: the stepwise liberation of small packets of energy by the oxidation (dehydrogenation) of sugars; the conversion of the released energy into the energy-rich phosphate bonds of ATP.

The utilization of ATP energy in the coupling of exergonic reactions: coupled exergonic reactions as a substitute for endergonic reactions.

The significance of small-change currency (ATP) and the stepwise oxidation of sugar.

The syntheses of polysaccharides, fats, and proteins: their enzyme control; their consumption of energy; their utilization of glucose fragments produced in respiration; the linking of constituent molecules by dehydration.

The interchangeability of cellular resources.

Biochemical systems: autotrophy and heterotrophy; degrees of heterotrophy; the evolution of heterotrophy.

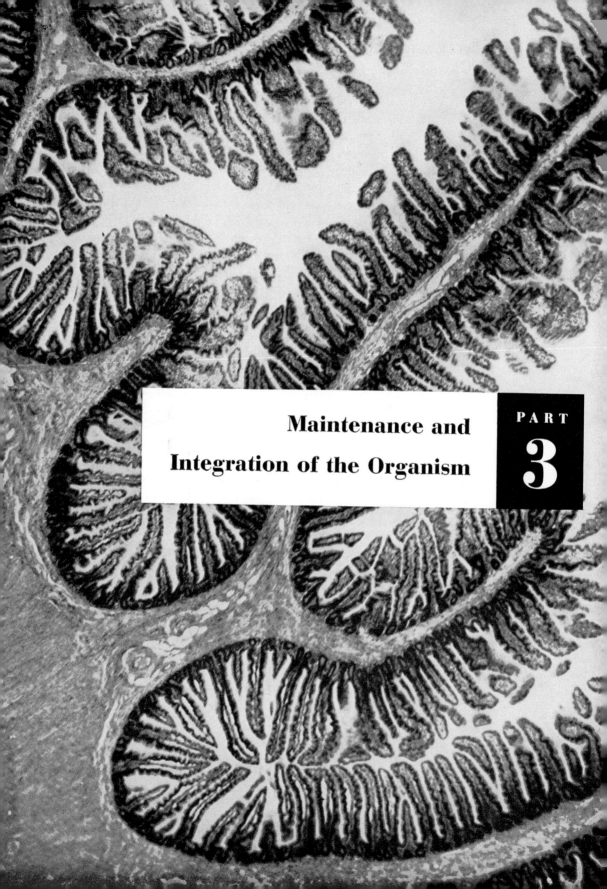

Maintenance and
Integration of the Organism

PART 3

Pictures of the single cell are deceptively simple; even from those obtained with the most elaborate modern techniques we get little concrete evidence of the system's complexity and organization. The illusion of simplicity in life is dispelled as soon as we turn to the structure of the whole multicellular organism.

The photograph introducing Part 3 shows a section through a very small piece of the wall of a human intestine. It contains a host of specialized cells—epithelial, glandular, muscular, connective, and nervous tissue cells. To the trained eye the cells' specialization of structure is obvious and can be related to the role each of them plays in the organized activity not only of the gut wall but of the entire organism. Here, then, is a situation very different from that of the single cell; we have a living system large enough to permit our direct observation of its complexity and organization, a system large enough to permit experimental manipulation of its component parts. It is from the study of the larger multicellular forms that much of our present knowledge arises on how living systems operate to integrate and maintain their organized state. Part 3 is devoted to these topics.

Chapters 6 and 7 discuss the procurement and processing of needed materials and energy. A major theme running throughout these chapters is the consequences of increased size in multicellular organisms. Large size brings advantages to the organism (as well as to the observer!), but it also raises problems of its own which demand special features in the living organization. One of these is the presence of rapid transport systems, like the blood, which play a central role in nearly all aspects of organic maintenance and integration.

Chapter 8 focuses attention on the idea of organization itself; it is concerned with the mechanisms that integrate the constituent parts and processes of the system into an ordered whole. Co-ordination between isolated parts demands mechanisms of communication within the organism. Chapter 8 discusses one of two such systems found in living things: the system of chemical messengers (hormones), which in animals are transported from place to place by the movement of the blood, and in plants are actively transported from cell to cell by a mechanism that is still obscure.

Chapter 9 is devoted entirely to the second type of communications network in organisms: the nervous system of animals. In addition to effecting communication between internal parts, the nervous system is concerned with obtaining and processing information about the external environment, and with regulating the organism's behavior.

The behavior of an organism (Chapter 10) consists of its ordered movements as a whole, its movements in relation to other organisms and the rest of the environment in which it must survive. This is an essential aspect of organic maintenance.

CHAPTER 6

Organic

Maintenance: I

THE CELL AND THE ORGANISM

The metabolism of energy and materials surveyed in the last chapter is the basic economy not only of cells but of all organisms and communities of organisms. It is the basic economy of life. Living systems differ only in the detail of how they meet those fundamental energy and material prerequisites they share in common. There are two broad, and never completely separate, categories of differences among living systems in respect to the *means* by which they fulfill their common metabolic requirements. The first is most fully exemplified by the difference between a green plant and an animal; they differ in their dependence on prefabricated resources of energy and materials.

The second category of differences is related to the dimensions of the living system. In the individual cell the procurement, transportation, and processing of raw materials is manifestly a different problem from that in a large multicellular organism like man or an oak tree. The total economy—the living system—is confronted with new technical problems as it grows in size. For example, the internal distances to be traversed become so great that transportation can no longer be entrusted to simple diffusion and protoplasmic streaming. Specialized systems for the mass movement of products, parts, and raw materials play a novel and major role in the economy of the multicellular organism. But these differences between living systems—plant or animal, large or small—never obscure a fundamental similarity in their ultimate material needs. In this chapter and the next, on the maintenance of the whole organism, you will recognize that, when we discuss diverse modes of digestion, assimilation, respiration, transportation, and excretion, we are discussing diverse ways of fulfilling ends already familiar from our study of the individual cell.

Procurement Processes

INTAKE

The passage of materials through an organic metabolic system clearly begins with their being taken into the organism. The most widespread method of intake of animals is the one we have ourselves: solids and liquids are

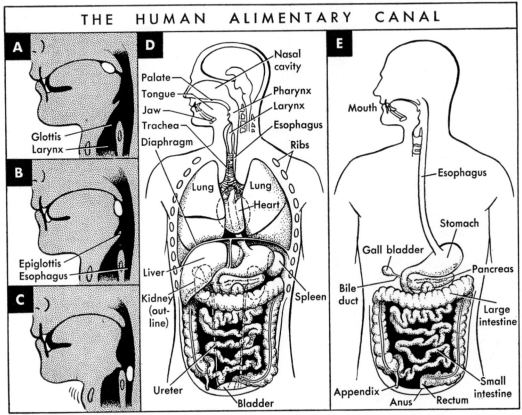

THE HUMAN ALIMENTARY CANAL

A

B

Epiglottis
Esophagus

C

Glottis
Larynx

D

Palate
Tongue
Jaw
Trachea
Diaphragm

Nasal cavity
Pharynx
Larynx
Esophagus
Ribs

Lung   Lung
Heart

Liver

Kidney
(out-
line)

Ureter

Spleen

Bladder

E

Mouth

Esophagus

Stomach

Gall bladder

Bile
duct

Pancreas

Large
intestine

Appendix

Anus

Rectum

Small
intestine

6-1   The alimentary canal in man. *A, B,* and *C.* Stages in the passage of food through mouth cavity and pharynx; the epiglottis prevents passage of food into the larynx and, hence, into the lungs. *D.* The alimentary system in relation to other internal organs in man. *E.* Part of the alimentary system.

taken into a tube, the alimentary canal, running through the body. Figure 6-1 outlines the alimentary canal in man, and identifies its parts. Within the alimentary canal parts of the solids go into solution, and liquids and substances in solution are absorbed through the wall of the tube.

Among the animals that take solid food into an alimentary canal there are many different systems for the actual acquisition of the food. Without attempting to consider all the details at this point, we can distinguish three main sorts. Some eat sizeable plants and animals or chunks of them. That is true of us, of course, and also of the animals most familiar to us. Usually such animals have a way of seizing food, a sizeable mouth, and some way of breaking up the chunks. Many animals, however, eat food in particles

very small in comparison with the animals themselves. These animals have filters to catch food, which is then swallowed whole in filtered masses (Fig. 6-2). The variety of filter feeders is surprising. They range from oysters to whalebone whales. Finally, there are some animals, fewer than those with other feeding habits, that simply take in samples of their whole environment, digest any food in it, and evacuate the rest. Earthworms are of this sort: they pass earth, in which they live, through the alimentary canal. Clearly this system will not work unless the environment is fairly nutritious; there are few worms in sand dunes.

Protists absorb water and dissolved materials directly through the body membrane. The body membrane is analogous to a cell membrane, if not exactly the same thing,

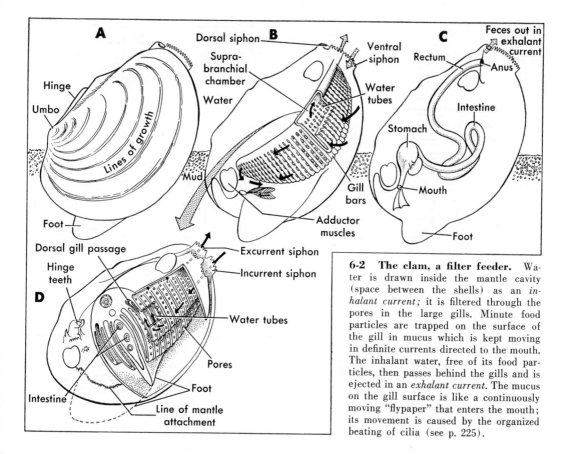

A

Hinge
Umbo
Lines of growth
Foot
Dorsal siphon
Supra-branchial chamber
Water
Mud

B

Ventral siphon
Water tubes
Gill bars
Adductor muscles

C

Feces out in exhalant current
Rectum
Anus
Intestine
Stomach
Mouth
Foot

D

Dorsal gill passage
Hinge teeth
Excurrent siphon
Incurrent siphon
Water tubes
Pores
Foot
Intestine
Line of mantle attachment

6-2   **The clam, a filter feeder.** Water is drawn inside the mantle cavity (space between the shells) as an *inhalant current*; it is filtered through the pores in the large gills. Minute food particles are trapped on the surface of the gill in mucus which is kept moving in definite currents directed to the mouth. The inhalant water, free of its food particles, then passes behind the gills and is ejected in an *exhalant current*. The mucus on the gill surface is like a continuously moving "flypaper" that enters the mouth; its movement is caused by the organized beating of cilia (see p. 225).

and of course the absorption involves diffusion and osmosis. It is really the same sort of process as absorption by cells lining the tube or sac—the alimentary canal—in multicellular animals. Many protists, especially among those that are often called animals, also take in solid food. They eat other protists and even small multicellular organisms, just as you eat plants and animals—although they are not so dainty about its preparation and often do not even bother to kill their food before eating it. The solid food of protists is simply surrounded or is captured by various devices. It is taken in through the body membrane and becomes enclosed in a food vacuole, in which digestion occurs. This method looks very different from our way of eating and digesting solid food, but the food vacuole corresponds with our stomach and intestine, and the same sort of processes go on in it. The only essential difference is not functional but structural: the food vacuole is not a

permanent part of the protist's anatomy but is improvised anew for each meal or "mouthful" (Fig. 6-6).

Some protists utilize solid food without actually taking it into the body for digestion. They secrete digestive fluid onto food outside the body wall and then absorb the dissolved products. Many starfish and some other multicellular animals do essentially the same thing: they hold their prey outside the body and surround it with digestive fluids in various ways. It could be said that they digest their food before they eat it. But from the point of view of food intake this is not fundamentally different from digestion within the alimentary canal. Why?

A few plants take in solid food in a way that is really the same as in carnivorous animals. These plants, including the pitcher plant, sundew, and Venus's-flytrap, have modified leaves which trap insects (Fig. 6-3). The traps also are cavities, fully analogous to

6-3 Carnivorous plants. From left to right, Venus's-flytrap (natural size), pitcher plant (one-third natural size), and sundew (slightly reduced in size).

an animal's alimentary canal, in which digestion occurs and from which the digested food is absorbed. These extraordinary plants have a special appeal to the imagination, and they are striking examples of both the unity and the diversity of life and its processes. They are, however, highly exceptional as plants.

The overwhelming majority of plants take in materials in only one way: by diffusion through the cell walls and membranes. In aquatic plants all materials, including water itself, are acquired from the water solution surrounding them. In terrestrial plants water and dissolved salts are acquired mainly by diffusion into root hairs and other cells on the surface of the roots. The other needed materials, oxygen and carbon dioxide, diffuse from their gaseous condition in the atmosphere into solution within cells of aerial parts, especially leaves. The intake of oxygen is part of the process of respiration, which will be discussed as a separate topic. Carbon dioxide, however, is a raw material for food.[1]

Separate problems are involved in the diffusion into plant roots of water and its dissolved inorganic materials (mineral salts). Water is pulled into the roots by an "osmotic pump." Figure 6-4 is a schematic section across a plant root from its hair cells to its xylem vessels. Suppose, first, that all the

1 See Chapters 4 and 5.

cells along the path from hair to xylem have the same osmotic pressure (Δ, p. 83). The pressure in the cells is much higher than that of the soil water because of the high concentration of sugars and salts in the cell. Water is consequently drawn by osmotic pressure into the root hair cell, slightly lowering its Δ value. The hair cell then yields water to the adjacent cell inside the root which has a higher Δ value. This continues across the whole cortex of the plant to the xylem, into which the soil's water is pumped by the *gradient of osmotic pressure.* The pressure developed by this gradient of Δ values across the root is often very large. It is called *root pressure;* we have more to say about it on p. 139 of the next chapter.

The movement into root hairs of dissolved substances in the soil water raises quite different problems. Where the incoming salt is immediately consumed in some synthesis or is bound to protein colloids in the cytoplasm, its concentration as a free molecule (or ion) in the cell may be kept very low. The cell is then assured of continued simple diffusion of the salt from higher concentrations in the soil to the lower concentrations in the cytoplasm. In other plants, however, the cell may require concentrations of salts far above those found in soil water. It has then to expend energy—in a manner still unknown—to pull salts into the cell against a concentration gradient (cf. Chapter 4, p. 86).

In general, then, substances taken in as food or as materials for food may be solid, liquid, or gaseous. Intake of a gas, in addition to oxygen for respiration, is essential in almost all green plants but is rarely important in other organisms. Solids are not actually absorbed and do not really enter into the life processes of the organism until they have been transformed into solutions. The ultimate, most common method of intake is thus absorption from aqueous solutions. (Small globules of liquid fats may, however, be absorbed without going into solution.)

THE PROCESS OF DIGESTION

The principal feature of digestion is that it transforms foods into forms that can readily be absorbed. Substances insoluble in water or with very large molecules or in large globules cannot as a rule be absorbed; they usually cannot pass through the membranes that surround cells and vacuoles. Most foods fall into these classes of substances difficult or impossible to absorb.[2] Simple carbohydrates (sugars) are generally soluble in water and are readily absorbed, but complex carbohydrates such as starch are insoluble. Fats (or lipides in general) are insoluble in water. Proteins have large molecules, and in water they usually form colloids to which cell membranes are impermeable, rather than simple solutions.

Here is something quite extraordinary. Most of the more complex compounds built up in cells cannot be passed on to other cells unless they are torn down again. Life would be impossible without elaborate organic foods. Yet in many cases these foods must be changed back into the substances from which they were derived before they can really serve as food for other parts of the same organism or for other organisms. Offhand this would seem to indicate profound inefficiency. It is true, certainly, that organisms are far from 100 per cent efficient, but further consideration shows that properties of life as it really exists depend on some apparently inefficient features of food utilization. If colloids could be absorbed through cell membranes, so that cells could take in complex proteins as such,

2 See Chapter 5.

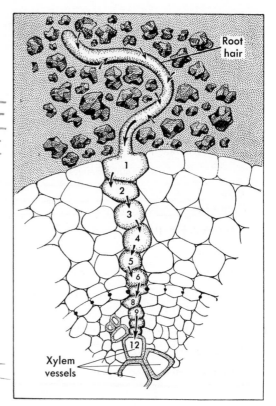

6-4 Water uptake by roots.

then colloidal protoplasm could not always be retained within the cell. If cellulose were soluble, then fluids moving in plants would dissolve the vessels through which they flow. If starch and glycogen were soluble, they could not be retained in cells in extra quantities available as storage against future needs. Moreover, the diversity of life and the actual characteristics of its different kinds depend on the fact that each kind has its own proteins. Each kind, therefore, cannot utilize the proteins of other organisms directly as they are taken in but must tear them down and rebuild them.

Many of the reactions of digestion are simply the reverse of those of synthesis. You already know the most basic processes of digestion; just look at some of the basic syntheses backwards. You already know, too, that organic reactions are frequently reversible; a number of equations for synthesis can be reversed and then become equations for digestion. Among the most fundamental of

TABLE 6-1

1. STARCH AND OTHER POLYSACCHARIDES

   Synthesis:

   n simple sugar molecules $\rightarrow$ Polysaccharide

   $+ \, n - 1$ water molecules

   Digestion:

   Polysaccharide $+ \, n - 1$ water molecules $\rightarrow$

   n simple sugar molecules

2. FATS

   Synthesis:

   Glycerol + Fatty acids $\rightarrow$ Fat + Water

   Digestion:

   Fat + Water $\rightarrow$ Glycerol + Fatty acids

3. PROTEINS

   Synthesis:

   Amino acids $\rightarrow$ Protein + Water

   Digestion:

   Protein + Water $\rightarrow$ Amino acids

these reactions are those in Table 6-1, given in very general and summary form.

You will recall that these particular syntheses are examples of condensation or *dehydration synthesis:* linking together of molecules with elimination of water from them. Digestion in general is the opposite process, *hydrolysis:* separation of molecules with addition of water to them.

In popular language we think of digestion as the first operation after foods are taken into the organism from outside. Exactly the same reactions may, however, occur over and over again in almost all cells of the body. Indeed, as a rule they must occur every time that insoluble or colloidal materials are passed on from one cell to another. In biological terms the reactions are called "digestion" whether they occur at the first intake of food or later on. An example is the first digestion of a polysaccharide (usually starch) to simple sugars, which are carried to the liver and there resynthesized into another polysaccharide (glycogen), which in turn is later digested in the liver cells into simple

sugar and passed on to other parts of the body.

This cyclic relationship between digestion and synthesis will suggest to you answers to many questions about the phenomena of metabolism. How does starch get into the underground tubers of a potato plant? How do stem and root tips obtain the amino acids necessary for their growth? What takes place before a bite of beefsteak affects the cells in your fingers or toes? How does sugar in your ice cream become a source of energy in your leg muscles during a dash around the block? Full answers to such questions may not yet be clear (really *complete* answers are not clear to biologists, either), but we have covered most of the essential principles involved.

DIGESTIVE ENZYMES

Organic catalysts, enzymes and enzyme systems, are usually involved in reactions in organisms.[3] Specifically, enzymes are necessary for all the reactions of digestion. Sometimes they are the same enzymes as those involved in the corresponding synthesis. What is summarized as a single reaction in digestion may require a number of different enzymes, because digestion actually proceeds as a series of smaller steps, each with its own enzyme. Enzymes are present in every living cell and usually also in fluids outside the cells, but the enzymes involved in the first digestion of food in the alimentary canals of animals are particularly well known. In the extremely complex and tiny chemical system of a cell, it is difficult to identify and isolate a single enzyme. In the alimentary canal, however, digestive enzymes are poured out from surrounding cells in relatively large quantities and in fairly simple mixtures.

In Table 6-2 we list some of the enzymes involved in human digestion. The usefulness of the list is that it provides a few concrete examples to give reality to the general principles of enzyme action and digestion. "Substrate" in the table simply means the substance digested with this particular enzyme as a catalyst.

Two solutions important in human digestion are *not* enzymes. First, the gastric juice

[3] See Chapter 5.

TABLE 6-2

Some digestive enzymes in man *

Substrate	Enzyme	Product	Place in alimentary canal
Starches	Amylase	Double sugars †	Enzymes from salivary glands, act from mouth to stomach
Proteins	Pepsin	Polypeptides †‡	Stomach
Starches and simpler carbohydrates	Amylase	Simple sugars	
Fats	Lipase	Fatty acids and glycerol	Enzymes from pancreas, act in small intestine
Proteins and polypeptides ‡	Trypsin	Amino acids	
Polypeptides ‡	Peptidases (a complex of enzymes)	Amino acids	
Double sugars	Disaccharases (a complex of enzymes)	Simple sugars	Small intestine

* See Fig. 6-1.

† Double sugars and polypeptides must be further digested before they can be absorbed. The other products shown are absorbed without further digestion.

‡ Polypeptides are combinations of amino acids simpler than proteins.

in the stomach is a rather strong solution of hydrochloric acid. Pepsin, the principal enzyme of the stomach, is not effective unless it is in acid solution. (Some other enzymes, such as trypsin, require an alkaline environment; acid from the stomach is neutralized by alkaline secretions when the food passes into the duodenum.) Second, bile from the liver is, in part, a solution of *bile salts.* These are poured into the small intestine, where they help to break up fats into small globules, forming an emulsion. This action does not change the fats chemically, but it puts them in a condition in which chemical reaction (catalyzed by lipase) occurs more readily.

Since the alimentary canal digests meat in the stomach and in the upper part of the small intestine (the duodenum) and is made of meat (of a sort), you may wonder why it does not digest itself. Obviously it must have a lining that is not normally susceptible to the action of the digestive juices, but just why it is not susceptible is far from clear. In fact the juices of the stomach and duodenum do sometimes digest parts of their walls: the result is an ulcer. That ulcers and, more commonly, indigestion may be brought on by worry and nervousness illustrates the great complexity of interactions in an integrated organism.

Enzymes like those in the human digestive system occur widely among other animals. Similar but not necessarily the same enzymes, catalyzing digestion of the same sorts of substrates, are usual in both plants and animals.

Some organic compounds widespread in nature are indigestible to most organisms. Probably the most striking example is the polysaccharide cellulose, a usual constituent of plant cell walls. Cellulose is entirely indigestible by man and most other animals, although some crabs, snails, and insects have an enzyme that hydrolyzes cellulose. In cows and termites, along with some other animals, cellulose is digested in a very interesting way: these animals cannot themselves digest it, but they have in their alimentary canals large numbers of bacteria or protists that can. The cow absorbs the sugars produced by the protists' digestion of the cellulose. Keratin, a protein in wool and other sorts of hair, is indigestible to practically all animals except the larva of the clothes moth. In that larva the keratin is first reduced and then hydrolyzed by a special enzyme—a neat trick, but one we humans cannot wholly admire.

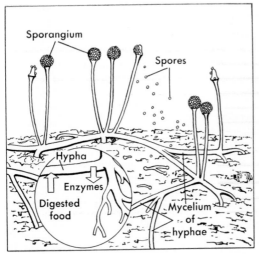

6-5 *Extracellular digestion by the bread mold (Rhizopus).* The body of the mold consists of a branching system (or mycelium) of threadlike structures called hyphae. Enzymes produced by the hyphal protoplasm are secreted to the outside, where they digest the complex carbohydrates in the bread. The sugars produced by this extracellular digestion are then absorbed by the hypha.

DIGESTIVE SYSTEMS

Since green plants do not ordinarily take in complex organic foods but make their own, they have no special system or organs for digestion.[4] Nevertheless, digestion does occur in green plants. It is necessary if food, manufactured or stored in one cell, is to be passed on to other cells. Digestion involved in this process may occur in any plant cell when food, enzymes, and other necessary conditions occur. Such digestion *within* cells, which is also common in animal cells, is called *intracellular digestion.*

In non-green plants obtaining food from outside the organism the situation is different. The actual reactions and processes of digestion are essentially the same, but the procedure is different. You are familiar with bread mold (Fig. 6-5), a common fungus growing on bread, cake, and other foods at room temperature. The food of this mold is in the bread or other material on which it grows. The organism cannot absorb the food until it is digested. Enzymes diffuse from the cells and catalyze digestion of starches and other foods

[4] Exceptions are the few insect-eating plants, mentioned above (pp. 119-20).

outside the organism, and the resulting compounds in solution diffuse into the cells. This is really the same way in which you and other animals digest solid food also: digestion is *extracellular* or outside the cells. Indeed, in all such instances, both in you and in bread mold, digestion occurs outside the organism altogether. (You recall that the inside of your stomach is *outside* you!) The only real difference is in the anatomical organs involved. In you, and the bread mold—and indeed practically all organisms—there is also intracellular digestion, involved in further movements and utilization of foods *after* they have been first absorbed into the organism.

Some protists have permanent mouths and a few have permanent anuses, but that is about as far as protists go with digestive systems. If solid food is taken in through the body membrane, temporary food vacuoles form. Most protists have no special digestive organs at all. Food manufactured in the cell or diffused in through the membrane is digested diffusely throughout the cytoplasm.

In the group of animals to which the corals and jellyfish belong, and also in the flatworms, there is a cavity surrounded by the body and freely open to the outside through a single opening (Fig. 6-6). Most of the food of these animals is first brought into this cavity, which is filled with the water in which the animals

---

6-6 **Digestive systems in animals.** *A.* Intracellular digestion in protists. *Trichonympha,* which inhabits the alimentary canal of termites, engulfs solid wood particles eaten by the termite. Digestion of the wood occurs in a food vacuole inside the cell. In *Paramecium* a food vacuole forms under pressure of the water driven down the gullet by the beating of cilia. Bacteria and other microorganisms are engulfed in the food vacuole, which moves along a fixed path through the cytoplasm. *B* and *C.* Digestion in *Hydra* (and other coelenterates as well as in flatworms) is partly extracellular and partly intracellular. The alimentary canal is a blind sac (one opening only) and lacks any specialization of parts. Partly digested (but still solid) food in the gut cavity is engulfed by cells into food vacuoles, as in protists. Digestion is completed as an intracellular process. *D.* Wholly extracellular digestion occurs in the earthworm (*Lumbricus*) and all higher animals. Here the alimentary canal has two openings, and food moves in one direction (mouth to anus). This permits specialization of the alimentary canal along its length.

DIGESTIVE SYSTEMS

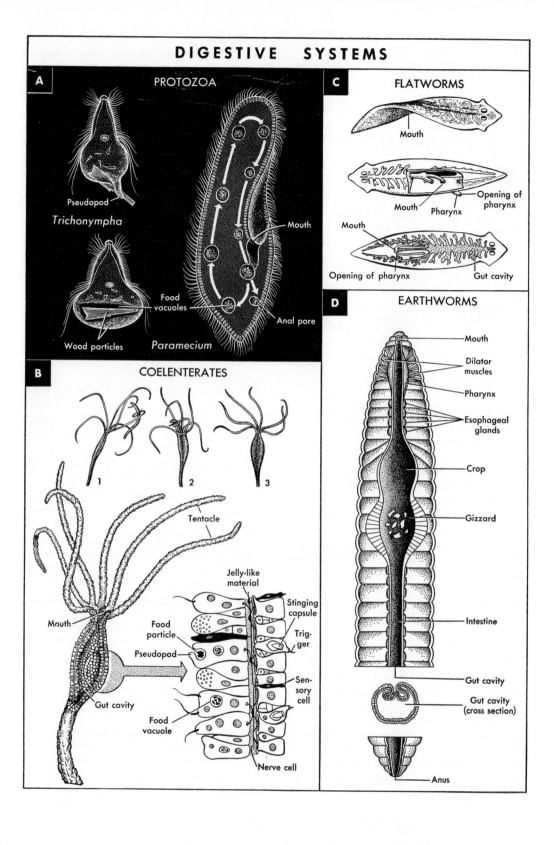

A PROTOZOA

Pseudopod

Trichonympha

Food vacuoles

Wood particles

Paramecium

Mouth

Anal pore

C FLATWORMS

Mouth

Mouth Pharynx

Opening of pharynx

Mouth

Opening of pharynx

Gut cavity

B COELENTERATES

1   2   3

Tentacle

Jelly-like material

Mouth

Stinging capsule

Trigger

Food particle

Pseudopod

Sensory cell

Gut cavity

Food vacuole

Nerve cell

D EARTHWORMS

Mouth

Dilator muscles

Pharynx

Esophageal glands

Crop

Gizzard

Intestine

Gut cavity

Gut cavity (cross section)

Anus

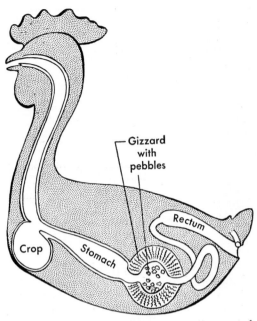

6-7 The gizzard in birds. Pebbles in the gizzard functionally replace teeth by grinding up food (cf. the earthworm, Fig. 6-6).

live but which also contains some enzymes secreted by the cells around it. Digestion begins here but in most of the animals it is not completed in the cavity. Usually small bits of food are taken bodily into the cells lining the cavity and are finally digested in food vacuoles in the cells, just as solid food is usually digested in protists. Thus digestion in these animals is interestingly intermediate between the food-vacuole system of protists and the alimentary-canal system of higher animals.

With innumerable modifications of form and of the organs into which it is subdivided, an alimentary canal occurs in practically all the animals above the lowly level of the coral or the flatworm. It is present and is even quite complex in the earthworm (Fig. 6-6), which is a much more advanced sort of animal than a flatworm and belongs to a different branch of evolution.

With such supplementary information as you now have about the processes of digestion (especially about enzymes, p. 122), the human digestive system (Fig. 6-1) will serve as an example of the system in a higher animal. Of course you understand that this

or any other example is not "typical." Every sort of animal has its own peculiarities of structure, enzymes, and so on, adapted to its particular way of life. Cows have an extraordinary series of stomachlike cavities and re-chew their food after digestion has started. (That is what they are doing when they chew their cuds.) Birds have no teeth and do not grind food in the mouth but do so in a specialized part of the alimentary canal called the gizzard (Fig. 6-7). Some insects do not swallow solid food but digest it in the mouth (or, more strictly, the pharynx), swallowing the solutions and spitting out the undigested parts. Many animals live on solutions such as nectar from flowers or blood from other animals, and their digestive systems and processes are correspondingly modified. In this, as in so many respects, the diversity of life seems almost endless. And yet, once more, there is basic unity in the principles involved.

ASSIMILATION

Digestion changes food into solutions which can enter cells and are actually incorporated into the body of the organism. Generally what happens next is some movement of these solutions from the region where they are formed or absorbed to other parts of the organism. How this movement occurs is a special topic for discussion in the next chapter (p. 141). Eventually the solutions containing digested food materials pass into tissues and usually into cells where they are stored temporarily or are more immediately utilized in metabolism. As you have already learned, storage usually involves resynthesizing insoluble foods, especially polysaccharides and fats. The stored foods are redigested and commonly redistributed and eventually enter into the same sorts of metabolic processes as the rest of the food materials.

Once in the cells, where they are utilized, the food solutions enter into all the reactions that occur in protoplasm. The foods usually arrive in relatively simple form, as the business of digestion is precisely putting them into simple forms: mainly simple sugars, fatty acids, glycerol, and amino acids. Some of these compounds may be utilized directly and in the same form, but usually the first thing that happens to them in the cell is a synthesis. They are used as materials for the far more complex compounds that make up much of protoplasm and that are involved in its reactions. We saw what some of these syntheses were in Chapter 5. Some material is incorporated into the actual structure of the cell, and some supplies energy for cell activities. We have also seen, however, that the distinction is not clear-cut. The cell-building materials are in a constant state of flux, perhaps as much so as the materials more largely utilized as energy sources, and the same materials may be used in both ways.

Cells form some compounds that are not useful within the cells themselves. Such compounds may be poured out from glands, as in the various digestive juices. They may be carried by the transportation system to other parts of the organism, where they influence other activities, as in the hormones. Or they may be final products of metabolism no longer useful anywhere in the organism. These processes of secretion and excretion are summarized at the end of the next chapter.

NUTRITION AND VITAMINS

The problem of nutrition is, on the face of it, a simple one. Adequate nutrition supplies the organism with all the materials it needs in order to synthesize the compounds that make up its structure and provide its energy. Some organisms, especially the green plants, can start their syntheses from simple inorganic compounds and elements. Others must start their syntheses with organic foods already of some complexity, such as sugars and amino acids. Man belongs to the latter class; he has low synthetic ability and requires a wide variety of elaborated foods. He thrives best on a diet containing, in addition to water and a considerable number of mineral salts, all three major classes of foods —carbohydrates, fats, and proteins—with some diversity in each class. Any digestible food of any of these chemical families can serve as an energy source. To this extent they are largely (although not entirely) interchangeable. They are not interchangeable as building materials or as sources for synthesis of enzymes and other compounds. For these needs, proteins (or a number of amino acids)

are absolutely indispensable. A man who ate enough carbohydrates to satisfy his hunger and supply all his energy needs would still be badly, and indeed fatally, undernourished if he ate nothing else.[5]

What you have already learned about the materials and processes of life would have led you to the foregoing inferences about human nutrition even if we had not expressed them. There is, however, another sort of nutritional need, only mentioned in passing hitherto: the requirements for *vitamins*. Advertisements and popular articles have made "vitamins" a household word, and you are sure to know something about them already. A brief review may clarify this knowledge, making it more precise.

Men who have an apparently sufficient diet of carbohydrates, fats, and proteins, with adequate material and energy (calorie) intake, may nevertheless develop serious deficiency diseases. A deficiency disease is one caused not by positive injury or attack of germs but by the lack of substances essential for normal metabolism. One of the earliest to be studied was scurvy, which causes bleeding gums, painfully swollen joints, and eventually death. It frequently appeared among sailors on long voyages in the days when fresh foods were not available on shipboard. Long before there was any real knowledge of the cause of the disease, it was discovered by trial and error that lime juice prevents scurvy.

Later experiments with animals and clinical investigations among humans revealed the cause not only of scurvy but also of a long list of other deficiency diseases. As you know, the cause is a lack of vitamins. Vitamins are *organic* compounds required in small amounts, essential to normal metabolism, but *not synthesized by the organism* and therefore necessarily present in the diet. This is not a very clear-cut definition. Vitamins do not belong to any particular family of chemicals. The same substance may be synthesized by one organism, for which it is therefore not a vitamin, and be required as a vitamin in the food of another. Some organic substances,

5 Incidentally, as a general rule foods rich in carbohydrates are cheap and those rich in fats and proteins are expensive. What social implications does this suggest? Is hunger the real problem of human nutrition?

such as particular fats or lipides, may be required in small amounts, and yet they are not usually *named* vitamins. But this is wholly a matter of convention because technically they are vitamins. Some other materials, such as iron and iodine salts, may also be required in small amounts and be similar to vitamins in the effects of deficiency, and yet they are not called "vitamins" because they are not organic compounds. Nevertheless, there is a definite list of chemical substances that are considered vitamins by general agreement. Some of the vitamins known to be required by man are listed in Table 6-3.

Although campaigns to sell patented vitamin mixtures give an opposite impression, the fact is that a varied diet such as is customary among all but the poorest Americans is more likely than not to supply all needed vitamins. This is especially true if the diet includes a considerable proportion of vegetables and fruit in addition to meat.

Heavy drinkers are likely to develop deficiency diseases, especially polyneuritis, from deficiency of thiamine. Alcohol supplies a large part of their energy requirements, and they tend to cut down on other foods on which the supply of vitamins depends.

A specific vitamin deficiency should be medically treated as such. Overdoses of vitamin D are definitely harmful, and the possibility of harm is not ruled out for overuse of some other vitamins.

Most vitamins can be synthesized by one plant or another, and therefore are not vitamins for these plants. The mere fact that plants do synthesize these compounds suggests that they are necessary in plant metabolism, but their roles are not always clear. Thiamine is utilized in growth of root tips. The roles of vitamins in animal metabolism are fairly well known. Requirements differ greatly in different groups.

The fact that vitamins are necessary, and yet that very small amounts suffice, strongly suggests that they help to form catalysts in the cells.[6] In general this does seem to be their method of action and the reason for need of them, but it is not the whole story. Vitamin A, for instance, combines with a

[6] Why do these facts suggest this inference?

TABLE 6-3

Some vitamins important in human nutrition

Vitamin	Some deficiency symptoms	Some sources
FAT SOLUBLE:		
A	Dry, scaly skin; night blindness	Milk, butter, liver oils, yellow and green vegetables *
D	Rickets (defective growth of bones and other hard tissues)	Milk, egg yolk, liver oils †
E	Degeneration of muscles (also sterility in rats and possibly in other organisms)	Green leafy vegetables, oils from seeds, egg yolk, meat
K	Delayed clotting of blood	Green leafy vegetables †
WATER SOLUBLE:		
Thiamine (B_1)	Beriberi, polyneuritis (inflammation and degeneration of nerves)	Yeast, whole-grain cereals, lean meat
Riboflavin (B_2, G)	Soreness around mouth, inflammation of eyes	Vegetables, yeast, milk, liver, eggs
B_{12}	Pernicious anemia	Liver
Ascorbic acid (C)	Scurvy	Citrus fruit, tomatoes, green peppers
Nicotinic acid or niacin	Pellagra (a disease affecting skin, alimentary canal, and nerves)	Yeast, meat

* Vitamin A is not required as such, since the human body can synthesize it from yellow pigments, carotenes, which are required if vitamin A itself is deficient.
† The human system can synthesize vitamins D and K, but the amount synthesized may be deficient.

protein to form an eye pigment involved in night vision, besides having other, possibly catalytic, activities elsewhere in the body.

Respiration

THE MEANING OF "RESPIRATION"

Nothing is more natural than breathing, and nothing is harder to do without. In the language of the physiologists, breathing in is *inspiration*, breathing out is *expiration*, and the whole process is *respiration*. Inspiration draws in oxygen, and expiration expels carbon dioxide. Oxygen is not used solely in the lungs, any more than food is used solely in the stomach and intestine. In both processes the organs named are involved in the intake of materials used throughout the whole body. The basic feature of respiration is therefore something that goes on not so much in the lungs as in cells and tissues through the whole organism.

It is unfortunate when the same word comes to be used in more than one way, and this has happened to the word "respiration": it means breathing in and out of the lungs, and it also means the consumption of oxygen and production of carbon dioxide by any metabolic process in an organism. Popular writers and a few biologists to the contrary notwithstanding, plants and a great many animals never breathe. Practically all organisms and separate cells within organisms do respire, in the broader sense of the word. In this book we shall apply the term "cellular respiration" to the processes in cells and tissues comparable with chemical oxidation.

CELLULAR RESPIRATION

Energy from solar radiation is bound into chemical compounds by photosynthesis. Among the first and simplest energy-rich compounds formed are simple sugars; the other, more complex, organic compounds also contain bound energy. Respiration, or oxidation-reduction, in cells includes the various processes by which this bound energy is released. We covered the fundamental chemical aspects of this respiratory energy release in Chapter 5. Here we must draw attention to variations on the basic pattern. One of these

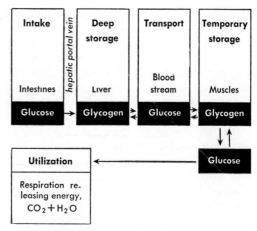

6-8 The absorption, transport, storage, and utilization of glucose.

variations—the cellular respiration of muscles —is related to transport problems arising from the rapid energy utilization and large size of some multicellular animals.

Carbohydrates enter the animal as glucose from the alimentary canal. Picked up in the blood, they are transported to the liver through a special short circuit in the blood system (the hepatic portal vein [see p. 150]). Glucose is converted in the liver into glycogen (animal starch), a polysaccharide suitable for deep storage. Carbohydrates are withdrawn from liver storage as glucose produced by digestion of glycogen. Glucose is transported all over the body in the blood stream; in muscles it is again converted to glycogen for temporary storage. Figure 6-8 summarizes these relations.

The respiratory breakdown of glycogen in muscle takes the usual pathway from glucose through a series of intermediates to pyruvic acid. This is the pathway outlined in Chapter 5 and diagramed in Fig. 5-9. In the presence of abundant oxygen it continues along the usual pathway, ending as CO_2 and H_2O. The energy is released as $\sim ⓟ$ and trapped immediately by ADP to form ATP. The ATP ultimately supplies the energy (again as $\sim ⓟ$) consumed in the contraction of muscle.

When a large animal, like man, performs very rapid movements, as in running, it consumes energy at a great rate. This implies that it demands a continuous supply of ATP, which it destroys at a great rate. In extreme exercise this rate of ATP consumption exceeds the rate at which it can be supplied by the normal *aerobic* (oxygen-consuming) *respiration* of glucose. The inadequacy of aerobic respiration is due to the relatively slow rate at which oxygen is transported from the lungs to the muscles through the circulation.

The oxygen supply does not, however, set an upper limit to the rate at which energy can be released in the muscle. In the last analysis this is because respiratory energy is released by removal of hydrogen, not by addition of oxygen. Oxygen, as we saw in Chapter 5, acts as a sponge to "clean up" the hydrogens stripped from sugar.

During violent muscular exercise the amount of hydrogen removed from sugar is too much to be removed by the inadequate oxygen supply. Instead, it is picked up by pyruvic acid itself, which is thereby transformed into lactic acid, which accumulates. So long as the demand for quickly supplied energy is maintained, lactic acid continues to accumulate. The muscle does its work on the ATP formed by the *partial, and anaerobic, respiration* of glycogen to lactic acid.[7]

The accumulation of lactic acid eventually fatigues the muscles, and the runner gets "cramps." When he stops he pants deeply for a long time until his system returns to normal. The rapid panting serves to bring in oxygen as rapidly as possible and pay off the *oxygen debt* he has accumulated. Actually the oxygen completes the final respiration of only a portion of the accumulated lactic acid. This is oxidized to CO_2 and H_2O, liberating, of course, some energy as ATP (energy 2 in Fig. 6-9). The energy released by this portion of lactic acid is utilized to resynthesize the remainder back into glycogen, ready again for heavy withdrawals.

One other aspect of energy release in muscle is noteworthy; like glycolysis itself, the other aspect relates to the very heavy demands that a muscle is likely to make at any moment. No cells carry a very large supply of ADP and ATP. *Quickly* withdrawable reserves of "ready-made" $\sim$(P) are stored by animals in compounds called phosphagens.

[7] This partial and anaerobic respiration of glycogen to lactic acid is called glycolysis.

In man and other vertebrates [8] the phosphagen is creatine phosphate. In Fig. 6-9 the creatine molecule is simply designated as C, creatine phosphate as $C\sim$(P). Of course, even when energy demands are low, muscle respiration (aerobic) nevertheless continues, and the $\sim$(P) radicals generated are passed, as usual, first to ADP to form ATP. As the ADP-ATP cycle becomes saturated (no more ADP), some ATP passes off $\sim$(P) to creatine, which *is* present in large amounts, for storage as $C\sim$(P). Later, when rapid exercise makes high demands for $\sim$(P), these are first paid from $C\sim$(P) reserves, but *through the agency of the ADP-ATP cycle*. All these relations are summarized in Fig. 6-9.

Anaerobic respiration also occurs in some plant cells, where it takes a slightly different course from that in animals: it proceeds to pyruvic acid, as in animals, but this compound, instead of becoming lactic acid, is transformed into ethyl alcohol and carbon dioxide. Anaerobic respiration in plants is, indeed, the process of *fermentation* which, carried out by yeast cells, supplies us with alcohol:

$$C_6H_{12}O_6 \xrightarrow{\text{enzymes}} 2C_2H_5OH + 2CO_2 + \text{Energy}$$
$$\text{Sugar} \qquad\qquad \text{Alcohol}$$

For comparison, we summarize the anaerobic respiration in muscle as follows:

$$C_6H_{12}O_6 \xrightarrow{\text{enzymes}} 2C_3H_6O_3 + \text{Energy}$$
$$\text{Sugar} \qquad\qquad \text{Lactic acid}$$

Although most organisms require aerobic respiration to complete the cycle, as we do, they can often get along on anaerobic respiration alone for shorter or longer periods. In us the period is very short, indeed, because our nervous system requires rapid aerobic respiration. If no oxygen is delivered to the brain, unconsciousness ensues in a few seconds. (Since this is true, how does it happen that you can hold your breath for two minutes or so without losing consciousness?) Some lower animals and plants can live by anaerobic respiration without oxygen for hours, days, or weeks, even though they do require

[8] See p. 558 for discussion of other phosphagens in animals and the evolutionary significance of their distribution in different animal groups.

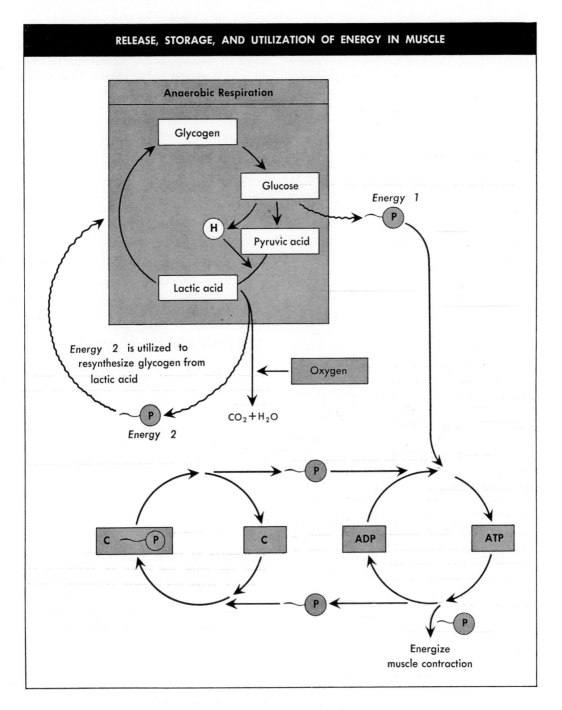

6-9 Intracellular respiration of muscle.

aerobic respiration eventually. Some organisms, too, are normally anaerobic throughout their lives. This fact has great importance for medicine and health, for these anaerobic organisms are mostly bacteria and intestinal parasites. The ability of tetanus germs to thrive in deep closed cuts and punctures, and of some worms to spend long periods in the intestines of men or other animals, is due to their anaerobic respiration.

Part of the energy released in cells by respiration appears as heat and is eventually lost. Even this energy cannot quite be said to be wasted. It helps to maintain body temperature in warm-blooded animals (birds and mammals), and even in other animals and in plants it influences the rates of other physiological processes. Much of the released energy is used in syntheses. The building up of complex from simpler compounds, for instance of proteins from amino acids, requires expenditure of energy, and the energy comes from respiration. This is the reason why all cells must respire. All need energy for building their own materials, even if the cell does not seem to be doing anything energetic. The released energy may also bring about physical changes in the protoplasm and in cell membranes. It may produce radiation and electrical phenomena. More familiarly, it may be expended as motion.

RESPIRATORY RATES

Even though anaerobic respiration also occurs, most plants and animals have respiratory cycles that are aerobic (oxygen-consuming) at one stage or another. This means that their oxygen consumption is at least roughly in proportion to their total energy consumption. This, in turn, is proportional to the total amount of activity, or work, of all sorts going on throughout the organism as a whole. Thus oxygen consumption is a valuable and interesting measure of organic activity. The amount of oxygen consumed per hour or day and in proportion to the weight of the organism is the respiratory rate.[9]

Many measurements of respiratory rates in plants and animals have been made, and some of the results are surprising. The rate in a man at rest is comparable to that in a carrot. It is much lower than in bacteria, some of which have far the highest rates known. Protists also tend to have high rates, but rates are generally low in the lower multicellular animals. Cold-blooded animals often have rates about as high as in man and other warm-blooded animals. Warm-bloodedness is not a matter of greater heat production but of more even production and better maintenance of heat level.

It is not surprising to find that respiratory rate increases greatly with muscular activity in animals. A butterfly's respiratory rate was found to be more than 150 times as high while flying as while resting. The rate in a mouse was eight times as high while running as while resting. In man, other mammals, and many other animals, the rate tends to be higher in small than in large individuals. The rate is usually higher in young than in old animals and also higher in males than in females. It will be no news to parents that a small, active boy is spending energy at a rate that is tops for mankind.

In plants most of the useful energy is expended in chemical synthesis and other metabolic activities. These activities tend to vary with the temperature (see p. 88) and with light, water supply, and other changing environmental conditions. Green plants produce oxygen in the course of photosynthesis and also use it in respiration. Conversely, they use carbon dioxide in photosynthesis and produce it in respiration. These relationships involve an interesting balance. When photosynthesis is most active, more food is being made and more oxygen produced than are used in respiration. As photosynthesis decreases, which it does as the light grows dimmer, a *compensation point* is reached where the two processes balance. Below that point respiration takes the lead: more food and oxygen are consumed than are produced and more carbon dioxide is produced than is

9 This is the principle of the basal metabolism test so commonly used by physicians for diagnostic purposes. The basal metabolic rate, or B.M.R., is usually expressed in terms of heat production per unit of body surface area per day. What is actually measured is oxygen consumption, and heat production is calculated from this. The surface area likewise is not actually measured but is calculated on the basis of height, weight, age, and sex.

used. What would happen to a plant if it were kept continuously at the compensation point?

RESPIRATORY SYSTEMS

As was seen to be true of digestion, respiration usually involves no special organs in protists or in aquatic plants and many small and relatively simple aquatic animals. The required oxygen simply diffuses from solution in the surrounding water into the organism through cell membranes. Carbon dioxide similarly diffuses out from the cell into the water of the environment. In land plants a similar process of diffusion occurs between cells and the surrounding air. Many of these forms also develop air-filled spaces among internal cells, and these spaces often have special openings—stomates—which open and close through the mechanism of guard cells. You have met this arrangement before (p. 86). More complex anatomical arrangements for O_2—CO_2 exchange do not occur among plants.

In higher animals, on the other hand, elaborate anatomical organs and systems have evolved (Fig. 6-10). Animals living in water or in a moist environment often do receive much of their oxygen by simple diffusion through the cells of the skin. This is still true in the frog, for instance, even though it has gills as a tadpole and lungs as an adult. Worms may have such diffusion not only through the outer skin but also through cells lining the gut. Some worms have an en-

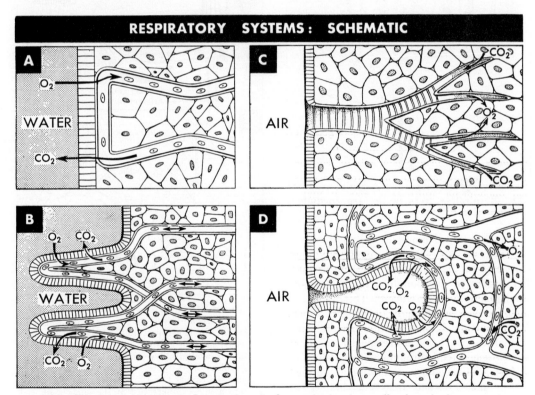

RESPIRATORY SYSTEMS: SCHEMATIC

6-10 Respiratory systems. In aquatic animals, respiration is usually through the external body surface, either (*A*) generally, or (*B*) in localized areas where the surface for O_2-CO_2 exchange is greatly increased by the development of gills. In land animals the respiration surfaces are internal because they must be kept moist. The two commonest systems are tracheae (*C*) and lungs (*D*). Tracheae (in insects and some other arthropods) are tubular ducts through which air passes directly to and from tissue cells. The fine ultimate branches (tracheoles) are filled with water and supply individual cells. Lungs are internal cavities whose moist surfaces are richly supplied with blood vessels that transport O_2 and CO_2 to and from tissue cells. Animals like the earthworm, which respire all over their body surface, are not fully terrestrial; they are restricted to moist soil. Why?

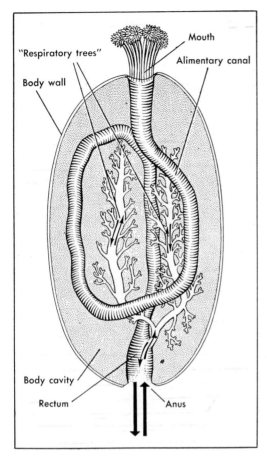

6-11 Respiratory trees in the sea cucumber, a starfish relative.

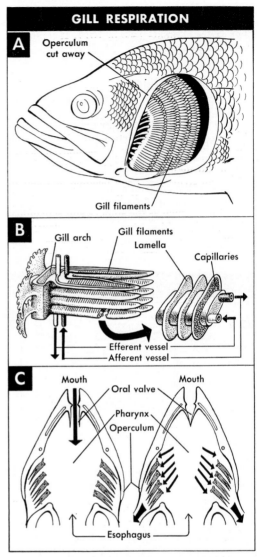

A Operculum cut away

Gill filaments

B Gill arch Gill filaments Lamella Capillaries

Efferent vessel
Afferent vessel

C Mouth Oral valve Mouth

Pharynx
Operculum

Esophagus

larged, thin-walled hind-gut and rhythmically take in and expel water through the anus. This part of the gut is thus a true respiratory organ, in addition to serving its more usual function. In sea cucumbers (Fig. 6-11) this type of respiration is further developed. Water, pumped in and out through the anus, circulates through much-branched *respiratory trees* which extend throughout the body.

Most relatively large and complex animals require more oxygen than can be readily taken in by diffusion through the unmodified body surface. Moreover, in many of these forms, both aquatic and terrestrial, there is

6-12 Gill respiration in fishes. The principal structural feature of gills is the way they are organized to offer as great a surface as possible to the water flowing over them; the greater their surface,

the greater is their capacity to pick up oxygen and give up carbon dioxide to the external water. In *A* the gill cover, or operculum, of the fish has been cut away, and four gills can be seen. Each gill carries a double row of gill filaments. Each gill filament (*B*) is organized as a series of lamellae. An afferent blood vessel carries blood to the gills; there it breaks up into a fine capillary bed at the surface of each lamella. Here gaseous exchange occurs. An efferent vessel carries the oxygenated blood away from the gills to the rest of the body. *C* shows the path of the water that carries oxygen into the gills. It enters through the mouth into the pharynx. As it is compressed by contraction of the pharynx, it is prevented from escaping through the mouth by the closure of oral valves. The water is thus forced through slits between the gills, finally leaving under the operculum.

a protective skin through which diffusion is slight or absent, a necessity for regulation of their water contents (see p. 761). It is among such animals that the most specialized respiratory organs have evolved. In aquatic forms these are usually *gills,* which have arisen independently in various groups and are highly diverse. Most of them have in common a filamentous or platelike structure, which crowds a large surface area into a small bulk, and some means of circulating water past or through the gills (Fig. 6-12).

Gill-like structures have become adapted to O_2—CO_2 exchange with the air in some land-living forms, such as the spiders and scorpions. Other air-breathing forms have developed lunglike pouches, as in certain snails. True *lungs,* like yours (Fig. 6-13), occur in some fishes, most amphibians, and all reptiles, birds, and mammals. A different and unique system for air breathing has evolved in the insects. In them there is a system of tubes, the *tracheae* (Fig. 6-14), with paired openings, *spiracles,* through the body wall. The tracheae branch repeatedly, and their smallest terminal extensions deliver air to the cells throughout the body. In many insects rhythmic movements of the abdomen and synchronized opening and closing of the spiracles produce a definite circulation of air through the tracheal system.

In animals with gills or lungs these organs facilitate O_2—CO_2 exchange between the blood and the external water or air. It is the blood that exchanges O_2 and CO_2 directly with the cells in which respiration occurs. In the in-

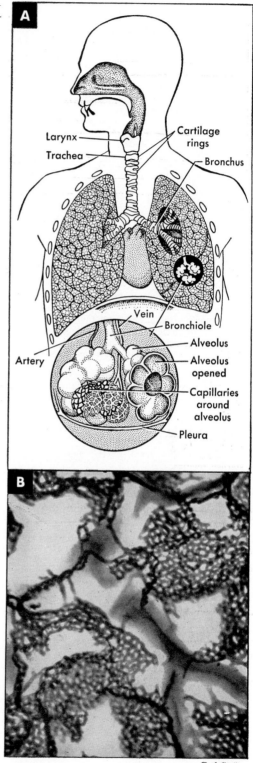

6-13 Lung respiration in man. *A.* Air, drawn in through mouth or nose, reaches the lungs through the trachea and its branches, the bronchi and bronchioles. The cartilaginous rings around the trachea give it sufficient rigidity to prevent its collapse, and thus guarantee a continuously open air passage to the lungs. The bronchioles lead into small cavities, alveoli, which are richly supplied with blood capillaries (p. 146). Gaseous exchange occurs in the alveoli. The increased internal surface of the lung achieved by its organization into alveoli may be compared with the increase in external surface of the gill achieved by its arrangement into filaments and lamellae (Fig. 6-12). What is the significance in both cases? All the alveoli in the lung are bound tightly together by a surrounding epithelium, the pleura. *B.* Photograph of the capillaries around the alveoli ($\times 250$).

Carl Strüwe

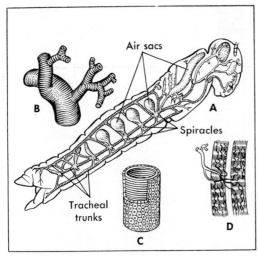

6-14 Tracheal respiration in the grasshopper. *A*. The distribution of spiracles, main tracheal trunks, and air sacs on one side of the insect. The air sacs are reservoirs. *B*. Portion of a main tracheal trunk and its branches. *C*. Portion of tracheal tube, showing its single layer of cells and the internal support of chitin (a protein substance) they secrete (cf. cartilage rings on the human trachea, Fig. 6-13). *D*. Ultimate tracheal branches supplying muscles.

sects, however, the body fluids are not involved in respiration (with unimportant exceptions), and O_2—CO_2 exchange is directly between air in the tracheae and the cells of the body (Fig. 6-14).

Chapter Summary

Effects of large size on multicellular organisms.

Modes of food intake.

Its acquisition in solid form by animals; its acquisition by diffusion in protists and plants.

Digestion, as the converse of synthesis: extracellular and intracellular digestion; the necessity of intracellular digestion for the movement of materials across cell membranes; digestive enzymes; digestive systems.

Assimilation, the incorporation of digested food into the organic system.

Nutrition and vitamins.

The two meanings of the term "respiration":

  (1) Gas exchange, as in breathing.

  (2) Intracellular processes of oxidation that liberate energy.

Cellular respiration: aerobic and anaerobic respiration, the former limited by the rate at which oxygen can be supplied; the anaerobic respiration of muscle; oxygen debt; energy reserves in the form of phosphagens.

Respiratory rates.

Respiratory systems: their diversity of form related to the peculiarities of the environment.

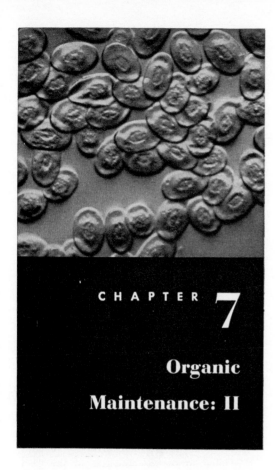

CHAPTER 7

Organic Maintenance: II

Transportation and Circulation

An organism may be as small as a bacterium or as large as a whale or a sequoia. Whatever its size and structure may be, substances have to move about in it. Each cell requires material from outside, and these materials must move to where they are needed within the cell. The cells have waste materials that must move out. In a multicellular organism substances formed in one cell are required by other cells. Products of digestion have to be distributed through the body. In aerobic respiration O_2 must be delivered and CO_2 removed. Transportation within organisms is just as important for their maintenance as is any other process we have discussed. The mechanisms of internal transportation—widely different in protists, plants, and higher animals—occupy us through most of this chapter.

TRANSPORT IN PROTISTS AND PLANTS

In protists and within single cells the movement of materials is largely by diffusion, atom by atom and molecule by molecule. In many of these organisms there is also some movement of the cytoplasm which helps to distribute materials around the cell. In the plants that have no transport vessels and that are called *nonvascular* [1] on this account, movement of materials is also almost entirely by diffusion and cytoplasmic motion. There is some specialization of roles among the cells of such plants—particularly for reproduction—but the majority of cells may still be relatively independent, making their foods with materials diffused directly from the environment. Such transportation of materials as must occur between one cell and another is across the cell walls and membranes or along cytoplasmic threads joining the cells, and not in distinct transport vessels. With more differentiation of parts and processes, however, and with development of organisms more complex and more fully integrated, more effective methods of transportation are necessary and have evolved.[2]

[1] Few biological generalizations are without exception. The so-called nonvascular plants are, as a group, relatively small and characteristically lack special transport vessels. A few of them—seaweeds—have attained considerable size and have developed phloem tissue comparable with that characteristic of the "true" vascular plants (ferns and seed plants).

[2] They did not evolve **because** they are necessary; the point is that if they had not happened

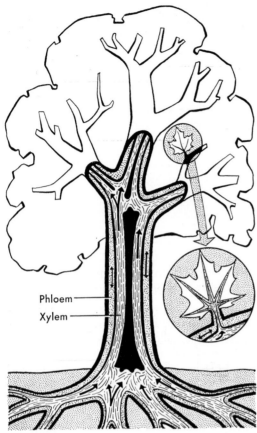

Phloem
Xylem

7-1 Direction of transport in the xylem and phloem of a tree.

The more advanced systems of transportation all involve the movement of fluids *outside* the living [3] cells but *inside* the organism. In plants this fluid is sap. In animals it is often blood, although other animal fluids are involved in internal transportation. Such fluids necessarily are contained in and move through otherwise open spaces within the organism. Frequently the spaces develop as long tubes, *vessels*, in which there is a definite and directional flow of fluid.

The vessels of the vascular plants are of two sorts, *xylem* and *phloem*; they occur in bundles in roots, stems, and leaves. You have

to evolve no such complex organisms would exist.

[3] It is debatable whether the phloem cells are dead. They are without nuclei but do contain cytoplasm, whose "life"—if it can be said to exist—may be rendered possible by the nuclei of the "companion cells" that are always immediately adjacent to each phloem cell. (See Fig. 3-18.)

already seen examples of them (p. 61), and you know that flow in the xylem is mainly upward from roots to stem and leaves, whereas products from leaves and other organs move both upward and downward through the phloem (Fig. 7-1). An enormous amount of water enters the roots of a plant, moves through the vessels, and eventually leaves the plant by evaporation. Of the 2000 tons of water absorbed by corn roots during one growing season on one acre in Illinois, all but 5 tons were lost by evaporation, or *transpiration*, as this sort of water loss by plants is technically called.

We speak of transpired water as lost, and you may be inclined to think of it as wasted.

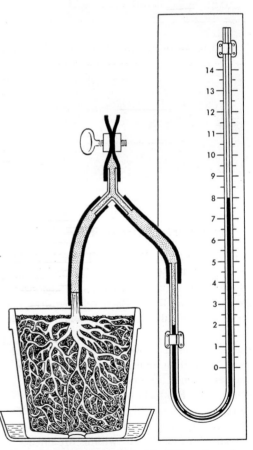

14
13
12
11
10
9
8
7
6
5
4
3
2
1
0

7-2 Root pressure. Sap forced up the xylem by root pressure (osmotic pump) exudes from the cut stem into the closed rubber tube and forces the mercury up the open arm of the manometer. This device permits quantitative determination of the force of root pressure.

But is it really lost? Where did it go? And where, before the plants got it, did it come from? Aside from that point, further study shows that the "loss" is essential to the life of the plant, and that transpired water may be as necessary and useful as water retained in the plant's cells. Plants have no hearts or other organs for pumping sap. Yet sap does rise in them, sometimes to an elevation of hundreds of feet in a tall tree. If you have ever operated a hand pump, you know that raising water is hard work. There has to be some sort of mechanism for raising sap, and energy is lavishly expended in the process. Transpiration is one part of the mechanism involved, and much of the energy comes from it. The other contribution comes from the *root pressure* described earlier (Chapter 6, p. 121).

The pressure developed by the gradient of osmotic pressures across the root and into the xylem serves to drive the water up the xylem for a considerable height. The power of this pressure is easily demonstrated in a laboratory experiment like that shown in Fig. 7-2. The effect of root pressure is also readily observed on the cut surface of a plant stem whose roots remain in the soil; sap continues to be forced up by the osmotic pumps in the roots.

It is very doubtful, however, if this root pressure can account entirely for the movement of water up to the top of very high trees. And it is here that we perceive the transportation of water to be not a "loss," but a functionally valuable process. Visualize columns of water extending through the xylem from roots to leaves. Now water has a high degree of *cohesion*; adjacent molecules tend to stick together and strongly resist separation. In the leaves especially, water molecules diffuse outward from the cells and evaporate into the air. As they go, other molecules move in behind them and exert a pull which affects

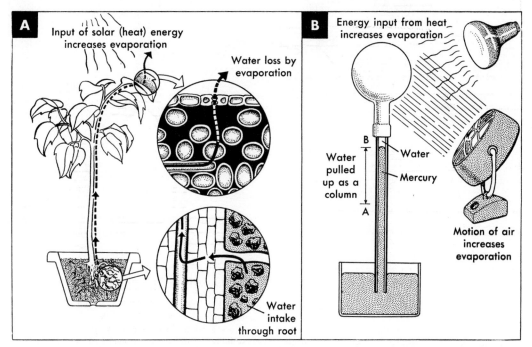

7-3 Transpiration pull. *A.* An unbroken column of water extends from the soil through root hair and root cortex (cf. Fig. 6-4) into the xylem and thence to leaves and leaf surfaces. The water column is maintained in upward movement because its apex is drawn off as transpired water vapor. *B.* The efficiency of evaporation in raising a continuous water column can be demonstrated experimentally by using a porous bulb at the head of a water and mercury column. As heat and wind from the lamp and fan increase evaporation from the bulb, the upward movement of the liquid column can be watched.

the whole column of water. This _transpiration pull_ is a principal factor in the supply of sap to the upper parts of vascular plants (Fig. 7-3). The energy expended comes mainly from the heat necessary to produce evaporation; anyone who has ever put a pan of water on a stove knows that heat energy speeds up evaporation. The heat comes directly or indirectly from the sun, and so in this process, as in photosynthesis, plants use solar energy. The total upward movement is

effected by the combined power of a solar engine and an osmotic pump.[4]

Most of the liquid in plants moves in one direction only, from soil into roots, up through the vessels, and out into the air through the

[4] The relative importance of the solar engine (transpiration pull) and osmotic pump (root pressure) is an unsettled and debated issue among plant physiologists. It should be added that, although transpiration is generally necessary to land plants, its results can be catastrophic if the lost water cannot be replaced from the soil.

ANIMAL SIZE AND THE PROBLEM OF INTERNAL TRANSPORT

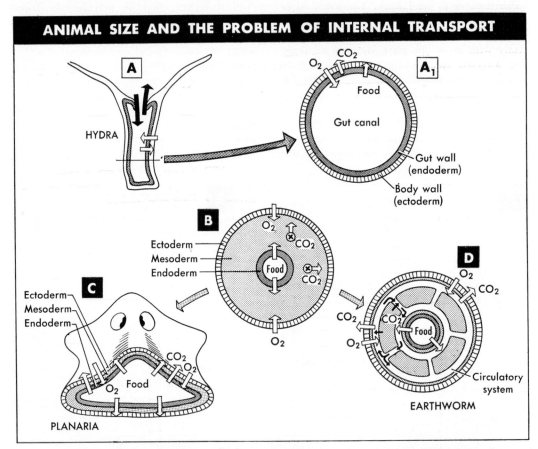

7-4 The significance of fluid transport (circulatory) systems in multicellular animals. _A_. In coelenterates, like _Hydra_, the body wall is essentially only two cells thick. Water circulates in and out of the body cavity, as indicated by the solid black arrows. Diffusion is sufficient for the transport of food substances, O_2, and CO_2 to and from all cells (white arrows). A_1. Cross section through the body wall of a coelenterate. _B_. Cross section through a hypothetical animal with extensive mesoderm tissues between the gut and body wall. The cells (marked X) in the middle of these tissues are too far removed from the gut and from the outside to rely on diffusion for transport of their food, O_2, and CO_2. _C_. The flatworms have solved this problem by evolving a flattened shape: no cell is a greater distance from the gut or body wall than can be maintained efficiently by diffusion. _D_. All animals higher than flatworms have evolved a more useful solution to the problem: a circulatory system which overcomes the limitations imposed by diffusion transport and permits animals to evolve to relatively enormous sizes. Food, O_2, and CO_2 are transported by the circulating blood over far greater distances than diffusion could cover.

7-5 Circulatory systems. *A.* A squid: a *closed* circulatory system with three hearts. *B.* An earthworm: a *closed* circulatory system with 10 hearts. *C.* A snail: a single heart drives blood through the *open* circulatory system. Blood from the heart reaches the muscular foot via a distinct artery; in the foot the blood enters an *open sinus*, from which it then drains once again into a distinct vessel (the circular vein) in the surface of the lung. Capillaries connect this vessel to other veins that return the blood to the heart.

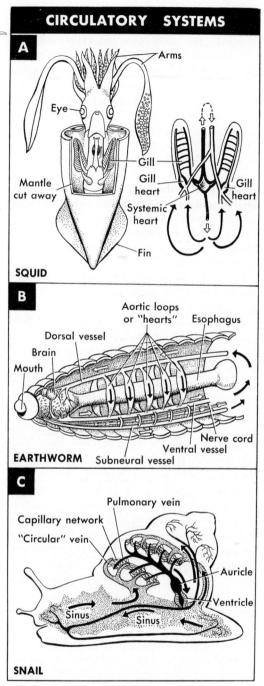

CIRCULATORY SYSTEMS

A

Arms

Eye

Gill

Gill heart

Gill heart

Mantle cut away

Systemic heart

Fin

SQUID

B

Aortic loops or "hearts"

Esophagus

Dorsal vessel

Brain

Mouth

Nerve cord

Ventral vessel

EARTHWORM Subneural vessel

C

Pulmonary vein

Capillary network

"Circular" vein

Auricle

Ventricle

Sinus

Sinus

SNAIL

leaves and other surfaces. Solutions do also move in the opposite direction (in the phloem), but in smaller amounts and generally with less regularity. There is no regular, directed *circular* movement of liquids, and to this extent plants do not have circulation or circulatory systems.

TRANSPORT IN ANIMALS

The simpler multicellular animals—sponges, corals, jellyfish, and their relatives—resemble the nonvascular plants in the absence of vessels or other special anatomical arrangements for movement of internal fluids (Fig. 7-4). They do, however, have passages or cavities in which there is movement of *external* fluids —the sea or fresh water of their environment.

There is one group of animals whose whole form dramatically emphasizes the profound importance of a vascular system to a multicellular organism. This is the group of flatworms (Fig. 7-4). The point of interest about these worms is their very flatness itself, and its relation to the absence of a vascular system. Their innermost cells can only obtain oxygen from outside, and get rid of carbon dioxide, fast enough if the cells are kept close to the epithelium. This end is accomplished by the flattening of the whole animal; like a pancake, nothing in the inside is far from the outside. Again, a problem arises in nourishing the whole cell mass in the absence of a circulation system to distribute food from the gut. This is offset by a branching of the gut so elaborate that no internal cell is far from part of it. Looking at a flatworm, one cannot help thinking, "If only it had a blood system, how different its life would have been."

Most other multicellular animals do have *internal* spaces or cavities between the outer body wall and the alimentary canal, and some of these spaces are devoted to transportation processes. Internal-transportation cavities usually take the form of definite vessels through which body fluids move. Local regions of these vessels are enlarged and have strongly muscular walls that contract rhythmically.

The contractions force fluid through the vessels, and a system of valves keeps the motion always in the same direction. These organs may properly be called *hearts* in all animals, although they have evolved independently in different groups and differ markedly in number, arrangement, and structure. Common earthworms, for instance, have ten hearts, arranged in pairs around a forward part of the alimentary canal and pumping blood from an upper (dorsal) to a lower (ventral) longitudinal vessel. A squid has one heart that pumps blood to the body as a whole, and two separate gill hearts that pump blood through the gills, from which it passes through vessels to the body heart. These are just two examples of the many arrangements of hearts in animals (Fig. 7-5).

In most animals one or more hearts constantly pump blood in the same direction, and there is no steady loss of body fluid analogous to transpiration in plants.[5] It follows that the blood must eventually return to the heart; it must somehow make a circuit of the body. There is, in short, true *circulation*. In some animals, including some worms and many mollusks (snails, clams, and their relatives) and insects, vessels from the heart pour blood into irregular spaces or channels, *sinuses*,[6] among the tissues. Here the blood moves rather sluggishly, exchanging materials with the cells in the various tissues and eventually seeping back into collecting vessels that return it to the heart. This is an *open circulatory system*, because the blood is not retained in distinct vessels through the *whole* circuit. In most worms, all vertebrates (fishes, amphibians, reptiles, birds, and mammals), and a few other animals the circulatory system is closed. The blood does not normally leave the vessels. Its exchanges with cells are accomplished in networks of very tiny, thin-walled vessels called *capillaries*.

Even in animals with closed circulation there are in addition sinuses and other internal spaces among the cells and tissues, and these spaces are normally filled with fluids. Thus two (or more) body fluids—*blood* and *lymph*—freely exchange many substances although separately contained in vessels or spaces. In the most complex sorts of animal transportation systems, there are two separate systems of vessels, one transporting blood and the other transporting lymph. There may even be a separate heart for the lymphatic system, as in the frog. Man has no lymph heart, but his circulatory system is otherwise one of the most complex. We will discuss something of the mechanism of man's circulation in a moment, but first it is advisable to learn a little more about blood, the fluid that is the main means of transportation in our bodies.

COMPOSITION OF THE BLOOD: PLASMA

If you look at blood under a microscope, you will see several sorts of cell-like objects floating in a colorless fluid. There is some technical question whether all the cell-like bodies are, in fact, cells. They are collectively referred to by the evasive term *formed elements*. The clear liquid is *plasma* and is a solution, partly colloidal, of an extraordinarily large number of different substances. Some of the formed elements and some of the substances dissolved in plasma are related to the maintenance of the blood itself, and to activities in it or involving it. Others are more strictly involved in transportation, which is the main but by no means the only function of the blood. Blood donation and the use of serum and other blood derivatives in transfusions are becoming so familiar that it is of interest to know the following relationships:

Whole blood = formed elements plus plasma (including fibrinogen and other clotting agents)

Plasma = whole blood minus formed elements

Serum = plasma minus fibrinogen and other clotting agents

Defibrinated blood = whole blood minus fibrinogen and other clotting agents
= serum plus formed elements

---

[5] There is a continuous water loss from our lungs—our breath is moist—but this makes no contribution to important movement of body fluids. Nor does the more occasional or sporadic loss of water in perspiration effect any significant internal movement of body water.

[6] "Sinus" is another word applied in a somewhat confused way to different things. The internal sinuses to which we are now referring have nothing to do with the nasal or frontal sinuses that may, if you are unfortunate, cause you headaches and other discomforts. The latter sinuses are not, strictly speaking, internal. They normally open to the outside and do not contain lymph.

Except for the respiratory gases, <u>most transportation takes place in the plasma</u>, which we examine first. The distinction between material in transport and substances involved in properties and processes of the plasma itself is far from absolute. The presence of dissolved materials in transport of course does affect the properties of the solution. Also, the same substances may play roles both in the plasma and in cells and tissues to which they are transported. Nevertheless, we can make a sort of rough division. First of all, we note that <u>virtually every substance used by cells is found dissolved in plasma at one time or another.</u> With a very few exceptions, every substance secreted or discarded by cells is also present in plasma. Of course we are not going to try to list all these substances, but some of the more important general sorts are given in Table 7-1. These substances are all dissolved

TABLE 7-1

Some materials in the plasma of human blood

MATERIALS IN TRANSPORT:

Name	*From*	*To*	*Significance*
Sugars (mostly glucose)	Intestine, liver	Whole body	Food to cells, especially energy source. Also transported to liver for storage.
Lipides, including fats and related compounds	Intestine, storage deposits in body	Whole body	Food to cells, energy source, also includes cholesterol (essential to nerve cells) and other special compounds. Fats are also transported *to* storage deposits.
Amino acids	Intestine	Whole body	Food, material for synthesis of proteins.
Inorganic salts	Intestine, storage, many tissues	Whole body	Essential in building protoplasm, enzymes, and other compounds, hard tissues such as bones, teeth.
Hormones	Endocrine glands	Whole body or specially affected tissues	Regulate and co-ordinate organic activity (see Chapter 8).
Urea, some other nitrogen compounds, and some other acids and salts	Whole body	Kidneys	Waste products being removed.
Gases:			
Oxygen	(Mainly in red cells rather than plasma [see p. 145])		
Nitrogen	Lungs	Lungs	Inert. Taken in and given out incidentally in gas exchange in lungs.
Carbon dioxide	Whole body	Lungs	Waste product being removed.

MATERIALS ACTIVE IN PLASMA:

Name	*From*	*Activity*	
Blood proteins:			
Fibrinogen	Liver	Clotting of blood.	
Others	Liver, or doubtful	Metabolism, viscosity, and osmotic pressure of blood; also, indirectly, CO_2 transport.	
Antibodies	Unknown	Act against bacteria, toxins, foreign proteins.	
Inorganic salts	Intestine, storage, other tissues	Maintain osmotic level, degree of acidity, internal environment favorable for cells. Calcium necessary for clotting of blood.	

or suspended in water, which makes up about 90 per cent of the plasma.

Plasma (minus its large proteins, which cannot pass through the capillary walls) is in contact with most of the cells inside the body. It is, in effect, the environment in which the internal cells live. It is an environment that provides all necessary materials—this is the function of transportation—and also one that maintains the chemical and physical conditions most favorable for the cells. This maintenance depends not only on the inorganic salts (as noted in the table) but also on the amount of blood sugar—indeed on the whole complex of dissolved materials as well as rate of flow and temperature.

Plasma and the blood as a whole are highly fluid and are being pumped around under pressure in a closed system of vessels. Even a small opening in this system as a result of injury or disease would lead to loss of most of the blood and rapid death if it were not for a defensive activity of plasma, clotting. The reactions involved are complex, but in summary what happens is about as follows. When an injury occurs, the injured cells and some of the formed elements in the blood release substances that react intricately, producing a compound called thrombin. Thrombin in turn reacts with fibrinogen, a protein dissolved in the plasma, which becomes fibrin. Fibrin comes out of solution as a tangled network of fibers, which shrink and form a hard clot that plugs the opening in the circulatory system. It is only because of this reaction that we do not bleed to death when we cut a finger or brush our gums too vigorously. There are a few unfortunate people, "bleeders," whose blood does not clot readily and who are in danger of death from the slightest injury. This condition, known as hemophilia, is hereditary and has become famous because of its prevalence among the male descendants of Queen Victoria.

There are some especially thought-provoking points about the clotting reactions, a couple of which can be mentioned, although we cannot pursue them far. Clotting depends on the fact that proteins can be coagulated. In most proteins, including some closely related to fibrinogen, this property is not useful and may be harmful in unusual circumstances. Would you say that the existence of this property in proteins as a whole and its usefulness in this specific protein (fibrinogen) under special conditions (injury to the vascular system) were providential? Or would you conclude that evolution had somehow worked with what happened to be at hand? Then consider the indirect way in which the reaction is produced. In fact, a bungling sort of improvization is almost a general characteristic of organic reactions. How does this bear on the two questions we have just asked? Note that the reaction has some very serious dangers, too, and often leads to accidents with which the organism cannot cope. A clot may form right across a vessel and cut off the blood supply of a vital organ; when it remains in place it is called a thrombus. Or a clot fragment (embolus) may break loose into the blood stream and finally lodge in a vessel essential for life. Both conditions are serious, and are known as thrombosis and embolism, respectively. Most of us have known people who have suffered one of these accidents and have died or become invalids as a result.

THE FORMED ELEMENTS OF THE BLOOD

The formed elements (Fig. 7-6) include red blood cells (technically called erythrocytes), white blood cells (leucocytes), and platelets (thrombocytes). Of these, only the red blood cells are involved in transportation. The white blood cells, of which five different kinds are commonly distinguished, are active mainly in combating bacterial infections. The platelets break down in the vicinity of an injury and liberate enzymes involved in turning fibrinogen to fibrin; they are thus part of the clotting mechanism.

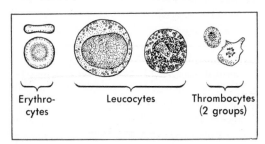

7.6 The formed elements of the blood.

In mammals (man included) the mature red blood cells have no nuclei and therefore are not organized like normal cells. For one thing, they cannot divide or reproduce. Young red cells, which do have nuclei and do reproduce, are not present in circulating blood. They form in connective tissue in the marrow of bones. As they lose their nuclei and mature, they pass into the main blood stream, where they live and function for ten to a hundred days. Eventually they are literally eaten and digested by cells in the spleen and liver. The numbers of red cells involved in this ceaseless activity are almost incredible. In an average adult there are about 25 million million—25,000,000,000,000—mature red cells at any one time. Every *second* about 10 million new cells pass from the marrow into the blood stream and about 10 million old cells are devoured in liver and spleen! If the replenishment is inadequate, anemia ensues. (Anemia may also result from a deficiency of hemoglobin in the red cells even when their number is near normal.)

The red substance in a red blood cell is *hemoglobin*, which we have mentioned before as being a conjugated protein, globin with heme as a prosthetic group (see p. 78). This compound has the all-important characteristic of combining *loosely* and *reversibly* with oxygen. When it is in an oxygen-rich environment, as in the capillaries of the lungs, it combines with oxygen. In an oxygen-poor environment, as in capillaries among cells in need of oxygen, it gives up the oxygen again. This is the mechanism of oxygen transfer from lungs to cells. Incidentally, hemoglobin is somewhat lighter and brighter in color when combined with oxygen. That is why the blood in arteries, on its way to the tissues, is bright red, and the blood in veins, returning from the tissues, is "blue" (actually a darker and more purplish red).

Hemoglobin has another property, and this one happens to be dangerous in our civilization. Hemoglobin combines with carbon monoxide, CO, even more readily than with oxygen, and is then incapable of picking up oxygen. Carbon monoxide is produced in large quantities in gasoline motors, and in fumes from gas ranges and heaters or charcoal grills. Carbon monoxide poisoning, quickly fatal, is a suffocation of the cells of the body because of loss of capacity of the red blood cells to carry oxygen.

Some carbon dioxide, CO_2, is transported in the plasma, as we have already noted, but the greater part is carried in the red cells (erythrocytes). About a fifth of the total CO_2 combines chemically with amino acids in the hemoglobin, but much more is carried within red cells as carbonic acid formed from CO_2 and water by a specific enzyme in the erythrocytes. The resulting acidity in the cell, which would rapidly become harmful if not counteracted, is reduced by a reversible combination between the protein in hemoglobin and hydrogen from the acid. On a lesser scale, the same sort of reaction occurs with some of the proteins in the plasma.

The white blood cells have nuclei and live in the blood almost as if they were separate, parasitic protists. In fact, some of them look and act very much like an ameba, which is an independent protist and sometimes a very harmful parasite. The white cells, however, are far from harmful under usual conditions. On the contrary, they are an indispensable part of the body's defenses. Their main role is in combating bacterial infections. When an infection occurs, white cells move out from the blood vessels (from the thin terminal vessels, the capillaries) in great numbers. They surround and digest bacteria, and some of them are killed by bacterial poisons. Soon there is a sort of battlefield strewn with living and dead bacteria and white blood cells, dead tissue cells, digestive enzymes, cell fluids, and fragments in all stages of disintegration. The resulting semifluid mass is pus. An abscess is a deeply imbedded, walled-off mass of pus. Marked increase of white cells in the blood is nearly always a sign of infection somewhere in the body, and a count of the cells is a useful diagnostic technique much employed by doctors.

Occasionally for no known reason the production of white cells gets out of hand and their numbers tremendously increase, even though there is no infection. This abnormal condition, known as *leukemia*, is usually fatal, and there is at present no known way to control it.

We have used human blood as the specific example most interesting to you. Properties and activities of the blood are generally similar in other animals, with the expected great diversity in detail. The most striking peculiarity of any one group is that the blood does not transport oxygen and carbon dioxide in insects.[7] The pigment involved in oxygen transport is usually hemoglobin, or rather *a* hemoglobin, since this compound is not exactly the same in different kinds of animals. There are several other sorts of pigments, however, such as hemocyanin, which occur in a number of snails and crustaceans. Hemocyanin contains copper rather than iron (as in hemoglobin), and it is blue rather than red. Crayfish and crabs are *really* blue-blooded. In these forms and some others, including a few with hemoglobin, the pigment is not in cells or formed elements but is dissolved in the plasma. All true blood in animals contains some cells, corresponding more or less to our white cells.

THE MECHANISM OF CIRCULATION

We shall also use man as a concrete example of the circulatory mechanism. The arrangement is practically the same in all mammals. The principles involved are similar in most other animals that do have a definite circulation, even though again the differences in details are legion. Examples of some differences have already been mentioned (p. 142).

The heart of the mechanism is just that— the heart. Maintenance of a constant flow of blood through the whole system requires the application of pressure at some point, and that is accomplished by the heart. In us (and other mammals) this organ is really two separate hearts (Fig. 7-7), placed side by side, beating in unison and yet quite distinct. The reason for this oddity, as you should anticipate, is historical (cf. p. 35). Our two hearts evolved by the gradual separation of a single heart.

[7] It is hard to find any generalization without exceptions, and when we make sweeping statements like this they sometimes override details that really are not essential for present purposes. Some oxygen and carbon dioxide do go into solution in the blood of insects, but since there is no oxygen-carrying pigment the amounts are practically negligible. Even that statement has an exception, however. In a few larvae of one family of insects hemoglobin does occur in the blood.

The heart is still single in fishes (Fig. 7-7). Our right heart, or the right half of our double heart, pumps blood to the lungs, and the left heart pumps it to the body tissues as a whole.

Blood coming to either side of the heart first enters a smaller and weaker upper chamber, the right or left *auricle*. When the heart relaxes—the part of the beat called *diastole*—blood surges through the auricle into the larger and stronger chamber below it, the *ventricle*. This blood surge into the ventricle is initiated by the ventricular relaxation (diastole), but it is completed by the contraction of the auricle (auricular *systole*). The filled ventricle itself contracts (ventricular systole) immediately thereafter (Fig. 7-8), pumping blood upwards and out of the heart through the main artery, the *aorta*. Flaplike valves between auricle and ventricle automatically close as the ventricular systole begins and prevent the blood from moving back into the auricle. If you listen with a doctor's stethoscope, at this point you will hear a sort of dull "boom," which is partly the sound of the valves closing and partly the sound of the ventricle's muscles contracting. When the ventricles relax in their next diastole, three smaller, crescent-shaped valves in each of the blood vessels close and prevent flow of the expelled blood back into the heart. The sound of these valves as they close is also distinctly audible with a stethoscope—a shorter, higher, almost clicking sound. If the valves do not close perfectly, some blood does leak back and the sound becomes softer, somewhat hissing. This sound is heart murmur, a sign that the valves are out of order.

The blood that leaves the left ventricle goes into a very large artery, the aorta. From this, repeated branching distributes the blood throughout the body in smaller and smaller arteries. (Vessels carrying blood from the heart are *arteries;* those carrying it to the heart are *veins.*) Eventually the blood goes through a capillary network, where the vessels are so extremely small that a red blood cell may be bent double in being forced through. Every organ in the body has capillary networks, and this is where the blood makes its deliveries and pickups (Fig. 7-9). From the capillary network the blood moves into small

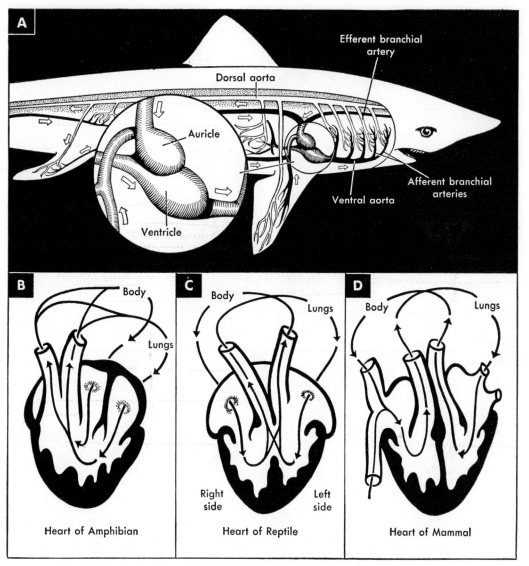

7-7   Vertebrate hearts.   *A.* Circulation in a fish (shark). The heart consists of a single auricle and a single ventricle. It drives blood forward through a ventral aorta to the gills. The blood enters the gills through afferent branchial arteries (cf. Fig. 6-12) and leaves them via efferent branchial arteries. It then passes to the rest of the body through a dorsal aorta. Thus in the fishes there is only a single stream of blood (deoxygenated) passing through the heart. In terrestrial vertebrates, however, there are two streams of blood surging through the heart: blood freshly oxygenated in the lungs first returns to the heart to be pumped again before it goes to the rest of the body. *B.* In the frog and other amphibia the freshly oxygenated blood enters the heart through a distinct auricle (the left) but becomes partly mixed with deoxygenated blood when it enters the single ventricle. This is clearly an inefficient system because some of the blood pumped to the body through the dorsal aorta is already exhausted of its oxygen. *C.* In reptiles this inefficiency is largely overcome by an incomplete partition in the ventricle. *D.* In mammals the partition is complete; two distinct ventricles are present. Freshly oxygenated blood returning from the lungs via the left auricle is now pumped by the left ventricle to the rest of the body without any admixture of deoxygenated blood.

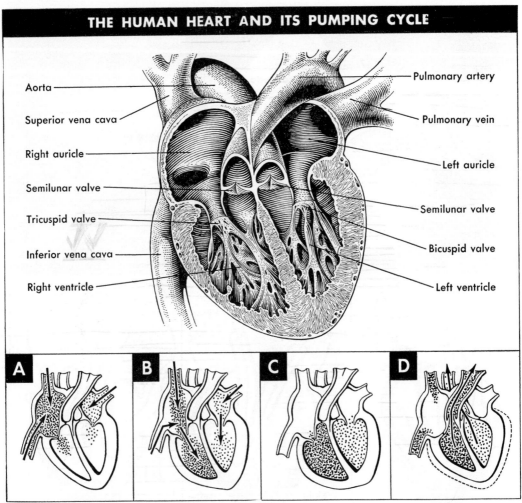

Aorta

Superior vena cava

Right auricle

Semilunar valve

Tricuspid valve

Inferior vena cava

Right ventricle

Pulmonary artery

Pulmonary vein

Left auricle

Semilunar valve

Bicuspid valve

Left ventricle

7-8   The human heart and its pumping cycle.   The upper figure shows the detail of the heart's four chambers and its valves. Note the heavier wall in the left ventricle. What is the significance of this? *A, B, C,* and *D* are successive stages in the pumping cycle. *A.* The auricles fill with blood as their walls relax (auricular diastole). *B.* The relaxation (diastole) of ventricles causes blood to flow into them from the auricles. *C.* Contraction (systole) of the auricles completes the filling of the ventricles. *D.* Contraction of the ventricles (ventricular systole) drives blood from the ventricles into the aorta and pulmonary artery. The blood is prevented from returning to the auricles by the bicuspid and tricuspid valves. During diastole it is prevented from returning to the ventricles from the arteries by the semilunar valves.

veins, thence into progressively larger ones, and finally into two venae cavae [8] which deliver it to the right auricle.

At this point the blood has not yet finished a complete circuit, because we started with it from the left heart and now it is back to the right, not the left, heart. From the right auricle it goes into the right ventricle and then is pumped to the lungs through the pulmonary artery and its two branches. In the capillary network of the lungs, it drops carbon dioxide and picks up oxygen. From there it is collected into the two pulmonary veins, which join and deliver the blood into the left auricle. Then it goes into the left ventricle, and so the circuit

[8] "Vena cava," singular; "venae cavae," plural. The superior vena cava delivers blood from the upper part of the body, the inferior vena cava from the lower part (Fig. 7-9).

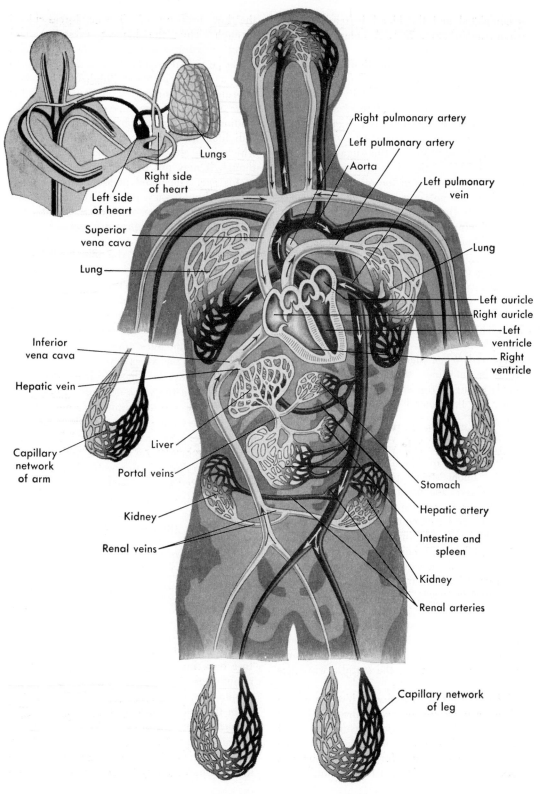

Right pulmonary artery

Left pulmonary artery

Aorta

Left pulmonary vein

Lungs

Right side of heart

Left side of heart

Superior vena cava

Lung

Lung

Left auricle

Right auricle

Left ventricle

Right ventricle

Inferior vena cava

Hepatic vein

Capillary network of arm

Liver

Portal veins

Stomach

Hepatic artery

Kidney

Intestine and spleen

Renal veins

Kidney

Renal arteries

Capillary network of leg

7-9   The human circulatory system.   (See p. 146.)

is completed and the blood is ready to go around again (Fig. 7-9). A complete round trip takes about 25 seconds.

There is just one complication in details of the blood circulation that we want to mention briefly because it is an unusually interesting example of effective correlation of mechanism and process. When digestion occurs, large amounts of sugar are absorbed by the capillaries of the intestines. If this sugar went into the general circulation, it would cause a sharp rise in blood sugar. On the other hand, when digestion was not occurring, the sugar level would drop. Body cells, especially nerve cells, are very sensitive to the sugar concentration in the blood. Sustained high sugar content produces the symptoms of diabetes, and low sugar content produces convulsions and unconsciousness. The sugar-rich blood from the intestinal capillaries does not go into the general circulation but into the *portal vein* (Fig. 7-9). This vein carries it to another capillary network in the liver, where sugar is removed and stored. When sugar is not being absorbed from the intestines, the liver feeds a steady supply of sugar from storage through its capillaries into the general circulation.

PULSE AND BLOOD PRESSURE

Every time the left ventricle contracts, it sends a surge of blood racing through the arteries under strong pressure. As the ventricle relaxes, the pressure drops. It is these alternations of pressure that we feel as the pulse. There is, of course, a pulse in all arteries and not only in the wrist, where it is usually taken for convenience. Feeling the pulse is simply a way of checking how fast and regularly the heart is working. Even when the ventricle is relaxing, in diastole, there is some pressure in the arteries because they are elastic. When the systolic surge reaches them they expand. Then they contract again, and the contraction keeps the blood under some, but less, pressure when the systolic wave has passed.

You have probably had your blood pressure taken and are familiar with the physician's procedure. The method used is compression of the arteries in the arm until the top of the systolic wave cannot force blood through them. The pressure is then relaxed until even

the low pressure of diastole forces blood through. Thus the highest (systolic) and lowest (diastolic) pressures of the whole pulse sequence are determined. You are likely to hear a great deal about "high," "low," and "normal" blood pressure and to see figures for these values, but the figures are often misleading. As with many physical variables, each individual has his own average blood pressure, which is healthy and normal for him even though it may not be average for all people of his age. The blood pressure also can and indeed should vary considerably under the influence of emotion or physical factors. Extremes of high or low pressure may, of course, be danger signals.

There is friction in the blood vessels, as there is in any system of tubes through which fluid is flowing. This friction reduces the pressure steadily as the blood moves progressively farther from the heart. In the capillaries friction is greatest. Here the pressure is radically reduced, and the pulse surge disappears. Blood returning in the veins has no pulse and is under little or no pressure from the heart. Blood flow in the veins depends in good part on breathing and other muscular motion. The motion alternately compresses the veins and lets them expand, and blood is kept moving toward the heart by a series of valves permitting flow in that direction only. You know that your feet are likely to swell if you sit or stand for a long time without moving. The swelling is caused by accumulation of blood in the veins in the absence of muscular movement around them.

THE LYMPHATIC SYSTEM

We have noted that there is fluid in various internal spaces of the body and, indeed, around almost all the cells. Much of this fluid, with the materials dissolved in it, has diffused from the blood in the capillaries and may diffuse back into it. It is, in fact, blood plasma minus those large proteins held back by the capillary walls. Other materials have diffused from the cells bathed by the fluid, and these materials, too, may diffuse into the blood in the capillaries. The fluid is thus intimately involved in the delivery and pickup activities of the transportation system of the blood. How-

THE LYMPHATIC SYSTEM

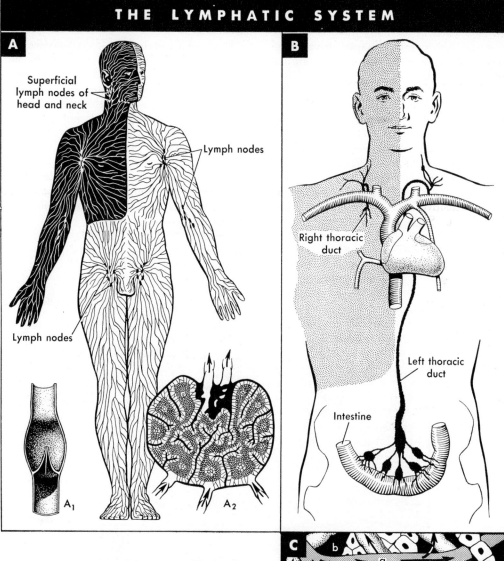

A

Superficial lymph nodes of head and neck

Lymph nodes

Lymph nodes

A_1

A_2

B

Right thoracic duct

Left thoracic duct

Intestine

C

b

a

c

c

b

a

c

7-10 The lymphatic system. *A.* The distribution of superficial lymphatic vessels and lymph nodes in man. A_1. A valve in lymph vessel. A_2. A lymph node. *B.* The left and right thoracic ducts emptying into the veins (subclavian) that drain the arms. The left thoracic duct is the larger one, draining the whole of the un-shaded area in *A* and *B*. It carries fats absorbed by the lacteals in intestinal villi (Fig. 7-11). *C.* Detail of blood and lymph capillaries. Plasma flows from blood capillaries (*a*) into intercellular spaces (*b*) and then into the lymph capillaries (*c*), which end blindly.

ever, not all the fluid finds its way back into the blood directly.

In most parts of the body there is another set of capillaries quite separate from those through which the blood flows. These are the *lymphatic capillaries*. Much of the fluid outside the blood vessels and cells in tissues finds its way by diffusion into the lymphatic capillaries (Fig. 7-10). From them the fluid, *lymph*, passes into successively larger vessels, much as the blood collects in veins after passing through the blood capillaries. The lymphatic system of vessels, however, runs in one direction only. Its capillaries end blindly and pick up materials only by diffusion through their walls. There is no delivery to them corresponding with the arterial part of the blood circulation.

The lymph vessels have internal valves, and flow through them depends on pressure and motion of surrounding tissues, as in veins, with no pressure from the heart. Eventually all the lymph in vessels reaches the upper part of the trunk and is emptied into veins near the shoulders (most of it on the left side). Thus the lymph, too, does finally enter the blood.

As you would expect from its relationship to the blood, the composition of lymph is similar to that of plasma, but it contains much

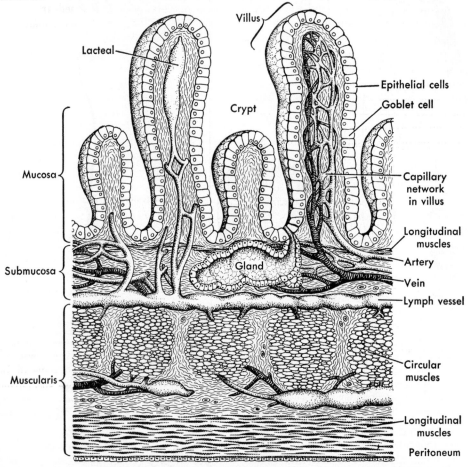

7-11 Lacteals and capillaries in the intestinal villi. The lining of the intestine in vertebrates, including man, is much folded into villi, which serve to increase the effective absorptive area in the gut (cf. earthworm, Fig. 6-6). Each villus contains blind-ending lymphatic vessels, called lacteals, into which fats enter. Each villus also is richly supplied with capillaries which absorb other foodstuffs. In the diagram the villi are shown, for simplicity only, with either a lacteal or a capillary net.

less of the blood proteins. Since it flows only from and not to the body tissues, it also contains less dissolved food materials in transit, but it does transport waste products from the tissues. There is one important exception to the statement that lymph is not involved in food transport: it picks up small globules of fat from the intestines and delivers them to the blood (Figs. 7-10B and 7-11). Undissolved fats seem to enter the lymphatic capillaries more readily than those of the blood. Red blood cells cannot normally leave the blood vessels, and they occur in lymph only as a result of injury. Some kinds of white blood cells can move out of or into vessels by an ameba-like movement through the walls, and these cells are abundant in lymph. Many are also formed in the lymphatic system and poured into the blood.

At points along the lymph vessels are lumpy enlargements, the *lymph nodes* (Fig. 7-10). It is here that certain of the white blood cells originate. The nodes are also filters. They remove and destroy bacteria and stop and store solid particles. Lymph nodes near the lungs of city dwellers are often black with soot and dust particles. During infection, the nodes may become swollen and sore. At one time or another you have probably been aware of their existence, for instance in the armpits or groin.

The lymphatic system, then, returns body fluid to the blood, assists with the intake of fats, filters out foreign particles, and helps to combat infection. It would seem that all these operations could be performed just as well by the blood circulatory system, and the need for a second system of vessels is not obvious. The reason is certainly historical—evolutionary—but is still obscure, although not beyond conjecture. Lymph in the sense of body fluid outside the cells and blood vessels occurs in all multicellular animals. A lymphatic vascular system is characteristic of the vertebrates. It seems odd that lymph nodes, which in man are involved in the more special activities of the lymphatic system, occur only in mammals and some birds. Many of the lower vertebrates, without lymph nodes, have lymph hearts that actively pump the lymph along. Why do you suppose we and other mammals lack lymph hearts? (We are not sure of the answer to that question, either.)

Secretion and Excretion

We have considered some of the complicated and interrelated processes in living things. We are now approaching the end of our discussion of the processes that are mainly *metabolic*, that is, involved primarily in the feeding and maintenance of the organism. Before we turn to other activities of organisms, there is a final point about metabolism to be considered: the end products of metabolism in cells and tissues. Such end products have already been mentioned from time to time, but now the knowledge should be correlated and rounded out.

Processes in cells and tissues have products that are not needed or useful where they are formed. Some of these products are necessary elsewhere in the organism, and some are not. The distinction is not always clear. For instance, CO_2 produced by respiration in plant cells is a useless, even a harmful, end product as far as respiration is concerned, but it is a necessary material for photosynthesis in the same cells or elsewhere in the plant. The plant releases it only when photosynthesis is not going on, or when the CO_2 produced is more than is used for photosynthesis. By and large, however, the distinction can be maintained. We may call the production of substances useful elsewhere in the organism *secretion*, and the elimination of those of no further use *excretion*.

SECRETION

Secretion occurs widely, in fact universally, in multicellular organisms. The cellulose and other constituents of the cell walls of plants are secreted by the cells. More specialized secretions include those responsible for odors and tastes and the poisons formed in mushrooms and many flowering plants. Numerous other organisms, from protists to snakes, also secrete poisons that are useful for defense or for the capture of food. All kinds of synthesized molecules in both plants and animals are called secretions if they are used by the organisms elsewhere than in the cells where they are elaborated.

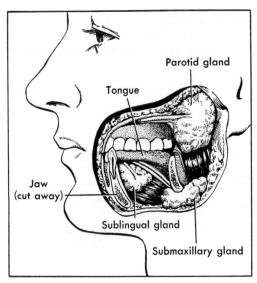

7-12 The human salivary glands. The three pairs of glands pour saliva containing digestive enzymes into the mouth cavity. As the names imply, the sublingual gland lies under the tongue, the submaxillary under the jaw, and the parotid near the ear.

Groups of cells active mainly in producing secretions and associated in distinct organs are called *glands* (Fig. 3-24). Glands are much more common and varied in animals but also occur in plants. For instance, the nectaries that produce a sweet secretion in some flowers are glands. In man, the action of the salivary glands (Fig. 7-12) and others secreting digestive juices is now familiar. You are also aware of the lachrymal glands, which secrete a fluid that keeps the eyeballs wet and which have a peculiar tendency to overflow when you are sad. The endocrine glands have received much publicity lately because of the sometimes spectacular effects of their secretions. These secretions—hormones—are, indeed, so important that we are going to discuss them separately in the next chapter.

EXCRETION IN PLANTS AND LOWER ANIMALS

Metabolism really ends not with such secretions as we have exemplified but with true end products, which are waste in the sense that they are no longer of any use to the organism. Such end products are commonly poisonous in any considerable quantity, and their elimination is a necessary part of metabolism.

Plants have no special organs of excretion. End products of their metabolism diffuse from the cells into the surrounding water or air, or they accumulate in harmless, insoluble [9] form somewhere in the organism. In protists and the simpler multicellular animals also, excretion is mostly by diffusion from the individual cells. Some protists do have an organ (or organelle) involved in excretion, the contractile vacuole (Fig. 7-13). The main or primary activity of this organ is to control water content of the cell, counteracting osmosis, and most of the excretion of these forms is by diffusion through the cell or body membrane. There is, however, some evidence that waste products dissolved in the water are also expelled by the contractile vacuole. This is the simplest level of a phenomenon that is widespread among animals: the excretory organs generally help to regulate water content in addition to eliminating waste products. Such organs are, however, absent in most protists.

Above the protists, three of the major groups of animals have no special organs for water regulation or for excretion: Porifera (sponges), Coelenterata (corals, jellyfish, etc.), and Echinodermata (starfish, sea urchins, etc.). It is significant that all these animals are entirely aquatic and that the great majority are marine. They include one widespread family of fresh-water sponges and a few fresh-water coelenterates such as *Hydra*, often used as a laboratory animal, but in both groups marine forms greatly predominate. All echinoderms are marine. What bearing do you think their marine environment has on their absence of water-regulating and excretory organs? The osmotic pressure (Δ) of the sea water is so nearly the same as that of their body fluids (see p. 86) that there is no serious tendency for excess water to move into the organisms by osmosis. Moreover, since they are completely bathed in water, they can simply excrete wastes from all their surfaces.

EXCRETION IN OTHER ANIMALS

From your present knowledge of metabolism, you can guess most of the kinds of sub-

[9] Why is an insoluble substance harmless to the life of the cell?

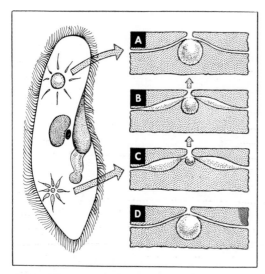

7-13 The contractile vacuoles in *Paramecium*.
Each vacuole goes through the cycle illustrated. *A.*
The central vacuole is full, and the radial collecting
vessels that penetrate the cytoplasm are empty.
B. Systole (contraction) of the central vacuole:
water is ejected through the pore. The radiating
canals are filling (diastole). *C.* Completion of central vacuole's systole, and the diastole of the radiating canals. *D.* Systole of the radiating canals fills
the central vacuole.

stances that have to be excreted by animals.
The end product of respiration is CO_2. This
usually leaves the body through the same organs that acquire O_2, that is, through the
respiratory organs—gills or lungs in most
animals. Respiration and numerous other metabolic processes also produce water, in addition to the water that is taken in as such.
Water formed by metabolism is as useful as
that drunk and is commonly retained for
longer or shorter periods. All animals do lose
some water. In some situations this is an unavoidable loss of a needed substance rather
than excretion of an unneeded end product;
but water is often in excess and actively excreted. Water is a necessary part of urinary
excretion, as we shall see in a moment. Water may also be lost in larger or smaller
amounts from any surface of the organism.
In man large quantities are lost from the
lungs. This is not active excretion, but evaporation as an incidental result of the lung
mechanism. We also lose much water through
our sweat glands. Even when we are not actively sweating (when no drops of water appear on our skins), we lose a pint or so of
water per day in this way. Several quarts may
be lost on a hot day. This water is secreted
by glands, but its significance is in heat regulation, not excretion. The loss of heat in the
evaporation of sweat serves as a cooling
agent (see p. 172).

Regulation of salt concentration and the
production of salts by the metabolic breakdown of some compounds require that there
be some mechanism for excretion of inorganic
salts. In fishes that drink sea water and thus
acquire excess salts, the gills are excretory
organs for salt, as well as for CO_2 (see Fig.
4-8). Some salts are always excreted in fishes'
urine, and this is usually the most important
way of salt excretion, as it is in man. Because
sweat is salty, there is a general impression
that this is our usual or main excretion of
salt. Such is not the case. Loss of salt in sweat
is insignificant in comparison with loss in
urine and usually plays no essential part in
our salt regulation. Exceptions may, however,
occur in situations where men sweat copiously
for hours at a stretch.

Contrary to another popular impression, the
intestine is primarily an organ of absorption,
not of excretion. The feces consist almost entirely of undigested food (or indigestible
matter taken in with the food) and masses of
bacteria from the intestines—materials that
have not been inside us and therefore cannot
have been excreted. There is, however, some
important excretion into the intestines. The
large intestine itself excretes salts of calcium
and other heavy metals, a little of which is
excreted in the urine. Dark brown bile pigments are excreted by the liver and flow into
the intestines. These pigments are mostly end
products of the destruction of red blood cells
in the liver (p. 145).

All these sorts and avenues of excretion in
animals still fail to account for a large, important, and often toxic class of end products:
those containing nitrogen. They are the end
products of protein metabolism; you recall
that proteins are the only really abundant body
materials that contain nitrogen. Among the
common end products are urea, $CO(NH_2)_2$;
uric acid, $(C_5H_4N_4O_3)$; and ammonia,

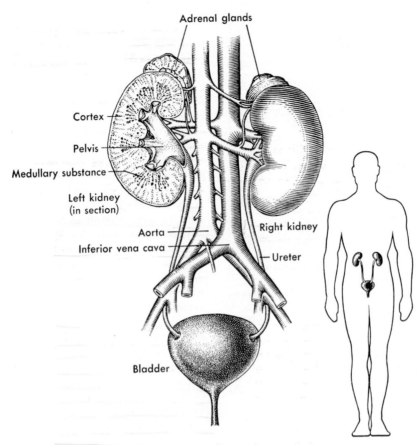

7-14 The urinary system in man.

(NH₃). All three occur in human urine, largely as the result of the breakdown of different proteins.[10] Urea is, however, about twenty times as abundant as the other two put together.

Animals differ greatly in their most abundant nitrogenous end products, and some interesting relationships are involved. Almost all aquatic animals, both invertebrates and vertebrates, excrete more ammonia than anything else. Ammonia is highly soluble, but it is also extremely poisonous. Its excretion involves solution in large amounts of water and copious, continuous or frequent flow of urine. Land animals excrete predominantly urea or uric acid. Almost all animals that lay eggs

10 Here is a curious fact. In almost all mammals uric acid is converted into a different compound before it is excreted. The exceptions are: men, apes, and Dalmatian dogs! Except for that one breed, dogs follow the general rule and differ from man in the composition of their urine.

outside of water secrete more uric acid: land snails, insects, reptiles, and birds. Land animals that lay eggs in water or that do not lay eggs at all secrete more urea: adult amphibians and mammals. Uric acid is almost insoluble and leaves the body in solid crystals. It may also be safely stored for long periods because its insolubility prevents absorption. Urea is highly soluble and must be excreted in solution, but it is not seriously toxic except in unusually strong concentrations. Can you think of any relationships between the ways of life of these various animals and their nitrogen excretion?

THE KIDNEY

All the animals we have just mentioned have special organs that excrete nitrogenous wastes. These organs also largely affect the amount of water that leaves the body. In vertebrates the organ involved is the kidney,

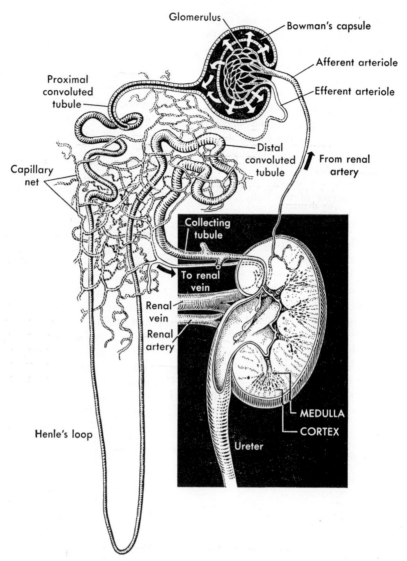

Glomerulus — Bowman's capsule

Afferent arteriole

Efferent arteriole

Proximal
convoluted
tubule

Distal
convoluted
tubule

From renal
artery

Capillary
net

Collecting
tubule

To renal
vein

Renal
vein

Renal
artery

MEDULLA
CORTEX

Henle's loop

Ureter

7-15   Detail of a single kidney tubule in man.

and we shall study the human kidney as an example (Fig. 7-14).

The work of the kidney is done in tiny tubules, over a million of them in each kidney. At one end of the tubule is a filter (called Bowman's capsule) closely applied to a ball of blood capillaries (the glomerulus) (Fig. 7-15). Here plasma is filtered into the tubule. Its composition is not much changed at this point, but the formed elements of the blood and colloidal proteins are filtered out and do not enter the tubule. As the plasma filtrate passes on down the tubule, which is also sur-

rounded by capillaries, most of the water is reabsorbed and returned to the blood. Other substances such as glucose are also returned. Oddly enough, so is about half of the urea. Some additional substances also here move from the blood into the tubule. At the end of the tubule the fluid, which is now urine and greatly altered in composition from the plasma, flows into branched collecting tubes and finally through the ureter into the bladder. The bladder is only a storage tank and does not further alter the urine.

This process does more than excrete waste

products. Selective absorption in the tubule and selective return of constituents of the plasma do much to regulate the composition of the blood. Substances in less than normal concentration in the blood are usually not retained in the tubule, and substances in more than normal concentration are usually retained in part. For instance, blood sugar is usually wholly returned to the blood, but if its concentration becomes abnormally high some is excreted in the urine. The tubules also retain and pass on to the bladder more water when the water content of the body is high and less when it is low.

The kidneys' control of the composition and volume of the blood, and hence the internal environment of our cells, is most effective. It must, however, be added that this is another natural process that is extremely inefficient from an engineering viewpoint. One-third of the whole flow of blood pumped by the heart is represented by the plasma pushed through the kidney filter. Of this, more than 99 per cent is returned. In effect, there is an endless battle by the heart to pump plasma out of the body and by the kidney to keep it in. Even in its excretion of the chief waste product, urea, it has been estimated that the kidney is only about 5 per cent efficient. Fortunately for us, this is enough.

Chapter Summary

Transportation within the organism: its simplicity in protists; one of the major functions demanding special adaptations in large organisms.

Transportation in xylem and phloem of vascular plants: the role of transpiration and root pressure in moving water up the xylem.

Circulatory systems in animals: hearts; open and closed circulations.

Composition and function of blood: plasma, serum, and the formed elements of the blood; the clotting reaction; hemoglobin and the transport of oxygen; transport of carbon dioxide.

The mechanism of circulation: diastole and systole of the heart; blood pressure.

The lymphatic system: the movement of plasma from blood capillaries through intercellular spaces to lymphatic capillaries; mechanism of one-way lymph movement; drainage into subclavian veins; lymph nodes; fat transport.

Glands and secretion.

Excretion: its simplicity in protists and plants; excretory problems and systems in multicellular animals; ammonia, urea, and uric acid; the organization and functions of the kidney in man.

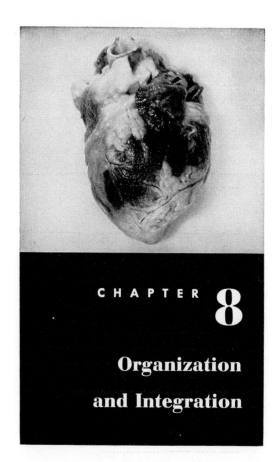

The ceaseless beating of the human heart, and its automatic regulation, exemplify that "wisdom of the body" which is the subject of this chapter. (Photo by Arthur F. Jacques, Rhode Island Hospital)

CHAPTER 8

Organization and Integration

A famous French physiologist, Claude Bernard (1813-1878), said that "Stability of the internal environment is the condition of free life." Before Bernard's time, life had been thought of as a series of separate processes which followed in sequence or were otherwise related but quite distinct one from another. Plants synthesize compounds, and animals tear them down; men think, fight, digest food, or feel warm—quite distinct activities, or so it seemed. By a series of ingenious experiments, Bernard led the way to a different attitude. Both plants and animals synthesize compounds and tear them down, and the processes are largely similar in all organisms. What did Bernard mean by the "stability of the internal environment"? It is part of a still grander principle, which Bernard also helped to develop: that an organism is more than the sum of its parts. The activities in an organism

are not only a chain of different processes: The apparently distinct structures and processes are linked together more intimately and in more curious ways than our predecessors could imagine. They are all aspects of the same thing: the organized life of an organism.

Organization

We repeat that an organism is more than the sum of its parts. The whole plant or animal has properties that are not possessed by any one of its cells or organs and that cannot be interpreted in terms of different parts and activities. This fact can be demonstrated by simple experiments that have spectacular implications. If you cut a piece of stem from a willow branch and keep it moist, it will grow roots at one end and leaves at the other. If you plant it, it will develop into a whole tree much like the one from which you cut it. The cutting contained only the cells and tissues of a stem, but it had properties that cannot be explained by those of a stem and its parts. It had an organization that could reproduce a whole organism of an intricate kind with the peculiarities of a particular species. Moreover, no matter where on the branch you cut the piece and no matter which end you place uppermost, leaves will sprout only from the end that was nearer the tip of the branch, and roots only from the other end. The cells of each sort, xylem, phloem, and the rest, seem to be exactly the

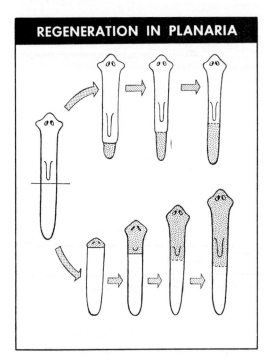

REGENERATION IN PLANARIA

8-1 Regeneration in planaria. The animal at the left is cut crosswise into two halves. The anterior (head) half regenerates a posterior (tail) half; the posterior half regenerates the missing anterior half. Note in the lower sequence that the head itself is regenerated first and the pharyngeal region later. As the regeneration of the anterior half proceeds, the posterior portion decreases in size until a whole organism of normal proportions is achieved. A similar reduction of the anterior half occurs when it regenerates a posterior half (upper sequence).

same at one end of the cutting as at the other, but the cutting as a whole has an *organization* different from a mere addition of similar cells. It has a kind of field orientation into *farther* from the trunk and roots and *nearer* to them; it is a bipolar field orientation. Nothing can be done to the cutting that will change the orientation it had when it was part of the original tree.

Many animals have properties of regrowth similar to those of a willow stem, and experimental results with them are even more striking. The experiment may be performed with a sort of flatworm called a planarian (Fig. 8-1). Planarians are little creatures, usually ½ to 1 inch long, having muscles, nerves, a primitive sort of brain, eyes, digestive organs, and rather complex excretory and reproductive organs. If a piece of reasonable size is cut from the front, middle, or hind end, the piece will regrow all the missing parts and become a whole, normal organism. Any piece cut off still has a front and rear. A new head will grow only at the end that was toward the head to begin with, and a new tail only at the end that was toward the tail.

The ability to maintain total organization and characteristic form is universal among organisms. It is part of the fact that they are *organisms*, and not merely casual associations of cells or parts of cells. Regrowth of missing parts is a special aspect of this ability. This particular ability occurs in all organisms, but in different degrees and with different manifestations. It is seen among animals, for instance, in the regrowth of a lost claw by a crab or of a lost tail by a lizard. These are both very complex animals, but as a broad generalization the capacity for regeneration is less the more complex the animal. In man, missing organs do not grow again, but parts of tissues such as skin, muscles, or nerves can regenerate if the loss is not too great.

The ability to maintain characteristic organization by regrowth of parts is more extensive in plants than in animals. In animals, the differentiation of tissues and organs normally occurs in a limited part of the life cycle, and any growth thereafter is mainly change in sizes of structures already differentiated. Plants, on the other hand, retain throughout life undifferentiated or embryonic cells from which new tissues and organs may be differentiated at any time. These embryonic cells form the *meristem* in higher plants. Deciduous trees shed an entire set of highly differentiated organs, the leaves, every year and grow an entirely new set from the meristem the following year. This evidence of integration in the organism, of its wonderful capacity for maintaining and renewing its characteristic organization, is so familiar to us that we seldom stop to think of it as the marvel it is.

Experiments and observations on regrowth of parts throw a great deal of light on reproduction and development, subjects we have not yet reached.[1] Our interest in such

1 See Part 4.

facts here is that they show clearly that the *whole* organism, willow tree, planarian, or any other, has a pattern and an orientation that runs through and includes all its parts. There is, indeed, an organization comprehensible only in terms of the whole and not of the parts. That point can be further demonstrated by other experiments on a planarian. If the animal is placed in a solution poisonous to it, the skin cells are destroyed first, but not all at the same time. In spite of the fact that these cells are similar all over the body and are reached all at once by the same amount of poison, destruction always begins at the front end and works back. Again we see evidence of a sort of organization that overrides the separate parts and includes them all. There is a *field of organization* in the planarian.

The planarian's field of organization has a center in the head, a longitudinal axis through the whole body, and orientation around and away from that axis with differentiation upward, downward, and laterally. Similar fields occur in most multicellular animals. Sometimes they are even simpler. In jellyfishes, for instance, there is a center, an axis, and differentiation around the axis radially, but no orientation corresponding with "up," "down," or "lateral" in a planarian. In other organisms, such as man, there is a field like that of a planarian but there are also other fields which greatly complicate the total organization. Consideration of the growth of the willow cutting, or of any part of a plant, shows convincingly that plants also have fields of organization. Precisely what these fields are and how they are maintained is another important biological subject on which research has not yet gone very far. No clear explanation of fields of organization has been found, but it is certain that they exist, and they can be described even if not fully explained.

The Internal Environment

Fields of organization show that what a cell is like and how it reacts depend on where it is. Not only the individual cell but also its relationships to adjacent cells and to the organism as a whole are involved. This is an other aspect of the principle that many activities of life are interactions between cells and their environments, a principle already familiar to you in a different setting.

CELL ENVIRONMENTS OF PROTISTS AND SIMPLER PLANTS AND ANIMALS

In protists the organization of the whole body is that of a single cell which is, necessarily, in direct contact with the external environment. For active protists, that environment is always a solution of various substances in water. The solution may be sea water or the water of ponds and streams. For the many parasitic protists it is blood, protoplasm, or some other solution in a multicellular organism. In simpler multicellular water plants or animals most individual cells are also in direct contact with the external environment. In an alga (plant) or in a sponge or coral (animals), the environment of a single cell includes the adjacent cells and the water in which the animal lives. Organization is brought about and maintained by contacts with other cells. Metabolism is maintained mostly by exchanges with the water of the external environment, which in these lowly organisms is partly contained in pouches and canals where the solution is modified by activities of the surrounding cells. There are internal cells in many of these organisms, but they are not far removed from the environmental solution. The internal cells also make metabolic exchanges with the external environment but do so through intervening cells and with fluids seeping between the cells.

The point is that in these organisms (protists and the simpler aquatic plants and animals) the environment of each cell is essentially that of the organism as a whole (Fig. 7-4). It is the general external environment, which is only slightly modified in the immediate vicinity of the organism by its own activities. The cells are thus affected by any change in the external environment. Any cell has a narrow range of conditions under which it can remain alive, and a still narrower optimum range in which its activities are most effective. In the organisms that we are now considering, life depends strongly on the environment, which must not fluctuate beyond the range in which all the cells of the organism can live. The outside environment must also be somewhere near the optimum during the most active periods of the organism's life. Put in another way, the evolutionary possibilities for such organisms are strictly limited. They can occupy only those environments that do not fluctuate too greatly; and the new metabolic processes they can evolve are restricted by the conditions existing in available external environments. This is true of all their cells.

What environments fluctuate least and which are most favorable to processes going on in all cells? The water of the sea is most stable and most favorable. Changes in composition, temperature, and other vital conditions are slower and less extreme in the sea. The inorganic material dissolved in sea water is similar to that in many cells, and the osmotic pressure is also similar. It is not surprising that the great majority of organisms with cells dependent on the external environment live in the sea.

Conditions are less favorable in fresh water. Fluctuations are greater, dissolved salts may differ more from those in cells, and osmotic pressure is lower. Many protists and simpler (nonvascular) plants and a few of the simplest animals do live in fresh water, but they are here much less abundant than in the sea. They have special adaptations which enable them to survive the fluctuations as well as the constant features of fresh water. For instance, the low osmotic pressure of fresh water may cause too much water to diffuse into cells. This may be countered by lower osmotic pressure in cells, by reduction of diffusion in various ways, by greater elimination of water, or by a combination of such protective adaptations.[2]

The land is the most difficult environment of all. Fluctuations in temperature and other physical conditions are far greater than in any body of water, even a small pool of fresh water. The air contains extremely few of the materials required by cells. Worst of all, it contains very little water, which constitutes most of protoplasm and is absolutely essential for cells. No protists or simpler ani-

mals truly live on land. Some live in damp soil, but there they are really in an aquatic environment. A good many nonvascular plants (among them fungi, lichens, mosses, and liverworts) do succeed in living on land by a variety of special adaptations to this unfavorable environment. All are small. Most of them grow in damp or downright wet situations, and others have special means of obtaining and retaining water.

VASCULAR PLANTS AND ANIMALS

Evolution early proceeded beyond the level of the forms of life that we have been talking about. Although this is a point for later discussion, it is of interest to note here in passing that such evolution happened much earlier in animals than in plants. Organisms evolved with more layers of cells and with greater differentiation and complication of internal tissues and organs. In them, the deeper cells are so far removed from the external environment that no effective interchange between deep cells and the external environment occurs (Fig. 7-4). In fact, the environment in which these cells live is quite different from the environment outside the organism. It is an *internal environment*. With further evolution along these lines, many of the external cells have become relatively inactive. Some still serve for absorption and excretion, but many are only protective, like cork cells in the bark of a tree. Most of the activities in higher organisms, especially animals but also plants, involve mainly internal cells.

The evolution of more abundant and complex internal tissues and organs was accompanied by the elaboration of internal fluids. This elaboration also involved the development of vessels in which the fluids move. All higher organisms, both plants and animals, are vascular. Life in such vast aggregations of internal cells, far removed from an external medium, would be quite impossible if there were not an internal medium and a mechanism for moving it. Complication of internal organs did not ensue because the vascular system made it possible, nor did the vascular system arise because it is necessary in such complex organisms. The two

2 See discussion of contractile vacuoles, p. 154.

necessarily developed together. If they had not, neither one would have evolved.

The evolution of internal fluids and vascular systems provided internal cells with an environment separated from that outside the organism. This carried the possibility that the _internal environment could be more stable than the external environment and more specifically adapted to the particular needs of each kind of organism. It resulted in a new and closer integration, bringing all or most of the internal cells in contact with a fluid environment specific to the organism. These cells became relatively independent of the environment of the organism as a whole,_ although, of course, the materials for construction and maintenance of the internal environment still had to come ultimately from outside.

Evolution of vascular systems and of distinctly separate internal environments _first occurred in aquatic organisms._ A later outcome was conquest of the land by living things. The difficulties of this most difficult of environments were in considerable part removed for vascular organisms. Most of their cells are not really living in the inhospitable open air but in a highly favorable internal liquid environment of their own. _All the truly terrestrial animals and an overwhelming majority of the terrestrial plants are vascular._

THE SEA WITHIN US?

In the course of evolution there has been a progression from organisms without a really separate internal environment to those with one. Most organisms without such clear separation live in the sea, and there are resemblances between sea water and the blood plasma of vascular animals. Some students of the subject have suggested that, when animals moved out of the sea, they preserved an environment of sea water for their cells by locking this up in the vascular system. Popularizers have gone so far as to say that the cells of our bodies are lapped by waves of the seas in which our ancestors swam hundreds of millions of years ago. That is very poetic, but unfortunately it is not quite true. Some matters of scientific attitude and principles, as well as of fact, are involved, so the point is worth looking into a little further.

TABLE 8-1

Relative amounts of some elements in sea water and some plasmas *

	So- dium	Potas- sium	Cal- cium	Mag- nesium	Chlo- rine
Sea water	100	3.61	3.91	12.1	181
Plasma of:					
King crab	100	5.62	4.06	11.2	187
Lobster	100	3.73	4.85	1.7	171
Man	100	6.75	3.10	0.7	129

* These data are from A. B. Macallum, the chief scientific supporter of the view that plasma and sea water are substantially the same. In each case the amounts are relative to the amount of sodium present.

Let us consider first whether the composition of sea water and of plasma really is the same. Some data are given in Table 8-1. There is considerable similarity between the composition of sea water and the three plasmas listed, but there are also remarkable differences. The plasma of man has relatively almost twice as much potassium but less than a fifteenth as much magnesium as sea water. Even the lobster, which lives in sea water as its ancestors have always done, has distinctly more calcium and much less magnesium. An attempt has been made to explain these differences by the hypothesis that the composition of sea water has changed and that the plasmas of different lines of descent were shut off in circulatory systems at different times. That will not work, however. To explain the amounts of magnesium would demand that the system arose first in the ancestry of man, somewhat later in that of the lobster, and much later (almost recently) in the king crab. The evidence of fossils and the relationships of these forms show that this certainly is not true. A circulatory system arose at the same time in the ancestors of king crab and lobster and probably later (surely not any earlier) in the ancestry of man.

There are distinct differences among these plasmas and between any one of them and sea water. These differences cannot be explained by any changes that may have occurred in sea water. They can nevertheless be explained in two other ways. In the first place, plasma is not really derived from sea water. Even in primitive marine forms plasma is a fluid that develops in organisms; it is not sea water somehow trapped in them. The fact that plasma is in a closed system separated from the water of the environment makes possible its *differences* from sea water. In the second place, plasma has evolved. It is different in different organisms and has specific characteristics developed in each, just as have the other materials and structures of various organisms.

It is still true that all plasmas have similarities and that they somewhat resemble sea water. The common-sense explanation of these facts is quite simple. The conditions under which cells can live actively are not exactly the same for all cells, *but they are closely similar for all.* Cells can live in both sea water and plasma. If sea water and plasma were not rather similar, this would not be possible. If sea water had a decidedly different composition, primitive life of the sort that did arise in the sea would have been impossible. *As animals with plasma evolved, their plasmas were necessarily similar to each other and to sea water because markedly different solutions would not have been compatible with the activities of cells.*

Control of the Internal Environment

The internal environment must be suitable for the life of all the cells it touches. It must also be adaptable to changes in organic activities. Further, it becomes involved in integration of the whole organism and co-ordination of various processes within the organism. All these facts require that there be some control of the internal environment. It must on one hand be kept constant within certain limits and on the other hand change within those limits as the activities of the organism change.

All vascular organisms do have mechanisms of control of the internal environment, but the mechanisms and the degree and nature of control differ greatly in different organisms. Control in plants is less rigid, less localized or more diffuse, and less independent of the outer environment than in most animals. The difference may be related to more definite and more complex differentiation of organs in animals, to the mobility of many animals, and, above all, to the fact that nerve reactions are usually involved in animals and do not occur at all in plants.

The composition of the ascending sap in plants necessarily depends on the materials that happen to be in solution in the soil. The initial composition of solutions entering the plant is further determined by the roots, which are to some degree selective and absorb some substances more readily than others. The composition of the sap is further modified by absorption and secretion from cells throughout the plant as the sap moves along. The rate of flow is largely, although not entirely, determined by the rate of transpiration (p. 139), which in turn depends on both external and internal factors. The humidity, heat, and light of the surrounding air play a part, and so do opening and closing of stomates (p. 86) and other conditions in the leaves. In some plants leaves may turn toward or away from the sunlight, or become reduced in area by rolling up, and these influence rate of transpiration as well as other processes.

In plants there is no mechanism for control of internal temperature, which is usually very near the external temperature.

Chemical co-ordination by secretion of substances which affect processes elsewhere in the plant is important in vascular plants. It is not fully understood but is certainly both extensive and complex. It will be discussed somewhat more fully later in this chapter.

Man belongs to a group of organisms (the mammals) in which the internal environment is most fully controlled. We may therefore draw more specific examples of such control mostly from human physiology, with some comparisons with other forms of life.

CONTROLS OF THE CHEMISTRY OF INTERNAL FLUIDS

The importance of the chemical constitution of the blood plasma and lymph is already clear. The main ways in which this is controlled need only brief review in this new context. New materials are picked up in the intestine, where the lymph acquires mainly fats and the plasma takes on many sorts of absorbed materials. The plasma and, to a somewhat less extent, the lymph exchange materials with all the active cells of the body. Excess foods and salts tend to diffuse from the plasma into tissues where they are stored. If the plasma solution develops a deficiency of any of these materials, diffusion tends to be reversed and substances pass from storage into the plasma. These more or less automatic diffusion processes help to maintain a balance between materials in tissues and in their internal environment. Such processes are not, however, sufficient in themselves to stabilize composition and concentration because they do not change the total amount of materials in the system.

The liver plays a special role in the regulation of plasma solutions. By means of the portal vein (p. 150) the liver removes much of the glucose formed by digestion before it circulates through the body as a whole. Glucose in temporary excess is stored as glycogen, which is redigested to glucose and poured back into the plasma as the blood sugar concentration tends to drop after digestion is completed (p. 150). Some of the plasma proteins are formed in the liver. (Where other plasma proteins come from is still a mystery.) The liver also has an essential, although intermediate, part in excretion. Excess amino acids are here converted into urea and other end products, and toxic products from other tissues or from infections may here be converted into less harmful substances. The end products thus formed are not immediately excreted from the body, but pass back into the plasma and are eventually excreted through the kidneys. Besides these processes that influence the composition of plasma, you will remember that the liver produces substances necessary for digestion of fats (p. 123) and that it destroys old red blood cells (p. 145). About a dozen other known processes involve the liver. No wonder that it is one of the largest organs of the body and that serious disturbance of liver function may be quickly fatal!

The final and most delicate regulation of plasma composition is in the kidney, the action of which was discussed on pp. 156-58. This regulation is purely negative. The kidney does not add anything to plasma, but it alters and controls the solution by selecting what substances it removes and how much of each. The concentration of the solution and, indirectly, the water content of tissues throughout the body are also controlled largely by the kidney. The mechanism for this is the balance between the amount of water filtered into the kidney and the amount reabsorbed and passed back to the plasma by the tubules.

Control of plasma solutions, mostly by the liver and kidneys, is essentially the same as in man throughout the vertebrates, from jawless "fishes" upward. Many invertebrates have glandular pouches along the intestine which resemble the vertebrate liver in the way they develop. These are sometimes called "livers" and may sometimes store glycogen, but they do not necessarily correspond with the true vertebrate liver either in structure or in function.

Practically all vascular animals have well-developed organs with the same sorts of regulatory functions as our kidneys. These organs selectively remove end products from the plasma and help to control the water content of the body. In all these animals, the basic mechanism is that internal fluid flows or is filtered into tubules and eventually is passed outside the animal. In all but the simplest animals, there is selective excretion along the tubule, much the same process as in man, although the organs may look quite different. In worms and some other invertebrates, separate tubules occur throughout the body. In some more advanced invertebrates, such as crustaceans, the tubules form in more complex and localized organs. Localization of such organs is related to the development of effective and complex circulatory systems. In worms it might be said that the excretory organs go to the plasma, while in lobster or man the plasma is brought to them.

We have been speaking so far of plasma and lymph. It is these solutions that bathe the cells and form the internal environment in the strictest sense. The formed elements of the blood (p. 144) are in the internal environment and are also a part of the mechanism of its regulation. The red blood cells carry O_2 and CO_2 (p. 145). The withdrawal of CO_2 from the plasma into the red blood cells, where it is not part of the internal environment, is an especially striking part of environment regulation. The removing of foreign invaders, such as disease-producing bacteria, by white cells (p. 145) is also an evident part of regulation of the environment. Finally, the prevention of loss of fluid due to injury is also regulatory, and the whole clotting complex (p. 144) may be mentioned again in this connection.

FLOW: THE HEARTBEAT

There is no more impressive example of the dynamic power of life than the beat of the heart, ceaseless day and night, week after week, and year after year. This incessant activity is evidence that the internal environment cannot be a static system. It must move constantly if it is to remain a livable environment for the cells of the body. Depleted materials must be restored, and waste products must be removed. It is this motion that makes the blood a powerful force of integration of the whole organism, for its motion can carry substances from any part of the body to all other parts.

The necessity of blood flow for life is dramatically established by the fact that cessation of the heartbeat is the symbol and the definition of death. That death in man seems to occur immediately when the heart stops beating is due to the extreme demands of our nervous system, especially the brain. If the blood flow stops, the brain is without oxygen or energy reserves, and it ceases to function adequately within a few seconds. In animals with less demanding nervous systems, activity may continue for considerable periods after the heart stops. Even in man other tissues retain vital activity for variable periods after the nervous system has died; death is not instantaneous throughout the organism.

William Harvey (1578-1657), who discovered that blood circulates, rather despairingly concluded that "The motion of the heart was to be comprehended only by God." Biologists cannot yet say that they have answered the last "why" about this or anything else, but the motion of the heart has now been described in fullest detail and a great deal is known about its causes and controls. In man and other vertebrates, the motion is inherent in the heart itself. A turtle's heart, for instance, entirely removed from the body of the turtle, can keep on beating for a long time. Even small bits of heart tissue, kept alive in solutions resembling lymph, may continue to contract rhythmically. The property of contracting, then relaxing, then contracting again, and so on, is, so to speak, built into vertebrate heart muscle, which is visibly different in structure from muscles which contract only when stimulated through nerves (Fig. 3-26).

The heartbeat starts at a point in the wall of the right auricle, picturesquely called the "pacemaker." From this point the impulse spreads to the left auricle, which starts to contract a little later, and then to both ventricles, which then contract together. Thus the contractions of the four chambers of the heart are kept in effective rhythm and sequence (Fig. 8-2).

In a man at rest the heart rate or pulse is usually around 70 beats per minute. In a hummingbird the rate may be as much as 1000, and in an adult elephant it is only about 30. Considerably slower rates occur in some lower animals. Pulse rate, like other activities, depends on the size and other characteristics of each particular sort of organism. Your own heart beats much faster, as much as twice as fast, at some times than at others. The tissues need more supplies from the blood, especially oxygen, at certain times. It is important to organic maintenance that the blood flow be variable to meet these varying needs. The amount of blood pumped by the heart can be increased in two ways: by increase in the volume pumped at each stroke, and by increase in the number of strokes per minute.

The volume of blood per stroke depends mostly on how much blood reaches the heart between contractions. Flow of blood through the veins to the heart is greatly increased by muscular action (p. 150). These relationships automatically ensure that your heart will pump more blood per stroke when you are active.

The rate of beating increases when you exercise, are excited, or have a fever. The rate is modified by numerous factors. It is in-

THE CONTROL OF THE HEARTBEAT

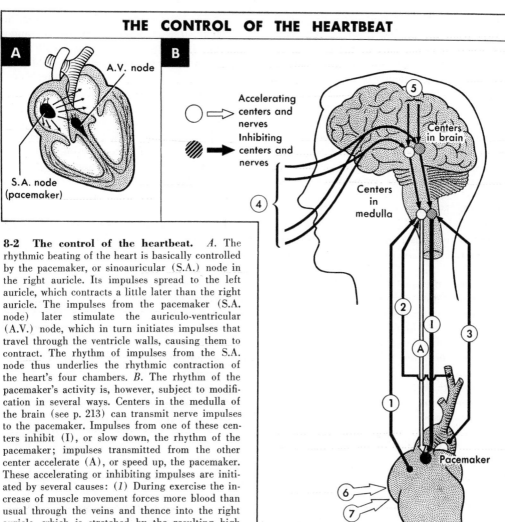

8-2 The control of the heartbeat. *A.* The rhythmic beating of the heart is basically controlled by the pacemaker, or sinoauricular (S.A.) node in the right auricle. Its impulses spread to the left auricle, which contracts a little later than the right auricle. The impulses from the pacemaker (S.A. node) later stimulate the auriculo-ventricular (A.V.) node, which in turn initiates impulses that travel through the ventricle walls, causing them to contract. The rhythm of impulses from the S.A. node thus underlies the rhythmic contraction of the heart's four chambers. *B.* The rhythm of the pacemaker's activity is, however, subject to modification in several ways. Centers in the medulla of the brain (see p. 213) can transmit nerve impulses to the pacemaker. Impulses from one of these centers inhibit (I), or slow down, the rhythm of the pacemaker; impulses transmitted from the other center accelerate (A), or speed up, the pacemaker. These accelerating or inhibiting impulses are initiated by several causes: (*1*) During exercise the increase of muscle movement forces more blood than usual through the veins and thence into the right auricle, which is stretched by the resulting high pressure. The stretching of the right auricle's wall initiates nerve impulses (transmitted through channel 1 in the figure) to the *accelerating* center in the medulla; this then sends further impulses back through channel A to the pacemaker, with a resulting increase in the rate of heartbeat. (Channel A is part of the sympathetic nervous system; cf. p. 219.) (*2*) The increase of respiration during exercise causes an increase in the CO_2 concentration in the blood stream. This is detected by special sense organs located at one site in the carotid artery. Nerve impulses initiated in the carotid artery by the high CO_2 concentration are transmitted (through channel 2) to the *accelerating* center in the medulla, thus ultimately causing the increase in pacemaker activity appropriate to exercise. (*3*) The heart is protected against beating at too high a rate by the presence of pressure-sensitive nerve endings in the dorsal aorta. As the rate of heartbeat increases, blood pressure in the aorta builds up and thus stimulates nerves which transmit impulses (through channel 3) to the *inhibitory* (or decelerating) center in the medulla. This in turn initiates

impulses (I) that appropriately slow up the pacemaker. (*4*) Wholly external stimuli, received through olfactory, auditory, or visual sense organs, can affect the rate of the heart's beating; these stimuli are relayed through higher centers in the brain to the centers in the medulla, ultimately accelerating or decelerating the pacemaker. What perceptions will ultimately stimulate the accelerating centers? What perceptions will affect the inhibitory centers? (*5*) Purely internal stimuli in the form of ideas arising in the cerebral cortex (cf. p. 213) can be similarly relayed to the centers in the medulla. Can you think of examples of ideas that affect your heartbeat? (*6* and *7*) The pacemaker's activity can also be influenced through non-nervous channels; increase of body heat (*6*) during exercise or fever increases pacemaker activity; increase in flow of the hormone adrenalin (cf. p. 219) into the blood also speeds up the heart's beat.

creased by heat, as from exercising or a fever. It is markedly increased by adrenalin (a hormone discussed later in this chapter, p. 178), which is poured into the blood stream when you exercise violently or are excited. The heart is also speeded up or slowed down by nervous impulses from elsewhere in the body. The heart beats whether it receives such impulses or not, but the rate is modified by the impulses. The nerves involved have connections with the brain, and this is another way in which emotions influence heartbeat. There are also nerve connections responding to pressure in the arteries, tending to slow the heart when rapid beating increases the pressure. This is part of the mechanism that keeps the rate near 70 when you are calm and at rest.

The whole mechanism by which blood flow and heart rate are controlled is remarkably intricate and complex. We have by no means gone into all the known complications, and there are still unknown factors involved. Even in summary, however, this is a good example of "the wisdom of the body," of how internal conditions are kept nearly constant under normal conditions but also respond to varying activities and needs.

RESPIRATION

The basic chemical processes of respiration occur in cells; in us and most other organisms the cells sooner or later use O_2 and produce CO_2.[3] These substances are carried from and to the lungs in the blood (Chapter 7). For the body as a whole, rate of respiration depends on how fast O_2 is taken up and CO_2 given off in the lungs. These exchanges in the lungs depend, in turn, on how rapidly and how deeply we breathe.

The lungs themselves have no muscles. They are forced to expand and permitted to contract again by movements of the ribs, which form a box around the lungs, and of the diaphragm, a muscular partition that closes the lower side of the box. Since this motion continues rhythmically even when you are paying no attention to it or are asleep, the muscles might seem to have an inherent rhythm like the heart muscles. It is, however, easy to see

3 See Chapter 6.

that this is not so. You can stop breathing immediately if you wish to, but you cannot commit suicide by holding your breath; even if you had will power enough to hold it as long as you were conscious, breathing would start immediately when you lost consciousness. This suggests that the rib and diaphragm muscles used in breathing are fully controlled by nerves (Fig. 8-3). The conclusion can be confirmed by experiments on animals: if nerves to these muscles are cut, breathing stops permanently. In man, these nerves may be attacked by disease, especially infantile paralysis, and the victim can then be kept alive only by continuous artificial respiration. You are probably familiar with pictures of the "iron lungs" used for such unfortunates. The mechanism forces air into the lungs, which function perfectly. It is only the nerves to the breathing muscles that are damaged.

The rhythm of breathing is maintained not in the lungs themselves nor in muscles of ribs and diaphragm, but in a nerve center. This *breathing center* is located in the *medulla oblongata*, which is the lower part of the brain at the top of the spinal cord (Fig. 8-4). From this center, rhythmic impulses are sent to the muscles of breathing, controlling their alternate contraction and expansion. The breathing center is situated in the central nervous system, with connections to the brain and to other parts of the body. Thus nerve impulses to the breathing center can modify the rate of breathing and co-ordinate it with other bodily activities. When you purposely hold your breath, an impulse travels from the brain and stops the rhythmic impulses from the breathing center to the muscles of breathing. Breathing also stops when you swallow, or quickly catch your breath when suddenly smelling irritating fumes. The mechanism is the same: a nerve impulse from throat or nose to the breathing center.

In usual circumstances the rate of breathing and even the fact that breathing occurs at all is controlled by the amount of CO_2 in the blood. CO_2 acts on the respiratory center and causes it to send out its impulses to the muscles of breathing. The more CO_2, the faster the rhythm of the impulses. If there is

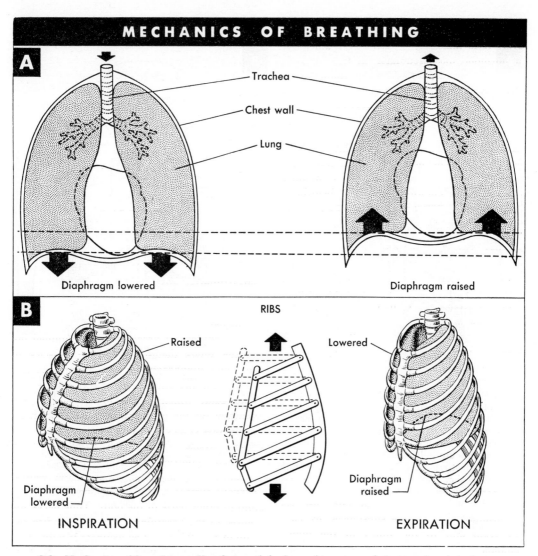

A

Trachea

Chest wall

Lung

Diaphragm lowered

Diaphragm raised

B

RIBS

Raised

Lowered

Diaphragm lowered

Diaphragm raised

INSPIRATION

EXPIRATION

8-3 Mechanics of breathing. Ventilation of the lungs (movement of air in and out) is due to the bellows-like action of the thoracic cavity (bounded by the chest wall and the diaphragm), in which the lungs lie. Air is forced into the lungs when the cavity is enlarged by (1) the elevation of the ribs and (2) the depression of the diaphragm. Air is forced out of the lungs when the thoracic cavity is decreased in volume by (1) the depression of the ribs and (2) the elevation of the diaphragm. *A* shows the extent to which the diaphragm is moved during inspiration (*left*) and expiration (*right*). The thoracic cavity, filled by the lungs, is shown stippled. *B* diagrams the extent to which the ribs move during inspiration and expiration. The central figure schematizes the way in which the ribs are loosely joined to the spinal column and the sternum (breastbone); it shows how elevation of the ribs enlarges the volume of the thoracic cavity.

extremely little CO_2 in the blood (a condition not normal but possible to produce experimentally), the impulses stop and so, of course, breathing stops. The effect of CO_2 on the respiratory center is very strong. When you try to hold your breath for a long time,

CO_2 piles up until its influence is so strong that you start breathing again in spite of yourself. Production of CO_2 by the cells and its diffusion into the blood are approximately proportional to the consumption of O_2. Thus there is an automatic regulation which is

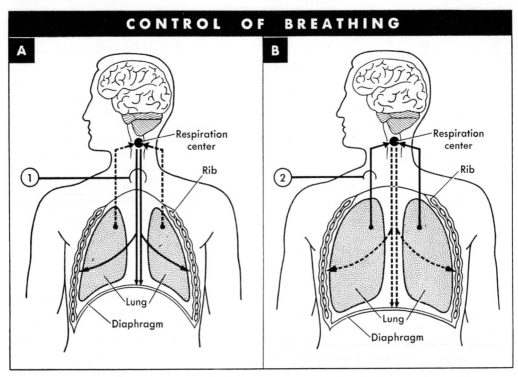

A

B

Respiration center

Rib

Lung

Diaphragm

Respiration center

Rib

Lung

Diaphragm

8-4 Control of breathing. The thoracic cavity is expanded by the muscles of the diaphragm and the intercostal muscles which elevate the ribs. *A.* These muscles are stimulated into action, thus enlarging the thoracic cavity, by nerve impulses that reach them (via channel 1 in the figure) from a respiratory nerve center in the medulla. *B.* The expansion of the thoracic cavity enlarges the lungs and thus draws air in. In the lungs are nerves sensitive to the tension developed when the lungs are fully stretched. Stimulated by the stretch of the lung walls, these nerves initiate impulses that are transmitted (via channel 2 in the figure) to the medulla's respiratory center, whose activity they inhibit. This inhibition of the respiratory center causes the diaphragm and the intercostal muscles to relax and, consequently, the thoracic cavity to collapse, causing expiration. When expiration is complete, impulses from the "stretch receptors" in the lung cease, and so, consequently, does inhibition of the respiratory center. Its renewed activity again stimulates (via channel 1) the appropriate muscles to expand the chest cavity.

unusually direct and simple as organic processes go. Consumption of O_2 in cells leads to increase of CO_2 in blood, which leads to increase in depth and rate of breathing, which leads to increase of O_2 in the blood available for use by the cells. Another interesting point is involved here. CO_2 is a waste product, harmful in any considerable concentration, and rapidly discarded by the organism. Yet it is also an essential part of the bodily mechanism, and on its way out it acts as a messenger from the body as a whole to the respiratory center. [Compare this picture of CO_2 as a "poison" and as an essential agent with what we had to say about blood clotting (p. 144) and water loss in plants

(p. 140). The general point arises again and again throughout biology.]

TEMPERATURE

Life can exist only within a relatively narrow range of temperatures. Particular sorts of organisms live or, at any rate, are at their best only in an even narrower range than that of life as a whole. The rates and even the kinds of reactions in cells are strongly modified by changes in temperature.

It is not surprising that temperature regulation should have evolved as part of the mechanism stabilizing the internal environment. It *is* surprising that such regulation is poor or absent in the great majority of organisms. We happen to be among the relatively few forms in which the temperature of the internal environment is closely controlled. This is so exceptional that use of man as an example should be preceded by a brief review of the very different conditions in other organisms.

The ranges of environmental temperatures in the sea are much narrower than those in other environments. The whole range of surface temperatures is about $-2°$ to $40°$ C. (about $28°-104°$ F.), and these are very local extremes in different places. The upper limit, especially, is most exceptional and can occur only in shallow rock pools in very hot climates. At any one place and depth, the range is usually only a few degrees. Marine organisms are markedly affected in their distribution by water temperature. Those living in warm seas are quite different from those of colder water. In each place, however, the temperature changes are slight. Occasional incidents such as the upwelling of cold water from the depths may cause death to millions of animals adapted to warmer surface waters. Yet the usual fluctuations pose no severe problems, and temperature regulation has never evolved in sea animals. (Penguins, seals, and whales have highly developed temperature regulation, but they inherited this from ancestors that lived on land.)

Fresh water has more variable temperatures than sea water, but still the variation is limited. Its temperature cannot drop much below freezing or rise above the temperature of the adjacent air. Organisms in waters with relatively great seasonal variation in temperature often pass the winter in an inactive state.

It is again (see p. 162) the land that is the most difficult environment. Here temperature ranges are extreme, not only over a continent but also in single localities through the year. In the tropics temperatures change little from one season to another, but they have a daily rise and fall that may be much greater than any seasonal change. Tropical animals, from mosquitoes to monkeys, commonly have a daily rhythm. They are active at the times of day or night when the temperatures suit them; they stay in shelter when temperatures are much higher or lower.

Most extreme seasonal changes occur in the so-called temperate zone, where the climates are most intemperate. If you live anywhere in the central region of the United States, you probably have some summer days hotter than any in the tropics and some winter nights as cold as those in the far north. In this zone land animals, even those that are "warm-blooded," frequently either hibernate (for example, bears and some rodents) or migrate southward (as birds do) in winter. There are many annual animals and plants. These die when cold weather comes, and their offspring survive the winter as inactive, well-protected eggs or seeds. Many insects and most herbaceous plants meet the problem of temperature range in this way, without internal temperature regulation. Perennial plants and trees become individually quiescent in winter, and most of them shed all their leaves in fall in the temperate zone. Practically the only organisms fully active here throughout the year are among those that do have internal temperature regulation—birds and mammals.

As far as has been detected, no protists, plants, or invertebrate animals have any means of temperature regulation.[4] They live in environments with relatively slight fluctuation in temperature, or they have adaptations (a great variety of them) permitting them to be physiologically inactive when temperatures are too low or too high for their normal activities. It is a striking anomaly that the two groups of land organisms that are much the most abundant and varied—flowering plants and insects—have no means of regulating their internal temperatures.

There are, to be sure, a few important exceptions among the insects. No insects maintain a constant body temperature; yet some do regulate their temperatures to a certain extent. Locusts move about so as to absorb more or less heat from the sun if they are too cool or warm. Ants move their larvae to warmer or cooler places in the nest. Some insects warm themselves up for action by exercise, much as athletes do. Honeybees maintain temperature in their hives within livable limits. If the temperature drops to $13°$ C.

4 Some invertebrates have evolved regulatory devices that maintain some vital processes at a constant rate in spite of variations in temperature.

(about 55° F.), the bees in the hive become very active and by release of body heat raise the temperature to about 25° C. (77° F.). In summer the bees ventilate the hive with their wings.

Among the vertebrates, some are "cold-blooded" (fishes, amphibians, and reptiles) and some are "warm-blooded" (birds and mammals). A "cold-blooded" animal may very well have a higher temperature than a "warm-blooded" one. The difference is not in coldness or warmth but in the fact that "warm-blooded" animals have mechanisms for keeping the internal temperature constant and "cold-blooded" animals do not. Since the terms "warm-blooded" and "cold-blooded" are therefore flatly wrong, it is necessary to call those with internal temperature-regulating mechanisms *homeothermous*, and those without *poikilothermous*.[5]

Poikilothermous animals tend to take on the temperature of their environments. This is only a tendency: poikilotherms do have some heat-regulating ability. A swiftly moving animal, even a fish, raises the body temperature well above that of its surroundings, and this warming in turn helps to speed up the reactions that produce it. Reptiles often bask in the sun on cool days, and absorption of radiation can raise their temperatures above that of the air. On hot days they avoid the sun and may burrow into cooler earth.

Only homeotherms tend to maintain a constant temperature by entirely internal mechanisms. The efficiency of the mechanisms varies. Variations of as much as 15° C. in internal temperature may not be fatal in some birds, but under usual conditions the temperature range is kept within a degree, more or less. Everyone knows that in man the body temperature is usually around 98.6° F. (37.0° C.) and that a rise or fall of 2° F. or so means trouble. (Of course, the fact that 98.6° F. is marked as "normal" on clinical thermometers does not apply precisely to all individuals. Perfectly healthy individuals may have somewhat lower or higher temperatures normal for *them*, and, in the same individual, temperature may vary a degree or so without

5 Homeothermous = same temperature; poikilothermous = variable temperature.

its meaning that he is ill.) The temperature of a normal, healthy man remains nearly the same, say 99° F. in round numbers, whether the air around him is at 115° F. or at 40° below zero. Obviously we have some means of producing heat, some means of losing it, and some means of striking a balance between the two.

Heat is produced by oxidation processes in cells. The important source is in muscles, which produce much heat when exercised or even when tensed. We tend voluntarily to move about more when it is cold than when it is hot around us. Even if we do not, our muscles automatically become tense in the cold. If the tenseness is extreme, the muscles begin to quiver, and we say we are shivering. When we warm up, the tenseness disappears and we feel relaxed.

Heat is lost by radiation and evaporation. The blood flows through a network of capillaries in the skin, where it is so near the surface that it loses heat by radiation. The more blood flows here, the more heat is lost. The amount of flow is regulated by constriction or enlargement (dilation) of the capillaries. In cold air the capillaries constrict; less blood flows near the skin, and less heat is radiated. In warm air the capillaries dilate; more blood flows, more heat is lost. Evaporation causes heat loss and hence is cooling, as everyone knows who has ever put a wet cloth on his brow. Cooling evaporation occurs all over our skin, mostly from sweat glands which secrete more liquid when the air is warm, less when it is cool. There is also much evaporation from our lungs.

Let us see, now, how these mechanisms work:

When it is cool	our skin capillaries are constricted —and we radiate less heat. our sweat glands are inactive— and we lose less heat by evaporation. our muscles are tenser— and we produce more heat.
When it is warm	our skin capillaries are dilated— and we radiate more heat. our sweat glands are active—and we lose more heat by evaporation. our muscles relax—and we produce less heat.

These diverse mechanisms are put into action by nervous impulses in nerves outside the sphere of conscious control. We cannot stop sweating when we want to, even to the extent that we can control breathing. The nerve impulses involved originate and are co-ordinated in a temperature-regulating center at the base of the brain.[6] The center reacts automatically (by reflex, see p. 242) to signals from sensory nerves in the skin where the sensations "hot" and "cold" originate. It is also possible that the center reacts directly to the temperature of the blood around it.[7]

Human beings differ in two ways from most of our fellow homeotherms. First, few other animals have as many sweat glands. Birds have none, and dogs and other carnivores very few. Heat loss is increased by more rapid breathing and by secretion of more fluid in the mouth. Everyone has seen dogs panting, with tongues hanging out and dripping, in hot weather. The second difference is that humans have no really useful natural insulation. Practically all other homeotherms are covered with thick fur or feathers, highly effective insulation both for keeping heat out when the sun is hot, and for keeping it in when the air is cool. There is another reflex which raises hairs and feathers, increasing the thickness of the insulating layer in very cold air. Oddly enough, man still has this reflex although we have lost the fur that makes it effective. In us it just produces goose flesh. We have made good our loss of fur, as we have many of our other deficiencies, by artificial means. We wear clothes, in cold weather at least. Do you suppose there is any relationship between our loss of fur and exaggerated development of sweat glands?

Chemical Co-ordination

We have repeatedly emphasized that the whole of a multicellular organism is a unit, with all its parts co-ordinated and interacting.

6 In the part called the thalamus.
7 Since cooling mechanisms operate when our body temperature is above 37° C. and heating mechanisms operate only when it is below 37° C., it follows that the thalamus must contain something equivalent to a thermometer capable of an absolute measurement of temperature. Or it may be thought of as a thermostat with a fixed temperature (37° C.) setting.

Now let us think a little more about how the organism is unified, what ties it together. In the first place, it is bound together mechanically. It is enclosed in a skin of some kind. The various internal cells and tissues are in contact with each other and fastened together in various ways and at many points. There are skeletons, a bony framework, an external shell, the united cell walls of plants, or other arrangements that enclose part or all of the organism and to which tissues are fastened.

Another sort of unification is achieved through the nervous system. A nervous system is absent in protists,[8] plants, and a few animals but is present in the great majority of animals. We know that it is of supreme importance in ourselves, so much so that it is to be considered at some length in the next chapter.

Still another mechanism of co-ordination exists, and this one is present in all organisms whatsoever: it is the movement of chemical substances from one part of the organism to another. Chemicals diffuse and flow in the protoplasm among the parts of a protist within its single, cell-like mass. In nonvascular multicellular plants and animals, substances also diffuse from one cell to another and may be carried by water of the external environment in cavities or otherwise in the immediate vicinity of the organism. In vascular organisms, movements within and between cells occur, too, and another feature has been added, especially apt for carrying chemical substances through the organism. There are internal fluids which, sooner or later, may move from any active cell of the body to any other.

As multicellular organization has been more intensively studied, it has become evident that all living cells must have some influence on adjacent cells. This influence is usually if not always chemical in considerable part, although of course mechanical, electrical, and other influences also occur. It has also become clear that any cell may produce substances that influence parts of the body quite distant from it. In other words, chemical co-ordination occurs everywhere in the organism, from and to all its cells, and not just between particular organs. A good but relatively simple example is

8 In Chapter 20 we describe the merest beginnings of a nervous system analogue in the most highly evolved protists, the ciliates.

that of CO_2 (p. 168). Produced by all actively respiring cells, CO_2 passes into the blood stream and produces a specific effect at one point, the respiratory center, through which it initiates changes that, again, affect the whole body.

Chemical co-ordination seems to be a completely general phenomenon of life, occurring in and between all the living parts of all organisms. That is the really important point, the general principle to which your understanding should cling. There are, however, certain specific chemical compounds produced by definite organs which diffuse into the blood stream and produce special, sometimes spectacular, results in the organism. These, the *hormones,* have been intensively studied in man and some other vertebrates. Remembering that hormone action is only a limited class of a much more general phenomenon, we may use the human hormones as first examples of chemical co-ordination.

THE HORMONES OF MAN

The hormones of man and the organs that produce them seem in the light of present knowledge to be more elaborated and advanced than they are in most other organisms. In such a situation there are two equally logical ways of going about a study of the subject. We can start with the more complex end product of evolution and then try to trace its relationships to simpler and also to earlier products. (The simpler are not *necessarily* the earlier.) Or we can start with the simpler or earlier and work up. In this book we have used both methods on different topics. There is no virtue in consistency that cannot be outweighed by other considerations. As regards the hormones, they are now fairly well known in man and are far less understood in other organisms. It seems wiser here to work from the better to the less known.

The human hormones are produced in *endocrine glands* or in *endocrine tissues* present in organs that also have other activities. For simplicity we may speak of *endocrines* in general, whether the tissue concerned forms the whole of an organ or not. The name is from Greek roots, meaning "inside separation"—in other words, *internal secretion.* By the way, it was Claude Bernard (p. 159) who

coined the term "internal secretion" and started biologists on the way to understanding chemical co-ordination. The secretion is called internal because the secreted substances, the hormones, diffuse directly into the blood and do not leave the tissue—go outside it—through tubes, as in other glands. In man, but not, as we shall see, in all other organisms, each separate endocrine is definitely localized in the body, whether it constitutes a whole gland or not. The various local endocrines are

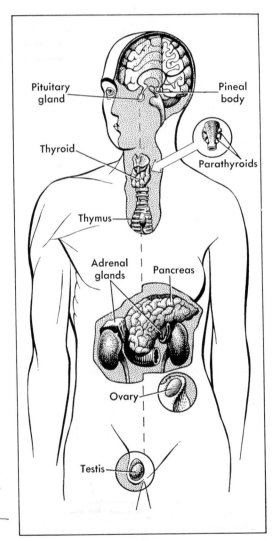

8-5 The location of the human endocrine glands. The left side of the figure includes the glands (testes) characteristic of the male, and the right side those (ovary) characteristic of the female.

TABLE 8-2

Some human endocrines and hormones, and some of their effects *

Endocrine	Hormones	Some processes affected or controlled	Some symptoms of excess	Some symptoms of deficiency
Thyroid	Thyroxin	Level of metabolism, oxidation rate, etc.	Irritability, nervous activity, exophthalmia [1]	Cretinism [2] when severe in infancy. Lethargy, myxedema [3]
Parathyroid	Parathormone	Calcium balance in blood	Bone deformation	Spasms; death if severe [4]
Adrenal medulla [5]	Adrenalin	Stimulation similar to that of autonomic nervous system [6]	Increased blood pressure, pulse rate, blood glucose	(See footnote 7.)
Adrenal cortex [8]	(Several)	Salt balance, carbohydrate metabolism, etc.	Excessive maleness [9]	Addison's disease [10]
Pancreas [11]	Insulin	Sugar balance in blood	Shock, coma	Diabetes [12]
Ovary [13]	Estrogen	Female sex development and menstrual cycle	——	Interference with menstrual cycle and sex activities
	Progesterone	Control of ovary and uterus during pregnancy	——	Sterility or miscarriage
Testis [14]	Testosterone	Male sex development and activity	——	Lessened development of male characters and less sexual activity
Pituitary	(Many)	Control of other endocrines, thyroid, sex glands, etc.	(Symptoms related to the glands controlled)	
		Growth	Gigantism	Midget
		Kidney action	Excessive water in body	Excessive loss of water
		Milk production	——	Lessened or no milk production

* Do not memorize this list. Read it through to get a general idea of endocrine activity, and then use it for reference on any particular questions that may arise.

[1] Exophthalmia is excessive protrusion of the eyes, "popeyes."

[2] Cretins are mentally deficient dwarfs.

[3] Myxedema is a disease the symptoms of which include loss of vigor, falling hair, and puffy skin.

[4] Parathyroid deficiency used to follow surgical removal of thyroid tissue when part or all of the parathyroids were accidentally removed at the same time. Surgeons are now aware of this danger and avoid it.

[5] The medulla is the internal part of the adrenal gland.

[6] On the autonomic (or sympathetic) nervous system, see p. 217.

[7] Deficient production of adrenalin or even entire removal of the adrenal medulla seems to have no ill effects. The symptoms noted under "excess" are apparently normal results of increased adrenal secretion, but they may appear even though no adrenalin is produced.

[8] The cortex is the outer part of the adrenal gland.

[9] Excessive maleness in either sex seems in some cases to result from overproduction of some adrenal cortical hormone, probably an indirect reaction through other endocrines. This is not one of the more essential activities of the cortical hormones.

[10] Addison's disease, fortunately rare, has among its symptoms coloration (bronzing) of the skin, low blood pressure, general weakness, loss of water from the body, and upset carbohydrate metabolism.

[11] The pancreas as a whole is not an endocrine gland, but it contains clusters of cells, the islets of Langerhans, that have an endocrine function and secrete insulin.

[12] The principal symptom of diabetes is marked increase of sugar in the blood.

[13] The ovary as a whole is not an endocrine gland, but some of the cells around the developing eggs produce the hormone estrogen. After an egg leaves the ovary a "yellow body," the *corpus luteum*, develops, and this secretes the hormone progesterone.

[14] Like the ovary, the testis is not an endocrine gland but does contain hormone-producing tissue.

scattered through the head, neck, and trunk without any particular anatomical relationship to each other or to their activities (Fig. 8-5). In fact, their activities characteristically affect many or all parts of the body.

Since the secretions of endocrines are rapidly carried everywhere by the circulatory system, no particular placement is necessary for their effectiveness. It seems logical, somehow, that the male hormone should be produced in the same organs that produce the male sex cells, sperms. Undoubtedly there is a relationship, but it is historical rather than functional. The male sex hormone also affects processes of the body far distant from the testis, for instance, growth of hair on the face and changes in the vocal cords. There is no obvious reason why the endocrine most involved in general metabolic level, the thyroid gland, should be in the neck. The reason is, again, historical: the thyroid has evolved from an organ that *did* have a functional relationship to this region of the anatomy.[9]

The hormones resemble each other only in being secreted into the blood and influencing processes at various other points in the body, or throughout the body. They are all chemical messengers, mechanisms of co-ordination. They do not belong to any one family of chemical compounds. At least one (insulin) is a protein, but others belong to quite diverse groups of simpler compounds.

Table 8-2 is a list of some of the better known endocrines, hormones, and their activities. The list is not exhaustive. For instance, the duodenum produces a hormone, secretin. The stomach also produces a hormone, and the liver may. Other organs, such as the pineal body in the brain or the thymus gland at the base of the neck, may be endocrine glands, but their activities are not yet clearly understood.

Note the kinds of things that hormones do. Some influence chemical balances, especially in the blood. In other words, they help importantly to stabilize the internal environment. Others affect rates of processes in growth and in general bodily activity. Still others go into action at particular times or periods in life and co-ordinate special developments and processes. Try making a classification of hor-

9 See Fig. 22-23.

mones along these lines: you will find that the distinctions cannot be made clear-cut. The hormones, too, interact and are parts of a balanced system in the unified organism.

The thyroid. We do not propose to discuss each endocrine and hormone in detail, but we will make further remarks about some of them to exemplify their action or to bring out a few points of special interest. We have already mentioned the thyroid and might consider it in most detail as an example. Its secretion, which has been precisely identified and synthesized chemically, is a combination of an amino acid with iodine; it is called *thyroxin*.[10] This substance influences the rate of metabolism, especially of oxidation-reduction or respiratory processes, in all the cells of the body. It normally is delivered to the blood and circulates in extremely small amounts. Decrease in this tiny but essential amount lowers metabolic activity in the whole organism, and increase speeds up activity.

Hormones were first discovered because an excess or deficiency of one of them may produce striking abnormalities or diseases. This is still the basis of the widespread interest in them. The association of thyroid degeneration with a disease was noted in 1874, one of the earliest definite recognitions of endocrine action. Much later thyroxin was isolated, and finally in 1927 it was artificially synthesized. The most striking and tragic effect of thyroxin deficiency occurs if severe deficiency starts in early infancy. The victim never grows up, physically or mentally, and becomes a mentally subnormal dwarf, a cretin. Thyroxin deficiency developed after normal growth has been completed has less drastic but still serious effects. If severe, it results in myxedema, a disease characterized by decreased bodily vigor, sluggish mentality, puffing of the skin, and often anemia.

In both cretinism and myxedema the symptoms reflect lowered metabolic rate, the difference depending on whether this affects early growth. Excess thyroxin production, which rarely occurs before early adulthood, has results that would be expected from heightened

10 As actually found in the thyroid gland, the iodine-containing amino acid is part of the larger molecule of a protein, but the amino acid alone has all the hormonal effects.

metabolism: loss of weight, nervousness and excitability, fast pulse, excessive sweating, and sometimes damage to the overworked heart and digestive upsets. It also usually has an oddly unexpected result, and one that may immediately identify a victim of this disorder: the eyes may bulge out markedly (Fig. 8-6).

Excess thyroxin production can be corrected by removal of part of the thyroid gland. Deficient production may be caused either by deficiency of the thyroid gland itself or by inadequate supply of iodine, an essential element in the thyroxin molecule. It can be corrected by continual doses of thyroxin or, if only the iodine supply is at fault, by adding iodine to food. Once cretinism has developed, it can be greatly ameliorated but hardly cured altogether.

The fact that iodine in very small amounts is necessary for thyroxin production has some interesting ramifications. Iodine must be acquired in foods or drinking water. With either source, the iodine must come ultimately from the soil. There are regions in which the soils contain little or no iodine, and in these regions people drinking local water and eating local foods develop thyroxin deficiency. It was noticed long ago that cretinism, myxedema, and less severe cases of thyroxin deficiency are much more common in certain areas, including parts of Switzerland and of the Great Lakes region of North America. Students were very slow to make the connection between this distribution of disease and the lack of iodine in the soil. Once they did, the remedy was obvious. Iodine is supplied in the diet, most conveniently by addition of small amounts to table salt. As you know, iodized salt is now sold everywhere in the United States. (In view of the fact that both thyroxin and iodine are decidedly harmful in excess amounts, what do you think of the indiscriminate use of iodized salt when no iodine deficiency is known or likely to occur?)

Goiters were common in many people in regions of iodine lack (as the cause was later learned to be). In fact, such regions are often called "goiter belts." A goiter is an enlarged thyroid gland. With low iodine supply, there is a compensatory enlargement of the thyroid which increases thyroxin output. Sometimes this suffices and the individual is entirely nor-

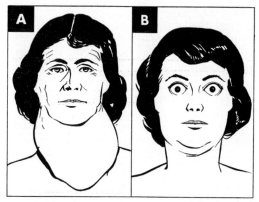

8-6 **Effects of thyroid gland malfunction.** *A.* Goiter. *B.* Exophthalmia.

mal except for having a goiter—which, incidentally, was considered a highly desirable female adornment by many of our forebears! Thyroxin deficiency may, however, persist even after great enlargement of the thyroid.

It seems simple enough: a goiter indicates iodine deficiency; therefore add iodine to the diet. But once again (and you are probably getting used to the fact that complications are plentiful in living organisms) things are not so simple. People with adequate iodine supply and *excess* production of thyroxin also frequently have goiters. Any enlargement of the thyroid *not* compensatory for scanty iodine brings on excess of thyroxin. Thus a goiter may mean either too much or too little thyroxin, and it is advisable to have a physician find out which (Fig. 8-6).

Insulin. Among the other hormones, none has been more widely talked about than insulin. This is because insulin represents a medical triumph that has alleviated a great deal of human misery. The disease of diabetes (more strictly, "sugar diabetes" or *diabetes mellitus*) is a disturbance of carbohydrate metabolism which results in abnormally large amounts of sugar in the blood plasma. It is diagnosed by the constant presence of considerable sugar in the urine.[11] The disease is rather common and had been well known for centuries before any way of checking it was found.

[11] Some sugar may occasionally be present in normal urine, as in times of stress (anger, fear).

In 1884 experiments on pancreas function revealed that dogs lacking the pancreas develop all the symptoms of diabetes. There are two kinds of glandular tissue in the pancreas. One secretes digestive enzymes (p. 122), as the experimenters knew. The other, forming what are called the islets of Langerhans (after their discoverer), was of unknown function. Further experiments showed that diabetes probably resulted from the lack of some substance secreted by this tissue. Years were spent by numerous investigators trying to extract a substance from the pancreas that would prevent diabetes. All efforts failed until Banting, collaborating with Best, McLeod, and Collip, worked out a method of extracting secretions not from the whole pancreas but from the islets only. The experimental difficulties had arisen from the odd fact that the other parts of the pancreas produce enzymes that destroy the secretion of the islets in the pancreas. The substance finally extracted in 1922 was, of course, insulin.

Since 1922 methods have been developed for producing insulin in bulk suitable for treatment of diabetes. The solution must be injected; it cannot be taken by mouth because insulin is destroyed by digestive fluids. Even now there is no known *cure* for diabetes, but periodic injection of insulin counteracts the symptoms so effectively that diabetics can now look forward to long and nearly normal lives. The procedure is merely supplying the blood with a hormone not sufficiently supplied by an abnormal endocrine tissue.

Adrenalin. It is worth while to comment briefly on adrenalin as a hormone of quite a different kind from thyroxin or insulin. The adrenal glands (Fig. 8-7) consist of two separate parts, inner and outer, which are of different origin, produce different hormones, and apparently have nothing to do with each other except that their history has brought them into nonfunctional contact.[12] Adrenalin, sometimes called epinephrin, is secreted by the inner part (the medulla). Unlike thryroxin or insulin, it is not necessary to life. The whole inner (but not outer) part of the adrenal glands can be removed without pro-

12 Incidentally, the same is true of the pancreas and the islets of Langerhans.

ducing any illness or apparently changing any reactions in the organism.

Although the gland producing it can be removed without any apparent effect, adrenalin is a very powerful drug. It has been isolated and identified chemically and is also made synthetically. Injection of either the natural or synthetic compound results in a number of strong reactions: the heart beats faster, blood pressure rises, the glucose content of the plasma increases, the pupil of the eye is dilated, and hair stands on end or goose flesh appears. There is a relationship between these apparently unrelated reactions: they all happen in man and in many other mammals, such as dogs, under the stress of fright, surprise, or great excitement. But, and this is itself very surprising, they also happen under these circumstances whether adrenalin is released into the blood or not. They are reactions produced not only by adrenalin but also and equally strongly by stimulation of part of the nervous system, in the autonomic or sympathetic system (p. 219).

There is a deep mystery here, and one that should not be glossed over by the usual statement that adrenalin mobilizes us for action in moments of sudden stress. If this is really a mobilization (and anyone who has been, as they say, frozen with fear may doubt it), then there are two systems of mobilization, one chemical and one nervous, which seem to do exactly the same thing. Perhaps there is a clue in the fact that the nerves producing these reactions also produce a substance very like adrenalin. Perhaps we are in an evolutionary stage of change-over from one system to the other. But the clue raises new mysteries. Which way is the change-over going, and above all, why? That is a question we do not expect you to answer; we cannot answer it with certainty, but it is worth thinking about.

The pituitary. The pituitary gland of man is a small nubbin only about 15 millimeters in greatest diameter and weighing about half a gram. It is situated inside the skull at the base of the brain (Fig. 8-7). In spite of its small size, it is the most complicated of all the endocrine glands. It produces at least fifteen different hormones and prob-

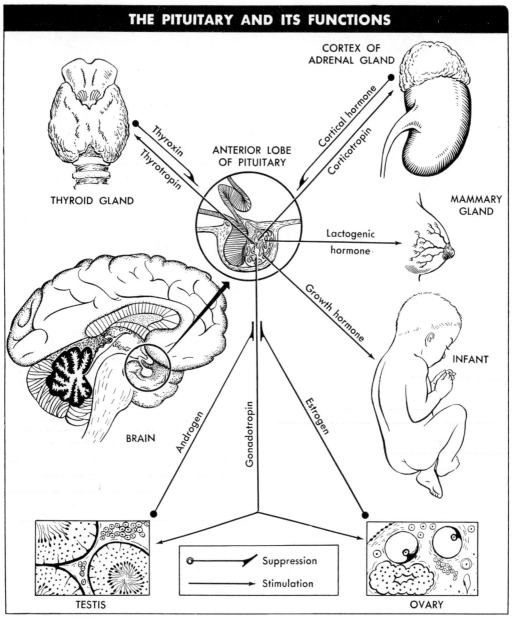

8-7 The pituitary gland and its functions. The pituitary gland lies at the base of the brain; most of its important hormones are secreted by its anterior lobe. Reading clockwise, these include: (1) a hormone (the adreno-corticotropic hormone, or ACTH), which stimulates the adrenal cortex to secrete its hormones; (2) a hormone that prepares the mammary glands for milk secretion; (3) a hormone promoting growth; (4) gonadotropic hormones, which stimulate the secretions of ovaries and testes; and (5) a thyrotropic hormone, which stimulates the thyroid gland to secrete thyroxin. The thyrotropic, ACTH, and gonadotropic hormones act as controls on the other endocrine glands. In these cases the pituitary is regulated by the concentration of the hormones it causes the other glands to secrete. Thus, thyroxin in the blood (a result of thyroid secretion) reaches a concentration which causes the pituitary to stop secreting thyrotropic hormone. The same is true of the adrenal-cortical and sex hormones: their concentration in the blood regulates the extent to which the pituitary gland secretes ACTH and gonadotropins. These are excellent examples of the way the body is *organized* to maintain automatically an optimum condition.

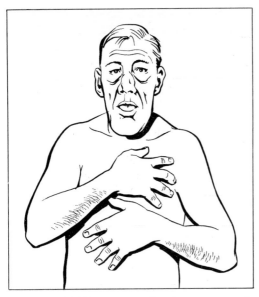

8-8 Acromegaly, an example of pituitary malfunction. Note the abnormal enlargement of hands, jaws, and facial bones caused by excessive secretion of growth hormone.

ably several more. It has been called "the master gland," and with some reason because it is the principal chemical co-ordinator of the activities of the other endocrines. The co-ordination is mainly by pituitary hormones that act on particular endocrines and stimulate their growth or activity. For instance, one hormone acts on the thyroid, which degenerates if the hormone is deficient; at least four act in different ways on the sex glands; and others act on the islets of Langerhans in the pancreas and the outer part (or cortex) of the adrenal gland. In at least one case the control is by a balance of opposite reactions: one pituitary hormone acts in a way *opposite* to that of insulin; that is, it increases blood sugar. Still other hormones balance similar reactions. Pituitary hormones affect metabolism of carbohydrates, for instance, and this metabolism is also affected by hormones from other endocrines.

Besides co-ordinating the whole system of hormones, the pituitary produces hormones with special reactions of their own. The most spectacular of these is the growth hormone, which promotes and controls normal increase in size of the body. Overproduction of the hormone during early life produces giants, and underproduction, midgets. Robert Wadlow, an American who was 8 feet 10 inches high and still growing when he died at the age of 22, was a pituitary giant; Martina de la Cruz, who lived to the ripe age of 74 without topping 1 foot 9 inches, was a pituitary midget.[13] Such giants and midgets are usually of fairly normal proportions and structure. If secretion of the growth hormone is excessive *after* growth is completed, however, serious deformity may result from enlargement of hands, feet, jaw, and facial bones (Fig. 8-8).

There is a saying that was current in ancient Rome and in various forms and languages ever since: "Who guards the guardians?" "Who watches the watchman?" ("Who takes care of the caretaker's daughter?" may be a debased form.) If the pituitary co-ordinates the other endocrines, what co-ordinates it? A good answer—and perhaps you will be the one to supply it—would make you a very famous biologist. Glimpses and partial answers are all we have as yet. There is some evidence that the other endocrines reciprocally help to regulate the pituitary by a mechanism something like the governor on an engine. When thyroxin concentration rises in the blood, production of thyroid-stimulating hormone in the pituitary is slowed down, and fall of thyroxin concentration speeds up production. We also know that external environmental conditions such as length of daylight can react on the pituitary through the nervous system. "In the spring a young man's fancy lightly turns . . .," and in the lengthening days of spring bird and animal pituitaries start the sex glands working. But how? That is one of the questions a future biologist will have to answer.

HORMONES OF OTHER ANIMALS

Other vertebrates. As would be expected, animals more nearly related to man resemble him more in endocrines and hor-

13 Most dwarfism is not of pituitary origin. We have seen (p. 176) that cretinism is due to thyroxin deficiency. The dwarfs usually seen in circuses, with large heads and trunks but short arms and legs, do not owe their deformity to endocrine disturbances but to the inheritance of a factor producing short limbs during prenatal development.

mones. Most or all mammals seem to have just the same endocrine system that we have. This makes it possible to obtain hormones used in human medicine as a by-product from our food animals. It has also made possible most of our knowledge of our own hormones by experimentation on other mammals, especially dogs.[14] The other vertebrates have similar endocrine systems, but differences begin to appear.

One interesting fact is that the same hormones may have different roles in different groups. There is in man and, as is more to the point, in woman a pituitary hormone, prolactin, which stimulates secretion of milk when a child is born. Prolactin has the same role in all mammals, as would be expected. But exactly the same hormone occurs in birds. In pigeons it stimulates the secretion of "pigeon's milk," which is not milk at all, but a secretion in the crop—part of the alimentary canal—that is regurgitated and fed to the young. In hens the hormone produces broodiness. It is even present in some fishes. The evidence suggests that prolactin evolved long before milk did, that it came to have various effects on maternal behavior, and that in mammals it somehow took over regulation of a new, related process.

In many fishes, amphibians, and reptiles pituitary hormones control variable coloration of the skin. The color is controlled by nerves in some species, but by hormones in most. It is a most peculiar fact that these hormones also occur in mammals, including man, although no mammals have the special cells in the skin that produce color variation. You have half the mechanism for matching yourself to your surroundings, but lack the effective half! Whether these hormones are only useless baggage inherited from our remote ancestors or whether they do have some other effects in us is entirely unknown.

It is less puzzling to find that different but

14 Let us point out here that most of our intimate knowledge of human and animal physiology has involved experimentation with animals. It has resulted in the saving of many lives and the alleviation of endless misery for both men and animals. It is unfortunate that we cannot explain things to the animals and call for volunteers, but anyone who understands the situation must conclude that experimentation, humanely performed, is justified—even from the dogs' point of view.

related processes may be regulated by the same hormone in different groups of animals. Change from a tadpole to a frog can be brought on prematurely by injection of thyroxin or can be prevented altogether by removal of the thyroid. This metamorphosis is quite different from anything in our life histories, but it involves heightened metabolism, and thyroxin raises our metabolism, too. Going still further back, there is convincing evidence that the thyroid gland in the earliest vertebrates evolved from a grooved structure that carried food particles into the front end of the digestive tract. This explains why the thyroid gland is in the neck. (We have said that there was an historical explanation, p. 176.) This raises a bigger question: why and how did a feeding mechanism turn into an endocrine gland? It is possible to frame a hypothesis, at least. Probably you can think of one.

When the older groups of vertebrates are compared with the younger, another tendency appears. The older groups seem to have simpler endocrine systems. At least some of the hormones present in mammals are absent, as far as has been determined, in fishes. Pituitary extract from fishes lacks the thyroid- and adrenal-regulating hormones and even the growth hormone. Fishes do grow, and they do so in a very well-regulated and co-ordinated way. It is impossible to believe that chemical regulation is not part of the process. The sensible conclusion is not that chemical growth regulators are absent, but that when fishes evolved these had not yet become localized as the product of one particular gland.

Invertebrates. Chemical co-ordination has been less studied in the invertebrate animals. This is natural enough, since the strongest motive for such study in vertebrates, and especially in mammals, has been immediate applicability to problems of human health and medicine. Even from this point of view, however, it is desirable and truly practical to learn all we can about other organisms. This knowledge can be expected to throw light on the most basic aspects of chemical control. It is from such wide comparisons that new points of attack and really fundamental advances are likely to arise.

Endocrine organs and hormones secreted by them are definitely known to occur among some of the more active mollusks (octopuses, cuttlefish) and in crustaceans and insects. These are all relatively advanced animals with well-developed circulatory and nervous systems. In several sorts of insects it has been demonstrated that metamorphosis from the larval ("worm" or caterpillar) stage to the adult involves hormones. In at least some of these insects hormones active in the process are secreted by endocrine glands in two different locations. One gland, closely associated with the brain, secretes a hormone that stimulates metabolism and secretion in the other, which is situated farther back in the thorax, the three body segments to which legs and wings are attached. The hormone from the thoracic endocrine then regulates the metamorphosis. In some insects there is also evidence that hormones from the glands in the head have an influence, probably indirect, on sexual processes, on molting, and on more general metabolic processes.

The known insect endocrines and hormones strongly invite comparison with some basic features in the vertebrate system. In both there are glands in the head (the pituitary in the vertebrates) closely associated with co-ordinating centers of the nervous system. In both, hormones from these master glands affect widespread metabolic activities, including the stimulation of endocrine glands elsewhere in the body. The two systems certainly evolved entirely separately. The ancestries of insects and vertebrates separated well over 500 million years ago and at a stage when there cannot have been a definite endocrine system. The similarity is adaptive. It bears witness to the fact that all animal tissues have fundamentally similar reactions. It also suggests that the development of local endocrine glands secreting specific hormones was based on a more primitive, more diffuse system of chemical co-ordination.

Some insects, mollusks, and crustaceans also have hormones that affect temporary changes in color. These hormones, too, have been shown to be secretions of definite endocrine glands in the head region—different glands in the different groups. You recall (p. 181) that vertebrates also have hormones that influence variable skin colors. Those vertebrate hormones injected into crustaceans sometimes produce color changes. There must actually be a close chemical similarity in some of the hormones in spite of the very distant relationships of the animals producing them. This, again, is good evidence of similar reactions in all animals and is suggestive of an extremely ancient basis for chemical co-ordination. There is more evidence to back up this suggestion. For instance, adrenalin has been identified in a sea snail and even in a protist, and the eggs of sea urchins contain a compound related to thyroxin and with similar (though not quite identical) effects on tadpoles.

Even in insects, with the most complex endocrine systems yet found among invertebrates, the systems are much simpler than in the vertebrates. In invertebrates other than insects and perhaps crustaceans (which are especially related to insects) the systems are still simpler. In fact, in the vast majority no endocrine glands or tissues have been identified. In this majority of lower animals it is thus unjustified to speak of endocrine systems at all. This does not mean that chemical co-ordination is absent.

It is, as you can readily imagine, extraordinarily difficult to isolate and identify a co-ordinating chemical unless this is produced by a definite gland or is involved in some distinct event such as the metamorphosis of an insect. A substance secreted diffusely or in small groups of cells scattered through the body and constantly involved in maintenance of a stable condition is especially hard to identify experimentally. Yet we do know (as mentioned on p. 173) that compounds similar to and even identical with hormones occur in animals that have no endocrine glands. This and other evidence is sufficient for the highly probable conclusion that chemical co-ordination is present in all animals, and even in protists.

Let us now turn around for a moment and look at the subject from the opposite direction. Chemical co-ordination appeared very early in the history of life. In protists and the simpler multicellular animals the co-ordinating chemicals, hormones by the definition of producing effects at a distance from their point of origin, moved and still move mainly by diffusion. The development of vascular circulatory systems provided a much more effective way in which the hormones could move throughout the body. In the earlier vascular animals and in their less modified descendants, the hormones were and are still produced throughout the body or in scattered cells. With further evolution came a tendency for complication in the system of hormones, for more hormones, and for each to be more specific in its action. The cells producing some of these also became more specific and came to be aggregated in local tissues and organs. This tendency has gone farthest in man and the other higher vertebrates. The organs formed are the endocrine glands. Even in man, however, there are activators or hormones that are not produced in endocrine tissues or glands, although they circulate in the blood, and there are still others that spread in the most primitive way, by diffusion.

Evolution of the nervous system was going on at the same time as the evolution of endocrine systems. Both the nervous system and the endocrine system are co-ordinating and integrating mechanisms for the organism as a whole. The two could hardly be independent of each other, and they are not. Part of the evolutionary trend has been toward closer co-ordination between the two co-ordinating systems. *In insects and vertebrates, independently, this trend led to development of a master endocrine which is actually attached to the main co-ordinating mass of the nervous system.*

Do not take the whole of this history as established fact. There is much inference in it, but the inferences are the most reasonable interpretations of the evidence that we now have.

THE HORMONES OF PLANTS

Everyone has heard of "plant hormones." They are widely advertised both as stimulants for the growth of desirable plants and as killers for weeds. Plants differ from the more highly evolved animals in that their hormones are secreted by unspecialized tissues. We concluded, above, that this was the primitive method of chemical regulation in animals

also, and it still persists to some extent even in animals that also have well-developed endocrine systems. It is therefore a universal mechanism of co-ordination in organisms. Indeed, in plants no other special mechanism has evolved, neither a more specialized chemical system nor a nervous system. The hormone system itself has certainly undergone evolutionary changes in plants, but there is still very little knowledge as to exactly what the changes have been.

Since plants have no other active system of organic co-ordination but are nevertheless well–co-ordinated organisms, their hormones are particularly important. Each plant grows at a particular time of the year; each grows in its own characteristic way, each flowers at a definite time, and the fruits and leaves of some perennials also drop at definite times. There is nothing haphazard about these activities. They are co-ordinated processes of the organism, and the co-ordination must be largely if not altogether chemical in nature. It is, in fact, well-established that hormones are involved in these and other processes. Yet only a few of the hormones have been definitely identified, so that this is a pioneering field of research at present. A special difficulty is the fact that the hormones are not secreted in endocrine tissues, where their isolation would be less difficult. The most fully known plant hormones are some called *auxins,* involved primarily in growth processes.

Auxins. Auxin is another invented word, coined from a Greek root meaning "to increase" or "grow." The term is still fairly precise in application to one definite class of plant hormones which promote elongation in growing cells, although they also have other activities. Their existence and some of their properties can be shown by simple experiments.

If oat seeds are germinated (Fig. 8-9) they first send upward a bluntly pointed, leafless shoot.[15] If you cut off the tip, the shoot stops growing. Now place the tip, cut side down, on a little cube of gelatin or, better, agar jelly (a seaweed product much used in

15 Actually the shoot has a leaf inside it. Botanists call the shoot a sheath or coleoptile because it surrounds the first leaf of the plant.

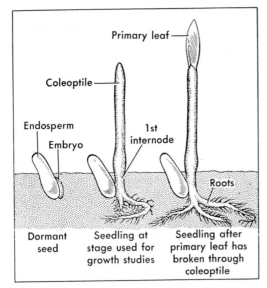

Primary leaf

Coleoptile

Endosperm

Embryo

1st internode

Roots

Dormant seed

Seedling at stage used for growth studies

Seedling after primary leaf has broken through coleoptile

8-9 The coleoptile of the germinating oat seed. On the left is the oat seedling before germination. In the middle figure germination has taken place. The young shoot system consists of a tubular sheath, the coleoptile, which contains within it the primary leaf. The primary leaf (*right*) eventually breaks through the coleoptile. The coleoptile itself is the subject of growth experiments undertaken to study plant hormones.

biological work) and leave it there for about two hours. Put the cube of jelly on the cut end of a decapitated shoot. The shoot starts growing again. Something diffused from the tip into the jelly, and that something—an auxin—promotes growth in the shoot (Fig. 8-10).

Does the experiment as we have outlined it really prove this? As a matter of fact, it does not. Before you read on, try to think of alternative explanations and of ways to test them as hypotheses.

There are at least two other possible explanations: (1) perhaps growth of the shoot was only temporarily stopped when it was decapitated and would have started again in a couple of hours anyway; or (2) perhaps the jelly alone would have caused growth. To test these hypotheses run the experiment with *controls*. Decapitate three shoots at the same time. On one, put a jelly cube that has had an opportunity to receive diffused material from a tip. On another put a cube exactly similar except that it has not been in

contact with a tip. On the third shoot do not put anything. Only the first shoot will grow, and the presence of a growth substance in the tip is substantially proved. It is still better to run multiple tests, giving each of the three treatments to a dozen or so shoots (equal numbers for each treatment).

Now try another experiment. Put a cube of jelly that contains diffused auxin on a cut shoot in such a way as to cover only one side of the cut end. As the shoot grows, it will bend away from the side in contact with the jelly. That side receives more auxin and therefore grows faster, and the shoot is forced into a curve. As you will see later on (Chapter 10), this important reaction explains many of the motions and growth patterns of plants.

Three distinct but chemically related auxins have been isolated from plants and identified. Oddly enough, the same substances are common in animals and one of them is present in human urine. Here is further evidence of the unity of life, but the relationship is not wholly clear.

In extremely small concentrations auxins cause elongation of cells and hence growth in length, but if the concentration increases they inhibit growth. The effect is different on different plant tissues. A concentration that causes most rapid elongation of stems stops the growth of roots. Thus auxins are not merely growth promoters. They are growth *regulators*, either stimulating or retarding growth depending on the circumstances.

A number of chemical compounds not normally present in plants have auxinlike effects due to resemblances to the natural auxins in molecular composition and structure. Such chemicals can be synthesized in commercial quantities and have many increasingly practical applications. Probably the most familiar at present is 2,4-D.[16] This compound produces abnormal, distorted growth and eventually death in wide-leaved plants but has little effect on the narrow leaves of grass. It can therefore be used as a spray to free a lawn of weeds. (It kills clover, though.) Auxins and auxinlike synthetics are also used to stimulate root formation on cuttings, to

16 2,4-D is a merciful abbreviation of 2,4-dichlorophenoxyacetic acid.

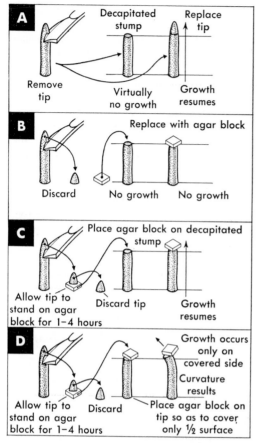

A		
Remove tip	Decapitated stump — Virtually no growth	Replace tip — Growth resumes

B		
Discard	Replace with agar block — No growth	No growth

C		
Allow tip to stand on agar block for 1–4 hours	Place agar block on decapitated stump — Discard tip	Growth resumes

D		
Allow tip to stand on agar block for 1–4 hours	Discard	Place agar block on tip so as to cover only ½ surface — Growth occurs only on covered side — Curvature results

8-10 Plant hormones. *A, B, C,* and *D* are a series of experiments demonstrating the existence of a diffusible growth hormone (auxin) in the tip of the oat coleoptile.

produce seedless fruits, to keep stored potatoes from sprouting, and to delay or force blooming in flowers.

Other hormones. There is plenty of evidence in plants of essential hormones other than the known auxins. It has, however, proved extremely difficult to isolate them, and we still have very little direct knowledge of them. For instance, indirect evidence strongly indicates that the local effect of auxins may depend on hormones from other parts of a plant, but these auxin activators have not yet been surely isolated.

Of all problems involving hormones in plants, none arouses more interest than that of the short-day and long-day plants. In these

plants the onset of blooming is somehow determined by the length of daylight. Short-day plants (such as ragweed or cocklebur) blossom as day length decreases below a characteristic value, and long-day plants (such as plantain or coneflower) as it increases. This interesting phenomenon has been intensively studied since it was first recognized in 1918. It seems quite impossible to explain the phenomenon unless there is a chemical flowering hormone, production of which, in these particular plants, is affected by relative lengths of darkness and light, among other things. Much, however, is known about this hormone (or, perhaps, hormones). For instance, its formation must begin, at least, in leaves, and it is transported only in living tissues, especially the phloem. The hormone is not an auxin, even though auxins can influence flowering. Just what the flowering hormone is may be discovered at any moment, and the discovery will be a great advance in our whole knowledge of the chemical regulation of organisms.

Chapter Summary

The condition of free life: stability of the organism.

The organism: more than the sum of its parts; its capacity to regenerate and heal itself; fields of organization.

Internal environment: its stabilization as part of evolutionary progress.

Vascular systems: the sea within us?

The roles of the liver and kidneys in regulating plasma composition.

Control of blood flow; heartbeat control; pacemaker and nervous regulation.

Controls on respiration, especially the role of CO_2 as chemical messenger.

Regulation of body temperature: devices that cool the body; devices that retain body heat.

Co-ordination through chemical communication: the special endocrine glands.

The hormones of man: thyroid functions; insulin; adrenalin; the pituitary secretions.

Hormones of other animals.

Plant hormones in the control of growth and flowering.

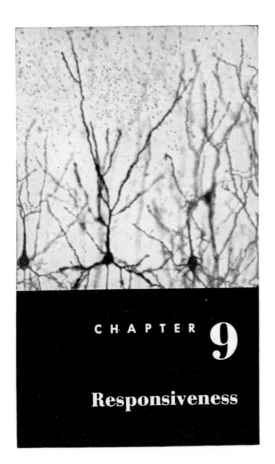

These cells (×188) are from the cerebral cortex of the cat's brain. Their special functions have evolved from an ancient and universal property of cells to receive and react—in a word, to respond— to stimulation. (Photo by J. Z. Young)

CHAPTER 9

Responsiveness

A sunflower turns to the sun. A hawk dives from the sky. There is more to life than vegetating, even for a vegetable. Most of the life processes that we have considered up to this point are of the sort sometimes called "vegetative." Whether they occur in plants or in animals (and we have seen many basic resemblances between the two), they involve primarily the maintenance of the organism, its metabolism, keeping it going, perhaps in the face of environmental difficulties and changes. While these processes of maintenance were being considered, it was obvious that they were a background for other activities. Organisms not only maintain themselves through environmental changes. They also *respond* to these changes by characteristic activities. Because everything cannot be studied at once, the existence of such responses has been taken for granted or mentioned in-cidentally in earlier chapters. Now we are ready to consider them more specifically and systematically.

The Reactivity of Protoplasm

If you touch an ameba with a very finely pointed needle or glass rod, it moves away (Fig. 9-1). An ameba has no organs (or organelles) for perception of touch—no nerves and no muscles. Nevertheless it obviously "felt" being touched. Its reaction involved putting out an extension on the opposite side of the animal, so that the "feeling" somehow was conducted from one side to the other. The end result was movement away from the foreign, inedible, and possibly harmful object. We have no right to conclude that it really felt the stimulus in the conscious way that we feel the prick of a needle, and we have every reason to believe that it did not. We also know that the conduction of an effect from this contact did not occur, as in us, along nerves. Nor did movement of the ameba involve muscles. Nevertheless the whole sequence was similar to what happens if you stick your finger with a needle. There was a *stimulus*, there was *conduction* of a signal of some sort set off by the stimulus, and there was an appropriate *response*. The response was appropriate in the sense that, by and large, movement away from inedible objects is likely to take the ameba into territory more propitious for its activity and survival.

The incident shows that an ameba can and does respond as a whole organism. It also shows, and this is our immediate concern here, that protoplasm reacts to environmental changes. It was the protoplasm as a whole, or more particularly the cytoplasm, that reacted in the ameba. This is a general property of living protoplasm wherever it is found, in a protist or in any cell of a higher plant or animal. If you kick a ball, it is also possible to say that the ball "responds" to a stimulus, but obviously there is a great difference. The "response" of the ball depended wholly on the stimulus, and not on any activity initiated in the ball. In protoplasm the response comes from inside and may have little relationship to the nature or strength of the stimulus. The ameba did not move away because it was pushed, and (within limits) its reaction does not depend on how hard you prick it. (Nevertheless there are nonliving mechanisms that respond in their own way, from within, and without reference to the strength of stimulus above a lower limit. Can you think of one?)

The usual technical term for the capacity of protoplasm to respond to stimuli is *irritability*. The term is in such wide use by biologists that it is necessary for you to know it. However, here is a situation in which technical usage runs up against everyday understanding of the same word. It is ludicrous to speak of an ameba or a plant cell as "irritable" in the usual sense of the word. It would have been better if biologists had called protoplasm *reactive* or *responsive;* and we prefer these terms in this book.

Even in the ameba we saw that the whole reaction involved three factors or phases. First, the stimulus was received and started some sort of process in the protoplasm. Second, reaction spread from the point where the stimulus was received; there was conduction of a signal. Third, there was a definite response to the signal; in this example the response was a movement. In the ameba the three phases are practically inseparable and certainly are not localized. The same reaction occurs regardless of where the stimulus touches the organism. Conduction is through its cytoplasm as a whole, and the response may also occur anywhere.

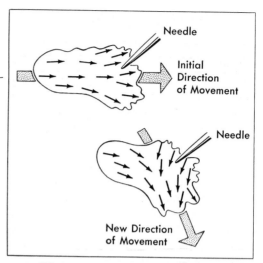

9-1 **The ameba's response to being touched with a needle.**

The evolution of multicellular animals has been accompanied by clearer separation of the three processes of reaction to a stimulus. In all but the simplest of animals special cells, tissues, and organs are involved in each phase. There are *receptors*, and these are practically always specialized to receive particular sorts of stimuli. They are sense organs. Then there are *conductors*, usually nerves, which carry signals from the receptors. There are also special organs of response, which are called *effectors* because they carry out, or effect (not affect), a response characteristic for the given organism. The conductors, of course, carry signals not only from the receptors but also to the effectors.

The specialization of receptor-conductor-effector organs is highly characteristic of animals. Plants are reactive or responsive to many environmental stimuli, but the mechanisms of the reactions are simpler and less specific. Their reactions, usually slow and not complex or varied, occur mostly through the relatively undifferentiated tissues of growth and maintenance. There are no special conductor cells comparable to the nerves of animals, and receptor or effector organs are few and simple. Here is another of the really basic differences between plants and animals. (What truly basic difference do you already know?)

Stimulus and Response

KINDS OF STIMULI

A stimulus is a change in the environment capable of producing a response in an organism. A stimulus carries information that something has happened around the organism. (Of course we do not mean that organisms as a rule are conscious of the information as such.) Any organism must, in order to survive, be sensitive to stimuli from *usual* environmental changes with *essential* effects on the organism. Such changes do occur in most environments for most organisms. Certain broad kinds of stimuli affect any protoplasm. Particular, narrower kinds affect some organisms and not others.

Let us be more specific. All protoplasm and therefore all organisms are affected by any considerable change in pressure, in chemical composition, in temperature, in radiation, and in electrical properties of the environment. An ameba reacts to all these kinds of stimuli, and so do you. So, too, do plants, although in them the reactions may not be apparent in a short time. In the ameba you saw reaction to pressure when you touched the organism. Reactions also occur if you add a bit of weak acid or salt solution (changing osmotic values) to the water around the ameba; if you heat the water; if you shine a light (radiation) on it from one side; or if you send a weak electric shock through it.

Within these broad classes, discrimination of particular stimuli and reactions to them differ greatly among organisms. Both plants and animals usually react to the pressure of gravity. In most plants, the main stem turns upward, away from the direction of gravity. Many higher animals, including humans, have special organs that signal the position of the body or, especially, of the head in relationship to the pull of gravity. Even with your eyes closed you know whether your head is upright or not. Fishes have (humans do not) special organs for reception of pressure changes in currents of water. The rhythmic pressure waves in air that we call "sound" are stimuli for many animals, and we and numerous other animals can distinguish the frequency with which such waves reach us as well as their intensity.

Discrimination of different chemical stimuli may also be highly developed in animals. Even an ameba moves toward some chemical stimuli, those associated with food, and away from others. We have the special chemical senses of taste and smell. Our sense of sight discriminates among radiations by direction, intensity, pattern, and frequency, the last of which we perceive as color.

No organism reacts to any and all possible stimuli from the environment. For instance, all organisms react to *some* wave lengths of radiation but not to *all* wave lengths (Fig. 9-2). Our special receptors for radiation, the eyes, react only to a limited range, from violet (shorter waves) to red (longer waves). Some animals, such as bees, can see radiation that we cannot. Bees see ultraviolet, invisible to us, but bees do not see red rays, which are visible to us. Other cells in our bodies do react to radiation that is not visible to us: we are tanned by ultraviolet, and we feel warm in infrared radiation.

No organism has receptors for or any reaction to the radiations that we use in radio communication, which are much longer waves than in light. We perceive them only by using devices that turn them into other sorts of stimuli: sound waves or (in television) visible light waves. It is improbable that magnetism, even when very intense, is a stimulus for any organisms.[1]

It is a striking fact that many possible stimuli capable of conveying information about the environment do not actually produce any reaction in organisms. As a rule, however, it seems that such information would not really be useful (and certainly is not necessary) to the organisms incapable of receiving it. The only radio waves in nature come from the stars or from lightning, and information about the stars or about lightning after it has struck could hardly be useful to a plant or animal. It certainly is not true that something or someone has neatly ar-

[1] There have been hypotheses that some birds detect the earth's magnetism and also that some of them react to radio waves, but at present these hypotheses are unproved and seem improbable.

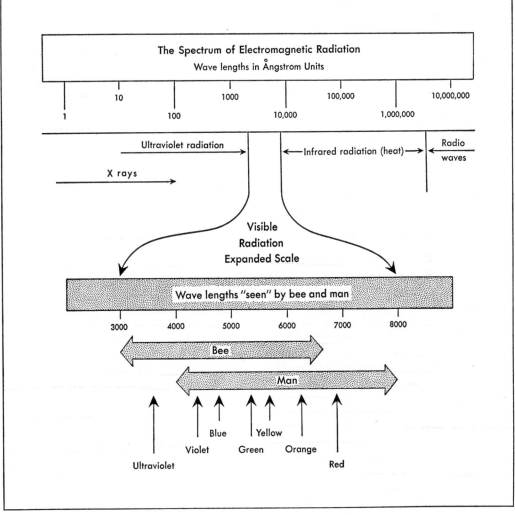

9-2 The sensitivity of man and the honeybee to radiation of different wave lengths. Living organisms perceive as visible light only a small fraction of the total spectrum of electromagnetic radiation. The radiation visible to organisms falls within the wave lengths of 3000 to 8000 Ångstrom units. The lower portion of the figure indicates, on an expanded scale, the wave lengths seen by the honeybee and by man. Note that the bees "see" ultraviolet but do not see red light.

ranged for each organism to receive precisely all the information of any use to it. That would require purposeful, efficient planning, which is conspicuous in nature only by its absence. It is true, for obvious reasons (answers to the first "why"), that all organisms receive the information *necessary to* their ways of life. Few if any receive more. What bearing would you say this has, if any, on the probability of mental telepathy?

EFFECTIVENESS OF STIMULI

A stimulus can produce a reaction only if an organism is capable of receiving it. That is a truism. There are, however, some less obvious points involved in the effectiveness of a stimulus. The first point is that a very weak stimulus may produce no reaction at all. For each sort of stimulus and for each organism there tends to be a strength or intensity below which no reaction occurs. This is the *thresh-*

old of stimulation. If you take a glass of pure water and add one drop of dilute salt solution, the water will still be tasteless. Keep on adding and tasting, drop by drop, and finally at a definite concentration the water will begin to taste salty. This threshold varies greatly in different people and in the same person at different times, but it is often around a 0.1 per cent concentration of salt in the solution.

For any stimulus there is generally an intensity below which a reaction is not produced. Above this intensity, whether a reaction is really produced, whether in fact the threshold is crossed, depends mainly on how long the stimulus continues and how rapidly it changes. In other words, there may be thresholds for duration and rate of change of stimulus as well as for intensity, and the actual threshold in an organism depends on all three.

RESPONSES

A stimulus may affect any process of change in a cell or organism. A response, then, may be anything that an organism can do. The common response to increase in heat, for instance, is simply a speeding up of metabolism. More complexly (p. 172) there may be an additional response which sets cooling mechanisms in operation. Such reactions are part of organic maintenance, which we have already reviewed in previous chapters. Now we are especially interested in more specific responses to immediate environmental changes, to particular stimuli.

The nature of the response depends more on the organism than on the stimulus. This is a special characteristic of responsiveness in living things. How a football responds to "stimulation" depends precisely on the stimulus. If you kick it or throw it, the result is always a motion fully determined by the speed, strength, and direction of the force applied to it. If you stick a pin into it, the response is quite different, and if you set fire to it, the response is different still. In organisms, the responses are built in, so to speak, and have no such simple relationship to the stimulus. The response built into the nerve of a tooth is pain, and an exposed nerve

gives a pain reaction whether you poke it, eat a lemon, drink cold water, or give it an electric shock. (Some dentists have a nasty way of finding out whether a nerve is alive by an electrical test.) If someone hits you in the eye, you see "stars"—actually a flash of light. A hard blow stimulates the optic nerve, the built-in response to which is the sensation of light. This specificity of response determined by the organism rather than by the stimulus is not confined to the nervous system. Some kinds and intensities of pressure, chemicals, radiation, and electricity may all produce the same response in an ameba, rounding into a ball. Muscular tissue responds to a variety of mechanical, chemical, and electrical stimuli, and always in the same way, by contracting.

There are some other special characteristics of responses in living matter. As a rule the response does not begin immediately when a stimulus, even a strong stimulus, is applied. There is a _latent period_ before the response begins. This period varies greatly in different tissues, but is usually very short, often about $\frac{1}{1000}$ second. Nervous and muscular tissue, in which these reactions have been most studied, also have the property of not responding again immediately after a response. For a short period, the _refractory_ period, no stimulus is sufficient to produce a new response. In the heart muscles this period is relatively long, up to $\frac{1}{5}$ second or so. However this property may have evolved, it has important and useful consequences. No matter how often or continuously the heart is stimulated, the muscle cannot remain contracted (which of course would stop its pumping and lead to death). In ordinary striped muscle (see p. 64) the refractory period is much shorter, often around $\frac{1}{1000}$ second. You can wiggle a finger faster than the heart can beat, and you can keep the finger muscles contracted indefinitely. There is some question whether a refractory period is a universal characteristic of protoplasm, but it does occur in amebas. An ameba that has rounded into a ball as response to a stimulus does not, and presumably cannot, do so again for several seconds.

Nerves and Nerve Action

In all but the lowest animals the most essential and characteristic part of the mechanism for specific responses to stimuli is the nervous system. *All special receptor organs transform stimuli into nerve impulses.* A nerve impulse is an electrical signal transmitted along fiberlike extensions of nerve cells. The nerves are the conductors from receptors to effectors. Their pathways and connections determine what, in the end, the response will be. Increasing complications along these pathways are mechanisms for co-ordination of actions, for memory, perception, association, and finally for all the richness of our own mental lives. The nervous system, too, has come to share with chemical integration the "wisdom of the body," automatic maintenance of the internal environment.[2] The nervous system of a clam or of a worm is one of the great marvels of the world. What can we say of the nervous system of man, so vastly more marvelous still? It is this that makes us mankind, organisms wholly beyond the potentialities of any others that have ever existed.

NERVE CELLS

One of the most remarkable facts about the nervous system is that, with all its complication and flexibility of reaction, it is made up of cells, all of which perform essentially the same action. The action is produced by the sort of extremely complex, interlocking processes so characteristic of life, but the action itself is rather simple: it is merely the transmission of impulses from one end of the cell to another. The impulses are of the same sort in all nerves. They may be involved in seeing red (either literally or figuratively), in composing a poem, in telling us that we are hot or cold, or in co-ordinated contracting of muscles that eventuate in a song or a swift kick. The impulses are of the same kind. It is not the separate nerve cells, but their arrangements and connections that determine the qualitatively different outcomes. Again, as on pp. 159-60, we see that properties of the organism are different from and much more complex than those of its separate parts.

2 See Chapter 8, p. 159.

The unit of the nervous system is the nerve cell or *neuron* (Fig. 3-27). For all their differences in size and shape, neurons are fundamentally alike in all animals that have them. The nucleus lies in a central cell body which is drawn out into two or more fibrous projections. The projections may be short, but usually are long fibers, much thinner than hairs. Nerve impulses can pass in either direction along these fibers. In some lower animals an impulse may come into the cell body along any fiber and then move away through all the others, out to their tips. Most neurons in higher animals, however, are so arranged anatomically that impulses always travel through them in the same direction. A frequent, although not the only, arrangement in these cases is with numerous, shorter branching fibers, the *dendrites*, on one side, through which impulses come into the cell body, and one longer fiber, the *axon*, on the other side, carrying impulses away from the cell body (Fig. 3-27). The fibers are often enclosed in one to three sheaths. The sheaths are not essential to conduction, for unsheathed fibers also occur and transmit impulses of the same sort. The sheaths look rather like insulation on telegraph wires, but probably are not insulators. They seem to be involved in regeneration of injured fibers.

A nerve such as you are likely to see when you dissect an animal in the laboratory is not a single fiber but a whole bundle of fibers belonging to different neurons. In vertebrate animals most of the cell bodies of nerves are in or near the brain and spinal cord. Some of the fibers may run through nerves for long distances. In man some extend down to the toes from cell bodies in the small of the back. It is exceedingly difficult to follow a single fiber through its whole length, and earlier students could not believe that a fiber in a toe was actually part of a cell with its nucleus several feet away (Fig. 10-14). Experimentation and more delicate dissection have proved that this is true.

THE NERVE IMPULSE

The nature of the nerve impulse has been the subject of long, ingenious experimentation and of much dispute. The main features now seem to be well established, although details of changes within the fiber are not wholly clear. How would you go about finding what chemical and electrical changes are going on in a fiber much smaller than a hair? Just to make it more difficult, the changes are over in a tiny fraction of a second and everything is back as it was before the impulse passed. It is surprising that anything is known. In fact, so much is known and the process is so complicated that we can only indicate its general nature here. The impulse is electrical, although apparently associated with and set up by chemical changes. It is not simple conduction of an electrical current, as in sending a message over a wire. The impulse accompanies a zone of change of electrical charges in the fiber, a zone that moves along with the flux of small, purely local currents from the fiber through the fluids immediately around it.

The mechanism of the nerve impulse has a bearing on the properties that, in turn, help in understanding the whole process of reaction to stimuli in animals. One consequence of the mechanism is that the impulse moves much more slowly than a current in a wire. The speed varies greatly from one nerve to another and one animal to another, but is always slow enough that conduction takes appreciable time. In the fastest fibers of mammals, including man, the rate is about 100 meters per second. That is a little less than 225 miles per hour, which no longer seems very fast to us in this age of much faster planes. In some of the slow invertebrate fibers the rate is as low as 5 centimeters per second, or about $1/10$ mile per hour. A tortoise can walk faster than that. Even in us, some fibers have rates lower than 2 meters per second, which is no faster than you can walk.

Another point about the mechanism of nerve conduction is that the strength of the impulse is standardized. It is not like putting an impulse of variable strength into a wire. The reaction is local in each part of the fiber. If an impulse is started at all, it starts at full strength and the strength is not affected by the length of the fiber. A usual way to make this sort of process understandable is to compare the fiber with a sprinkled line of gunpowder. If the powder is lit at one end, the flash travels to the other end.

The rate of travel and the strength of the flash do not depend at all on the heat of the match with which it was lit or the length of the line. A nerve fiber similarly transmits impulses by local power at each point and has an *all-or-none reaction*. Comparison with the gunpowder cannot be carried further, because the reactions involved are really quite different.

No matter how strong the stimulus is, the nerve impulse has a fixed strength. How, then, does it happen that the impulses do have varied intensities in their effects? The answer is that a stimulus seldom starts a single impulse. Unless the stimulus is extremely brief, repeated impulses pass along the fiber one after the other. A stronger stimulus results in impulses that are closer together, hence more frequent. More of them arrive at the other end, and so they can have a stronger effect even though each has the same intensity.

All protoplasm reacts to stimulation and conducts impulses. Nerve cells do not have unique properties, but are only specialized in the sense of heightening the particular property of conductivity and directing it anatomically. Nerve cells also carry on respiration and other metabolic processes of protoplasm in general. In fact all nerve cells have particularly high oxidation rates and are especially sensitive to variations in concentration of sugar, the principal source of energy. Thinking really is work, not just because some of us are reluctant to indulge in it, but because it does use energy.

NERVE CONNECTIONS

In some lowly animals, receptor cells are in direct contact with an effector. The receptor or sensory cell may receive a stimulus and transmit an impulse (as if it were a neuron) direct to a muscle cell (Fig. 9-3*A*), which contracts when the receptor is stimulated. In a next stage of complication, the sensory cell starts an impulse in a separate nerve cell, through which the impulse travels to a muscle fiber or other effector (Fig. 9-3*B*). In either of these reaction systems, the reaction is necessarily simple and entirely inflexible. A sufficient stimulus, one above threshold, on the sensory cell invariably and necessarily results in an impulse to one particular effector which responds in a way that can vary only in duration.

In higher animals sensory cells are rarely in direct contact with effectors—and never in vertebrates. Almost always there is more than one nerve cell between receptor and effector, with branches in the possible lines traveled by nerve impulses. A *sensory neuron* carries impulses from the receptor and passes them on to a *motor neuron*. The motor neuron in turn conducts the impulse to an effector, characteristically a muscle fiber, which reacts. This is still a simple chain from receptor to effector. It is a reflex arc (Figs. 9-3C and 10-14). Even this relatively simple arrangement brings in the possibility of more effective and flexible response than direct connection between a receptor and an effector. When there are separate sensory and motor neurons, a sensory neuron can stimulate more than one motor neuron (Fig. 9-3D). Response to stimulation can be more extensive, and continued stimulation can spread so as to involve more and more effectors. Yet the reaction must still be a simple reflex, a connection from one particular receptor to one particular set of effectors.

The next complication, which has become practically universal among higher animals such as insects or vertebrates, is the occurrence of still other nerve cells, one or many, between the sensory and the motor neurons (Fig. 9-3E). These additional cells are *association neurons*. Through them, an impulse may be passed on selectively to any of a number of different effectors. Impulses from different receptors may also be brought together and routed to the same or different effectors. Simple reflexes can still occur, but the possibilities for more complex and flexible reactions are tremendously increased.

The fibers through which an impulse is passed from one neuron to another are not continuous or fused to each other. They may be pressed close together, but there is always a tiny gap between them, a separation by cell membranes, at least.[3] The point of transfer, with its tiny gap, is called a *synapse*. The

[3] Of course it would be impossible to prove that they never fuse, but it is now reasonably well established that they do not normally do so.

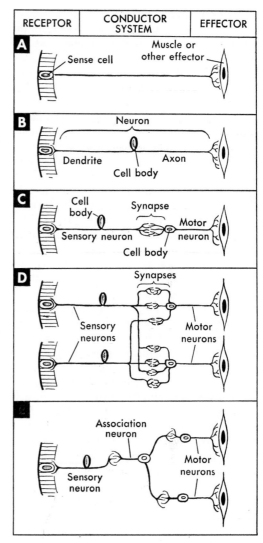

9-3   Receptor-conductor-effector systems.

actual mechanism of transfer is still disputed. When an impulse reaches a synapse, a minute quantity of a chemical compound often appears there. The compounds that have been detected (there are at least two of them) have a stimulating effect on nerves. One of them is very like adrenalin (p. 178). The transmission may be by diffusion of these chemicals across the synapse: the chemical is produced by one nerve fiber and stimulates the other. Or the transmission may be electrical, and the chemicals in question may facilitate the passage of an electrical impulse.

It seems probable that this is one of many questions that have not been asked in the right way. Recent studies suggest that the question "Is transmission chemical or electrical?" is not sensible. Transmission probably involves a complex interplay of chemical *and* electrical processes.

The fact that impulses are not conducted through fibers from one neuron to another has some important consequences. One or a few impulses or widely spaced impulses may arrive at a synapse and not cross it. If numerous impulses arrive at close intervals, they add up (*summation* occurs, technically speaking), and finally they are transmitted across the synapse. A brief, weak stimulus produces few and widely spaced impulses. These may cross no synapses, so that no response occurs, or few synapses, so that response is weak and local. A long, strong stimulus produces many and closely spaced impulses. These readily cross synapses, so that response definitely occurs, and can cross many synapses, so that response may become strong and widespread, especially as associative neurons become involved.

Another important property of synapses is that once an impulse has been transmitted across them, subsequent impulses pass more readily. It may take a long volley of closely spaced impulses to cross a synapse, but once this has occurred, a short sequence of impulses or even a single impulse may cross. The fact that impulses have already been transmitted facilitates transmission of later impulses, and the phenomenon is called *facilitation*. If no further impulses do come along, the effect fades out, often in a matter of seconds or minutes. If impulses keep coming along before facilitation has entirely faded out, the facilitation is maintained and increased. Continual crossing of a particular synapse at appropriate intervals can maintain facilitation there for a lifetime. Thus there are established pathways in the nervous system, routes across facilitated synapses, along which impulses move more readily and rapidly.

Once a response or an association has occurred, it occurs more readily soon thereafter. If it occurs often, its readiness increases and it may be maintained indefinitely. Clearly this is a mechanism that goes far toward explaining habit, learning, and memory.

The termination of a nerve fiber on an effector, such as a muscle (Fig. 9-3), is anatomically unlike a synapse, but it has similar properties of summation and facilitation.

NERVE PATTERNS AND RESPONSES

In rather rapid succession you have met *neurons, dendrites, axons, sensory neurons, motor neurons, reflex arcs, association neurons,* and *synapses.* This is a bare minimum of terms necessary to describe nerves and their arrangement, but you may begin to feel a little bogged down in anatomy. The whole business should become clearer and less burdensome if you will stop a moment and think about what nerve actions and nerve patterns mean in you and in other animals—especially in you.

In animals with well-developed nervous systems, *specific reactions to stimuli depend mainly on how nerves act and how they are arranged.* The *kinds* of reactions that *may* occur depend on the nerve pattern: how many nerves there are, what receptors stimulate them, how they run to synapses and to effectors, what associative paths are present, and so on. This arrangement is determined mostly by heredity, although it is also more or less affected by the conditions of early development. The reactions that actually *do* occur depend first of all on the stimuli that an individual happens to receive, next on the mainly inherited nerve pattern, and finally on the past experiences and current condition of the individual. Facilitation, in particular, depends largely on what responses the individual organism has already made.

Thus in higher animals what an animal does, its whole pattern of behavior, and indeed what sort of creature it is, are more closely related to its nervous system than to any other one factor. As neurons become more abundant and patterns more complex, culminating in man, there is more anatomical variation within the normal pattern of the species. Responses and associations become more varied, too, and so do the experiences imprinted on the nervous system. Herein is the basis not only of the high and numerous capacities of mankind, but also of individuality and of personality.

Receptors

The nervous system is largely involved in handling information about the environment. (It also handles information about the organism itself, but that is a different point for later consideration.) It is involved in responses to changes in the environment and also, with increasing complexity, with sorting out and associating information, storing impressions for future responses, varying responses according to current situations, and other activities all of which go back to the receipt of information about the environment. (Can you imagine what your mental life would be like if you had never known anything about things outside your own body?) Before further discussion of the nervous system as a whole, it is advisable to know something about receptors, the means by which information is first acquired.

We have inherited from antiquity the popular notion that we have just five senses: sight, hearing, taste, smell, and touch. A little thought or simple experimentation suffices to show that this is false. We have five large, complex, and definitely localized sets of sense organs: eyes, the hearing mechanism of the ears, an organ of equilibration connected with the inner ear but producing very different sensations, the taste organs in the mouth, and the smelling organs in the nose. It is significant that all these localized organs are in the head. Elsewhere throughout most parts of the body we have an extremely large number of tiny, anatomically simple, scattered receptors. These vary and intergrade so much in structure and in the sensations produced that it is really impossible to say how many senses they represent.

In the skin, especially well provided with scattered receptors, there are at least four distinct "senses," that is, there are at least four kinds of receptors each of which on stimulation produces a different sort of sensation. The sensations are: warmth, cold, pain, and touch or pressure. A little exploration with a pin and small warm and cold rods will convince you that these have receptors definitely localized at certain spots and distinct from each other. Many other receptors of diverse sorts occur within the body. We feel the tenseness of muscles, the motion of joints, hunger, thirst, internal pain, nausea, sexual orgasm, and other distinct sensations that originate inside ourselves.

Probably the best answer to "How many senses have we?" is "Lots!"

We noted above (p. 186) that undifferentiated protoplasm as in an ameba or almost any cell reacts to stimuli of many different sorts. Now we are interested in the development of special receptors that react to particular sorts of stimuli. Such specialization clearly depends on protoplasm and has evolved from its general reactivity. In all but the simplest animals it has resulted in the development of organs in which stimulated receptor cells start impulses in nerve fibers. The most conspicuous, at least, of these organs can be classified as follows (we have given the technical names in the second column for reference):

Receptors of	Names of organs
Light	Photoreceptors
Sound	Phonoreceptors
Touch and pressure	Tangoreceptors
Gravity and motion	Statoreceptors
Taste and smell	Chemoreceptors
Temperature	Thermoreceptors

LIGHT RECEPTORS

All protoplasm is sensitive to radiation, including the radiation which is visible to us and which we therefore call "light." (But sensitivity in most protoplasm is usually greater to ultraviolet, which is invisible to us.) As a stimulus giving information about the environment, light is in a class by itself in the amount of information it can give and in giving information about things at a distance from the organism. Comparisons of simple and more complex light receptors are especially interesting because they show how more and more information can be gained from the same stimulus.

The very simplest sorts of light receptors—you could hardly call them "eyes" at this stage—occur even in some protists as well as in simple multicellular animals (Fig. 9-4). They are sensitive spots of light-absorbing

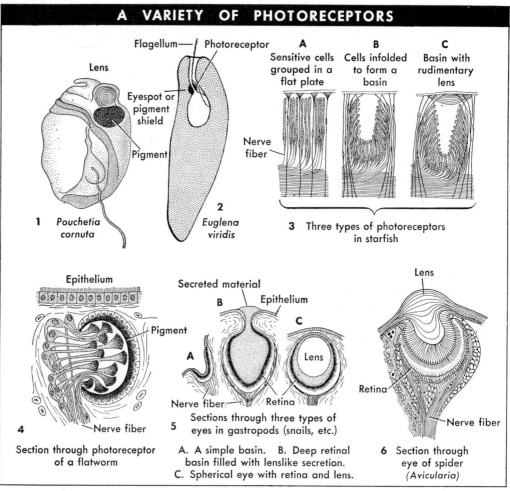

Lens

Flagellum—

Photoreceptor

Eyespot or
pigment
shield

Pigment

1 Pouchetia
cornuta

2 Euglena
viridis

A
Sensitive cells
grouped in a
flat plate

B
Cells infolded
to form a
basin

C
Basin with
rudimentary
lens

Nerve
fiber

3 Three types of photoreceptors
in starfish

Epithelium

Pigment

4 Section through photoreceptor
of a flatworm

Nerve fiber

Secreted material

B

Epithelium

C

A

Lens

Nerve fiber

Retina

5 Sections through three types of
eyes in gastropods (snails, etc.)

A. A simple basin. B. Deep retinal
basin filled with lenslike secretion.
C. Spherical eye with retina and lens.

Lens

Retina

Nerve fiber

6 Section through
eye of spider
(Avicularia)

9-4 A variety of photoreceptors. The eyes illustrated belong to a diversified array of organisms. In groups as different as snails, starfish, and spiders there has been an evolutionary tendency to develop (a) special light-absorbing cells and (b) a lens that concentrates or focuses the light on these cells. The frequency with which this system has evolved in unrelated organisms attests to the importance of photoreceptors. Light energy is actually absorbed by pigment molecules in the receptor cells of the eye. The absorbed light energy initiates in these cells chemical reactions that ultimately stimulate associated nerve cells. 1 and 2 are examples of very simple photoreceptors in unicellular organisms. In some protists like *Pouchetia* (1) a simple lens concentrates the light on the absorbing pigment molecules in the cell behind the lens. 3. A simple kind (A) of photoreceptor in starfishes consists of a flat plate of nerve cells which contain the light-absorbing pigments. Other starfish photoreceptors (C) illustrate the evolution of a more efficient system in which a simple lens is formed by a thickening of the epithelium. 4. In the flatworm's eye light-absorbing pigment is concentrated in a separate layer of cells lying in front of the nerve cells they ultimately stimulate. 5. The snails (gastropods, p. 567) have evolved eyes of varying degrees of complexity. The simplest (A) is a basin of pigment-carrying cells supplied with nerves. The most complex (C), which have surely evolved from simple beginnings like A, are complete with a spherical lens. 6. The eye of the spider *Avicularia* is an example, in a completely unrelated group of animals, of an eye similar to that of the snail (5B).

pigment. They really give no information from a distance but only indicate whether light is present or absent where the animal is. Some or all of these simple animals also react to increase or decrease in intensity of light.

More complex eyes, such as occur in most invertebrates, have evolved with great diversity of details in form and structure. They almost always involve one or both of two features: the presence of a lens and of several to many separate light-sensitive cells, each capable of starting impulses in a nerve fiber. A lens concentrates light on the sensitive cells. It therefore permits reaction to weaker intensities of light and also finer discrimination between different intensities. An eye with a lens also gives a new sort of information: the direction from which light is coming. This clearly facilitates and directs the response, widespread in animals, of moving toward or away from light. Increase in number of sensitive cells also makes response to light and to changes in intensity more delicate. Moreover, if there are many sensory cells back of a lens, different cells will be stimulated in succession when light or dark objects move in front of the lens. In such simple forms of eyes no true image is formed. The organism cannot tell *what* is moving in front of its eye, but it can distinguish and respond to the fact that motion has occurred. This is a great advance in amount of information received, and it can include information (even though of a vague sort) about happenings at some distance from the animal.

There is no doubt that lenses first evolved not as image-formers but merely as mechanisms for concentrating light from particular directions. It is, however, a fact (you can call it a peculiarly fortunate coincidence) that lenses can form images by focusing light on a surface. If a lens is of appropriate shape, if the number of sensitive cells increases greatly, and if all the cells are arranged as a *retina* on the curved surface where the lens focuses an image, then it is possible for the eye to receive an image and to translate it into a pattern of nervous impulses (Fig. 9-5).

These evolutionary developments have occurred more than once. There need not have been, and quite surely was not, a definite point or sudden change when eyes began to receive images. Increased discrimination of light intensity, direction, and movement would gradually begin to produce a vague image. Variation such as occurs in all groups of animals would mean that the image was a little less vague for some than for others. It is definitely an advantage for a sufficiently complex animal to be able to discriminate what is approaching it; this becomes possible as even vague images are formed. On an average, animals with clearer images would have better chances to survive and to pass their characteristics down to posterity. Thus extremely slow but steady improvement in the image would occur. What do you think of the claim, sometimes made by philosophers or in a few popular works on evolution, that eyes like ours must have appeared all at once because they would be of no use at all until they were perfect?

Eyes with lenses forming useful images have evolved, entirely independently, at least three times: in some of the more active and complex mollusks (such as the octopus), in some spiders, and in the early vertebrates, from which we and all other vertebrates have inherited them.

There are several other ways besides lenses by which images can be formed mechanically, or rather, optically. Insects and some of their relatives evolved image-forming eyes that work on one of these other principles. Their *compound eyes* have a large number of tubes, *ommatidia*, each of which is an independent light-sensitive unit. Since each tube points in a slightly different direction, each receives light from a different part of the insect's surroundings. Each ommatidium therefore responds to more or less light from one area of the surroundings, and the sum of all ommatidial reactions is a rather crude but often fully recognizable image (Fig. 9-6).

There is another sort of information that can be conveyed by light and that may be useful in identifying objects and discriminating among them; this is *color*, which depends, as you know, on the wave lengths of light

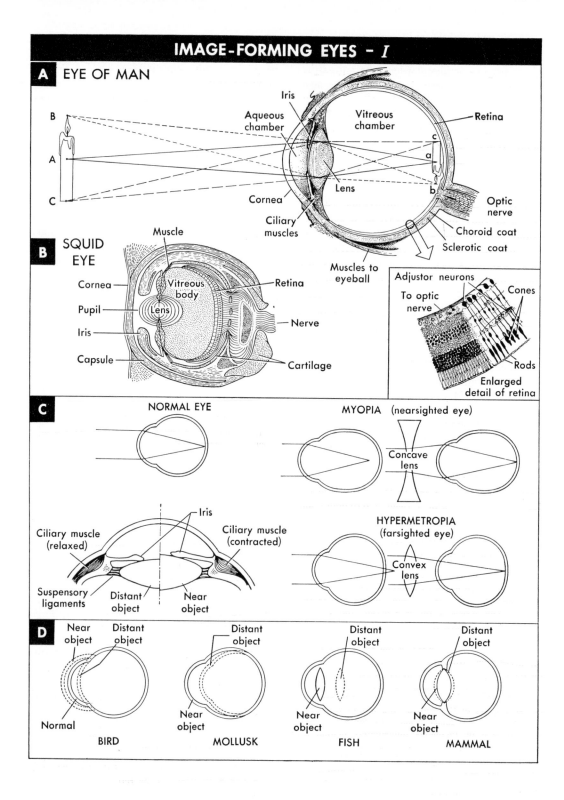

A EYE OF MAN

B
A
C

Iris
Aqueous chamber
Cornea
Ciliary muscles
Lens
Vitreous chamber
Retina
c
a
b
Optic nerve
Choroid coat
Sclerotic coat
Muscles to eyeball

B SQUID EYE

Muscle
Cornea
Vitreous body
Pupil
Lens
Iris
Capsule
Retina
Nerve
Cartilage

Adjustor neurons
To optic nerve
Cones
Rods
Enlarged detail of retina

C

NORMAL EYE

MYOPIA (nearsighted eye)
Concave lens

HYPERMETROPIA (farsighted eye)
Convex lens

Iris
Ciliary muscle (relaxed)
Ciliary muscle (contracted)
Suspensory ligaments
Distant object
Near object

D

Near object
Distant object
Normal
BIRD

Distant object
Near object
MOLLUSK

Distant object
Near object
FISH

Distant object
Near object
MAMMAL

transmitted or reflected.[4] Animals may, and many do, see very well by light of various wave lengths without discriminating *differences* between the wave lengths. Such animals do not have *color vision*. (It really is not correct to call these species color blind, because most of them simply never had color vision.) Color vision, the ability to distinguish different wave lengths of light, has evolved several times. Some crustaceans have it, and so do many insects. Some insects, including honeybees, not only see ultraviolet (as we noted, p. 188) but also see it as a color, as different from, say, green. Of course we have not the slightest idea what ultraviolet color looks like to a bee, any more than a bee could imagine (if it had an imagination) what red looks like to us. Red is black,

[4] There is, indeed, yet another kind of information about light that organisms can obtain; this is the polarization of the light. We cannot enter into this topic here, and refer the interested reader to Von Frisch's "The Dancing Bees" (Harcourt, Brace, 1955). For a lucid account of both polarized light and its role in the navigation of bees, see pp. 81 and 95.

absence of light, to a bee as ultraviolet is to us. (Did you know that red flowers are generally not pollinated by bees? Why do you suppose this is so?)

Strangely enough, color vision may have been lost and regained in our ancestry. Many fishes and reptiles and most birds have color vision, but most mammals do not. Primitive mammals probably lacked color vision. At least this is slight or absent among most present-day mammals except man and his nearest relatives, the apes and some monkeys. Dogs, cats, horses, and most other mammals may see some colors very faintly, but more probably they have no color vision.

The evolution of image-forming eyes has involved other refinements and extensions of the capacity to obtain information from light. Many of these refinements can be seen in our own eyes, which are about as highly developed as any. The whole apparatus is enclosed in a ball, which can be turned by its own muscles. Both eyes habitually focus on the same point, and the stereoscopic effect is

---

9-5 Image-forming eyes of the camera type. Image-forming eyes comparable to a camera have evolved in at least three groups of animals (p. 197). The lens system has been transformed in the course of evolution from a mere light concentrator to a precise optical device that focuses an image on a light-sensitive retina. *A* and *B*. The structure of two camera eyes is shown in *A* (man, a vertebrate) and *B* (squid, a mollusk; cf. the note to p. 566). Essentially both eyes consist of: (1) a light-sensitive *retina*; (2) a *light-focusing system*, cornea and/or lens; (3) an *iris* that controls the amount of light entering the eye by adjusting the diameter of the *pupil*; (4) a protective coating. In the squid this is a complex and heavy cartilaginous casing; in man it is the sclerotic coat, a strong elastic connective tissue. (The cornea is the transparent and strongly curved anterior portion of this sclerotic coat.) The detail of the inset figure shows how the rods and cones (p. 201) are arranged in the retina. Note how the nerve fibers from the retina run over its surface on their way to the optic nerve. *C*. Accommodation (or focusing) of the human eye. Incoming light rays are focused on the retina mainly by the strongly curved surface of the cornea (top left in *C*). Final adjustment of the focus is made by the lens, which is suspended by ligaments immediately behind the iris. The lens adjusts by changing the curvature of its surface. This, in turn, is adjusted by the tension of the ciliary muscles (lower left in *C* and also in *A*). When the ciliary muscles contract, the curvature of the lens surface increases and the focus is changed

for near objects. Myopia (top right in *C*) is an abnormal condition in which the affected person cannot focus on distant objects. Its usual cause is an eyeball too long for its lens system, so that, even when the ciliary muscles are fully relaxed, the focal plane lies in front of the retina. The condition can be compensated for by the use of concave lenses in eyeglasses. Hypermetropia (bottom right in *C*) is the reverse condition, in which the eyeball is too short. Convex lenses are used to compensate for this condition. *D*. Diverse methods of accommodation in camera eyes. Mammals generally, like man, accommodate, or make fine adjustment of focus, by varying the curvature of the lens surface (far right in *D*). Other ways of adjusting focus have, however, been evolved in various animal groups. Accommodation is of unusually great importance in birds of prey; the animal must retain focus on its prey not only when at a great distance above ground but also, following its swoop to earth, when its victim is immediately in front of it. These predatory birds accommodate by a radical change in the curvature of the cornea rather than the lens. Some mollusks accommodate, not by changing the curvature of the refractive surfaces, but by shortening the eye itself. Thus, by bringing the lens closer to the retina, the eye accommodates to distant objects. Fish lack ciliary muscles and hence cannot change the curvature of the lens. The eye accommodates because muscles within the eye change the position, not the curvature, of the lens. The lens is pulled back closer to the retina to accommodate to distant objects.

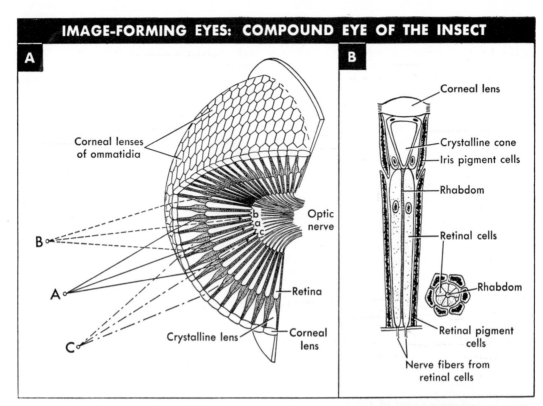

A

Corneal lenses
of ommatidia

Optic
nerve

B

A

C

Retina

Crystalline lens

Corneal
lens

B

Corneal lens

Crystalline cone

Iris pigment cells

Rhabdom

Retinal cells

Rhabdom

Retinal pigment
cells

Nerve fibers from
retinal cells

9-6 Image-forming eyes of the compound type. *Above,*
A. The compound eye of an insect cut away to show the hundreds of individual ommatidia. *B.* A single ommatidium. The corneal lens and crystalline cone focus incoming light rays onto the rhabdom, a clear, rod-shaped structure. Light passes from the rhabdom into eight retinal cells that surround it. Each retinal cell contributes a nerve fiber to the optic nerve. The whole ommatidium is surrounded by pigment cells, which prevent leakage of light from one ommatidium to another. Compound eyes of this type form erect images (cf. *A* in this figure with Fig. 9-5*A*). In the camera-type eye the image is inverted when it falls on the retina, and has to be inverted again in the brain. No such inversion is involved in the mechanism of the compound eye.

Center, the face of a robber fly.
The individual ommatidia in the compound eye are readily seen.

Edwin Way Teale

Right, a photograph made through the eye of a firefly.
It represents the erect image transmitted to the insect's
brain. The picture is of a church steeple seen through a
window, on one of whose panes a capital *R* has been written.

a clue to distance. (This is almost unique to man; man also uses other clues to distance, and many other animals rely wholly on other clues than the stereoscopic effect.) The lens is elastic and can be focused. A variable diaphragm, the iris, automatically adjusts to light intensity. The sensory, retinal, cells are of two sorts, one set (the rods) especially sensitive and active in dim light, the other set (the cones) active in bright light. (Only the cones are involved in color vision, but just how nobody knows.) Altogether, the eye in the higher vertebrates—perhaps even more in birds than in man or other mammals—is the most complex receptor that has ever evolved.

Before leaving the subject of light reception, we must mention another point of great importance here. There is much more involved in the sense of vision, or any other sense, than the receptor. Complex as it is, the eye does no more than send a series of signals, all of the same sort and intensity (cf. p. 192) but varying in frequency, along a large number of nerve paths. If these signals were diverted to a muscle, the muscle would contract and that is all. The fact that an optical image was involved in their formation would have no meaning. The image becomes meaningful—it is really information to the organism—only if all the separate signals are somehow associated into a whole pattern simultaneously grasped. This process certainly does not occur in the eye. It occurs by means of an incredibly complex arrangement of extremely numerous associative and conductive neurons in the brain. So far as its usefulness to the organism is concerned, the image may correctly be said to be formed in the brain and not in the eye.

It follows that an eye that is optically image-forming is not really image-forming for the organism unless it is accompanied by a complex associative system precisely related to it. The advanced sort of receptor could not evolve without this accompaniment of evolution in the brain. Organisms without brains or with simple brains can have only simple light receptors or none. At each level of complexity there is only so much information that can become meaningful for the organism

and that can, therefore, really be information for it.

The effector system is also involved in the interrelationship that starts with the receptor. The more complex receptors make finer discriminations. A simple eye receives the information adequate to conclude: "Something is moving." But a complex eye provides enough information for the discriminating observation: "A yellow house cat a foot long is coming toward me slowly from ten feet away a little to my left." Such varied and detailed discrimination is of no use to the organism unless the possible responses are also varied and detailed in accordance with the information. An ameba's responses are just about exhausted by rolling into a ball, moving one way or another, or putting out a projection and engulfing a food particle. Discriminating precisely what was touching it would have no significance in the life of an ameba because the reaction would be precisely the same in any case. _Discrimination in receptors simply does not evolve unless it is accompanied both by a correspondingly complex association system and by appropriately varied effector responses._ Does this have a bearing on the near lack of receptors in plants?

TOUCH, PRESSURE, AND SOUND RECEPTORS

Reviewing the animal kingdom, we will find it difficult to distinguish sound receptors from touch and pressure detectors. Protoplasm as a whole—protists, plants, and lower animals—is sensitive to touch and pressure, but not to sound _as such_. Sound receptors, however, clearly evolved in higher animals on the basis of this primitive sensitivity to pressure. These receptors are more discriminatory organs for pressure reception, specialized for reaction to vibratory changes of pressure (i.e., a sound wave) in water or air. Besides these special organs, higher animals, including man, also have simpler receptors for other sorts of touch and pressure.

In most aquatic invertebrates touch and sound receptors, if present, are the same. Frequently they are sensitive hairs that respond to a touch and also vibrate when affected by sound. Insects also receive sound

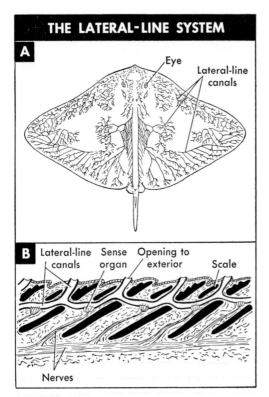

THE LATERAL-LINE SYSTEM

A

Eye

Lateral-line canals

B Lateral-line canals — Sense organ — Opening to exterior — Scale

Nerves

9-7 The lateral-line system in fishes. *A* shows the distribution of the lateral-line canals on the surface of a ray. *B* is a section through the surface of a perch. It shows the scales embedded in the skin; a lateral-line canal with its openings to the exterior; and pressure-sensitive sense organs supplied with nerves.

stimuli with vibratory hairs, but in addition they have small, special sound receptors that may be scattered in the body or grouped in rather simple special organs. These organs discriminate intensities (loudness) and modulations (change of frequency) in sounds. They do not, however, permit the organism to recognize the absolute pitch or frequency of a sound.

Fishes have a special sensory system lacking in terrestrial vertebrates. This consists of a series of grooves or canals with clusters of sensory cells on head and body, the *lateral-line organs* (Fig. 9-7). They are sensitive to changes in pressure or currents in the surrounding water. These organs also occur in the aquatic, larval stages of amphibians, as in the tadpoles of frogs, but are lost in the adults. They are absent in reptiles, birds, and mam-

mals, even those such as whales that have become secondarily aquatic.

Aside from their evident importance to most aquatic vertebrates, the lateral-line organs are of special interest because they seem to be the primitive, simple pressure receptors from which organs of hearing and equilibrium have evolved. In fishes the ear is entirely internal and is mainly an organ of equilibrium. There has been some argument as to whether fishes really hear, in the sense of discriminating the sort of vibrations that we detect as sound. The answer seems to be that some do and some do not. Many fish do not respond at all to sound vibrations, but some quite specialized forms do respond and also discriminate between different frequencies or pitches of sound waves.

The land vertebrates have specialized organs of hearing which seem to have evolved from parts of the pressure and equilibrium receptors of fishes and are still closely associated with those receptors in the ear. The anatomical details of sound receptors differ markedly in diverse groups and have evolved in an interesting way, but the same principles are involved in amphibians,[5] reptiles, birds, and mammals. Air vibrations (sound waves) hit an eardrum (technically, the tympanic membrane) and cause it to vibrate at the same rate as the sound wave. The membrane is attached to a small bone which vibrates with the membrane. Either directly or through one or two other bones, this bone passes the vibrations on to a fluid-filled cavity of the inner ear. Here vibrations in the fluid stimulate sensory cells on another membrane in a special sac or tube, technically the cochlea (Fig. 9-9).

The hearing organ is most highly developed in man and other mammals. Here there is an outer ear, with a tube leading to the eardrum. In the middle ear there is a chain of three small bones. The final receptor in the inner ear is a strongly coiled tube with an elaborate arrangement of membranes and sensory cells. Such an arrangement is highly sensitive and discriminates delicately among all the changes that occur in sound, those of intensity (loud-

[5] In recent amphibians the hearing organs are usually aberrant or degenerate.

ness), frequency (pitch), and timbre (pattern or quality).

THE SENSE OF EQUILIBRIUM

For an animal leading a free life, swimming in water, walking on land, or flying in the air, it is important to know which way is up. In other words, such animals usually need to orient themselves in the field of the earth's gravity. Most of them have special organs sensitive to gravity. In invertebrates the organ is usually a sac in which there is a small stony ball. The ball is acted on by gravity and stimulates sensory hairs or cells (Fig. 9-8). It is curious that insects, although usually well oriented, only exceptionally have a special gravity receptor.

Vertebrates have the same kind of receptor as that described for invertebrates. In the inner ear are two sacs, each with a usually stony secreted mass. Vertebrates also have a more specialized receptor, connected with this one, which responds to changes in rate and direction of motion. This consists of two (in the most primitive forms) or three (in almost all recent vertebrates) semicircular canals (Fig. 9-9). The canals, which are connected, are arranged approximately at right angles to each other and are full of fluid. Any increase or decrease of motion causes the fluid to flow in the canals, and the pattern of flow in the three canals depends on the direction of motion. The flow is detected by sensory cells. You can readily recognize the sensations from this apparatus if you close your eyes and nod or shake your head. For some reason not at all clear, there is a reflex connection from this mechanism to the abdominal region. If you go up or down in a fast elevator, the motion is really sensed in the semicircular canals, but it is felt in the pit of the stomach. This connection is also instrumental in sea or air sickness. Do you suppose that there is any connection between the fact that up or down motion is disturbing to us and the fact that extensive motion in these directions seldom occurs to land animals or primitive men?

THE CHEMICAL SENSES

The chemistry of the environment is extremely important to any organism. It is not surprising that all protoplasm is sensitive to chemical changes around it and that in many animals special chemical receptors have evolved. Even without special receptors many protists and lower animals detect their food through a general chemical sensitivity. Molecules in the food diffuse through water and act as stimuli. Harmful chemicals are also detected and produce defensive responses such as motion away from the stimulus or contraction into a less penetrable mass. Most aquatic invertebrates are sensitive to chemicals over their whole bodies, and many have developed rather simple local receptors. For instance, clams and some other marine mollusks have little patches of yellow cells that "taste" the water drawn in and circulated through the gills. The most specialized chemical receptors among invertebrates occur in insects. They have scattered simple receptors, rather like short, blunt hairs, and also have special taste receptors in or near the mouth and special smell receptors on the antennae. Some insects can taste things with their legs.

Our own sense of smell is so feeble and, by and large, plays so small a part in our lives that we are inclined to underestimate the importance of this sense in other vertebrates. We rely on our eyes for most of our information about the world around us, and derive relatively little useful or (to us) interesting information from the nose. Smell does greatly increase our esthetic pleasure in food, but aside from that it is more likely to be a useless annoyance. Yet this sense is of supreme importance to most fishes, amphibians, and reptiles, and even to most of our fellow mammals. The last point is clear to anyone who has ever owned a dog. Dogs can see, hear, and feel very

9-8 A statocyst from the mollusk _Pecten._ The central body is a _statolith_, a stony concretion of calcium carbonate. Gravity causes it to press on sensory hairs that line the hollow sphere of cells. Which sensory hairs are being stimulated is the animal's cue to its orientation to gravity.

THE HUMAN EAR: SENSE OF SOUND; SENSE OF EQUILIBRIUM

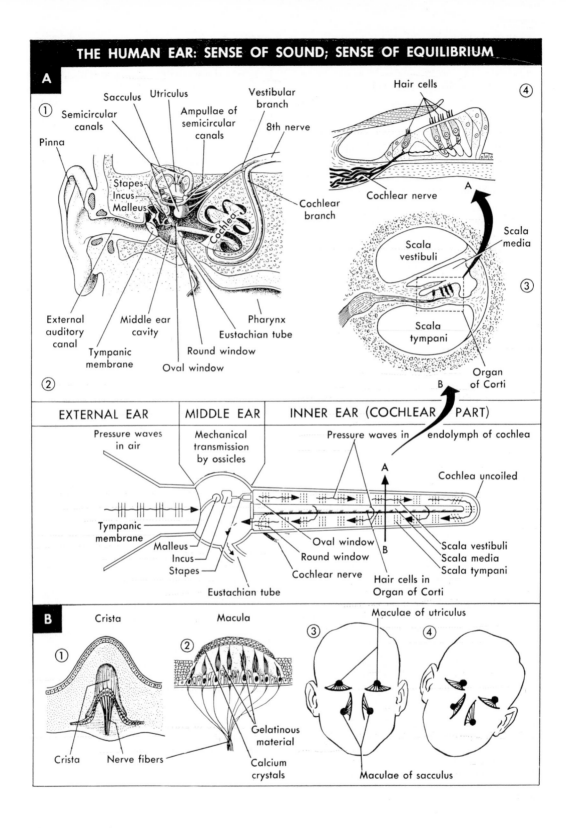

A

① Pinna — Semicircular canals — Sacculus — Utriculus — Ampullae of semicircular canals — Vestibular branch — 8th nerve

Stapes — Incus — Malleus — Cochlear branch

Hair cells ④

Cochlear nerve

Scala vestibuli — Scala media ③

Scala tympani

Organ of Corti

External auditory canal — Middle ear cavity — Pharynx — Eustachian tube — Round window — Oval window — Tympanic membrane

②

EXTERNAL EAR	MIDDLE EAR	INNER EAR (COCHLEAR PART)
Pressure waves in air	Mechanical transmission by ossicles	Pressure waves in endolymph of cochlea

Cochlea uncoiled

Tympanic membrane — Malleus — Incus — Stapes — Eustachian tube — Oval window — Round window — Cochlear nerve — Hair cells in Organ of Corti — Scala vestibuli — Scala media — Scala tympani

B

Crista ① — Macula ② — ③ Maculae of utriculus — ④

Crista — Nerve fibers — Gelatinous material — Calcium crystals

Maculae of sacculus

well, but for them smell is obviously the main source of really reliable and meaningful information. They agree with the other vertebrates in this, with man and most birds among the conspicuous exceptions. It is clear that dogs smell things that we do not.

Nostrils first evolved among early fishlike vertebrates as inlets for water to specialized chemical receptors. When air-breathing animals arose, this chemical sense was retained in the same place although it became sensitive to molecules diffused in air rather than dissolved in water. Use of the nose for breathing was incidental and is still unnecessary (Fig. 9-10). All air breathers can and on occasion do breathe just as well through the mouth.

Even man, with his comparatively poor sense of smell, can detect extraordinarily small concentrations of some molecules in air and can discriminate among a very large number of smells. This ability to discriminate smells is very baffling. Anatomically the odor-sensitive cells are simple and all look alike. The nervous impulses from them are all alike. Discrimination can only be explained on the basis that different cells respond to different stimuli and send impulses to different associative connections in the brain. But how can cells that are apparently exactly alike have different specific reactions to particular molecules? At present the best-supported theory is that the cells contain different enzymes which somehow fit against or are otherwise activated by molecules of particular shapes. (Cf. p. 95.)

The sense of taste is somewhat less puzzling because it makes much less complex discriminations, and those it does make are anatom-

---

9-9 The human ear. A. Sense of sound. 1. The components of the ear of man: the external ear includes the pinna (the ear of common language) and the external auditory canal. The middle ear is the cavity between the tympanic membrane and the two "windows" (oval and round) to the inner ear. The three ear ossicles (malleus, incus, and stapes) lie in the cavity of the middle ear; the malleus attaches to the tympanic membrane, and the stapes to the membrane covering the oval window. The middle cavity vents into the throat, or pharynx, via the Eustachian tube. The Eustachian tube thus serves to maintain the air pressure of the middle ear cavity at equilibrium with atmospheric pressure. (Temporary closure of the Eustachian tube during rapid change of altitude in an airplane or elevator causes unpleasant sensations in the ear. This is because the air pressure in the middle ear cavity is higher or lower than the outside pressure exerted on the tympanic membrane. Chewing motions serve to open the Eustachian tube and equalize the pressure of the middle ear with that outside.) The inner ear comprises two major elements: (a) The vestibular apparatus, consisting of the semicircular canals, sacculus, and utriculus, which are all concerned with the sense of equilibrium; and (b) the cochlea, concerned with sound reception. The cochlea is a long coiled tube, shown in A_1 as though opened up. The cochlear tube is partitioned lengthwise into three distinct chambers: the scala vestibuli, the scala media, and the scala tympani. The ultimate auditory sense cells of the cochlea are hair-bearing cells in the organ of Corti, which separates the scala media from the scala tympani. The anatomical relations of the cochlea are clarified in A_2, A_3, and A_4. 2. The mechanism of sound reception: pressure waves in the air pass down the external auditory canal and cause the tympanic membrane to vibrate. The vibration is transmitted mechanically by the three ear ossicles (malleus, incus, and stapes) to the membrane that covers the oval window of the inner ear. Vibration of the oval membrane sets up pressure waves in the fluid content of the inner ear's canals. Pressure waves in the fluid of the scala media strike the organ of Corti and stimulate its hair cells. The hair cells then initiate impulses in the fibers of the cochlear nerve which supply the hair cells. The pressure waves in the inner ear ultimately leave it via the round window back into the middle ear cavity and thence through the Eustachian tube to the pharynx. 3. Cross section through the cochlea to show the three cavities and the position of the organ of Corti. 4. The organ of Corti. B. Sense of equilibrium. The position of the head is detected through sensory devices in the vestibular part of the inner ear. Each semicircular canal, filled with a fluid, terminates in an ampulla (see A_1) which contains a sense organ, the crista. Each crista (B_1) is a group of hair cells whose hairs are embedded in a gelatinous mass. When the head moves in a given direction, the fluid in the semicircular canals tends, because of its inertia, to move in the opposite direction. In so doing, it strikes the crista and thus stimulates its hair cells, initiating impulses in the fibers of the vestibular nerve which supply the hair cells. The sacculus and utriculus (see A_1) of the inner ear contain similar structures, called maculae (B_2). In each macula calcium crystals are deposited in the gelatinous material that surrounds the hairs of the sense cells. This added mass makes them sensitive to gravity. Any change in the position of the head displaces the maculae relative to the hairs that suspend them; the "push" or "pull" exerted on the hairs (B_3 and B_4) is registered through the stimulation it initiates in the nerve supply to the hair cells.

ically localized. The receptors are clusters of cells on the tongue and on the roof and back of the mouth. Only four tastes are discriminated: salt, sweet, bitter, and sour. Salt and sweet are tasted mainly at the tip of the tongue, bitter at the base, and sour along the sides (Fig. 9-11). You may object that you detect far more different flavors than these four in your food. This is true, but the complexity is due to the fact that you also smell the food you eat and do not wholly distinguish taste and smell in the blend of flavor. This is why food tastes odd and flat when you have a bad head cold. What you sense then really is the *taste* of food. The rest is smell, plus impressions of texture and temperature.

OTHER SENSES

We have mentioned (p. 195) the considerable and indefinable number of other sensations that we receive from various parts of our bodies. Complex sensory reactions are evidently present in all higher animals, but they are seldom associated with well-defined and specialized organs except those we have mentioned. Of course we have not listed every single type of organ related to these senses. For instance, snakes and lizards have two little pouches in the roof of the mouth into which they run the tips of their forked tongues. The pouches are a special chemical receptor organ. When a reptile flicks its tongue in and out rapidly, it is not sticking its tongue out at you or expressing emotion: it is tasting the air.

There are also exceptions to the generalization that other senses, such as that of warmth, usually do not have complex and local receptor organs. Some snakes, called "pit vipers" on this account, have sensory pits on each side of the head between eyes and nostrils. The pits are extremely sensitive warmth receptors. They can detect the presence of a warm-blooded animal, such as a mouse, up to several feet away. Pit vipers, of which rattlesnakes are the most familiar examples in this country,

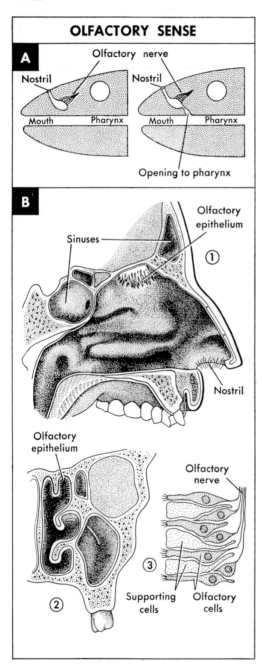

OLFACTORY SENSE

A

Olfactory nerve

Nostril   Nostril

Mouth   Pharynx   Mouth   Pharynx

Opening to pharynx

B

Olfactory epithelium

Sinuses

①

Nostril

Olfactory epithelium

Olfactory nerve

②   ③

Supporting cells   Olfactory cells

9-10   The vertebrate nostril and olfactory sense. *A.* Schematic, showing the relationship of the nostril in aquatic vertebrates (*left*) and terrestrial vertebrates (*right*). The nostril is primitively an opening and duct leading to a sensory epithelium devoted to smell. In terrestrial vertebrates the nostril's respiratory function is secondary; the duct leading to the olfactory epithelium has, so to speak, been extended to enter the pharynx. *B.* The nostril and olfactory epithelium in man. ① and ② show the position of the olfactory epithelium in the nasal cavity. ③ is a cross section of part of the olfactory epithelium, in which the ciliated olfactory sense cells lie between supporting cells.

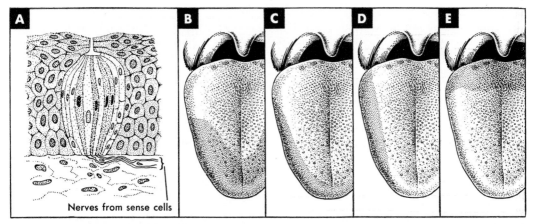

9-11 The taste receptors on the human tongue. *A* is a section through an individual taste receptor on the surface of the tongue. It is a pit in which lie the sensory cells supplied with nerve fibers. Each such "taste bud" is sensitive to only one of four basic tastes: salt, sweet, bitter, and sour. The shaded areas of *B* show the distribution on the tongue of salt receptors, *C* the distribution of sweet, *D* of sour, and *E* of bitter.

feed on small warm-blooded animals, and the pits help to detect their prey.

It is an interesting speculation, in which we have all indulged, that other animals may have some senses quite different from ours. The lateral-line system of a fish has sense *organs* different from any of ours, but the *sense* is one of pressure, and we can detect the same sorts of pressures in water. Animals certainly have some senses more acute or discriminatory than ours—witness the dog's nose—but the sense is the same. Animals may also be sensitive to different ranges of stimuli—witness bees' eyes (p. 189)—but again the sense is the same.

Many insects sense and respond to humidity differences, but it is doubtful whether this represents a special sense. In the insects studied, the sense organs occur either on antennae or are bristles on the back. It is still unknown exactly how any of the sense organs operate, but it is likely that they exploit one or both of the known sensitivities to temperature and pressure. The rate of water evaporation from the antennae varies in relation to the air's moisture content, and could well be registered by temperature receptors which must be cooled by the evaporation. The large bristles on an insect's back bend as their moisture content varies, and this bending could well flex the pressure-sensitive skin where they

are attached. And there are still other possibilities in relation to known senses.

Indeed, there is no really convincing evidence that any animal has a sense altogether different in *kind* from any of ours. As for dogs that "know by a sixth sense" that a man is honest, or when their masters die—surely we do not have to tell you that these are old wives' tales. If a dog does something you do not immediately understand, the odds are ten to one that he is simply reacting to a smell you have not detected. In scientific circles, discussion of a wholly different sense has often centered around homing and similar phenomena. Birds fly thousands of miles to a more or less precise destination. Bees and ants return unerringly (sometimes!) to their homes. Salmon (also sometimes!) find their way back from the open sea to the mountain stream where they were born. Male moths fly long distances to an unseen and unheard female. Such phenomena suggest a homing sense, or the use of clues, such as the earth's magnetism, undetectable by us. Strict study, however, has negated those ideas. Male moths can smell females from miles away, which is wonderful, certainly, but does not involve a sense absent in ourselves. Ants lay and follow scent trails. Even the homing of bees and birds does not seem to demand any new sense, although recent studies have revealed something almost as spectacular. Some brilliant experiments in Germany have shown that homing pigeons keep a true course by constantly referring to the position of the sun, like some ancient mariner. But, like the mariner, the bird needs a chronometer when it navigates, because it must compensate for the steady movement of the sun across the sky as the day wears on. Incredible as it seems, it has been proved that the pigeon does possess such a clock, which is almost certainly in its brain, but in exactly what form is still unclear.

Many, and possibly all, organisms have built-in "clocks" which control the timing of various activities; some of these examples come up in a later chapter, 26. And a few other organisms perform time-compensated navigations like the pigeon. The bee can do this; [6] and so can some shrimps on the wide beaches of the Adriatic Sea. When these shrimps are disturbed they head straight for the sea, even though they cannot see it. They can, however, detect the position of the sun and, using their internal clock, unconsciously compute the shortest route to the sea, which they follow. You are probably aware of some ability to measure time in yourself. Many people can beat the alarm clock by minutes if they set themselves to do it; and there are people, not too rare, who always "know" the time within an accuracy of fifteen minutes.

The History of the Nervous System

Our approach to the study of nerves and receptors has been partly historical. We have pointed out a number of changes and trends that have occurred in the course of evolution. Now we are going to consider briefly some major features of the history of the nervous system as a whole. The only direct approach to such a history is by means of fossils, remains of the organisms of the past. For the nervous system, that approach is quite inadequate. Nervous tissue is practically never preserved in fossils. Fossils of invertebrate animals give no good evidence of what their nervous systems were like. Fossil vertebrates

6 The bee also uses its internal clock to arrive on time for the opening of a flower which yesterday proved rich in nectar. The flower also uses a "clock" to time its opening hour!

do give valuable evidence about part of the nervous system, especially the brain, because the brain in these animals was surrounded more or less closely by bone. The bone is preserved, and its shape gives good clues as to the nervous structures once contained in it. Still the evolution of the brain from early fish to modern man is only half, or considerably less, of the story.

In such a situation the historian of life must therefore fall back on the study of living animals. Judicious comparison of their nervous systems gives evidence as to the history. Some animals have evolved farther and more rapidly than others. It is fair to assume that a clam of a few hundred million years ago had a nervous system somewhat like that of a clam today. By comparing animals that have changed less with those that have changed more, some inferences about the history become reasonably probable. There are, however, dangers in this method. All animals have changed somewhat in the course of evolution, and comparison of living animals is fundamentally nonhistorical. It should be obvious (although even professional biologists sometimes forget this fact) that no living animal is ancestral to any other. Moreover, no living animal is exactly like the ancestor of another.

Above all, it is necessary to keep in mind the relationships of the animals being compared and the fact that many sorts of ancestral animals have disappeared altogether and were not like any animal now alive. These points can be illustrated by consideration of the nervous systems of vertebrates and of insects. Vertebrates have much more complex nervous systems than invertebrates, and they evolved from invertebrates. Insects have about the most complex nervous systems among living invertebrates. It is therefore tempting to assume that the insect nervous system represents the next stage below the vertebrates, that it tells us something about the transition from invertebrate to vertebrate nervous systems. But the assumption is not warranted.

The ancestry of insects and of vertebrates separated well over 500 million years ago, long before insects or vertebrates themselves had arisen. The very remote forms ancestral to both insects and vertebrates probably had nervous systems, but if so these were very simple and we can learn less about them from insects than we can from other and simpler animals. Unfortunately no living animal is likely to resemble that common ancestry closely, and we can infer what its nervous system was like only in general terms. The insect nervous system of today certainly is not like any stage in the ancestry of the vertebrate system, and it can tell us little about the history of the latter. Since nerve action is much the same anywhere, we can learn things about vertebrate or other nerves from insects or from any animals with nerves. We can also detect evolutionary tendencies that occurred separately in both insects and vertebrates. This must, however, be done cautiously and in the light of the long separate histories of the two groups.

We have made this rather long introduction to the present subject because it applies more widely than to this subject alone. In any discussion of anatomy, processes, and their histories, remember that the comparative study of living animals is not historical. It can give evidence on history, but that evidence is likely to be misleading if it is not interpreted cautiously and in the light of evidence that is historical.

ORIGIN OF THE
NERVOUS SYSTEM

We have seen (p. 186) that in protists the whole body may conduct impulses of some sort. Stimulation at any point may be followed by response at any other point. In sponges, the only major group of multicellular animals without nerves, the protoplasm of each individual cell shows similar capacity to conduct impulses within that cell. In most ways the various cells operate quite independently of each other, but it is possible for a stimulus on one cell to be transmitted across another cell and to evoke a response in more distant cells. Sponges have evolved along a line all their own, but it is almost a logical necessity that some such stage as this existed in the earliest multicellular ancestors of other animals. Increasing cell specialization and the beginning of differentiation of tissues would result in the more regular activity of some intermediate cells as conductors between others. These intermediate cells, mainly involved in the con-

duction of impulses, would be primitive nerve cells.

Next simplest after the sponges among living animals are the coelenterates, the corals, jellyfishes, and their relatives, including the little fresh-water *Hydra*, which you may be able to study at first hand. The coelenterates, too, are somewhat off any main line of further evolution but they are nearer than sponges, and again there is some inherent probability that higher nervous systems passed through a stage like theirs. They have a *nerve net* composed of neurons, all nearly alike, each with several fibers of about equal length (Fig. 9-12). The neurons are spread rather evenly and thinly through outer layers of the body. The fibers are short and have synapses with fibers of adjacent neurons, roughly in a circle around each neuron. This is just the system you would expect if intermediate cells, such as we spoke of in the last paragraph, became specialized for conduction.

In a nerve net the main or only response to stimulation is local contraction. A stimulus anywhere can eventually spread to the whole net, and conduction through fibers is in either direction, depending on what point is stimulated. A stimulus must, however, be strong and long to spread far because the fibers are short and many synapses have to be passed. For the same reason, conduction is slow. Such a nervous system can co-ordinate and spread simple responses, mostly contractions of the whole body or parts of it, but that is about all it can do. It has little or no associative activity, and it cannot control or co-ordinate complex reactions. It does permit simple reflexes, for there are scattered sensory cells, and the nerves conduct impulses from them to effectors, muscular cells. The barest essentials of nervous reaction are present.

TRENDS IN HIGHER
INVERTEBRATES

Free-living flatworms, such as the planarians (p. 530), are very instructive animals because they show in simple and probably primitive form many of the most fundamental features of all higher animals. Such features as are shared by most higher forms are almost sure to be primitive. Complications peculiar to one group, such as the special characteristics of

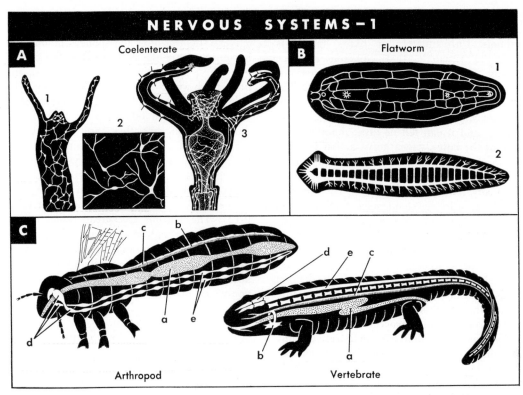

A Coelenterate

1
2
3

B Flatworm

1
2

C
c b
d e c
a e
d
a e
b a
Arthropod   Vertebrate

9-12 Nervous systems—1. *A.* In the coelenterates (p. 525) the nervous system is a simple network formed by the connected branches of individual neurons. *1* indicates the distribution of the nerve network in *Hydra*, part of which is enlarged in *2* to show individual neurons. *3* is the nerve net in the coelenterate *Obelia*, showing a concentration of nerve cells around the mouth region. *B.* In some flatworms (*1*) also, the nervous system is basically a simple net of neurons. In others (*2*) the beginning of a central nervous system is discernible in the tendency to form nerve cords running lengthwise down the animal, and an anterior brain in relation to the sense organs of the head. *C.* Fully evolved central nervous systems are exemplified schematically here in the two most complex animal groups, the arthropods and vertebrates. The arthropod schematized is an insect, and the vertebrate a salamander. The arthropod nervous system is typical of most invertebrates in being a double nerve cord *ventral* (*e*) to the alimentary canal; the brain (*d*) is a concentration of nerve ganglia that forms a ring around the esophagus. [Note, too, that in the arthropod the heart (*b*) and main blood vessels (*c*) lie *dorsal* to the alimentary canal (*a*).] The vertebrate central nervous system is a single tubular nerve cord (*e*) that, along with the brain (*d*), lies completely *dorsal* to the alimentary canal. [The vertebrate heart (*b*) lies *ventral* to the alimentary canal (*a*).]

the insect brain, probably are not primitive for other groups. Such considerations suggest that the *general* characteristics of the planarians' nervous system (Fig. 9-12) probably are primitive. The detailed anatomy of the system is undoubtedly specialized in living planarians, but its basic structural and functional characteristics were probably present in the common ancestry of all the more complex animals.

There is still an outer nerve net in planarians. Indeed, this simple type of nervous structure may persist or reappear in all sorts of higher animals: there is a nerve net in the wall of the human intestine. Planarians also have the rudiments of a *central nervous system*. This includes a series of *nerve cords* and an enlargement of them which may be called a *brain*, although so rudimentary as barely to deserve the name. The nerve cords are main lines of conduction, each containing many neurons. The neurons have long fibers along the cord and are so arranged that impulses pass along the fibers in one direction only.

From cell bodies in the nerve cords, fibers also connect with the nerve net and with other cells of the body.

Planarians have a definite front end in the direction of usual motion. Here sensory cells (which also occur all over the body) are especially numerous, and here are the eyes. The eyes are definite and well-developed receptor organs, sensitive to light intensity and direction, although they have no lenses and do not form an image. The nerve cords converge at the front end of the body and merge with an enlarged mass of nervous tissue which for courtesy we have called a brain. The eye and many sensory cells connect directly with the brain, which contains associative cells and a fairly complex arrangement of synapses between the sensory nerve fibers and other fibers from the nerve cords.

Simple as it is, the planarian nervous system permits control and co-ordination of special responses throughout the body. It mediates between sense organs and effectors, and it involves association and some variability of responses in addition to simple reflexes. All the rest of the evolution of the nervous system can be viewed as elaboration of characteristics already present in a planarian— as really tremendous elaboration. Among the important trends already suggested, at least, in planarians and carried further in the ancestors of the vertebrates are the following:

1. Formation and concentration of a *central nervous system.* Most cell bodies of neurons come to be concentrated in one or a few nerve cords or in masses (ganglia) near the cords. Connections from here to all other parts of the body are by a *peripheral nervous system.* The peripheral system does have some ganglia with cell bodies, but it is mainly composed of *nerves,* bundles of long nerve fibers from the cell bodies in the central nervous system.

2. Differentiation of *afferent* and *efferent* fibers and nerves. Most of the nerve impulses occurring in the body (although never all of them) become routed through the central nervous system, and a particular nerve carries impulses in one direction only. Those bringing impulses to the central nervous system are afferent ("carrying to"), and those conducting impulses away from it are efferent

("carrying away"). Sensory nerves (p. 193) are of course afferent, and motor nerves are efferent. A result of this arrangement is that even the simplest reflex passes through at least two neurons and is more flexible than a one-neuron reflex, which does not occur in higher animals. Usually many neurons are involved in a stimulus-response reaction.

3. Increased complexity of *association.* The afferent-efferent system accompanies increase in associative neurons throughout the central nervous system and in the number and complexity of nerve routes and connections.

4. Development and complication of a *brain.* The front end of the nerve cord (or cords) becomes enlarged, principally by the development here of large numbers of associative neurons and tracts. Eventually a large proportion of nervous impulses in the body are routed through this associative mass. Fully central co-ordination for complex responses is thus provided.

5. Increase in number, complexity, and sensitivity of *special sense organs.* Scattered and simple sensory cells and organs persist, but the progressive trend is for the development of complex organs at the front end of the organism, in the head. Here these organs are directly connected to the brain. As we have already noted (p. 201), this development is necessarily accompanied by that of complex associative mechanisms in the brain, where volleys of nerve impulses from the receptors become transformed into *perceptions* (recall the discussion of the brain and the eye, p. 201).

THE VERTEBRATE BRAIN

The precise number and pattern of nerves of course differ greatly from one species to another, and even among individuals of the same species. Those anatomical details do not concern us here. *In the vertebrates* the tendency for concentration of central control reaches a peak, and *the evolution of the brain is the most important single factor in this group.*

The central nervous system of all vertebrates consists of a *single, hollow* nerve cord which runs along the *back* (dorsal part) of the body. These basic anatomical characteristics of the nervous system do not occur in

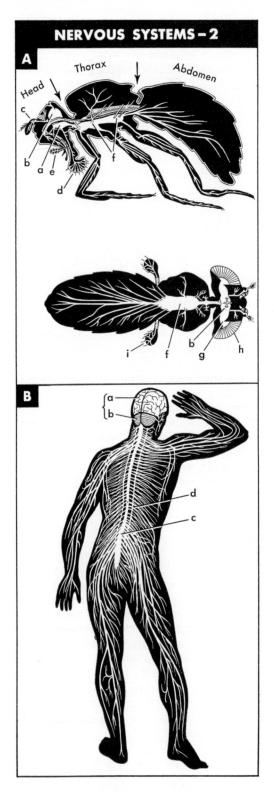

NERVOUS SYSTEMS - 2

A

Head   Thorax   Abdomen

c
b a e
d
f

i f g b h

B

{ a
{ b

d
c

any *living* invertebrates—reason enough to infer that none of them *preserve* just the same structure that was present in those *ancient* invertebrates from which vertebrates evolved. The brain of the great majority of modern higher invertebrates is a ring of nervous tissue surrounding the esophageal part of the alimentary canal (Fig. 9-12). The ring consists of two ganglia (masses of nerve-cell bodies) lying above the esophagus, and connected to two others lying below. *Two solid* nerve cords leave the *sub*esophageal ganglia and extend backwards along the length of the body under (or *ventral* to) the gut. The fact that the brain is an anterior inflation of the nerve cord is the principal similarity in the gross anatomy of the central nervous system of the more advanced living invertebrates and vertebrates (Figs. 9-12 and 9-13).[7]

The most primitive vertebrate brain consisted mainly of three irregular swellings of the hollow nerve cord, each with various thickenings of the walls. The three enlargements are the *fore-, mid-,* and *hindbrain*, which can still be distinguished in the human brain, with its vastly greater complications.[8] Very early,

[7] Some ingenious but completely unconvincing arguments have been made to the effect that invertebrates like those still living turned into vertebrates by rolling over on their backs.

[8] There are of course more technical terms for these parts, derived from Greek roots. Full de-

9-13 Nervous systems—2. *A* is an actual arthropod nervous system, that of the fruit fly *Drosophila*. *B* is an actual vertebrate nervous system, that of man. In the upper figure of *A* note how the central nervous system (CNS) (white) lies ventral to the gut, which is stippled and shown only as it passes through the head and thorax. The brain (*a-b*) encircles the esophagus (stippled) in the head; *a* is the ventral, and *b* the dorsal portion of the brain; *c* is the antenna which carries diverse kinds of sense organs; *d* is a sucking structure leading to the mouth; it and *e*, the maxillary palp, are also endowed with sense organs; *f* is a large concentration of nerve cells in the thorax. The entire *Drosophila* CNS is seen from above in the lower figure of *A*: *g* is the optic nerve leading from *h*, the compound eye; *i* is the balancer, a remarkable sense organ that functions like a gyroscope, assisting the fly to maintain its orientation in flight. *B* shows the organization of the human nervous system into brain (*a* is the cerebrum, and *b* the cerebellum; see p. 213) and dorsal spinal cord (*c*), from which individual nerves supply all parts of the body. The two sympathetic nerve trunks (*d*) lie on either side of the spinal cord (cf. Fig. 9-19).

even in primitive fishes, further complications occurred. The forebrain became divided into three parts: (1) the *thalamus* and associated structures; (2) a pair of swellings farther forward and higher, the *cerebral hemispheres* (or, taken together, the *cerebrum*); and (3) the *olfactory bulbs*, which project as swellings from the lower front of each cerebral hemisphere (Fig. 9-14). The midbrain developed various swellings, especially an upper pair, the *optic lobes*. A large swelling developed on the forward, upper part of the hindbrain and became the *cerebellum*. The much thickened lower wall of the hindbrain is the *medulla oblongata*.

There are dozens of other distinguishable parts even in fairly primitive vertebrate brains, but the *main* parts from front to back are as shown in Figs. 9-14 and 9-15.

Forebrain { Olfactory bulbs
Cerebral hemispheres (the cerebrum)
Thalamus (with an upper epithalamus, lower hypothalamus, etc.)

Midbrain Optic lobes, in mammals four (two pairs) swellings called the *corpora quadrigemina*, "quadruplet bodies"

Hindbrain { Cerebellum (forward and above)
Medulla oblongata (below)

All parts of the brain connect directly or through chains of neurons with the spinal cord through the medulla oblongata, which grades into the spinal cord without sudden change. The brain also has a series of paired nerves of its own which connect it directly with some sense organs and muscles. The forebrain is connected with the smell receptors in the nose. The midbrain is connected with the light receptors in the eyes and, by two separate pairs of nerves, with the eye muscles. The hindbrain has a whole series of nerves—usually six pairs in lower forms and eight in higher forms, including man—which connect with the more scattered receptors and with the muscles of the head.

The main features of the vertebrate brain, as we have just outlined them, were already present in rudimentary form, at least, in the jawless "fishes" that are the earliest known

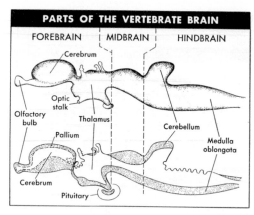

PARTS OF THE VERTEBRATE BRAIN

FOREBRAIN | MIDBRAIN | HINDBRAIN

Cerebrum
Optic stalk
Olfactory bulb
Thalamus
Cerebellum
Medulla oblongata
Pallium
Cerebrum
Pituitary

9-14 Parts of the vertebrate brain. A generalized and schematic representation of the vertebrate brain to illustrate the parts discussed in the text. The lower figure is a longitudinal section to show the local differences in thickness of the brain wall.

vertebrates. Many and important changes in details have occurred, but the most striking later developments have involved the forebrain, especially the cerebrum. At first the cerebrum was greatly outweighed in bulk by the rest of the brain. It was only a pair of small, smooth swellings involved mainly in association of sensations of smell. (We have noted, p. 203, how important smell is to most vertebrates.) Even the most progressive fishes and the amphibians have small, smooth cerebra which are dominantly olfactory: they are "smell brains" (Fig. 9-15).

In early reptiles very significant changes began to appear. The cerebrum, although still forming less than half of the whole brain, became definitely larger. Most of it was still concerned with smells, but at the forward, upper part a new sort of nervous tract began to appear. This was and is involved in association and co-ordination of all kinds of impulses from various other receptors and brain centers, and not primarily with smell. This new part of the brain is the *neopallium*, which means "new cloak." It is a new sort of covering of gray matter on the cerebrum. This covering in general is the *cerebral cortex*, and the neopallial part can also be called *neocortex* (Fig. 9-16).

Birds and mammals arose separately from reptiles, and each group evolved in its own way. In both the brain became larger and the

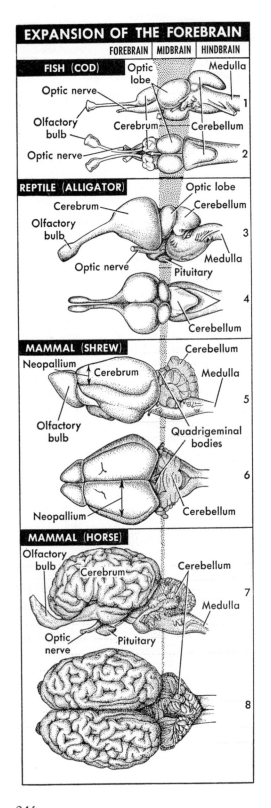

EXPANSION OF THE FOREBRAIN

FOREBRAIN	MIDBRAIN	HINDBRAIN

FISH (COD)
Optic lobe
Medulla
Optic nerve
Olfactory bulb
Cerebrum
Cerebellum
Optic nerve
1
2

REPTILE (ALLIGATOR)
Cerebrum
Optic lobe
Cerebellum
Olfactory bulb
Optic nerve
Medulla
Pituitary
Cerebellum
3
4

MAMMAL (SHREW)
Neopallium
Cerebrum
Cerebellum
Medulla
Olfactory bulb
Quadrigeminal bodies
Neopallium
Cerebellum
5
6

MAMMAL (HORSE)
Olfactory bulb
Cerebrum
Cerebellum
Medulla
Optic nerve
Pituitary
7
8

cerebrum became the largest part of the brain, but the expansion of the cerebrum was very different in the two groups. In birds the smell areas were reduced and the neopallium or cortex as a whole did not expand. The expansion of the cerebrum in birds is almost entirely in a basal region which remains relatively small in all other vertebrates. This peculiarity of the brain is certainly related to the special behavior of birds, which is also unlike that of any other animals, although its significance is not well understood. It is of interest, at any rate, that the part of the brain where we form more complex associative patterns—where, indeed, we think—is practically absent in birds. The epithet "bird-brain" therefore has some justification. On the other hand, birds perform very complicated *unlearned* procedures in courtship, nest-building, and the like, and we are deficient in a part of the brain well developed in them. So a bird would be justified in calling a particularly clumsy mate a "man-brain."

In primitive mammals the smell brain was not reduced. It remained large, as in reptiles, or even increased in size. The most significant evolutionary development was that the neopallium became separated from the rest of the cortex by a furrow and expanded greatly. In the most ancient and primitive known mammalian brain, which is some 140 million years old, the neopallium already forms the whole upper part of the cerebral cortex. A stage almost as primitive survives in some living mammals, notably the opossum. In most mam-

9-15 The expansion of the forebrain in vertebrate evolution. Four vertebrate brains are shown in side view (odd numbers) and from above (even numbers). The proportionate size of fore-, mid-, and hindbrains is to be judged by noting the width of the stippled pathway, which includes the midbrain in each case. The huge proportionate increase of the forebrain is clearly seen in comparing four vertebrates. Although the forebrain was originally principally concerned with olfaction, its expansion is due to the growth of the cerebrum, which is concerned with general association and control. In the later stages of forebrain evolution, the most important feature is development of the cerebrum's neopallium (p. 213). This is still relatively small and unconvoluted in the shrew, a primitive mammal. The huge convoluted surface of the horse cerebrum is entirely neopallium.

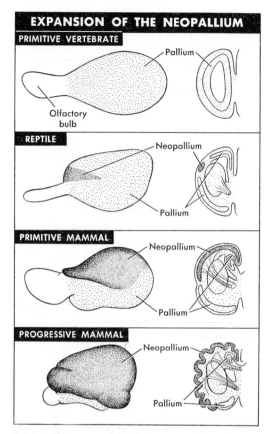

EXPANSION OF THE NEOPALLIUM

PRIMITIVE VERTEBRATE

Pallium

Olfactory bulb

REPTILE

Neopallium

Pallium

PRIMITIVE MAMMAL

Neopallium

Pallium

PROGRESSIVE MAMMAL

Neopallium

Pallium

9-16. The expansion of the neopallium in vertebrate evolution. *Top,* a generalized primitive vertebrate forebrain seen in side view (*left*) and in cross section (*right*). The cerebral hemisphere, lying behind the olfactory bulb, is stippled. Its outer wall is a *pallium* of neurons. The second figure shows comparable views of a generalized reptilian forebrain. The neopallium (dark stipple) is a small area on the front side of the cerebrum. In primitive mammals (third figure) the neopallium is more extensive. In advanced, or progressive, mammals the neopallium covers virtually the entire cerebrum (fourth figure). Indeed, the growth of neopallium is such that it has become folded, or convoluted, on the cerebral surface.

mals, however, there has been considerably further increase in the area of the neopallium, and consequently in its number of associative neurons. This increase has occurred in two ways: by expansion of the whole upper part of the cerebrum, and by folding or *convolution* of its surface. A convoluted hemisphere has more surface than a smooth one of the same size, and it is the surface area that determines the functional extent of the cortex of the brain.

Increase in size of the cerebrum, increase in relative extent of the neopallium, and increase in its surface by convolution have all occurred in varying degree in the evolution of most groups of mammals. All three are carried to an extreme in man. The cerebrum has expanded right over the other parts of the brain so that nothing but cerebrum is visible from above. The surface of the cerebrum is almost entirely neopallium. Only a small bit of smell brain is still visible in the middle of the bottom side of the cerebrum.

BRAIN FUNCTION IN MAMMALS

In all animals that have this organ, the brain is primarily an associative and co-ordinating center for nerve impulses. It receives impulses from sensory receptors, organizes them, and transfers or initiates impulses to various effectors. In the vertebrate brain the number of associative neurons is enormous and their arrangement is extremely complex. In one group of vertebrates after another there has been a tendency for intensification of these characteristics, and the tendency culminates in mammals, especially in man.

In lower vertebrates the hindbrain is a sort of message center. Impulses in both directions between most of the body and the brain pass through here, and here preliminary associations are made. Some regulatory responses are started here: automatic or reflex adjustments of posture, changes in rate of heartbeat or breathing, and the like. Messages involved in more complex or modifiable responses are, however, passed on to the parts of the brain farther forward. The functional relationships of the hindbrain are essentially the same in mammals. This is the part of the brain that has changed the least in vertebrate evolution.

In lower vertebrates the forebrain is also a message center, but a simpler one than the hindbrain. It receives information from a single sense, that of smell, makes preliminary associations, and passes on the organized information to the midbrain. In these animals the midbrain is the main center of control and co-ordination. Here final associations are made with data from forebrain and hindbrain, and here the more complex and diversified responses are started.

In the rise of mammals from reptiles and

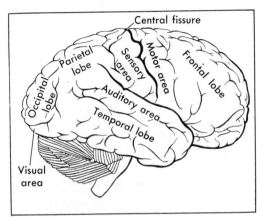

9-17 Localization of function in the cerebral cortex of man. Only the major convolutions of the cortex are drawn. They are remarkably constant from individual to individual and provide landmarks in the task of mapping the distribution of special functions in different parts of the cortex. Note especially the sensory area and motor area, which lie posterior and anterior, respectively, to the central fissure (or convolution). Details of further localization of function within these areas are given in Fig. 9-18.

further evolution among mammals, a great change has occurred. Central control has passed almost entirely from the midbrain to new centers in the neopallium of the forebrain. The midbrain has been much reduced in relative size. It has become a comparatively unimportant reflex center and a secondary message center. It relays messages between the forebrain and hindbrain (and thence to the spinal cord) and also between the forebrain and the eyes. Some secondary associations occur here, and most of the information is passed on to the neopallium.

Thus, in mammals, final co-ordination and control of most information and responses are concentrated in the neopallium, which makes up most of the cortex of the cerebrum. This development reaches its height in man. It is, indeed, what makes us human. It is the mechanism back of the extreme complexity and variability of our behavior and mental activity. To accomplish such results, even in mammals less complicated than man, the neopallium itself must be highly complex and must have some differentiation of structure, connections, and functions.

Perhaps you have seen in an old book or in a fortuneteller's display a "phrenological chart." This is a picture of a human head marked off neatly into sections labeled "combativeness," "amativeness," and the like. It was an old idea that each such personality trait had a center in the brain. If a person was particularly amorous, say, his or her "center of amativeness" would be large, so large as to cause a bump on the skull. We can afford to smile at such nonsense now, although people still go to fortunetellers. Yet it has been learned, little by little, that there is localization of functions in the brain. Phrenology has about the same relationship to our present study that astrology has to astronomy.

Particular receptors and effectors have regions of the cortex with which their connections are most direct and where messages from and to them are normally received and sent (Fig. 9-17). Sensory messages from the nose still go to the smell brain at the bottom of the cerebrum. Messages from the eyes go to an upper hind part of the neopallium. It may seem a little odd that messages from the eyes in front of the brain go to the *back* of the cerebrum, but remember that in our reptilian and earlier ancestors they went to the midbrain. They are still routed through the midbrain. Messages from the ears go to an area below or in front of the visual area. Farther forward on the upper part of the neopallium is an area which receives messages from scattered receptors all over the body and is therefore called the somatic sensory area (*somatic* means "bodily"). Just in front of this is a motor area that sends messages to muscles all over the body. It has even been possible to show where the various parts of the body are represented in these areas. The *right* side of the body is represented on the *left* side of the brain. (No one has ever discovered why the nerves happen to cross over to the other side in the nervous system.) In general the lower part of the body connects with areas along the midline of the brain. Areas for the upper part of the body are farther out, and those for the head are on the sides of the cerebrum (Fig. 9-18).

In mammals that have a relatively small neopallium, most of the region is occupied by fairly definite receptor (sensory) and effector (motor) areas like those we have just men-

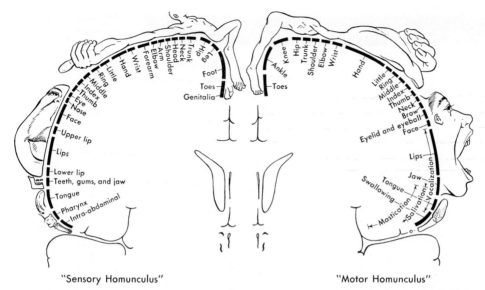

"Sensory Homunculus"   "Motor Homunculus"

9-18 Localization of function in the somatic sensory and motor areas of the cerebral cortex of man. The figure represents a section through the cerebrum. The left side of the figure is a section just posterior to the central fissure. Thus the surface on the left is that of the sensory area. The right side of the figure is a section just anterior to the central fissure and thus is the motor area. The heavy black line represents the cortex and has been broken into fragments which are labeled as to function. Outside the heavy line is a drawing of the corresponding body (or somatic) areas serviced by the cortex. The distorted representation of the body obtained in this way has been called a "homunculus." Compare the relative importance of various parts of the body as to sensory and motor function. Note, for example, that more cortex is given over to the motor than to the sensory function of hands, while the sensory area devoted to lips is greater than the motor area.

tioned. Nevertheless there are regions that have no specific connection with receptors and effectors, and these apparently blank areas are proportionally larger when the neopallium as a whole is larger. Man has an enormous neopallium, and most of it is not specifically either sensory or motor. It is certain that these areas are not really blank or functionless. Some, at least, are involved in associations of a higher and less localized sort, one or many steps further removed from specific sensations and muscular actions. This is confirmed by such relationships as those between the front end of the brain and emotions and between lower lateral parts of the brain and speech. Conscious emotions and control of reactions to them are on a high level of mental activity and are definitely localized, in part, in the front of the brain. Similarly speech, or language in general, represents a supreme sort of generalization and symbol formation and is also definitely localized in an area that is not *directly* either sensory or motor. There is much dispute

regarding other parts of the "blank" areas in man and other mammals. Some of them may be a sort of general-purpose associative mechanism, ready to take on such work as turns up, so to speak. At least, experiments on rats and other mammals have shown that if part of the cortex is removed its functions may be taken over by other parts.

The Nervous System and the Internal Environment

When we discussed the internal environment and its maintenance in Chapter 8 we were especially concerned with chemical controls. Even so, we noted many relationships with the nervous system. It was apparent that the controls are partly chemical and partly nervous, and that the two are not independent but interact closely.

In the vertebrates and in some of the more complex invertebrates (including insects) nervous control of the internal environment is

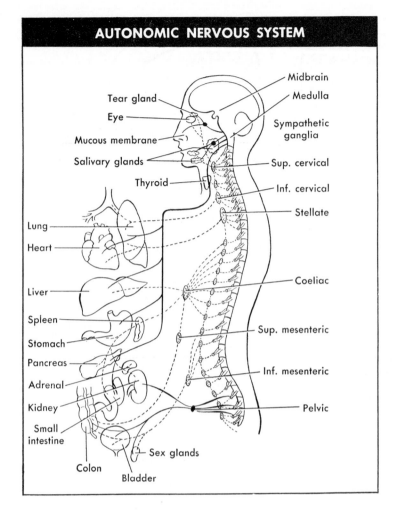

AUTONOMIC NERVOUS SYSTEM

Midbrain
Medulla
Tear gland
Eye
Sympathetic ganglia
Mucous membrane
Salivary glands
Sup. cervical
Thyroid
Inf. cervical
Stellate
Lung
Heart
Coeliac
Liver
Spleen
Stomach
Sup. mesenteric
Pancreas
Adrenal
Inf. mesenteric
Kidney
Pelvic
Small intestine
Sex glands
Colon
Bladder

9-19 The autonomic nervous system. The autonomic nervous system is shown in relation (*a*) to the central nervous system (brain and spinal cord) and (*b*) to the viscera it controls. The sympathetic and parasympathetic divisions of the autonomic system are distinguished by broken and solid lines, respectively. Note how the sympathetic system includes a distinct chain of ganglia (superior cervical, stellate, coeliac, and superior and inferior mesenteric) lying to the side of the spinal column (cf. Fig. 9-13). The parasympathetic system comprises two main elements, one arising from the medulla and the other from the lower (sacral) region of the spinal cord.

largely through a *visceral* [9] *nervous system.* This visceral system is closely connected with the central nervous system, but can act with some independence. The arrangement is most highly developed and best known in mammals, but the principles of its operation are about the same everywhere. Afferent nerves from the various internal organs run to the central nervous system, to the spinal cord or the medulla oblongata in mammals. Here they form reflex arcs with efferent visceral nerves and also have associative connections with the central nervous system itself, including the brain. Much of the activity remains within the visceral reflexes: most of the

[9] Internal organs, such as stomach, intestine, bladder, and kidney, are collectively designated as viscera.

processes of digestion, glandular secretion, and other internal regulations go on without our being aware of them or having any conscious control over them.

The efferent visceral nerves, which carry regulatory messages to the internal organs, form the *autonomic nervous system* (Fig. 9-19). There are two complete sets of these nerves, which run to most of the same organs but which have different connections with the central nervous system. The effects of the two sets of nerves are generally opposite. For instance, one set, called *sympathetic*, speeds up the heart and slows down digestion. The other set, *parasympathetic*, slows the heart and speeds digestion. The balance between the two normally keeps bodily processes near a constant rate. Comparison can be made with keeping an automobile at a steady speed by using the accelerator on upgrades and the brake on downgrades. The balance is an important part of the maintenance of stability in the internal environment.[10]

Like the chemical regulators (Chapter 8), the autonomic nervous system is involved not only with maintenance of a steady state of activity but also with altering this state in exceptional circumstances. Stimulation through the central nervous system can increase the activity of the sympathetic nerves so that they overbalance the parasympathetic nerves. Then the heartbeat increases, blood pressure rises, and in general the effects of the hormone adrenalin (p. 178) appear. In fact, the nerve fibers secrete adrenalin (or something very like it) at their terminations, and sympathetic nerves also stimulate the adrenal endocrine to pour adrenalin into the blood. The reaction occurs when you are frightened or excited. Its net effect is to make you keyed up and ready for instant action.

We may now again consider the question (p. 178) about the relationship between nervous and hormonal control of reactions to fright and excitement. We see that they are not really alternative or duplicate systems, but are parts of the same system. The nerves deliver immediate, small doses of adrenalin at particular points in organs involved in the reaction. Acting through endocrines, the same nerves also produce the somewhat slower but more widespread and lasting delivery of adrenalin to the whole body through the blood stream. There is, indeed, some evidence that the endocrine concerned, the adrenal medulla, evolved later than the sympathetic nerves, as a secondary mechanism increasing and spreading the adrenalin production normal for these nerves. If this is so, there is no question of a hormonal system replacing a nervous one, or the other way around. What has happened is only an increase in capacity and spreading of the action of a combined nervous-chemical system.

Most endocrines are not under direct nervous control. Their action is controlled, in one way or another, by pituitary hormones

(p. 180). The pituitary, in turn, is closely connected with the midbrain, and its activities are largely controlled by autonomic nervous reflexes[11] through the hind- and midbrain. Thus the whole regulatory system of hormones and nerves is closely and intricately interrelated.

In all but the simplest animals, the role of the nervous system in bodily regulation is still more extensive and complex. When water begins to run low in your body, drying of throat tissues and reduction of saliva flow signal "Thirst" to brain centers. Those centers make appropriate associations and send coordinated volleys of signals to your muscles; you go and get a drink of water. Water balance is restored. Here is a stabilizing mechanism, just as much as the activity of a hormone or of an autonomic reflex, but clearly much more complicated. Even animals with quite simple nervous systems often have this sort of stabilization. They seek food when they are hungry and in other ways respond with the whole organism to meet internal needs. Such responses are on a different level of activity. They are *behavior*, which is the subject of the next chapter.

Chapter Summary

The responsiveness of protoplasm; stimulus-conduction-response; receptors-conductors-effectors.

Stimuli: their diversity; their significance in terms of survival; their effectiveness; thresholds.

Responses; determined by the organism, not by the stimulus; latent and refractory periods.

Nerves; structure of neurons; nature and speed of the nerve impulse; all-or-none reaction; sensory, motor, and association neurons; synapses and their properties; summation; facilitation; nerve patterns and behavior.

The diversity of receptors:

Photoreceptors: their diversity; lenses as light concentrators and their subsequent utilization in image-forming eyes; com-

---

[10] If you read more advanced biological literature you will encounter a technical term for this maintenance of stability by both chemical and nervous mechanisms: homeostasis.

[11] There is a possibility that the pituitary is also controlled by some hormonal influence through a blood vessel which reaches it from the hypothalamus (see p. 213) of the brain.

pound eyes; color vision; complex eyes related to complex brains.

Touch, pressure, and sound receptors; lateral-line systems; the vertebrate ear; sense of equilibrium.

Chemical receptors: taste and smell.

"Other senses" in other animals: navigation by birds, bees, and shrimps; chronometers in many organisms.

History of the nervous system: dangers attending historical conclusions based on comparison of living forms.

Origin of the nervous system: nerve nets; a central nervous system (or CNS) (cords and brain); relation of CNS to peripheral nervous system; differentiation of afferent (sensory) and efferent (motor) nerves; association fibers; evolution of special sense organs.

The vertebrate brain: its complexity; comparison of vertebrate and invertebrate CNS's; three parts of the vertebrate brain (fore-, mid-, and hindbrain); their subparts and functions.

The forebrain: its initial association with the sense of smell; its evolution in higher vertebrates; importance of the cerebrum and the development of its neopallium in mammals; contrast between bird and mammal forebrains.

Brain function in mammals:

Hindbrain: message center and seat of much automatic or reflex control.

Midbrain: secondary message center.

Forebrain: site of important associations and final control of co-ordination; localization of function in the neopallium.

The visceral nervous system and control of the internal environment; sympathetic and parasympathetic fibers in the autonomic (efferent) system; adrenalin secretion by nerves; nervous control of endocrine glands.

CHAPTER 10

Behavior

WHAT IS BEHAVIOR?

An eagle perching quietly at the top of a tall tree is a wonderful sight. But how much more wonderful when the eagle spreads his wings, soars overhead, and dives at a scuttling rabbit! You have learned that the motionless eagle and also the tree on which it perched were not inactive. Ceaseless, intense activity was going on at tremendous rates in every living cell of those organisms. They were also responding to stimuli. The rays of the sun, for instance, evoked responses in the heat-regulating mechanism of the eagle and in the photosynthetic cells of the tree. When the eagle flew, however, there was a different level of response and a quite different order of activity. We all feel this difference strongly, even after we have learned about the incessant internal activities of the organism. The bird

sat, "not doing anything"; then it flew away, soared, and dived. That was really doing something, in the usual conceptions of our speech and thought. It is their doing things, in this sense, that makes animals so interesting, that makes them impressive as whole and individual creatures. This different order of activity is *behavior*.

Behavior is another term difficult or impossible to define with absolute precision. This is true of almost all terms that involve abstraction and do not apply to a separate, concrete object; you have encountered several previous examples. Perhaps as good a definition as any is that behavior is simply doing things, in the popular sense of the words. We still cannot define "doing things," but everyone has a reasonably accurate idea of what the words mean. A fairly good definition in more scientific terms would be that behavior is externally directed activity. Activity is behavior if it is related to the surroundings of the organism and if it brings about some external change in the relationship between organism and environment.

Although we define behavior as involving an external change, it arises from within the organism and obviously also involves all the sorts of internal mechanisms discussed in previous chapters. It may be a direct response to an external stimulus—to a change in the environment—and it almost always is this in plants and lower animals. The mechanism of response is nevertheless internal. In many organisms, especially in higher animals, behavior may not have any immediate outer stimulus. The eagle may fly off even though it does not see a rabbit and nothing has changed in the environment. It just was hungry, or it was tired of sitting. Even so, the behavior involved previous experience with external stimuli. Such behavior requires complex associative processes and usually also memory, whether conscious or not. It is usually dependent on a well-developed nervous system.

All behavior directly or indirectly involves the sequence of stimulus-conduction-response, discussed in the preceding chapter. Behavior therefore is strongly influenced and in large part determined by receptors and conductors, and further by associative mechanisms when these are present in the conductor system. It is also necessarily influenced and in part determined by the mechanisms of response, the effectors. We have not hitherto paid much attention to effectors. Since they are so important in behavior, we had better preface this chapter on behavior with a brief discussion of effectors.

Effectors

MOVEMENTS

When the eagle flew away its behavior was a sequence of motions, and the effectors were the bird's muscles. It is possible to think of responses that involve no motion—or at least motion of nothing larger than molecules—but which could be called behavior. Some simple organisms, especially bacteria, release poisons without any visible motion of the organism. The action does lead to an external change of the environmental relationship, but would you call it behavior? Then, too, if we are thinking of the whole life pattern of activity of the eagle, we are likely to say that one of the things it does—part of its behavior—is to perch motionless on trees. Such points underline the difficulties of definition and the complexity of the concept labeled "behavior." It is nevertheless clear that the one common factor in practically every activity clearly recognized as behavior is motion.

Behavior certainly depends on a great deal more than motion, but we almost always recognize that behavior is occurring by the fact that there is motion. Behavior is also described almost entirely in terms of motion and of the relationship of motions to the circumstances in which they occur. The motion may involve movement of the entire organism from one place to another; then it is *locomotion*. It may, however, involve movement of only a small part of the organism. A wink is behavior (or misbehavior) just as much as is dashing a hundred yards or driving an automobile. In behavior, then, the effectors to be discussed are those that produce motion either of a part or of the whole of an organism. Can you think of any other sorts of effectors?

EFFECTORS IN PLANTS

Plants are characterized (as we noted on p. 187) by having few, simple, and poorly differentiated receptors, conductors, and effectors. Most plant motions of a sort that can be called behavior depend not on special effector cells or organs but on activities of the ordinary plant cells. The experiment outlined on p. 184 showed that more rapid elongation of cells in one place than in another can cause a plant to bend, a distinct motion. This mechanism is involved in most of the natural movements of plants, and in nature it is usually if not always affected by auxins, as it was in the experiment.

The only other mechanisms commonly involved in motions of parts of plants are changes in the turgidity (stiffness or flabbiness) of cells and in their water content. Leaves and stems droop or stiffen according to whether their supportive cells are less or more turgid. Some pods pop open, often quite violently, when they dry out. Among the very few definite effector organs in plants is one that operates by changes in water content and turgidity. In sensitive plants (Fig. 10-1) there are little swellings (called *pulvini*) at the base of each leaf attachment (petiole, see p. 60) and also at the bases of each branch within the compound leaf. The swellings are loosely packed with thin-walled cells. When the leaf is touched, the upper or lower cells of the pulvinus lose water and become less turgid. The leaf then bends toward the side of less turgidity. That is

10-1 Complex behavior in a plant. *Above,* the carnivorous Venus's-flytrap, seen here capturing a housefly, displays relatively complex plant behavior. The leaf, shaped like a bear trap, is sensitive to touch and responds by rapidly closing the two halves of the blade, thus trapping whatever touches it. *Below,* the sensitive plant (*Mimosa*) also exhibits behavior that is unusually elaborate for a plant. Its leaves close rapidly (*right*) on being touched.

about as far as plants have gone in developing effectors related to behavior in the usual sense of the word.

EFFECTORS IN PROTISTS

Behavioral motion occurs in almost all protists and animals and is usually produced by special effectors. Protoplasm has among its characteristics an ability to expand and contract. Motion in protists and animals involves various specializations of this general property of protoplasm.

Ameboid motion occurs not only in amebas but also in many other protists, slime molds,

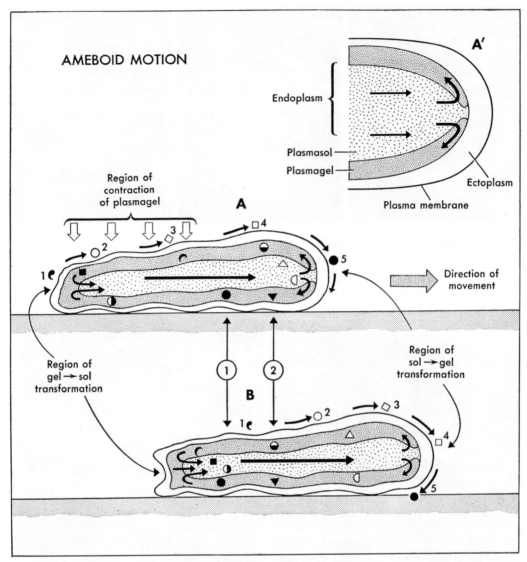

10-2 Ameboid motion. *A* and *B* represent consecutive positions of an ameba moving to the right. The motive force is the contraction of the plasmagel (*A'*). This contraction squeezes the sol portion of the endoplasm forward. At the anterior end the forward-moving endoplasm becomes converted to plasmagel and moves backward to the region of plasmagel contraction (*A*). At the posterior end of the animal there is a reconversion of plasmagel to plasmasol. The animal is schematically marked with symbols (in practical study it may be marked with small particles) which permit visualization of the whole complex movement. The movement is like that of a caterpillar track on a bulldozer. Note how, as the animal moves forward on its rolling ectoplasm, the ● and ▼ symbols remain fixed at positions ① and ②. The rolling motion of the ectoplasm may be visualized by the shifting symbols numbered 1 through 5.

and many cells within multicellular organisms —our own white blood cells, for instance. When an ameba starts to go somewhere, it bulges on one side. Part of the cytoplasm becomes a sol (p. 50) and flows toward the

bulge, where it spreads to the sides and becomes a gel again. At the opposite side of the ameba, gel turns to sol and flows forward, and remaining gel near the membrane here moves up after the sol. Thus the whole protist moves slowly in the direction of the bulge (Fig. 10-2).

The turning of gel to sol and the streaming forward of the sol provide a first answer to "Why does an ameba move?" The next "why" is "Why does the sol flow forward?" The most probable answer is that the gel around the sides and rear contracts and forces the sol forward, much as when you squeeze a tube of tooth paste. The next two "why's" are "Why does the gel contract?" and "Why does gel turn to sol and sol to gel?" No very good answers are available as yet. A great deal of work is being done on these questions. This is not so much because biologists are especially worried about how amebas get about. The main reason for spending so much time on rambling amebas is that the answers would cast light on the nature of protoplasm and on problems of energy release and contractility. Those answers would bear on important processes in all organisms, including man, and even on the nature of life.

Other protists move about by lashing whip- or hairlike projections called _flagella and cilia._ There are more technical differences between these two kinds of protistan "whips" but the most obvious is their size and number on each cell. Flagella are always longer and usually few in number. In ciliated protists the whips (cilia) are very short and usually cover the whole surface of the cell. Flagella are used in various ways; some "pull" the cell by executing a gentle rippling motion, others drive it with a more vigorous lash. Moreover, these diverse flagellary motions can be executed by one and the same cell (Fig. 10-3). In ciliates the ciliary beat can be reversed,

backing up the cell from its former path (cf. p. 235). The motion of flagella and cilia is probably caused by very local contractions of the cytoplasm, although whether this occurs in the moving "whips" themselves or around their base in the cytoplasm is not certain.[1]

Ciliary motion is also important in higher animals and plants. In some plants and most animals including man, the male sex cell moves by means of a flagellum and in this way encounters the female cell. There are many other cells with cilia in higher animals. For example, in the gills of an oyster or the lung tubes of man, the cells are fixed and the cilia move fluids (on the gill) or dust particles (in the lung) past the cells. Certainly these motions are important, but they are not part of behavior as we are using that word.

Even in some protists there are contractile fibers, which of course in these acellular organisms are not made of cells (cf. Fig. 3-13). They are localized strands within the cytoplasm that have the capacity of contracting more rapidly and pulling in a more definite direction than the rest of the protoplasm. In almost all multicellular animals there are specialized cells in which part, or usually all, of the cytoplasm has these properties. These are muscular cells, usually united into strands or layers of muscular tissue and clustered in bundles forming separate muscles. Movements of parts or wholes of animals above the level of sponges are generally the results

[1] In Chapter 11 we point out that flagellary motion is in part controlled by the centriole of the cell. The centriole is also associated with the movements of spindle fibers in mitosis.

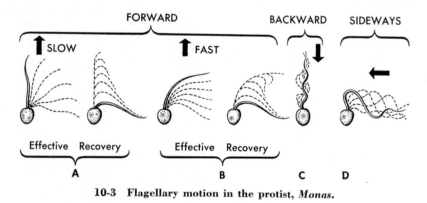

10-3 **Flagellary motion in the protist, _Monas._**

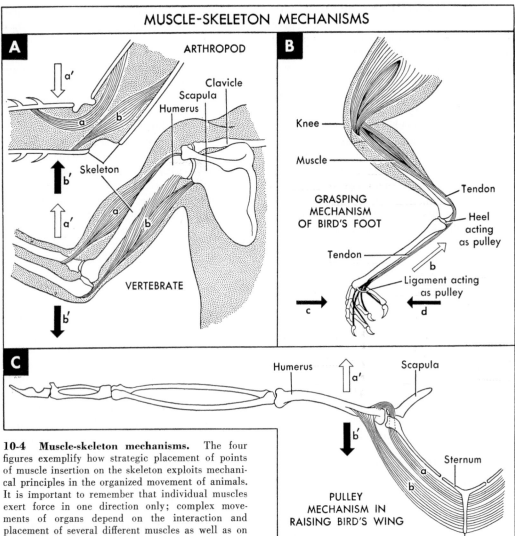

MUSCLE-SKELETON MECHANISMS

A ARTHROPOD

Clavicle
Scapula
Humerus
Skeleton

VERTEBRATE

B GRASPING MECHANISM OF BIRD'S FOOT

Knee
Muscle
Tendon
Heel acting as pulley
Tendon
Ligament acting as pulley

C Humerus
Scapula
Sternum
PULLEY MECHANISM IN RAISING BIRD'S WING
Keel

10-4 Muscle-skeleton mechanisms. The four figures exemplify how strategic placement of points of muscle insertion on the skeleton exploits mechanical principles in the organized movement of animals. It is important to remember that individual muscles exert force in one direction only; complex movements of organs depend on the interaction and placement of several different muscles as well as on the geometry of the skeleton. *A.* The movement of a limb joint in an arthropod (external skeleton) is contrasted with that in a vertebrate (internal skeleton). In each, contraction of the muscle *a* causes limb movement in the direction *a'*; contraction of muscle *b* causes movement in the direction *b'*. When comparing the arthropod with the vertebrate, note that the difference in *a'* direction depends on the geometrical relations of the muscle insertions on the skeleton. The controlled motion of the limb in any one direction depends on the balance of the opposing contractions of both muscles, *a* and *b*. *B.* When a bird squats on a branch, its claws execute a complex grasping motion caused by the contraction of a single muscle in the upper part of the leg; there are no muscles in the lower leg or toes. Simple muscular contraction is translated into complex claw motion by the geometry of the whole limb. The single muscle responsible is inserted on the pelvis near the spinal column; it ends in the lower part of the leg as a long tendon that passes over the heel and through a pulley formed by a ligament

at the base of the claws. Here it branches, sending parts to the tip of each toe. Contraction of the leg muscle pulls the long tendon upward (*b*, white arrow) and drags its separate parts through the ligament pulley, causing the claws to move inward in the two directions *c* and *d*. *C.* Birds also provide a striking example of how a pulley may invert the direction of motion inherent in a muscle's contraction. Both the up and down beats of a bird's wing are caused by muscles (*a* and *b*, respectively) lying side by side. They are both inserted on the keel of the sternum, or breast bone. And both are inserted on the humerus of the wing; *b* pulls the humerus directly down (*b'*, black arrow) when it contracts; *a* raises the wing (*a'*, white arrow) in spite of its position, simply because before inserting on the humerus it first passes over the pulley formed by the scapula or shoulder blade. Its contraction is thus translated into an upward movement of the humerus.

of *muscular motion.* It is in these organisms that behavior is most elaborate and most significant, from our human point of view, at least. Muscular effectors are therefore worthy of special consideration.

MUSCULAR EFFECTORS

In practically all animals above the level of a sponge a muscle (Fig. 10-4) is the usual effector in a stimulus-conductor-effector sequence, whether this occurs in just that form, as a simple reflex, or with associative complexities. In all but the simplest forms, a fairly clear distinction can be made between muscles that produce the sorts of motions that we have defined as behavior and those involved only in internal processes. In higher animals the distinction may be so clear that even a small segment of a muscle can be identified as *behavioral* (or *skeletal* in a vertebrate, or *voluntary* in man) or *visceral* (*involuntary* in man, see p. 65).

A well-developed but still quite simple muscular system can be exemplified by that of an earthworm. As in man, a cylindrical sheet of muscular tissue around the intestine moves food along by rhythmical contractions. There are also muscles in the walls of some blood vessels, especially in the five pairs of hearts. The intestinal and circulatory muscles are of course visceral muscles. The behavioral muscles form two nearly complete cylinders, one inside the other, throughout the body just inside the outer wall. The outer layer has its fibers arranged in circles, and in the inner layer the fibers run in the direction of the length of the body. A section of the body with the outer layer contracted and the inner layer relaxed becomes long and thin. Conversely, when the outer layer relaxes and the inner contracts, the section of the body becomes short and fat. There are also paired bristles down the sides of the body, each with its own small muscle fibers that erect it or pull it back (Fig. 10-5).

An earthworm in its burrow moves along by bracing itself with its bristles and then sending waves of long-thin and short-fat along the body. The contractions forming the waves are controlled by nerves. The nerve cords (two of them) exercise central control, but what is by courtesy called the brain has

little to do with the process. An earthworm with its front end cut off moves along just about as well as before, as you have doubt-

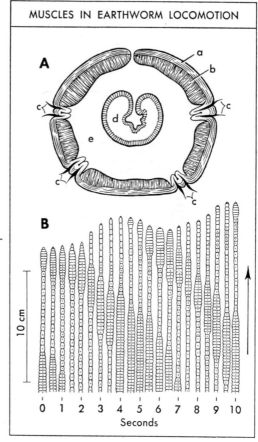

MUSCLES IN EARTHWORM LOCOMOTION

10-5 Muscles in earthworm locomotion. *A.* Cross section through the body of an earthworm: *a,* outer layer of circular muscles, whose contraction narrows the animal; *b,* inner layer of longitudinal muscles, whose contraction fattens the animal; *c,* the four pairs of bristles, which serve to grip the animal against its burrow; *d,* the alimentary canal; *e,* the body cavity, or coelom. *B.* The shape and progress of an earthworm moving forward through 10 successive seconds. At the beginning, note that the anterior segments are fat (local contraction of longitudinal muscles), gripping the burrow. Subsequently, contraction of longitudinal muscles moves backward as a wave, while contraction of circular muscles begins at the anterior end, thrusting the anterior segments forward. Part of the forward advance is conserved (seconds 5 through 7) when the anterior segments initiate a new wave of longitudinal muscle contraction. This contraction fattens the animal anteriorly, slowing down the initial advance as the bristles engage the burrow wall.

less observed. This simple reaction is nearly, although not quite, all there is to an earthworm's behavior. You are likely also to have noticed that an earthworm can contract the whole body at once and snap back into its burrow.

Development of really complicated motions and of the most complex sorts of behavior depends on a system of rigid braces, attachments, levers, and joints worked by muscles. Such an arrangement is a *skeletal system*. The skeleton often has other functions as well, particularly that of protection, but in its relationship to the behavioral muscles it is an integral part of the effectors of the organisms that have it. In animals with skeletons almost all the behavioral muscles are attached to skeletal parts and move them, the other tissues naturally coming along. There are exceptions. For instance, the muscle most involved in kissing is not directly attached to the skeleton, and kissing is definitely behavior.

There are two possible relationships between muscular and skeletal systems (Fig. 10-4), and both arrangements have evolved more than once. They contrast characteristically in the two groups in which the most elaborate behavior has also evolved: insects and vertebrates. In insects the skeleton is a hollow shell on the *outside* of the body, and the muscles are attached *inside* the skeletal tubes and other parts. In vertebrates, as you well know, the skeleton is inside and muscles are attached around it, fastened to outer surfaces of bones. In rather small animals the two systems are about equally effective mechanically, and in extremely small ones an external skeleton may be more effective. In larger animals, however, sufficient strength in an external skeleton would require inordinate increase in its bulk, and almost insuperable difficulties in forming workable joints and lodging muscles strong enough to work the heavy mechanism. As everyone knows, insects are smaller than most vertebrates, and this is one of the reasons. As usual, there are other factors, too, but this alone would make an insect as big as a man impossible. Do you think a man as small as an insect would be possible?

The study of bones, or of insect skeletons,

and muscles has great fascination for anyone who is at all mechanically minded. Most of the mechanical principles of simple and compound levers, for instance, may be illustrated in animals. We cannot here take the time to discuss these details, but we have illustrated a few examples (Fig. 10-4). It is, of course, outside the plan of this book to name and describe the vertebrate muscles and bones one by one.

We must make just two other biological points about muscles: The first is that they work in only one direction. Force is exerted only when a muscle contracts. When it relaxes again, it may slowly resume its former shape spontaneously or it may be pulled back into shape, but in any event it releases no energy by its return. A consequence of this fact is that in a workable system there must be something pulling in the opposite direction from each muscle. This opposing force may be an elastic tissue of some sort, but with the skeletal muscles it is usually another muscle, or group of them (Fig. 10-4). That system of opposing forces makes possible the delicacy and precision of behavioral motions. You can illustrate it and feel it by bending your arm into any position. The arm can be moved and then held, with precision in small fractions of an inch. While in the set position you can flex the arm muscles strongly without moving the arm at all. Obviously, then, you are putting in play opposing sets of muscles, and are applying exactly equal force in opposite directions.

The second and last point on this topic is that muscle fibers, like nerves, normally respond by an all-or-none reaction. If they contract at all, they go all the way. This is an effect in part of their own character and in part of the fact that the nerve impulses stimulating them are all-or-none phenomena. You will be right to question this statement from your certain knowledge that you can exert greater or less force with the same muscle, but perhaps you can think of a hypothesis to account for this fact.

The answer is that each muscle consists of a large number of fibers divided into many groups stimulated by different nerve fibers. Each group contracts fully or not at all, but the total force in the muscle depends on how many groups contract. Thus more impulses through more nerve fibers produce greater contraction of the whole muscle.[2] Even when we think we are not using our nerves and muscles, they are usually slightly active. A few fiber groups in any skeletal muscle are contracted all the time. This is muscle *tonus*. It does not tire the muscles, because the same groups do not remain contracted for long; one relaxes and rests while another contracts.

OTHER EFFECTORS

There are sorts of effectors that we have not mentioned, but they are of so much less importance for an understanding of general biology that it is not worth while to devote much space to them. We will mention two by way of examples. Coelenterates (the big group of corals, jellyfishes, and so on that you have met before) have special cells scattered over the surface which explode when touched (cf. Fig. 22-3). They shoot out threads or darts, some of which help the animal to adhere to a surface. Others cling to prey or pierce it and inject poison. If you have ever brushed against a jellyfish while swimming, you know how painful these can be. They are fatal to the usual prey of jellyfishes, and, indeed, even men have been killed by them. Their discharge is certainly behavior, an externally directed activity, and it involves motion, although of a different sort from any previously noted.

Our second example is the discharge of an electric shock by any of the several sorts of electrical fishes. The discharge may involve as much as 2000 watts at 200 volts, a tremendous jolt. This is "externally directed activity" with a vengeance, so it must be considered behavior. It is one of the few sorts of behavior that do not necessarily involve motion—except on the part of the unfortunate recipient! [3]

[2] In some invertebrates there is evidence that nerve impulses of certain frequencies or along certain channels may prevent contraction instead of stimulating it. If so, this is another way of balancing the amount of contraction.
[3] Note the interesting point that electric-organ effectors in fish are modified muscles.

The Study of Behavior

We have now entered a field that is at the same time both biology and psychology. Since psychology is often defined as the science of behavior, it may, indeed, appear that the present subject is psychology rather than biology. But behavior is obviously a living activity, and it is impossible to pursue the study of life, which is biology, and to ignore behavior. There is a large area in which biology and psychology not only overlap but are actually the same subject. We shall not attempt to follow the psychologists far into their most complex and distinctive subject matter, human mental life and personality, but even that is inseparably grounded in biology.

It is useless to try to establish a boundary between biology and psychology. Behavior certainly cannot be understood without some knowledge of effectors. Behavior is equally dependent on conductors and associative mechanisms and on receptors. The properties and actions of receptors are clearly a part of biology and are studied intensively by biologists, but they are also studied by other investigators who approach them from a psychological point of view. Such overlaps in science are all to the good. They are fruitful sources for discovery of new relationships.

It is also clear that understanding of the mechanisms of behavior demands knowledge of processes of maintenance, which in turn depend on syntheses and other processes in cells, and so ramifications reach into all the life sciences.

The study of behavior is one of the most difficult branches of biology. Behavior is extremely complex in the manifestations of most interest and importance to us. It depends on a multiplicity of factors, all extremely hard to isolate and identify—many of them internal processes that seem to defy observation. Men have always been interested in the behavior of other men and of all the animals around them. This interest must date from a time before our ancestry became human, for it is obvious that nonhuman animals also show interest in the behavior of their associates. Study of behavior is one of the oldest occupations, but it is one of the youngest sciences.

The problems of interpreting, of understanding, the behavior of other organisms are so great that a really rational approach to them has been developed only in recent years.

We see only the external aspects of behavior. An environmental stimulus and the response of some effector may be observed. Until very recently even the specialists in such studies had no way of examining what occurs between the stimulus and the response, and even now the information about this is extremely incomplete. We cannot see into the minds of even our nearest and dearest, let alone into whatever corresponds to a mind in a rat, a bug, a worm, or an ameba. We usually have to infer the internal process from its external result, which is almost always some form of motion. If our nearest and dearest goes through the motions we call "kissing" or "hitting," we judge the accompanying mental processes by the processes we would have if we performed the same actions.

Judging others by ourselves is all very well to the extent that others are really like ourselves. We can be quite mistaken even about our nearest and dearest. We are more likely to be mistaken about an Eskimo, although there is no biological difference in the mechanisms that determine his behavior. How much more likely we are to be mistaken about a dog, a fish, or a fly, in which there certainly is a difference in mechanisms! Yet from time immemorial most people have assumed that, if some nonhuman animal performs an action, its reasons for doing so (that is, the accompanying processes inside the organism) are the same as ours would be.

Interpretation of nonhuman actions in terms of human motives was one of the two greatest impediments in development of a *science* of animal behavior. The other was that animals were observed in surroundings so complicated that the stimuli really involved could not be accurately identified. Observations were *anecdotes* as to what an animal was seen to do in complex natural situations, in which the stimuli important to the particular animal were often wholly unknown to the observer. The anecdote was invariably interpreted *anthropomorphically*,[4] as if the animal were a man. You know that this entirely non-

4 From the Greek, meaning "man form."

scientific and non–common-sense procedure is still usual. Some popular magazines make a special point of gathering anecdotes about pets and other nonhumans and giving anthropomorphic interpretations of their behavior.

There is an old principle of logic and science sometimes called Occam's razor, after a Scholastic who expressed it in the fourteenth century, and "razor" because it is supposed to cut out nonsense. The principle, which has been stated in many different ways, is that if several different explanations are possible, the simplest is to be considered the most probable. The science of behavior can be dated, more than by any other one event, from the application of this principle by Lloyd Morgan (1852-1936). "Morgan's canon" (stated by him in somewhat different words) is that the actions of an animal should be interpreted in terms of the simplest possible mental process.

This application of the razor has certainly cut out a great deal of nonsense. When an ameba puts out a projection, surrounds a food particle, and digests this in a food vacuole, we do not say that it *smelled* food, *liked* the smell, *decided* to eat, and therefore seized the particle. We attribute to the ameba no mental activity at all. Even before Lloyd Morgan, few would have been quite so anthropomorphic about an ameba. Yet many bird lovers still assume that a mother bird sits on eggs because she *wants* to have babies and that she cares for the hatched young because she *loves* them and knows they need food and warmth. Application of the razor would suggest that the bird reacted *instinctively* to physiological needs in *herself*, without the slightest idea that young would hatch from the eggs, with no conscious knowledge of the needs of the young, and no tender emotion toward them. In fact, control of the stimuli confirms this view. Birds will react to pebbles or to cuckoos' eggs in the same way as to their own eggs. A slight change in appearance or behavior of the hatchling can turn maternal care into a vicious attack.

The razor can cut both ways, and most students of behavior now recognize that its previous use was sometimes in the wrong direction. On the face of the facts, the simplest hypothesis about what happens between stimulus and response is that nothing happens except conduction from receptor to effector—in other words, a simple reflex. Some researchers did go so far as to conclude that all reactions should be interpreted as reflexes and that the study of behavior reduces to correlation between stimuli and responses. This *behavioristic or objective* approach, as it was called, can be applied to man, and it leads to the remarkable conclusion that our actions have nothing to do with our thoughts; nothing, at least, beyond the fact that we may notice our own actions. Now, we cannot get into the minds of others, but we are in our own minds. We know beyond any common-sense doubt that our actions—not all of them, but the great majority—*are* determined by complex mental processes and are not simple reflexes. The question arises whether, after all, it is a correct use of the razor to insist that nothing of the sort happens in other animals.

A dog sees its master and wags its tail. According to Morgan's canon we must conclude that this is no more than an established reflex: stimulus (sight of master)—conduction (from eyes to tail muscles)—response (wag). Is this the right application of the razor? We know the dog and know that recognition of his master has been built up by learning and is equally possible by different cues, not only sight but also sound and, above all, smell. We know that the dog responds to the master in different ways, not only by tail wagging but also by barking, running, cringing, picking up its leash, or otherwise, depending on the situation. We also know that the dog has a very complex brain, with all the parts that occur in ours although they are different in proportions and shapes. We can also determine that there is activity in the *cortex of the brain,* not only in reflex conductors, when the dog sees its master. This last is a recent technical development that makes it no longer true that behavior can be studied only through responses. By use of suitable electrical equipment it is possible to determine that nervous activity is occurring, and where. Surgical interference with the nervous system can also determine what parts are necessary for perception of a stimulus and production of a given response.

In the light of *all* the facts about the dog, should we infer that the dog recognizes its master, likes him, and responds by tail wagging, or that nothing but a reflex is involved? The reflex does not explain what is known about the whole of the dog's behavior in the presence of its master and about the dog's associational equipment and its activities. To begin to explain all this would require an extremely complicated set of reflexes. It is actually *simpler,* and more consistent with the whole body of data, to conclude that the dog thinks. That is the way to apply the razor. In *this* case it cuts out Morgan's canon.

We still are not justified in concluding that the dog thinks like a man. Of course it does not. Its receptors, conductors, associators, and effectors are characteristic of its species, with variations peculiar to this individual. It thinks like a dog, and like this particular dog. To find out what that thinking is like we have to steer clear of anthropomorphism, of course, but we must steer equally clear of the unjustified application of Morgan's canon.

Modern study of behavior follows principles of good experimentation applicable in any field. Tests are made in a standardized situation kept as uniform as possible except in one respect. One environmental factor is varied, and this is a controlled stimulus. Responses, mainly motions, are observed. Stimuli are varied in kind and intensity in successive experiments. Finally, the mechanisms between stimulus and response are also studied by their anatomical relationships, by their activities, and by the effects of interference with them at various points.

Suppose you want to find out what sounds a dog can hear, what tones it can discriminate, whether it has an established reflex to any tones, whether it can learn a response to a tone, whether it can learn different responses to different tones, and whether it can learn to make two successive responses to a single tone. (You can readily think of still other things you might want to know about relationships between hearing and behavior in dogs.) Can you set up a series of experiments to find out these things?

Tropisms and
Other Reflex Movements

TROPISMS

The observation of an organism's behavior reduces, in one sense, to the observation of its movements. The first behavioral movements to be well understood were those of plants. Here behavior takes a very simple form: a plant stem moves away from, or towards, a stimulus such as light (Fig. 10-6). The same stimulus invariably produces the

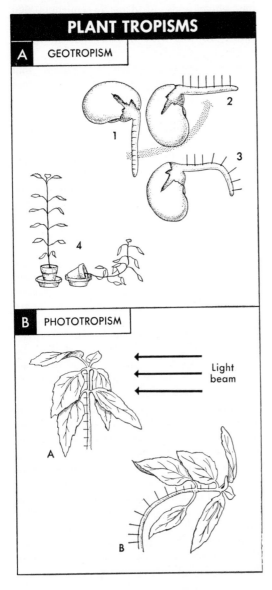

PLANT TROPISMS

A GEOTROPISM

B PHOTOTROPISM

Light beam

same response; there is no evidence that memory or learning is involved. The word *tropism* was originally coined for plant responses of this kind. Tropism derives from the Greek word meaning "turning," and in its original use it had a very precise meaning. Indeed, botanists carefully reserved the term "tropism" for the bending movements of stems and roots which are caused by differences of stimulation (e.g., by light or gravity) on the two sides of a growing organ. They employed *taxis* for the movements of freely swimming unicellular plants. However, the word "tropism" was subsequently carried over by zoologists into the description of animal movements. We will see in this section that its meaning has been seriously blurred as a consequence. Nevertheless, we begin by noting its precise meaning, because it is important to understand what the early students of animal behavior had in mind when they borrowed the term.

Two elements are involved in the tropism concept. (1) The movement in a tropistic response has a definite direction which is determined by differences in the intensity of stimulation on the two sides of the moving organ. (2) The mechanism of the turning response is *innate*—it is an inflexible part of the organism's inherited physiological apparatus. It is not subject to modification or control by the organism. A tropism is what

10-6 Plant tropisms. *A. 1, 2,* and *3.* The *positive* geotropism of roots. *1.* A germinated bean seed with root growing downward toward gravity. *2.* The root (marked with India ink at equal intervals along its length) is experimentally rotated upward through 90 degrees so that it lies perpendicular to gravity. *3.* The root now grows downward toward gravity. Inspection of the original ink marks shows that the point of curvature is the point of greatest growth. The root has grown less rapidly on the side toward gravity and more rapidly on the side away from gravity. *4.* The shoot system exhibits a *negative* geotropic response when it is rotated through 90 degrees. When the plant is placed on its side, subsequent growth leads the shoot upward away from gravity. *B.* The positive phototropism of the shoot system. When subjected to a lateral source of light *(A)* the shoot system curves toward it *(B).* Again the use of ink marks shows that the region of curvature has the greatest growth. Growth in the growing region is inhibited on the illuminated side.

one famous student, Loeb, called a "forced movement." The organism which executes a tropism has no choice about the matter. A man may turn his head when a pretty girl passes by, but he does so on his own responsibility. That is *not* a tropism.

TROPISMS IN PLANTS

Much of the behavior of plants consists of tropisms, the most obvious of which are responses to gravity and light. Doubtless you are already familiar with both reactions in garden plants, and they can easily be shown in experiments.

When you plant seeds, you do not bother to put them in right end up. No matter how the seed is oriented, the roots grow down and the stem grows up. There is a gravity (or earth) tropism, which is positive in the root (it grows toward the center of gravity) and negative in the stem (it grows away from the center). If you sprout some beans, a little cylinder, the developing root, appears. Turn a seedling so that the root is horizontal. Next day the tip will have turned and will point downward (Fig. 10-6). Only the growing tip turns downward; response to gravity is confined to this region. Tropism of the stem can be demonstrated equally simply: turn a pot containing a growing, tall-stemmed plant on its side. The growing end of the stem (and again *only* this part) will turn upward in a day or so.

Differences in growth rates are the mechanism of tropistic responses in plants: there is greater elongation of cells on one side of the root or stem than on the other. Auxins (p. 183) become more concentrated on one side. But *how?* the force of gravity results in this concentration on opposite sides in root and stem is another of the things that no one knows—yet.

Tropistic response to light is equally familiar and easy to demonstrate. Most green plants grow toward light and they may, like the sunflower, keep parts turned to the sun in its daily movement. If an oat shoot (like those used in the experiment on p. 183) is lit from one side, it bends toward that side. Or if one side is covered with carbon black, the shoot bends toward the uncovered side. (Charles Darwin carried out many experiments of this kind and determined most of the phenomena of light tropism.) In these tropisms differential growth stimulated by auxins is involved, although again the reason why auxin distribution is affected by light in just the ways observed is not yet clear. At any rate the crucial point is clear enough: the direction of the stem's movement is ultimately determined by the difference in intensity of light stimulus on its two sides.

Many other stimuli determine direction of growth in parts of plants and therefore produce tropistic responses. Roots grow toward water. Tendrils twine around what they touch.

Loeb and animal "tropisms." The general nature of plant tropisms as "forced movements," due to differential growth stimulation on the two sides of an organ, was well understood by the end of the nineteenth century. However, the description and analysis of animal behavioral movements was still encumbered by anecdotal techniques and anthropomorphic interpretation. As we noted earlier, Lloyd Morgan led a rebellion against this approach; and he was joined in his revolt by one of the most dynamic personalities in biology of the early twentieth century, Jacques Loeb (1859-1924). Loeb set out to place the study of all animal behavior on as sound a footing as that of plants by developing a theory of *animal tropisms*. His main aim was to show that the pattern of animal movement was—like that of a plant—caused by differences of stimulation on its two sides.

We can illustrate Loeb's ideas with the behavior of a pill bug (or wood louse) in the presence of a light source, like a lamp. The animal moves directly towards a single light source, following a path like that in Fig. 10-7*A*. If it is placed near two lights, it moves along the path shown in Fig. 10-7*B*. Loeb explained movements like these simply by substituting amount of muscular activity for amount of growth. Just as the two sides of a plant stem differ in the amount of light stimulus they receive, so do the two sides (eyes) of the pill bug; just as the difference in stimulation automatically causes a difference in growth in the stem, so does it automatically cause differences in muscle movement in the pill bug. The less illuminated side moves faster, and the animal curves in towards the light. As soon as the pill bug is oriented head-on to the light, its two eyes are equally stimulated and a straight path is maintained. Do you see how this explains the two-light experiment? The animal moves along the line where stimulation from the *two* sources is equal.

Loeb's theory of animal tropisms—as *forced movements*—is a zealous application of Morgan's canon, and attractive in its simplicity. It tempted many biologists into believing that a fully mechanical and simple explanation of animal movements (and therefore behavior, if one follows Morgan's canon to its limit) was at hand. Loeb devoted much of his life to pressing this extreme mechanical view of animal behavior. The story of his campaign—and such it was, for it lacked nothing in vigor and outspokenness—is fascinating but complex enough to prevent our telling it fully here. It is to Loeb's credit, as well as to Morgan's, that behavioral study was freed from anthropomorphism; but on the debit side of his campaign we must place the ruination of tropism as a term with precise meaning and usefulness. Loeb stubbornly attempted to explain all animal movements as tropisms; yet the fact is that comparatively few of them are like those of the pill bug in the presence of light. And for that matter, many plant movements are not tropisms in the true meaning of the word. Let us look into these nontropistic movements before finally evalu-

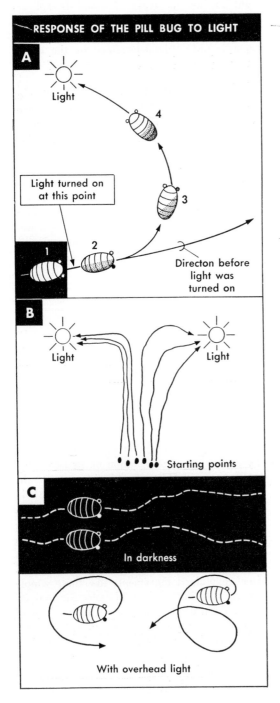

RESPONSE OF THE PILL BUG TO LIGHT

A

Light

4

Light turned on at this point

3

1 2

Direction before light was turned on

B

Light   Light

Starting points

C

In darkness

With overhead light

10-7 Phototaxis of the pill bug. *A. 1, 2, 3,* and *4* are successive positions of the pill bug. Before the light is turned on it is in position 1, headed in the direction indicated. When the light is turned on it is illuminated differentially on its two sides, as the shading on the body and eyes indicates. Subsequently it turns until, in position 4, it is illuminated equally on its two sides and eyes. It then maintains a straight path to the light. *B.* The tracks of six animals exposed to two lights. They move up the path on which they experience equal light intensity on their two sides. Ultimately they swing toward one or the other. *C.* Two animals have had their right eyes covered with black paint. In darkness they maintain an essentially straight path. When exposed to an overhead light they both start what is called a "circus movement": their pathways are circular and the direction of movement is to the left, that is, toward the more illuminated eye. (How might you have improved this experiment? Would it have been better to paint the left eye in one of the animals? Why is the experiment in darkness necessary?)

ating the meaning and utility of the tropism idea in general.

NONTROPISTIC MOVEMENTS

The direction of many plant movements is not controlled by differences in the intensity of the stimulus on the two sides of the moving organ. Such movements are, therefore, not tropisms. When the sun rises many leaves move upward from a "sleep" or nighttime position; when darkness arrives the leaf droops. The direction of neither petal nor leaf movement is determined by differences in intensity of light on its two surfaces; it is determined by their anatomy. At the base of the leaf is a special organ (called a pulvinus) that functions as a hinge; when water is withdrawn from some of its cells these "collapse" and so does the hinge, causing the leaf to droop. Restoration of water into these cells opens the hinge and raises the leaf. A similar mechanism is responsible for the surprisingly rapid (one or two seconds) closure of the leaflets of the sensitive plant *Mimosa* (Fig. 10-1). The Venus's-flytrap's very rapid leaf movements trap those flies which trigger three sensitive hairs [5] in the middle of the leaf (Fig. 10-1). Like other leaves, the leaves of the Venus's-flytrap close in a direction inherently determined by their structure and not by the pattern of stimulation.

In protists and multicellular animals there

5 A rare case of specialized receptors in plants.

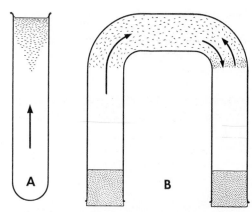

10-8   The negative geotaxis of *Paramecium*. *A.* Paramecia accumulate near the surface of an open test tube. The question arises: are the paramecia congregating there because of negative geotaxis or because of a positive taxis to high oxygen concentration? *B.* The experiment illustrated shows that geotaxis is indeed involved. A U tube is filled with water, stoppered at both ends, and inverted. Paramecia are introduced at the bottom left and immediately move upward into the horizontal part of the tube. When, in moving across the tube, they find their path going downward, they reverse their direction of movement. No differences in oxygen concentration exist in the tube, and the pattern of movement is precisely that expected on the hypothesis of negative geotaxis.

is much behavior that looks tropistic—movements apparently away from or toward a source of stimulation. *Paramecium* (Fig. 10-8) is a complex ciliated protist much used in laboratory studies. It performs many seemingly tropistic movements: it moves up-

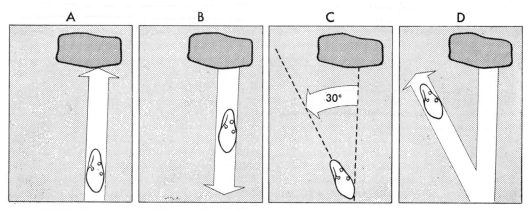

10-9   Trial-and-error behavior in *Paramecium*. *A*, *B*, *C*, and *D* represent successive positions of a paramecium before and after encountering an obstacle. The broad white arrow indicates the direction of its path. In *B* the animal backs directly away from the obstacle and executes a fixed turn of 30 degrees (*C*) before starting off in another "trial" direction (*D*).

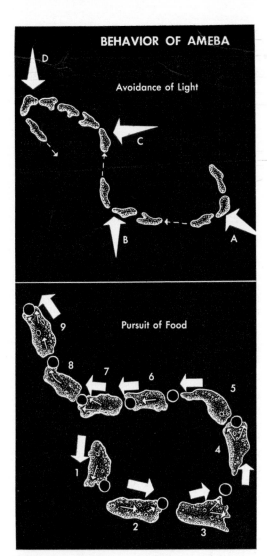

BEHAVIOR OF AMEBA

Avoidance of Light

D

C

B   A

Pursuit of Food

9

8

7   6

5

4

1

2   3

10-10 The behavior of *Ameba*. *Above*, successive positions of an ameba after being subjected to successive lights coming from the directions indicated at A, B, C, and D. Each time it turns away from the light. *Below*, successive positions of an ameba "in pursuit" of a food particle. Inspection of the figure shows that, even when it loses actual contact with the particle, it can still detect its position, presumably by chemical stimuli.

ward away from the center of gravity (Fig. 10-8), and when confronted with an obstacle it moves away from it (Fig. 10-9). Many flagellated protists can photosynthesize, and react markedly to light. They move toward a light that is not too strong but away from a light above a certain intensity. Many

protists are sensitive to chemical stimuli and, like the ameba in Fig. 10-10, they will move directly toward food, guided by "taste" stimulation. Even bacteria, which have about as little behavior as any organisms, move away from acids. Planarians, the little flatworms we discussed in Chapter 8, move against a current, and they aggregate in the darker side of a dish. Fruit flies congregate in the drier side of a dish. Everywhere we find animal movements that are guided somehow by external stimulation: gravity, light, chemicals, temperature, moisture, and so on. But by far the majority of these movements are not tropisms in the real meaning of that term.

The paramecium that "avoids" an obstacle does not turn tropistically, forced by stimulation differences on its two sides. When it blindly bumps into an obstacle it has a shock reaction; it stops. It then reverses its ciliary beating and, backing up a way, makes a turn of about 30 degrees, and goes forward again (Fig. 10-9). The angle of turn is not controlled by the pattern of stimulation; it is fixed. If the paramecium hits the same obstacle on its re-try it repeats the backup and 30-degree change of course. Sooner or later the obstacle is avoided. But in twelve repetitions the animal might be back where it started after missing several escape channels in the meantime. Similarly, flagellates do not, as a rule, move *directly* toward or away from a light. They have shock reactions to strong light and darkness. Sooner or later trial and error lead them into light of intermediate intensity. Fruit flies in a dish that is drier on one side do not move directly to the dryness. They move about at random and eventually congregate in the dryness simply because they slow up there. This is no more a tropism (a directed movement) than the congregation of automobiles in the congested *slow* traffic at intersections and the approaches to big cities.

Indeed in none of the examples we have mentioned (other than the pill bug) is the *net direction* of movement controlled by differences in stimulation on the two sides of the organism. The only resemblance they have to Loeb's tropisms is that many of them are "forced movements"—they are *fixed* or invariant responses that are released (forced

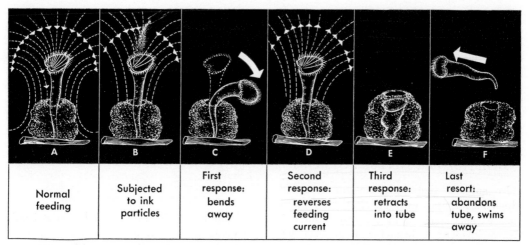

| Normal feeding | Subjected to ink particles | First response: bends away | Second response: reverses feeding current | Third response: retracts into tube | Last resort: abandons tube, swims away |
| A | B | C | D | E | F |

10-11 The behavior of the protist *Stentor* when irritated with ink particles. The pipette used to apply the ink particles is shown only in *B*.

as a mousetrap is forced) by a set stimulation. They are therefore best thought of as reflex or automatic movements.

Unfortunately, we cannot even leave it at that. Close scrutiny reveals that many of the responses are not wholly reflex and automatic. What the animal does is often open to modification in the light of past experience. *Stentor* (Fig. 10-11) is a relatively complex, stalked, tube-building protist. If it is continuously irritated by a stream of India ink particles, it goes through a series of changing responses in spite of the fact that the stimulus remains constant. First it bends to and fro in different directions; if the stream of particles continues it *then* reverses its cilia so as to "blow" the particles away; when this fails it pulls itself inside its tube. Whenever it ventures out, only to find the stimulus still present, it goes straight back into the tube. It does not make the responses (bending, "blowing") it earlier made to the same stimulus. Finally (Morgan and Loeb forbid us to say "in exasperation") it breaks away, moving off to build a new tube elsewhere. Such is genius among the protists.

THE ADAPTIVE NATURE OF BEHAVIOR, AND ITS MODIFIABILITY

The net impact of Morgan's canon and the personality of Loeb was to free behavioral studies from silly and obstructive human comparisons. This was indeed a great step forward, and for the most part the only price paid for this advance was loss of useful meaning to the word "tropism." However, for a while there were other consequences: the insistence that conscious manlike purpose played no part in animal behavior tended to obscure the fact that "purpose" in another, quite different, sense is indeed involved. For it is a reasonable generalization about behavior in all organisms that it is *adaptive*. With some exceptions behavior in any species has *average* results beneficial to the species. Behavior *serves a purpose* when by means of it an animal gets food, avoids enemies (and India ink!), and not only finds but wins a mate. Behavior serves purposes, and benefits the species not because animals are sensible or because their behavior is planned to help them. The reason is quite simple; behavior is adaptive because it has to be. A species with inadaptive behavior would not last long. This does not explain how particular sorts of adaptive behavior arose. That is another question, a much harder one that we postpone until Chapter 18.

Finally we note that Loeb's campaign for "forced movements" as a general explanation of all animal behavior founders on another hard fact. Most behavior is never wholly automatic and forced, whether by this we mean a true tropism or some other simple reflex movement. It is open to some degree of control and modifiability by the animal in the light of its experience—as even *Stentor* shows! We will, however, certainly do well to follow Morgan and Loeb in avoiding "wisdom," "conscious purpose," and such like in explaining this fact. Its understanding will come from knowledge of how the workings of the nervous system underlie behavior.

Behavior and Nervous Systems

In animals that have nervous systems, which means practically all multicellular animals excepts sponges, the nervous system is always involved in behavior. It at least acts as the conductor that sets off the effector response. Usually it does much more. It is not surprising, then, that the broad features of behavior in these animals run roughly parallel to differences in their nervous systems. Complex behavior requires a complex nervous system. *Alternative responses require alternative routes in the conductors. Co-ordination of different effectors in a single response requires associative mechanisms.* Assembling of complex stimuli into units of information producing selective responses to different elements in the total situation require still more complex associative mechanisms. *Centralized control requires a centralized message center of conducting and associating neurons. Delayed response to stimulus requires a storage mechanism, a memory of some sort.*

In considering the evolution of the nervous system (p. 209) we saw certain broad trends beyond the stage of a diffuse nerve net. Conducting paths were centralized, lengthened, and speeded up in nerve cords. Associative neurons multiplied in these cords. Co-ordination of information from receptors and action by effectors began to be centralized in nerve masses near the front end of the body. These masses—brains—tended to take over more and more of the co-ordination and control of effector activities, and hence of behavior. In the vertebrates this tendency was particularly evident, with development of extremely complex secondary and higher-level association centers in the brain. Finally, in mammals new centers of still higher level and greater complexity evolved.

All these major changes in nervous structure are paralleled by changes in sorts and complexities of behavior. That the nervous system became more complex and that behavior did also is broadly true, but it leaves out some extremely important points. In the first place, animals comparable in complexity may and usually do differ in their kinds of behavior. Still more striking is the changing balance between innate—built-in or instinctive—behavior and modifiable, or learned, behavior.

NERVE NET BEHAVIOR

Your own behavior may serve as a handy example of one extreme in kind and complexity of behavior and an associated nervous system. Insects represent another extreme, of quite a different kind and along a widely separate line of evolution. Among living animals, the simplest nervous system and behavior [6] occur in the coelenterates, with their undifferentiated nerve nets. If a tentacle of a sea anemone touches a small bit of food, that tentacle alone bends toward the mouth. If the food is large or struggling, the stronger

[6] Exceptions occur among various parasites with secondarily simplified nervous systems and behavior. Parasitism is a turning of evolutionary direction into a one-way bypath. It takes the animals out of any main line of evolutionary change. It is, nevertheless, highly adaptive, and whether it is degenerate depends on the point of view.

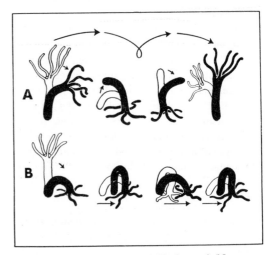

10-12 The locomotion of *Hydra*. *A*. Movement by somersaulting. *B*. Movement by looping, like a caterpillar.

stimulus may spread and other tentacles may join in the reaction. There is no centralization or evident co-ordination. The reaction simply spreads out from wherever the stimulus occurs. In a swimming jellyfish, on the other hand, the whole bell rhythmically contracts at the same time. This certainly is co-ordination, but of a simple sort and without local control. The nerve net is circular and has practically simultaneous rhythmic impulses throughout.

Perhaps the most complex and certainly the most amusing behavior in a coelenterate is the locomotion in *Hydra*. *Hydra* often creeps along very slowly by ameboid movements in the basal cells by which it usually clings to a plant or to the bottom of the pool or stream in which it lives. Once in a while, however, it moves more rapidly. Then it bends double, clings with its tentacles, lets go at the basal cells, bends double again, clings with the basal cells in a new position, and straightens up (Fig. 10-12). It thus turns a complete somersault and comes up in a different place. This is not really a very elaborate maneuver, but still it is rather surprising that it can be done without central control or developed associative mechanisms. It looks like a chain reaction, one in which each step is the stimulus for the next step. [Much more elaborate chain

reactions have been intensively studied (Fig. 10-13).] The locomotion of *Hydra* does not seem to be directive. It is not going after anything, but is only moving to new and possibly better feeding grounds by trial and

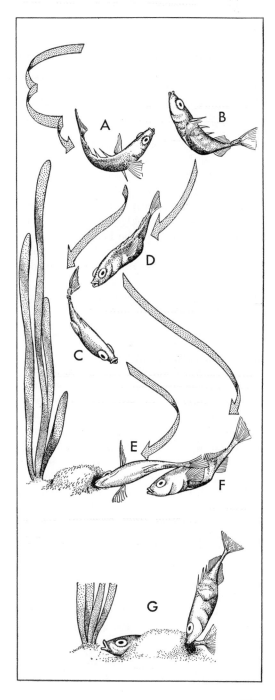

10-13 "Chain reaction" behavior in the stickleback. In the three-spined stickleback the male is responsible for all the family chores: he builds the nest, induces a female to lay eggs in it, and attends the eggs after they have been laid and fertilized. The female's only contribution is to lay the eggs, and even for this she has to be led to the task in an elaborate behavioral dance initiated by the male. This courtship dance illustrates well the principles of "chain reaction" behavior. Each step made by the male is a stimulus that elicits the next, fixed step from the female; in turn, each female response stimulates the male to the next step. *A*. Male performs zigzag dance directed at female; this stimulates female to *B*. *B*. Female courts by turning toward male and adopting an upright posture; this stimulates male to *C*. *C*. Male swims toward nest; this stimulates female to *D*. *D*. Female follows; this stimulates male to *E*. *E*. Male "shows" female the nest by putting his snout in entrance and rolling on his side; this stimulates female to *F*. *F*. Female enters nest; this stimulates male to *G*. *G*. Male nuzzles female at base of tail; this stimulates female to lay eggs. She then leaves nest. Male enters nest and fertilizes eggs.

error. In spite of the odd method of locomotion, its behavior is not much if any more advanced than that of *Paramecium*.

Echinoderms (starfishes, sea urchins, and their relatives) have a nerve ring and radial nerve cords in addition to a nerve net. There are associative neurons and true nervous reflex arcs from receptors and effectors. As you would expect, their reactions are more highly co-ordinated and varied than those in coelenterates, but the difference is not very striking. Most of their behavior is still of the trial-and-error variety, although once a stimulus is encountered, such as a succulent clam, it is dealt with by directive and unified actions of the whole body. There is even some evidence that a starfish can be trained to avoid unfavorable stimuli or to use one arm more than others, but the learning ability is slight at best. A disturbed starfish reacts very sluggishly and in a seemingly aimless way. The reactions of its cousins, the brittle stars, seem equally aimless but are far from sluggish. Violent lashing of the arms follows any disturbance, an example at a simple level of marked differences of behavior in animals with similar nervous systems.

BEHAVIOR WITH THE BEGINNINGS OF BRAINS

We have noted (p. 227) that an earthworm has rudiments of brains, anterior enlargements or *ganglia* of the nerve cords. We have also noted (p. 227) something of its behavior. Reflexes through the central nervous system are highly developed, but these occur locally in the segments of the nerve cords and involve the brain scarcely or not at all. Locomotion and other behavior is not seriously affected by removal of the brain. Nevertheless, the brain has some control over the tonus (see p. 229) of the muscles and general sensitivity. Removal of the upper of the two anterior ganglia causes the front end to bend upwards (because tonus is reduced in upper muscles), and removal of the lower ganglion results in downward bending. Removal of the upper ganglion also makes the worm more sensitive and restless. Almost everyone has noticed that a worm with its head cut off squirms more than one that is intact, but this is not a reaction to pain; it is due simply to loss of inhibitory messages from the brain. There is extremely little central control in an earthworm, but the beginnings are there.

A flatworm such as a planarian (which is not at all closely related to an earthworm) has slightly more central control. A planarian moves in several different ways: by beating cilia on the lower surface, by rippling motions of the body, and by a looping crawl a little like an inchworm caterpillar. Removal of the brain does not interfere at all with ciliary locomotion, interferes seriously with rippling but does not wholly prevent this motion, and stops crawling altogether. Thus the more complex behavioral reactions, or those requiring more extended co-operation of muscles, are co-ordinated and largely controlled in the brain.

Both flatworms and earthworms can be trained in simple ways. Planarians can be taught not to cross a rough surface in a dish by shaking the dish every time they come to the rough part. After a great many repetitions, they turn away from the rough area even when the dish is not shaken. Earthworms can be trained to turn to the right or left in a Y- or T-shaped passage by giving them an electric shock when they take the wrong turn. Some training is possible when the brain has been removed, but it usually takes longer. In other words, earthworms can learn with their nerve cords alone, but the brain helps.

Offhand, there is something mildly ridiculous in the sight of a scientist solemnly spending hours and hours teaching an earthworm which way to go. This, however, is an example of highly meaningful information. No one, not even its trainer, really cares much about the poor earthworm as an individual or even as a representative of its species. But it helps to demonstrate relationships between learning and the nervous system, and every thinking person does care about that. The results have wide significance and apply (with suitable precautions) to all sorts of animals, including man, in which these simpler reactions are more difficult to study because they are overlaid by so many other complexities.

Innate and Learned Behavior

INSTINCT AND LEARNING

In plants beyond any doubt, and in protists and coelenterates with only a whisper of a doubt, we were dealing with completely innate behavior. The whole mechanism of behavior is built into these organisms and is rigidly fixed. A certain stimulus always produces exactly the same response, and the organism can do nothing about it. Other individuals of the same species (if they are in the same physiological condition) have exactly the same responses to the same stimuli, whatever their past history has been. In the echinoderms dimly and questionably, and in the flatworms and earthworms simply but definitely, something else has appeared. Most of the behavior here still seems to be innate, but not all. Reaction to a given stimulus, a roughened surface, a right or left turn (or a dark or light passage in other, similar experiments) is not rigidly fixed. It is changed by training. After the training, the response is not the same as in other individuals of the same species. There are differences due to the past experiences of the animals.

Innate behavior is what is commonly called *instinct.* Instinct has usually been understood as something quite different from learned behavior. An action was *either* instinctive *or* learned. The task of the investigator was to find out which. There used to be a tremendous amount of discussion as to whether a particular item of behavior was learned or instinctive, or as to the relative amounts of the two sorts of behavior in a given animal. It was found out that many supposed instincts are not *purely* instinctive. Researchers began to shy away from the word "instinct" and to talk about "innate behavior" instead. Changing the name does not change the problem, but it does help a little in getting away from some of the wrong ideas that had become attached to the old name.

Scientists have recently been learning, rather slowly and painfully in some subjects, to be suspicious of "either-or" questions. Such questions offer only two choices, and it is entirely possible that neither choice is correct. This is notably true of questions about whether a thing is inherited or acquired. It usually turns out, not only in the field of behavior but also in intelligence, size, blue eyes, or almost anything else, that many things are neither solely inherited nor solely acquired. The wrong question was being asked. We smile now at all the sound and fury of the "nature or nurture" battles that were raging up to a few years ago. (Some biologists are still fighting the battle, but they are few and are decreasing.)

Some behavior is probably *completely* innate, although this is open to question except, perhaps, for true tropisms in plants. It is practically impossible to say that any behavior is *completely* learned in that it depends in no way on inherited mechanisms. To take an extreme example, nothing is more obviously learned, one might say, than human language. Infants born deaf and blind never talk unless they can be taught through the sense of touch as Helen Keller was.[7] Language is always learned from those around us,[8] and we learn totally different languages, depending on who raises us. Nevertheless, there is a considerable and essential innate element in language. We are born with the nervous mechanism and the effectors for talking. Without them, as when the left temporal area of the brain is accidentally damaged, we cannot talk. Other animals are *innately* unable to talk.

The real point about linguistic behavior is not that it is not innate, but that it is highly *modifiable.* Its mechanism is innate, but it can be used in many different ways. The ability to talk is innate, but the particular language we talk is not.[9]

[7] Helen Keller became deaf and blind at 19 months as a result of illness. Some of the important aspects of her education in relation to language are described and discussed in Cassirer's "Essay on Man" (Anchor Books), cited later in this chapter.
[8] The Greek historian Herodotus wrote that Psammetichus, king of Egypt, had two children raised without ever hearing anyone speak. He claimed that the children started talking Phrygian to each other, which proves—or does it?— that language is innate and that Phrygian is the oldest language. Or does it prove something about the accuracy of Herodotus?
[9] There is inconclusive evidence of heritable differences in the ease with which some words are pronounced. If this proves to be true, then there are innate differences in ability to learn particular languages.

At the opposite extreme, when a doctor taps just below your knee with a rubber hammer, you normally give a little kick. This is a highly innate response, a simple reflex. Yet you can learn to prevent the response. You can also learn to make the same response, or what looks exactly the same from outside you, whether the doctor taps you or not and without using the reflex arc. This behavior, too, is modifiable, although it is much less modifiable than linguistic behavior.

From this point of view, the significant thing about behavior is not so much whether it is innate or not but whether it is less or more modifiable. Every gradation exists from practically unmodifiable to almost endlessly modifiable behavior. The songs of birds illustrate this point very well. Individuals of some species of birds, if raised without ever hearing another bird, will nevertheless produce a song completely characteristic of their species. Not only the ability to sing but also a particular song is innate. If raised with another species, such birds still sing the song of their parents, which they never heard. Other birds, if raised with a different species, produce the song of that species and not of their own. Sometimes the song will have characteristics of both species. Some birds have one, fully stereotyped song, and some have wide variation of song. Some never alter their songs, and some can imitate the songs of almost any other birds and even the sounds of human voices. There is, in short, almost every degree of modifiability, and the question whether bird song is instinctive is not a "yes or no" one.

REFLEXES

Any individual nervous system develops with a distinct and definite pattern. The nerve pattern is mainly, although not altogether, dependent on the inherited pattern of growth in general. Nerves are not moving parts within the body. They grow into their pattern, which does not change its arrangement in accordance with behavioral reactions. For instance, an efferent nerve does not move from one effector to another in the production of different responses. Each effector must have its separate, fixed nerve, and difference in response must involve impulses through different nerves.

What is most innate and least modifiable in connection with behavior is the pattern of the nervous system. In animals with nervous control of behavior, a particular sort of behavior cannot occur unless there is an established nerve channel for it. Modifiability of behavior implies the presence of alternative channels. Even in the maze of associative neurons in the vertebrate brain, with millions of alternative channels across the various synapses, the synapses are fixed. Impulses can only move through an existing and fixed, even though extremely complex, pattern. The modifiability of behavior cannot, therefore, depend on changing the pattern of neuron connections. It consists of making some alternatives through a fixed maze of *possible routes* more easily followed than others. In the last analysis this must depend on something like the facilitation of synapses we described in Chapter 9.

The simplest and the only inherently unmodifiable behavior involves direct nerve connection from a receptor to an effector. Such connections occur in a few very simple nervous systems, but never (as far as known) in higher invertebrates or vertebrates. The simplest connection in them involves at least two and usually (always in vertebrates, at least) more neurons between receptor and effector. The connection is usually through a nerve cord and the arrangement is a reflex arc (Fig. 10-14). Even at its simplest, the reflex arc involves the *possibility of modification,* because there are possible channels other than the one direct from receptor to effector. This is, however, the mechanism of the most strongly innate and least modifiable behavior of higher animals.

If you accidentally put your hand on a hot stove, the hand jerks back very rapidly. This is a reflex, and its retention in man is adaptive: speed minimizes injury, and a reflex is a lot faster than thinking. At the same time a message does go to the brain, where further behavior (quite possibly linguistic behavior) is started. We have a number of such emergency reflexes, as well as maintenance reflexes like those that narrow the pupil of the eye in strong light and widen it in dim

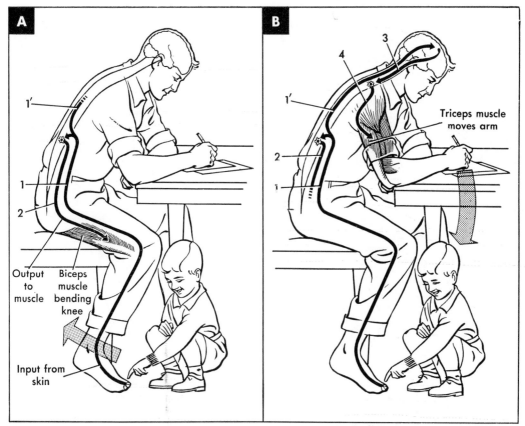

10-14 A human reflex action and its simple modifiability. *A.* A child tickles his father's toe. The stimulus is conducted along a very long sensory neuron (1), which in turn stimulates a motor neuron (2). The motor neuron, originating in the spinal cord, in turn stimulates the biceps muscle in the thigh, causing the knee to bend back reflexively from the stimulus. The stimulus, traveling along the sensory neuron (1), also reaches the brain via the path 1'. *B.* When the child continues to "stimulate" and the simple reflex of knee-bending proves inadequate, a second response (a modification of the initial reflex) results. The renewed stimulus follows the pathway 1-3-4, eventually activating the triceps muscle of the arm and causing a more effective "response" to the "stimulus." Modification (arm swipe) of the initial reflex follows only after many stimulations because the pathway 1-3-4 involves synapses less easily traversed, requiring facilitation by several stimulations.

light, or those that flex our muscles and keep us standing erect without our thinking about it. Reflexes are pretty well at a minimum in us, however. Most of our behavior is much more modifiable. (Cf. Fig. 10-14.)

As a generalization, open to many exceptions in detail, lower animals have more of the simpler, least modifiable reflexes than higher animals have.[10] Most of an earth-

[10] This is one of the reasons why we call them "lower" and "higher." The terms are vague and can be quite misleading, but it is a convenience to use them here and should not confuse you seriously. You have been warned against the common mistaken belief that lower living ani-

worm's behavior is controlled by quite simple reflexes through the nerve cords, probably even simpler than your heat-hand jerk reflex. If an earthworm gets near something too hot, its reflexes move it away without troubling the brain to act at all in the matter.

CONDITIONED REFLEXES

A conditioned reflex is one in which the response has been transferred from one stimulus to another. The classical experiment, by

mals represent ancestral stages of higher animals (p. 208).

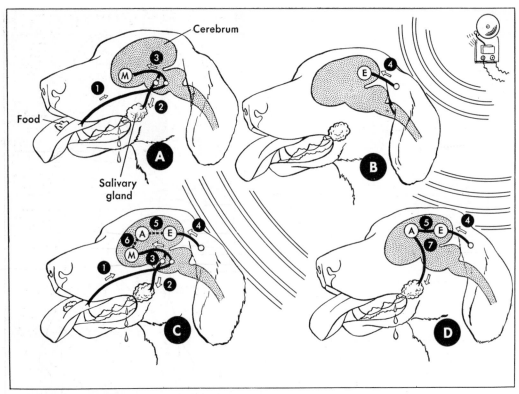

10-15 A simple conditioned reflex. *A.* A dog salivates when food reaches his tongue. A nerve impulse, initiated at the tongue's taste buds, passes along a sensory neuron ① and then an afferent neuron ② ultimately stimulates the salivary glands into activity. The nerve impulse in passing along the sensory neuron ① also reaches a part of the cerebrum (M, mouth) concerned with mouth sensations such as taste; in other words, the dog has some consciousness of the taste. *B.* When a bell is rung, impulses pass from the ear to the auditory region (E) of the cerebrum. These impulses have, however, no way of passing into the afferent channels leading to the salivary glands. No salivation occurs. *C.* Food reaches the tongue at the same time as the bell is rung. The dog salivates because impulses reach the salivary gland via the old routes ① and ②. Impulses also reach a cerebral *association center* (A) from the mouth (M) and auditory (E) centers via routes ⑤ and ⑥. The dog learns to associate sound with food. *D.* When the association between sound and food has been well established, impulses initiating in the ear can reach the salivary glands via the routes ④, ⑤, and ⑦.

the Russian physiologist Pavlov (1849-1936) was based on the reflex that causes a dog to secrete more saliva when it smells food. Dogs were *conditioned* by ringing a bell every time food was placed before them. In time, ringing a bell produced the flow of saliva even though food was absent. The response, saliva flow, was transferred from one stimulus, smell of food, to another, sound of a bell (Fig. 10-15). Many other experiments have since been performed, and it has been found that responses of all sorts can be attached by conditioning to almost any sort of stimulus that the animal can receive.

The conditioning of a reflex is clearly a modification of behavior, and in that sense it is learning: the dog "learned" to salivate at the sound of the bell. For a time after publication of Pavlov's work (his major works appeared in English translation from 1902 to 1929), some enthusiasts believed that *all* behavior could be put in terms of reflexes. Innate behavior involved a simple reflex, learned behavior a conditioned reflex. This apparent simplification fitted in well with then current devotion to Morgan's canon. What could be simpler, and therefore more probable, than the hypothesis that all behavior, including human behavior, is reflex behavior?

Gradually it has been realized that instead

of simplifying the concept of learned behavior, ascribing it to conditioned reflexes only complicates the concept of a reflex. A conditioned reflex is no longer a reflex in the strict meaning of the term. Association has occurred; a different path through the nervous system has been made habitual by constant use. It is, then, largely a matter of degree when the pathway becomes more and more complicated, leading through increasingly larger parts of the brain. If all these reactions are reflexes, then a reflex is any impulse following any route in the nervous system. It is simply nerve conduction. If conditioning is any change in such a route, then conditioning necessarily accompanies any modification of behavior. "Conditioned reflexes" became synonymous with "learning," and explained learning only by saying, in effect, that learning is due to learning.

The failure of the conditioned reflex to reduce learning to simple (truly) reflex processes does not mean that conditioned reflexes are of no significance. They cast a great deal of light on associational processes and the facilitation of nerve impulses along alternative routes, in other words, on what are accepted as the basic processes of learning. The point is that so-called conditioned reflexes are learned responses, whether or not they are reflexes strictly speaking. Recent students use the Pavlov technique, in varied forms, under the name of "conditioned response." It is an extremely useful technique not only for the study of learning but also for such investigations as those of discrimination. An animal may, for instance, be conditioned to respond differently to stimuli such as two tones. By making the tones more and more alike, the point at which the animal can no longer distinguish them is determined.

If you were instructed to find out whether bees recognize different colors, the task might appear hopeless because you cannot ask the bee—at least you cannot ask it outright and in English. But you *can* ask it indirectly by using the technique of conditioned responses. The problem is to determine whether or not the bee can distinguish a color from that intensity of grayness to which the color would correspond if the bee were color-blind and recognized therefore only degrees of bright-

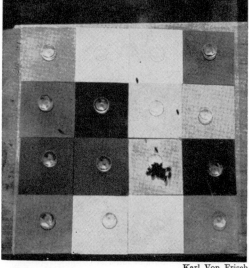

10-16 Using a conditioned response to demonstrate color vision in the honeybee. *Above,* bees that have been fed regularly on a blue paper are offered blank sheets of paper, one blue, the other red. They all settle on the blue paper, ignoring the red in their search for food. They have become conditioned to the blue card. It now remains to be proved that the bees distinguish blue paper because of its *color* and not because of its apparent grayness, which clearly differs from the red. *Below,* the table is covered with squares of paper, each carrying an empty dish. The squares are different shades of gray except for one, which is blue. All the bees come to this square, proving that they recognize the *color* as such, distinguishing it from the equivalent shade of gray, which lies just above it and to the right.

ness in a series of grays. The problem is solved—and the bee is asked our question—as shown in Fig. 10-16.

CONDITIONED RESPONSES, HABITS, AND LEARNING

The learning seen in experiments on conditioned responses is the association of a particular, usually quite simple, response with

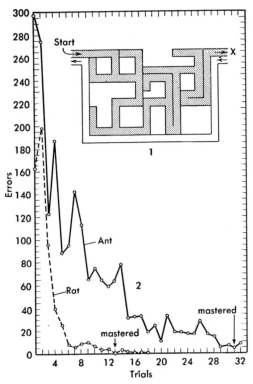

10-17 Maze learning. *1.* The ground plan of a maze offered to rats and ants. *2.* Graphs showing the progress of rat and ant in mastering the maze. The rat learned the maze more rapidly than the ant; it had mastered it by the thirteenth trial, while the ant required thirty-one trials.

a particular stimulus. A sheep is given an electric shock in one leg a few seconds after a metronome is started. After many repetitions the sheep learns to lift the leg as soon as it hears the metronome and before the shock is given. A stimulus (the sound of the metronome) which at first produced no response now produces a specific response which is invariable for a time. This invariability is not innate, however. The animal may forget the response from lack of practice, and the experimenter can purposely change it. The experiment is more similar to habit formation than to what we ordinarily think of as learning in ourselves. Habits are responses which, through long repetition, we come to (really *learn* to) make in a given situation, which is the stimulus. The habitual response becomes automatic in time, but it is not innate and it remains modifiable. We can

change our habits, and they die out if they are not repeated more or less frequently. We can purposely break a habit by preventing or changing the response or by avoiding the stimulus.

Unless an animal is kept in controlled, experimental conditions all its life, it is extremely hard to distinguish reflexes from habits. In fact there is no sharp distinction, because both do depend on the innate nervous connections and both may be developed and are strengthened by repetition. The habit usually involves a more complex nerve path; it is more modifiable; and it does not become fixed without repetition. A distinction between habit (or conditioned response) and other or, as we feel, higher types of learning is still less clear. The difference is one of degree only. The nerve paths become still more complex; they often bring in more evident control; they are more modifiable as a rule; and the greater central control may also reduce the requirement for repetition. Not much, even in ourselves, but some learning can occur at one trial, without repetition.

Most experiments on learning in nonhuman animals have involved, besides response conditioning, mazes or problem apparatus. A maze is a series of pathways with one or more points where the animal must choose which way to go. With the wrong choice the animal comes up against a blind end, is punished, or fails to achieve a reward. A Y- or T-shaped passage is a one-choice maze, and we have seen (p. 240) that even an earthworm can learn this. Animals with more complex nervous systems learn more complicated mazes. One often used with rats is illustrated in Fig. 10-17. The rate of learning is scored by the number of mistakes made on successive trials. The graph shows that the error rate decreases (the rat learns) on successive trials. Ants tested in the same maze learned less rapidly. By varying rewards or other factors, the influence of different conditions on rate of learning can be determined.

Problem apparatuses of many different kinds have been used. One frequently used device is to place food in a compartment that can be opened by operating one or more pedals or catches.

MOTIVATION

Learning experiments always involve some system of rewards or punishments. The animals are rewarded, usually with food, for a "right" choice, that is, the choice the experimenter wants them to learn, and are punished, usually with an electric shock, for a "wrong" choice. As you would expect, most experiments show faster learning if both reward and punishment are used. This doubtless applies to humans, too. Many mothers offer a piece of candy or a whack depending on whether little Johnny does "right" (that is, what mama wants) or "wrong" (what mama does not want, but Johnny probably does). The method generally works. Some experiments with rats indicate that the animals learn faster if they are punished for "wrong" and not rewarded for "right" than if they are rewarded but not punished.[11] It is not at all clear whether this is a general rule for humans or for other animals. Some human mothers seem to assume that it is and deal out far more whacks than candy. Most of us, however, like to think that humans and other animals respond best to kindness (that is, learn more rapidly to do what *we* want if we reward them than if we punish them). It is possible that this is only what we *like* to think, but there are other factors than learning in this behavior. For instance, most of us feel better ourselves when we give rewards than when we deal out punishment.

Psychological experiments on learning may not seem very realistic when compared with learned behavior in animals (including man) not undergoing experimentation. Learning may be rewarded by food or in some other concrete way, but often it is not. Punishment in the form of an electric shock never occurs (except in extreme cases among humans), and usually there is no obvious punishment. Nevertheless, it is clear that animal behavior, including learned behavior, depends on something similar to reward and punishment. Animals do things because they "want" to. They learn new behavior because they "like" the

results, and they learn to avoid behavior with results that they "dislike." "Want," "like," and "dislike" are anthropomorphic words and were put in quotation marks for that reason. They perhaps apply correctly to some animals rather like ourselves, but they are misleading if applied, say, to an ameba or a worm. A stuffier but scientifically better way to put the matter is to say that animal behavior is *motivated*. Motivation need not be conscious or involve any emotion.

The most widespread motivation for behavior is the maintenance of stability in the organism. We have seen that there are elaborate chemical (p. 173) and nervous (p. 217) internal stabilizing mechanisms. Behavior is another powerful stabilizing mechanism, closely interrelated with the other two, as they are themselves. A lack of energy and materials in the organism upsets its stability. The upset is translated into a felt (but not necessarily consciously felt) need: hunger. The organism, whether it is *Hydra* or *Homo*, responds by behavior that is likely to bring in food and restore stability. The behavior may be mostly innate, as in *Hydra* or a human infant, or mostly learned, as in more mature humans. It is very different in form in different kinds of organisms. But in all it has this in common: as a rule or on an average it tends to satisfy the organic need.

Motivation arising from a need to stabilize the organism is called a *biological*[12] *drive*. Hunger and thirst are obviously such drives. Sex is also so considered, but here there are other and more complex factors. At its simplest, the sex drive corresponds with an instability arising not from deprivation but from the internal release of chemical substances, hormones. In higher animals, including most vertebrates, sex behavior also involves more or less complex patterns not related simply and directly to satisfaction of the drive.

Learned behavior motivated by biological drives does involve rewards and punishments. Restoration of internal stability is definitely a reward. In fact the food usually used as a reward in experiments is a reward precisely because it restores stability, and the same

[11] Curiously enough, rats sometimes learn almost as fast if they are both punished and rewarded for "right." This is as if Johnny were given a piece of candy and whacked when he was good but just ignored when he was bad, and learned to be good faster than if he were not whacked at all.

[12] Or biogenic, "born of life," as opposed to psychogenic, "born of the mind." There is much question as to whether this is a real distinction. What do you think?

reward is frequent for learning in nature. Continuation and increase of internal instability is similarly a punishment.

Much behavior is not obviously related to internal instability. When a bee builds a honeycomb, gathers honey, and stores it in the comb, it is not satisfying any hunger it feels at the time. It seems nevertheless to be satisfying a need built into its nervous system. An inherited behavior pattern exists, and it is probably not going too far to conclude that there is an internal instability unless this pattern is carried out in action.

When you study this chapter and learn something about learning, you do not feel an organic drive or a restoration of your internal stability. Nor do you have an innate behavior pattern that is carried out when you read what we have written. Yet you do have motives for studying, and if you search far enough through the intricacies of your mind you may find that your motivation is not wholly divorced from biological drives.

As to the general relationships of motivation and learning, no learning occurs unless it is motivated in some way. That is a redundant statement, because motivation is definable as the cause of behavior. It is not so redundant to say that learning is faster if motivation is stronger. Degree of hunger can be measured, and learning with a food reward is faster in hungrier animals. (An animal that is not hungry at all usually has sense enough not to bother with the experiment.) Much study has been devoted to the relative effectiveness of different drives. For instance, some experiments with rats suggest that hunger is a stronger incentive than sex. One trouble with this conclusion, however, is that no one can measure equal intensities of hunger and sex drives. And rats, at least, do not die for lack of love, although they do for lack of food.

OTHER INFLUENCES ON LEARNING

Many factors other than motivation influence rate and kind of learning. We shall leave these to the psychologists on the whole, but perhaps we should mention a few of them. With rats learning a maze, a little help from teacher early in the learning period speeds things up. A great deal of help, or help late in the learning period does not. Up to an age

that corresponds with about sixty in man, old rats learn about as fast as young rats. Undernourished rats sometimes learn more slowly and sometimes faster than well-nourised rats. The results depend on the particular dietary deficiency and on motivation rather than on the general level of nutrition.

These are facts about learning in rats. To a biologist, it is extremely interesting to compare learning and other behavior in all sorts of animals, and we only wish that as much were known about others as about rats. The psychologists who have done most of these experiments were not (with certain exceptions) really interested in rat behavior. They really wanted to find out about behavior and learning in humans. Rats are used because they are convenient and cheap laboratory animals, and because they are simpler. An old rat is not likely to have habits and motivations that interfere with learning. (At least, rats can be raised so as to avoid such interference.) But an old man is almost certain to have interfering habits and is likely to lack motivation for learning. Basic biological factors, including those of the nervous system, are closely similar in rats and men, but due allowance must be made for some quite radical additional factors in man.

Many behavioral processes are similar in kind throughout much of the animal kingdom. This applies in essence to all the processes we have considered up to this point. Man's peculiarity depends largely on having more modifiable behavior and more extensive learning. Man also has mental faculties that are rudimentary or absent in most other animals. Before alluding further to these, we may briefly consider a group of animals in which both innate and learned behavior are well developed, but developed in quite different forms and degrees from man.

Behavior in Insects

Anyone who has ever spent much time watching ants or bees will agree that the behavior of insects has a peculiar fascination. Some of it looks so clever and farsighted! Bees build their elaborate, mathematically aligned combs and fill them with honey for the winter's needs. Some insect behavior looks so abysmally stupid! An ant, lugging a burden larger than itself, completely exhausts itself trying to pull the load over a stone or stick, when it could have gone around in a few steps. Some insect behavior seems so baffling as to require senses other than ours. Bees react as if they were following guiding patterns on flowers that are plain white to us. *To us, insects have truly alien minds* and have the puzzling attraction of something completely foreign.

The puzzle of insect behavior results in part from their different sensory equipment, to which we have referred several times (pp. 189 and 199). The bees *are* following patterns on the "plain white flowers"; the patterns are in ultraviolet, which they can see but we cannot. More of the puzzle, however, arises from the peculiarities (as we consider them) of the insect nervous system. Insects have the most complex behavior, and correspondingly the most complex nervous systems, of any invertebrates. As higher forms, they also show more evidence of modifiable behavior and learning than other invertebrates, although one reason why they baffle us is that they perform complicated maneuvers that are *not* learned. We tend to think of animals by degrees of intelligence in comparison with ours. The outstanding point about insects is not that they are less intelligent than we are (although of course this is true), but that their intelligence is so very different in kind. They are at the end of a long evolutionary progression that has been diverging from ours for half a billion years and more.

We cannot here go into detail about the extremely diverse, incredibly strange activities of the innumerable sorts of insects. There are many good books on the subject, and we have cited a few in our bibliography (p. 819). Here we can consider only some generalizations and principles bearing, especially, on the balance of innate and learned behavior and the nature of some behavioral sequences.

Although it is often overemphasized, undoubtedly the most striking fact about insect behavior is that the large proportion of it is innate. Most insects live quite alone, never seeing their parents or their offspring, and seldom with any relationship to other members of their species except for brief mating.

(A few insects do not even mate; the females carry on the race without benefit of males.) Yet each species has a distinct, frequently a very complex, behavior pattern carried on without training and with little variation from one generation to the next. The constancy of these behavior patterns can be explained only by innate characteristics of the nervous system. Social insects, in which learning is most evident, also have much innate behavior. Honeybee workers make their precise, six-sided cells without any learning.[13]

A solitary wasp, which has never seen its parent and need not have seen any other wasp doing the same thing, goes through a sequence of actions. It hunts for a nest site and digs a nest. It then hunts prey, usually a caterpillar, paralyzes the victim, drags it to the nest and shoves it in. This is repeated several times. Then the wasp lays an egg in the nest, seals the opening, and smoothes it over so the location is invisible. Later the egg hatches and the larva eats the food provided, but the wasp that made the provision knows nothing of this. In the course of this chain of actions there are immediate reflexes to separate stimuli; the stinging of the caterpillar has this appearance, at least. There is also learned behavior; the wasp's unerring return to the nest cannot be explained otherwise. But the sequence of acts as a whole is innate. *Each act,* nest building, food hunting, and so on, *is the stimulus for the next.* The wasp cannot vary the sequence, omit a step, or go back and repeat one. For instance, if the caterpillars are removed from the nest when enough have been provided, the wasp lays an egg and seals it in anyway. It is perhaps in such complex combinations of innate chain behavior, simple reflexes, and learning that insects differ most from us, even though we also have innate behavior, reflexes, and learning. The combination of these in the wasp is so nonhuman! (See Fig. 10-18.)

Bees have no innate sense of direction that enables them to return to the nest. Part of their homing is learned behavior, and young bees have to learn their way around just as

[13] This is not quite so much of a feat as it may seem. A series of equal cylinders crowded into a confined space automatically takes on the hexagonal precision of a honeycomb. It would be harder to build the cells in any other pattern.

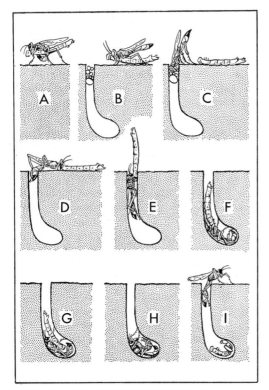

10-18 Innate behavior in the digger wasp.
A. Having dug its nest, the wasp captures and stings a caterpillar, paralyzing it. *B.* Transports prey to nest. *C.* Opens nest, having left prey nearby. *D, E, F, G.* Packs victim into nest. *H.* Lays egg on the still-paralyzed caterpillar. *I.* Crawls from nest before reclosing it and leaving it permanently.

limits, but none is highly modifiable. In itself this fact is not so striking; the same might be said of an earthworm. *The remarkable specialization in insect behavior is that it may be very complex, comparable in this respect to that in many higher vertebrates, even in mammals, and yet is so little modifiable.* Here must be a nervous system with many pathways established at birth, but with few connections and alternatives between them.

A final important point is that all insect behavior seems to be interpretable in terms (1) of innate structural pattern and reflexes, quite complex as to number and sequence, and (2) of learning of the simplest conditioned responses—limited modifications of responses to surrounding stimuli. There is little or no evidence of what we would call in ourselves sizing up a situation, thinking things over, solving a problem, deciding on a course of action, and the like. There is no evidence of foresight, in spite of storage for the winter. An insect does not plan; it acts. The apparent foresight is built into the species, not decided on by the individual. There is very little evidence of emotion. Certainly there are in our own behavior many factors weak or absent in insects. These factors have arisen in our own line of evolution, among the vertebrates.

Concepts and Symbols

When we come to the higher mental faculties, those just alluded to in most unpsychological terms, we are leaving the field of the biologist and are more definitely entering that of the psychologist. Thus far a background knowledge of general biology carries us. As we approach the most special aspects of human behavior and thought, a more specifically psychological background is required. We shall therefore be particularly brief in this section. Something must be said, however, because the biological status of man—that is, his place in the world of life and his special characteristics as an organism—depends largely on his psychology. It is also important to mention that even man's highest faculties have biological bases that can be seen in other animals and down to the lowly protists.

The usual maze experiment prevents learn-

much as we do, although of course they do so in their own way. The bee learns landmarks around the nest and recognizes them by sight. On longer flights the direction of the sun is noticed and used as a guide. But if the bee is moved to another, unfamiliar spot, it will fly in what *was* the right sun direction but here is not, and it will miss the hive altogether. The behavior is modifiable, but not very. The behavior, even the most modifiable of it, is innately limited. Modification can take place only as between a few simple alternatives.

Clearly it is not true that insects operate by instinct only. Their behavior can be modified. It is, however, reasonable to conclude that the whole of their behavior is innately limited. Some behavior is so restricted as to be practically unmodifiable. Some has broader

ing by any process except trial and error. Even a man, placed in a maze of suitable size, can only choose at random and learn which way is right and which wrong by what happens after he has made the choice. This is not the characteristic human way of learning or solving problems. Trial and error cannot be wholly eliminated, but we usually try to size up the whole of any new situation as well as we can. Then when we act, our behavior is often right the first time. If it does prove to be wrong, it was still based on a great deal more than blundering along a path taken at random until we were punished or thwarted.

Biologically speaking, "right" behavior in any situation is behavior more likely than not to benefit the organism. All organisms do tend to have right behavior in this sense (see p. 237). In animals, the usual primitive basis of such behavior is perception, the dim beginnings of which occur also in protists and in plants. "Perception" is another word hard to define, but a rough definition is that it is the process of organizing stimuli in such a way as to give them meaning for the animal concerned.

If a *Paramecium* hits the stem of a water plant, it experiences a touch stimulus. A *Paramecium* has no mind and probably is not conscious or aware of anything, but its reactions show that there was in a broad sense a sort of meaning derived from this stimulus within the organism. The meaning was "obstacle," and the response was to back up. "Meaning" here merely labels a relationship between stimulus and response. This is an extremely dim and primitive perception, but it shows the beginnings of the process. At the other end of the scale, a botanist might come along and perceive the same water plant. He would have much more extensive sensations from stimuli, mostly light stimuli in his case, and would form a fully conscious, meaning-packed, very complex perception. He would, further, attach to this perception a symbol which would relate it to all his other perceptions of the same sort. He would call it *Spirogyra*.

The word *Spirogyra*, spoken or written, does not have the slightest resemblance to the little, filamentous water plant of which it is the name. It is a symbol that stands in our minds for the plant. It does not stand, however, just for the particular plant that the botanist perceives at a given moment. It stands for *all* plants that are like this one in certain well-defined ways. Strictly speaking, then, it does not really stand for the plant as a concrete object at all. It stands for the idea of a whole group of plants, of the things they have in common, and of their relationships with each other. Such an idea is a *concept*.

Aside from intensification of abilities common to many other animals, man's most distinctive characteristic is the ability to form abstract concepts and by this means to grasp complex relationships between things. This is the ability concerned in, among many other things, the human way of sizing up a problem and solving it without trial and error. The ability to form concepts has surely evolved from increasingly complex processes of perception, and, as we have seen, the rudiments of perception occur even in protists. Nevertheless, there is no evidence that the particular quantity and quality of mental activity that we call "concept formation" occurs in any lower animals. Its rudiments probably are present in our nearest living relatives, monkeys and apes, so that even in this capacity we are not *absolutely* different from other animals. Rhesus monkeys and chimpanzees have been taught to match objects by *either* color *or* form depending on still another cue presented at the same time. Some degree of abstract thinking must be involved. Recently some experiments in Germany have shown that parrots can abstract numbers up to 7. No other animals, however, not even our useful friends the laboratory rats,[14] are known to do anything requiring such high mental faculty.

The further step of attaching a definite symbol to a concept seems a natural outgrowth of concept formation, but it is even more peculiarly human. Again, there are rudiments in a few higher animals, but fully developed

[14] But rats and other animals have been trained in ways that suggest their formation of still more rudimentary concepts. Rats apparently can form a concept "triangle." Even bees readily react to a color, such as blue, regardless of form or other characteristics, but it is extremely unlikely that an abstract concept of blueness is involved.

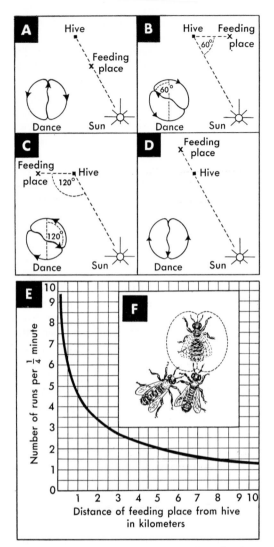

10-19 **The language of the bee.** A worker bee, returning to the hive after finding a food supply, imparts information to her fellow workers about the distance and direction of the food. The information is transmitted in a "language" illustrated in *F*. The bee dances along a line, wagging her abdomen; she turns a full half-circle and again dances along the line; she then makes a full half-circle in the other direction. All the while, she is followed closely by other workers. The speed of her dance, plotted in *E* as the number of runs down the diameter of the circle per ¼ minute, is the code in which she tells of distance. As the graph shows, the farther away the feeding place, the slower is her dance. The dance is performed on the dark vertical face of the honeycomb inside the hive. The dancing worker gives the direction in which food will be found by the orientation of her dance relative to gravity, as indicated in *A*, *B*, *C*, and *D*.

symbolization occurs only in man. Our most complete and systematic set of symbols is language, which has had tremendous biological and social consequences. It has done more than any other one factor to make us altogether unique organisms.[15] And it has done this not just because it is a language in some broader sense, but because it is language employing symbols for abstract concepts like numbers and relationships. We can best show what this means by contrasting our own language with the so-called "language" of bees.

When a worker bee returns to the hive having found a rich supply of honey (the nectar in flowers), she can promote the efficient use of her fellow workers' time and effort by "telling" them where she found her rich harvest. To do this, she dances on the vertical face of the honeycomb; and in the details of her movements is a message to fellow workers "saying" how far and in what direction the honey will be found. The dance (Fig. 10-19) is made in a circle which she transects on a line whose angle to the vertical (defined by the sense of gravity) corresponds with the angle between the sun and the honey source. As she makes her dancing transect across the circle the bee "waggles" her body, and the number of waggles denotes the distance of the honey source from the hive. This is all a nearly incredible degree of refined communication. In a sense it is a language—but is it really? Does the bee *tell* her fellow workers how far and in what direction to fly? Or is she simply forced by her own recent experience to make a set of motions that act as a stimulus eliciting a predetermined, but appropriate, response from her fellows? In short, is she using a language or exhibiting innate, instinctive behavior of the most elaborate kind? Here we are caught in the cross fire of Morgan's canon, which confronts us wherever we turn for an explanation! For neither alternative is really simple; common sense demands a little of both views, and much uncertainty. At any rate there is surely no evidence that the dancing movements that constitute the bee's

15 Many readers will greatly enjoy the chapters in Cassirer's "Essay on Man" (Anchor Books) which treat the use of symbols by man as his truly unique ability.

language are abstract symbols like the sounds or written words of our own language. They have a fixed denotation; they are *signs* for one concrete situation, and refer only to distance and direction of flight. The bee has not freed these signs from their unique concrete meanings and used them to develop, for instance, a simple arithmetic.

Other Aspects of Behavior

In this chapter we have now mentioned, at least, most of the aspects of behavior that are biologically important. Other aspects are touched on in other chapters. Still others may now be no more than just mentioned, so that you may have a more rounded idea of the contents of the science of behavior.

In Chapter 8 it was noted in passing that *hormones may influence behavior*. For instance, excess or deficient thyroxin is accompanied by more nervous or more phlegmatic behavior. When the importance of hormones was just becoming generally understood, it was a popular fad to describe behavior patterns and personality in terms of endocrines. "You are what your glands make you." Now we know that was a gross exaggeration. Any bodily function or disturbance can influence behavior. So can drugs and many other things. But in man and other higher animals the essential control is in the nervous system, through which these other influences secondarily affect behavior.

We have discussed behavior mostly, although not entirely, in terms of responses to external stimuli. It should be added that the signal for action may come from the *central nervous system* without any immediate environmental change. This is particularly true in higher animals and in man, because of processes of association, memory, and concept formation. We know that we sometimes decide to do a thing when there is no present stimulus for the action. There is, however, generally an association with a past stimulus. The initiation of behavior in the central nervous system of nonhumans is extremely difficult to study, because we cannot get inside their nervous systems. It is, however, clear that this process is common only in man, and

it is probably absent altogether in many lower animals.

The subject of *emotions* is another that is extremely difficult to study in any animal but man (and rather difficult in man, too). Emotions are internal phenomena and, unlike behavioral movements, not open to simple observation. They influence animal behavior in ways often erratic, but they cannot be directly observed. We almost have to judge emotions anthropomorphically. We have no way of telling whether a worm has emotions or what they are like, any more than we can tell whether a worm is conscious.

Personality is a subject that can be studied in other animals to the extent that it involves consistent individual differences in behavior. It is a fascinating subject, too. Personality depends on modifiable behavior. Invertebrates and lower vertebrates have little personality. Every bee behaves almost exactly like any other of the same species and caste. Personality is evident in most mammals, and culminates in man. We must leave these complexities to the psychologists.

In our brief consideration of innate behavior we have not referred to *maturation*. Changes of behavior in the course of life depend not only on experience, that is, on learning, but also on development of mechanisms. A butterfly's behavior is quite different from that of a caterpillar, but it is innate in equal degree. In almost all organisms one of the factors of changing behavior is growth, which will be discussed in Chapter 14.

Social behavior is another extremely complex subject that must be left mostly to the specialists: social psychologists, sociologists, ethnologists, and politicians. As far as it is directly biological, it will be mentioned in Chapter 25.

Chapter Summary

The nature of behavior; "doing"; externally directed activity; its intimate dependence as stimulus-conduction-response systems, especially on effectors.

Effectors; behavior as movement; effectors in plants; in protists (ameboid motion, cilia, flagella); effectors in multicellular animals (muscles).

Muscular effectors; types of muscles (behavioral and visceral); muscles and skeletal systems; endo- and exoskeletons; control of movement by opposing muscles; all-or-none response of individual fibers; a muscle as a group of fibers.

Other effectors: stinging organs in coelenterates; electric organs.

The study of behavior: its relationship to psychology; its difficulties; dangers of anthropomorphism; Morgan's canon as a special case of Occam's razor relevant to study of behavior; dangers in Morgan's canon.

Tropisms and other reflex movements; initial botanical meaning of tropism; Loeb's extension of concept to animals; behavior of the pill bug and the notion of forced movements—zealous application of Morgan's canon; nontropistic movements in plants and simple animals.

The adaptive nature of behavior and its modifiability—a simple case of learning, even in protists.

Behavior in relation to the structure of nervous systems: simplicity of behavior in animals with nerve nets—Hydra, echinoderms, and planarians; increased complexity and learning capacity in animals with brains.

Innate and learned behavior: instinct *or* learning as a falsely simple problem; language as learned behavior dependent on innate human capacities; the learning of song in birds, and its modifiability in some species.

Reflexes and conditioned responses: the modifiability of reflexes; conditioned responses as simple cases of learning; habits; maze learning; motivation; maintenance of the organism's stability the most general source of motivation; age and other influences on learning.

Behavior in insects: its great complexity and relative lack of modifiability, exemplified by the digger wasp.

Concepts, symbols, and language.

Other aspects of behavior: endocrine effects; personality; social behavior.

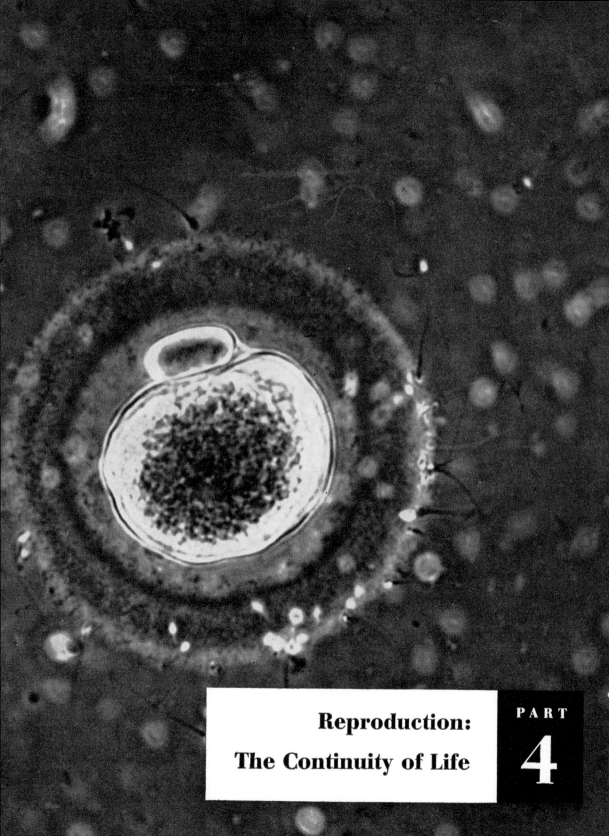

Reproduction:
The Continuity of Life

PART
4

Self-reproduction, the most characteristic feature of all living systems, is the subject matter of Part 4. It is introduced by a remarkable photograph of a human egg cell with sperm cells attached. One of the sperms will fertilize the egg; in other words, its nucleus will migrate into the egg and there fuse with the egg nucleus. The fertilized egg cell—or zygote—contains nuclear material from both parents. It marks the beginning of the life of a new human being and is a useful focal point for introducing all the diverse aspects of organic reproduction.

In the first place, the nature of the zygote—a single cell—points up the fact that organic reproduction is basically a *cellular process*. Second, the origin of the zygote through fertilization introduces the generalization that organic reproduction nearly always involves the added complication of *sex*; the egg and sperm cells are produced by different types of adults—different sexes—specialized for their role in reproduction. Third, the certain fate of the human zygote is to develop into a human being—not, for instance, into a mouse. A generalization about organic reproduction is that it involves *heredity*, the production of like by like. Fourth, an essential feature of virtually all reproduction is elaborate *development* whereby the parent's complex organization is created afresh in the offspring out of the simple beginnings afforded by a single cell (usually the zygote).

This last point lies at the heart of our discussion in Part 4. We emphasize that the processes of development, which are essentially a creative job of construction, cannot take their orderly course leading to a particular kind of adult (man *versus* mouse, for instance) without a set of specifications or instructions to guide and control them. Such control specifications must be present in the zygote; what an organism inherits from its parents—its heredity—is a "message" with specifications for proper development; and, since the organism in turn transmits a copy of this same message to its own offspring, it is clear that reproduction is ultimately concerned with duplicating an "inherited message."

Chapter 11 shows that the inherited message is in the nucleus and presumably in the chromosomes; it describes how duplicate sets of chromosomes are transmitted to new cells in mitosis and meiosis.

Chapter 12 traces the growth of the major tenets of genetics, including the rigorous demonstration that the genes which constitute "the inherited message" are arranged in linear order as parts of chromosomes.

Chapter 13 discusses the chemical nature of genes; it details modern ideas of how genes act to achieve their control over the life of the cell—in other words, ideas on how the inherited message is decoded by the cell.

Chapter 14 discusses the processes of development and suggests how they might be controlled by the inherited message in the chromosomes.

Chapter 15 is concerned in particular with adaptive specializations related to the sexuality of organisms.

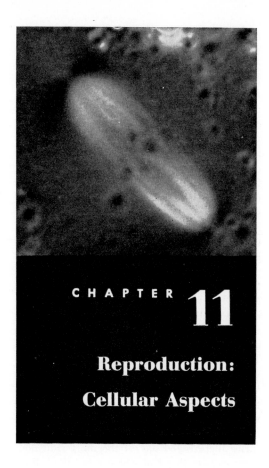

A microphotograph, taken with polarized light, of the mitotic spindle in a living cell of the worm Chaetopterus *(see Fig. 22-11). This minute structure, about 8 μ long, is one of the wonders of biology and lies at the heart of life's orderly reproduction.* (Photo by Dr. Shinya Inoué, U. of Rochester)

CHAPTER **11**

Reproduction: Cellular Aspects

THE CONTINUITY OF LIFE

The individual organism—bacterium, rosebush, mouse, or man—is an elaborate and complex system whose structure and activities are, as we have now seen, highly organized. It can maintain its organization and its activities for varying lengths of time by capturing energy and expending this appropriately in the maintenance of its ordered state. The organism can adjust its structure and behavior, within limits, in such a way as to remain adapted to changing environmental conditions. Again within limits, it can repair damage due to accident and the inescapable ravages due to use and aging. We do not understand precisely how the machinery of the body wears with age, but clearly it does; and ultimately this damage gets beyond the organism's capacity to repair. Death comes to all living things—indeed, there is

no surer or wider generalization that we can make in biology.

The persistence of life on earth in the face of death's certainty points up the universal ability of organisms to reproduce themselves as one of their most characteristic, and most defining, features. The long-term endurance of life is not due, like its short-term endurance, to the ability of the individual organism to repair, patch up, and adjust itself. It is due to the fact that, in a sense, it can throw off the worn-out machinery and start again in the form of its offspring. These in turn can repair and adjust for only so long; ultimately they face the same fate as their parents. They will live into posterity only insofar as they leave offspring. What endures on earth over the millennia is not the individual organism but the race, and its endurance depends on the act of reproduction as a vital bridge that spans successive mortal generations.

The Major Features of Organic Reproduction

HUMAN REPRODUCTION: PROBLEMS AND PRINCIPLES

The subject of reproduction is many-sided. It involves several different kinds of problems and several different features of the organism's structure and activities. We will begin by sorting out the major features of reproduction as they are more or less familiar to

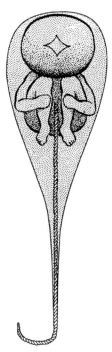

11-1 The homunculus, or little man, as "seen" in the human sperm by an early member of the "spermist" school.

us in humans, and in doing this we will define the general problems to be given detailed attention in later sections.

In man, as in the vast majority of other species, the individual organisms fall into two categories, male and female, with respect to their roles in reproduction. The new human begins its life inside the body of its mother, and the role of the male is restricted to the act of copulation, during which he introduces into the female a fluid known as semen. It has been realized in Western culture for well over 2000 years that the act of copulation in man was causally related to pregnancy and the production of offspring. In spite of this, the real significance of copulation in man and other organisms remained obscure until the advent of the microscope and the clear formulation of the cell theory. The microscope revealed facts which imply that reproduction, like so much else in biology, is to be discussed and understood primarily in terms of cells.

The thick seminal fluid ejaculated by the male in copulation is a heavy suspension of single cells, sperm cells, or *spermatozoa.* In-

troduced from the penis of the male into the female vagina (Fig. 15-24) these cells swim upward in special ducts, down which there migrates a cell or cells, contributed by the female. These are egg cells, or *ova.* The ultimate sexual event is the union of one egg cell with one sperm, an event known as *fertilization.* The product of fertilization is the *zygote,* or fertilized egg cell. In man, only one fertilized egg usually proceeds to grow further, although occasionally two or more may do so, leading to twins [1] or triplets, and so forth.

The zygote marks the real beginning of the new organism's life. In humans it lodges on the wall of the mother's uterus, where it remains for nine months, undergoing growth and the initial creative development of the adult human's complex structure. The discovery of the cellular nature of fertilization was a crucial step forward. But the early observers did not grasp its full significance. The early microscopists, excited at the new world of minute life their microscopes revealed, let their imaginations fill in the detail their imperfect instruments could not resolve. During the latter part of the seventeenth and early part of the eighteenth centuries there raged one of the most ridiculous controversies that has ever marred the history of biology. One school of opinion (we should really say one school of imagination) asserted that in the egg cell there existed a preformed human being, minute but complete in its every detail. These scholars viewed the sperm as serving only as a kind of trigger to initiate the growth of the minuscule creature contained within the egg. An opposing group—anxious perhaps to uphold the dignity of the male—claimed that the preformed adult lay in the sperm head (Fig. 11-1). This group, called the *spermists,* in contradiction to their opponents the *ovists,* claimed as a member no less a figure than the great Van Leeuwenhoek himself. Both views were what are now called *preformist,* that is to say, they assumed that *the adult was preformed* in the germ cells (sperm or ova), and for them what we call development today did not exist. The history of the young human in its moth-

[1] This is not the only manner by which twins come into being (see p. 340).

er's womb was a simple history of expansion or unfolding of all the adult complexity already present from the start. Both groups recognized, but were not seriously embarrassed by, the astonishing logical end point of their position—that within the minute germ cell (sperm or egg) there was a minute human with a reproductive organ, which contained eggs or sperms which in their turn contained still more minute human beings. This meant that in the eggs of Eve or the sperm of Adam (according to whether you were ovist or spermist) there were contained minute humans which contained minute humans which contained minute humans— and so on *ad infinitum*. One mathematically minded ovist at the time came forward with the "precise" conclusion as to how many million such human generations were packed one inside the next, all within the egg of Eve.

Ridiculous as these views were, they are interesting for the following reason. The alternative, which turns out to be correct, is a truly astonishing fact. *From a single cell* (the zygote, or fertilized egg), which is visibly simple and unspecialized, *the entire staggering complexity of the adult human is created or developed afresh in each generation.*

In the photograph used to open Part 4 (p. 255) the human egg cell is shown as it normally appears in the mother during fertilization. The egg proper is the large cell (bright in the photograph) at the center of the mass. At its side lies a smaller cell (a polar body, p. 338), which will play no further role in development. The egg is surrounded by a wide membrane into which many spermatozoa are seen entering. Only one of these ultimately enters the egg cell proper and causes fertilization. The single cell resulting from fertilization proceeds to divide into two replicas of itself; each of these in turn divides, and the embryo becomes four-celled. This multiplication of cells continues and is one of the basic elements in the increase of the bulk of the embryo as a whole. Increase in bulk through cell reproduction is clearly not the entire story of development, however. Figure 11-2 shows that the cell mass of the embryo soon takes on a definite form although not, to begin with, a form that is recognizably human. The cell mass becomes elongate, cor-

responding with the future long axis (head to tail) of the body. At the side of the future spinal column one can see regularly repeated bulges which are destined to develop further into the musculature of the adult. Only after about five weeks can the grotesque outline of a head be recognized as such by the uninitiated; it is a head grossly out of proportion (by adult standards) with the rest of the embryonic form. At later stages the heart and limbs become evident, but each is only a gross outline of the fine detail of the adult which is developed gradually in successive stages of embryonic life. There are two curious features of the early embryo's form which are of interest to us as evolutionary biologists: (1) a pronounced tail, extending well beyond the point where the hind-limb buds attach to the body; and (2) a set of so-called "gill arches" in the region of the pharynx just below the head. Neither of the features survive to appear in the adult; they reflect, as we discuss later (p. 352), the early evolution of man and are relics of embryonic processes in early primates and fish, respectively.

We are not here concerned with an exact treatment of details in human development. It is our purpose only to illustrate the cardinal point that each reproductive cycle involves the *fresh creation* of adult form, and that the *development* concerned is not a simple unfolding of detail present in the egg from the outset. *The development of adult complexity in each generation is an integral part of the problem of reproduction as a whole.*

Sexuality, development, and its cellular foundations are not the only major features of reproduction illustrated by humans. The simple fact that new humans arise only as offspring of pre-existing humans implies two more major generalizations. First, living things arise from other living things and do not appear spontaneously (without the intervention of life) from nonliving materials; this is the principle of biogenesis. Second, humans have human babies; flies reproduce flies; bacteria reproduce bacteria. This is the phenomenon of heredity: like begets like.

There are thus five general features of reproduction: *sexuality, development, cellularity, biogenesis,* and *heredity.* Of these, sex-

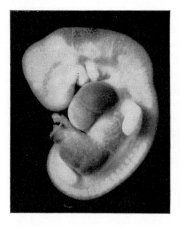
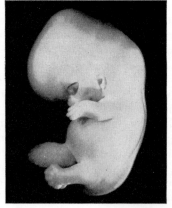
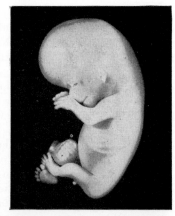

Top three photos, Chester F. Reather, FBPA, Johns Hopkins U. School of Medicine; lower picture, Richard D. Grill, Carnegie Inst. of Washington

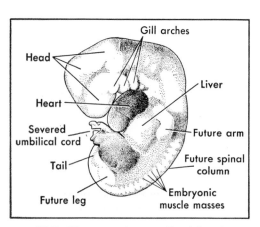

Gill arches

Head

Heart

Severed
umbilical cord

Tail

Future leg

Liver

Future arm

Future spinal
column

Embryonic
muscle masses

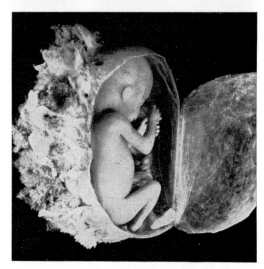

11-2 Human embryos. *Top left*, a human embryo in its fourth week of development. *Bottom left*, the same embryo with some major parts labeled. *Top center*, embryo in its sixth week of development. The eye and ear are now recognizable, as well as the fore and hind limbs. Note how, in the hind limb, the five toes are only roughly sketched out, so to speak. *Top right*, embryo in eighth week of development. The mouth is clearly evident; the digits (fingers and toes) on the limbs are fully formed. Note also the ribs. *Bottom right*, fetus, about sixteen weeks old, lying in the fetal membranes.

uality is the least general; many organisms reproduce themselves without the complication of sex. This asexual reproduction is common and familiar in horticulture, where many plants are propagated by cuttings, suckers, or bulbs. Most, probably all, bacteria reproduce principally in an asexual fashion. A bacterium can produce a replica of itself without any sexual fusion comparable with that seen in man.[2] A fuller discussion of the diverse forms of sexual and asexual reproduc-

2 But see p. 360.

tion is reserved for Chapter 15, when the full implications and meaning of sexuality can be better appreciated.

We have seen that reproduction is basically a matter of cells rather than of whole, adult organisms. Its most general features—biogenesis, development, and heredity—are best approached as problems in cellular reproduction, and such will be our program. First, however, we will briefly examine these three great principles to see how they are related to each other.

Biogenesis

ARGUMENT FROM EXPERIMENT

It was the general opinion for many centuries that lower organisms can originate from mud or, especially, from the flesh of dead animals. Aristotle (384-322 B.C.) taught that fleas and mosquitoes arise from putrefying matter, and no one ventured to contradict him during the long course of antiquity and the Middle Ages. An eminent seventeenth-century scientist was sure that he had seen rats develop from bran and old rags. It was even easier to be certain that maggots arise spontaneously in rotten meat. Another seventeenth-century scientist, Redi (1627-1697), disproved this idea. By careful experiments he showed that maggots never appear unless flies have laid eggs in the meat.[3]

Perhaps Redi's work should have settled the matter, but it did not. A really popular error dies hard, if it ever completely dies out. This one is still alive, and some people in the United States are still sure that a horsehair can turn into a worm if soaked long enough in water. As far as biologists are concerned, however, the matter was finally settled in the nineteenth century by the work of Pasteur (1822-1895), among others. It was then known that microorganisms appear in milk, wine, meat broth, and other substances even if they are protected from flies and other apparent sources. Pasteur examined every known example of such supposed spontaneous generation of living things. He showed that heating could kill microorganisms still present and that if the sterile substance was then protected from air, no others appeared. (We still call this procedure "pasteurization" after him.) It was demonstrated that microorganisms are carried through the air and that spontaneous generation does not occur in any known case.

All life comes from life. That is one of the really great and fundamental generalizations of biology. Since Pasteur there has been no reasonable doubt that it is true of the life around us today and that represented in the

[3] The particular flies look somewhat like bees, so much so that they fooled some ancient writers, who recommended their use for the replenishment of beehives!

known fossil record. However, another aspect of the matter is not settled: the origin of life. Life now comes only from other life, but the sequence must have started some time.

Redi was attacked by theologians who interpreted some passages in the Bible as implying that spontaneous generation of maggots does occur. By the time of Pasteur the theologians were on the other side: they denied spontaneous generation on the grounds that it contradicted the creation of life solely by acts of God. They hailed Pasteur's results as confirming their doctrine.

Now the results of Pasteur and other nineteenth-century biologists were reasonably conclusive as regards conditions on earth today and through the last few hundred million years of geological history. They prove nothing whatever, one way or the other, about the still more remote time when life really appeared for the first time and when conditions were clearly quite different. Most biologists think it probable that life did originally arise from nonliving matter by natural processes. With some nonbiologists it is an article of faith that this did not occur. Since neither side can produce real *proof*, and since the two do not agree on what is and is not evidence, the controversy is likely to continue. Incidentally, do you think that Pasteur's experiments really *proved* that life is not originating from nonliving materials even now?

Whatever you may think about the origin of life or a complete generalization from Pasteur's results, the fact remains that reproduction of life from previous life is, *as far as known,* the only process involved in the rise of organisms today or through the course of *recorded* evolution. It is the great principle underlying the continuity of life as we know it.

ARGUMENT FROM THEORY:
COMPLEXITY AND INFORMATION

Quite apart from the strong argument that experiment raises against the idea of the spontaneous generation of life under present world conditions, there are very strong theoretical reasons for rejecting the whole possibility. An attempt to understand these theoretical reasons is worth while because the argument forces us to frame the problems of organic reproduction in terms of concepts that are most useful for further study.

We referred in Chapter 1 to the tendency of the physical world toward a state of uniform disorder—the tendency which is referred to technically in the Second Law of Thermodynamics. The most probable state for any system of matter, the state it tends ultimately to assume, is one of simplicity and disorder. The idea of complexity embodies within it the idea of improbability; the more complex a thing is, the less probable it becomes that it arose by chance. This is also true of the ideas of order and organization. A complex organization is in itself improbable, and if left alone it will decay. If no work is put into the system to maintain its organization, it will tend to assume its most probable state—simple disorder.

We first introduced these notions about simplicity and disorder versus complex organization in Chapter 1 in relation to the universal demand in organisms for an energy supply. In the face of the universal tendency for order to be lost, the complex organization of the living organism can be maintained only if work—involving the expenditure of energy—is performed to conserve the order. The organism is constantly adjusting, repairing, replacing, and this requires energy.

But the maintenance of the complex, improbable organization of the living creature needs more than energy for the work. It calls for *information* or instructions *on how the energy should be expended* to maintain the improbable organization. The idea of *information* necessary for the maintenance and, as we shall see, creation of new living systems is a concept of great utility for approaching the group of biological problems associated with reproduction.

In the nonliving world of bricks, stones, and raw metals, the appearance of a skyscraper immediately indicates for us the presence of life, and not simply because we associate people with buildings. Nobody would ever assume that the complex organization of a modern building could come into existence spontaneously, of its own accord. The ordered nature of the arrangement of bricks, girders, etc., is *too improbable to arise by chance*. There is an enormous number of possible ways in which the bricks, girders, and other constituents of a building *could* be arranged. The particular arrangement that is a functional building is only one out of the total ensemble or array of possible arrangements.

In what way is the element of chance removed in the appearance of a skyscraper? It is removed because the work which was expended in creating it followed instructions or information on how to put together the constituents in the one particular way (out of the many possible) that results in a skyscraper. The information contained in the architect's plans is the agent that removes chance from the work of the construction engineer and leads to the development of a complex organization that is in itself too improbable to arise by chance.

A modern building is certainly a complex and highly ordered structure, but its complexity cannot begin to compare with that of the living system. And for precisely the same reasons that make us reject the idea of a building coming into existence spontaneously, we are forced to reject the idea that anything as complex as an organism could arise spontaneously from the materials of the nonliving world. *The materials that go into the construction of an organism*—chemical elements like carbon, nitrogen, hydrogen, oxygen, and the rest—*could assume so many possible configurations that the chance origin of the particular arrangement which is a particular kind of living cell is utterly negligible.*

It is interesting to note in passing that a precise and quantitative way of talking about information has been developed in recent years, and that by using these mathematical techniques it has been possible to estimate just how improbable the *chance* origin of a living organism is. This is simply another way of saying how much information is needed to guarantee the creation of an organism. The basic notion in the exact treatment of this information is simple enough. It is obvious that if someone has to perform a particular task and there are only two possible courses of action open to him, one of which is correct, then it takes less information to control and guarantee his correct performance than in situations in which a hundred possible courses of action have to be discriminated among. The idea of information, in the sense in which it can be treated as an exact and useful scientific concept, is the idea of how much specification is necessary to exclude all but the correct or desired alternative out of an array of many that are possible. The more possibilities that exist, the greater is the information that must be given to specify one in particular. Since we know roughly the numbers of atoms of each kind of chemical element that occur in the human body, for example, we can estimate how many possible combinations these elements could make in the numbers in which they occur. By estimating how many *possible* configurations they could assume, we at the same time estimate roughly how much information is needed to specify that particular configuration which is man. The numbers involved are, of course, in the present state of our knowledge, rough and only estimates, but they are staggering. The quantitative estimates obtained indicate an amount of information that if translated into human language would fill all the books of several major libraries. That anything requiring as much specification as this should arise by chance is indeed utterly out of the question. Theory and experiment combine to dismiss the ancient myth of spontaneous generation; and the theoretical argument helps us formulate what it is we must seek to understand in reproduction as a whole.

One further point should be noted before we return to the subject of reproduction. Our discussion of life's complexity and the impossibility of its spontaneous origin applies strictly to the physical world and to life as we know them today. The argument does *not* exclude the spontaneous origin of life in simpler form under highly special conditions long since passed on the earth. This is a topic to which we return in Chapter 30.

HEREDITY AS INFORMATION FOR THE CONTROL OF DEVELOPMENT

The hallmark of living systems is their complexity and their organization, and the *focal point of the reproduction problem is how complexity and organization can be reproduced.* You cannot reproduce skyscrapers by cutting them in two. This process yields half-skyscrapers, not skyscrapers, because the essential complexity and organization of the building is three-dimensional in space; it is destroyed by being cloven in two. To duplicate a skyscraper, the information in the initial blueprints must be taken again—or at any rate a copy of them—and the duplicate must be built or developed from scratch.

Precisely the same considerations apply to living organisms whose organization is also three-dimensional in space.[4] Simple cleavage of a living system like man into two parts does not lead to reproduction; it leads to the destruction of his essential complexity of structure. The reproduction of man, as of all other living systems, involves the *development* or building from a simple start of the complexity that is to be duplicated. The phenomena of embryonic development, of which we have had a glimpse in man, are an integral part of the process of reproduction which, in our scientific study, we seek to explain.

Our understanding of the need for the initial blueprint (or a copy of it) as a prerequisite for the reproduction of a building forms the proper starting point for defining the problems involved in organic reproduction. We have seen that the construction of an organism without information to control the construction is as out of the question as the unguided construction of a skyscraper. The redevelopment of the organism's complexity in each successive act of reproduction demands a source of information for the control of its construction. Now the same construction is undertaken generation after generation in living systems. Embryologically, we and you were constructed in the same fashion, and so were our parents and grandparents before us. In each generation there is a supply of information which regulates or controls development, and in each generation the "blueprint" containing this information is the same. What we inherited from our parents at the outset of our lives as single cells was a supply of "information" that controlled our

4 Actually, the organization of the living system is four-dimensional in that organized sequences of events in time are an essential aspect of it.

development and that determines our fundamental behavior as adults even today.

This is the way we can approach the problem of *heredity*. In its immediate aspect heredity is the phenomenon of like begetting like in the successive acts of reproduction. Like begets like *because* parent and offspring were each in their turn *developed* by processes controlled by the same set of information. Clearly there must be a sense in which it is true to say that what is reproduced and transmitted from generation to generation of living organisms is the correct set of information for their creation. We will direct our search in the study of development and heredity along these lines.

We must discover

1. What the nature of the information is that controls the development of the organism.
2. How the information is reproduced.
3. How copies of it are transmitted from generation to generation.
4. How the information acts to achieve control.

The Cellular Basis of Reproduction

VIRCHOW'S DOCTRINE: "ALL CELLS FROM CELLS"

The cell theory in its explicit form, the doctrine that all living systems are built of cells, was announced in 1838-39 by Schleiden and by Schwann, but it was not until about 1860 that its full implications began to be evident. The decade from 1850 to 1860 still saw much discussion about what was called "free cell formation," a discussion of the "spontaneous origin" of cells from noncellular materials. As the whole notion of spontaneous generation began to fall, it became increasingly clear that the old aphorism, "All life from life," could be translated, as it was by the German physiologist Virchow in 1855, into a more precise formulation, *"Omnis cellula e cellula"*—"All cells from cells."

Cells are the elementary building blocks of living systems; if new life arises from old, it must take the form of new cells from old. The life of each organism begins, as we have seen in man, as a single cell, the zygote. The growth and development of this one cell to the massive complexity of adult man is, in one major respect, due to the activity of the original cell and its progeny of cells reproducing themselves. When the multicellular organism is mature and, as an organism, reproduces itself, the fundamental event is again one of producing a new cell—egg or sperm.

Clearly the single-celled zygote from which the adult develops contains within its minute structure the controlling information we have argued must be present—the real inheritance of the child from its parents. We now proceed to show where in the cell the control center must be and how copies of it are transmitted to new cells as they are produced.

THE NUCLEUS AS CONTROL CENTER

Several kinds of observation combine to show that the nucleus is the control center for the whole cell's activities. In the first place, the nucleus can be removed from some cells that are sufficiently big to permit operation on them with suitable micromanipulating equipment. Cells devoid of a nucleus soon die, showing at least that the nucleus is indispensable for the enduring welfare of the cell. But by other means it can be shown more directly to be the actual site of the cell's controls, the store of information for the control of its organization and behavior.

There is a group of fresh-water protists that are especially favorable for experiments bearing on the role of the nucleus. These protists are plants which, in spite of their single-celled nature, assume a surprisingly large size and complexity of structure. Figure 11-3 shows two species (*mediterranea* and *crenulata*) of these protists which belong to the genus *Acetabularia*. For simplicity we will refer to species concerned as *med* and *cren*. In both species three parts of the plant can be distinguished: a cap or hat, a "stem," and a base which branches in a way suggestive of roots.

11-3 The nucleus as control center of the cell. The plants being used in this experiment are species of the fresh-water protist *Acetabularia*.

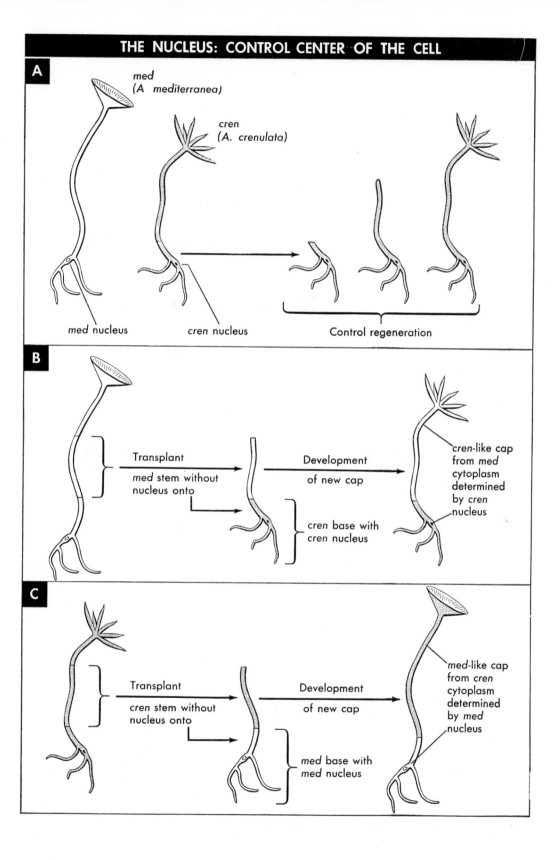

A

med
(A. mediterranea)

cren
(A. crenulata)

med nucleus

cren nucleus

Control regeneration

B

Transplant

med stem without
nucleus onto

Development
of new cap

cren base with
cren nucleus

cren-like cap
from med
cytoplasm
determined
by cren
nucleus

C

Transplant

cren stem without
nucleus onto

Development
of new cap

med base with
med nucleus

med-like cap
from cren
cytoplasm
determined
by med
nucleus

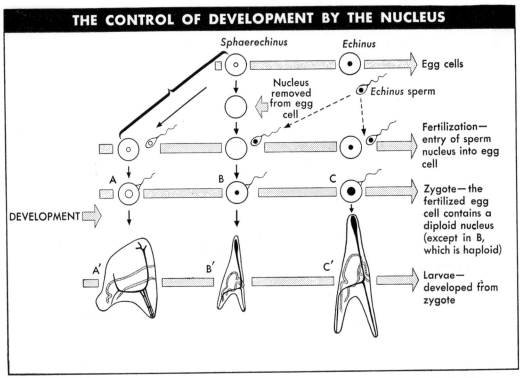

11-4 Control of development by the nucleus in sea urchins. The structure of the *Sphae-rechinus* larva is markedly different from that of *Echinus*. Entry of the haploid *Echinus* sperm nucleus (shown in black) into the enucleated *Sphaerechinus* egg produces a larva which in spite of its small size (because it is haploid) is clearly *Echinus* in its morphology.

The nucleus of the single cell lies in the base. In *med* the cap is disc-shaped, and in *cren* it is branched. The plants, although single-celled, are sufficiently big that operations can be performed on them with ease. If their stem and cap are cut away the cell *redevelops* a new stem and cap; and under the control of the normal nucleus this development repeats the original and produces the typical cap. Another kind of operation is possible. The stem and cap can be cut away, and the stem (lacking the cap) of the other species can be transplanted or grafted onto the cut base. This is illustrated in Fig. 11-3, where a capless stem of *cren* is grafted on the base of *med*. The *med* base contains a *med* nucleus, and, when a new cap is regenerated from the *cren* stem material, the cap assumes the form of *med*. Clearly the course of development which the *cren* stem material follows is controlled by information in the *med* nucleus. The converse experiment gives similar results: a

med stem transplanted to a *cren* base regenerates a *cren* cap.

The experiments of Boveri on sea-urchin eggs illustrated in Fig. 11-4 lead to the same conclusion. If the nucleus is removed from the egg of *Sphaerechinus* before it is fertilized, and if it is then fertilized by the sperm of a different sea urchin, *Echinus,* then the egg develops solely under the control of the *Echinus* nucleus. Minute as the *Echinus* nucleus is in relation to the mass of *Sphaerechinus* cytoplasm which it enters, it nevertheless reveals its controlling nature. Its entry into the *Sphaerechinus* brought in the specifications for development of the *Echinus* form which the developing larva assumes.

MITOSIS: THE SEQUENCE
OF STAGES

The experiments with *Acetabularia* and the sea urchins show that we are on the right track in our search for the controlling information in the organism if we pursue our study of the nucleus and its structure.

When it is not in the process of reproducing, the nucleus gives little evidence of its detailed or intimate structure. Figure 3-1 shows the visible structure of a generalized cell. The nucleus lies in the cytoplasm, showing only its nucleolus and a fine granular appearance. Outside the nucleus in animal cells (although not in most plants) lies the centrosome or aster, which is a star-shaped body. At the very center of the centrosome there is a minute body called the centriole. Details of nuclear structure become abundantly evident, however, as soon as the cell begins to reproduce.

Chromosomes and mitosis. The onset of reproductive activity is marked by the division of the aster and its centriole into two parts and the separation of these toward opposite sides of the nucleus. Within the nuclear membrane changes become evident and one begins to see elongate threads in place of the previous fine granular structure (Figs. 3-2 and 11-5). These threadlike structures are chromosomes (see p. 52). The chromosomes, as we shall see, are the carriers of the cell's inherited controls, and the details of their structure and behavior are, therefore, what we want to understand.

The diagrams in Fig. 11-5 represent the succession of events that occur during the division of a cell into two new daughter cells; the whole process is called mitosis.[5] This word derives from the Greek root mitos ("thread") and refers, obviously, to the threadlike nature of the chromosomes which are evident at mitosis. The nucleus that is drawn in Fig. 11-5 belongs to a purely hypothetical organism in which the number of chromosomes is kept small for diagrammatic purposes. It is convenient to treat the long [6] and continuous process of mitosis by recognizing in it a sequence of more or less distinct stages or phases. This sequence of stages is prophase, metaphase, anaphase, and telophase.

[5] Strictly speaking, the division of the cell itself should be called cytokinesis. The events involved in the division of the nucleus as such are called mitosis.

[6] The duration of mitosis varies in different cell types; known durations vary from minutes to several hours.

Prophase. In prophase the chromosome threads are elongate to begin with and progressively shorten, becoming at the same time apparently thicker and more heavily stainable if laboratory preparations are treated with dyes. The shortening and thickening are in a sense only an appearance and are due to the fact that the elongate thread seen in the earliest prophase is thrown into a helix (Fig. 11-6), which becomes coated with a matrix of material derived from the nucleolus. The nucleolus accordingly becomes progressively smaller during prophase.

Even from the earliest prophase stage we can recognize two characteristics about the chromosomes that are fundamental and shared by almost all organisms: (1) They occur in pairs. In our hypothetical form there are two pairs (A^f and A^m, B^f and B^m). The members of each pair are similar and are said to be homologous. (2) Each chromosome is itself double-stranded. The two strands of each chromosome are held together by a small body called the centromere. Each chromosome has one centromere.

As the prophase of mitosis progresses, the two strands of each chromosome coil into helical form independently of each other; when the prophase is complete, each chromosome has the appearance shown in Fig. 11-6.

Metaphase. This is the name given to the stage of mitosis that follows prophase. At the end of prophase the nuclear membrane disappears, and in the space between the two centrioles there develops a remarkable structure called the spindle. The spindle consists of fibers which radiate from the two centrioles, producing a biconical structure (Fig. 11-5). At metaphase the chromosomes migrate onto the equator of this spindle. The arms of the chromosomes may lie loosely off the equator of the spindle itself, but the centromeres lie precisely on it. Some fibers of the spindle somehow become attached to the centromere of each chromosome. The centromeres now split in two in a definite plane (Fig. 11-5), and the anaphase of mitosis has commenced.

Anaphase. Each of the two "daughter" centromeres of a chromosome is attached to a

MITOSIS

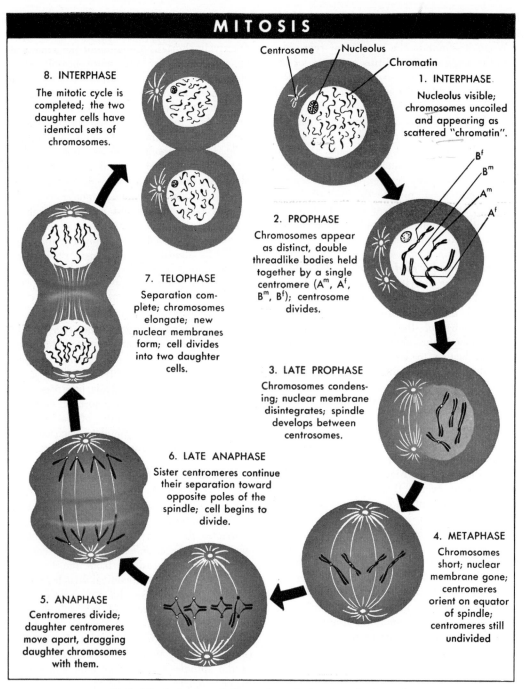

8. **INTERPHASE**
The mitotic cycle is completed; the two daughter cells have identical sets of chromosomes.

Centrosome Nucleolus Chromatin

1. **INTERPHASE**
Nucleolus visible; chromosomes uncoiled and appearing as scattered "chromatin".

B^f
B^m
A^m
A^f

2. **PROPHASE**
Chromosomes appear as distinct, double threadlike bodies held together by a single centromere (A^m, A^f, B^m, B^f); centrosome divides.

7. **TELOPHASE**
Separation complete; chromosomes elongate; new nuclear membranes form; cell divides into two daughter cells.

3. **LATE PROPHASE**
Chromosomes condensing; nuclear membrane disintegrates; spindle develops between centrosomes.

6. **LATE ANAPHASE**
Sister centromeres continue their separation toward opposite poles of the spindle; cell begins to divide.

4. **METAPHASE**
Chromosomes short; nuclear membrane gone; centromeres orient on equator of spindle; centromeres still undivided

5. **ANAPHASE**
Centromeres divide; daughter centromeres move apart, dragging daughter chromosomes with them.

11-5 The behavior of the nucleus during its mitotic cycle.

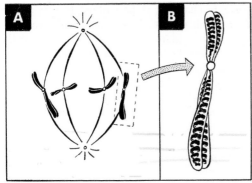

11-6 The helical structure of the metaphase chromosomes. *A.* The four chromosomes of Fig. 11-5 seen on the metaphase spindle. *B.* One of the chromosomes enlarged to show how the chromosome thread is thrown into a helix and embedded in a matrix.

spindle fiber. The centromeres now begin to move apart, one to each centriole. As they move they carry with them the daughter chromosomes. Thus at each of the two ends, or poles, of the spindle there accumulates a complete set of chromosomes: A^m, A^f, B^m, and B^f.

Telophase. This phase follows anaphase and, in a way, is the reverse of prophase: a new nuclear membrane develops around the chromosomes, which uncoil and resume their original appearance as elongate, poorly stainable threads. As they uncoil, they lose their surrounding material, which coalesces again into the body of the nucleolus.

Interphase. "Interphase" is the name given to the state of the nucleus when it is not involved in mitosis. During the interphase the chromosomes remain virtually unstainable. We know, however, from a series of observations too involved to enumerate here, that during the interphase the chromosomes retain their identity as distinct bodies.

MITOSIS: A DEVICE FOR
ORDERLY TRANSMISSION

Movements of the chromosomes. The highly organized movement of the chromosomes, first in the way they orient themselves on the spindle equator at metaphase, and later in their separation and movement to the

spindle poles, is one of the great wonders in biology. We still do not by any means understand fully how these movements are caused. Is the anaphase movement caused by the spindle fibers contracting, like muscles, and in this way dragging the daughter centromeres to the poles? Or does the middle region of the spindle expand and push the centromeres towards the poles? Again it could be that the movement of the chromosomes is to some extent autonomous, by which we mean that the forces responsible for their movement may be internal to the chromosomes so that they *go* to the poles rather than being *forced* to the poles.

The problem of explaining the chromosomes' movements at mitosis has attracted and baffled many biologists. Perhaps the most widely held view at present is that the spindle fibers do exert a pulling effect on the centromeres to which they are attached so that the chromosomes are pulled to the pole rather than moving there independently. One thing is certain. *Both the centromere and the spindle fiber, which is organized by the centriole, are essential for the movement.* Chromosomes without centromeres cannot execute a poleward movement; and chromosomes which in spite of having a centromere fail to get onto the spindle and attach to a fiber fail to reach the pole. The centromere and the centriole which organizes the spindle fibers are therefore indispensable for orderly chromosome movement, and in some way responsible for it.

As evolutionists we are interested but not surprised to find that the centriole has been put to use by the cell in another form of organized movement. In flagellated single cells like protists and sperm cells, the flagella, which are organelles [7] of movement, are organized and controlled by the centriole. Nor are we surprised by another related point: the centromere and centriole are evidently essentially the same structures. There is a group of snails in which the centromeres seem to be poorly anchored to the chromosomes, sometimes getting quite loose from them. When this happens the chromosomes without centromeres never get onto the spin-

[7] The word "organelle" is used to denote a functionally distinct part of a cell, just as "organ" is used to denote a functionally distinct part of the whole organism.

dle; and the free centromeres aggregate around the centrosomes. Later they reveal their essential identity with the centriole because, like it, they organize a flagellum. These atypical snail sperms come, in this way, to have not one but several sperm tails; and the number of extra tails corresponds, of course, with the number of chromosomes that get lost from the spindle—stranded without their organelles of movement.

These relations of centriole and centromere are the kind of thing which, as evolutionists, we expect to find in living organisms. As we shall see later in greater detail (Chapter 18), living systems evolve in an opportunistic way, making use of what is already available and suitable for the "solution" of new problems as they arise. Clearly the cell in its long evolutionary history has made use of essentially one and the same body, centromere-centriole, for three quite distinct tasks whose only common denominator is involvement in organized movement. The essential properties of this kinetic center (or movement organizer) must surely have evolved first in relation to one of the three functions it now serves, but which we do not know. At a later time its presence and properties were put to use in solving other problems.

The ordered separation of duplicates. We digressed briefly to the problems of the cause of the chromosome movements not only because it is one of the major biological problems studied today, but for the more general reason that the organized and controlled movement of the chromosomes at mitosis merits emphasis as a focal point in organic reproduction in general.

If we survey mitosis throughout the plant and animal kingdom, fascinating differences in detail can be discovered, but these are studied largely because they are so rare. It is the other side of the picture that we want to stress: *mitosis is virtually co-extensive with life, and its major features are amazingly constant.* The universality and constancy of mitosis bespeaks something fundamental, and what is fundamental is clear enough in the light of our earlier discussion of heredity as information. The mitotic mechanism is the basic mechanism of hereditary transmission. As a result of mitosis two cells are developed from one, and to each of the daughter cells is transmitted—by virtue of the orderly movements of the chromosomes on the spindle—a copy of all the chromosomes.

Transmission versus duplication. At the beginning of each prophase we see that each chromosome is already duplicated and the duplicates are "tied together" by the single centromere. Mitosis is concerned, so to speak, only with the orderly separation of the two duplicate sets and their transmission to different cells. It is important to note that the mitotic process is not concerned with the reproduction of the chromosomes, but only with their separation once reproduced.

When and how does the actual duplication take place? At anaphase and telophase the chromosome consists of only one of the two strands seen at the previous prophase. It follows that the single strand is duplicated sometime between telophase, when it is single, and the following prophase, when it is clearly double. Exactly *when* during the interphase replication, or duplication, takes place and, *how* it is effected we do not know (Fig. 11-10). However, one point must be emphasized. Sometimes biologists do speak of a chromosome splitting in two, but this is at best an unfortunate way of putting it. If the duplex nature of the prophase chromosome resulted only from a longitudinal split of the earlier telophase chromosome, this could go on for only so long—a cake can be cut into smaller and smaller pieces but eventually none is left! Obviously the duplication of chromosomes is a real re-creation, or reproduction, of a copy of the already existing one; it cannot be simply a cleavage or splitting in two of the existing one. In the next chapter we will return to the problem of how the chromosome is reproduced in interphase.

DIPLOIDY: ITS ORIGIN
IN FERTILIZATION

One point that will have impressed you and that demands explanation is that the chromosomes in the nucleus occur in pairs.

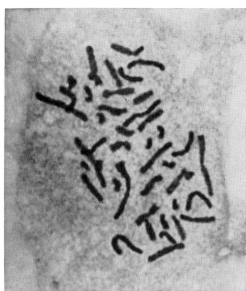

11-7 The diploid (2n = 48) set of chromosomes in a cell from the spleen of man.

Biologists usually symbolize the number of pairs as *n*. In our simplified hypothetical organism in Fig. 11-5 there are 2 pairs (A^m and A^f: B^m and B^f); $n = 2$. In man there are 24 pairs (48 chromosomes) (Fig. 11-7). In some relatives of the lobster there are 100 pairs. In the fruit fly *Drosophila*, to which we give much attention in the next chapter, there are 4 pairs. What is the significance of this regularity—the fact that the nucleus of each species contains a definite number, *n*, of *pairs of chromosomes?*

The explanation is found in the nature of sexual reproduction. The sexual act leads to the union of two cells, one contributed by each parent. These gametes (sperm and egg) prove to be special with respect to their chromosome contents. Each gamete contains half the number of chromosomes seen in the nuclei of *adult* organisms. Thus in our hypothetical organism with four chromosomes (2 *A*'s and 2 *B*'s) the sperm and egg contain only two (1 *A* and 1 *B*); the union of egg and sperm is followed by a pooling of their chromosomes so that the fertilized egg contains four (Fig. 11-8).

The nucleus of the gametes is said to be

*ha*ploid, or to have *n* chromosomes. The nucleus of the fertilized egg with two sets of chromosomes, one from each gamete, is said to be *di*ploid or to have $2n$ chromosomes. Thus in each pair of chromosomes (such as the *A* pair) within the diploid nucleus, one chromosome is derived from the male parent through the sperm (A^m), and the other from the female parent through the egg (A^f). The two *A* chromosomes are said to be a homologous pair; A^m is homologous with A^f; B^m with B^f; A^m is not homologous with either *B* chromosome.

The diploid nucleus of the fertilized egg contains two complete sets of information, one set from the egg and one set from the sperm. These two sets are each faithfully copied in each interphase, and the duplicates are separated during mitosis into the two new daughter cells. Thus from the single-celled zygote produced by fertilization the multicellular adult arises as a result of repeated cell divisions, and all the nuclei throughout the organism contain their own copy of the controlling instructions.

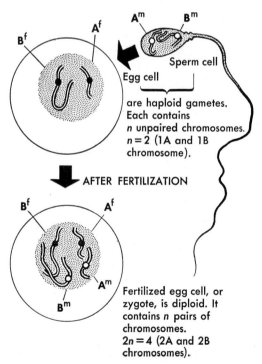

11-8 The origin of diploidy at fertilization.

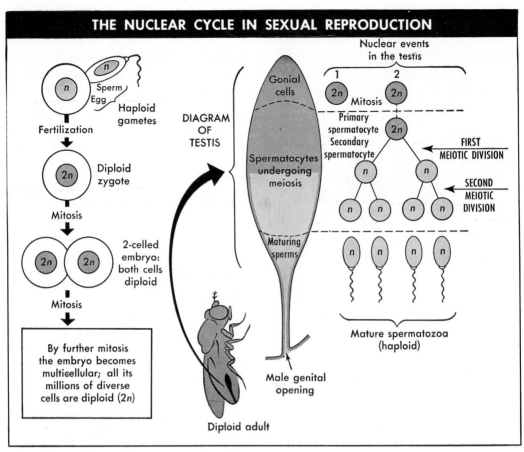

THE NUCLEAR CYCLE IN SEXUAL REPRODUCTION

Nuclear events in the testis

Sperm / Egg
Haploid gametes
Fertilization
Diploid zygote
Mitosis
2-celled embryo: both cells diploid
Mitosis

By further mitosis the embryo becomes multicellular; all its millions of diverse cells are diploid (2n)

DIAGRAM OF TESTIS

Gonial cells
Spermatocytes undergoing meiosis
Maturing sperms
Male genital opening
Diploid adult

Mitosis
Primary spermatocyte
Secondary spermatocyte
FIRST MEIOTIC DIVISION
SECOND MEIOTIC DIVISION
Mature spermatozoa (haploid)

11-9   Where meiosis occurs.

HAPLOIDY: ITS ORIGIN IN MEIOSIS

A further problem must now be obvious. In all organisms that reproduce sexually a union of two cells takes place. The two gametes pool their chromosomes, and the zygote therefore has double the chromosome number of the gametes. In spite of this the number of chromosomes remains stable and characteristic of the species from generation to generation. Evidently a special form of mitosis must occur in the production .of gametes whereby the diploid number of chromosomes, present in all other cells of the body, is reduced to the haploid number that is found in the gametes. This special mitosis is called *meiosis.*

Where meiosis takes place. Let us suppose that the hypothetical organism we

have been discussing so far is some kind of fly whose adult form is outlined in Fig. 11-9. The figure shows that, after the fusion of haploid gametes, the diploid zygote undergoes successive cell divisions during which the duplicated chromosomes are transmitted faithfully by mitosis to all new cells. All the tissues of the adult fly are composed of diploid cells, including those of the reproductive organ (Fig. 11-9). Let us suppose further that this individual fly is male; the reproductive organ is therefore a testis. The sperms produced by this testis are, we know, haploid, so that it is evident that *meiosis*—the special nuclear division yielding haploid cells —must occur in cells in the testis.

The cellular organization of the testis is represented in highly schematized form in Fig. 11-9. At the head of the testis are cells called *spermatogonia* (or *gonial* cells), which divide mitotically. One of the daughter cells produced by a spermatogonial mitosis remains as a gonial cell, and the other becomes a *spermatocyte*. A spermatocyte is the cell in which meiosis takes place. The entire meiotic process comprises two cell divisions, conveniently designated as meiosis I and meiosis II. The cell in which meiosis I takes place is diploid, being derived by mitosis from a gonial cell; it is called the *primary* spermatocyte. Meiosis I produces two *secondary* spermatocytes which then undergo meiosis II, thus yielding four cells, all of which are haploid and are gametes (Fig. 11-9).

Our task is to understand the special chromosome movements in meiosis that are responsible for the transition from the diploid condition of the primary spermatocytes to the haploid condition of the four sperms derived from each primary spermatocyte.

Synapsis, or pairing, at prophase I. The complexities of meiosis are best understood if we focus our attention on the behavior of the centromeres, and confine our discussion initially to one of the pairs of homologous centromeres with their attached chromosomes. We will follow the A pair (A^m and A^f) in our hypothetical fly. The description applies equally well to the B pair, or for that matter to any of the 24 pairs of chromosomes in man. Thus the problem in understanding the events of meiosis is essentially the problem of explaining how in meiosis *only one member of a homologous pair of centromeres* (with its chromosome) *is transmitted to each new nucleus* instead of both members, as in mitosis.

In *mitosis* the two homologous A centromeres with their attached chromosomes behave absolutely independently of each other. They move onto the equator of the spindle at metaphase quite separately, and then each splits in two so that both an A^m and A^f centromere move to each pole of the spindle.

The behavior of the centromeres during the first meiotic division is different in two respects. First, the homologous centromeres (A^m and A^f) do not behave independently of each other; and second, they do not split as they do in mitosis, but move instead one to

each pole. We will follow these differences now in more detail.

The specialized nature of the first meiotic division (Fig. 11-10) is indicated from its very beginning by the fact that the individual chromosomes are seen to be still single-stranded, as they were at the previous telophase. The duplication of the single strand, which normally occurs during interphase, has been delayed. You will recall that the mitotic prophase chromosome is already duplicated.

These single-stranded chromosomes now begin to pair up; A^m pairs with A^f, and B^m with B^f. Strictly corresponding, or *homologous*, points of the chromosome pairs are brought next to each other (Fig. 11-10). Only *after* this pairing, or synapsis, do the individual chromosomes undergo the normal process of duplication. As a result of duplication the chromosome pair is four-stranded and includes two centromeres.

Separation (or segregation) at anaphase I. This paired condition persists throughout prophase. When the spindle is formed the chromosomes move onto its equator at metaphase, still in their paired condition. The homologous centromeres A^m, A^f, etc.) do *not* now split. Instead, one intact centromere moves to each pole of the spindle at anaphase, and in doing so it carries its two chromosome strands with it.

Thus each nucleus that re-forms at the two ends of the spindle at telophase I contains only one A centromere and only one B centromere. (See Fig. 11-10, bottom drawing.)

The second meiotic division (meiosis II). In the interphase following meiosis I the nucleus contains only one of each kind (A, B, etc.) of centromere. Each centromere already carries two chromosome duplicates with it, and accordingly no further duplication takes place. When the second division (meiosis II) commences, each centromere moves onto the spindle at metaphase and now splits, separating the two strands, one going to each pole.

The arithmetic of meiosis. The four strands present in the paired chromosome at

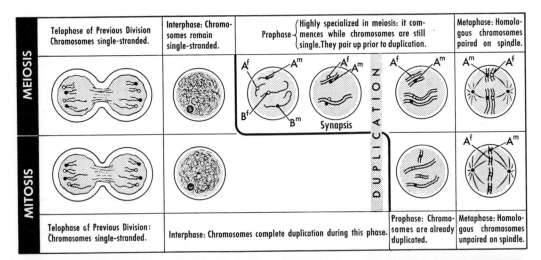

	Telophase of Previous Division Chromosomes single-stranded.	Interphase: Chromosomes remain single-stranded.	Prophase { Highly specialized in meiosis: it commences while chromosomes are still single. They pair up prior to duplication.			Metaphase: Homologous chromosomes paired on spindle.
MEIOSIS			Synapsis			
MITOSIS						
	Telophase of Previous Division: Chromosomes single-stranded.	Interphase: Chromosomes complete duplication during this phase.			Prophase: Chromosomes are already duplicated.	Metaphase: Homologous chromosomes unpaired on spindle.

DUPLICATION

THE CHROMOSOME CYCLE IN 2 **MITOTIC** DIVISIONS

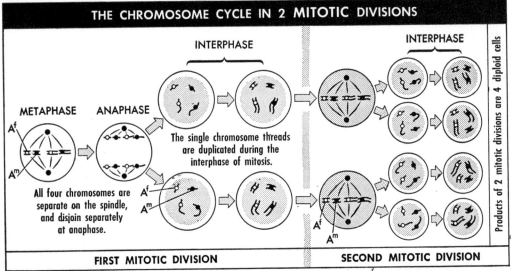

INTERPHASE

INTERPHASE

METAPHASE   ANAPHASE

The single chromosome threads are duplicated during the interphase of mitosis.

All four chromosomes are separate on the spindle, and disjoin separately at anaphase.

FIRST MITOTIC DIVISION

SECOND MITOTIC DIVISION

Products of 2 mitotic divisions are 4 diploid cells

THE CHROMOSOME CYCLE IN 2 **MEIOTIC** DIVISIONS

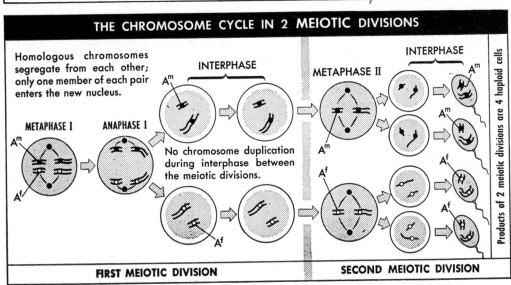

Homologous chromosomes segregate from each other; only one member of each pair enters the new nucleus.

INTERPHASE

METAPHASE II

INTERPHASE

METAPHASE I   ANAPHASE I

No chromosome duplication during interphase between the meiotic divisions.

FIRST MEIOTIC DIVISION

SECOND MEIOTIC DIVISION

Products of 2 meiotic divisions are 4 haploid cells

metaphase I finish up separated, one in each of four gametes. In the whole process of meiosis there are two sets of chromosome separations on a spindle—one at the first division and another at the second division. But chromosome duplication precedes only one of these divisions, the first; and the centromere only divides once, at the second division. The chromosome separation at the first division is based not on the *division* of individual centromeres but on the *separation* of paired homologous centromeres.

The random assortment of chromosomes.

In our account of meiosis so far we have paid attention to the sequence of chromosome movement responsible for separating the members of a single pair of homologous chromosomes. The account applies to all such pairs of homologues. One further point of great importance must be added to make the picture complete. In Fig. 11-11(1) note that A^f, the A chromosome derived originally from the mother of the organism we are studying, goes to one pole of the spindle in meiosis I and A^m to the other. The figure also shows B^f going to the same pole as A^f. This is not the only possible way that the chromosomes could behave. The orientation of the B pair on the spindle is quite independent of the A pair. We will find the metaphase arrangements shown on the spindles in Fig. 11-11 equally often, since they are equally probable. As a consequence B^m may go to the same spindle pole just as often with A^f as with A^m. The following combinations of chromosomes in

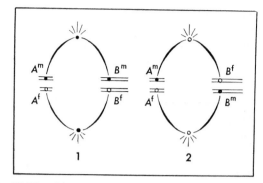

11-11 Independent chromosome assortment. The orientations of the chromosomes at metaphase I shown in (1) and (2) are equally probable.

the gametes are, therefore, all equally probable and frequent.

A^m and B^m
A^f and B^f
A^m and B^f
A^f and B^m

All that the mechanism of meiosis guarantees is that the gametes produced by an organism will contain one member of each pair of homologous chromosomes. It does not guarantee that the two groups of maternal and paternal representatives remain together in the gametes in the combinations in which they were inherited (Fig. 11-11).

The significance of mitosis and meiosis.

We began our discussion of cellular reproduction (1) by noting that it must involve, somehow, the transmission, from one cell generation to the next, of the controlling information responsible for the maintenance of the next cell generation's complexity and organization, and (2) by demonstrating experimentally that the site of the control was the nucleus.

We have found that the nucleus contains a number of elongate threads, the chromosomes. The chromosomes prove to be the seat of nuclear controls. We have found also that when the cell reproduces, it provides—in the form of the mitotic mechanism—for a highly ordered transmission to the new cell of the information (the chromosomes) it needs.

When mitosis begins, the information needed has already been copied. The two

11-10 Mitosis and meiosis compared. The top figure compares mitosis and meiosis from the previous interphase through metaphase. Homologous chromosomes, like A^f and A^m, are single-stranded at the beginning of the meiotic prophase (cf. mitosis) and pair up before duplication. Note how A^m and A^f, for example, are paired together at the meiotic metaphase; they are separate entities at the mitotic metaphase. (Space does not permit representation of the true size and proportions of the B chromosomes on the mitotic spindle.) The two lower figures continue the comparison of mitosis and meiosis from metaphase through two divisions. Chromosome duplication (suppressed in the interphase *between* the first and second meiotic divisions) occurs normally during interphase *after* the second meiotic division.

copies are held together by the centromere. The centromere does not divide until it is properly oriented on the spindle. The spindle's fibers guide the duplicates of each chromosome to two opposite poles. These poles are foci for the gathering together of all necessary information into two strictly equivalent packets promptly enclosed in a new nuclear membrane at telophase. The significance of the spindle is, therefore, clear: it is a device for the orderly separation of the two copies, or blueprints, of the chromosomes.

Other features of the system need further clarification, however. What is the significance of the fact that the cell is usually diploid, carrying two basic and equivalent sets of information, one of which seems, in a sense, surely redundant? There is a simple and obvious answer to this question: diploidy is a consequence of sexual reproduction, since it results from the fusion of representative nuclei from two parents. Each parent contributes one complete copy of the total information necessary. To understand fully why diploidy is so nearly universal in organisms, we must answer a second question: "Why is sexual reproduction so nearly universal?" This is a question that we are not yet ready to treat, for the answer emerges only from an understanding of the mechanism of evolution, taken up in Chapters 15 through 18.

Similar considerations apply to meiosis. There are simple features about meiosis that are obviously understandable in terms of sexual reproduction. Since this does involve nuclear fusion in each generation, the meiotic process must occur if the number of chromosomes is to be held constant. Again, however, we must emphasize that, like diploidy, meiosis can be understood in all its detail only in terms of the mechanism of evolution, so we must return to it later.

Chapter Summary

The continuity of life dependent on the universal ability of organisms to reproduce themselves.

The major features of reproduction illustrated by reference to the familiar case of man; sexuality; embryonic development—preformationism *vs.* epigenesis (the creation of adult complexity); biogenesis; and heredity.

Biogenesis; experimental evidence against spontaneous generation in the modern world; theoretical argument against modern spontaneous generation.

Complexity and information; heredity as information for control of development.

The study of reproduction must reveal:

(1) The nature of the information that controls the development of the organism.

(2) How the information is reproduced.

(3) How copies of it are transmitted from generation to generation.

(4) How the information acts to achieve control.

The cellular basis of reproduction: "all cells from cells"; nucleus as control center.

Mitosis: nuclear division; chromosomes at mitosis; the sequence of stages: prophase, metaphase, anaphase, telophase, interphase; mitosis as a cellular device for the orderly separation of duplicate chromosomes; chromosome movements; transmission *vs.* duplication of chromosomes.

Diploidy: its origin in fertilization.

Haploidy: its origin in meiosis; where meiosis takes place; chromosome pairing at prophase I; segregation at anaphase I; the second meiotic division; the arithmetic of meiosis; the random assortment of chromosomes; the significance of mitosis and meiosis.

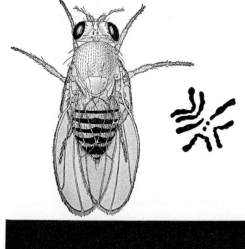

The development of the chromosome theory of heredity is one of the great achievements of twentieth-century science. The little fruit fly Drosophila (2 mm.), illustrated here with its eight chromosomes, has played a major role in the growth of genetics as a principal object of study. (Fruit fly after Sturtevant and Beadle; chromosomes after Dobzhansky; both from Srb and Owen, *General Genetics*, Freeman)

CHAPTER 12

The Chromosome Theory of Heredity

ORIGIN OF THE CHROMOSOME THEORY

"We hold these truths to be self-evident: that all men are created equal. . . ." Those stirring words are deeply familiar to every American. All men are equal before the law, and all are equal in dignity as human beings: that is what the writers of the Declaration of Independence meant. It is, however, one of the profound lessons of genetics that only identical twins are born equal biologically. Unless you are an identical twin (and only about 0.4 per cent of births are those of identical twins), you are not equal to anyone else on earth. No judgment is involved here as to who is better and who is worse, or as to whether "better" and "worse" have a valid meaning in this connection. Nevertheless, the fact remains that the mechanisms of heredity make it highly improbable that any two non-twins ever are truly equal in the sense of hav-

ing inherited just the same genes. And how fortunate that this is true! The interest of life, the texture of society, and the progress of evolution all are enhanced by the differences among us.

Centuries of human striving—political, moral, and physical—have gone into establishing the truth of the political equality embodied in the Declaration of Independence. There is an equally long history of human endeavor behind the truth of the biological inequality of man, even though the deliberately straightforward account of the physical basis of heredity that we developed in the last chapter may have left some impression that the problem was simple and straightforward.

In the last chapter we showed that heredity involves the transmission of controlling information, not only from generation to generation, but also from cell to cell. We showed that the controls were in the nucleus. Their physical basis is in linear "tapes" of information (the chromosomes) that were neatly copied and transmitted to new cells in orderly fashion like so many blueprints for the government of the cells' activities. The logical sequence we followed was dictated by our present understanding of the problem. We wish to emphasize now that the logical sequence bears little or no relation to the historical sequence of discovery and development of understanding. Cell division and the details of mitosis were studied well before there was rigorous proof that the nucleus was the cell's control center. Indeed, the facts of cell and nuclear division were being studied at the same time that many able students still argued for a kind of "spontaneous generation" called "free cell formation."

Whenever a great advance is made in science, the advance is in the form of a theory—a scheme of explanation and understanding in terms of which all the facts, previously scattered and "difficult," seem clearly and simply to fall into a pattern. T. H. Huxley is said to have remarked after reading Darwin's great book *The Origin of Species*, "Why didn't I think of it?" However, until a theory is found, the facts themselves are in no sense simple and clear; nor is the path to the theory simple and clear.

The historical development of a theory nearly always involves several distinct lines of investigation. In the development of *the chromosome theory of heredity* there were two distinct lines that ultimately fused. One of these we have looked at already, although not in an historical way: the study of the cell's visible structures and how they behave in cell reproduction. The other main line of inquiry sought to find general rules of inheritance by studying differences and similarities between parents and offspring. We may call this the direct study of heredity. This direct study of the regularities of heredity is very much older than the study of the cell. Democritus and Aristotle, among other ancients, had discussed the problem of heredity. Eighteenth- and nineteenth-century biologists were much preoccupied with the same problems before the cell theory gave biology its firm start around 1840, and long before the facts of the last chapter were discovered (1870 to 1900). We will shortly see that these two lines of study came to conclusions that supplemented and demanded each other. The theory that emerged from their fusion in 1902 was like the opening of a floodgate. It opened up a flood of biological investigation and new insight that is still at its height over fifty years later. This, as we argued in Chapter 2, is the character of all good theories; they not only explain old facts but also point the way to new knowledge.

Pre-Mendelian Ideas on Heredity

We may well ask the question, "If a theory, once discovered, is the main guide to inquiry and research after it is discovered, what guided inquiry before?" There are really two answers to this question.

First, much of the earlier inquiry was indeed in effect random, helter-skelter, and unguided. Consequently it produced relatively little but oddities such as the ideas about strange hybrids issuing from the mating of camels and leopards; or myths concerning the lingering effect of a first husband on the children a woman has by a later husband. Some other erroneous ideas more important for the history of the subject are discussed below.

However, there is a second answer to our question. Men are really never at a loss for some kind of scheme in terms of which they talk about their problems. The natural human tendency to seek order in the world they live in leads people to find analogies or models of some kind that offer a way of talking about things. There is no doubt that the search for analogies or models for comparison is a basic tool of human thought and the search for understanding. Somehow there is a trace of satisfaction derived from every comparison we make that reveals some similarities between the things compared. The search for analogies is essentially an attempt to find something familiar, something already known, a model for the "explanation" of the new and unfamiliar; and this search goes on continuously, sometimes consciously and often subconsciously.

It is not surprising that the most common source of analogies or models to which men have turned in the absence of exact theories is the realm most familiar to them: human nature and human society. Before the scientific development of the modern Western world the universal tendency was for men to "explain" nature by talking about it in the familiar terms of human attributes; the "forces of nature" took on the form of human will and motivations. The conscious attempt to avoid such analogies and to depersonalize our understanding and explanation of the nonhuman world is a real hallmark of the

Western scientific movement. But the influence of "human models" has nevertheless lingered on, often subconsciously. For instance, the cytologist Virchow was led to the most direct model human experience offered when he sought to understand how discrete cellular units work in subservience to the welfare of the whole organism: he regarded the organism as a "cell-state."

BLENDING INHERITANCE

It used to be believed that blood was particularly involved in inheritance. Even those of us who know better still speak of "blood lines," "bad blood," "blue-blooded," and the like. It was supposed that the blood of our ancestors mingled and was finally poured into us. According to that notion, your inheritance is a half-and-half blend of blood from your father and mother, and hence a quarter each from your grandparents, an eighth each from your great-grandparents, and so on.

This erroneous idea about heredity springs from two distinct sources. First, there is the notion that somehow "blood" is fundamental to life; therefore, it must be what we inherit. Second, the notion of blending which is involved fits not only the model of mixing bloods but also the intuitive but erroneous notion that all our ancestors must necessarily contribute their due share to our make-up. If we have a great man somewhere in our lineage it is nice to consider precisely how much he has contributed to our inheritance. The nearly universal tendency in human cultures to revere ancestors must have contributed to the plausibility of blending inheritance on the one hand—and on the other hand have received some justification from it.

We saw in the last chapter that it is chromosomes we inherit rather than blood; and the briefest consideration of the rules of chromosome inheritance reveals a fact that must be disquieting to people unduly concerned with pride in their ancestry. Families proud of their descent from some famous Revolutionary or Pilgrim ancestor have a good chance of lacking any chromosomes at all from that famous ancestor!

The familiar idea of "blending"—of mixing and getting intermediates as we do with paints —must have been at the root of those other quaint and amusing speculations about heredity that take the form of strange hybrids. A giraffe was supposed to have issued from the mating of camel and leopard—blending the leopard's spots and the camel's long neck (but not long enough!). Camels were indeed favorite and versatile hybridizers. One authority stated that an ostrich is a cross between a camel and a sparrow—a curious blend to say the least. Arabian scholars thought that sea cows were crosses between humans and fishes, and Greek mythology is full of hybrids half-human, half-animal. Many a visitor to the zoo still explains the queer animals as crosses between the most diverse parents.

Of course, as you already know, only animals of the same or very closely related species can cross and produce offspring. Even when the species are closely related, the offspring produced are usually not fertile: witness the mule. It is entirely impossible for animals as distinct as man and ape, cat and dog, or horse and cow (let alone camel and sparrow) to engender offspring.

THE INHERITANCE OF ACQUIRED CHARACTERISTICS

The persistence of other errors about heredity is as nothing compared with the persistence of the belief in inheritance of acquired characteristics. A man who exercised and developed large muscles would of course pass on his muscular development to his children. An animal that stretched its neck reaching for leaves would have offspring with longer necks than if he had been content to browse near the ground. Hence, in time, a giraffe.

In more modern times this theory has been especially in vogue in relation to problems of evolution. The belief in the inheritance of acquired characteristics has gone under the name of Lamarckism after Jean Baptiste de Lamarck, the French evolutionist of the late 1700's and early 1800's. However, the idea is at least 2000 years older than Lamarck. It was discussed by many Greek scholars, and its origin was independent from evolutionary thought. The idea doubtless arose because it has a common-sense plausibility about it, but for a notion to have "common-sense plausibility" it must be familiar in some form. A familiar analogy to the inheritance of acquired characteristics is not hard to find. The everyday experience of man has confronted him with the fact of inheritance of acquired characteristics in the social and legal realm. A man inherits his father's estate—what his father acquired by dint of work, good fortune, and, in his turn, inheritance. One generation inherits all the cultural advances and setbacks acquired by the last. Such social, legal, or cultural "Lamarckism" was doubtless the model initially predisposing human minds to such a view of biological heredity. The word "heredity" itself, which now has a strictly biological meaning, is a derivative of the original form "inheritance," which refers to the social and legal phenomenon. Nothing illustrates better than this example the dangers of the use of analogies.

The catch in the whole situation is that the mechanism of social or legal heredity is utterly different from the mechanism of biological heredity. The mechanism of biological heredity renders the inheritance of acquired characteristics impossible. The idea is historically important only because it was part and parcel of the first full and consistent theory of evolution—Lamarck's (see p. 442); and it is politically important only because the Communist Party professes it.[1]

PANGENESIS

Pangenesis, like the idea of the inheritance of acquired characteristics, which demands it, was in vogue in the latter nineteenth century before the discovery of the chromosome theory of heredity. Again, the Greeks, Democritus in particular, had discussed pangenesis in only slightly cruder form 2000 years earlier.

If a blacksmith's enlarged muscles, acquired by virtue of his work, are inherited by his son, there must be some mechanism whereby the condition of his muscles can be represented in what heredity transmits to his son.

[1] In 1948 the Party decided that all good communists must teach and say that acquired characteristics are inherited. More recently this political dogma seems to have stumbled against the cold biological facts. At any rate, there is evidence of a change in the Party's position.

Democritus spoke of representative particles, pangenes, coming from all parts of the bodily organization and entering the semen introduced into the female in copulation.[2]

In his later years Charles Darwin resorted to a theory of the inheritance of acquired characteristics, and to a revived form of Democritus's pangenesis. He spoke of "gemmules," representative particles again, entering the germinal material.

It has been fashionable in learned circles to heap endless blame on Aristotle for the confusion and myth in medieval biology; certainly much of later myth had its origin in his writings. But in a curious and somewhat ironical way it is also true that Aristotle had some remarkable biological insights, and among his other real achievements must be counted the rigorous demolition of the Democritean theory of pangenesis, as well as its Darwinian form 2000 years later. How, asks Aristotle, can we believe that the hereditary material consists of representative particles derived from all over the body when a man who has lost an arm nevertheless has a child with the usual complement of two? Where did the pangenes for the missing arm come from? His argument and his illustrations are more extensive, but this itself is final—for Democritus, for Darwin, and for all other versions of this same line of human thought.

The Aristotelian conclusion about heredity has an astonishingly modern ring to it: Aristotle concluded that what was inherited was a *potentiality to develop*.

WEISMANN: THE ONE-WAY RELATIONSHIP BETWEEN GERM CELLS AND SOMA

The advent of the cell theory in mid-nineteenth century brought with it the seeds [3] of many advances, including especially a clari-

[2] The lengths to which a speculative theorist may be driven in his search for facts supporting his theory—rather than facts critically testing it—is illustrated by one of the arguments Democritus offered in support of pangenesis. The intensity of orgasm, he claimed, was explained by the simultaneous rush of pangenes into the semen from all over the body.

[3] Notice again how models or analogies from the realm of practical everyday human experiences affect how we talk about other things. We use such a model when we say that further scientific advances grew from "seeds" in the form of the cell theory.

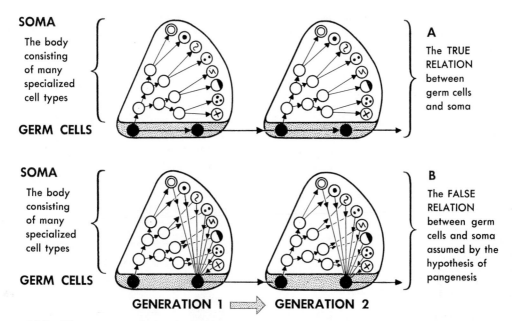

SOMA

The body consisting of many specialized cell types

GERM CELLS

SOMA

The body consisting of many specialized cell types

GERM CELLS

A

The TRUE RELATION between germ cells and soma

B

The FALSE RELATION between germ cells and soma assumed by the hypothesis of pangenesis

GENERATION 1 ⟹ GENERATION 2

12-1 The one-way relation between germ cells and the differentiated cells of the soma.

fication of ideas about heredity. We saw some detailed fruits of the cell theory in the last chapter. Once it became clear that all organisms are derived from single cells, an immense difficulty arose for all forms of pangenesis and associated ideas.

We may diagram the relations between the germ cells and the body cells as in Fig. 12-1. All the diverse body cells (muscle, nerve, bone, etc.) are descendants of the single zygote cell, as the arrows indicate. From which type of cell is the egg or sperm derived? It cannot be a descendant of all these differentiated types: a cell is a descendant of a single cell. Weismann provided the answer to this problem by pointing out that the germ cells of each generation were direct descendants through a lineage of unspecialized cells from the germ cells of the previous generation. That is, the specialized *body cells of each generation are related to germ cells in a one-way fashion: they are derived from germ cells but do not give rise to them.* This insight is a death blow to pangenesis in all its forms. The very essence of pangenesis is the basic assumption that the hereditary material transmitted from one generation to the next is derived from, and represents—like members of a parliament from various dis-

tricts—the various specialized regions of the "cell-state" that is the organism. As Fig. 12-1 indicates, the demand of pangenesis for the two-way relationship between soma (body) and germinal (or hereditary) material does not, in fact, exist.

The great clarification that Weismann's insight brings is due again to the study of the cell itself, and its behavior. Direct study of heredity—the study of resemblances between parent and offspring—was the other main line of investigation leading to the great theoretical advances of 1902. To this we now return by going directly to the discoveries of Gregor Mendel in 1866.

Mendel's Principles of Heredity

Gregor Mendel (1822-1884) was a monk in the Augustinian monastery of Brünn, Austria (now Brno, Czechoslovakia). He taught natural science in the monastery school and became interested in problems of heredity. He devised ingenious and careful experimental techniques, and by crossing different strains of garden peas he discovered the fundamental principles of *genetics*, the science of heredity.

Mendel's results were published in 1866, but they were long neglected by other students.

Mendel himself did not follow up his discoveries, and their importance was not recognized by other biologists for thirty-five years. Finally, around 1900, three other experimenters independently rediscovered the Mendelian principles: Correns in Germany, De Vries in the Netherlands, and Von Tschermak in Austria. This is a striking example of a phenomenon mentioned in Chapter 2. A theory, even though it is correct, may not be accepted and bear fruit until the general progress of science creates an atmosphere receptive to it.

MENDEL'S FIRST EXPERIMENTAL RESULTS: A SINGLE CHARACTER DIFFERENCE

Mendel chose the garden pea for his work. Among other advantages, the pea offers an abundance of variant types which can be crossed or hybridized. Many garden varieties differ in a clean-cut, either-or way. Some have

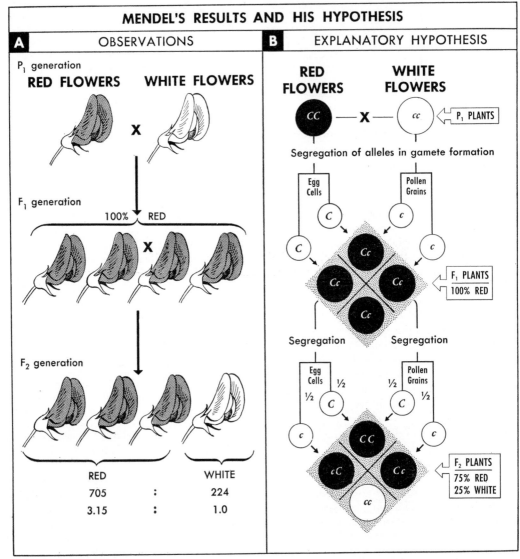

12-2 The results of Mendel's experiments in crossing red- and white-flowered peas and his interpretation of the results.

colored flowers, others white; some have yellow seeds, others green; some are tall, others dwarf; some have flowers clustered at the apex of the stem, and others spread out. The most advantageous feature is that these differences in character are clean-cut. Mendel seems to have been aware that this was an advantage; he sensed that he was correctly attempting to study and analyze the simplest possible kind of heredity. This was indeed the case, and a major reason for the success of his work. The complexity involved in the inheritance of most commonly studied human features had been a block to their successful analysis.

Mendel's first experiments involved crosses between varieties that differed in only one visible respect. He crossed tall with dwarf plants; colored flowers with white ones; and so on. He had seven pairs of alternative characteristics for study, and in all seven cases he found the same result as he did, for example, in the cross between red-flowered and white-flowered types.[4] When red-flowered were crossed with white-flowered plants, the hybrid offspring were all red-flowered. This result was obtained whether the red form was used as the male (pollen) parent or as the female (ovule) parent. However, when two hybrid reds were crossed, the offspring surprisingly contained both reds and whites in a ratio of about three reds to every white

[4] The flower color is actually a violet-red, simplified here as red.

(Fig. 12-2). These results can be summarized schematically as follows:

P_1 plants Red-flowered x White-flowered
F_1 plants   100%   Red-flowered x Red-flowered
                                    ↓
F_2 plants   Red   :   White

Mendel's actual results in F_2:

Number of plants	705	:	224
Percentage	75.9%	:	24.1%
Ratio	**3.15**	:	**1.0**

The symbol P_1 designates the initial parents; F_1 is the name applied to the first hybrid (or "filial") generation; and F_2 is the name given to the second generation of hybrids, the generation arising from the crossing of F_1 plants.

The two important results are: (1) the F_1 consists entirely of plants resembling only one of the parents; and (2) the F_2 consists of plants resembling both parents in the P_1 generation. The parental characteristic missing in F_1 appears in about one-fourth of the individuals in F_2. Table 12-1 lists the actual counts Mendel obtained from his other experiments. In every instance the same general result was found: F_1 was all of one type, and F_2 contained both, the type missing in F_1 being 25 per cent of the F_2. The generality of the result indicates immediately that something important is involved. Mendel perceived this and proceeded to seek an explanation, which he found and then tested.

TABLE 12-1 *Mendel's results in crosses involving seven pairs of alternative characteristics*

Characters	F_1	F_2: Number of plants			F_2: Percentage	
		DOMINANT *	RECESSIVE	TOTAL	DOMINANT	RECESSIVE
Seeds: round *vs.* wrinkled	All round	5,474	1,850	7,324	74.74	25.26
Seeds: yellow *vs.* green	All yellow	6,022	2,001	8,023	75.06	24.94
Flowers: red *vs.* white	All red	705	224	929	75.90	24.10
Flowers: axial *vs.* terminal†	All axial	651	207	858	75.87	24.13
Pods: inflated *vs.* constricted	All inflated	882	299	1,181	74.68	25.32
Pods: green *vs.* yellow	All green	428	152	580	73.79	26.21
Stem length: tall *vs.* dwarf	All tall	787	277	1,064	73.96	26.04
Totals		14,949	5010	19,959	74.90	25.10

* "Dominant" means the character found in *all* F_1 plants.
† Axial = flowers spread all along the stem (axis) of the plant; terminal = flowers clustered at the end of the stem.

MENDEL'S HYPOTHESIS OF PAIRED FACTORS: SEGREGATION AND DOMINANCE

The most significant feature of Mendel's results is the reappearance of the white-flowered plants in the F_2 generation. It follows that, although the F_1 plant does not itself show any white flowers, it nevertheless must possess some hereditary factor for them because it transmits such a factor to at least $\frac{1}{4}$ of its offspring (indeed, we shall see that it transmits the factor to $\frac{1}{2}$ its offspring). This line of argument *suggests* two other conclusions. First, each plant carries at least two hereditary factors for each flower color; and, second, the factor for white is completely dominated by the factor for red when both are present in the same plant. Hence arise the terms *dominant* (red in this case) and *recessive* (white in this case) to describe the relationship between the two alternative forms of the hereditary factor concerned.

Mendel saw that he could explain his results if he made the following assumptions:

1. There is in each plant a pair of hereditary factors controlling flower color.

2. The two factors in each pair were derived from the plants' parents—one member of the pair from each parent.

3. *The two factors in each pair separate, or **segregate**, in the formation of germ cells, each germ cell receiving only one factor.*

4. The factors for red flowers and white flowers are alternative forms of the same factor, the red being dominant over the white.

These assumptions and the way they explain Mendel's results are summarized in Fig. 12-2.

For discussion and understanding of this scheme, and for the whole science of genetics which is founded on it, we need to define several terms:

1. The paired hereditary factors are called *genes*.[5]

2. The alternative forms of the same gene are called *alleles*. Thus the genes for red flowers and for white flowers are *alleles* of each other. Again, the gene for plant size

occurs in two *allelic* forms; there is an allele for tallness and an allele for dwarfness. Tallness, however, is not an allele of redness. (The original term, also proposed after Mendel, was *allelomorphs*, "alternative forms," now universally abbreviated to "alleles.")

3. The red allele is *dominant* over the *recessive* white allele. The alleles of a gene are symbolized by the same single letters or brief combinations of letters. The dominant allele is written as a capital letter (C = red allele), and the recessive allele is written as a small letter (c = white allele).

4. When both members of the pair of alleles in a plant are the same (for example, cc or CC), the plant is said to be a *homozygote* ("like joined"). When the two alleles differ (for example, Cc), the plant is said to be a *heterozygote* ("differently joined").[6]

5. Although all the plants in the first hybrid generation (F_1) are red-flowered and indistinguishable in appearance from the red-flowered plants in the P_1 generation, they nevertheless have a different hereditary constitution (see scheme in Fig. 12-2B). We will constantly have to make this distinction between appearance and hereditary constitution. In doing so it is useful to speak of the *phenotype* ("visible type") and *genotype* ("hereditary type") of the organism.

Now we can follow Mendel's scheme (Fig. 12-2B).

In the P_1 generation both red-flowered plants and those with white flowers are homozygotes. The genotype of the red-flowered plant is CC, and the genotype of the white-flowered plant is cc. When they produce gametes the genes segregate, and the red-flowered plant produces only C gametes; the white-flowered plant produces only c gametes. Union of these in the zygotes formed at fertilization can produce only an F_1 plant that is heterozygous with a Cc genotype (we can equally well write cC; the order of the symbols is meaningless). The phenotype of the plant is, however, red-flowered and indistinguishable from the parent red.

The F_2 arises from crossing two F_1 reds, each genotypically Cc. What gametes will

[5] This term was introduced long after Mendel's analysis.

[6] The adjectives are "homozygous" and "heterozygous."

There are two kinds of gametes from the female parent ($\frac{1}{2}$ *are C;* $\frac{1}{2}$ *are c*)	*and they may be fertilized by*	*either one of two kinds of gametes from the male parent* ($\frac{1}{2}$ *are C;* $\frac{1}{2}$ *are c*)	*to give the following zygotes in* F_2
1. C	x	C	CC ($\frac{1}{4}$ of total possible)
2. C	x	c	$\left.\begin{matrix}Cc\\cC\end{matrix}\right\}$ ($\frac{1}{2}$ of total possible)
3. c	x	C	
4. c	x	c	cc ($\frac{1}{4}$ of total possible)

these F_1 plants produce? In both parents the Cc pair segregates so that each parent produces two kinds of gametes, C and c. Mendel *assumed*,[7] moreover, that these two kinds of gametes (C and c) must be produced in equal numbers by each parent. Thus, if the F_1 plant used as male parent produces 1000 pollen grains, 500 will be C and 500 will be c.

Only one kind of fertilization was possible in the formation of F_1 plants—the union of C and c, giving Cc as the F_1 genotype. However, in the mating of the two F_1 plants, more than one kind of fertilization is possible. In fact there are four types, and all four are equally probable, or frequent:

Figure 12-2 shows a checkerboard system making it easy to visualize fertilizations listed in the chart. The second and third types of fertilization in the chart produce F_2 plants with the genotypes Cc and cC: these two heterozygotes are identical. Thus we conclude that, on the basis of the Mendelian scheme, the F_2 generation should contain three kinds of genotypes in the following proportion:

$$
\begin{matrix}
CC & : & Cc & : & cc \\
\frac{1}{4} & & \frac{1}{2} & & \frac{1}{4} & \text{genotypic ratios} \\
& \frac{3}{4} & & & \frac{1}{4} & \text{phenotypic ratios} \\
\text{Red} & & & \text{White} &
\end{matrix}
$$

Because the CC homozygotes and Cc heterozygotes are phenotypically the same, only two classes of phenotypes will appear in F_2, and they will tend to appear in the ratio of $\frac{3}{4}$ to $\frac{1}{4}$. The class of plants that are cc homozygotes are those with white flowers that Mendel had found were missing in F_1. They constitute about $\frac{1}{4}$ of the F_2.

MENDEL'S TESTS OF THE HYPOTHESIS

Let us, in spite of our present greater knowledge, assume ourselves to be in Men-

[7] His assumption proved to be correct (see p. 289).

del's position for a moment. We have no knowledge of chromosomes and their role in heredity. Indeed, we have no knowledge at all of the real physical basis of heredity. What we have done is to perform some crosses with garden plants of differing flower color and have obtained some quantitative results that are summarized in Fig. 12-2B. Then to explain these results we have *created a hypothesis* which assumes the existence of hereditary factors which we will call genes, although at this stage we have no knowledge of what they are physically, or how they are related to cell structure. We did not observe the hypothesis; it was a pure invention, as given in Fig. 12-2B.

The fact that the hypothesis will explain the facts is not in itself a sufficient basis to accept it as true; there may be other hypotheses that could explain the facts equally well. What we now seek, therefore, is some further basis in fact for the acceptance or rejection of our scheme: we must *test the hypothesis.*

Chapter 2 showed how testability distinguishes a good from a bad hypothesis; Mendel's hypothesis is good because it *is* testable. The test takes the form of finding out whether or not certain predictions arising out of the scheme hold good. We must look, in the theory, for predictions as to the outcome of new crosses yet to be performed.

The most obvious tests of the scheme hinge around the fact that red-flowered plants are of two kinds genotypically. The red in the P_1 generation is, on hypothesis, homozygous CC and when crossed with a white-flowered plant (cc) can produce only red-flowered offspring that are Cc heterozygotes. But the superficially similar mating of F_1 red x white will have a very different outcome. The prediction (see Fig. 12-3) is that the progeny in this case will be $\frac{1}{2}$ red and $\frac{1}{2}$ white

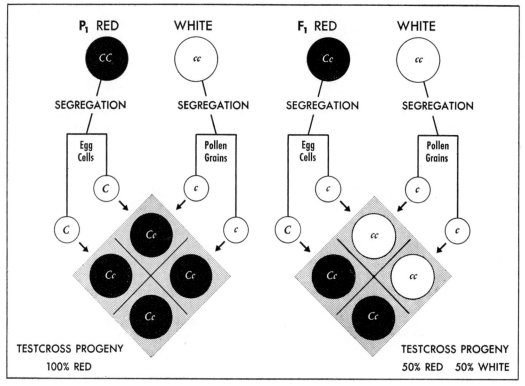

12-3 A testcross that distinguishes the genotypes of P_1 and F_1 red-flowered peas. P_1—red crossed with white—gives a progeny that is 100 per cent red. F_1—red crossed with white—gives a progeny that is 50 per cent red and 50 per cent white.

because, while the white parent produces only c gametes, the red parent produces $\frac{1}{2}$ its gametes C and $\frac{1}{2}$ c, so that Cc and cc fertilizations will be equally frequent (see Fig. 12-3). Mendel performed such a cross and obtained 166 plants, of which 85 were red-flowered and 81 white.

It is of great importance to notice that the prediction was not just a *qualitative* one. The scheme predicted not only that red-flowered plants would occur in this cross of F_1 red x white plants, but also that they would tend toward a specific *quantitative* relationship—$\frac{1}{2}$ red : $\frac{1}{2}$ white. When specific quantitative forecasts are fulfilled in this way we have very good reason to believe in the validity of the hypothesis that produced them. It is guiding us successfully to new knowledge.

It is clear from these and other experiments that the Mendelian hypothesis is formally or mathematically valid. Mendel did not know at this stage what the paired factors

or genes were, but it was clear that they did exist, and in pairs that segregate when gametes are formed.

TWO CHARACTER DIFFERENCES: INDEPENDENT SEGREGATION

Having understood the rules governing the hereditary transmission of genes controlling one character difference (e.g., flower color) Mendel proceeded to a more complex case. He followed the inheritance of two distinct character differences simultaneously: seed shape and seed color. Both of these character differences he had studied separately, finding them to obey the same rules as flower color (Table 12-1).

We will see in a later chapter (15, p. 373) that seeds contain young or embryonic plants in which root, stem, and two embryonic leaves (cotyledons) can be distinguished. The peas in a pod thus contain young offspring of the parent plants.

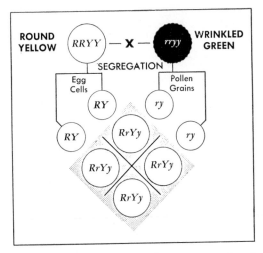

12-4 All F_1 plants from the cross round yellow x wrinkled green have the genotype $RrYy$.

The two seed characters—color and shape—whose inheritance we will now follow both relate to the embryonic leaves or cotyledons. First, the cotyledons may be either yellow (controlled by the dominant gene Y) or green (y, recessive). Second, they may be fully swollen, making the whole pea seed round (controlled by the dominant gene R) or shrunken, making the seed wrinkled (r, recessive). For each pair of characters (yellow *vs.* green, round *vs.* wrinkled) there are, as with flower color, three possible genotypes:

	Homozygous dominant	*Hetero- zygote*	*Homozygous recessive*
Seed shape	RR	Rr	rr
	Round phenotype	Wrinkled phenotype	
Seed color	YY	Yy	yy
	Yellow phenotype	Green phenotype	

Mendel began by crossing plants raised from round, yellow seeds ($RRYY$) with plants raised from wrinkled, green seeds ($rryy$). In meiosis, when gametes are formed, each pair of alleles (for example, RR and YY) segregates independently of each other. Thus the round yellow plants ($RRYY$) produce only RY gametes, never RR or YY: *Each pair of alleles is always represented in the gametes by one of its members.* The wrinkled green plants ($rryy$) produce only ry gametes. The F_1 consists of seeds that are round and

yellow, with the genotype $RrYy$ (Fig. 12-4); the F_1 is heterozygous for both pairs of alleles, and is called *dihybrid*. (Why?)

What are we to expect when two F_1 plants are crossed to produce an F_2? We know from the study of each character separately that in the formation of gametes R will segregate from r, and Y will segregate from y. However, we are left with an uncertainty as to whether there will be two or four kinds of gametes. Thus:

P_1	plants	$RRYY$	$rryy$
P_1	gametes	RY x	ry
F_1	plants	$RrYy$	

What kinds of gametes?
There are two possibilities
either (*a*)   or   (*b*)

F_1	gametes	RY, ry	RY, ry, Ry, rY

When the F_1, $RrYy$, was formed the gametes from the parental plants were of two types, RY and ry. The two dominant alleles were associated in one gamete, and the two recessives in the other. Are they necessarily always associated? If so, we expect only two classes of gametes to be produced by the F_1: RY and ry. These two types of gametes (*a* above) are said to contain *parental* combinations of alleles. (Why?) However, if the Rr pair of alleles segregates independently of the Yy pair, and the original combinations are not necessarily maintained, then two new kinds of gametes would be produced by F_1 (Ry and rY) in addition to the two original ones (*b* above). Ry and rY are said to be *recombination* types of gametes. (Why?)

It is easy to find out which of these two possibilities (list *a* or *b*) is in fact realized because they will lead to different F_2 generations, as indicated in Fig. 12-5: (1) If the only combinations produced by the gametes are the *parental* ones—RY and ry—there will be only three classes of genotypes in F_2 and two classes of phenotypes: round yellow ¾ and wrinkled green ¼ (Fig. 12-5*A*). (2) If the two *recombination* types of gametes are produced in addition to the *parental* types, and all four occur in equal frequencies, there will be nine classes of

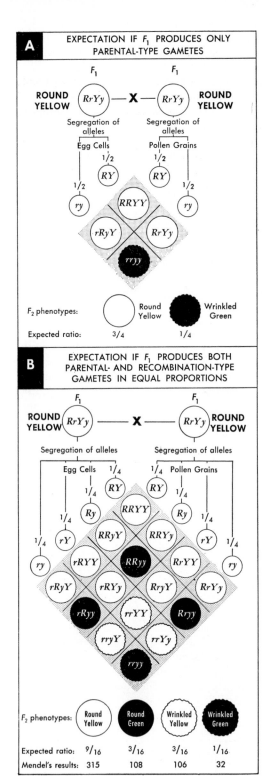

A
EXPECTATION IF F₁ PRODUCES ONLY
PARENTAL-TYPE GAMETES

F₁   F₁

ROUND
YELLOW (RrYy) — X — (RrYy) ROUND
YELLOW

Segregation of   Segregation of
alleles   alleles

Egg Cells   Pollen Grains
1/2   1/2
(RY)   (RY)

1/2   1/2
(ry)   RRYY   (ry)

rRyY   RrYy

rryy

F₂ phenotypes: Round   Wrinkled
           Yellow   Green

Expected ratio: 3/4   1/4

B
EXPECTATION IF F₁ PRODUCES BOTH
PARENTAL- AND RECOMBINATION-TYPE
GAMETES IN EQUAL PROPORTIONS

F₁   F₁

ROUND (RrYy) — X — (RrYy) ROUND
YELLOW   YELLOW

Segregation of alleles   Segregation of alleles

Egg Cells   1/4   1/4   Pollen Grains
1/4 (RY)   (RY) 1/4
   RRYY
1/4 (Ry)   (Ry) 1/4
   RRyY   RRYy
1/4 (rY)   (rY) 1/4
rRYY   RRyy   RrYY
(ry)   (ry)
rRyY   rRYy   RryY   RrYy
   rRyy   rrYY   Rryy
     rryY   rrYy
       rryy

F₂ phenotypes: Round   Round   Wrinkled   Wrinkled
           Yellow   Green   Yellow   Green

Expected ratio: 9/16   3/16   3/16   1/16
Mendel's results: 315   108   106   32

12-5 Alternative expectations concerning the cross *RrYy* x *RrYy*, and the fit of Mendel's actual results to the second alternative.

genotypes in F_2 and four classes of phenotypes. The four phenotypes and their expected frequencies are round yellow $\frac{9}{16}$: round green $\frac{3}{16}$: wrinkled yellow $\frac{3}{16}$: wrinkled green $\frac{1}{16}$ (Fig. 12-5*B*).

Figure 12-5*B* gives results from Mendel's own experiment. It is clear that the four kinds of genotypes are produced; the parental combination *RY* and *ry* can be recombined in the F_1 to yield gametes that are *Ry* and *rY*. Moreover, all four are produced in equal frequency, as indicated by the close agreement between expected and observed proportions.

Mendel's demonstration of the independence of the *Rr* and *Yy* pairs of alleles in their segregation is often referred to as the "law of independent assortment." We shall shortly see that it is not a universal law. Exceptions to the so-called law of independent assortment were soon found in the outbursts of genetic work that followed the rediscovery of Mendel's principles in 1900, and it is by understanding the causes both of the rule and of its exceptions (which outnumber the "rule") that still further advances are opened up.

The Physical Basis of Heredity

THE CHROMOSOME THEORY

The reader, armed with the facts given in the last chapter, will long ago have perceived the significance of the main Mendelian results: the paired nature of the genes, one derived from each parent, and their segregation in gamete formation. Clearly these characteristics of genes must be related to the like characteristics of chromosomes discussed in Chapter 11. We have deliberately avoided using knowledge of chromosome behavior in the discussion of Mendel's results to emphasize the brilliance and adequacy of his analysis; Mendel was actually ignorant of chromosome behavior when (1865) he performed and analyzed his experiments. He lived until 1882, by which time much, but not all, of our basic knowledge of chromosomes had been discovered. Mendel himself did not perceive the relation; at least he did not publish such insights. As a matter of fact, in his later years he was drawn more and more away from science into monastery affairs, being embroiled in some rather bitter wrangles within the church.

On the other hand, the people who worked out the behavior of the chromosomes overlooked the significance of Mendel's work. It was not until after De Vries, Correns, and Von Tschermak had rediscovered the Mendelian phenomena themselves that the biological world could put the two lines of study together.

Sutton's formulation of the chromosome theory. In 1902 an American cytologist named Sutton[8] saw the implications of Mendel's analysis in relation to the behavior of chromosomes. Sutton maintained that the hereditary factors—or genes—that Mendel had studied are carried on the chromosomes, or part of the chromosomes. *The theory that genes are chromosome parts explains: (1) why they occur in pairs (because chromosomes do); (2) why the two members of a pair are derived one from each parent (chromosomes are so derived); and (3) why genes segregate at meiosis (because chromosomes do so).* Other features of Mendel's results are immediately explainable by the assumption that the genes are carried on the chromosomes.

Chromosomal basis of segregation: the 1:1 segregation ratio. Mendel assumed that the Cc genes in his F_1 (red-flowered) heterozygotes segregated to produce two types of gametes, C and c; and he *further assumed* that the two types were produced in equal numbers (cf. Fig. 12-2B). The chromo-

8 Two other men, Boveri and De Vries, perceived the same significance independently, but Sutton's is the first and fullest analysis.

12-6 The chromosomal basis of the 1:1 segregation ratio. *A.* The origin of the F_1 plant and its nucleus, which carries the genes C and c on its large B chromosomes. *B.* Meiosis in the F_1 plant, leading to the production of c and C gametes in equal numbers.

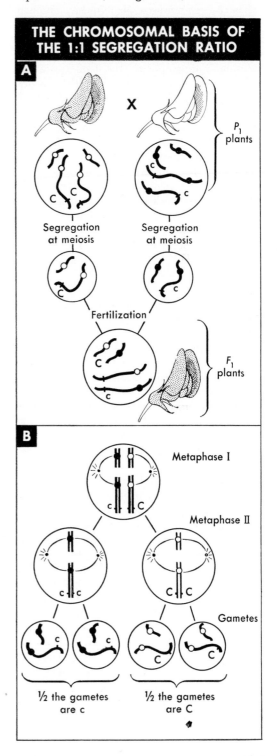

THE CHROMOSOMAL BASIS OF THE 1:1 SEGREGATION RATIO

A

P_1 plants

Segregation at meiosis

Segregation at meiosis

Fertilization

F_1 plants

B

Metaphase I

Metaphase II

Gametes

½ the gametes are c

½ the gametes are C

some theory shows his assumption to be correct and explains it.

The F_1 red-flowered plant must contain a pair of chromosomes carrying the alleles C and c. Figure 12-6A shows schematically the origin of the F_1 red and its chromosome constitution. For simplicity, the figure uses the same hypothetical nucleus on which earlier discussions (p. 277) were based. At metaphase of meiosis I in this F_1 plant, the equator of the spindle carries the chromosomes indicated in Fig. 12-6B. The A pair of homologous chromosomes carries C and c. Each member of the chromosome pair has duplicated, and the two members are going to different poles. Each telophase I nucleus contains an A chromosome carrying either C or c. The two strands of each A chromosome are separated at meiosis II, so eventually each cell that undergoes meiosis produces *precisely* two gametes with C and two gametes with c. If the pea plant produces 4000 pollen grains, these must have arisen from 1000 diploid cells in which meiosis occurred. Each of the 1000 cells yielded four gametes, two of which are C and two of which are c. No matter how many gametes are produced, the segregation ratio will always be 1:1.

Chromosomal basis of independent segregation.

Sutton pointed out that the chromosome theory could explain another feature of the Mendelian results—the independent assortment (or independent segregation) which Mendel had discovered in his experiment on the inheritance of two characters. Figure 12-7 shows how independent segregation occurs if the two pairs of genes (Rr and Yy) are carried on different chromosomes. Suppose that the Yy alleles are carried on the larger (B) pair of chromosomes, and that Rr is carried on the smaller (A) pair of chromosomes. The way in which the large pair of chromosomes is oriented on the equator of the spindle is independent of the way the small pair orients. Thus the arrangements given in Fig. 12-7A and Fig. 12-7B are equally likely, and, accordingly, the allele Y is just as likely to enter the same nucleus with r as it is with R. Four types of gametes (YR, yr, Yr, and rR) are produced with equal frequency (check with Fig. 12-5B).

Statistical nature of Mendelian heredity.

The ratios of different genotypes and phenotypes occurring in F_2 generations are often referred to as "Mendelian ratios." For instance, when two F_1 red-flowered plants are crossed, the Mendelian ratios expected in F_2 are as follows: (1) phenotypes, ¾ red : ¼ white; (2) genotypes, ¼ CC : ½ Cc : ¼ cc (see p. 285). In actual experiments the ratios are realized only as statistical approximations. Why is this so? Why did Mendel, for example, obtain 75.9 per cent red, 24.1 per cent white, and not exactly 75 per cent and 25 per cent respectively? The answer to this question emerges from understanding that any *sample* is only an *approximate representation* of the population of events or things from which it is drawn.

Consider, first, what happens in spinning a coin. We expect heads half the time and tails half the time. If we were to throw a coin a million times the ratios of heads and tails would be very close to 500,000 heads : 500,000 tails (½ : ½). But if we throw it only four times there is a good chance (actually 1 in 16) that we might get four heads instead of the expected ratio—2 heads : 2 tails. The more times you spin the coin, the better is your chance of getting exactly ½ : ½. To put it another way, the larger the sample you take from a conceivably immense "population" of throws, the more nearly will the ratio of heads to tails approximate ½ : ½.

When a geneticist crosses two F_1 red-flowered pea plants, he obtains a relatively small number (say, 100) of F_2 plants. The 100 ovules and 100 pollen grains that gave rise to the F_2 plants were only a sample of the entire population of gametes produced by the F_1 plants. Like a small sample of coin throws, the sample of gametes only ap-

12-7 The chromosomal basis of independent assortment. The figure diagrams the chromosomes at meiosis in the dihybrid plants $YyRr$, showing the location of the Yy genes on the large B pair of chromosomes and the Rr genes on the smaller A pair. A and B are equally probable ways in which the chromosomes can orient themselves at metaphase I (cf. Fig. 11-11). The consequence is that the four kinds of gametes YR, yr, Yr, and yR are produced in equal numbers.

CHROMOSOMAL BASIS OF INDEPENDENT ASSORTMENT

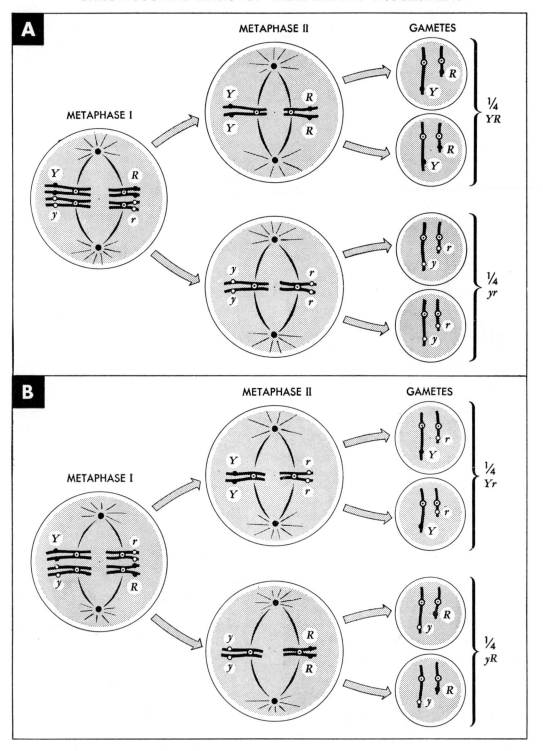

proximates the exact ratio of $\frac{1}{2}\,C:\frac{1}{2}\,c$ which applies to the gamete population as a whole. Consequently, the sample of zygotes obtained merely approximates the $\frac{1}{4}\,CC:\frac{1}{2}\,Cc:\frac{1}{4}\,cc$ ratio to be expected were an infinitely large progeny raised.

TESTS OF THE CHROMOSOME THEORY

With the announcement of the chromosome theory of heredity in 1902, the science of genetics in its modern form was born. It was *born as a theory* which, unlike all other theories about heredity, was precise and quantitative and had its foundations in cellular structures (chromosomes) whose behavior and properties were open to direct observation and analysis. The earlier theory of pangenes (which nobody could see) offered virtually no specific predictions [9] by which its merits could be judged. On the other hand, the chromosome theory offered abundant predictions, the testing of which led to the rapid growth of genetics as an exact science. From 1906 onward, much of the experimental work in genetics was carried out using the common fruit fly *Drosophila melanogaster*, which is familiar to everyone as the small yellowish fly that hovers around garbage cans and fruit in the later summer and fall.

Drosophila melanogaster.[10] Someone should erect a much larger-than-life monument to this tiny (2 millimeter) insect. It is an ideal laboratory animal and has done more than any other to give us our knowledge of genetics. It is big enough to work with, but small enough to raise by the hundreds in milk bottles or similar containers without crowding a laboratory. It breeds readily in captivity, it is prolific, and it has short generations (as little as two weeks). All these advantages make genetical experimentation relatively easy, quick, and cheap. The experiments that took Mendel seven years with peas

[9] Except that which Aristotle had seen and pounced upon 2000 years ago.

[10] Rapid progress in genetics began in 1906, when T. H. Morgan (1866-1945) started experiments with **Drosophila** at Columbia University. Morgan got the idea of using **Drosophila** from another pioneer geneticist, W. E. Castle (1867-), who had been conducting other sorts of experiments with fruit flies at Harvard since 1901. **Drosophila melanogaster** (a female) and its chromosomes are figured in our chapter opening.

and required a large garden can be repeated with *Drosophila* in a few months in a dozen or so bottles tucked away on a shelf. *Drosophila* has two other advantages not realized when experiments with it were begun. It has a small number of chromosomes (four pairs in the most used species), and its salivary glands contain chromosomes enormously larger than those of other parts or of most other organisms. The small number of chromosomes simplifies the study of the grouping of genes in chromosomes. The giant chromosomes greatly aid in correlating heredity with the anatomy of the chromosomes.

Genetical experiments have been carried out with many organisms besides *Drosophila*, from bacteria and protists to corn, pine trees, chicks, and mice. Many interesting peculiarities of heredity occur in one species or another. Thousands of experiments on hundreds of species have, nevertheless, confirmed that the *principles* of heredity are basically the same in all organisms. The principles learned most fully from *Drosophila* apply in the widest way to all living things.

Sex and the chromosome theory. *Sex Determination.* In brief, Sutton's theory said simply that the coincidence in, or correlation between, the behavior of Mendel's *inferred* (but not seen) genes and the behavior of the *visible* chromosomes is so great that we must conclude that the genes are in the chromosomes. Clearly a first step in developing this theory must be the attempt to associate a specific gene and a specific chromosome; we must try to find where particular genes are located in the visible chromosomes.

For this task it would be convenient if there were in the nucleus one pair of chromosomes different in appearance and behavior from all the others. If its behavior were sufficiently aberrant, but understood, we ought to be able to predict how the genes it carries will be inherited. There actually is such a pair of special chromosomes in the nucleus of nearly all higher animals—the sex chromosomes. It is no coincidence that the history of modern genetics has been focused strongly on the behavior of the sex chromosomes in our fruit fly *Drosophila*.

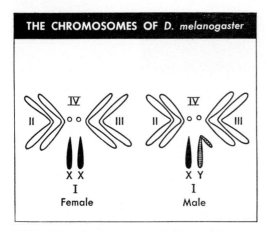

THE CHROMOSOMES OF D. melanogaster

12-8 **The chromosomes of *Drosophila melanogaster*.**

Figure 12-8 shows the chromosomes seen at metaphase of mitosis in a male and in a female *Drosophila*. There are only four pairs of chromosomes. One pair is dotlike, and very small; it is called the IVth pair. There are two larger V-shaped pairs with the centromere in the middle of the chromosome; these are called the IInd and IIIrd pairs. The IInd, IIIrd, and IVth pairs of chromosomes are collectively designated *autosomes* in distinction to the Ist pair, which are called *sex chromosomes*. The sex chromosomes are different in the two sexes. In the female they are both rod-shaped, with the centromere near the end. In the male there is one rod-shaped chromosome, but its partner (unique to the male) is J-shaped, the centromere being at the bend. The sex chromosomes in the female are said to consist of two X-chromosomes; in the male there is one X- and the special Y-chromosome, which is the J-shaped member. It is obvious that, while the female will produce only one kind of gamete so far as the sex chromosomes are concerned, the male will produce two kinds. All the females' eggs will carry an X-chromosome, but of the sperms produced by the male, ½ will carry an X-chromosome, the other ½ Y.

Figure 12-9 indicates the outcome of this at fertilization. One-half the fertilizations yield zygotes with two X-chromosomes; the other half yield zygotes with one X- and a Y-chromosome. The former become females, and the

latter males. Thus sex determination, which like other aspects of heredity had been discussed in vague and mythical terms for over 2000 years, is cleared up immediately by the chromosome theory. In most cases, *sex is determined at the moment of fertilization, and the decisive factor is whether the sperm carries an X- or a Y-chromosome.*

Offhand, it looks as if X-chromosomes carried genes for femaleness and Y-chromosomes for maleness, but, as often happens in biology, things turn out not to be so simple. The Y-chromosome probably has nothing to do with sex determination. At least, there is no evidence that it does in man, and it surely does not in some other animals. In some, indeed, there is no Y-chromosome (Fig. 12-10). It has been established in some animals, and probably is a valid generalization, that the development of sex is determined by interaction between genes on the X-chromosomes and genes on various autosomes. As

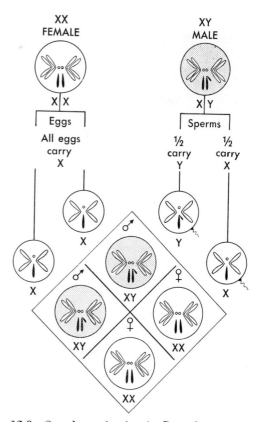

12-9 **Sex determination in *D. melanogaster*.**

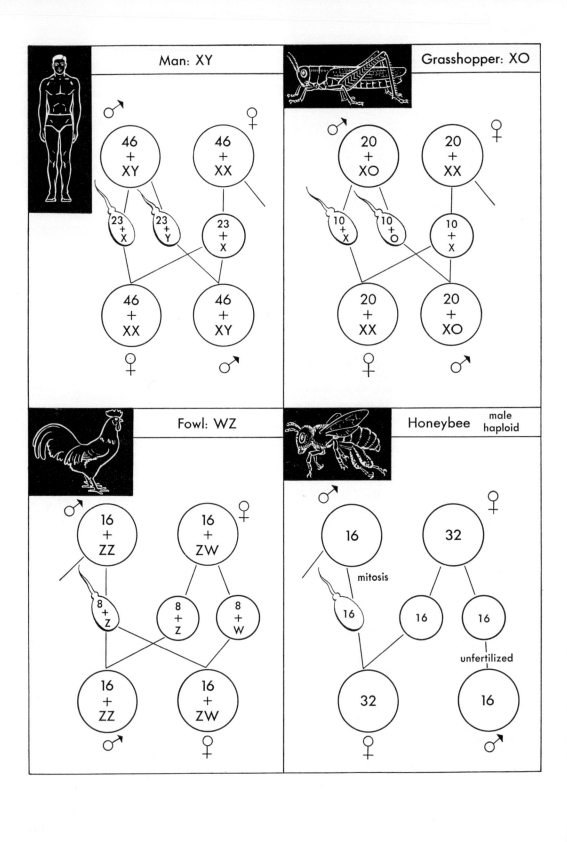

usual, the best evidence comes from *Drosophila.*

In experiments with *Drosophila* it has been possible to obtain individual flies differing in the ratio of autosomes to X-chromosomes. Table 12-2 illustrates the different ratios obtained, and shows how the scale of X/A ratios from 0.3 to 1.5 is a scale of increasing femaleness. The normal male has an X/A ratio of 0.5 (1 X-chromosome/2 sets of autosomes); the normal female has an X/A ratio of 1.0 (2 X-chromosomes/2 sets of autosomes). Evidently the genes of the autosomes tend to produce males, and genes concentrated on the X-chromosomes interact with those, producing females when they overbalance the autosomal genes.

Sex Linkage. The sex chromosomes are the special pair the theorist wants, and the pair the early workers seized upon for particular study. Among the many characters in *Drosophila* which Morgan and his students first studied were many, like that of vestigial wings, which followed precisely the simple pattern of inheritance Mendel had discovered in peas. There were other characters, like white eye color, however, which showed a strikingly aberrant pattern of inheritance which suggested that these characters were controlled by genes on the sex chromosome.

First let us note the inheritance of vestigial *versus* normal wings in the fly. As in Mendel's pea experiments, it does not matter which

---

12-10 Types of sex determination. In man ($2n = 48$), as in *Drosophila,* the male is the *heterogametic* sex; that is, the male produces two kinds of gametes (X and Y). The female is *homogametic;* all her gametes are of one kind (X). In the grasshopper ($2n = 22$ in the female, 21 in the male) and many other insects, the male is heterogametic again, but the two kinds of gametes are X and no X, rather than X and Y. In the fowl ($2n = 18$), as in all birds and also butterflies and moths, the female is *heterogametic.* The sex chromosomes are designated Z and W to distinguish female heterogamety from male heterogamety (XY). In some butterflies and moths the condition analogous to XO has evolved: some have ZO females. The honeybee ($2n = 32$), and many other members of the insect order Hymenoptera (bees, wasps, ants), have a remarkable sex-determining mechanism: unfertilized eggs develop into (haploid) males; fertilized eggs develop into (diploid) females. (See Fig. 15-27.)

TABLE 12-2

Number of X-chromosomes	Sets of autosomes (A) (three in a set)	Ratio X/A	Sex phenotype
3	2	1.5	Superfemale *
2	2	1.0	Normal female
2	3	0.67	Intersex
1	2	0.5	Normal male
1	3	0.33	Supermale *

* Both supermales and superfemales are weaker flies than their normal counterparts. Indeed, there is nothing "super" about them except that their chromosomal balance exceeds that characteristic of their sex.

---

parent—male or female—carries a particular character. Whether the vestigial-wing character is in the male or female parent, the F_1 is always all normal-winged, and the F_2 contains three normals to one vestigial. Moreover, the 3:1 ratio applies to both the male and female members of F_2.

The situation is very different in the case of white eye color versus red eye color. Figure 12-11 shows that the constitution of the F_1 is strikingly different, depending on whether the white-eyed parent is father or mother. And the F_2 differs in both cases. Hopelessly aberrant as this inheritance looks at first sight, it is exactly what we would expect if the genes for white and red eye color were carried by the X-chromosome, and if the Y-chromosome were an empty shell of a chromosome carrying no genes at all.

Figure 12-11 shows how the results are explained by these assumptions. Note especially Fig. 12-11A, which explains the cross between the white female and the red male. All the male offspring are white-eyed because a male's X-chromosome is always derived from its mother; from its father a male receives only the Y-chromosome, which evidently is empty of genes, at least as far as this character is concerned. On the other hand, every female always receives one X from its father and one from its mother. Since red (R) is dominant over white (r), all daughters *in this cross* must be red-eyed because the father was red-eyed; all sons must be white-eyed because both the mother's X-chromosomes carry the recessive gene r. Follow the segregation and fertilizations involved in both figures to see

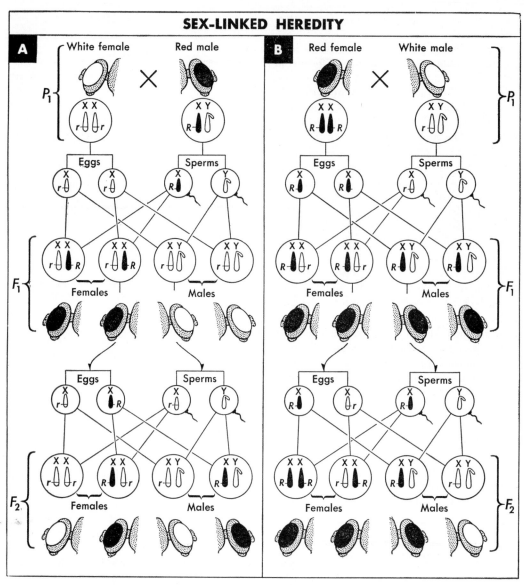

12-11 Sex-linked heredity.

how the assumption that the genes are on the X-chromosome explains all the results.

The conclusion that the Y-chromosome is just an empty shell carrying no genes fits in with observation of other insects, such as the grasshopper, where it has been dispensed with altogether. Here the female has two X-chromosomes again, and the male simply carries one. As in the XY system the male produces two kinds of gametes, but the two kinds are X and no-X rather than X and Y (see Fig. 12-10).

Nondisjunction (or failure to segregate): proof of the chromosome theory. The assumption that the gene for white eye color is on the X-chromosome explains all the unusual patterns of eye color inheritance in such a precise way that we have the strongest grounds for believing the assumption to be true. We have correlated the behavior not just of genes and chromosomes in general, but of a particular gene and a particular chromosome. This particular gene—for eye color—was studied intensively by the early American geneticists. One of them, C. B. Bridges (1889-1938), discovered a further anomaly in its inheritance. The discovery led to final and convincing proof that the gene was carried from cell to cell, from generation to generation, by the X-chromosome in the fashion we have outlined above.

Figure 12-11 showed that, when a white-eyed female is crossed with a red-eyed male, all the daughters will be red (heterozygotes *Rr*) and all the sons will be white (*r* plus the "empty" Y). Bridges discovered that *very* rarely (about once in three thousand) a daughter was produced that had white eyes. This is clearly not as it should be. The normal mechanism demands that the daughter must have one X-chromosome carrying the dominant *R* from the father. Similarly, it was noted that red-eyed sons were produced with about the same frequency. These again were anomalous: they should have received their X-chromosome from their mothers (*rr*), and thus have been white-eyed.

Once a general theory has proved itself valid and useful, as the chromosome theory had up to this point, anomalies like the exceptional daughters (red-eyed) and exceptional sons (white-eyed) in Bridges' experiment become of the greatest importance. The maxim in science, "Treasure your exceptions," implies that, when apparent exceptions become explainable by general theory, the theory becomes the better established and the more advanced.

Bridges perceived that the exceptional offspring could be explained by the hypothesis that the two X-chromosomes in the white-eyed mother sometimes failed to segregate (or "disjoin") during the first meiotic division. Figure 12-12 contrasts Bridges' hypothesis with the normal course of events in the first meiotic division. In the exceptional case envisaged by Bridges the X-chromosomes do not segregate at anaphase, but go instead to the same pole of the spindle. This leads to the production of eggs that either lack an X-chromosome altogether or else have two X-chromosomes (both of which carry the gene *r*). The figure also shows the four kinds of zygotes produced when the exceptional eggs are fertilized by the red-eyed father.

Two of these fertilizations we may ignore. (1) The zygote that gets only a Y dies because at least one X is essential for development; it carries indispensable parts of the total blueprint. (2) The zygote with three X-chromosomes turns out to be female, and for the moment we need only note that she is red-eyed like her normal sisters.

It is the other two fertilizations which are important for us now: *one will lead to a red-eyed son and the other to a white-eyed daughter*. The red-eyed son will arise from the egg that received no X-chromosome from the mother; it received an X-chromosome (and therefore an *R* gene) from the father. XO, like XY, leads to a male. The real difference between male and female is not the presence of the Y in the male, but rather the fact that the male has only one X. XO is the same as XY as far as sex determination is concerned: each has one X; the female condition is determined by two X's. Similarly, the presence of the Y will not cause the XXY fly to be male; the fly will be female because it has two X's, and it will be white-eyed because both X's came from the white-eyed mother.

Figure 12-12 summarizes Bridges' guess as to how a breakdown in the usual mechanism causes the appearance of the exceptional offspring. This "guess," based on the general theory of chromosomal inheritance, assumes very great importance indeed because it yields two highly specific *testable* predictions. The testable predictions are: (1) the exceptional *white-eyed daughters will carry a Y-chromosome*, unlike all their much commoner sisters. They are white and not red because they received the father's Y-chromosome, not his *R*-carrying X-chromosome; (2) the exceptional *red-eyed sons will entirely lack a Y-chromosome*, unlike all their much commoner brothers. They received their father's X-chromosome (with its *R* gene), not his Y. From their mother they received no sex chromosome at all.

Bridges tested and confirmed these predictions by looking through the microscope at the chromosomes of the exceptional offspring. His analysis of "nondisjunction" of X-chromosomes (1913-18) is one of the great landmarks in the history of genetics.

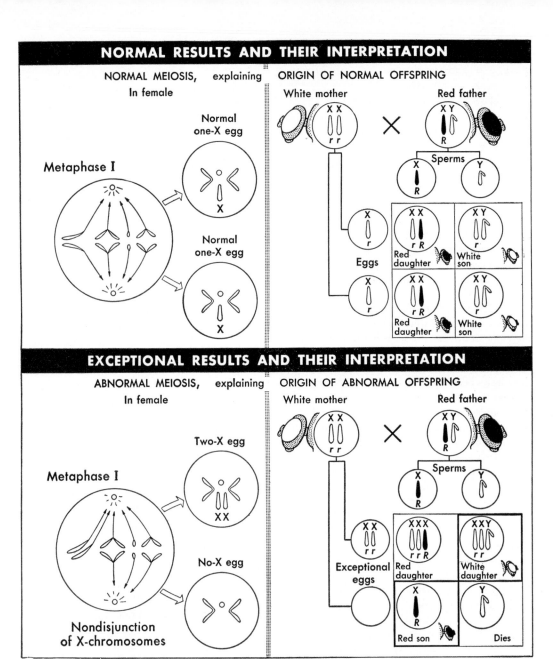

12-12 Nondisjunction of the _X_ chromosomes in _D. melanogaster._ The upper left figure shows the normal course of meiosis I leading to eggs that have one X-chromosome each. The upper right figure summarizes the normal genetical results of a cross between a white female and a red male. The usual form of the genetic checkerboard has been modified to include a summary of the chromosome, as well as the gene, content of each fertilized egg. The lower left figure shows the abnormal form of meiosis I, which Bridges guessed was the cause of the exceptional offspring he had found. On the right the genetical results _predicted_ by this hypothesis are given in the form of a genetic checkerboard. The two squares in heavy outline explain the exceptional offspring and lead to the crucial prediction which made this study of Bridges' a landmark in genetics. What is the prediction? For diagrammatic simplicity we have represented the oöcyte (at metaphase I) as giving rise to two eggs. In reality, as we detail later (p. 338), an oöcyte gives rise to only one egg. This does not, however, affect the implications of our diagram. Thus, while in the lower half of the figure, we show the abnormal oöcyte giving rise to _both_ a two-X egg and a no-X egg, in nature it gives rise to _either_ one or the other. But since a female lays large numbers of eggs she will produce in the long run _both_ the two-X and the no-X eggs as the result of nondisjunction.

Gynandromorphs. Gynandromorphs literally, "female-male forms") are rare monsters, part female and part male. Gynandromorphs had been known long before the development of the general chromosome theory of heredity and its derivative, the special theory of sex determination by sex chromosomes. Clearly, whatever theory of sex determination ultimately proved valid, it would have to account for these exceptional forms.

The sex-chromosome theory explains the origin of gynandromorphs. Figure 12-13 indicates how an X-chromosome can be lost off the spindle at mitosis in an early cell division in the embryonic life of a female. All

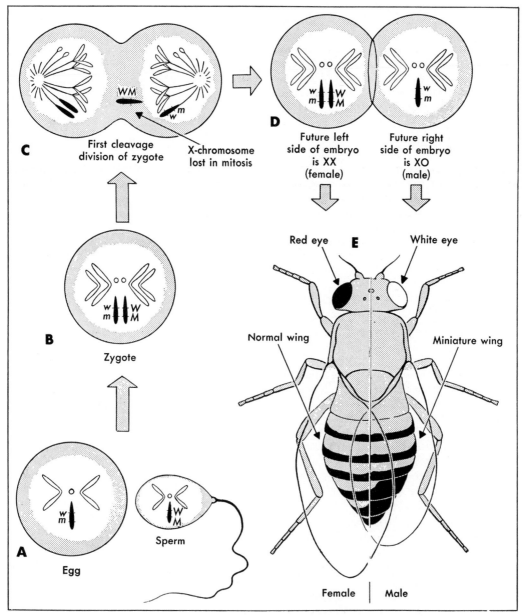

12-13 The chromosomal basis of the origin of gynandromorphs.

the tissues that later derive from the right-hand cell in the diagram will carry only one X-chromosome. Consequently the mature fly is male on the right side and female on the left. In the case illustrated in Fig. 12-13 the fly has a white eye and miniature wing on the right (male) side of the body. Here again is precisely what is expected if the chromosome theory is correct and gynandromorphs originate because of the loss of an X-chromosome. The zygote (Fig. 12-13) from which this fly arose was heterozygous for the genes controlling eye color and wing length, both of which are on the X-chromosome. Moreover, the recessive genes for miniature (*vs.* long) wing and white (*vs.* red) eye color are together on one of the X-chromosomes. The fly would normally be long-winged and red-eyed because of the dominance of these characters. This is true of the left side of the body, where both X-chromosomes are retained, causing femaleness. The X-chromosome lost early in the life of the fly was in this case the X that carried the dominants, long and red. The single surviving X-chromosome causes maleness, and miniature wing and white eye on the right side.

LINKAGE AND CROSSING OVER

There remains one striking prediction of the chromosome theory of heredity that may have occurred to the reader long before now: the independent segregation that Mendel discovered when he followed the inheritance of two pairs of genes simultaneously must be the exception rather than the rule. Sutton explained independent segregation by assuming that the two gene pairs must be on separate chromosomes; the physical basis of genic segregation is chromosome segregation. In *Drosophila* there are only four pairs of chromosomes. It follows that independent segregation of genes could only be a valid generalization for *Drosophila* if there were only four genes in its entire hereditary blueprint—one gene pair on each chromosome pair.

We must surely anticipate far more than four gene pairs (or four pieces of information) in the entire hereditary blueprint of an organism as complex as *Drosophila*. And we must therefore anticipate that many gene

pairs will not segregate independently at meiosis because they will be linked together, carried by the same chromosome. Such a linkage—or nonindependence—between genes was soon discovered in the early growth of genetics after 1900. It was found, in fact, that in *Drosophila* all the genes that were discovered (several hundred) fell into four groups called *linkage groups*. All the genes within a linkage group tend to segregate as a unit. The fact that there are four such groups in *Drosophila* is obviously significant: there are four pairs of chromosomes. One of the four groups is very small and clearly belongs to the dotlike IVth pair of chromosomes. Another group is sex-linked and belongs, as we have seen, to the X-chromosomes. The other two groups are very large and are associated with the two big V-shaped pairs of chromosomes (pairs II and III, Fig. 12-8).

Let us take an example of linkage between two genes in corn, which is one of the plants best known genetically. In corn there are two genes, each with two alleles, which affect the color and texture of kernels as follows:

	Alleles	Effect on kernel
1st gene pair	$\begin{cases} C \\ c \end{cases}$	Colored Colorless
2nd gene pair	$\begin{cases} S \\ s \end{cases}$	Smooth (or full) Shrunken

We begin with the following cross:

P generation	$CCSS$ x $ccss$
P gametes	$CS \downarrow cs$
F_1 generation	$CcSs$

If these two genes follow Mendel's rule of independent assortment (p. 286) we would anticipate: (1) that the F_1 would produce the following four types of gametes: CS, cs, Cs, cS; and (2) that they would be produced in equal numbers, each type constituting $\frac{1}{4}$ of the total "pool" of gametes produced. Furthermore, if all four classes of gametes were produced in these frequencies we should expect the F_2 generation (F_1 x $F_1 \rightarrow F_2$) to contain $\frac{9}{16}$ colored smooth kernels, $\frac{3}{16}$ colored shrunken, $\frac{3}{16}$ colorless smooth, and $\frac{1}{16}$ colorless and shrunken. (Why? Cf. Fig. 12-5B.) We would test whether or not the F_1 did produce all four kinds of gametes expected on the basis of independent segregation by making such an F_2. There is, however, a more direct and generally useful way—known appropriately as a *testcross* [11]—of finding out what kinds of gametes the F_1 produces. It is performed by crossing the F_1 ($CcSs$) to a plant that is homozygous for both recessive alleles ($ccss$). The double recessive ($ccss$) plant is known as the tester; clearly it can produce only cs gametes.

It will be noticed from Table 12-3 that, of course, the phenotypes of the testcross offspring indicate immediately what kinds of gametes came from the "tested" plant ($CcSs$) because the tested plant alone contributed dominant alleles. Scoring the frequency of phenotypes in testcross progeny amounts to scoring the kinds and frequencies of gametes produced by the tested plant ($CcSs$ in the present case). It follows that if the Cc and Ss gene pairs segregate independently we can expect that all four possible phenotypes in the testcross progeny will occur in equal numbers, $\frac{1}{4}$ colored smooth: $\frac{1}{4}$ colored shrunken: $\frac{1}{4}$

colorless smooth: $\frac{1}{4}$ colorless shrunken (row 4 in Table 12-3: no linkage). If, however, the two kinds of genes are on the same chromosome, and cannot segregate independently, we can expect the tested plant to produce only CS and cs gametes in equal numbers, leading to a testcross progeny containing $\frac{1}{2}$ colored smooth: $\frac{1}{2}$ colorless shrunken (row 5 in Table 12-3: complete linkage).

Row 6 in Table 12-3 shows what kinds of testcross progeny were *actually* obtained in this experiment.[12] It is clear that the two genes are not independent in their segregation; the ratio among CS, cs, Cs, and cS gametes is far from $\frac{1}{4}:\frac{1}{4}:\frac{1}{4}:\frac{1}{4}$. The ratio is much closer to $\frac{1}{2}\,CS:\frac{1}{2}\,cs$, which is what we would expect if linkage were complete. We must be on the right track in explaining the results obtained by attributing them to linkage; the commonest allele combinations produced by the $CcSs$ plant are the combinations (CS and cs) which existed in the gametes

[11] Compare our earlier use of a simple testcross (Fig. 12-3).

[12] Carried out in 1922 at Cornell Agricultural Experiment Station by C. B. Hutchinson.

TABLE 12-3 *A testcross to determine what kinds and proportions of gametes the F_1 plant ($CcSs$) produces*

	F_1 plant $CcSs$	x	Tester plant $ccss$		
	Possible F_1 gametes				
(1) Genotypes of F_1 gametes	$C\,S$	cs	Cs	cS	
(2) Genotypes of F_1 testcross progeny	$CcSs$	$ccss$	$Ccss$	$ccsS$	cs There is *only one possible* kind of gamete from the tester plant
(3) Phenotypes of testcross progeny	CS colored smooth	cs colorless shrunken	Cs colored shrunken	cS colorless smooth	
(4) Ratios indicating *no linkage* between C and S	25%	25%	25%	25%	50% recombination gametes
(5) Ratios indicating *complete linkage* between C and S	50%	50%	0	0	0% recombination gametes
(6) Observed ratios indicating *incomplete linkage* between C and S	[4030] 48.25%	[4030] 48.25%	[150] 1.75%	[150] 1.75%	3.5% recombination gametes

that produced the plant. These combinations are appropriately called the "parental" combinations; the new types (*cS* and *Cs*) are called the "recombinations." It is clear, however, that we cannot ignore the few recombination gametes: our notions about linkage so far demand that we anticipate progeny in the ratios given *either* by row 4 *or* by row 5. We cannot have our cake and eat it, so to speak: either the genes are linked or they are not.

This is another excellent example of how important exceptions are in scientific progress (recall the other which was important in this chapter). "Exceptions" in science do not create a dilemma; they create—as one great student has said—an opportunity. By focusing attention on the exceptions in the present case—the recombination gametes—genetics made one of its most significant advances.

A close study of the behavior of chromosomes in the prophase of the first meiotic division reveals details that explain the appearance of a small number of recombination gametes. When the homologous chromosomes, such as those carrying *CS* and *cs* in our tested plant, pair up in meiosis, it can be seen that the two homologous partners often undergo an exchange of parts. This exchange of chromosome parts between homologous chromosomes at meiosis is called *crossing over*. The process is diagrammed in Fig. 12-14, where the *C* and *S* genes (and their alleles *c* and *s*) are placed on one pair of homologous chromosomes. We have used again, for diagrammatic purposes, our simplified nucleus with only two chromosome pairs. Actually in corn there are ten pairs. The genes for seed color and texture are placed on the B-chromosomes. *C* and *S* are on the B^f chromosome that came from the female parent (*CCSS*). Both chromosomes received from the male parent (A^m and B^m) are drawn in black to contrast with those (A^f and B^f) from the female parent.

In Fig. 12-14*A* the exchange, or *crossover*, has taken place *between* the genes *C* and *S*. Notice that the diagram implies a fact the discovery of which is one of the greatest achievements of genetics since 1900: the genes (such as *C* and *S*) have a definite and fixed place, or *locus*, where they occur on the

chromosome. The crossover involves only two of the four strands. It arises because the B^m and B^f strands broke at strictly homologous points; when the broken ends reunited they did so in such a way that the B^f strand joined with the B^m strand. The figure shows the consequence of this: ½ of the four gametes produced contain B-chromosomes that are a mixture of B^m and B^f parts, and are the recombination types (*Cs* and *cS*) we had to explain.

In the particular meiosis shown in Fig. 12-14*A*, the crossover occurred between *C* and *S*. It does not always occur in this region of the chromosome, however. Sometimes it will occur outside the region bounded by *C* and *S*, and when this happens no recombination gametes for those genes will be formed (Fig. 12-14*B*). A moment's thought shows that, *once we have the data given in row 6 of Table 12-3, we actually know how often a crossover occurs between the genes C and S*. Altogether, there were 8067 parental combination gametes produced by the *CcSs* plant; and there were 301 recombination gametes. Let us round these numbers out to 8060 (96.5 per cent) and 300 (3.5 per cent). All told, we have 8360 gametes derived from 2090 cells by meiosis (2090 × 4 = 8360). Remember that in every cell in which a crossover occurs between *C* and *S* half the gametes will be crossovers and half will not. It follows that a crossover occurred between *C* and *S* in only 7 per cent of all cells undergoing meiosis.

What is the significance of the fact that a crossover occurred between *C* and *S* in only 7 per cent of all cells that underwent meiosis in the corn plant? Why is it 7 per cent and not, for example, 20 per cent? The answer to this question was perceived by Morgan and his collaborators at Columbia University between 1910 and 1915. The development and use of their answer form one of the most exciting chapters in the history of genetics. They provide us with a tool for making maps of chromosomes and pinpointing on the map the position of individual genes.

Their answer was as follows: Each chromosome is a long thread on which the genes are located at fixed places in a definite sequence.

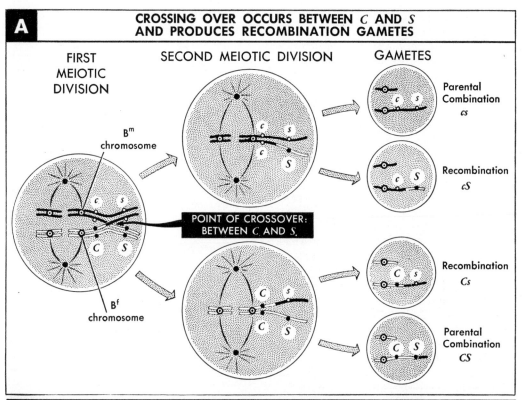

A — CROSSING OVER OCCURS BETWEEN *C* AND *S* AND PRODUCES RECOMBINATION GAMETES

FIRST MEIOTIC DIVISION

SECOND MEIOTIC DIVISION

GAMETES

B^m chromosome

B^f chromosome

POINT OF CROSSOVER: BETWEEN *C* AND *S*.

Parental Combination *cs*

Recombination *cS*

Recombination *Cs*

Parental Combination *CS*

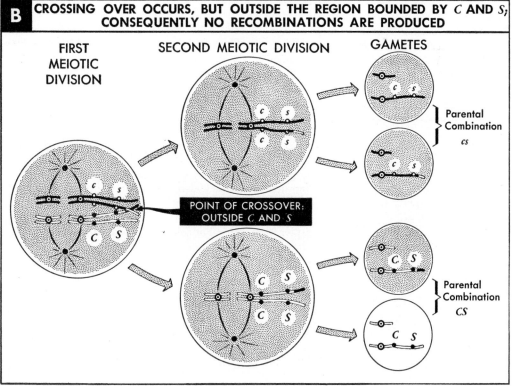

B — CROSSING OVER OCCURS, BUT OUTSIDE THE REGION BOUNDED BY *C* AND *S;* CONSEQUENTLY NO RECOMBINATIONS ARE PRODUCED

FIRST MEIOTIC DIVISION

SECOND MEIOTIC DIVISION

GAMETES

POINT OF CROSSOVER: OUTSIDE *C* AND *S*

Parental Combination *cs*

Parental Combination *CS*

12-14   The chromosomal events involved in crossing over.

The frequency of crossing over between two genes is approximately proportional to the distance between them. Thus, if genes are arranged in linear order on a chromosome as follows:

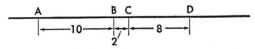

the frequency of crossing over between *A* and *B* (10 per cent) is greater than between *B* and *C* (2 per cent), which are closer together. By measuring crossover frequencies between genes, we can obtain a measure not only of their relative spacing on the chromosome but of the sequence, or order, in which they are arranged. This is done as follows. Suppose we study another gene, *E*, which is on the same chromosome as *A*, *B*, *C*, and *D*. First we measure the frequency of crossing over between *D* and *E*. It turns out to be 6 per cent. Where does *E* lie? It could be in either of two places:

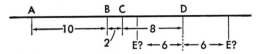

To settle the issue we measure the frequency of crossing over between *C* and *E*. It proves to be 2 per cent. We now know the following map is correct:

Where would *E* lie if the *C-E* value had been 14 per cent?

Many of the hundreds of genes so far discovered in *Drosophila* have been mapped in this way. Maps showing the location of many of these genes are given in Fig. 12-15. A start has even been made in mapping human genes, although only the barest of starts. With his long generations and aversion to controlled breeding, man is the worst of all animals for genetical experiments. What little we know about human genes is of course not due to experimentation but to the fact that some genes with known effects can be counted in populations, and to pedigrees of families in

which there are known alleles, usually causing hereditary defects.

Quantitative Inheritance

THE THEORY OF MULTIPLE FACTORS

The new science of genetics, which Mendel founded and later workers developed as the chromosome theory, is based on the assumption of distinct genes arranged in linear file on the chromosome. The success of genetical analysis, from Mendel onward, has been dependent on the distinctness of the gene. The gene's transmission from one generation to the next can be followed as *the transmission of a distinct particle*. Genetics, like physics and chemistry, owes its precision and quantitative nature largely to its particulate—or "atomic"—foundation. For, in a sense, the gene is an atom of heredity.

During the first decades of this century an important class of genetical phenomena seemed intractable to the new theoretical scheme. Mendelian experimentation has been based almost entirely on characters in which there are only a few easily distinguishable alternatives. A flower is red or white; a seed is full or shrunken; a chicken is black, blue, or spotty white. It is, however, clear that many of the characteristics of organisms are not like that. Instead of falling into a few sharply distinct classes, they have a long range of intergrading conditions. Men are not either tall or short, either black or white. Cows do not produce either much or little milk. Field mice are not either pale or dark. Ears of corn are not either small or large. In all these examples and indeed in a majority of the characters of plants and animals there is ingrading between extremes. Individuals cannot be classified simply as one thing or another but can only be placed somewhere along a continuous scale.

The widespread occurrence of continuous, quantitative variation was a serious problem of genetics. It seemed at first that the Mendelian principles do not apply to such characteristics. If that were true, a great and important part of heredity would remain unexplained and the Mendelian principles would have decidedly limited value. It was, however,

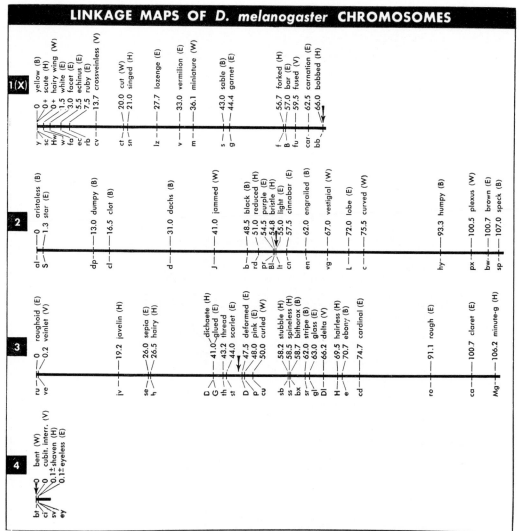

12-15 Linkage maps of *D. melanogaster* chromosomes. The map is to be read by turning the page on its side. The chromosomes are numbered 1 through 4, corresponding with the usage of Fig. 12-8: chromosome 1 is the *X*-chromosome; 2 and 3 are the large V-shaped autosomes, and 4 is the small dot-shaped chromosome. On the map of each chromosome given here, the centromere is marked by an arrow. The descriptive name of each gene (e.g., "bent") is given to the right of its position, and the standard symbol for the gene (e.g., "bt") is given to the left. The capital letters in parentheses following the name designate the part of the fly most affected by the gene: *W* = wing, *V* = veins of wing, *H* = hairs, *E* = eyes, *B* = body. On each map one gene is taken as an arbitrary starting point; its "map distance" is taken as zero. The positions of the other genes are then mapped in relation to this. The number given for each gene (e.g., 13.0 for "dumpy" on the chromosome 2 map) is the standard "map distance" for that gene; it is discovered experimentally through a study of crossing over. The map distance for "dumpy" implies that there is essentially 13 per cent crossing over between "aristaless" and "dumpy"; there is 3.5 per cent crossing over between "dumpy" and "clot."

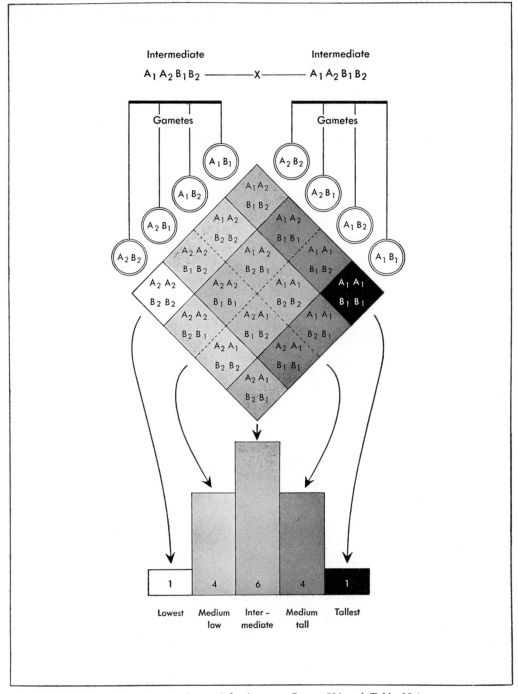

12-16 Multiple-factor inheritance. See p. 304 and Table 12-4.

TABLE 12-4 F_2 progeny from the cross $A_1A_2B_1B_2$ x $A_1A_2B_1B_2$

Genotypes	Expected ratio	Phenotypes	Expected ratio
$A_1A_1B_1B_1$	1	Tallest	1
$A_1A_1B_1B_2$	2 ⎫	Medium tall	4
$A_1A_2B_1B_1$	2 ⎭		
$A_1A_1B_2B_2$	1 ⎫		
$A_1A_2B_1B_2$	4 ⎬	Intermediate	6
$A_2A_2B_1B_1$	1 ⎭		
$A_1A_2B_2B_2$	2 ⎫	Medium low	4
$A_2A_2B_1B_2$	2 ⎭		
$A_2A_2B_2B_2$	1	Lowest	1

possible to frame and test a hypothesis that would explain control of continuous variation by genes inherited in accordance with the Mendelian principles. The hypothesis is that (apparently) continuous variation is controlled by numerous different genes, the effects of which add up *without distinct dominance*. This is a reasonable hypothesis because it is clearly established in simpler examples that two or more genes can affect one character and that gene effects can add up without dominance. Let us see how the hypothesis would explain continuous variation.

Suppose a character such as height in a plant were effected by only two genes, A and B, each with two alleles, A_1 and A_2; B_1 and B_2. Suppose A_1 and B_1 make for taller, and A_2 and B_2 for lower, height. Then the tallest plants would have the genotype $A_1A_1B_1B_1$, and the lowest would have the genotype $A_2A_2B_2B_2$. If these two were used as parents, all the offspring in F_1 would have the genotype $A_1A_2B_1B_2$. Since we have postulated that no dominance is involved, these offspring with half tall and half low alleles would be intermediate in height. Now suppose the intermediate F_1 is interbred. The checkerboard (Fig. 12-16) predicts that five height classes would appear in F_2 in the proportions indicated in Table 12-4.

If tallest and lowest were crossed as parents, and if, instead of just two genes, a great many were involved, the hypothesis would predict that:

F_1 would be intermediate between the parents, with few size classes, and no individuals as tall or as low as the extreme parents.

F_2 would have many size classes, so close together as to intergrade in practice.

The extreme size classes of F_2 would be about equal to the tallest and lowest parents.

There would be very few individuals in the extreme size classes of F_2, and increasing numbers of individuals in classes nearer intermediate size.

Do you see how these predictions follow by extension from the simple two-gene situation? These predictions can be checked experimentally. The results in Table 12-5 were obtained by E. M. East (1879-1938) in an experiment now classical. Corn with short and long ears was used for the parents.

The predictions from the hypothesis are well confirmed. Many similar tests have been made, and other sorts of tests have been devised and carried out. They leave little doubt that the hypothesis is correct and that continuous variation is due to *multiple factors*, which are genes inherited according to Mendelian principles (Fig. 12-17).

There is another interesting agreement with the theory of multiple factors. Continuous

TABLE 12-5   *The inheritance of ear size in corn*

Length of ears in centimeters	Numbers of individuals		
	P_1	F_1	F_2
21	2	—	1
20	7	—	2
19	10	—	1
18	15	—	12
17	26	—	11
16	15	—	10
15	12	4	13
14	11	9	21
13	3	17	27
12	—	14	33
11	—	12	33
10	—	12	33
9	—	1	17
8	8	—	5
7	24	—	2
6	21	—	—
5	4	—	—

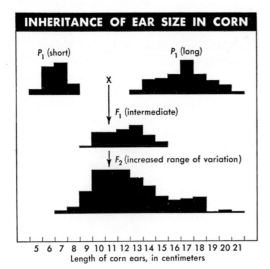

INHERITANCE OF EAR SIZE IN CORN

P_1 (short)

P_1 (long)

X

F_1 (intermediate)

F_2 (increased range of variation)

5 6 7 8 9 10 11 12 13 14 15 16 17 18 19 20 21
Length of corn ears, in centimeters

12-17 The inheritance of the ear size in corn.
Based on the data of Table 12-5, from E. M. East's classical experiment.

variation in natural populations almost always has the sort of distribution seen in F_2 of experiments like that of East. Most individuals are near the intermediate or average condition, and the number of individuals becomes smaller the farther they are from the average. This is one of the most important generalizations about variation in nature (Chapter 17). It is explained by the theory of multiple factors.[13]

Chapter Summary

The chromosome theory of heredity: two lines of investigation leading to it and fused by it; discovery of the theory opened up the flood of work that is modern genetics.

[13] As an exercise explain the following facts: The offspring of a Negro without white ancestors and a white without Negro ancestors are always intermediate in skin color, with little variation. The offspring of couples of mixed

Pre-Mendelian ideas on heredity: their derivation from analogies with human nature and human affairs; blending inheritance, related to the idea of blood as vehicle of heredity; inheritance of acquired characters, an ancient idea derived from legal and cultural inheritance; pangenesis, and its dismissal by Aristotle and by Weismann, who showed the one-way relationship between germ line and soma.

Mendel's principles of heredity (1866): results of a single character cross; Mendel's hypothesis of paired factors to explain his results; his tests of the hypothesis; the results and interpretation of a two-character cross: independent segregation (or assortment).

The physical basis of heredity: Sutton's (1902) formulation of the chromosome theory: genes as parts of chromosomes; the chromosomal basis of the 1:1 segregation ratio, of independent assortment, and of the statistical nature of Mendelian heredity.

Tests of the chromosome theory: the role of *Drosophila melanogaster* in the history of genetics; sex linkage; nondisjunction; gynandromorphs.

Linkage and crossing over:
Linkage groups; their number equal to the number of chromosome pairs.
Crossing over, and its basis in chromosome behavior; crossover maps.

Quantitative inheritance: an early difficulty of the Mendelian theory; explained by the theory of multiple factors; illustrated by East's experiments with ear size in corn.

Negro and white ancestry and of intermediate ("mulatto") color also tend to be intermediate in color more often than not, but they vary greatly, all the way from pure black to pure white.

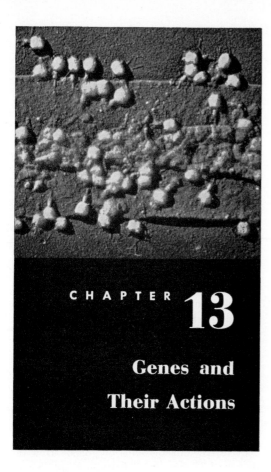

What is a gene? How does it act to control the life of the cell? Partial answers to these questions have come from many experiments, including studies on the heredity of viruses. This is a photograph ($\times 36,000$) of viruses attached to a bacterial cell they are about to parasitize.
(Photo by E. Kellenberger, University of Geneva)

CHAPTER 13

Genes and Their Actions

The Inherited Message in Living Systems

The advent of atomic power, with its frightening capacity for destruction and its staggering possibilities for human welfare, has tended to obscure the significance of a very different technical revolution that has begun since World War II. This is the advent of automatic machines. Self-regulating machines that can perform the most complex tasks, and thus mimic living systems, were once encountered only in science fiction, but they are a realized fact in the mid-twentieth century.

Dr. W. Grey Walter in England has built a sort of mechanical tortoise that he has called *Machina speculatrix*, the speculating machine (Fig. 13-1). *Speculatrix* is a remarkable "creature." It wanders all around the laboratory un-

der its own steam, so to speak, although its energy supply is in fact a storage battery. It has a quite complex behavior pattern. It continually moves around the room, and keeps out of trouble by recognizing and avoiding obstacles. It avoids strong lights but is attracted to light of moderate intensity. It has a weak light shining from its own "head," and when two or more *Machina speculatrix* are present in the house they are eventually attracted by each other's lights, and congregate, leading a sort of social existence for a while. What, incidentally, do you suppose is the significance of the flashing of fireflies? And have you ever seen a kitten playing with its own image in a mirror? *Speculatrix* does this too; it loiters before a mirror, as Dr. Walter nicely puts it, "like a clumsy Narcissus." But its most remarkable feature is the way *Speculatrix* behaves when its batteries run low. Its response to light becomes modified in such a way that it automatically wanders back to its illuminated home. Home is a hutch it bumbles into. Once within, the sides of *Speculatrix* touch the walls, which are electrical outlets, and the creature's batteries are recharged. Now, as though with a feeling of well-being, it leaves the hutch and resumes its ceaseless wandering exploration. For us, as biologists, Walter's tortoise with its elementary "behavior" and self-feeding habits is the most striking of the new automata. But many other more complex automata exist and are put to practical use. Everyone now is

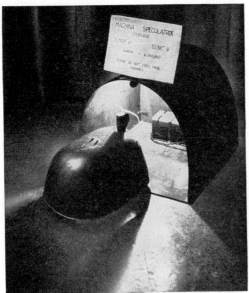

Courtesy LIFE Magazine
© TIME, Inc., 1950

13-1 *Machina speculatrix* about to enter its hutch in order to recharge its batteries.

familiar with the elaborate electronic computing machines that solve mathematical equations arising in weather forecasting, not to mention presidential elections. The twentieth-century army is equipped with self-aiming guns and guided missiles. In all these automata the significant principle for us is that, once they are given a goal, they pursue it *automatically*. They themselves meet each exigency as it arises, compensating for any deviation from their pre-set goal.

Let us compare automata with an ordinary machine like an automobile. The ordinary motorcar, unlike *Speculatrix* or a real tortoise, does not know when its tank is running low on fuel, and accordingly it does not turn automatically into the nearest gas station and tank up. Nor does the automobile avoid obstacles. It does not know when a detour has deflected its path from a pre-set destination. It does not stop at a red light. It is the driver who has in his head all the information that maintains the orderly behavior of a motorcar and is responsible for its reaching its proper goal. But not so with *Speculatrix,* self-aiming guns, guided missiles, and electronic computers. Once given its task—the solution of a mathematical equation—the electronic

computer needs no further attention from an operator because it possesses all the necessary information specifying how to proceed, no matter what unexpected circumstances develop.

The information that makes these modern machines automata, is, of course, ultimately provided by man. In different kinds of automata the information may be provided in different ways, either on punched cards, magnetic drums, or on a long tape which, to the untrained observer, seems only to carry a sequence of irregularly spaced holes. However, the pattern of holes in the tape is not really irregular and chaotic. It is carrying, in a sort of code, the complex message that tells the machine how to behave.

Let us turn to science fiction for a moment and suppose a "humanoid" from Mars visits a modern electronic computer laboratory. If he attempted to understand the behavior of the machines, he would be faced with problems exactly comparable with some of those that baffle the biologist today—problems we introduce in this chapter and the next.

What would the Martian's problem be? Like a biologist, he is confronted with very complex and highly organized systems that achieve recognizable ends or goals. "How do they work?" may be his first question. Shortly he discovers the source of the energy they expend while operating. Then he studies the way the electronic circuits work inside the machine; at this stage he is probing into the physiology of his nonliving automata, just as we have done with living organisms in earlier chapters. But his principal problem is how to account for the elaborate organization of the machine. Where, he asks, is the information supply that guarantees all the order? He finds it in the form of the tape on a reel. At this point he might be compared to the biologist discovering chromosomes as the supply of specifications for the behavior of the cell and organism. Like the biologist, he now realizes that his most difficult problems are still ahead: What is the code to the "language" of the tape? Can he decipher the code and thus understand fully how the information on the tape controls the machine?

This is the stage the biologist has reached

today. We know where the "tape of information" is in our living organisms. It is the array of chromosomes usually carried in duplicate (the diploid condition) in each cell. In a sense the biologist is even a slight step ahead of the Martian as we left him. The biologist even knows how the tape got there: in living systems it is faithfully copied in each cell generation, and the copy is transmitted as an *inherited message*. But, like the Martian, we are still confronted with the knottiest problems. We must now try to decipher the coded message in the chromosomes and thus learn *how* it specifies the wonderful order of the living cell. We must also find out how the cell copies the message (makes duplicate chromosomes) before each mitosis. Ultimately we will have to ask how the message in the chromosomes came into being in the first place. The answer to this last question lies in the mechanism of evolution, discussed later in Part 5.

The problem of decoding the language of chromosomes is really what we are attempting to solve when we discuss, in this chapter, how genes act. We will begin by looking more closely into the nature of chromosomes and genes, and into their reproduction. Examining the physical make-up of chromosomes is the first step in the attempt to decode their message.

Perhaps we have cheated the reader in attempting to impress him with the truly exciting stage that genetics has reached today, by formulating current problems in the fashion of a mystery story. It would certainly be cheating if we withheld for long the fact that nobody has so far cracked the code, and that we cannot proceed in the next two chapters as we did in the last, with a clearly laid out historical and logical approach to a definite answer. The answer is one of the major prizes of biology in the future.

We are not cheating, however, in conveying an atmosphere of high incentive. The attempt to unravel the language of chromosomes and the way its message regulates the living system is one of the major focal points of biological thought and investigation today. We could have decided that what little is known about chromosome and gene action is too fluid, too uncertain, and too difficult to occupy the beginning student. In rejecting this decision we must emphasize that much of what we say concerning the nature of genes, precisely how they are reproduced and act, falls into a different category from material in other chapters. Here there is no universal agreement among biologists concerning even the little we have to tell. On the other hand, the problems are so central to biology and an appreciation of its present trends that they cannot be omitted without really cheating the reader. Furthermore, we can convey some features of the scientific process as a vital activity by indicating the way the problem is being approached from diverse lines, and how ideas from other and currently better understood systems (like man-made automata) serve to stimulate new lines of thought and new approaches.

The first steps seem obvious enough. What are the chromosome and the gene made of? How many genes are there? How big are they? How are detailed specifications carried in the stuff the chromosome turns out to consist of? A distinct, and equally obvious, line of questioning is: What kinds of things have to be controlled in the cell and in development? By understanding what goes on in the cell and in development we should gets hints on how the cell might be controlled.

The Nature of the Genetic Material

We will begin by following up the first line of questions. What are the physical and chemical characteristics of the genetic material?

THE SMALL SIZE OF THE INHERITED MESSAGE

The number and the size of the chromosomes are fixed characteristics [1] of any particular species. All humans have a diploid number of 48, and all *Drosophila melanogaster* flies have a diploid number of 8. The number and size of chromosomes differ considerably between species, as illustrated by the comparison of fruit flies and men. The commonest

[1] There are cases in which the number and size of the chromosomes differ in different tissues of the same organism. But these are exceptions that need not distract us from the generalization.

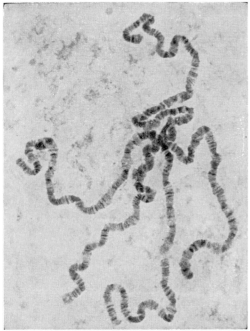

B. P. Kaufman

13-2 Salivary gland chromosomes in Drosophila melanogaster. In the salivary glands of many flies, including *Drosophila*, the chromosomes are enormously enlarged and clearly visible even during interphase. Moreover, as the photograph clearly shows, they are strikingly cross-banded. The bands (local concentrations of nucleic acid) are constant in position from nucleus to nucleus and have made it possible to construct topographic maps of chromosomes. Particular genes have been localized in some bands.

diploid number in organisms is 12 or thereabouts, although the known range extends from 2 to hundreds. There is no correlation at all between the chromosome number and the degree of complexity of the organism. It is true that man (48) has more chromosomes than the fly (8), but there are algae and garden weeds and some crabs with chromosome numbers in the hundreds!

The most significant fact about the number and size of chromosomes is that together they indicate the extremely small bulk of material that constitutes the inherited message. It is not more and probably much less than $\frac{1}{1000}$ of the material in the fertilized egg. Moreover, it is by no means certain—it is even unlikely—that all the material of the chromosomes is directly concerned with carrying hereditary information. Some chromosome material is probably only a sort of skeleton carrying the rest. Furthermore, the comparison of the chromosome with the tape of information in a machine must not blind us to the fact that the chromosomes are *living* tapes. As such, they carry out some metabolism of their own, and contain enzymes and products of metabolism which are not necessarily part of the message-carrying material; rather, they are concerned with its maintenance.

GENES: HOW BIG? HOW MANY?

It has been possible, by using ingenious and indirect approaches, to obtain estimates of both the size and number of genes in the nucleus. One method of estimating gene size can be briefly recounted here. It utilizes the same principle that would be used in determining the size of a target at the far end of a darkened room. We can find out how big such a target is if we have a shotgun that fires volleys of small shot. If we know that there is one pellet per square inch within the area covered by a volley, and that the target is hit (suppose a bell rings when it is hit) twice every time we fire a volley, then we have found out that the target covers an area of 2 square inches. But if we hit it, on the average, only once every two times we fire a volley, then the target is clearly only one-half of a square inch in area.

To determine the size of a gene in a *Drosophila* we use volleys of X-ray particles instead of lead pellets! The density of X-ray showers can be controlled. Although nothing as convenient as the ringing of a bell occurs every time the gene is hit, there is something nearly as good as a bell. When the gene is hit by an X-ray particle, its structure is changed. It is said to be mutated. The mutated gene produces a recognizably different fly in the next generation. Thus we have a technique for knowing how often we hit the target with an X-ray beam whose particle density we know. We can therefore calculate how big the target is. The results from these, and other, studies show that the gene is an astonishingly small part of the chromosome, about 10 to 100 millimicrons in diameter. (A millimicron is 0.000,001 millimeter.)

Similarly indirect approaches tell us that in the four chromosomes of *Drosophila* there are altogether about 10,000 genes (not less than 5000 and not more than 15,000).

WHAT IS A GENE?

We cannot *see* genes as distinct parts of the chromosome even when we use the most powerful microscope available. Most chromosomes give no visible evidence at all of linear differentiation. Some chromosomes, however, show a linear sequence of small swellings (*chromomeres*) at prophase of mitosis and meiosis; others, in special tissues like the salivary glands of *Drosophila*, are enormously enlarged, showing clearly defined crossbands (Fig. 13-2). Some geneticists have suggested that these swellings and bands represent individual genes. However, this is unlikely to be true in general because it has been discovered that at least *some* chromomeres and bands contain more than one gene.

If we cannot *see* the separate genes on the chromosome, how do we know they exist? Let us briefly recount why geneticists have concluded that there are two distinct and *separable* genes controlling eye color (red *vs.* white) and wing length (normal *vs.* miniature) on the *Drosophila* X-chromosome.

If we crossed a "white" and "miniature" fly to a normal one, we would get a normal F_1 because the alleles for red eyes and long wings are dominant over those for white and miniature (Fig. 13-3). Crossing this F_1 normal fly to a "white, miniature" fly will give us a progeny that will tell us what gametes the F_1 produced (cf. p. 301).

Suppose that we obtained from this cross only two classes of flies in equal numbers: 50 per cent normal and 50 per cent "white, miniature." What would be the simplest hypothesis about the genetic control of eye color and wing length? For simplicity, we would have to assume that they were controlled by one factor, or one gene [2] (Fig. 13-4*B*).

Entirely different conclusions are forced on us if we find four classes of flies in the testcross progeny (Fig. 13-4*A*). In this case the two new types of fly—white eyes, normal wings, and red eyes, miniature wings—tell

[2] As we shall see later, it is not uncommon for one gene to affect more than one character.

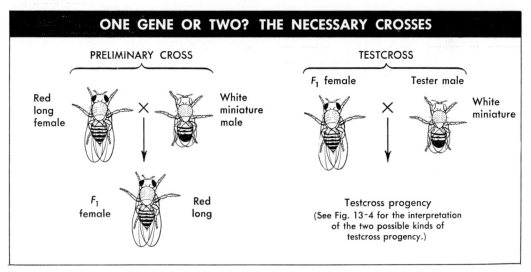

ONE GENE OR TWO? THE NECESSARY CROSSES

PRELIMINARY CROSS

TESTCROSS

Red long female × White miniature male

F_1 female × Tester male → White miniature

F_1 female   Red long

Testcross progency
(See Fig. 13-4 for the interpretation of the two possible kinds of testcross progeny.)

13-3 One gene or two? I. Genetic tests show that white (*vs.* red) eye color, and miniature (*vs.* long) wings are controlled by the genetic material in the X-chromosomes: they are sex-linked characters. Are these two characters controlled by two separate genes or by one? This question is attacked by making the following crosses: (1) Preliminary cross: red, long female x white, miniature male. The F_1 is red and long since these characters are dominant. (2) Testcross: F_1 female x "tester" male, who is white and miniature. Since white and miniature are recessive, the testcross progeny immediately reveal what kinds of gametes the F_1 female produces. (Cf. Table 12-3, where the testcross technique is illustrated.)

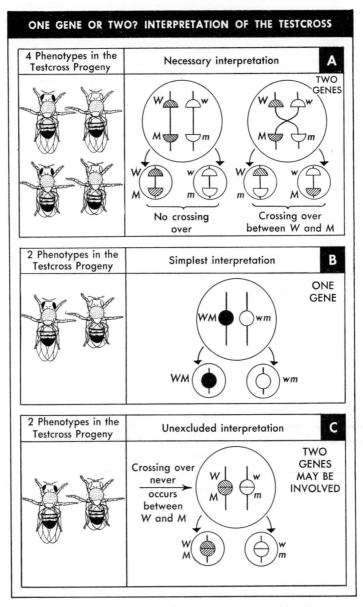

13-4 One gene or two? II. The two possible kinds of progeny from the testcross illustrated in Fig. 13-3 are: (1) Four phenotypes present: white miniature, red long, white long, and red miniature; and (2) only two phenotypes present: red long and white miniature. The interpretation of these alternatives is as follows: *A.* Four phenotypes present: the X-chromosome carries two physically distinct genes. One of these (W) affects the eye, and the other (M) affects the wing. These genes are separated by crossing over in some cells that undergo meiosis. The F_1 female, therefore, produces four kinds of eggs: WM, Wm, wM, and wm. *B.* Two phenotypes present: simplest interpretation. A single gene (call it WM) on the X-chromosome affects both eye color and wing length. Thus the heterozygous F_1 female is WM wm, and produces only two kinds of eggs: WM and wm. *C.* Two phenotypes present: unexcluded possibility. The X-chromosome carries two physically distinct genes: W and M. They lie close together, and crossing over never separates them. The heterozygous F_1 female is Ww Mm, and produces only two kinds of eggs: WM and wm.

us that eye color and wing length must be controlled by quite separate pieces of the chromosome (separate genes), for it is possible to recombine these pieces by crossing over (Fig. 13-4A).

Here is a most important point: in any study of inheritance we can be sure that two genes, rather than one, are involved *only if* crossing over occurs between them and so proves they are distinct parts of the chromosome. On the other hand, even though there actually were two genes present, *if* crossing over did not occur between them we would be forced to the erroneous conclusion that there was only one.

The answer to our question, "What is a gene?" must therefore be as follows: genes are the smallest pieces into which the chromosome can be broken up by crossing over. There may well be smaller distinct units within the gene, but if so we need new techniques to recognize them.

In recent years it has been found that some of the most thoroughly studied "single" genes in *Drosophila* are in fact compounds of "subgenes" like Fig. 13-4C. This is true of the white eye gene in *Drosophila*. Crossing over occurs between the constituent parts so rarely that it has required special methods to detect it. Previously the compound structure had been thought to be a single unit.

We are thus led to conclude that genes must be relatively large [3] and complex portions of the total message inherited in the chromosomes. If we are to probe more deeply into the fine structure of the genetic material we must turn to new techniques. In a sense we must focus our attention on words and sentences—not whole paragraphs (genes)—to crack the code of the genetical language.

THE CHEMISTRY OF THE GENETIC MATERIAL

When we ask what the chromosomes are made of, difficulties immediately appear to confront us. How can we pick up a chromosome—much less a gene—and put it in a test tube for standard procedures of chemi-

cal analysis? The beginnings of chromosome chemistry consisted of side-stepping such an approach by devising special indirect methods of microchemical analysis. If we have a colorless solution which produces a specific color when it reacts with chemical x, then we have a tool for detecting the location of chemical x in the cell. Thin sections of cells can be treated with the test solution and the section studied under the microscope: the local appearance of color within cell structures identifies the presence of chemical x. Test-staining techniques have revealed the fact that the chromosomes contain, principally, two classes of molecules: the ubiquitous *proteins,* and *nucleic acids.* It is thought that these two kinds of molecules are widely present in the chromosome in loose chemical combination as *nucleoprotein.*

The nucleic acids are of special interest. They occur in the cell in two forms: ribose nucleic acid (RNA for short) and desoxyribose nucleic acid (DNA for short). DNA differs from RNA, as its name indicates, in lacking an oxygen atom in each of its constituent sugars. DNA is the form that is most interesting to us; it is found only in the chromosomes of the nucleus, and thus seems to be correlated with *reproduction* at the subcellular level. RNA, while present in the chromosomes in small amount, occurs principally outside the nucleus in the cytoplasm, although it is apparently made in the nucleus.

This knowledge of chromosome chemistry, based on staining procedures, is confirmed in recent studies. It has been possible to get, literally, test tubes full of chromosomes from tissues like calf thymus gland and liver which are available by the ton from slaughterhouses. These studies have shown that the visible structure depends on both DNA and protein, for if either is removed the structure is destroyed.

Which is the genetic material (the carrier of specifications) in the chromosome? Is it the nucleic acid, the protein, or both?

NUCLEIC ACID (DNA): MESSAGE-CARRYING MOLECULE

The first strong indication that desoxyribose nucleic acid (DNA) was the message-carrying fraction of the genetic material came in the

[3] Genes are, of course, very tiny in absolute size; we mean here that they are large fractions of the total message, which itself is extremely small in absolute size.

1930's from studies on pneumonia-causing bacteria (*Pneumococcus*). In *Pneumococcus* there are many different hereditary cell types, and it was discovered that a particular type (e.g., type III) could be changed into one of the other known types (type II) by using a chemical extract taken from type II. The chemical extracted from type II was called "the transforming principle"; it transformed the heredity of type III to that of type II.

The transforming principle was subjected to intensive chemical study and found to consist of DNA; the most careful scrutiny revealed only a minute trace of protein. This was a history-making experiment in biology because it was the first time that part of the hereditary message of one cell was extracted as a chemical and introduced into another and different organism which accepted it.

An interesting experiment in recent years has given strong grounds for favoring DNA still more as the actual carrier of hereditary information. This experiment concerns the heredity of viruses.

The nature of viruses is much disputed. They are extremely small particles, many of them no bigger than some protein molecules (Fig. 3-5). Some, like the virus causing mosaic disease in tobacco plants, TMV (tobacco mosaic virus), have actually been obtained in large quantities from diseased tissue purified and *crystallized.* The success in crystallizing some viruses led some students to the conviction that they were single molecules. Because they seemed to reproduce themselves, it was supposed that they were alive, and therefore were *living molecules.* It is doubtful whether they should be called alive, and still more doubtful whether the distinction between living and nonliving has any useful meaning when applied to a single molecule. We cannot really say the virus is a molecule that reproduces itself; all we know is that when a virus successfully enters a cell we can recover hundreds of similar viruses from the infected cell when it later dies. Did the virus reproduce itself, or did the cell copy the virus? This may seem a petty distinction, but it may be important in understanding the minimum degree of complex organization necessary for reproduction. In this light the virus may prove too simple *to reproduce itself* in the sense in which we can confidently state that cells reproduce themselves. At any rate, the important fact is that new viruses are made in the cell of an organism once it is invaded by a virus. Furthermore, virus reproduction has the same characteristic of all reproduction by living systems: the new viruses are like the old ones, and we may speak therefore of *virus heredity.* Viruses, like chromosomes, contain both protein and desoxyribose nucleic acid (DNA).[4] We are again faced with the query, "Is it the protein or the nucleic acid molecules that carry the hereditary message?" An experiment in 1952 gave the answer to this question—again in favor of the DNA.

The particular virus studied is one that infects, and ultimately destroys, the common colon bacillus (*Escherichia coli*) of man. This bacterial virus is often called bacteriophage, or phage, for short. It has been studied under the electron microscope and found to have a definite shape (illus., p. 309). When the virus attacks the cell it does so tail first. Evidently the tail enters the cell membrane. After this initial contact, the contents of the main body of the virus enter the cell *as though* squeezed from a syringe through the tail, which we could liken to a hypodermic needle. The empty shell of the virus is left outside. What entered the bacterium is the carrier of virus heredity because, once inside the cell, the material is copied again and again until the whole cell is destroyed and bursts, yielding hundreds of new phage particles complete with case and tail.

In the 1952 experiment bacterial cells (*E. coli*) were grown on a nutrient medium containing both radioactive phosphorus and radioactive sulfur. The bacteria that grew on this medium incorporated both radioactive elements into their photoplasm. When, in turn, these cells were infected with virus, the new virus particles produced in the infected cell also incorporated both radioactive elements. The point of using phosphorus and sulfur in radioactive form is very simple: all DNA contains phosphorus in large

---

[4] A minority of viruses (e.g., the influenza virus and those attacking plants) contain RNA.

amounts, but it contains no sulfur; on the other hand, proteins do not contain phosphorus, but they do commonly contain sulfur.

When, therefore, we have viruses that contain radioactive phosphorus and sulfur, we know that the phosphorus is in the nucleic acid and the sulfur is in the proteins. Such "radioactive viruses" can now be used to infect fresh bacterial cells free of all radioactivity. After the message-carrying hereditary material enters the cell, the empty virus cases on the outside can be shaken off. It is then discovered that these empty cases contain radioactive sulfur but no radioactive phosphorus; it follows that the empty cases contain protein but no nucleic acid. On the other hand, the infected cells contain radioactive phosphorus but no radioactive sulfur. This in turn tells us that the hereditary material that entered the cell contained nucleic acid (DNA) but no protein.

This experiment confirms the inference, made from the earlier study of *Pneumococcus*, that DNA is the principal genetic material.

There is a problem that must have begun to worry the reader. We speak of one kind of chemical substance—DNA—as being the message-carrying molecule in *Pneumococcus* bacteria, in viruses, and presumably in all organisms. How can one kind of molecule carry all the detailed and different specifications involved in such diverse cases? The answer, of course, is that all DNA is not the same.

The chemical analysis of this molecule shows that it contains sugars (ribose), phosphoric acid groups, and four different nitrogen compounds (bases). The four nitrogen bases we will simply designate as numbers 1, 2, 3, and 4. These constituents—sugars, phosphoric acid, and four bases—still do not seem to add up to a very complex molecule, somehow not complex enough to be a full message specifying the construction of a cell, much less a fly. There is a catch here, however. To say that DNA consists only of sugars, phosphoric acid groups, and four bases is like saying that this textbook consists only of 26 letters in the English alphabet and a few numbers; or that a message from an admiral to his destroyer consists only of dots and dashes. The fact is that the DNA molecule is immensely long; monotonous though its constituent parts are, the possibilities for complicated sequences are nevertheless endless. The message in the DNA molecule must consist of the sequence of its parts.

In 1953 it was discovered that the DNA molecule is constructed like a ladder, as diagramed in Fig. 13-5. The "uprights" of the ladder are formed by a sequence of phosphate and sugar parts; the cross rungs are the bases. The "cross rungs" of the ladder are always formed by bases 1 and 2 or 3 and 4. 1 never pairs with 4, and 2 never pairs with 3. This pairing is a physical necessity due to the shape of the bases. It is now thought that the information—the message of hereditary specifications—is coded in terms of the sequential pattern, or order, in which the 1-2 and 3-4 crosspieces occur. This is comparable to the way in which a very complex message in Morse code reduces to the pattern in which just two alternatives (dots and dashes) follow each other in time.

Knowledge of the structure of the DNA molecule is recently acquired, and we are far from certain about some aspects of it. However, there seems little doubt that in its structure lies coded the inherited message every cell gets. We are brought face to face with the challenge of decoding this message. Some suggestions have been made; one will be discussed in a later section of this chapter (p. 320).

The Reproduction of the Genetic Material

So far we have approached our study of the nature of the hereditary material by following up the line of questioning that begins: What is its physical nature? What is it made of? We can now turn to the other questions: What, precisely, does it do? How does it do it? Genetic material does two things: (1) it reproduces itself (or is somehow reproduced by the cell); and (2) it effects general control over the activity of the cell and organism as a whole. In this section we will turn our attention to the problem of gene reproduction.

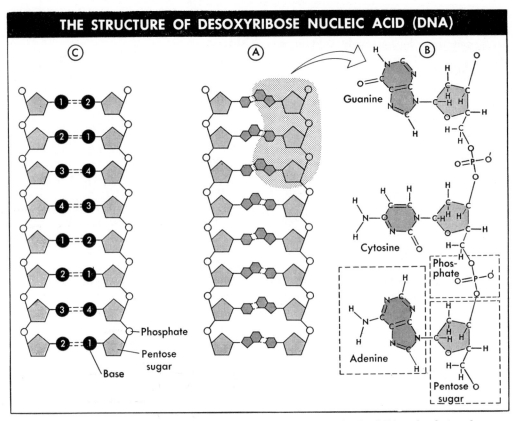

Ⓒ   Ⓐ   Ⓑ

Guanine

Cytosine

Phos-
phate

Adenine

Pentose
sugar

Phosphate

Pentose
sugar

Base

13-5 The structure of desoxyribose nucleic acid (DNA). *A.* The DNA molecule is a long ladderlike structure that is twisted into a helix; in these figures and in Fig. 13-8, the ladder is shown in untwisted form for diagrammatic simplicity. The "uprights" of the ladder consist of pentose sugars (light gray pentagons in the figure) and phosphate groups (open circles). The cross rungs of the ladder consist of pairs of nitrogen bases (dark gray in *A* and *B*), of which there are four: thymine, guanine, cytosine, and adenine. *B.* The detailed chemical structure of part of the DNA ladder. *C.* The structure of the molecule is further simplified, the four bases being represented by black discs numbered as follows: (*1*) cytosine; (*2*) guanine; (*3*) thymine; (*4*) adenine. The important point is that the "cross rungs" of the DNA ladder always consist of one of the two pairs: *1-2*, cytosine-guanine; or *3-4*, thymine-adenine.

THE MECHANISM OF
GENE REPRODUCTION

Needed: a living template. Reproduction, as we saw even in Chapter 1, is surely the most characteristic and defining feature of all living systems. Organisms exist today, and persist from generation to generation, only because they possess the ability to make copies of themselves. They are too complex to arise *de novo* (unguided by inherited information) from the materials of the contemporary nonliving world. In the last analysis, this capacity of organisms to make copies of themselves therefore boils down to their ability to make copies of their hereditary information. We must now distinguish carefully between the problem of chromosome reproduction and the mitotic mechanism for separating the copies once they are made. At the end of one mitotic cycle, at telophase, each chromosome incorporated into the nucleus is single-stranded; when that nucleus later enters prophase to initiate a new mitotic separation, the chromosomes are double-stranded. The chromosome was copied in the *inter*phase between mitoses.

It has been commonly said that between mitoses the single chromosome strand simply splits into two strands. But this is clearly a useless way of discussing reproduction: splitting could only be done just so many times before nothing would be left. Simple as it may appear, use of the word "splitting" covers up the real problem.

We must point out that nobody yet knows for certain just how the genetic material is reproduced. However, the general difficulty of copying anything except an external surface has led biologists to channel their thoughts about the problem in one particular direction. It is interesting to note here how we have been influenced by models or analogies from the well-understood world of everyday human affairs. For a long time people have been able to copy very complex surfaces, such as the sculptor's work, by making molds or templates of them (Fig. 13-6). The use of templates in industry for the easy mass copying of all kinds of products is too familiar to need further emphasis. In the search for a method whereby the genetic material *might* be copied, much thought has been given to the possibility that this process, too, involves a template—a living template.

Antigens and antibodies. It has long been held that the familiar and obvious differences between organs, tissues, and cells—indeed, all important biological differences—ultimately reduce to differences in the structure of the most complex class of molecules, the proteins that occur in living cells. Different organs and tissues can be characterized by differences in the proteins they contain. For an almost equally long time biologists have thought that the really significant differences between proteins were their differences in surface structure. This view is strongly supported by the remarkable property of animals to develop antibodies to foreign substances, especially proteins. Often proteins and other kinds of molecules that are part of the normal organization of one living thing prove to be toxic to another. Thus the proteins produced by some bacteria are seriously toxic to man and other animals. One remarkable property of animals is their capacity to produce what are called *antibodies* to these foreign, sometimes disease-producing, pro-

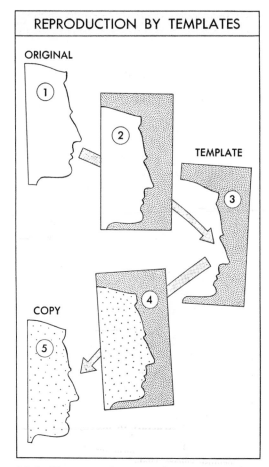

REPRODUCTION BY TEMPLATES

ORIGINAL

TEMPLATE

COPY

13-6 **How a template is used to copy a surface.**

teins. Antibodies are protein in nature themselves, and their functional significance for the organism is that they inactivate the foreign protein, called the *antigen*. There are strong reasons for believing that the antibody does its job of inactivating the antigen because its surface is a perfect complement to the surface of the antigen, which, once covered by the antibody, is no longer able to upset the normal activity of the invaded organism. It is as though the organism manufactured scabbards to fit every shape of sword that entered its blood, rendering them harmless (Fig. 13-7).

These surface relations of antigens and antibodies have suggested one way genes *might* be copied. Since the organism *can* make a mold (a negative cast, or template) to a molecular surface, why could it not then

Antigen

Antibody

13-7 Antigen-antibody surfaces. The antibody surface is a complement to that of the antigen.

make another cast from this mold? The second cast would be a perfect copy of the original molecule's surface. Many biologists have favored this as a *hypothesis* of how genes are reproduced, and experiments, still inconclusive, are being made to test it.

DNA: built-in templates. The present-day view, as we saw earlier, is that the DNA in the chromosome, not the protein, carries the hereditary detail. DNA is therefore the crucial molecule to be copied. This does not detract from the general plausibility of the template theory of gene reproduction, because we know that antibodies, themselves always protein, can be made to antigens that are not proteins. However, the new knowledge we have of the DNA molecule suggests how it *might* be copied, following the template principle, but not involving protein antibodies. Indeed, the most remarkable feature about the DNA molecule is that, in a sense, it has built-in templates. The two "uprights" in its ladder-like structure are unique complements of each other. As we noted earlier (p. 317) base 1 is always paired with base 2; and base 3 is always paired with base 4. It is this feature that suggests a second hypothesis as to how the DNA molecule might be copied. Suppose that the chemical bonds linking the paired nitrogen bases are broken (Fig. 13-8). The molecule is then opened up, somewhat like an opened zipper. The two pieces of this opened "zipper" now have exposed unsatis-

fied chemical bonds of such a kind that base 1 in the molecule will always pick up base 2 from the nearby protoplasm; 2 will pick up 1; 3 will pick up 4; and 4 will pick up 3. By picking up the appropriate complementary bases (and also the sugar and phosphate) in this fashion, the two halves of the opened "zipper" each become identical DNA molecules. Thus the DNA molecule might be compared to a compound structure consisting of a piece of sculpture and its own negative mold: the two surfaces separate and each acts as a mold for its complement (Fig. 13-8).

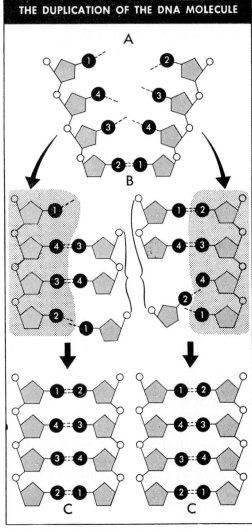

THE DUPLICATION OF THE DNA MOLECULE

A

B

C   C

13-8 The duplication of the DNA molecule.

Many biologists are currently studying DNA with these ideas in mind, but it will be some time before we are certain as to exactly how the genetic material is copied. However, whatever the detailed answer proves to be, nearly all biologists are convinced that it will involve a template of some kind. And this itself is an important point. *It implies the notion that the significant feature of the genetic material is its surface shape.* We will see later (p. 325) that this idea agrees very well with another fundamental feature about genes—how they manage to regulate the activity of the cell.

MUTATION

Mutation as the rare error in reproduction. If we were asked to supply a symbol of durability and stability, it would be a natural human tendency to name a landmark, such as a mountain, which is simple and solid in structure. By comparison the living thing seems fragile, complex, prone to decay. Yet of all the things on earth we know, living things are in some respects the most durable and stable. A biologist recently pointed out that the main features of mammalian organization appeared on earth many millions of years before the Himalayan Mountains were formed. This same mammalian organization has been faithfully preserved with minor modifications ever since. More amazing still is the thought that the major features of cellular organization, including, for instance, mitosis, must be much older than 500 million years— more nearly 1000 million. In this sense the world of life, while surely fragile and complex, is incredibly durable through time— more durable than mountains. This durability is wholly dependent on the almost incredible accuracy with which the inherited information is copied from generation to generation.

Accurate as the reproductive process is, however, accidents do happen, and errors occasionally creep into the copy of the chromosome blueprint that is passed on to the next generation. The cell, being possessed of a completely blind copying process, proceeds in the next generation to copy the error. In this way new forms of heredity arise and are perpetuated. *Mutation* [5] is the name given to

13-9   Ancon, a dominant mutation in sheep. The short-legged ram on the right carries a mutant gene ("ancon") that causes a shortened leg. Bred to a normal ewe (*left*) it produces an ancon F_1. This particular mutant is agriculturally useful: it cannot jump fences.

all those processes which result in change in the hereditary material.

Plant and animal breeders have long known that an individual sharply different from its parents may suddenly appear in the most uniform, carefully bred strain. Such "sports," as the early breeders called them, or *mutants*, as they are now called, have been a source of numerous distinctive breeds or true breeding varieties. The Ancon mutation (Fig. 13-9), producing animals too short-legged to jump fences, has occurred at least twice among sheep. The bulldog-faced (locally called *ñata*) breed of Argentine cattle represents a sort of mutation that has also occurred in swine and other animals as well as dogs. Mutations for hornlessness have occurred among many horned animals and have been used to develop hornless breeds. Horses that pace naturally by heredity rather than training have been bred from mutants. Many popular horticultural varieties—dwarf, double-flowered, variegated, and so on—have appeared spontaneously as mutants. Many mutations have also been observed in humans. Queen Victoria's tragic hemophilia gene was a mutation in the germ cells of either herself or her parents,

5 "Mutation," from the Latin for "change," was a natural but unfortunate choice of name for

the process. Unknown to De Vries, who introduced "mutation" for the genetical process, the term was already used with a different meaning by paleontologists. The double usage caused confusion and misunderstanding between geneticists and paleontologists for a long time, but now the genetical usage has prevailed.

although of course this was unknown at the time.

Mutations have all sorts of effects, from barely perceptible (or very likely imperceptible in usual studies) to great and obvious. Mutation is, indeed, the ultimate source of all *new* genetic materials, which then are endlessly shuffled in the processes of sexual reproduction. All evolutionary change depends in the final analysis on mutation.[6] Of course, not all mutations lead to evolutionary change. Most of them are eliminated eventually. What happens to mutations after they occur— whether they are eliminated, remain as rare variants, or spread and lead to significant change—these are parts of another story to which we will come later on (Chapter 16).

Kinds of mutations. Mutations have sooner or later been seen in all organisms that have been carefully studied over considerable periods, from bacteria to the highest plants and animals. There is no doubt that mutations can and do appear in all sorts of organisms. That is a very fundamental generalization: capacity for mutation is one of the universal and definitive characteristics of life. It is certainly the basic process on which all organic evolution is dependent.

The combination of breeding experiments with microscopic observation of chromosome sets and structures has shown that mutation may occur in several different ways. In fact, it occurs in as many ways as there are ways for the copying and transmission mechanism to go wrong. All mutations fall into one of the following broad categories:

1. Change in chromosome number ⎫
2. Change in chromosome structure ⎬ Chromosome mutations
3. Change in single genes — Gene mutations

Of these classes, the gene mutations are believed to have the most far-reaching sig-

6 It seems strange to conclude that evolution, so often a progressive process, should depend on "errors" in the reproducing mechanism. In a way, this is akin to the fact that the blood-clotting mechanism (p. 144) is a two-edged phenomenon; it protects but it may kill. Mutations are in one sense errors, in that they are not planned; but they are errors that populations of reproducing organisms have turned to good use in natural selection.

nificance. Indeed, when the word "mutation" is used without specification as to whether gene or chromosome mutation is meant, gene mutation is usually implied. Chromosomal mutations do, however, play an important role in some phases of variation and evolution. Let us briefly consider them before we discuss gene mutation.

Changes in chromosome number: polyploidy. We have seen that organisms normally have a basic set of chromosomes, the *haploid* (simple) set, in which the number of chromosomes may be symbolized as n. Biparental organisms usually receive one full set from each parent and therefore have paired sets with n pairs, or a total of $2n$ chromosomes. $2n$ is the diploid (double) number. In both mitosis and meiosis there is a stage at which the pairs are doubled, and for a brief time $4n$ chromosomes are present in each cell. In mitosis a single division then produces two diploid cells, with $2n$ chromosomes each. In meiosis two divisions produce four haploid cells, with n chromosomes each.

Now suppose something goes wrong with these mechanisms. Like man-made machines, the mechanisms of nature work most of the time but do occasionally break down. If the mitotic spindle mechanism fails (again in any one of several ways) to operate properly, the two duplicate diploid sets will not be moved apart into the usual separate nuclei of two new daughter cells. Instead they will remain clumped together and reconstitute a nucleus with double the usual number: $4n$ instead of $2n$. Other irregularities in division may drop out single chromosomes or duplicate some. For instance, if the spindle mechanism fails on only one of the metaphase chromosomes we would get one cell with $2n + 1$, and the other with $2n - 1$. All sorts of such irregularities of chromosome distribution can, but rarely do, occur in both mitosis and meiosis.

By variation of these processes individuals can originate with not only $4n$ but also $3n$, $5n$, $6n$, and so on, as well as various odd numbers of chromosomes. Such numbers are *polyploid* (multiple), the new sorts of individuals are polyploids, and the various processes

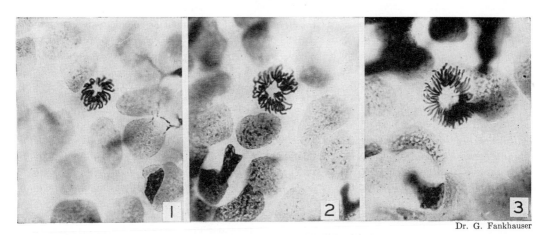

13-10 Polyploid nuclei in salamanders. *1.* A normal diploid $(2n = 22)$. *2.* A triploid nucleus $(3n = 33)$. *3.* A pentaploid nucleus $(5n = 55)$.

giving rise to such conditions are summed up as polyploidy (Fig. 13-10).

Polyploids differ in various ways from their parents. Their cells, containing more chromosomes, are usually larger. Often the whole organism is larger. Polyploids, derived from crossing or hybridization of different races and species [7] may be more or less intermediate but often also have some new characters of their own. Thus polyploidy results in the sudden appearance of new kinds of organisms. It is a form of mutation.

Chromosome rearrangements. Genes are arranged in single file along a chromosome. In any chromosome they have a definite sequence, so that if we indicate genes as *A, B, C, D,* and so on, a chromosome could be represented as *A-B-C-D-E-F-·· ·*. Actually, as we have seen, there are at least hundreds and possibly thousands of genes in most chromosomes, but you can get the picture without going so far. In the course of meiosis, paired chromosomes often exchange segments in the normal process of crossing over (p. 300). This process does not change the gene arrangement. Sometimes, however, this mechanism, too, acts irregularly and gene sequences are changed. Different sorts of changes are as follows:

[7] Hybridization may be successful without giving rise to polyploids.

1. A gene is dropped out. *A-B-C-D-E-F* becomes *A-B-D-E-F* (the technical term is *deficiency*).

2. A gene is duplicated. *A-B-C-D-E-F* becomes *A-B-B-C-D-E-F* (*duplication*).

3. Part of the gene sequence is turned around. *A-B-C-D-E-F* becomes *A-B-E-D-C-F* (*inversion*).

4. A chromosome exchanges parts with one belonging to another pair and not with its own mate. Two nonpaired chromosomes, *A-B-C-D-E-F* and *G-H-I-J-K-L* become *A-B-C-J-K-L* and *G-H-I-D-E-F* (*translocation*).

It is easy to see that a deficiency or a duplication would be likely to change development. Since genes control development, the absence of one, or a double dose, would be expected to have an adverse effect. This is confirmed in *Drosophila*. For instance, a particular short deficiency in the X-chromosome produces a notch in the wings in the phenotype. You might think, however, that inversions and translocations would make no difference. The same genes are present, only their positions are changed. Sometimes, indeed, no difference in the phenotype is seen even though inversion or translocation is visible by microscopic study of the chromosomes. The change does affect the way the chromosomes pair in meiosis, and this may cause a decrease in fertility or various peculiarities in inheritance. Sometimes the effect of a gene is changed simply because it has new neighbors. In *Drosophila* it has been found that size of the eye is affected by which genes are next to each other. This *position effect* is evidence that genes interact in producing their results, a topic we will say more about later in this chapter.

Gene mutations and their rates. Individual genes can and do change their characteristics. What the actual change is below microscopic level in the chromosome remains doubtful, but the changes—gene mutations— are evident by their effects. The different alleles of genes, such as those extensively exemplified in the last chapter, have all arisen as mutations. This was certainly true of the alleles used in Mendel's experiments, although the mutations occurred at some unknown time before he began his work. Since then, hundreds of mutations have been seen to arise in laboratories, and many have also been observed in nature.

The frequency of mutation in any one gene varies greatly from gene to gene, but it is always low. Tests for mutations with distinctly visible effects in corn have given rates for single genes from 0 to about 500 mutations per 1,000,000 gametes. There are so many genes that the total rate for all genes is much higher. The percentage of individuals with a mutation in some gene may be around 5 to 10 per cent in many organisms. Such figures are necessarily only estimates. They are probably underestimates because the most frequent mutations may be those with such slight effects that they are overlooked. By ingenious statistical procedures it is possible to estimate rates of some mutations with strong effects in man. Mutations producing hemophilia occur in 1 to 5 X-chromosomes in every 100,000. Fortunately this is a small figure, but it is enough to keep hemophilia present in human populations even if no one ever passed the gene on to descendants. It is possible that at least 1 per cent of babies born have some mutation, although of course most of these mutations produce little or no evident effect. Some students place the figure at 10 per cent or even higher.

The rate of mutation is subject to a certain amount of control by mechanisms within the organism itself. In *Drosophila*, for instance, it was found that a particular population of flies in Florida possessed a gene that increased the mutation rate of the other genes in the chromosomes. In the Florida strain the mutation rate was 10 times higher than the comparable rate in an Ohio population of the same species.

Experimental production of mutations. Experimentation on mutations (mostly in *Drosophila*, as you would expect) went very slowly when the geneticists had to wait for a particular mutation to turn up spontaneously. The whole subject was revolutionized when H. J. Muller discovered that mutations could be produced at much greater rates by applying X rays. Since then several other ways of speeding up mutations have been found, mostly by various radiations or by chemicals. For the most part these methods do merely speed things up. The mutations produced are those that would occur naturally at lower rates. Also, as with natural mutations, there is no way to predict what particular mutation will occur in any given experiment.

Gene Action

THE SINGLE GENE IN ACTION

Genes and enzymes: a language of specific surfaces. On a microscope slide or on a textbook page, a cell may seem a static and simple thing—a mere sac of apparently structureless protoplasm. Such a view is thorough illusion. In reality the cell, like the whole organism, is an active system of biochemical change. Compounds are constantly being synthesized, while others are broken down in an endless, but highly organized, shuffling of energy and materials. The ordered structure and activity of the whole organism, so obvious to us, must in the last analysis be based on equally ordered, if less obvious, biochemical activity in the cell.

The fact that the biochemical activity of the cell must be orderly and organized is just another way of saying that it must be controlled. How might this be done? Our discussion in Chapter 5 noted that chemical reactions will proceed only when the necessary activation energy is somehow provided by enzymes specific to each reaction which occurs. A moment's consideration of this fact gives us a first and important lead on how genes act in controlling cellular activity. Enzymes are potential agents of control: produce the necessary enzyme, and a particular reaction will proceed; without it, the reaction stops or never starts. Could this be how genes act? Perhaps the genes ultimately regulate cell life through the agency of enzymes which the genes alone have the power to produce.

This hypothesis is now more than fifty years old, but only in the last fifteen years has it been followed up by a number of geneticists. They have found that in many different organisms genes are, indeed, associated with the formation of specific enzymes. For instance, it has been found that one of our genes controls, through the production of the appropriate enzyme, the oxidation of the compound alcapton. This fact was uncovered by study of a mutant allele of the normal gene. The mutant allele fails to produce the enzyme. In a person homozygous for the mutant allele, alcapton is not destroyed, as it normally is. It is excreted in the urine, which turns dark on exposure to air. (Only about one person in a million is homozygous for the mutant.)

The pink bread mold, *Neurospora*, has proved to be as useful for experiments on chemical genetics as the fly *Drosophila* has been in classical Mendelian experiments. *Neurospora* grows along the surface of some nutritive medium like stale bread or, in laboratory experiments, agar jelly supplied with sugar and biotin. Apart from sugar as an energy supply, the only molecule *Neurospora* needs in ready-made supply is the vitamin biotin. All other molecules involved in its biochemical system are made by the mold itself. The meshwork of synthesis that the cell is constantly effecting is diagramed very schematically in Fig. 13-11. Some molecules are transformed directly into others (e.g., $A \to B$, $E \to F$, $F \to G$); some are compounded from two others (e.g., $D + C \to E$). On the other hand, some may become involved in the synthesis of more than one other com-

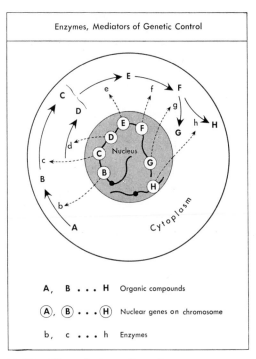

Enzymes, Mediators of Genetic Control

A, B ... H   Organic compounds

Ⓐ, Ⓑ ... Ⓗ   Nuclear genes on chromosome

b, c ... h   Enzymes

13-11   The relation of nuclear genes to enzymes and cellular reactions.

pound (e.g., $F \to G$ or H). Each reaction is enzyme-controlled, and our hypothesis, as indicated in the diagram, is that the enzymes are themselves gene-controlled. Thus gene B ultimately is responsible for the reaction $A \to B$ because it is responsible for the production of enzyme b.

Our hypothesis predicts that if we could get mutants of gene B which failed to produce the enzyme b, then the reaction $A \to B$ would not take place, and, if B were indispensable to the cell, growth would cease. Earlier in this chapter we saw how the production of new alleles through mutation can be speeded up by subjecting the organism to high energy radiation such as ultraviolet or X rays. When *Neurospora* spores are bombarded with such rays, it is found that mutants are indeed produced that will not grow unless some specific compound (like B in Fig. 13-11) is supplied. What has happened is that the radiation caused the gene B to mutate to an allelic form B that fails to produce the enzyme b (Fig. 13-12).

Chemical genetics has so far been focused

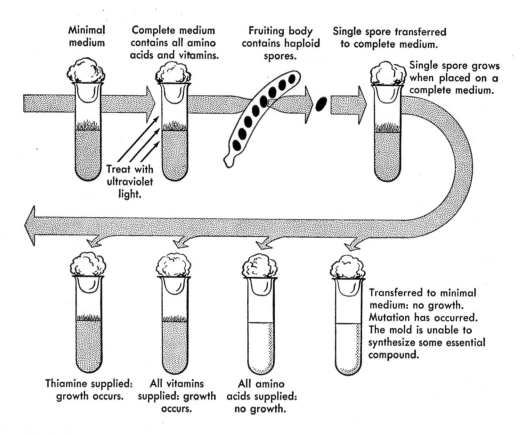

Minimal medium

Complete medium contains all amino acids and vitamins.

Treat with ultraviolet light.

Fruiting body contains haploid spores.

Single spore transferred to complete medium.

Single spore grows when placed on a complete medium.

Thiamine supplied: growth occurs.

All vitamins supplied: growth occurs.

All amino acids supplied: no growth.

Transferred to minimal medium: no growth. Mutation has occurred. The mold is unable to synthesize some essential compound.

13-12 The production and isolation in *Neurospora* of mutations affecting single chemical reactions. The sequence of steps illustrated demonstrates that a mutation has been induced which affects the synthesis of the vitamin, thiamine.

largely on *Neurospora* and bacteria because, like *Drosophila* in earlier studies, these organisms were the most convenient for the particular problems attacked. There are strong reasons for believing that the major conclusions from these studies on microorganisms have as general an application to all organisms as do the *Drosophila* results. In other words, we are confident that at least one of the major ways, and probably the principal one, in which genes exert their control is through the enzymes they produce.

This is a tremendous step toward our general goal of decoding the inherited message in the nucleus. We have discovered, so to speak, the kind of language the nucleus talks. It is a language of chemical control, of enzymes. This is a very significant point because it relates to our other knowledge of the genetic ma-

terial discussed earlier in this chapter. We concluded that the hereditary specifications the gene carries are probably in the form of a complex surface. Our reasons for this were: (1) the capacity of the gene to be automatically copied in each cell generation is its most certainly known property; and (2) a surface is the form for which we can most readily imagine a plausible copying process, as in the casting of a mold. This conclusion conforms with our new one—that genes produce enzymes—because the chemist maintains that the really significant feature of enzymes, all of which are proteins, is the nature of their surface.

In Chapter 5 we showed how the surface of the enzyme-protein could promote specific reactions. Acting as a temporary mold, the enzyme surface brings the chemical reactants together in just the right way (Fig. 5-4) for the appropriate parts of the reacting molecules to contact and react. Figuratively we may imagine the enzymes of the cell as so many Yale keys on which the precise pattern of nicks is the opener of specific reactions. All these keys were cast by the cells against the living templates, or molds, on the chromosome surface. We can now be more specific than we were earlier when we described the language of the chromosomes as one of chemical control: it is a language whose code is couched in *specific surfaces. It is through the specific surfaces first of gene, then of enzyme, that control is brought about.*

Earlier we found that present evidence implicates nucleic acid (DNA) as the chemically important part of the gene. The structure of DNA suggested that the sequence of its constituent parts might be the basis of the detailed specifications it carries. Future research must show how this sequence of parts in the DNA molecule is related to the surface it ultimately forms, and through which it exerts its chemical control by molding enzyme surfaces.

Dominance and multiple alleles.

When the hypothesis of gene action through enzyme production was first advanced, a simple interpretation was also given to the well-known genetic phenomenon of dominance. It was supposed that, although the dominant allele of a gene was capable of making its specific enzyme, the recessive was not. Referring to the enzyme, this was summed up as the presence and absence theory of dominance and recessiveness. It is certainly attractive in its simplicity and nicely explains the similarity of the heterozygote (*Aa*) to the homozygous dominant (*AA*): both of them have the enzyme necessary for a particular reaction which fails in the recessive homozygote for complete lack of the enzyme. Unfortunately, the hypothesis has proved too simple.

Dominance has turned out to be relative and seldom complete. It is only sometimes true that the heterozygote (*Aa*) has precisely the same phenotype as the homozygous dominant (*AA*). Often the heterozygote is different from both homozygotes (*AA* and *aa*). This is obvious, for instance, in Andalusian chickens. One allele for feather color produces black when homozygous. Another produces white with small spots. When both alleles are present, in heterozygous combination, the feathers are blue. It is hardly accurate to say that either allele is dominant. Their *effects* blend. But note that the *genes* do not blend. They segregate as usual when gametes are formed. When blue fowls are interbred, the characteristic ratio appears: 1 black:2 blues:1 spotty white (Fig. 13-13).

It is impossible to reconcile such cases of dominance with the presence and absence theory of the enzyme. Two distinct forms of the gene must be present and active in this case. This is even more clearly shown in the inheritance of the human blood groups A, B, AB, and O.

The reader probably knows already that all people fall into one of four groups—A, B, AB, and O—of blood types. Each type or blood group is characterized by a particular protein antigen (p. 319) on the surface of the red blood cells. Thus people in blood group A have the protein antigen A on their red cells; group B have antigen B on their cells; group AB people have both antigens A and B; and group O people have neither A nor B. It is a curious and unexplained fact that group A people also have another special protein (an agglutinin) in their blood *serum* (cf. p. 329) which is like an antibody in that its surface is the complement of the surface of B proteins. This is the reason why, when blood of group B people is transfused into group A people, the incoming red cells with their B antigen are clotted or agglutinated; they are hooked together by the β agglutinins in the type A person's serum (Figs. 13-14 and -15). Clotting can be very serious, even causing death by blocking up smaller blood vessels and stopping circulation. Comparable difficulties arise in the transfusion of A blood into B people who contain α agglutinins in their blood. AB people are sometimes called *universal receivers* because their blood serum lacks both α and β agglutinins and therefore will not clot any type (A, B, AB, or O) of blood cells that are transfused into them. O-group people, on the other hand, are *universal donors* of blood because their

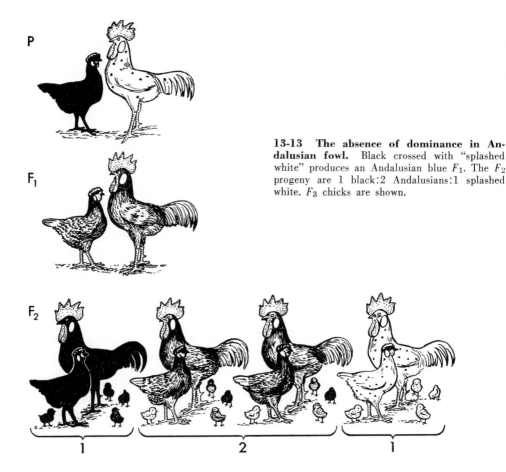

13-13 The absence of dominance in Andalusian fowl. Black crossed with "splashed white" produces an Andalusian blue F_1. The F_2 progeny are 1 black:2 Andalusians:1 splashed white. F_3 chicks are shown.

red cells lack both the A and B antigens.

The points of immediate interest to us concern the inheritance of these blood groups. They are absolutely determined by alleles at a single gene locus. It turns out that three alleles of the gene are concerned.[8] They are L^A, L^B, and L^O. Each allele produces its own characteristic antigen on the surface of red blood cells. The L^A gene produces A antigen; L^B produces B; and L^O produces neither. Type A blood is produced by either of two genotypes $L^A L^A$ and $L^A L^O$; $L^B L^B$ and $L^B L^O$ produce B type blood; $L^A L^B$ produces AB blood; and $L^O L^O$ produces O type blood.

There are three interesting points about the heredity of these blood groups. First, the genes concerned here are seen in direct action,

[8] The gene is labeled L for Karl Landsteiner, who first discovered the A, B, AB, and O blood groups.

manufacturing proteins with specific surfaces. Second, there is no dominance involved. In the $L^A L^B$ heterozygote each allele independently does its own job in producing its own specific protein product. Third, one gene can exist in more than two forms. This situation in blood groups, with three alleles, is by no means exceptional. Geneticists believe most, or all, genes can occur in many allelic forms. In *Drosophila* there are known to be at least twelve allelic forms of one gene controlling eye color.

The existence of multiple alleles and the common absence of dominance force us to reject the idea that the total range of possible actions for a particular kind of gene is the simple pair of alternatives—actions making, or not making, the enzyme. The relations between the gene and the reaction it normally controls can be far more varied than this.

It is easy to envisage how mutations could produce a wide range of alleles whose surface pattern was slightly deformed from the normal. The greater the departure from the normal, the less efficient would the enzyme be in doing its job of fitting reacting chemicals together on its surface. To be sure, this is not the only possibility.

Some mutants are known in bacteria and *Neurospora* in which a particular chemical reaction fails to take place in spite of the fact that the enzyme necessary for the reaction is known to be present. Enzymes are certainly necessary for a given reaction, but evidently other conditions must also be satisfied.

Geneticists believe, in discovering the relation between genes and enzymes, that we have come a long way toward our goal of unraveling the mystery of how the gene controls the activity of the cell. But we still have much more to discover.

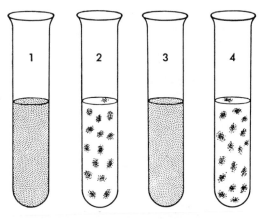

1. Serum of A, cells of A → No agglutination
2. Serum of A, cells of B → Agglutination
3. Serum of B, cells of B → No agglutination
4. Serum of B, cells of A → Agglutination

13-14 Tests for human blood groups. When serum and cells from different blood groups are mixed, the cells agglutinate, or clot together.

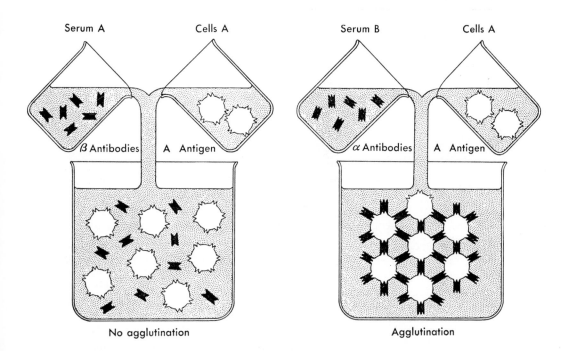

13-15 The mechanism of agglutination. α antibodies have a complementary surface to that of A antigens; β antibodies do not. α antibodies serve to bind together A antigens, and hence to bind together those red blood cells that carry A antigens.

THE ACTION OF THE GENOTYPE
AS A WHOLE

Genes and development. Our discussion of how the individual gene ultimately effects its control must seem somewhat remote from the more familiar aspects of the organism. After all, are not size, shape, pattern, and color the features whose development we want to understand? How does the chemical basis of gene action relate to them?

In the case of color the connection is clear enough. Red petals or white—here the observable difference between fully developed organisms is an obvious chemical difference in the pigments of the flower. Indeed, in some cases the detailed chemical differences are fully known, as well as the particular reaction which did or did not take place, leading to the development, or lack of development, of the pigment concerned.

In size and shape the connection between cell chemistry and final organism is less clear.

13-16 The action of modifying genes in mice. All six mice are heterozygous (Ww) for a gene producing white spots; the six mice differ in the number of modifying genes they carry for bolstering the effect of the primary (white-spotting) gene: (1) fewest modifiers present; (6) most modifiers present.

But even here it seems necessary to conclude that the primary action of the genes concerned must be chemical. Difficulty in envisaging the connection between the primary chemical action of a gene and its ultimate morphological (size, shape) effects is only likely to arise if we overlook how all the genes in the total inherited message tend to act together as an integrated whole in the control of development. We speak of a single gene for red flowers in peas, for wrinkled seeds in corn, or baldness in man. This is all very well and reflects a scientific truth. In each case—redness, wrinkledness, baldness—the development of the character concerned is known to be dependent on the presence of one particular gene allele that we have been able to study. But the character is also dependent on many other genes. As a result of our habit of speech, it is easy to fall into the habit of thinking that an organism has a set number of characteristics with one gene controlling each character. This is quite incorrect. The experimental evidence indicates clearly that genes never work altogether separately. Organisms are not patchworks with one gene controlling each of the patches. They are integrated wholes, whose development is controlled by the entire set of genes acting co-operatively. The rules are: (1) that *each character is affected by many genes*; and (2) that *a single gene may affect many characters*.

Many genes affect one character. In the blue Andalusian fowl two different alleles of the same gene work together, and the result is a phenotype distinct from that produced by either allele alone (that is, when homozygous) (Fig. 13-13). It is also common for different genes to interact, so that phenotypic characters depend on two, three, or many genes and not on one alone. In mice there is a gene that tends to produce white spotting, but its effect is modified by a whole series of other genes, which are *modifiers* in genetic terminology. If few or no modifiers are present, the animal is almost pure white. Practically all intermediate conditions also occur, with various numbers of modifiers (Fig. 13-16). Another example is that of a Norwegian family in which for over four generations about half the children had short index fingers. In some children the finger was very short, and in others it was just barely shorter than usual. Study of the pedigree strongly suggests that two genes are involved, one determining that a short finger will occur, the other determining the degree of shortness.

We have already seen experimental evidence (Chapter 12) demonstrating the multiple gene control of an organism's more general aspects like size and shape. Sometimes, as in the inheritance of corn size (p. 307) the many gene steps seem to be simply additive. The many genes determining sex in *Drosophila* also seem to act on a simple plus-minus, additive basis; sex is determined by the net balance of autosomal and X-chromosomal genes. Often, however, the various genes controlling a character—like that of the Andalusian fowl—interact in a way that is not simply additive. In *Drosophila* the two genes "purple" (eye color) and "arc" (wing shape) separately reduce the vigor and longevity of flies that carry them in homozygous condition. However, when both genes are homozygous in the same fly (Table 13-1) this individual has a life expectancy almost as great as the normal fly, and much greater than that of either the purple or arc homozygotes. Again, the effects are complexly interactive rather than simply additive.

When multiple-factor effects can be traced to a few genes, the genes can sometimes be identified and counted. More commonly, as in corn size, so many genes are involved that their separate identification is a practical impossibility. When a single gene has a more obvious effect on the mature organism clear-cut Mendelian inheritance can be seen, but even then we are merely picking out one element in a system that works as a whole.

One gene affects many characters: pleiotropy. The analogy of organic development with a construction job was used earlier (p. 262) in likening the inherited chromosomes, with their specifications (the genes) for development, to the builder's instructions. The analogy may help us here in elucidating how some genes affect more than one character of the organism while a few seem more restricted in their effects.

TABLE 13-1
Gene interaction in Drosophila

Genes	Length of life (days) *
"Purple" (eye color), alone	24.5
"Arc" (wing shape), alone	26.8
"Purple" and "arc," together	33.7
The nonmutant fly	39.7

* The mutants "purple" and "arc" each reduce length of life when compared with nonmutant flies; when both mutants occur in the same fly they interact, producing a new effect.

In the development of a building or an organism, a single constructional step will have trivial or far-reaching effects depending on when it occurs or how basic is the process involved. It makes little difference if the architect's single specification for door color is misread; the doors might be painted blue instead of green, but no other aspect of the building is affected. The step was terminal, isolated, and trivial. Like doors, which are painted last, the majority of clean-cut inherited differences in living organisms involve trivial and terminal steps in development; the formation of a pigment in a particular organ, eye, or petal may fail, but little else is affected.

But failure or abnormal execution of other single steps will have far-reaching, ramifying consequences. If the single specification for girder or brick size is wrong, or if the workman's square is not exactly 90 degrees, the entire building will finally be affected. In mice a particular gene mutation is known which improperly specifies a single step in bone formation. Its consequences—like those of the builder's untrue square—are seen everywhere in the body where bone formation is important. In *Drosophila*, the gene "vestigial" is so called because its most obvious effect is to reduce the single pair of wings to mere vestiges of the normal (Fig. 13-17). But careful observation shows that this allele also affects the balancers behind the wings, certain of the bristles, the reproductive organs, and other parts. More significantly, it also shortens life and lowers egg production capacity. Clearly the gene has

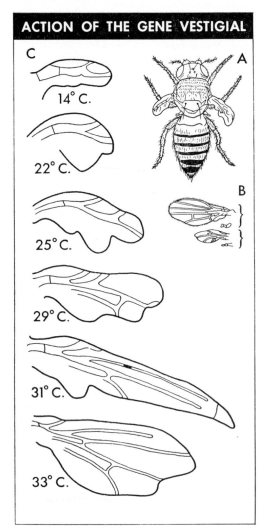

C

14° C.

22° C.

25° C.

29° C.

31° C.

33° C.

A

B

13-17 The action of the gene "vestigial" in Drosophila. *A.* An adult female fly homozygous (*vg vg*) for the gene "vestigial." Note the rudimentary nature of the wings. *B.* The normal (*upper*) and vestigial (*lower*) wings and balancers compared. *C.* The wings of *vg vg* flies reared at different temperatures. The action of the gene is dependent on the temperature: at lower temperatures its effect (in causing departure from normal) is greatest; at 33° C. the wing is nearly normal.

directly or indirectly had a hand in the development of a wide range of the organism's characteristics.

In man there is a recessive mutant allele which, when homozygous, produces imbeciles who are pale in coloring. They also excrete phenyl-pyruvic acid, a compound that is ab-

sent from the urine of normal people who possess the nonmutant form of the gene. These widely diverse effects—skin color, urine constituents, brain function—are all effects of one gene; and probably they are all ultimately due to the single enzyme (either its absence or abnormality) produced by the gene. This normal enzyme evidently controls (like the builder's true square) one step in a complicated process—in humans a metabolic cycle which involves phenyl compounds and produces at various points in the organism not only pigments but also substances necessary (in some unknown way) for proper brain development.

Many single errors early in the construction of a building will cause it ultimately to collapse. Many single genes control early developmental steps so fundamental that their effects also ramify throughout the whole structure of the organism. Their defection or abnormal function has lethal consequences.

The phenomenon of genes affecting a diversity of characters is called *pleiotropy* ("more changing"), and is a genetical generalization of great width and importance. Some students point out that the facts we currently possess concerning pleiotropy do not exclude the possibility that the gene has many primary actions, that is, that one gene produces more than one enzyme, and so on. We do not need to pursue this difficult question here. It is only necessary to note that the multiple effects of a single gene *can* be understood in terms of its having a single primary action (like the use of the builder's square) which has diverse consequences all over the completed structure. This is true not only because a single primary action could occur over and over again in different places (all cells have a complete genotype), but because the products of the primary action may be used as building parts in diverse subsequent developmental processes. The consensus among geneticists studying the developmental effects of genes favors the one gene → one primary product (enzyme) interpretation of pleiotropy. This may turn out to be too simple when all the facts are better understood, but in the meantime it is the most useful working hypothesis.

Environment affects gene action: nature and nurture. In the previous section we have shown that how a gene acts is dependent on what other genes are present. We could say the gene's action is affected by the genetic environment it is in. And it is similarly affected by the physical environment in which it acts. Flies homozygous for the recessive gene "vestigial" (*vg vg*) served us earlier for illustration; the gene *vg* affects many characters besides the wings, and its action is affected by many other genes. Its action is in turn strongly dependent on the temperature at which the fly develops. At high temperatures (30°-31° C.) the wing grows nearly as long as it does in the fly carrying the normal gene (Fig. 13-17).

A tendency to develop *diabetes mellitus* (manifested as an excess of blood sugar) is hereditary in man. The manner of gene control is unknown, but the facts are consistent with the hypothesis that an enzyme or other compound essential for formation of insulin is produced by one allele of a gene and not by another allele. Insulin, in turn, affects the metabolism of carbohydrates, and hence the level of sugar in the blood; high levels are reflected by the presence of sugar in urine (p. 177). This is an example of multiple effects forming a chain from, quite probably, a single primary gene action, the sort of thing we have just been talking about. Let us go on and look at some additional facts.

It has been found that persons who have the genotype for diabetes do not necessarily develop the disease; that is, it does not always appear in their phenotype. An investigator who studied 63 pairs of identical twins, one or the other of whom had diabetes, found that in 10 of the pairs only one was afflicted. Identical twins are so called because they have identical genotypes (p. 340). Therefore in these 10 pairs the twins who did not have the phenotype diabetes nevertheless had a diabetic genotype. In some instances it has been found that the twin with phenotypic diabetes had a different diet, one that made larger demands for carbohydrate metabolism. You already know (p. 178) that, when diabetes has appeared, its symptoms can be almost fully controlled by injections of insulin. As in the twins, the symptoms do not depend on the genotype alone but on the genotype plus phenotypic influences of diet or of medication.

Is *diabetes mellitus* caused by inheritance or by environment? This is another "either-or" question that is not sensible in view of the facts. The disease is caused neither by inheritance alone nor by environment alone, but by the interaction of the two.[9] This is true of the great majority of the characteristics of organisms. It is one of the most important principles of biology that development is an interaction between heredity and environment. That is the broad principle, one special case of which you have already encountered in the relationship between innate and learned behavior (p. 241).

Human blood types are already genetically determined in the zygote, even before blood itself has developed. As far as is known, no environmental influence thereafter changes the blood type in the least. That is one extreme. At the other extreme, human behavior seems to be almost endlessly modifiable. Yet it only seems to be, as a moment's thought will confirm. No human being really "crawls on his belly like a reptile," as some sideshow barkers would have us believe. None swims literally like a fish, and no airman truly flies like a bird. Genetic limitations on human behavior are extraordinarily wide, but they certainly exist.

There is every gradation between characters that are not (as far as we know) modifiable by the environment and those that are greatly modifiable. Height is strongly affected by heredity, but it may be equally influenced by diet and even more strongly affected by disease of the pituitary (p. 180) or medical administration of pituitary hormones. Skin color is primarily determined by heredity, but it is also much modified by exposure to radiation, as well as by some diseases and chemicals. It is common knowl-

9 Symptoms of **diabetes mellitus** may also appear in persons who do not have the diabetic genotype involved in previous discussion. The symptoms may, for instance, follow some damage to the pancreas. In such cases are these symptoms entirely independent of the genotype? (Remember that the whole developmental system, including the presence of a pancreas and the biochemical cycles of carbohydrate metabolism, is influenced by the genotype.)

edge that plants of the same varieties and races (hence closely similar in genotype) have different sizes and shapes (different phenotypes) when grown on different soils, with different fertilizers, with different water supply, or in different climates.

All this boils down to the fact that *what is inherited is a developmental mechanism*. The mechanism determines how the organism will develop under given environmental conditions. It sets narrower or wider limits to the developing organism's reactions to different environments. This is the principle of the reaction range. All phenotypes that actually occur, including those we consider abnormal or pathological, are necessarily within the reaction ranges of the underlying genotypes. The sensible question about any characteristic is not "Is it hereditary or environmental—due to nature or to nurture?" but "What is the reaction range of its genotype, and what are the environmental factors correlated with this particular position in the range?"

Chapter Summary

The inherited message in living systems: information; chromosomes compared to the tape of information that controls the organized work of automatic machines; the study of gene action an attempt to decode the control "language of chromosomes."

The nature of genetic material: the small size of the inherited message; the number and size of genes; difficulty in defining a gene; genes as smallest units of chromosome separable by crossing over.

The chemistry of the genetic material: proteins and nucleic acids; DNA as the message-carrying molecule; experiments with *Pneumococci* and bacteriophage.

The reproduction of the genetic material: templates for reproduction of surfaces in art and industry; the complementary nature of antigen and antibody surfaces suggests a protein template mechanism of gene reproduction; DNA, built-in templates.

Mutation as error in gene reproduction: meanings of "mutation"; chromosome and gene mutations: kinds of chromosome mutations; rate of gene mutations; the experimental production of mutations by high-energy radiation and by chemicals.

Gene action: the single gene in action; enzymes as agents of biochemical control; gene control of enzyme production; genes and enzymes—a language of specific surfaces; dominance and multiple alleles argue against the simple presence-absence hypothesis of dominance-recessiveness.

Action of the genotype as a whole: genes and the control of development; many genes affecting one character—modifier genes; one gene affecting many characters—pleiotropy; the environment affecting gene action; nature and nurture a falsely simple "either-or" question.

This is a developmental stage (the veliger larva) of a marine snail. Its subsequent development will be so accurately controlled that its mature form will duplicate nearly exactly that of the adult snails which produced it. (© Douglas P. Wilson)

CHAPTER 14

Development

"And so the gametes fused and formed a zygote, which developed into an adult." That sounds like ". . . and so they were married and lived happily ever after." In both stories the most interesting part comes after the happy ending. In the whole realm of biology there is nothing more extraordinary or more baffling than the development of mature organisms from zygotes. Here is a single cell, often of microscopic size and always very small in comparison with the developed organism. It divides; the two cells divide again; and the resulting cells divide again and again. Unerringly from this process there emerge all the tissues and organs of a rosebush or a man, an immensely complex, patterned organism, the essential characteristics of which were somehow determined from the start by the specifications in the zygote's chromosomes. In the previous chapter we discussed

the nature of the inherited chromosomal message whose specifications control development. We saw that the language in which the message is couched is one of chemical control. More specifically, we considered it to be a language of molecular surfaces. This knowledge is a substantial step toward our goal of decoding the language of hereditary messages in general, but it is only a beginning. It is a far cry from knowing how one egg becomes a rosebush and another a man. In the present chapter we turn directly to the processes of development. By knowing in more detail what has to be controlled, we may get hints as to how it is controlled.

Processes of Development

In the development of a multicellular organism from the zygote it is useful to distinguish the three constituent processes briefly outlined below: (1) growth, with cell division; (2) morphogenesis; and (3) differentiation.

GROWTH AND CELL DIVISION

Offspring are always smaller than their parents at first. When protists divide, the two offspring are necessarily about half the size of the single parent. In higher plants and animals parents are commonly thousands or millions of times as large as the zygote that is the beginning of a new generation. The process of development, then, always involves growth. Cell division and consequent increase in the number of cells is one aspect of the over-all growth process. But of course growth also necessarily means that individual cells increase in size. (Why cannot multiplication of cells produce growth unless cells themselves become larger at some stage in the process?)

MORPHOGENESIS: THE CREATION OF PATTERN AND SHAPE

Compare yourself with the tiny, spherical zygote from which you developed. You are enormously larger than the zygote, and contain a trillion times as many cells, or more. In a word, you have grown a great deal. But there is clearly more to it than that. You differ from the zygote even more strikingly in having, as a whole organism, a definite, very complex structure and functional *pattern* and shape which were created by the foldings and mass movements of groups of cells as the embryo developed.

DIFFERENTIATION: CELL SPECIALIZATION

You also differ strikingly from the zygote in that your constituent parts (cells and tissues) are visibly *differentiated* into several highly specialized types. Cellular differentiation is a distinct developmental problem in itself, to which we will pay detailed attention later; but it is also almost inextricably a part of morphogenesis. For much of the characteristic pattern of the adult organism derives from the intricate interrelationships that develop between specialized tissues.

differentiated cells in animals and those that longest retain the embryonic capacity for repeated division are the *germ cells*. Concentrated in the primary sexual organs, these continue to divide and to produce gametes through most of the life of the organism.

In plants differentiation is also generally irreversible once the plant is fully developed. However, even the higher plants, in which differentiation is most elaborate and complete, retain throughout life extensive tracts of undifferentiated cells. These constitute the *meristem*, a persistently embryonic tissue (p. 58, Fig. 3-16). From it irreversibly specialized tissues, such as those of wood and bark, and organs, such as leaves and flowers, continue to be differentiated periodically throughout life. This is *open development.*

Like so many distinctions between plants and animals, that between open and closed development is not absolute. Even here there is a unity in the diversity. The capacities of the germ tissue of animals are more restricted than those of meristem tissue, but both are composed of persistent, relatively unspecialized cells more or less embryonic in type. Both give rise to the reproductive cells from which the next generation originates.

The actual continuity between generations does not occur through the differentiated cells that form most of the developed organism. Continuity passes by way of embryonic tissues and the germ cells derived from them. The following mode of continuity applies to the majority of multicellular organisms, both animals and plants (see also Fig. 12-1):

Differentiated cells, P	*Differentiated cells, F_1*
Embryonic tissue → Germ cells ⟶	Embryonic tissue → Germ cells ⟶ to F_2, etc.
P generation	F_1 generation

It is characteristic for differentiation to affect most of the cells and to be irreversible. Specific kinds and arrangements of tissues arise; after they are well differentiated they cannot revert to an undifferentiated form. By the time a human infant is born, its organic pattern is fully established. Later changes are almost entirely in size and shape. Such development is called *closed.* The least

This is the modern form of the principle of *continuity of the germ plasm,*[1] first developed by August Weismann (1834-1914). We do not now accept the principle precisely as Weismann first stated it, but his essential point was correct. That point is that differentiated body cells usually have nothing to do with the production of the next generation and

1 See p. 281.

therefore that they have no direct influence on heredity.

PHASES OF DEVELOPMENT

The three major processes of development do not go on uniformly through the life of the organism. There are phases in which one process or another predominates. The phases intergrade and have no sharp division points, but they are often distinguishable.

In most plants there is a rather rapid early phase of morphogenesis. In higher plants, for instance, the root-stem-leaf pattern is soon evident in the seedling. The next phase is mainly characterized by over-all growth and the creation of more units of the pattern: more roots, more stems, more leaves. Later comes a new phase of more specialized patterning, when reproductive organs (flowers in the flowering plants) are formed.

In animals the over-all pattern is usually established once and for all (the development is closed, p. 336) during an early morphogenetic phase of development. Multiplication of pattern units, then, usually does not accompany growth of animals, as it does the growth of plants, whose development is open (p. 336). Usually, too, the reproductive organs of animals are laid down as part of the original pattern, even though they may not function until much later. Frequently the following phases can be more or less clearly distinguished in the development of animals:

1. A phase before fertilization when the cytoplasm of egg cell grows and undergoes some internal patterning and differentiation.

2. Immediately after fertilization a short phase of cell division or *cleavage*, with little or no over-all growth (individual cells become smaller) or differentiation. The pattern remains simple and has no clear resemblance to the definitive pattern. In man this phase lasts for the first week or ten days after fertilization.

3. Then follows a principally *morphogenetic* phase during which the main outlines of the adult pattern are established in the multicellular embryo.

4. The next phase, *differentiation* of cells and tissues, is never wholly separate from the preceding one. Most cell differentiation does,

however, tend to come after the major pattern of the organism is established. In man this phase occupies the greater part of life in the uterus. Around the end of the seventh month it begins to merge with the next phase.

5. A phase in which *growth* predominates, changes being more matters of proportion than of introduction of new elements in the pattern. This is often the longest developmental phase. In man it begins before birth and lasts into the late teens.

The sequence in particular animals may have further complications. For instance, the many animals with larvae go through a radical second phase of repatterning. Some of the specific details are treated in the next chapter. Here a broader summary suffices as introduction to some of the principles of pattern formation.

Patterns of Morphogenesis and Differentiation in Animals

THE MATURATION OF THE EGG CELL

The process of meiosis is the same in both sexes as far as chromosome behavior is concerned. It follows the course outlined in Chapter 11, whereby the chromosome number is reduced from the diploid to the haploid number. In the female, however, nonchromosomal aspects of gamete formation are profoundly modified in a manner directly bearing on the general problem of development.

The differences between spermatogenesis (sperm production) and oögenesis (egg-cell production) are outlined in Fig. 14-1. A single (diploid) spermatocyte gives rise to four (haploid) sperms as a result of the two meiotic divisions. In the female the diploid cell in which meiosis begins is called an oöcyte. It gives rise to only one (haploid) egg cell. Before meiosis the oöcyte becomes surrounded by a *follicle* of other cells in the ovary. They appear to provide the oöcyte with food. Certainly the oöcyte grows substantially. Part of its growth is due to the storage of food materials as yolk. The human oöcyte grows to a size of 0.2 millimeters; that of the frog to 2 millimeters; and that of the ostrich to 10 centimeters.

When meiosis takes place in the oöcyte, one of the two cells formed by the first division is a very small *polar body* which contains almost no cytoplasm. Similarly, in the second meiotic division one of the nuclei is nipped off in a second polar body. In this way a single egg

cell is produced,[2] retaining all the food materials accumulated during the long period of maturation before meiosis.

The maturation of the egg cell, however, involves more than the accumulation of food

2 The polar bodies degenerate.

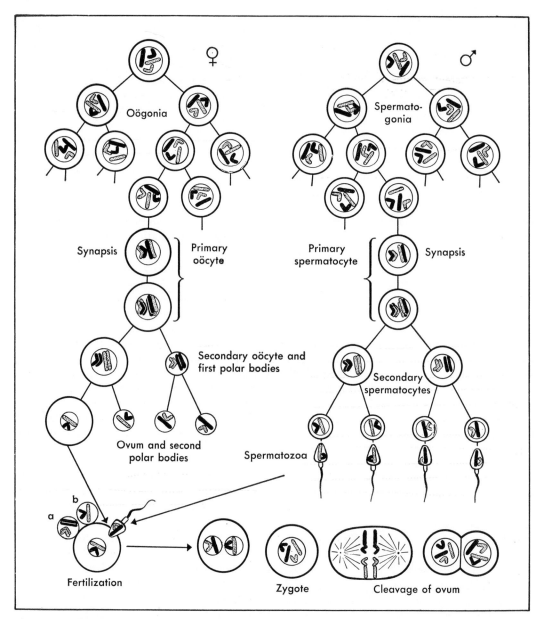

14-1 Differences in the course of meiosis in male and female. The organism is represented as having 4 chromosomes ($2n = 4$), one pair of rod-shaped chromosomes and a pair of smaller V-shaped chromosomes. At fertilization (*lower left*) *a* and *b* are two polar bodies that degenerate.

for the early growth of the embryo. One essential feature is an initial spatial organization, or differentiation, of the egg-cell cytoplasm, paving the way for later differentiation of the multicellular embryo derived from it. The extent of visible cytoplasmic differentiation in the egg varies in different groups; it is especially marked in some invertebrate animals like sea squirts, annelid worms, and mollusks (see Chapter 22). This difference is related, as we shall shortly see, to the capacity of different groups to undergo twinning. But some differentiation—visible or invisible—of the cytoplasm seems to be characteristic of all eggs.

FERTILIZATION

Cytoplasmic organization is complete by the time meiosis occurs in the egg. Meiosis commonly is arrested at the metaphase of the second meiotic division and is completed only when the entry of the fertilizing sperm cell acts as a signal to proceed. Indeed the response of the egg cell to the sperm's entry is not only to complete meiosis but also to proceed with the rest of development.

In some species artificial stimuli such as the prick of a fine needle can cause the egg to complete meiosis and to start development. This shows that the sperm's nucleus is not essential for development. The haploid egg cell can go ahead and complete nearly all of development and, in some cases, absolutely all. Haploid salamanders have been raised in this way.[3] Haploid embryos can also be raised by removing the egg nucleus before fertilization. The haploid nucleus of the fertilizing sperm proves adequate. Indeed, in a few instances some early development can be achieved by an egg cell artificially deprived of any nuclear controls. To be sure, such eggs do not develop far along the normal path and they do die. But the fact that they develop at all tells us that the cytoplasm itself carries some information on how to proceed. This probably reflects the early differentiation of the egg cytoplasm that took place in the egg's maturation (which was nuclear-controlled) before the time of fertilization.

[3] As noted earlier (p. 276), the importance of diploidy is principally in relation to the mechanism of evolution.

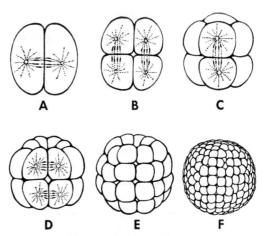

14-2 Cleavage of a fertilized egg. Note that successive cell divisions proceed without cell growth; at the end of cleavage (*F*, morula) the embryo, though many-celled, is no larger than the zygote was at the first cleavage division (*A*).

CLEAVAGE

In normal development the fertilized egg proceeds to divide immediately following the formation of a diploid nucleus by union of egg and sperm chromosomes. Cell division continues for some time in the absence of any protoplasmic growth. Thus the cleaving embryo remains constant in over-all size, and cell dimensions steadily decrease with successive divisions until the growth accomplished by the egg's maturation is canceled out (Fig. 14-2). The result of egg cleavage is a raspberry- or mulberry-like cluster of cells called a *morula* (Latin for "mulberry"). With further divisions the number of cells increases and a cavity develops in among them. The whole embryo then has the gross form of a hollow sphere, the *blastula*.

Experiments with cleavage-stage embryos are very instructive. With many species it is possible to shake apart the individual cells and observe their subsequent behavior. In some animals, these separate cells are able to start all over again and complete development; in other animals this is not possible.

When renewed development is possible, as with sea urchins and frogs, we must conclude that the cells were not irreversibly differentiated; that is, they all were still essentially alike, and each was capable of complete development, just like the original egg. Lack of

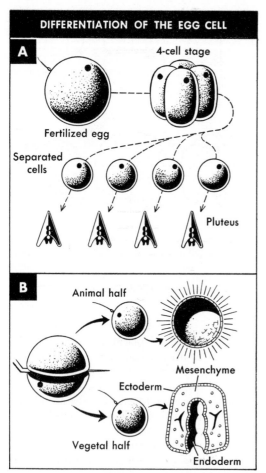

DIFFERENTIATION OF THE EGG CELL

A

4-cell stage

Fertilized egg

Separated cells

Pluteus

B

Animal half

Mesenchyme

Ectoderm

Vegetal half

Endoderm

14-3 Experimental evidence of differentiation in the zygote's cytoplasm. *A.* The fertilized egg cleaves along the axis of differentiation, producing four cells, all of which are the same and contain a complete sample of the field of differentiation; shaken apart, all four cells can produce a complete embryo. *B.* When the fertilized egg is experimentally cleaved with a needle *across* the axis of differentiation, a different result is obtained. The two halves ("animal" and "vegetal") do not contain a complete sample of the field of differentiation; consequently, neither can develop into a complete embryo. One half of the egg reaches only an advanced gastrula stage (*below*), and the other stops development while a blastula (*above*).

differentiation in the cells of young embryos is surprising, for we noted earlier that the mature egg cell is often differentiated, even visibly so. How is it that the cleavage of the egg cytoplasm into distinct cellular compartments does not produce differentiated cells? For instance, the sea urchin, whose egg is

visibly differentiated, is one of those animals whose early cleavage stages (up to 4-cell stage) can be shaken apart to produce cells that are still capable of further development. The explanation lies in the plane of cleavage in the egg. The first divisions of the zygote cleave the egg *along* the axis of differentiation (Fig. 14-3). If, however, another egg cell is experimentally cleaved *across* the axis of visible differentiation the separated halves fail to develop into normal embryos (Fig. 14-3). In those animals like snails and worms, in which cell differentiation starts with the first cleavage, the first cleavage plane cuts across the field of differentiation in the egg cytoplasm.

Embryos that develop from separate cells derived from the same morula do, of course, possess exactly the same heredity. Their nuclei were produced by the mitotic division of a single zygote nucleus. This is the way in which identical twins arise. The potentiality for separate development may persist later than the two-celled stage. Identical quadruplets can arise by separation of cells in the four-celled stage, after two cleavages. (How could identical triplets arise?) In man this potentiality for total development persists even after three cleavages. This is one way the Dionne quintuplets may have arisen. There are other possible ways in which identical twins, triplets, and so on, can arise from one zygote, but all depend on the absence of irreversible differentiation among cells in the young embryo.[4]

[4] Twins are not necessarily identical. Sometimes two eggs are liberated from the ovaries at the same time, are fertilized by separate sperms, and develop simultaneously. Twins developed in this way are neither more nor less similar in heredity than brothers and sisters born separately. They are called fraternal twins (even if both are girls). Identical twins are necessarily of the same sex. (Why?) Fraternal twins may or may not be identical. Triplets may be all fraternal, all identical, or two identical and one fraternal. What are the possibilities among quadruplets?
Multiple births are relatively rare in humans. The numbers vary considerably in different groups, but in the United States about 1 birth in 90 is of twins among whites and about 1 in 70 among Negroes. Of these, about a third are identical and about two-thirds fraternal twins. Triplets occur about once in 8000 or 9000 births, and quadruplets only once in 600,000 or 700,000. A tendency to produce twins or other multiple births is sometimes hereditary, and the proportion may be much higher in "twin-prone" families. Oddly enough, this applies only to fraternal twins. There is no clear evidence that

Sooner or later there is some differentiation of cells within the developing embryo. Thereafter a single cell removed from the rest will not develop into a whole organism, and development of the remaining cells does not produce a normal organism. Parts that would have developed from the removed cell are missing.

The cleavage of the zygote is often profoundly modified by the amount of food materials (yolk) and other factors in the embryo. Figure 14-4 compares cleavage in amphioxus, frog, and bird—a series of embryos with increasing amounts of yolk material. In the hen's egg the zygote cell is the whole yellow mass we designate as yolk. The nucleus and cytoplasm from which the embryo develops are localized on a part of the surface of the yolk. Much of the original zygote cell is never involved in cleavage. Cleavage of the cytoplasm occurs first in a platelike area on one side, and the growing embryo gradually consumes the yolk proper, finally occupying the whole available space.

In general, species whose eggs have little yolk develop in one of two ways. The immature organism, still midway in its development, (1) becomes self-feeding, or (2) is nourished directly by its mother, as in the mammals (see p. 386). Self-feeding immature stages are called *larvae* and are familiar in caterpillars (to develop further into moths and butterflies) and maggots (immature flies). Larvae are common in many invertebrate groups of animals (p. 384).

GASTRULATION: A PRINCIPAL MORPHOGENETIC PHASE

Even in the earliest stages, development follows different lines in various groups of animals. As the process goes further, there

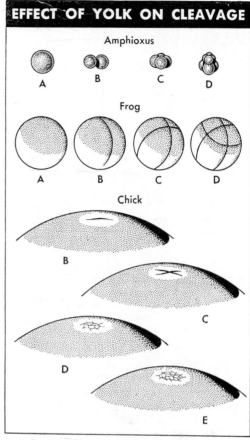

EFFECT OF YOLK ON CLEAVAGE

Amphioxus

Frog

Chick

14-4 **The effect of yolk on the cleavage of the egg.** (1) In the Amphioxus egg, which contains virtually no yolk, cleavage is complete. (2) In the frog's egg there is considerable yolk on one side (unstippled). The yolk material is an inert mass incapable of cleavage. The cleavage plane consequently is displaced above the yolk. (3) The hen's egg cell is almost entirely yolk, and consequently cleavage is restricted to a very small area. *B, C* and *D* are identical stages in all three animals.

production of identical twins runs in families, that is to say, is influenced by heredity.

Most of the larger mammals agree with man in usually having one young at a time, with occasional twins and still rarer triplets. Small mammals, especially the rodents, usually have multiple births. In members of the mouse family quintuplets are common, and ten, fifteen, or even twenty young may occasionally be born at once. Multiple offspring are also the rule among other vertebrates and especially among invertebrates, some of which produce thousands and even millions of eggs in one breeding season. Such multiple births are usually fraternal, and identical twinning is comparatively rare in nature.

is tremendous diversity in detail. However, some features can be seen in more or less modified form in most animals. Among such features is the formation of separate layers of cells, which we shall describe in its simplest form—a form so simple, indeed, as to be rare in actual occurrence. Almost always the process is profoundly modified, sometimes almost unrecognizably so. Nevertheless, even the most complex forms of development do involve layer formation analogous to that in the simple cases we describe.

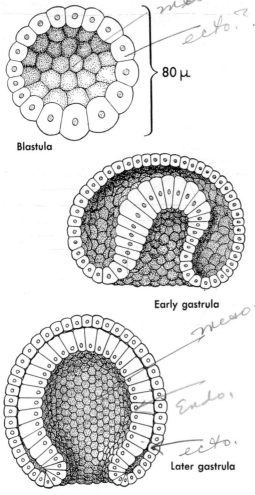

meso.
ecto.

80 μ

Blastula

Early gastrula

meso.

Endo.

ecto.

Later gastrula

14-5   The gastrula of *Amphioxus* and its formation by invagination.   The endoderm of the gastrula has larger cells than the ectoderm.

The process of gastrulation, whereby the embryo becomes a two-layered structure, follows the morula and blastula stages (p. 339). The simplest, though not the most common, form of gastrulation is for one side of the blastula to cave in, much as does the side of a soft rubber ball you poke with your finger. The result is a cup- or bowl-shaped *gastrula* with two layers of cells forming its walls (Fig. 14-5). The outer layer is the *ectoderm* ("outside skin"); the layer lining the cavity of the gastrula is the *endoderm* ("inside skin"). Figures 14-5 and 14-6 compare the simplest mode of gastrulation as found in amphioxus (p. 543), for instance, with the

gastrulation of the frog's embryo. In the frog one region of the blastular wall grows more rapidly than the rest, and a lip of cells is formed, where the more rapidly growing tissue folds inside the cavity of the blastula.

The cavity inside the double-walled gastrula becomes the alimentary canal of the adult animal. Here in the gastrula we can recognize the gross outlines of the adult's future pattern. Gastrulation is indeed principally a morphogenetic phase of development, producing the main outlines of organic pattern rather than differentiation of cells into special types.

In coelenterates (corals, *Hydra*, etc., p. 526) gastrulation is more than the main outline of morphogenesis. It is *almost* as far as the whole process goes because these animals are essentially just pouches with two well-defined layers of cells (Fig. 22-3), although a few other cells may migrate between the bases of the distinctly layered cells.

In most other animals a more complex third layer of cells (the *mesoderm*) develops between the ectoderm and endoderm. The mesoderm may arise by pouchlike foldings

---

14-6   Early development of the frog.   *1.* Sperm enters the egg. The arrow indicates the future head-to-tail axis of the embryo. *2.* Sperm nucleus migrates to egg nucleus—fertilization. *3.* Blastula in cross section. Note the large yolk cells in the lower ("vegetal") half of the egg. *4, 5.* Early gastrulas. The sheet of cells forming the upper ("animal") half of the blastula is beginning to grow actively and roll inward at a place known as the blastopore. The actual point of involution of cells is known as the dorsal lip of the blastopore. *6-10.* Later stages of gastrulation. The blastocoel (original cavity of the blastula) is nearly obliterated (*6*). The new cavity formed by the ingrowth of cells at the blastopore is the archenteron, or primitive digestive tract (*7*). The blastopore (at this stage closed by a plug of yolk cells) is destined to become the anus of the adult. The mouth remains to be developed at the other end of the archenteron (cf. *16*). The sheet of cells that has grown in from the blastopore is the future mesoderm (*8, 9*). Endoderm on the floor of the archenteron grows upward and arches over to form the future digestive tract (*9, 10*); the sheet of mesoderm then lies between the roof of the digestive tract and the ectoderm (*10*). The notochord arises from the mesoderm immediately above the archenteron (*10*). The coelomic cavity arises as a split within the mass of mesoderm. *10-15.* On the dorsal surface of the embryo two folds of ectoderm grow upward as the neural folds; the flat layer of ectoderm between them

THE EARLY DEVELOPMENT OF THE FROG

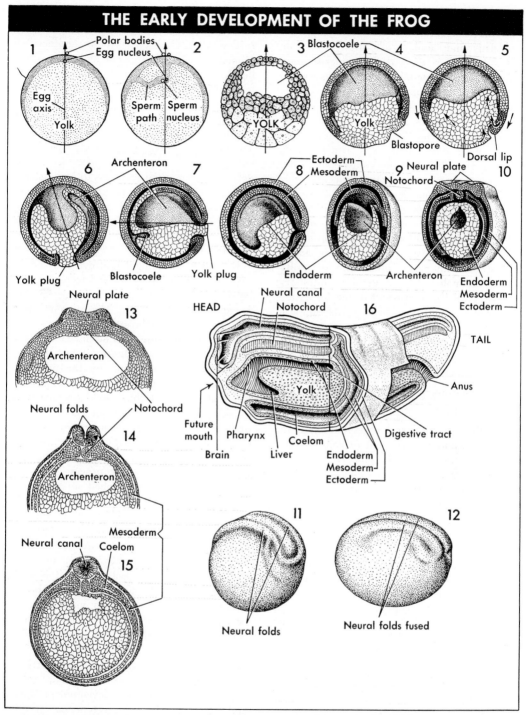

is known as the neural plate; the tube eventually formed by closure of the folds is the neural canal; in this manner the tubular dorsal nerve cord—typical of all vertebrates—is formed. In the anterior portion of the neural canal three swellings correspond with the future fore-, mid-, and hindbrain portions of the adult brain (cf. p. 213). *16.* Late frog embryo, showing major outlines of adult form: head-tail axis is clear; neural canal and brain lie above the notochord. The digestive tract still lacks a mouth opening, which will later develop as an invagination of ectoderm; an evagination from the digestive tract marks the beginning of the liver; mesoderm and coelom are clear.

from the endoderm region or as individual cells that migrate into the space between ectoderm and endoderm and proliferate there. In either case the mesoderm soon becomes quite complex and loses whatever clear resemblance to a layer it may have had. Usually at a rather early stage a cavity, the *coelom*, appears in it, lined with mesodermal layers or masses. A distinction, often not at all clear in actual study, can be made between a coelom that develops from endodermal pouches and one that appears later within a mesodermal mass (Fig. 22-20). The former process seems to be primitive for echinoderms and vertebrates, at least, and the latter process is primitive for most other animals that do have a coelom. This is, again, evidence for an early subdivision of multicellular animals into two great evolutionary groups (p. 554). As a result of the formation of a coelom, the mesoderm at its simplest and most truly layerlike really forms two layers, one closely applied to the ectoderm and one to the endoderm, with the coelomic cavity between them (Figs. 14-6 and 22-20).

DIFFERENTIATION AND
ORGAN FORMATION

The three germ layers represent an early sorting out and arrangement of cells as they increase in number in the embryo. The cells in the layers still are not strongly differentiated. When the cells do later form distinct tissues and organs, the layer arrangement is

TABLE 14-1

Tissues derived from germ layers

Ectoderm

Epidermis of the skin (cf. Fig. 3-25), nails and hair; sweat glands in skin; all nervous tissue; receptor cells in sense organs; epidermis of mouth, nostril, and anus.

Endoderm

Epidermis lining gut, trachea, bronchi, lungs, urinary bladder, and urethra; liver; pancreas; thyroid gland.

Mesoderm

All muscles; blood; connective tissue (including bone); kidneys; testes and ovaries; epithelia lining body cavities.

no longer evident. Many of the tissues can, however, be traced back more or less clearly to derivation from one layer or another. The alimentary canal and glands and other organs developed from it, and the respiratory system are lined with tissue from the endoderm surrounded by other tissues of mesodermal origin. Skin has outer parts that arise from ectoderm, and inner parts from mesoderm. The nervous system and parts of sense organs closely associated with it arise from ectoderm by a remarkable process to be illustrated below. Most connective tissue, muscles, bones, blood vessels and blood, and many internal organs such as the heart, kidneys, or gonads (testes and ovaries) arise from the mesoderm (Table 14-1).

It used to be thought that every tissue was clearly and necessarily derived from one germ layer and always from the same germ layer for any one sort of tissue. The inference, then, was that the germ layers, as such, represent early and irreversible differentiation of the cells in them. For instance, it was believed that ectoderm cells were, by the mere fact that they are in the ectoderm, partially differentiated so that they could become nerve or skin cells; they could not become muscle or bone cells. This has been proved incorrect. Gastrulation and germ-layer formation are processes of morphogenesis rather than differentiation; they are the processes whereby adult form is roughly sketched out and masses of potentially multipurpose cells are stockpiled ready for later cell differentiation and development of detailed organs. The later differentiation of a cell depends not so much on whether it is broadly ecto-, meso-, or endoderm, as on precisely *where* it is in the over-all pattern of the embryo. Muscles and bones usually develop from mesoderm only because mesoderm normally happens to occur in those parts of the embryo where muscle and bone are differentiated. But if by some variation of development in a particular species ectoderm happens to come into a region of muscle or bone development, muscle and bone develop from ectoderm. In other words, final and definitive differentiation depends on regional relationships and on later anatomical controls, not basically on the germ layers.

INDUCTION AND ORGANIZERS

Our discussion of germ layers emphasized the fact that later differentiation of a cell depends not only on what but especially on where it is. Many experiments have revealed something of the nature of the interactions among developing cells. Some of these experiments involve tissue culture. Bits of tissue removed from a living organism will continue to live, grow, and divide if they are kept in a solution of suitable temperature, osmotic pressure, and composition. If kidney cells from a mouse are so cultured, they grow in a formless way, like undifferentiated embryonic cells. If, however, kidney connective tissue is added to the culture, the cells differentiate and tend to form kidney tubules. The connective tissue evidently releases some substance that *induces* differentiation in the kidney cells.

Experiments on embryos show that *induction* likewise and even more elaborately occurs in normal development. The German experimental embryologist Hans Spemann (1869-1941) showed that there is a special inducing region at the upper edge of the infolding lip of the gastrula (Fig. 14-6) in frogs and salamanders. He called this region the *organizer*. Its removal prevents normal differentiation. Transplantation of the organizer into another embryo at a similar stage of development causes double differentiation and development of a sort of Siamese twins (Fig. 14-7).

The organizer of frogs and salamanders is ultimately responsible for much of their differentiation. Specifically, the tissue [5] just inside the organizer lip induces formation of the nervous system in the overlying ectoderm. In these animals, as in all vertebrates, the nervous system arises first as a plate or thickening (the neural plate) in the ectoderm along what is to become the back of the animal. Later the sides of the neural plate are elevated, forming the neural folds, which fuse together to form a tube that eventually becomes the brain and spinal cord (Fig. 14-6). Experiments readily prove that this process is induced by the organizer tissue, which nevertheless does not itself form any of the nervous

[5] This tissue, destined to become mesoderm, is technically known as chorda mesoderm.

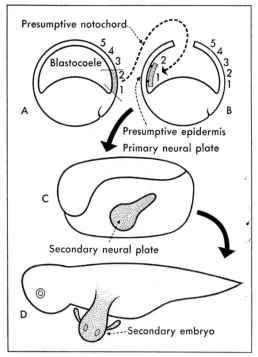

14-7 Experimental demonstration of induction by the organizer. *A.* The piece of the organizer (dorsal lip of blastopore) that normally ultimately induces the formation of neural plate is presumptive notochord: it will become notochord eventually. *B.* This presumptive notochord is removed from one embryo and transplanted into the blastocoel of another, where it attaches at a point corresponding with the future left side of embryo. *C.* It here induces a secondary neural plate, and (*D*) the result is a two-headed monster.

system. If the organizer tissue is removed just before the neural plate would have been formed in the ectoderm, no neural plate develops. If the organizer is transplanted and placed beneath another area of ectoderm, a neural plate will develop there instead of in the normal position.

Further experiments indicate that the induction of the neural plate, at least, is due to a chemical diffused from the inducing organizer tissue into the differentiating ectoderm.

Other experiments involving the transplantation of pieces of the embryo to new locations elucidate further aspects of the process of normal development. In the gastrula stage of the amphibian embryo, careful observation and experiment have enabled embryologists to draw a map showing what organs various parts of the gastrula will eventually produce. Figure 14-8A shows the location of a mass of cells that in normal development would give rise to an eye. These gastrula cells can be transplanted to various locations

on an older embryo. When this is done (Fig. 14-8A) their future development is again controlled by the particular environment of cells into which they have been transplanted. Transplanted to the head region, they develop into the brain and eye, characteristic of that region; behind the mouth they develop into gills; and when placed in the tail end of the embryo they develop into, among other things, the kidney duct characteristic of the region.

All the embryo's cells, arising by mitosis from the single-celled zygote, arrange themselves into a definite form and differentiate in a gradual process. What they differentiate into is initially controlled *purely by their location* in the embryo. Their differentiation cannot be controlled by differences in heredity *because all the cells receive one and the same set of chromosomes from the zygote by the process of mitosis.* However, their differentiation, initially guided by embryonic location, eventually does reach a point of no return, so to speak. In the normal embryo a stage of differentiation is ultimately reached by the cells we have discussed when their ultimate fate to be eye cells is no longer *presumptive* but *determined.* After differentiation has reached this state of determination, the cells can be transplanted and will go ahead and become an eye independent of their new location (Fig. 14-8B).

THE PROBLEM OF GENETIC CONTROL

After our brief survey of the kinds of processes that go on in the normal development of the organism, we must now return to our earlier problem. How does the inherited blueprint, the set of chromosome specifications, control these processes? There is a fundamental problem that faces us in attempting to answer this question. How can we reconcile the two following facts?

1. Development involves the organization of a multitude of cells into a complex but definite pattern and the differentiation of these cells into many diversified and specialized cell types.

2. All these cells with their widely different fates in the organism have an identical heredity. They arose by mitosis from the single-celled zygote.

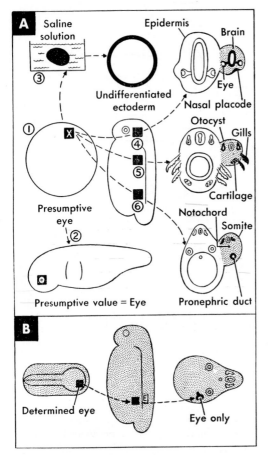

14-8 **Determination *vs.* presumptive fate in embryonic development.** *A.* (*1*) A piece of embryonic tissue (marked *X*) in the amphibian gastrula will normally develop into an eye: its presumptive fate is eye. (*2*) If, however, it is removed from the gastrula and allowed to develop in saline solution it does not differentiate into an eye (*3*). If it is transplanted to unusual locations (*4, 5,* and *6*) in older embryos it differentiates, not into an eye, but into structures characteristic of the location to which it has been moved. In the gastrula the fate of *X* as an eye is only *presumptive* and is contingent on its embryonic location. *B.* If the same tissue is transplanted from a much older embryo than a gastrula, its fate is found to have become *determined:* no matter where it is transplanted it differentiates into an eye.

There is *no evidence whatsoever that*, in successive cell divisions in the growth of the embryo, neatly packaged fractions of the total blueprint are partitioned out—one set to presumptive leg tissue, one set to presumptive eye, and so on. Indeed there is evidence that this is *not* the case. The chromosome set remains visibly complete in different tissues. And, as we have seen, cells can proceed along one path of differentiation for quite a while and still retain their capacity to differentiate into something entirely different if they are transplanted. *To reconcile these facts we must show how it is possible for the diverse cells to behave so differently in spite of possessing the same nuclear controls.*

A lead to the solution of this problem comes from our earlier survey (p. 325) of gene action. The evidence points to the conclusion that the gene acts through its control of unitary chemical processes. This control in most, if not all cases, is effected through the intermediary of enzymes. But, as we saw, the gene's action is not an absolutely fixed affair. There is not even a flat alternative of producing or not producing an enzyme—of a reaction taking place or not. We know of cases in which a reaction (the synthesis of pantothenic acid in some bacteria) fails to occur in spite of the fact that the necessary enzyme is present. Any reaction, such as the conversion of a substance A to B, depends on many conditions, only one of which is the presence of the enzyme. It depends on the rate of supply of A, and also on the rate at which B is removed by conversion into other substances in other reactions. Since these events—the supply of A and the removal of B—are the products of the action of other genes, it is clear that genes must interact, as we earlier found they did. The reaction is also sensitive to physical conditions, such as acidity and temperature. A gene's action is, in short, profoundly influenced by both the genetic and physical environment in which it finds itself.

Here then is our lead to the riddle of different cell types developing in different parts of an embryo in spite of possessing identical chromosome sets. *Ultimately the diverse effects of the same genotype must be due to the different cellular environments that exist in the embryo.*

Let us look at one very clear example of this principle. In rabbits there is a gene which when homozygous produces a characteristic color pattern (Fig. 14-9). The coat is white except for the nose, ears, paws, and tail, which are black. The blackness is due to an enzyme-controlled synthesis of pigment. Our

14-9 The effect of temperature on the action of a gene. The Himalayan rabbit is homozygous for a gene that controls synthesis of the black pigment, melanin. The gene acts, however, only at low temperatures. Thus pigment is regularly formed only on the extremities: nose, ears, paws, and tail. If the rabbit is shaved on the back and the new hair grows under the cooling influence of an ice pack, black pigment is formed.

basic problem can here be stated in clear-cut terms: we are sure that the enzyme is gene-controlled and that each cell of the body contains the gene. How is it that the gene acts, ultimately producing pigment, in only some cells (nose, ears, etc.)? Experiment reveals that the pigment is produced only—that is, the reaction proceeds only—below a certain temperature (92° F.). When the temperature is higher, the reaction fails in spite of the presence of the gene. The restriction of pigment to the paws, tail, and nose is due simply to the fact that the high surface/volume ratio of these extremities causes them to be slightly colder than the rest of the body, as anyone knows who has gone out in freezing weather. If the back of the rabbit is shaved and cooled with an ice pack while new hair is grown, it comes in black.

The general results of transplant experiments point in the same direction. What a cell becomes depends at first entirely on where it is in the embryo; later it also depends on both where it is and what it is; and what it is depends on where it was earlier. The direction of differentiation seems then to be determined by differences in strictly local physical and chemical conditions in the embryo. All the embryo's cells have identical controls, but which genes act and how they act in any particular cell depend on the strictly local environment in which the gene finds itself. This principle involves a kind of chain reaction. Gene Z's action may be dependent on products of X and Y; and gene X's on the products of W. A slight peculiarity in local conditions of, say, one part of the mesoderm might inhibit the action of gene W only; but this in turn will affect genes X and Z. Evidently minute environmental differences within the embryo can have profound, snowballing effects on the genotype as a whole.

This line of argument takes us right back to the zygote and egg cell itself. The prolonged maturation and differentiation of the egg cytoplasm now assumes great significance. Local differences in the egg cytoplasm are partitioned into separate cells by the process of cleavage. And though the nuclei that enter these cleavage cells are fundamentally identical in their gene content, they enter different

physical and chemical environments. Hence arises the process of evoking different actions from identical nuclei; and this process continues with increasingly marked consequences in later stages of development.

If we revert to our analogy of heredity as the transmission of a message for the control of development, we may view the early maturation of the egg cell in a new light. The maturation of the egg is a process which organizes the cytoplasm properly to decode the message of the nucleus.

Patterns of Growth in Animals

In most multicellular animals, the anatomical pattern of differentiated cells, tissues, and organs is achieved rather early in the life cycle. As development continues, there are further changes in functioning as the organism matures. For instance, in vertebrates the integration and co-ordination of the nervous system may continue long after its anatomical pattern is complete, and the sex organs are not effectively in operation for a long time after they are present and differentiated. The phase during which these changes in *maturation* occur is more strikingly marked by changes in size than by changes in structure. A period of *growth* intervenes between the period of embryonic differentiation and the relatively static period of adult life (p. 337).

THE GROWTH CURVE

An over-all pattern of growth is obtained if an organism is measured at suitable intervals and the measurements are plotted against time. Measurements of individuals are of course likely to show a good many irregularities, especially if environmental conditions are not absolutely uniform. (Even in a laboratory it is extremely difficult to keep conditions wholly uniform, and they never are in nature.) Nevertheless, the pattern of growth frequently looks more or less like Fig. 14-10A. Marked deviations from this pattern can usually be explained by special circumstances.

The curve of Fig. 14-10B shows that increase in size is at first rather slow but soon becomes rapid and then finally tapers off again as adult size is reached. This sequence is familiar in ourselves. The slow beginning occurs in the embryo. By the time of birth, growth is going on very rapidly, and it continues so into adolescence. Then growth slows down and finally stops altogether. The timing differs considerably for different individuals, sexes, and measurements. In humans increase in height usually stops in the early twenties, or in almost all healthy individuals sometime between 18 and 30, at least. Increase in weight continues longer, frequently into the forties, but also usually stops eventually. When growth stops, an actual decrease in size soon sets in. You are likely to reach your greatest height in the early twenties, and then to start shrinking in height, even though your waistline may increase for another twenty or thirty years. The decrease in height will be slow and not noticeable for a long time, but it is likely to speed up in your fifties. If you reach a ripe old age you will probably be visibly shorter and lighter than you were in your prime.

When the whole animal kingdom is considered, it is not usual for growth to reach a definite stopping point, and it is still less usual for growth to be followed by shrinking. Definite cessation of growth is especially characteristic of mammals. The reason or, at least, the mechanism involves the way the vertebrae and limb bones grow in man and other mammals. While growing, these bones have separate plates or pieces at their ends, and growth occurs by addition of bone tissue between these pieces and the main body of the bone. Eventually fusion occurs, and then normal bone growth is subsequently impossible. However, birds also tend to grow to a definite size and then stop, although they do not have this particular mechanism of bone growth. In other vertebrates and in many invertebrates growth may continue throughout life. Growth becomes very slow in the adult, however, and such species do have a maximum size that is never exceeded. Thus there are two patterns, which do not really differ very much.

In insects and their relatives with hard external skeletons (most of the arthropods, p. 569) another variation in growth pattern occurs. The skeleton does not grow, and it

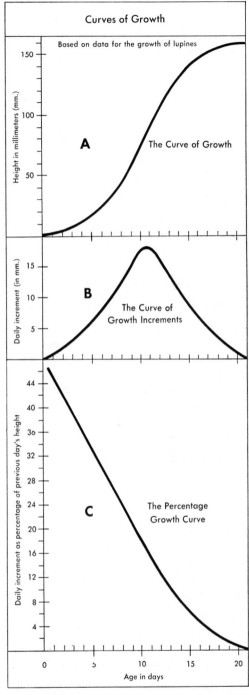

14-10 **Curves of growth.** The data from which the curves were plotted relate to the growth of lupine plants. See pp. 350 through 355.

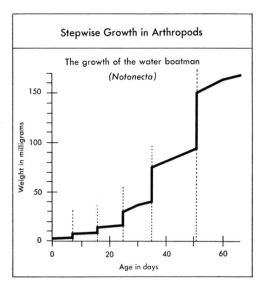

Stepwise Growth in Arthropods

The growth of the water boatman
(Notonecta)

14-11 Stepwise growth in arthropods. The hard exoskeleton of arthropods must be shed periodically to permit growth, which therefore takes on a stepwise character. Each abrupt step in the growth curve occurs at a time when the old hard skeleton has been discarded and the new one below is still soft enough to permit growth.

confines the other tissues and prevents growth of the animal as a whole. Growth therefore occurs in spurts, with the shedding or molting of the old skeleton and the growth of a new, larger one (Fig. 14-11). Growth ceases after the last molt. Insects do not molt after the adult stage is reached, and adult insects are therefore fixed in size. (In us, too, the outer layer of the skin is dead and does not grow. How is it, then, that we can grow continuously without outgrowing our skins?)

It is obvious that growth varies with variations in environment and food. All organisms have a temperature range, for instance, in which growth is most rapid, and all have an optimum (best) combination of foods and other materials for growth. Growth may also be strongly influenced by normal changes in the internal environment, especially those directly or indirectly influencing the growth hormones (p. 180). This is well illustrated by changes in human growth rates at puberty, when the sex glands begin to function and the general hormonal balance of the body changes. There is then a quite marked and

relatively rapid increase both in height and in weight. On an average this occurs around the age of 12 or 13 in girls, who then shoot up and become gawky, in some groups averaging taller than boys of the same age. When they are 14 to 16, the boys shoot up in their turn and become (on an average) decidedly taller than the girls. (See Fig. 14-12.) When they are 15 to 17 girls often have a second period of rapid increase in weight (but not, or not so evidently, in height). Then they fill out in the magic transformation from gawkiness to femininity.

PERCENTAGE GROWTH

It is one of the principles of growth and, indeed, of life that the products of growth are themselves alive and capable of growth.[6] The process is not like building a wall of bricks, which stay put. In growth, as soon as a "brick" is added, the brick itself adds others around it. The activity of growth thus depends on how much material is already there—in other words, on how much growth

[6] This is a valid generalization for growth as a whole, but it does not always apply to all the separate parts of organisms. Notably, it is not true of the noncellular parts of supportive and connective tissues (p. 67).

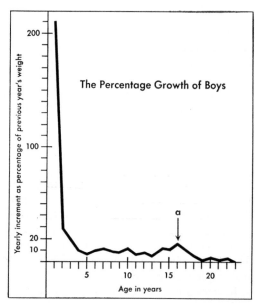

The Percentage Growth of Boys

14-12 The percentage growth of boys (Minot's data). Note the slight increase in growth rate around 14 to 16.

has already occurred. In judging how active the growth process is, it is therefore more enlightening to consider the *percentage* increase rather than the absolute increase. If a baby weighing 10 kilos (22 pounds) gains 2 kilos in a year, it is growing more actively than an adolescent weighing 50 kilos and gaining 5 kilos in a year. This essential fact is brought out by saying not that the baby gained 2 and the adolescent 5 kilos, but that they gained 20 per cent and 10 per cent, respectively.

If growth curves are plotted by percentage they tend to take the form of Fig. 14-10C instead of that of Fig. 14-10A. In terms of percentage increase there is no early period of slow growth that later increases to a maximum. Once growth starts at all,[7] the percentage increase is fastest right at the beginning and then tends to slow down steadily throughout life or until growth stops. Perhaps you will agree with C. Minot, a leading student of growth, that the capacity for rapid growth is a youthful characteristic and that its loss is a sign of aging. If so, you must also agree with Minot that you started to grow old before you were born, and that you were aging most rapidly during your first days in your mother's womb. The young grow older rapidly but the aged age slowly (Fig. 14-12).

This may be related to something you have probably noticed, or if not, will before you are much older. Time seems to pass more slowly when you are young than when you are older. This is *perhaps* because the young grow and live faster. An extension of this idea is that a dog, for instance, has used up about as much of its life span and is physiologically about as aged at 10 as a man at 70. This is the concept of *physiological time*, which, according to another student of growth (P. B. Medawar), is "biology's claim to be considered at least as obscure to the lay mind as theoretical physics." Obviously an animal with a short life span *ages* more rapidly than one with a long span. Whether, however, it *lives* more rapidly is indeed obscure. What do you think?

[7] You recall that growth usually does not occur in the very earliest phase of development (p. 337).

RELATIVE GROWTH

So far we have talked as if growth were just a matter of becoming larger. If you look at a calf and a cow or at a baby and yourself, you will see that there is more to growth than that. There are changes in shape as well as in size. Frequently, the changed shape results from the fact that something new has been added, such as horns on a cow or breasts on a human female. Even more frequently,

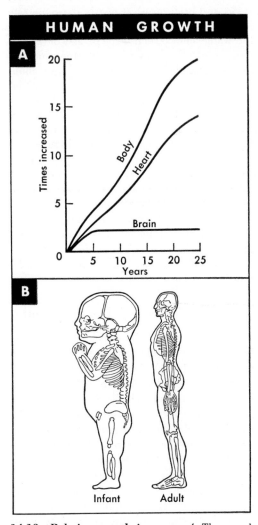

14-13 Relative growth in man. *A.* The growth rates of body, heart, and brain compared: the heart and brain grow at a relatively slower rate than the body, especially in later years. *B.* The effects of differences in the relative growth of parts of the body are strikingly brought out by a comparison of the proportions of infant and adult.

shapes change because parts grow at different rates. A calf or a baby has a relatively larger head than a grown cow or you. Evidently in cattle or men (and this is true as a generalization about mammals) the head either grows more slowly or stops growing earlier than the body as a whole.

Figure 14-13 compares growth rates for the human body and some of its organs. Body weight continues to increase fairly steadily up to the age of 25 (and beyond). Heart and brain grow at nearly the same rate initially but they grow more slowly than the whole body. Their growth also levels off long before the body's weight stops increasing. The weight of the brain increases about as rapidly as that of the heart up to about 4 years, but then it stops growing. Of course this agrees with and in a "first-why" way it explains the fact that the head is relatively larger in infants than in adults. Figure 14-3 shows how markedly external proportions change in man as a result of different growth rates of different parts. (Note that an adult man has relatively longer arms and legs than a human infant. Adult man has relatively shorter arms and longer legs than an adult ape. What bearing, if any, does this have on recapitulation [see below] or on the relationships of men and apes?)

The Evolution of Development

In some respects the development of embryos may be singularly indirect. Human embryos (Fig. 14-14) develop tails, which later disappear. They also develop gill-like pouches in the neck region, which also disappear as such and are in part transformed into quite nongill-like structures, including the ear canal. At this stage the embryo looks a little like a fish, although the resemblance is not so close as is sometimes suggested.[8] Still it seems very roundabout for a developing human to go through a stage even remotely fishlike and to have structures so little related to adult anatomy. Until the reality of evolution was

recognized such facts were inexplicable. Then it was realized that they have a historical, evolutionary basis.

THE BIOGENETIC LAW

The fact is that the tailed, gill-pouched stage of the human embryo is not much like an adult fish but is very like an *embryonic* fish. K. E. von Baer (1792-1876) noted this fact even before the fact of evolution was recognized. He considered it an example of the so-called *biogenetic law*, which is not really a law but a descriptive generalization with a number of exceptions. According to this generalization the earlier stages of embryos resemble those of other animals lower in the scale of nature, or, as we would now say, more like those of related or ancestral groups. As development proceeds, the embryos of different animals become more and more dissimilar. In its very earliest cleavage stages, a human embryo is rather like that of a starfish. In somewhat later stages it is still very similar to that of a (true) fish, amphibian, or reptile. Even later, it is quite like the embryos of other mammals. Finally, well before birth, it becomes clearly human and unmistakably distinct from any other species (Fig. 11-2).

Early evolutionists, especially E. H. Haeckel (1834-1919), rephrased the "biogenetic law" as the *principle of recapitulation:* "ontogeny repeats phylogeny,"[9] that is, successive stages of individual development correspond with successive adult ancestors of the line of evolutionary descent. The vaguely fishlike stage of the human embryo was believed to represent the stage when our adult ancestors were fishes. Von Baer had more correctly generalized the facts, but at a time when the principles underlying those facts could not be understood. Haeckel correctly pointed out that the observed facts must result from evolution, as Darwin had already done, but Haeckel misstated the evolutionary principle involved.

It is now firmly established that ontogeny does *not* repeat phylogeny.[10] Ontogeny re-

[8] The human embryo does not have any differentiated gill tissue, and the gill-like pouches do not have open gill slits as in fishes. Fins are lacking. The tail is not at all like any fish's tail. Indeed, the resemblance to an adult fish is vague and superficial.

[9] Ontogeny is the "development of being" (the individual organism), and phylogeny the "development (or descent) of races."
[10] You may well ask why we bother you with principles that turned out to be wrong. There are two reasons. In the first place, belief in recapitulation became so widespread that it re-

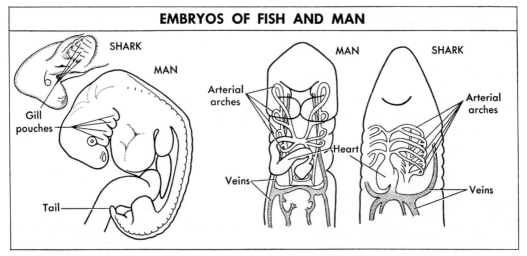

EMBRYOS OF FISH AND MAN

14-14 The biogenetic law. At the left embryos of shark and man are compared, showing the presence in both of gill pouches in the neck region. (See Fig. 19-5 for the subsequent developmental history in man of the skeletal arches in these gill pouches.) At the right embryos of shark and man are again compared, showing the great similarity in their circulatory systems.

peats ontogeny, with variations. Phylogeny is a series of ontogenies. Evolution is not manifested by a sequence of adults giving rise to later, modified adults. An individual organism has a time dimension. It is the same organism from zygote to death and is to be understood only as a dynamically developing living system. What is passed on from one generation to the next is a developmental mechanism. It is also the developmental mechanism that evolves. Heritable change in the adult can occur only on the basis of change in that developmental mechanism.

The developmental mechanism that produced a fish in our ancestors of about 300 million years ago has been inherited by us. In the meantime, however, it has undergone many and profound evolutionary changes and it produces quite a different kind of adult organism. The changes are more evident in later than in earlier developmental stages, and that is why an early human embryo is still rather like a correspondingly early fish embryo. There have, however, been some important evolutionary changes even in the earliest stages.

CHANGES IN ONTOGENY

Haeckel's principle of recapitulation would be correct if changes in the developmental mechanism were usually additions of new stages at the end of development. For instance, a sequence of stages *a-b-c-d* might produce an adult fish, and addition of new stages after this, making the ontogeny *a-b-c-d-e-f-g*, might produce a reptile or a mammal. Students who followed up Haeckel's lead did at first think that this is what commonly happens. Something more or less (mostly less) like it may, indeed, sometimes happen, but simple addition of new stages at the end of ontogeny is certainly not the usual course of evolution. An adult fish has developed about as far from the zygote as has an adult man, but it has developed in a different direction.

The changes in ontogeny that produce evolutionary change are usually changes in direction of development. Often, in accordance with Von Baer's generalization, they are more evident in later stages. Usually, however, they have some effect throughout the whole course

is still evident in some writings about biology and evolution. You should therefore know what recapitulation is supposed to be and you should know that it does not really occur. In the second place, this is a good example of how scientific knowledge is gained. Von Baer and Haeckel were not flatly or wholly wrong. They made successive approximations to truth, and our present closer approximation is based on their accumulation of facts and attempts at explanation.

of development, and they may be most apparent at any one stage. As would be expected, the earlier the effects of a change in direction, a *deviation*, become evident, the greater the usual difference in adult structure. Up to a point, gill-like structures develop similarly in fishes and in mammals, but deviation occurs early, and the adult differences in this region are profound.

In some instances, which are exceptions to Von Baer's generalization, the young of related species differ more than the adults. This is especially likely among the many animals that have feeding larvae quite different in form from the reproducing adults; caterpillars and butterflies are a familiar example. The larval forms have special adaptations for their own way of life, usually strikingly unlike the way of life of the same animal when adult. Larval adaptations may evolve without any great influence on adult structure. Thus it happens among some flies or worms that the larvae differ greatly and the adults are closely similar.

Even in forms without larvae, there are usually special adaptations to embryonic life that never occurred in any adult form and that may be quite different in different groups. In man and other higher mammals, the umbilical cord, the placenta, and the membranes surrounding the fetus (p. 386) are embryonic adaptations of essential evolutionary importance. They differ in several respects from adaptations in marsupial mammals (pp. 598 ff.) and are profoundly different from the embryonic adaptations of, for instance, fishes or birds.

Apparent oddities and indirections in development may give helpful clues as to the way structures evolved. For instance, the way jaws develop in some fishes clearly indicates that they arose from gill arches of earlier, jawless vertebrates (Fig. 18-12). Of course this is not because the jawless stage is "recapitulated." It is because the developmental mechanism for jaws and for a particular pair of gill arches started out as the same and has not deviated unrecognizably. In other instances almost unrecognizable deviation has occurred. For example, there is little question that the liver in vertebrates originated in the evolutionary sequence (phylogenetically) as a

pouchlike protrusion from the intestine. In mammals, however, it does not arise embryologically (ontogenetically) in that way, but as a compact mass of cells that differentiates directly into liver tissue. Stages present in the ancestral developmental sequence, but no longer functionally significant, have been dropped out of ontogeny.

There is another mode of evolution of ontogeny that may have had exceptional importance in some instances. This is the retention in adults of features that occurred in earlier stages in the ancestors.[11]

It does happen, although not commonly, that a final stage of development is simply dropped off the life history. Salamanders (a group of amphibians, p. 589) normally have a larval stage in which they are aquatic and have gills, and an adult stage in which the gills are lost and they breathe with lungs. However, some salamanders become sexually mature and reproduce without ever losing the gills or acquiring the fully adult form. Many anatomical features of man have been interpreted as retention in the adult of characteristics that are juvenile in apes and the ancestry of man. These features include the relatively large skull, absence of ridges above the eyes, the angle between the skull and backbone, and even the reduction of body hair. Adult man resembles the young decidedly more than the adults of apes and monkeys.

There are other ways in which ontogenies have changed in the course of the history of life. The preceding few examples suffice to emphasize and illustrate the fundamental principle that phylogeny, evolutionary descent, is a sequence of ontogenies and that the course of evolution is through changes in ontogeny. Some other striking examples, among both plants and animals, will appear in the discussion of life histories in the next chapter.

RELATIVE GROWTH AND EVOLUTION

Changes in the relative sizes of parts because they grow at different rates and stop growing at different times are extremely com-

---

11 There are complicated and sometimes conflicting technical terminologies for the many kinds of changes that can occur in ontogeny. The term most often applied to this particular process is neoteny.

mon among animals. Often they are even more striking than in man. Since it is really the growth mechanism that produces changes of form in the course of evolution, this phenomenon has profound significance in the history of life.

Striking changes can occur as a result of relative (or differential) growth persisting for longer or shorter periods. A famous example is the extinct Irish elk (Fig. 14-15), which had tremendous antlers, the largest known. In the smaller living allies of this animal, the antlers increase in size at a rate faster than the body as a whole.[12] The larger the animal, the larger its antlers, not only in absolute size but also in proportion to the rest of the body. Now if the living elk, which are much smaller, grew to be as large as the extinct Irish elk, they would have antlers as disproportionately large as in that animal. This strongly suggests that the Irish elk had the same sort of growth mechanism as its living relatives. The evolutionary change that produced that species was, then, just an increase in total body size. The established growth mechanism automatically resulted in the enormous antlers. Change in body size is one of the commonest evolutionary events,

12 The comparison is complicated by the fact that the antlers are shed and regrown once a year. Relative rates can, however, be studied by comparing body size and fully grown antlers from year to year.

American Museum of Natural History

14-15 The extinct Irish elk (*Megaloceros*).

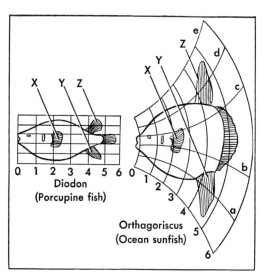

14-16 Evolutionary change in the pattern of growth. A grid of co-ordinates is drawn over both the porcupine fish and the sunfish in such a way that homologous points (X, Y, and Z in the figure) in the two fishes fall on corresponding points on the overlying co-ordinate grid. Comparison of the grids shows that the sunfish grows relatively much faster from top to bottom in the tail region than does the porcupine fish.

and usually results in differences of shape through the mechanism of relative growth.

In the example of the Irish elk, the pattern of relative growth was not changed. It only continued further in a larger animal.

Figure 14-16 shows a comparison of two related recent fishes by a method developed by D'Arcy Thompson. The porcupine fish has more usual proportions and probably resembles the ancestor of both fishes. The extraordinary form of the sunfish results mainly from a change of growth pattern such that the nearer a part is to the hind end, the faster it grows in the top-to-bottom direction.

Chapter Summary

The developmental processes controlled by the inherited message in the chromosomes: growth and cell division; morphogenesis, the creation of pattern and shape; differentiation, the specialization of cell types; closed development in animals; open development in plants; continuity of germ cells; phases of development in which one or another of the developmental processes predominates.

Patterns of morphogenesis and differentiation in animals: maturation of the egg cell consists of differentiation of egg cytoplasm; polar body formation; fertilization; cleavage—cell division without growth; the blastula; twinning in relation to the plane of cleavage and the axis of the egg's differentiation; the effect of yolk in cleavage.

Gastrulation and morphogenesis: ectoderm and endoderm; gastrulation in amphioxus and frog compared; origin of mesoderm and of coelom; differentiation of tissue types; their derivation from germ layers; organ formation.

Induction and organizers: the organizer in frogs; experimental demonstration of its inducing action; presumptive fate, dependent on embryonic environment; determination.

The problem of genetic control of development—in essence the problem of how the same inherited message (identical chromosome sets) controls the differentiation of diverse tissue types: its solution to be sought in knowledge of how gene action is affected by the chemical and physical environment; known to be different in different parts of the egg cell after cleavage (the gene controlling pigment formation in rabbits as an example).

Patterns of growth: the general form of the growth curve; variations in vertebrates; stepwise growth in arthropods; endocrine effects on growth in man; percentage growth; relative growth.

The evolution of development: similarity of human and fish embryos; the biogenetic law; Haeckel's misstatement of the correct principle involved in the biogenetic law; changes in ontogeny—deviation, larval specialization; relative growth and evolution (the case of the Irish elk).

CHAPTER 15

Reproduction: Organismic Aspects

If Mars had intelligent inhabitants and if one of them should happen to land in the northern United States in winter, his first impression would be that most of life on earth had become extinct. Many of the plants would be plainly dead. Most of the others, especially among the larger woody plants, would stand skeletonlike, gaunt and bare. The visitor might find a few insects, all dead or seeming so. If wider investigation revealed some rodents or a bear, these, too, might be so profoundly quiescent as to seem dead at first sight.

What amazement the Martian would feel if he stayed until spring! Everywhere he would see a resurrection of life. Plants would burst out from germinating spores and seeds. Trees would show a new surge of life and break out into vividly living greenery. From tiny eggs and mummy cases millions of insects would emerge. Birds would appear, seemingly from nowhere, and bustle about the business of nesting and reproducing. The hibernators would awaken, among them the she-bear already followed by her cubs. The visitor would conclude that life on earth is cyclic. Each longer life has a recurrent pattern through the cycle of the seasons. All lives, long or short, are links in reproductive cycles in which one life follows another, each life repeating the pattern of its forebears within its species.

The seasonal cycle is not everywhere so apparent as in the so-called Temperate Zone, with its intemperate alternation of summer and winter. The reproductive cycle is completely universal. It exists for all living things wherever they may be on earth and whether their life spans be measured in minutes or in centuries. All kinds of organisms are born and differ only in the manner of their origin. "Birth" may be a fission of the parent, the germination of a seed, emergence from an egg or from the womb; but the resemblances are more fundamental than the differences. Among all kinds of organisms, an individual in its turn gives birth in its own fashion to others, and so begins another cycle of life, a new link in the long, long chain of the race.

The Generalized Reproductive Cycle

The individual life cycle begins with reproduction from a parent or two parents. Development of the individual follows (Chapter

14) and then reproduction again, starting another cycle. There has thus been in all organisms a continuous sequence: reproduction-development-developed organism-reproduction-development-developed organism- . . . , and so on through the centuries and millennia, ever since life begin. It would be foolish to say that one phase is more important than another in a process that is continuous, with each phase dependent on the others. However, in some sorts of studies (for example, those of transfers of energy and materials in communities) attention is naturally focused on the developed organisms. Then reproduction may be viewed merely as part of the background, as the process that keeps up a continuous supply of organisms. In consideration of the life cycle, on the other hand, reproduction is a particularly crucial phase. It begins the individual cycle and is the connection between the generations that are links in the long chain. From this point of view the developing and developed individual is the medium of reproduction, or is what intervenes between the crucial episodes of reproduction. The hen, as Samuel Butler said, is the egg's device for laying another egg. The subject of life cycles may, then, be considered first of all in terms of reproductive cycles.

ASEXUAL AND SEXUAL REPRODUCTION

In Chapter 11 the subject of reproduction introduced us to the study of heredity, and the distinction was there made between sexual and asexual reproduction. In *sexual reproduction* there is a fusion of two nuclei from different cells (gametes) into one (zygote); and in *asexual reproduction* there is not. Asexual reproduction is necessarily uniparental. Sexual reproduction is usually biparental, but may also be uniparental as, for instance, in the many self-fertilizing flowering plants.

One of two usual forms of asexual reproduction (Fig. 15-1) is *vegetative reproduction,* which (p. 159) occurs in both animals and plants but is more common among plants. Both protists and multicellular organisms may reproduce vegetatively by fission of the body, each part developing into a separate organism. In many plants and a few animals almost any reasonably large part will grow into a new organism under proper conditions. This method is familiar to you in the *cuttings* often used to propagate cultivated plants,[1] and a planarian (p. 159) provides an animal example. Quite a few animals, of

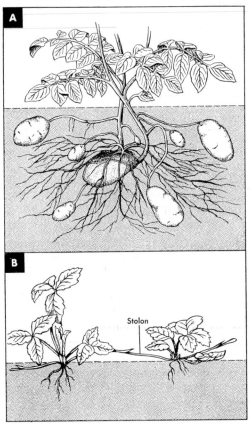

15-1 Vegetative reproduction. *A.* Tuberous swellings of the stems in the potato plant serve to propagate the species vegetatively. The bulk of tissue is a food reserve (starch), but embryonic tissue is present in the "eyes" of the potato, and from these new shoot and root systems can develop. *B.* In the strawberry the shoot system effects vegetative reproduction. Shoots known as stolons, growing along the surface of the ground, may develop new root systems and establish a new plant.

[1] A special sort of propagation by cuttings is grafting, the attachment of a cutting from one plant to the growing stem or root of another. The graft and its host become part of the same physiological system and look and grow like a single plant, but there is no exchange or mixture of chromosomes and each part retains its own heredity. A peach may be grafted to a plum, and then the same tree will bear both peaches and plums on different branches.

which *Hydra* is an example (Fig. 15-2), reproduce vegetatively by *budding*. Many plants develop special *organs of vegetative reproduction*. Some of these are surely familiar to you: the tubers of potatoes, the bulbs of onions or tulips, the bulblike organs of gladioli, the runners of strawberries, and the runner-like underground structures of many grasses. Many different parts and processes may be involved in vegetative reproduction, but the principle is always the same and is simple: a part of the parental organism, genetically identical with its other parts, develops into a separate organism.

The other common form of asexual reproduction is by *spores*, single reproductive cells each of which develops into a separate organism without fertilization. (See Fig. 6-5, p. 124.)

The essential feature of sexual reproduction is the fusion of two nuclei within a single cell, which develops into a separate organism. You will recall from Chapter 11 that the specialized sexual reproductive cells of plants and animals are called gametes and that they usually are of two kinds: smaller, more mobile male gametes, or *sperms*, and larger, more passive female gametes, or *eggs*. The union of male and female gametes is called fertilization, and the resulting single cell is a zygote. In some protists and lower plants the two cells whose nuclei fuse are not visibly different from each other or from ordinary cells (or, in protists, whole organisms) of the species. The male and female are not distinguishable, and the lack of apparent specialization for reproduction may make the term "gamete" seem inappropriate. Nevertheless, such cells have gone through meiosis and are fully comparable with gametes in this preparation for fusion by reduction of chromosome number.[2]

Hugh Spencer

15-2 Vegetative reproduction in *Hydra*. A "bud" in *Hydra* consists of an evagination of the polyp wall that contains both ectoderm and endoderm tissue layers. It develops tentacles (barely visible in the photo) and a mouth; eventually, severing itself completely from the parent, the bud becomes a new individual.

Modes of achieving sexual reproduction have become amazingly diverse in plants and animals. The gametes have acquired numerous different characteristics in different groups. Organs associated with their production, with fertilization, and with subsequent development of the offspring have become extremely specialized and have also taken innumerable different forms. Nevertheless, sexual reproduction is essentially the same and has the same evolutionary and biological significance whether it occurs in paramecia, roses, or humans. In each the basic phenomenon is that half the chromosomes from each of two individuals have been united in a single new individual.

THE DISTRIBUTION AND SIGNIFICANCE OF SEX IN ORGANISMS

It is almost certain that the first organisms, more than a billion years ago when life was young, had a simple vegetative, asexual reproductive cycle. They must have reproduced solely by fission—division of protoplasm and genetic materials—with each fission product becoming an individual of the same kind.

[2] Some biologists object to applying the term "fertilization" to fusion of nuclei in protists and do not consider this as sexual reproduction. They call passage of the nucleus, only, from one individual to another "conjugation," and fusion of two individuals, both nuclei and cytoplasm, "syngamy" (see Fig. 20-7). Nevertheless, in essence and real biological significance conjugation or syngamy in protists and fertilization in multicellular organisms are fundamentally the same. In both, haploid cells (or their nuclei) fuse and produce a new diploid individual. It is not confusing two different things but recognizing their essential equivalence when the same terms are applied to the process in protists and in other organisms.

Even today, simple cell division, and the mitotic transmission of identical nuclear controls to each new daughter cell is the basic—and asexual—mode of reproduction.

Sex is clearly something added to and, in a sense, not an essential part of the basic reproductive process. Yet from its nearly universal occurrence, we must conclude that the added complication of sex plays a vitally important role in the reproduction of whole organisms (as against the reproduction of their cellular constituents).

The significance of sex in organisms is that it is a device for promoting genetic variability among the offspring left by one generation to initiate the next. We saw in Chapter 12 how some of the gametes produced in meiosis may contain a recombination, or reshuffling, of gene combinations present in the parents' gametes. Consider two organisms that are homozygous for two gene pairs as follows: *AABB* and *aabb.* So long as each reproduces only by asexual means they can produce only *AABB* and *aabb* offspring, respectively, generation after generation until the comparatively rare process of mutation changes one of the alleles. But were these organisms to reproduce sexually—were they to mate, producing hybrids (*AaBb*), the very next generation of sexually produced offspring (*F*$_2$) would contain a variety of recombination genotypes: *AABB, AABb, AAbb, AaBB, AaBb, Aabb, aaBB, aaBb,* and *aabb.* Of course, normal sexual reproduction produces an even richer array of variants than the nine types listed above. An organism contains thousands of gene pairs, not just two, as we saw in Chapter 13; and, correspondingly, the amount of variation among offspring is extremely great.

Here, then, is the biological importance of sex in organisms: it promotes variability among offspring. The basic materials for evolution are genetic variations in populations (pp. 399 ff.). Asexual reproduction keeps such variation at a minimum, while sexual reproduction maximizes variation. There is, therefore, no mystery attaching to the nearly universal occurrence of sex as a complication added to the reproduction of organisms. Those populations of organisms most able to

vary have been those most able to survive varying conditions in the environment, and those most able to evolve into new ways of life as the opportunity arose. Sex is widespread because, like any other adaptation, it has promoted the long-term survival of those populations that possessed it.

Until recently it appeared that some primitive groups of organisms lacked sexuality altogether: viruses, bacteria, the blue-green algae, and miscellaneous other forms including the common ameba. (But some close relatives of ameba do have sexuality.) It has, however, now been discovered that viruses and bacteria—the most primitive of all now-living organisms [3]—do have mechanisms for recombining genes. Thus they, too, have survived and flourish even to this day in part because of their capacity, as populations, to face the world in each new generation with some depth of genetic alternatives to offer. At the present time the blue-green algae are the only major group of organisms that are not *known* to possess some device for recombination between genotypes. It could well be that this is simply because they have yet to be studied with the special techniques that revealed the existence of recombination among bacteria and viruses.

Leaving aside the blue-green algae as a temporarily uncertain group, we are led to the generalization that *all now-living organisms have some device for genetic recombination or, if they lack it, are modified descendants of* organisms that recently possessed such a device.

You may have noticed that in our discussion of viruses and bacteria we said "device for recombination" rather than simply "sex." The exact process of recombination in bacteria and viruses is uncertain, and it may not be truly sexual. It is known that if there are bacteria of two genotypes, such as *AB* and *ab,*[4] in the same culture, the recombinations, *Ab* and *aB,* may turn up among their descendants. It is also known that recombination in bacteria has a characteristic frequency for any two genes (such as *A* and *B*) and

---

[3] If, indeed, viruses can even be considered organisms. See pp. 43 and 316.
[4] Bacteria seem to be haploid.

is different for different genes (e.g., the frequency between *A* and *B* may be 10 per cent, and that between *A* and *C* only 3 per cent). In fully sexual organisms those same phenomena (gene recombinations at fixed frequencies) are due to chromosome crossing over at meiosis following nuclear fusion. They make it possible to draw crossover maps of the sequence of the genes in each chromosome (p. 304). Maps based on fixed recombination frequencies have, indeed, been drawn for genes of the common colon bacterium of man (*Escherichia coli*) and for genes of the bacterial virus (bacteriophage, p. 316) that parasitizes it. But we cannot as yet confidently infer that the physical basis of these gene maps for bacteria and viruses is the sexual process—nuclear fusion and meiosis with chromosome crossing over. Although bacteria do have visible chromosomes, no one has ever seen bacterial cells fuse, as would be expected if the sexual process (involving nuclear fusion) occurred in the usual way. Moreover, there is evidence of strange happenings in bacterial reproduction unknown in higher organisms. It seems that pieces of chromosomes (perhaps free genes?) can migrate from one bacterium to another. In that case there is recombination without the essentials of sex—meiosis and nuclear fusion. Here is a radically distinct system of recombining genetic materials wholly unknown in any organisms other than bacteria.

Sex as we ordinarily use this term is defined by nuclear fusion and meiosis. As such it is evidently only one of at least two methods of genetic recombination that organisms have hit upon; there are more ways than one of skinning a cat, or for that matter of executing almost any biological function, including genetic recombination. Sex is the method of recombining genes that occurs in cellular organisms with fully evolved chromosomal and mitotic equipment for transmission of the genetic material. The hallmark of sex is the cyclical process of pooling (via fertilization) two duplicate sets of chromosomes, and reshuffling "new hands" from the "double deck" in each new generation (via meiosis, including independent segregation of chromosome pairs, and crossing over). The chromosomal and

mitotic system of carrying and transmitting genes evidently proved so efficient that few organisms lacking it have survived. (Which are they?) And few, as we have already seen, have survived without sex to promote their variability. Indeed, we shall argue later that, in those species in which sexual reproduction is lacking, it has been lost secondarily. Why and how it has been lost is another question, also to be taken up later (p. 390).

THE HAPLOPHASE-DIPLOPHASE REPRODUCTIVE CYCLE

Most protists, a great many plants, and quite a number of animals have both asexual and sexual reproduction. In simplest form this combination of reproductive cycles may be visualized as in Fig. 15-4. This we regard as the primitive, ancestral condition for cellular organisms equipped with chromosomes.[5] The numbers and sequences of asexual and sexual cycles vary greatly. Most protists go through the asexual cycle (by fission) repeatedly and then once in a while go through a single sexual cycle, followed by more asexual cycles. In animals and plants the sequences may be quite irregular. Not infrequently asexual and sexual cycles are simultaneous (in different offspring). For instance *Hydra* often reproduces sexually and by budding at the same time.

Fertilization is the definitive process of sexual reproduction. You have seen (p. 272) that fertilization must be preceded by meiosis, cell division with halving of chromosome number. Otherwise the number of chromosomes would double in each repetition of the cycle and would soon become impossibly large. On the other hand, if meiosis recurred in a cycle and fertilization did not, the chromosome number would be cut in half in each repetition of the cycle, which is also impossible because normal life demands the presence of at least one full *set* of chromosomes in each cell. Therefore the sexual cycle must include both of two key processes: meiosis and fertilization.

Meiosis and fertilization divide the whole

[5] This excludes, for the moment, the blue-green algae, which are not known to possess the usual form of nucleus with chromosomes.

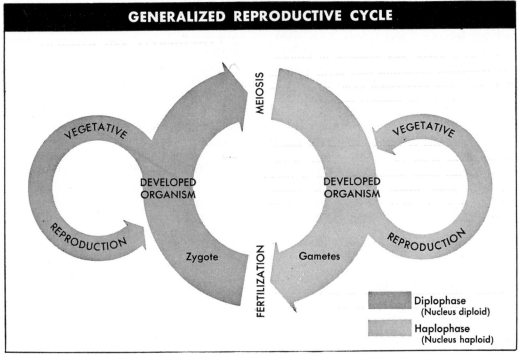

15-3 The generalized reproductive cycle.

life cycle of sexual organisms into two parts. After meiosis and before fertilization cells and organisms have a reduced number of chromosomes; they usually have *n* chromosomes and are haploid (p. 271); this phase of the reproductive cycle is the *haplophase*. After fertilization and before meiosis they have the full complement of chromosomes: the number is usually *2n,* and they are diploid; this is called the *diplophase* of the reproductive cycle.

Among most organisms, especially those most familiar to us, the developed organism occurs in the diplophase of the sexual cycle. The more conspicuous and longer part of the cycle, the one in which the organism matures and lives an independent life, acquiring its own materials and energy from the environment, involves development from the (diploid) zygote and subsequent maturity. The developed organism of the diagrams of the sexual reproductive cycle (Fig. 15-3) is then on the left side of the diagram. Then it may be that only gametes, sperms and eggs, occur on the right side of the diagram, in the haplophase of the cycle. This is the situation in ourselves and most other animals.

Gametes are, in fact, haplophase organisms themselves. They have only a single set of chromosomes, but they do have one complete set, and this is sufficient for an organism to live and carry out all necessary metabolism. Specialized gametes usually are short-lived, acquiring materials only from the parent and having a brief period of independent life during which they acquire little or nothing on their own. Then they unite into a zygote, or die. Nevertheless it is possible for a cell produced by meiosis, hence haploid, to lead a longer life, and even for it to acquire materials on its own and have all the characteristics of an independent organism. It may go so far as to develop and become multicellular. The occurrence of a developed organism (some development in meiosis) in the haplophase of the sexual cycle (to the right in our diagrams) is rare, but not absent, among animals.[6] It is usual in plants.

There are three possibilities for the oc-

6 Male bees, for instance, are haploid.

currence of developed organisms in the sexual cycle. (1) They may occur in the diplophase only (Fig. 15-16). This is usual in animals, as has been noted, and common in protists. (2) Developed organisms may occur in *both* diplophase and haplophase (Fig. 15-6). This occurs rarely as an unusual modification in animals, but it is almost universal in plants. (3) Finally, it is also possible for the developed organism to occur only in the haplophase of the cycle (Fig. 15-5). This is the rarest of the three possibilities, but it does occur in some protists and lowly plants (algae). Note also that, wherever they occur in the sexual cycle, whether diplophase or haplophase, many developed organisms can reproduce vegetatively as well as sexually. All the descriptive facts reviewed up to this point can be summarized in a diagram of a *generalized*[7] *reproductive cycle*, as in Fig. 15-3. No one organism is known to go through *all* the specific processes indicated in this complex cycle. However, all the reproductive cycles that do occur in organisms are present in the diagram.

The valuable thing about the diagram (Fig. 15-3) is that it shows the biological relationships between the numerous kinds of reproductive cycles that occur among organisms. For instance, the reproductive cycles of most animals may seem to be fundamentally different from those of most plants, and they are usually so represented. Yet if, as we go along, the special cycles in plants and animals are compared with the generalized cycle, they will be seen to be fundamentally similar. The only essential difference is that in animals the cells (the haplophase) resulting from meiosis usually develop no further before fertilization (they are simply gametes) while in plants the haplophase usually does develop somewhat further, becoming multicellular and, in some cases, even an independent organism.[8]

[7] Some students feel that "generalized" somehow implies vagueness. This is not necessarily true. This generalized diagram is perfectly definite; there is nothing vague about it. A scientific generalization is usually definite: it sums up all that various separate things or occurrences have in common or, as in this instance, it includes all the possibilities as parts of a single pattern.

[8] Some exceptions are diatoms and a few other algae.

Reproductive Cycles in Plants

GAMETOPHYTE AND SPOROPHYTE

The occurrence of development in the haplophase of the reproductive cycle is so nearly universal in plants and so rare in animals[9] that this difference is even more definitive than the fact that most plants are photosynthetic (p. 522). Since developed organisms commonly occur in both the haplophase and diplophase of plants (both to the right and to the left in our diagrams), it is convenient to distinguish these by their technical names. The developed haplophase organism (between meiosis and fertilization and therefore haploid or with reduced chromosome number) is called the *gametophyte* ("gamete plant") because it produces gametes. The developed diplophase organism (between fertilization and meiosis and therefore diploid) is called the *sporophyte* ("spore plant") because it produces spores. One of the striking things about reproductive cycles in plants is their great diversity in relative development of gametophyte and sporophyte.

PLANTLIKE PROTISTS

Chlamydomonas (Fig. 15-4) is a single-celled photosynthetic organism. The cell, which swims around actively photosynthesizing for most of the life cycle, is haploid. It is capable of asexual reproduction in the haplophase. Occasionally two cells fuse to form a diploid zygote which immediately undergoes meiosis, yielding four new haplophase cells. Thus in *Chlamydomonas*, as in all other flagellated protists (which are the most primitive of cellular-chromosomal organisms), the life cycle is spent mostly in the haplophase. The diplophase is not extended beyond the time necessary to execute meiosis leading to another generation of haploid cells.

ALGAE

Algae is a name applied to numerous plants, relatively simple in structure, almost all aquatic. Various groups of algae probably

[9] You will recall (p. 337) that the animal egg cell does undergo some internal differentiation —which is development, to be sure—but it never becomes either multicellular or an independently feeding organism before fertilization.

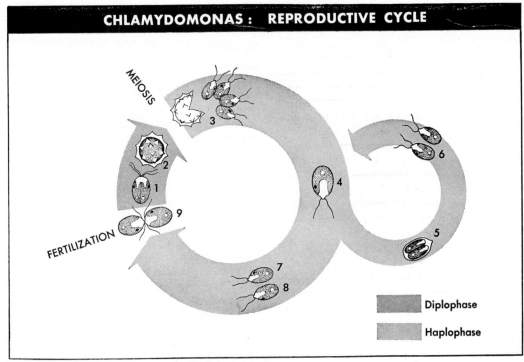

15-4   The reproductive cycle in the protist *Chlamydomonas*. The diplophase is of minor significance; most of the life cycle is passed in the haplophase, which alone undergoes vegetative reproduction. *1.* Young zygote. *2.* Mature zygote, in which meiosis occurs. *3.* The liberation of four haploid cells (products of meiosis) from the old zygote case. *4.* Mature haplophase cell. *5, 6.* Vegetative reproduction. *7, 8.* Two haplophase cells acting as gametes. *9.* Fertilization by union of the gametes.

arose independently from protists.[10] In many algae like *Spirogyra* (Fig. 15-5) the primitive form of the haplophase-diplophase cycle persists; that is, the diplophase undergoes no special development but immediately enters meiosis to yield new haplophase organisms that grow and propagate asexually before renewed sexual reproduction. There is, then, no sporophyte[11] in these plants; the actively growing and dividing plant is a gametophyte.

Within the algae themselves—most primitive of all multicellular plants—there has been an evolutionary tendency to switch emphasis from the haplophase to the diplophase part of the cycle. We will find that this trend applies broadly to plants as a whole. In *Ecto-*

carpus, a common brown seaweed that often grows on other algae, a definite sporophyte is present. Indeed, it is equally as prominent as the gametophyte, and the two generations[12] cannot be distinguished without microscopic study. The cycle in *Ectocarpus* is shown in Fig. 15-6.

The sporophyte in *Laminaria,* a brown alga commonly known as kelp, is far more conspicuous than the gametophyte (Fig. 15-7). The sporophyte is a flat, crinkly blade, often two meters or so in length, single or forklike, attached to rocks by what look like roots. (The "roots" are, however, anatomically and physiologically unlike true roots,

[10] Indeed, photosynthetic protists and their allies are classified as algae by most botanists. This is true of **Chlamydomonas,** for instance.

[11] Recall that the terms "gametophyte" and "sporophyte" are to be applied to developed (some nuclear division) organisms in the haplophase and diplophase, respectively.

[12] In plants where distinctly developed multinucleate organisms (gametophyte and sporophyte) occur in both haplophase and diplophase parts of the reproductive cycle, it has been customary to speak of an "alternation of generations." Strictly speaking, this is a confusing usage, because both gametophyte and sporophyte are essential constituents of one full generation (a full reproductive cycle).

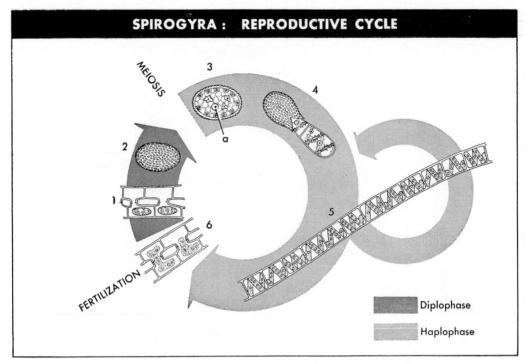

SPIROGYRA : REPRODUCTIVE CYCLE

15-5 **The reproductive cycle in the green alga** *Spirogyra*. As in *Chlamydomonas*, the diplophase is of minor significance; most of the life cycle is passed in the haplophase, which alone undergoes vegetative reproduction. *1*. Two young zygotes in the cells of a former haplophase filament. *2*. A single mature zygote which has developed its own cell wall (or case). *3*. Four haploid nuclei (products of meiosis) can be seen within the old zygote case. Three of these disintegrate; one (labeled *a* in the figure) develops further. *4*. A young haploid filament, developed from the surviving cell in *3*, is germinating from the old zygote case. *5*. The mature haplophase filament, which can vegetatively reproduce. *6*. The conjugation of two haplophase filaments. The cytoplasm and nuclei of the cells in one conjugating filament migrate through specially developed conjugation tubes to the cells of the other conjugating filament; zygotes are formed in each cell of this latter filament.

which do not occur in algae.) In some of the surface cells in the blade the nuclei and cytoplasm divide repeatedly and give rise to tiny spores. Meiosis occurs in the course of these divisions, and the spores are therefore haploid. The spores are released from the parent plant into the surrounding water, where they swim by means of flagella. The spores develop into separate male and female [13] gametophytes, each mi-

croscopic in size and consisting of only a few cells. The male plants produce and release tiny sperms,[14] which also have flagella and swim about. The female plants produce somewhat larger gametes—eggs—which are pushed out of the cell walls but remain attached to the gametophyte. *If* a sperm in its wanderings encounters an egg, fertilization occurs. The zygote begins to divide while still attached to the female gametophyte, and there forms an embryonic sporophyte. After just a few cell divisions, the sporophyte becomes detached from the parent gametophyte, attaches itself

[13] It is useful here to introduce in the diagrams the biological symbols for the sexes: ♀ for female and ♂ for male. These are easy to remember because ♀ is Venus's mirror (a round hand mirror with a handle below), and ♂ is Mars's round shield with his spear sticking out from behind. Venus was considered the most beautiful and feminine of the Roman goddesses, and Mars the most male of the gods, probably because he was so quarrelsome. (As-

tronomers use these same symbols for the planets Venus and Mars.)

[14] Another botanical name for them is "antherozoids."

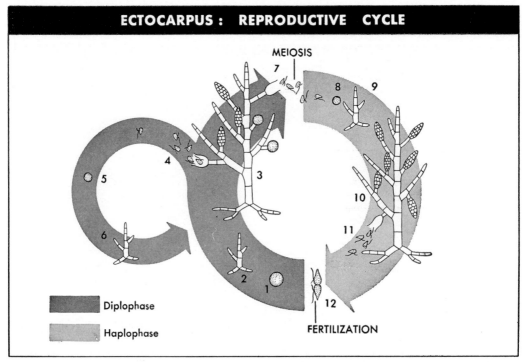

MEIOSIS

Diplophase

Haplophase

FERTILIZATION

15-6 **The reproductive cycle in the brown alga *Ectocarpus*.** Gametophyte (haplophase) and sporophyte (diplophase) generations are equally prominent and very similar. Vegetative reproduction occurs only in the sporophyte generation. *1.* Zygote. *2.* Young sporophyte. *3.* Mature sporophyte. *4, 5.* Diploid zoospores liberated from sporangium. *6.* Young sporophyte. *7, 8.* Haploid zoospores (products of meiosis) liberated from sporangium. *9.* Young gametophyte. *10.* Mature gametophyte. *11.* Gametes being liberated from gametophyte. *12.* Fertilization.

by holdfasts, and develops into the large, familiar seaweed.

Fucus is another brown alga (Fig. 15-8). In it the emphasis on the diplophase has reached a limit: there is no gametophyte generation.

MOSSES

Mosses have evolved or have inherited from ancestral algae a reproductive cycle opposite in tendency from those of higher plants (ferns and seed plants). In mosses the conspicuous developed organism, the one that has leaves and that carries on most of the vital syntheses for the whole cycle, occurs in the haplophase; it is a gametophyte. The gametophytes develop sperms and eggs, on the same plant in some species and in others on different male and female plants. The sperms are swimming, flagellated cells. Most mosses are nonaquatic but, if fertilization is to occur, there must be a film, at least, of water through which the

sperms can swim to the eggs.[15] The eggs are retained in the special organs (archegonia) in which they develop. After fertilization the zygote also remains there and develops into a sporophyte that is attached to the parental (maternal) gametophyte. The usual form of the sporophyte is simply a long, slender stalk with a capsule at its upper end. Within this capsule meiosis occurs, producing spores. Liberated spores are widely distributed through the air, and under favorable conditions they settle down and develop into gametophytes. The cycle is shown in Fig. 15-9.

[15] The way in which the sperms find the eggs is amusing. The egg-bearing organs release sugar which diffuses into the surrounding water. The sperms are attracted by sugar (a forced movement [pp. 232 ff.] and not a preference!) and move toward higher sugar concentration. They thus wind up at an egg. Aesop might have made something of this way in which the female attracts the male if he had known about it.

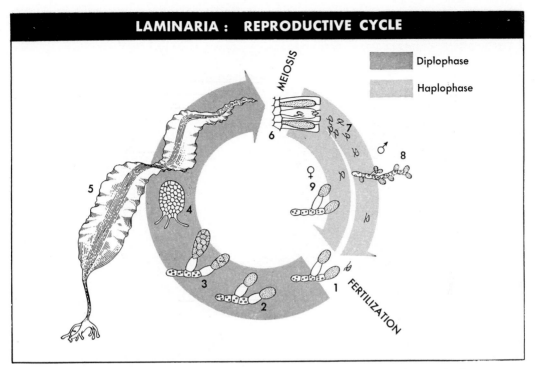

Diplophase

Haplophase

15-7 The reproductive cycle in the brown alga *Laminaria*. The diplophase is the dominant part of the cycle: a large sporophyte is developed. The gametophyte generation is a small filament of cells, and occurs as two distinct sexes. *1*. Fertilization: a sperm approaching a female gametophyte on which there are two egg cells, one of which has extruded from its cell wall and is ready for fertilization. *2*. Female gametophyte carrying two fertilized eggs or zygotes, each of which marks the beginning of the diplophase. *3*. Young sporophytes, each still consisting of only a few cells, attached to the old female gametophyte. *4*. Older sporophyte. *5*. Mature sporophyte, about six feet long. *6*. Meiosis occurs in some surface cells of the sporophyte, liberating haploid motile spores (*7*) that mark the beginning of the haplophase. *8, 9*. Male and female gametophytes, respectively, which have developed from the haploid spores.

Mosses also have remarkable powers of vegetative reproduction, which occurs only in the haploid phase (in our diagrams, the right side) of the reproductive cycle. In a few species sporophytes are unknown and sexual reproduction has apparently been lost.

FERNS

In ferns and all higher plants the conspicuous leafy organism is the sporophyte (Fig. 15-10). You have noticed brownish dots on the underside of fern leaves. These are the spore-producing organs, or *sporangia*. If a spore falls on a favorable spot, it develops into a small, flat, more or less heart-shaped multicellular organism, the gametophyte of the fern. The gametophytes are seldom more than five or six millimeters in diameter, so small and inconspicuous that they are almost never noticed except by botanists, who know what to look for and where to look. The same gametophyte produces both sperms and eggs in different organs and at different times, the sperms first. The sperms swim to the eggs, which are retained in the egg-producing organs (archegonia, Fig. 15-11), much as in mosses. As in mosses, too, the sporophyte embryo starts developing on the gametophyte and is at first parasitic. Unlike the mosses, however, the sporophyte soon develops its own roots, stems, and leaves and grows into a relatively large, independent plant, while its parent gametophyte dies and disappears. The parallel with the alga *Laminaria* (p. 364) is

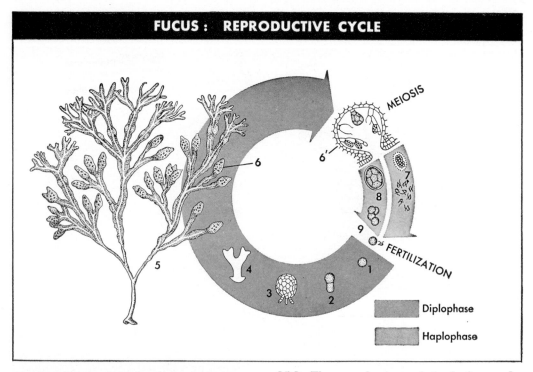

MEIOSIS

FERTILIZATION

Diplophase

Haplophase

Hugh Spencer

15-8 The reproductive cycle in the brown alga *Fucus*. The dominance of the diplophase (sporophyte) generation is here complete. The haplophase never produces a fully developed (gametophyte) organism: it is restricted to the gametes, which are of two distinct sexes. *1*. Zygote. *2, 3, 4*. Successively older stages in the development of the sporophyte. *5*. Mature sporophyte, of which Fig. 15-8*A* is a photograph. *6*. The swollen end of a sporophyte branch in which there are cavities containing tissue that undergoes meiosis, producing gametes. *6'*. Diagram of one such cavity. For simplicity the cavity is shown producing both male (*7*) and female (*8*) gametes. In fact each individual cavity produces only eggs or sperms. *9*. Fertilization.

obvious. In fact, the reproductive processes in these two plants are practically identical, even though the anatomy of the sporophytes is very different.

SEED PLANTS

The highest plants, that is to say, those most complex and belonging to groups of most recent evolutionary origin, were derived from fernlike ancestors. In them, as in ferns and the brown alga *Fucus*, the conspicuous, vegetative plants are the sporophytes. The gametophytes are greatly reduced in comparison with the ferns and are microscopic in size. The female gametophyte is parasitic in the tissues of its parent sporophyte, and the free existence of the male gametophyte is only the period when it is being transported as pollen, during which little or no development occurs. These characteristics are associated with the production of seeds, in which the sporophyte embryo is enclosed with nutritive material inside a protective coat. Seeds are an adaptation to plant life in the open

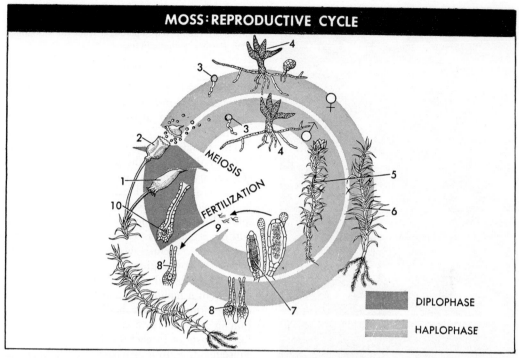

DIPLOPHASE

HAPLOPHASE

15-9   The reproductive cycle in a moss. The gametophyte generation dominates the cycle; the sporophyte is a small structure, completely parasitic on the gametophyte. It consists of only a stalk and a sporangium. *1.* The sporangium (capsule) of the sporophyte generation. *2.* The liberation of haploid spores that have been produced (through meiosis) in the sporangium. *3.* Germination of the spores to produce young gametophytes, which are of two distinct sexes. *4.* Older gametophytes. *5.* Mature male gametophyte. *6.* Mature female gametophyte. *7.* Male sex organ, or antheridium, which produces motile sperm (*9*). *8.* Female sex organ, or archegonium, containing a single egg cell. *8'.* The egg cell at the base of the flask-shaped archegonium is fertilized by the sperm (*9*), which swims over the surface of the female plant and eventually down the neck of the archegonium to reach the egg. *10.* The zygote, marking the beginning of the diplophase, at the base of the archegonium.

air and have made possible the great diversity and abundance of land plants.

The flower.   The sporophyte in flowering plants, like that of ferns, bears special spore-producing organs, or sporangia. They are of two kinds, male and female. The male sporangia are *anthers,* and the female sporangia are *ovules.* These sporangia are not uniformly distributed over leaf surfaces, as they are in ferns; they are clustered together in a *flower.* Thus the familiar flower is essentially an aggregate of sporangia surrounded by modified, often colored, leaves called petals and sepals (Fig. 15-12). The significance of the (often) colored petals is something we return to later; it is related to

the problem of getting the male gametophyte from one flower to the female gametophyte of another.

The gametophytes.   The *microspores* are those destined to develop into male gametophytes. They originate as products of meiosis in the anthers (male sporangia). Development of the male gametophyte, which starts while the spore is still in the anther, consists simply of division of the nucleus into two and then of one of these into two more, which become the male gametes (Fig. 15-12). Sometimes there is also a division of the cytoplasm by cell membranes, but often there is not. The partly developed male gametophyte when it leaves the anther (it usually has two nuclei

15-10 Ferns. *Top*, clusters of sporangia on the back of the polypody fern's leaf. *Middle*, a single cluster of (about ten) sporangia from the Christmas fern. *Bottom*, gametophytes.

at this stage) is a *pollen grain*. It is carried, generally by wind or insects, to the sticky upper end (stigma) of the pistil of the same or another flower.

The female organs of the flower are collectively designated the *pistil*. This comprises stigma, style, and the ovary, inside of which are several ovules (Fig. 15-12). Each ovule is destined ultimately to become a *seed*. Anatomically it is basically a sporangium, for within it meiosis takes place, producing *megaspores*. Meiosis occurs within only one cell of the sporangium, producing four megaspores. Three of these megaspores degenerate [16] in a manner that strikingly recalls the degeneration of polar bodies in egg production in animals (p. 338). The single remaining megaspore in each ovule undergoes three subsequent mitotic divisions, becoming an eight-nucleate female gametophyte.[17] Only one of the eight nuclei becomes the female gamete (egg). The remaining seven represent much-reduced gametophyte tissue. The eight nuclei characteristically assume the positions shown in Fig. 15-12. The egg nucleus is associated with two others that are thought to be evolutionary vestiges of the flask-shaped archegonium that surrounds the egg in gametophytes of mosses and ferns (cf. Fig. 15-10). The remainder are thought to be vestiges of the general photosynthetic tissues of these earlier gametophytes. Two nuclei are of special interest; they fuse, giving rise to a diploid *fusion nucleus*.

Fertilization. By one means or another, the pollen grains (mobile male gametophytes) reach the stigma at the head of the pistil. There they germinate. A protoplasmic tube (the *pollen tube*) emerges from each pollen grain and grows down the style to enter the

[16] There are (we are tempted to add "of course") exceptions among lilies and other plants. But these are clearly secondarily evolved modifications we may here ignore.

[17] The eight-nucleate female gametophyte is technically known as an embryo sac. There may be as few as four or as many as sixteen nuclei in the embryo sac of other seed plants.

FERN: REPRODUCTIVE CYCLE

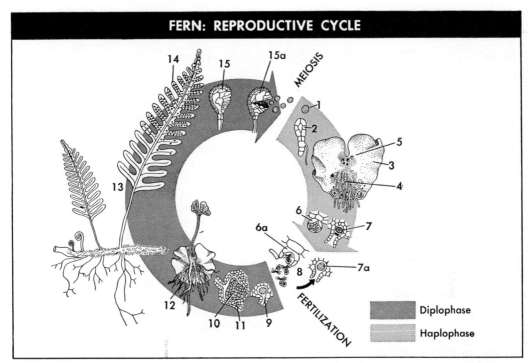

15-11 The reproductive cycle in a fern. The sporophyte generation dominates the life cycle; the gametophyte is a small, short-lived structure bearing male and female organs. *1.* The haploid spore (meiotic product) shed by the sporophyte. *2.* Young gametophyte. *3.* Mature gametophyte. *4.* Antheridia (male sex organs) among rootlike structures on the underside of the gametophyte. *5.* Archegonia (female sex organs). *6.* Individual antheridium, liberating (*6a*) sperms. *7.* Individual archegonium with egg cell at base (*7a*) being fertilized (*8*) by sperm. *9.* The diploid zygote at the base of the archegonium. *10.* Embryo sporophyte still in the archegonium (*11*). *12.* Young sporophyte still attached to the parent gametophyte. *13.* Mature sporophyte. *14.* Clusters of sporangia, on the back of the sporophyte leaf. *15.* Individual sporangia bursting (*15a*) to yield haploid spores produced by meiosis in sporangial cells.

ovary, penetrating an ovule and ultimately the female gametophyte within the wall. The two sperm nuclei move down the tube, entering the female gametophyte. One sperm nucleus unites with the egg nucleus to form a zygote: fertilization occurs. The zygote then begins development and forms an embryo sporophyte. Note that this embryo is still within the ovule (sporangium) and the ovule is in turn still within the ovary of the sporophyte.

The second sperm nucleus unites with the fusion nucleus. You recall that the fusion nucleus is already diploid, so when another haploid nucleus joins it, it becomes triploid, with three sets of chromosomes. The triploid cell then divides and develops into a multicellular mass called the endosperm. This is a most extraordinary structure, which really has no parallel in reproductive processes outside the flowering plants, not even in the other (nonflowering) seed plants.[18] It looks almost like the start of a third kind of developed organism in addition to the haploid gametophyte and the diploid sporophyte. There is, however, no evidence that such is its evolutionary significance. In any event, no real differentiation occurs in it. It becomes merely a uniform tissue, rich in foods usable by the growing sporophyte embryo. (It is the starchy endosperm that forms the bulk of our food grains, corn, wheat, and so on. Peas and beans,

[18] In the seeds of pines and some other non-flowering plants there is a tissue that looks like endosperm and is sometimes so called. It is, however, really the nonreproductive part of the female gametophyte.

however, have no endosperm, and the food is in the embryo.)

Seeds and fruit. The ovule (sporangial) tissues around the young embryo harden to form a tough *seed coat*. The final product, the seed, is thus a sporangium containing an embryonic sporophyte, usually with triploid endosperm as a sort of developmental sideline. Often the seeds are shed free (as in the pea) and may or may not have various devices that facilitate their dispersal (see p. 377). Sometimes, however, the seeds may be retained within the ovary, which itself undergoes further growth to become a fruit. Fruits are modified ovaries, or other flower parts, in which seeds are imbedded. Commonly their growth produces succulent and sweet tissues attractive to animals. The significance of such modified ovaries is, again, in their relation to problems of dispersal.

THE PROBLEM OF PLANT IMMOBILITY

Plants are usually anchored or rooted in place. This is one of their striking differences from most animals (although there are anchored animals, too). Their immobility is undoubtedly related, through the processes of evolution, to many special developments in the reproductive structures and cycles in plants.

Getting the sexes together. In the first place there is the problem of biparental reproduction, which has been a condition of most progressive evolution throughout the history of life. Two immobile plants cannot get together to reproduce, as can any two mobile animals. In lower plants the immobility of the developed organisms is counteracted by the mobility of gametes. The male gametes of attached algae are water-borne and are often motile (self-mobile) by means of flagella (p. 225). Fern sperms are also motile, even though limited in range. In seed plants it is the pollen grains, partly developed male gametophytes, that are mobile. In most nonflowering seed plants pollen is produced in enormous quantities, and the grains are so light that they are spread far and wide, even for hundreds and thousands of miles, by winds and air currents. This was undoubtedly the primitive condition for the first plants that were able to rise well into the air, dispensing with a requirement for water in which gametes could be dispersed. Many flowering plants, notably among the grasses, have retained or, perhaps, have returned to wind dispersal of pollen.

It is probably significant that so many plants, including the vast majority of seed plants, are *hermaphroditic*. That is, both sexes are present in one and the same individual plant. In spite of devices (reviewed below) to promote safe transmission of pollen from one plant to another, there is always a chance that this transmission will fail. Very many plants can self-fertilize themselves; this may be viewed in broad perspective as a last resort, assuring some seed production.[19] But self-pollination, if sustained over several generations, is effectively an abandonment of

[19] We will note later that hermaphroditism in animals is common in sessile (immobile) forms and in others (like specialized parasites) where the risk is great of never encountering a mate.

15-12 Reproductive cycle of a flowering plant. *Above,* broad features of the cycle. The sporophyte generation is the dominant part of the cycle. The male and female gametophytes are minute structures with a transient existence associated with fertilization. *1.* The mature sporophyte with a flower: *a,* sepals; *b,* petals; *c,* the stamens, consisting of filament (*d*) and anther (*e*); *f,* the pistil, consisting of stigma (*g*), style (*h*), and ovary (*i*). *2.* The pollen tube (male gametophyte) growing out of the pollen grain. *3.* The embryo sac (female gametophyte). *4.* The seed, containing embryo sporophyte (*a*) and nutritive endosperm (*b*). *5.* Seedling sporophyte. *Below,* detail of the gametophytes and fertilization. *1.* Mature sporophyte with flower. *2.* The young pistil. The ovary (black in the figure) is, historically speaking (see Fig. 21-7), a modified leaf (or leaves) folded over to enclose the sporangium (or sporangia) which it bears. This female sporangium is the ovule (gray in the figure); within the ovule is a single cell which will undergo meiosis, producing four haploid megaspores. *3.* Ovule containing the four megaspores. *4.* Ovule with the one surviving megaspore, which marks the beginning of the female gametophyte (haplophase). *5, 6,* and *7.* Successive mitotic divisions in the development of the female gametophyte (embryo sac) leading to its eight-nucleate state. *8.* The mature embryo sac with eight nuclei. Three of these (*a*) are called the antipodal nuclei; two others (*b*) are the future fusion nucleus; of the other three (*c*), the largest is the female gamete (egg cell); the other two are sometimes

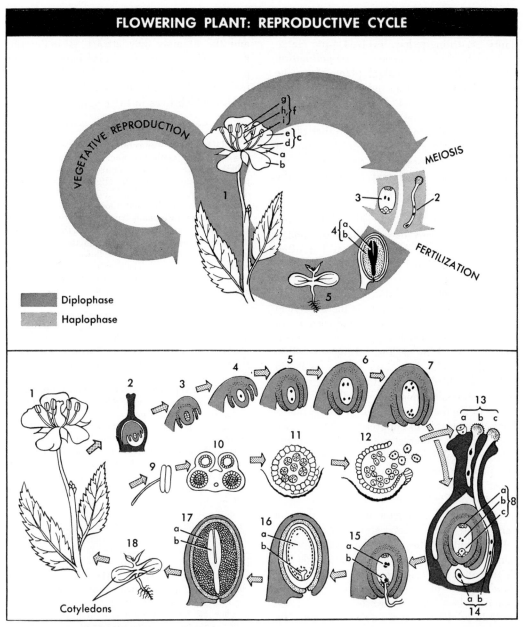

Diplophase

Haplophase

Cotyledons

thought to represent the vestigial remains of an archegonium. *9*. The stamen. *10*. A cross section through the anther (sporangium), which has four separate chambers; in two of these can be seen cells that will undergo meiosis, yielding microspores (pollen grains). *11*. Section through a single anther chamber with cells in which meiosis has occurred. *12*. The same anther chamber at a later stage, bursting and yielding pollen grains that have already developed into young male gametophytes: the nucleus in them has divided. *13*. *a*, pollen grain on the stigma. *b*, *c*, germination of the pollen grain and growth of the male gametophyte (pollen tube) down the style to the embryo sac (female gametophyte)

in the ovule. *14*. The nuclear constitution of the male gametophyte: *a*, the tube nucleus, which is not a gamete; *b*, the two male gametes. *15*. Fertilization: *a*, one of the male gametes fuses with the diploid fusion nucleus of the embryo sac, producing a *triploid* nucleus that will later develop into the endosperm of the seed (*16a*); *b*, the other male gamete nucleus fuses with the egg cell, producing a *diploid* zygote that marks the beginning of the new sporophyte. *16*, *17*. Younger and older seeds including (*a*) endosperm and (*b*) embryo sporophyte. *18*. Seedling sporophyte still showing its embryonic leaves (cotyledons), of which there are two in this particular (dicotyledon) flowering plant.

true sexuality, the very essence of which is the reshuffling of different genotypes. Many plants, accordingly, have evolved quite elaborate mechanisms to assure *cross-pollination* between different individual plants. In some species the anthers of an individual plant mature before its stigma, thus minimizing the amount of (last-resort) self-pollination. The pollen is available to fertilize only other plants that are slightly ahead in their development and therefore possessed of ripe stigmas. In other species the order may be reversed; the stigma may ripen first. The effect is the same in either case.

It is especially characteristic of flowering plants that so many of them have the pollen carried by animals, usually insects but often birds and occasionally other animals. It is clear that many features in the evolution of flowers are related to this complex process of pollen dissemination. Here is the biological significance of color, scent, and nectar in flowers. Nectar is a rich sugary secretion much prized as food by a host of insects—flies, butterflies, moths, bees, and so on—and also by hummingbirds. The nectar is an attraction to these animals whose busy traffic from one flower to another is exploited by the plants—themselves unable to congregate of their own accord. Many flower structures have evolved as guarantees that the visiting nectar-seeker will pick up and transmit pollen from one flower to another in the same species (Fig. 15-13). *Salvia* (Fig. 15-13C), a kind of wild sage, has flowers with a trigger that pulls down a stamen and dusts a nectar-seeking visitor with pollen. Scent and flower color act as advertisements or recognition signals that guide the visiting insects to *their* goal of food, and the *plant's* goal of cross-pollination. Flowers visited by bees are often white, yellow, violet, or "ultraviolet," colors distinguishable by bees, and rarely red, which looks black to a bee. Hummingbirds, however, can see red as a distinct color. Many flowers, especially in the tropics, where hummingbirds abound, are brilliantly red, advertising a nectar supply to which hummingbirds are partial. The structure of hummingbird-flowers is often long and tubular, preventing nearly all visitors other than the long-tongued hummingbird from getting the nectar.

There are many amazing and more elaborate relationships between flowering plants and the animals they attract as pollinating agents. Three of these we give here as a sample. Some orchids have evolved flowers that look remarkably like the female of a particular bee which lives in the neighborhood (Fig.

15-13 Insect-flower relationships. *A.* The *Yucca* flower and the moth *Pronuba. 1.* The moth collects a ball of pollen from the stamens. *2.* She packs the pollen onto the head of the stigma. *B.* The flowers of *Aristolochia* are among those in which the sex organs mature at different times; in this particular plant the female organs ripen first. Small insects enter the young flower (*1*) and push their way past the downward-pointed hairs (*a*) on the corolla tube to reach the dilated base of the flower where the ripe young stigma (*b*) is. Their exit is prevented, however, by the same hairs they pushed by on entry. Thus they are trapped in the flower for some days until the stamens mature and shed their pollen, which dusts the insects. Then the hairs wither (*d*) and the insects leave, only to enter another, younger flower whose ripe stigma is inevitably dusted by the pollen the insects bring with them. *C.* The flowers of *Salvia* (sage) are among those in which male organs ripen first. The flowers have, moreover, evolved very elaborate morphological adaptations to exploit bee visitors as cross-pollinating agents. The essential feature is best seen in *3:* the filament of the stamen (*c*) is short; the anther is highly asymmetrical, one part (*d*) being extremely short and shaped like a shield that gets in the way of the bee's proboscis when it seeks the nectar (*1*). This short arm acts as a lever: pushed by the bee's proboscis, it is lifted, and the other, long arm of the anther (*e*) is pushed down and touches the bee's abdomen. *2* shows the anther in its "rest" position; *3* shows it in the position to which it is forced by the bee. In young *Salvias* (*1*) the style has not completed its growth, so that the stigma (*a*) does not reach to the bee's abdomen; the anther (*b*), on the other hand, does. In older flowers (*4*), however, the style has completed its curved growth and the stigma is always brushed onto the bee, receiving pollen from other, younger flowers the bee has recently visited. *D.* The Australian orchid *Cryptostylis leptochila* is one of the flowers that mimics a female insect and leads to cross-pollination by seducing males of the insect species concerned. In this case the insect is the ichneumon wasp *Lissopimpla semipunctata* (*1*). *2.* Part of the flower (*a*) is strikingly like the female's abdomen; other parts (*b, c*) simulate legs and antenna. *3.* The male ichneumon attempts to copulate with the flower; when he leaves he carries away pollen which he transmits to the next plant he mounts. *E.* The Mediterranean orchid *Ophrys fusca,* and the male bee *Andrena trimmerana* that copulates with it.

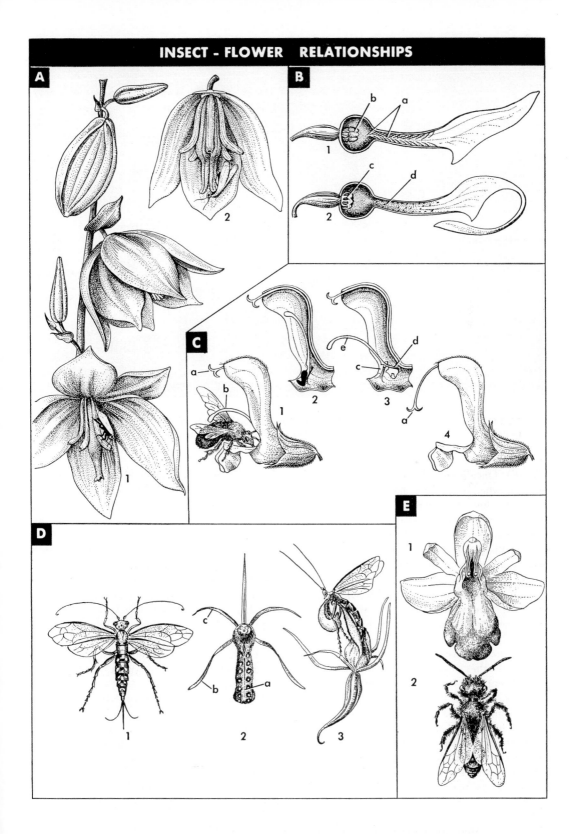

15-14 A bee gathering pollen and nectar from a *Lobelia* flower. Her traffic from flower to flower serves to transport pollen and cross-fertilize the *Lobelia* population.

15-13*E*). Once a year this orchid flowers, and does so when male bees have emerged and are flying but the females are still in pupal cases. So good is the flower's mimicry of the female that even the male bee is deceived. He mounts the flower as he would a female bee, and copulates with it. The stamens of the orchid are so arranged that the male bee's genital organs become dusted with pollen. The bee then carries the pollen and transmits it to the next orchid that seduces him.

When Smyrna fig trees were first grown outside the regions where they had long been cultivated, the trees failed to produce any fruit. Eventually it was found that the reason for the failure was the absence of a particular kind of small wasp. The female wasp lays her eggs in fig flowers, which are the only places where the larval wasps develop normally, and in turn the wasp is the only means of pollinating the figs so that they bear fruit. The figs have separate male (staminate) and female (pistillate) flowers. Wasps can develop only in

the male flowers. When the female wasps emerge from the flowers in which they were born, they are dusted with pollen. They then enter some other flower, lay their eggs, and die. The greatest peculiarity is this: if the female lays her eggs in a male flower, her eggs develop but no pollination occurs; if she lays them in a female flower, her eggs do not develop, but pollination occurs and fig seeds and fruit are produced. If all the wasps laid eggs in male flowers, there would soon be no more figs, and then no more wasps. But if all eggs were laid in female flowers, there would soon be no more wasps—and then no more figs!

Some yuccas bear seeds only if yucca moths are present. The moth collects balls of pollen and stuffs them into the tubular end of the pistil, which assures fertilization of the yucca and development of seeds and fruits. The moth then lays her eggs in the ovary of the yucca, and when the larvae hatch they eat the developing fruits. There is more than enough for their appetites, so some yucca seeds mature (Fig. 15-13*A*).

Do you think that fig wasps and yucca moths know what they are doing and have decided on these ways of assuring the future of their species? If not, how can such intricate relationships and behavior have arisen?

A final noteworthy point relates to the problem of getting the sexes together. If fertilization is to occur (and therefore if the species is to persist), it is necessary that availability of pollen and access to a mature stigma be simultaneous. This would be impossible if liberation of pollen and opening of flowers with stigmas occurred at different times of the year or, in some cases, even at different hours of the day. Plants have evolved the necessary means to synchronize flowering time among individual plants in the same species population. It is commonly known that all crocuses bloom at the same time early in spring, and chrysanthemums only in the fall. But how is this *timing* accomplished? Many factors seem to be involved, like temperature and light intensity, but probably the most important of all is the relative length of day and night. No matter how fickle the temperature

and other conditions may be, the length of daylight [20] is a rigorously constant *signal* of the season. It is the signal that synchronizes flowering.

Many plants control flowering time not only as to season but also as to time of day. Their flowers open and close rhythmically with a twenty-four–hour frequency controlled by some internal timing device that establishes "opening time" at a fixed hour relative to dawn. Bees make use of the fact and economize on time and effort by visiting the right flowers at the right time of day. Can you imagine what advantage this elaborate control confers on the plant?

Dispersal. So much for the problem of getting the sexes together in biparental reproduction. There is the further question of how plants spread geographically. In lower plants dispersal usually occurs in the spore phase of the cycle, and in those plants spores can develop into independent organisms. Like their motile gametes, the spores of algae are water-borne and are often motile, having flagella. Fungi and ferns produce clouds of

[20] Most plants actually measure night length!

Hugh Spencer

15-15 Seed dispersal. The cocklebur (*left*) seed is armed with hooks that attach it to passing animals, who unwittingly aid dispersal of the plant. The milkweed's seeds (*right*) are supplied with a delicate parachute of many fibers. They are dispersed by wind.

light spores that are carried by air currents far and wide, a few of them even for thousands of miles. The air you breathe is seldom free of spores. In seed plants the spores as such do not leave the parent organism (only pollen, which cannot by itself produce a new plant as spores can). In them dispersal is by means of seeds. The great success of the seed plants is clearly related to two characteristics of seeds: they protect the embryo through a dormant period and during times of drought or cold, and they are readily dispersed.

Adaptations for dispersal in seeds (Fig. 15-15) are as varied as those for pollination in flowers. Dandelions and many other plants have parachute seeds scattered by winds. Burrs stick to passing animals. Tempting fruits have hard-coated seeds that pass unharmed through the digestive systems of fruit-eaters. Coconuts and mangroves have floating seeds, resistant to long voyages in the currents of the sea. Vetches and a number of other plants have pods that open suddenly and scatter seeds like the fragments of a grenade. In Russian thistles—the tumbleweeds of Western song—the globular plant breaks off from its roots and rolls across the countryside, scattering seeds as it goes. Can you think of other ways in which seeds are dispersed?

Most individual plants are immobile as developed organisms, but seed dispersal is so effective that *populations* of plants may spread more widely and rapidly than populations of mobile animals.

Reproductive Cycles in Animals

DOMINANCE OF THE DIPLOPHASE

We have seen that both within the algae (most lowly of plants) and in the plant kingdom as a whole there has been a strong evolutionary tendency to emphasize the diplophase (sporophyte). In the most elaborately evolved algae like *Fucus* [21] and in the seed plants, the haplophase has been greatly reduced.

[21] Recall (note 1, p. 137) that **Fucus** is highly evolved, for an alga, in another significant respect; it has evolved vascular tissue not unlike that of true vascular plants. Both in its possession of vascular tissue and its elimination of the gametophyte, **Fucus** evolution has converged with that of seed plants (see p. 470).

What is the significance of this trend? To be honest, biologists must admit they do not know the full answer to this question. There are several suggestions, one of which is certainly part of the true answer. This relates to the fact that populations of diploid organisms can *store* more genetic variability than populations of haploid organisms; and diplophase organisms have been therefore favored in evolution for the same general reasons that sexuality itself has been favored. This point will become clearer after we discuss population genetics in the next chapter. In the meantime we note it as the only reasonable explanation offered for the clear emphasis of the diplophase in plants, and the fact that virtually all animals are diplophase organisms.

Indeed, the history of animals reveals only slight traces of any original emphasis on the haplophase. Biologists suspect that multicellular animals may have evolved from animal-like (nonphotosynthetic) flagellated protists (pp. 112 and 551), much as algae probably evolved from photosynthetic flagellates like *Chlamydomonas*. So far as is known, the animal-like flagellates are also haplophase organisms, the diplophase being restricted to the zygote itself. But *once animal life evolved above the protistan level, it became exclusively diplophase,* [22] the haplophase being represented only by the gametes. Why more plants than animals have been able to survive as haplophase organisms is not really clear.

The usual reproductive cycle in animals is, then, that which is familiar to you in man; there is no analogue of a gametophyte. Modifications of that cycle relate mainly to secondary regression in sexuality and to addition of vegetative (asexual) reproduction in the diplophase of the basic cycle (Fig. 15-16). Both of these processes are less common in animals than in plants, but they also occur rather widely in animals. Other evolutionary changes in reproduction and life histories in animals have involved not so much the overall reproductive *cycle* as the structures and processes of reproduction and development. In these respects animals are extremely diverse.

[22] There are the usual exceptions, such as the male bees noted earlier in this chapter. But they are clearly secondary specializations and outstanding by virtue of their rarity.

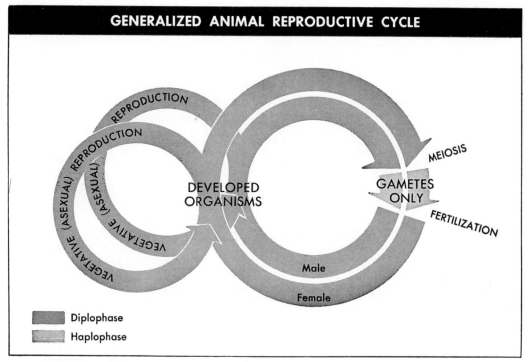

15-16   Generalized animal reproductive cycle. There is no analogue of the gametophyte generation in plants; the haplophase is represented by the gametes only. (There is one remarkable exception to the generalization given by this figure: male bees [and other Hymenoptera] are haploid. See Fig. 15-27.)

SEXUAL PLUS VEGETATIVE REPRODUCTION

Vegetative reproduction is lacking in ourselves and in the animals most familiar to us, the other vertebrates, so that it may strike you as strange that animals do reproduce vegetatively. Such reproduction is not the rule in animals and there are few—perhaps no—animal species in which it is the *sole* means of reproduction. Nevertheless, it does occur in many different kinds of invertebrates and even in tunicates (p. 543), animals related to the vertebrates. Vegetative reproduction in animals is usually by budding (as in *Hydra,* p. 359) or by fission (as in planarians, p. 160), processes not always clearly distinguishable.

In some insects a mass of cells formed early in embryonic development may bud off into many smaller clumps, each of which develops into a separate organism. When the process occurs before tissue differentiation, it does not differ in principle from multiple identical twinning (p. 340). In other insects, however, division into several individuals may occur later in the life history, in larval or pupal (p. 385) stages.

In many coelenterates, relatives of the jellyfishes, sexual and vegetative reproduction alternate regularly. In *Obelia* (Fig. 15-17), a classic example, the zygote develops (through a larval stage) into an attached individual which grows into a branched colony of polyps by budding without separation. Parts of the colony then produce further buds that do become detached and that swim off as medusas,[23] which look like small jellyfish. The medusas are male or female (in separate individuals), and they produce eggs and sperms that unite in fertilization and give rise to new attached colonies. The complex cycle, summarized in

[23] After the girl in Greek mythology whose hair was turned into snakes. The animals have numerous tentacles hanging down all around, and someone with a lively imagination thought that the unfortunate girl must have looked like this.

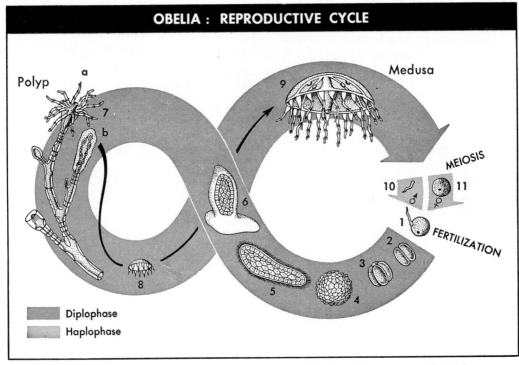

15-17 The reproductive cycle in coelenterates like *Obelia*. There is a so-called "alternation of generations" (medusa-polyp-medusa-polyp, etc.) in certain coelenterates like *Obelia*. However, this is not at all comparable to the alternation of sporophyte and gametophyte in plants: in coelenterates both polyp and medusa are diplophase. As in other animals, the haplophase is represented by the gametes only. *1*. Fertilization—union of egg and sperm. *2, 3,* and *4*. Successive stages in the cleavage of the egg and growth of the embryo. *5*. Ciliated swimming larva. *6*. Larva metamorphosing into polyp adult. *7*. Adult colony of polyps: *a*, a feeding polyp; *b*, a reproductive polyp which asexually buds off medusas. *8*. Young, free-swimming medusa. *9*. Adult medusa which produces sperms (*10*) and eggs (*11*).

Fig. 15-17, thus includes developed organisms of two strikingly distinct forms: the attached, sexless, colonial polyps and the free-swimming, sexed, noncolonial medusas. Both forms are diploid and belong on the left side of our reproductive cycle diagrams—the diplophase. Their anatomical structure is fundamentally the same beneath the superficial differences of attachment and proportions. Although it is most common in coelenterates, alternation of sexual and vegetative reproduction also occurs in several other groups of invertebrates. You already know (p. 363) that this same alternation also occurs (usually with less regularity) in plants. It is, however, fundamentally different from the other alternation of sporophytes (diplophase) and gametophytes (haplophase), with which it is often confused under the misnomer of "alternation of generations."

FERTILIZATION IN ANIMALS

Almost all animals produce specialized and sharply distinct female and male gametes: relatively large, approximately spherical eggs, immobile except as they may be passively moved by surrounding fluids, and relatively small, tailed or flagellated sperms, actively motile. The egg may remain attached within the maternal tissues until it is fertilized and starts to develop, as is usual in plants and also in sponges among animals. Much more often in animals the egg is detached from the maternal tissues before fertilization, although it may remain in cavities or passages in the maternal body and the developing organism may even, as in man, become re-attached.

In the majority of aquatic invertebrates—American oysters will serve as a concrete example—both eggs and sperm are simply shed into the water. There some of the swimming sperms, so enormously numerous that the water may be milky with them, eventually encounter eggs. Fertilization and development follow, with no special relationship to the parents. There are, however, innumerable modifications and complications of this simple process. In European oysters, for example, the eggs are retained in cavities in the mother, and these are fertilized and developed into larvae. In some fresh-water clams the eggs, after leaving the organ (the ovary) in which they are formed, are retained under the gills. Water currents passed through the gills draw in sperms, which fertilize the eggs. Development of small larvae proceeds, still within the interior of the gills. After being expelled, the larvae die unless they encounter a fish on the fins or gills of which they live as parasites until they have developed far enough to take up independent life.

In many fishes, also—indeed in an extremely wide range of aquatic animals—eggs and sperms are shed into the surrounding water, where fertilization occurs. This seems, and sometimes is, an extremely haphazard process (Fig. 15-18). A small pond, not to mention an ocean, is a vast volume in which a sperm can wander and never contact an egg. Animals have evolved, as have plants, a variety of devices that synchronize their sexual activity and so reduce the chance of wasting gametes. Most have seasonal periods of sexual activity, just as flowers are seasonal. And as in the flowering plants, many animals achieve synchronized seasonal reproductive

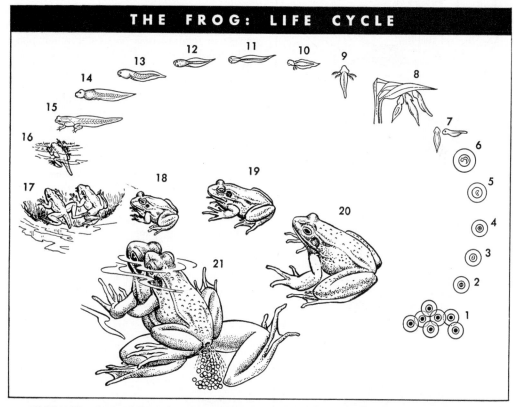

THE FROG: LIFE CYCLE

15-18   The frog: a life cycle involving external fertilization. Stages *1* through *6* show development of the fertilized egg, which floats freely and unprotected in pond water. *7, 8.* Freshly hatched larvae—tadpoles. *9-15.* Progressively older larvae (*15*, larva with limbs). *16, 17.* Metamorphosis from tadpole larva to adult frog. *18.* One-year-old adult. *19.* Two years old. *20.* Three years old. *21.* Adults spawning in water. Eggs are shed by the female (below); the male ejects sperms onto them when they are outside the female and free in the water.

COURTSHIP OF GREAT CRESTED GREBE

15-19   The courtship of the great crested grebe. The behavioral device of courtship that serves to synchronize release of gametes (and prevent interspecific matings, p. 431) is often an elaborate ritual. The figure shows several incidents in the grebe's courtship display. *1.* Mutual head shaking. *2.* The female is displaying before the male, who has dived and shoots out of the water in front of her. *3.* Two views of the male rising from his dive and displaying his "collar" of feathers. *4.* Both sexes have dived and brought weeds, which they display to one another.

activity by "recognizing" day-night length as a reliable season marker. Of course, this is not a conscious recognition; the relative lengths of day and night act as purely physiological triggers to initiate sexual activity. Many animals, again like plants, also use internal timing devices—we could call them "clocks"—to synchronize activity more finely to time of month and day. Thus many marine animals release their gametes on a twenty-eight–day cycle in relation to a particular moon phase. The palolo worm in Pacific coral reefs makes the sea milky with eggs and sperm, but only at full moon.[24]

In addition to these broad physiological processes which tend to synchronize sexual activity, motile animals have evolved elaborate behavioral adaptations that synchronize their release of gametes. Males and females may be stimulated to expel gametes only in the presence of each other. There may even be a more or less elaborate *courtship* which has the result that eggs and sperms are discharged at the same time and place (Fig. 15-19; see also Fig. 10-13, illustrating stickleback courtship).

Fertilization is possible only in watery surroundings and with eggs that do not have a complete tough coating. Such a coating excludes sperms. An egg without a coating, a shell of some kind, must be surrounded by fluid or it dries and dies. Fluid is also a necessary medium through which sperms may swim and reach eggs. Fertilization cannot take

[24] Lunar cycles of reproductive activity are also known in some mammals; the twenty-eight day periodicity of the oestrus cycle in women (Fig. 15-25) seems to be regulated by a timing system inherited from earlier mammals whose sexual activity occurs in phase with the moon. The lunar clock in women, however, has lost capacity to be synchronized (brought into phase) with the moon.

15-20 The copulation of Cecropia moths, female (*left*) and male (*right*).

place in the open air, where an egg without a shell rapidly dies and where a living sperm cannot reach the egg. The same limitations apply for the same reasons to fertilization in plants, and the limitations are really overcome in the same way in land plants and land animals even though the organs and activities are so different in the two: in both, fertilization takes place within the maternal organism. In the immobile higher plants, as you know, the male gamete is brought to the egg (somewhat indirectly) by the mobility of the pollen. Land animals are mobile and, in simpler fashion, the male takes the sperms to the female and injects them into her: copulation occurs. In all animals fully adapted to life on dry land, notably insects, reptiles, birds, and mammals, fertilization is internal

following copulation (Fig. 15-20).[25] In insects the shell is formed before fertilization, but there is a small hole in the shell through which a sperm enters. In reptiles and birds the shell forms after fertilization. In (true) mammals no shell forms, the zygote and resulting embryo being retained within the mother.

Copulation entails anatomical specializations (Fig. 15-24). The male must have an organ (a penis) that can be inserted into the female and through which sperms are ejected. The female must have a receptacle from which the sperms can move to the eggs through a fluid internal medium. In insects but not in

[25] Copulation also occurs in some aquatic animals, such as sharks, in which the egg either is surrounded with a protective shell before being expelled or is retained and develops inside the mother.

vertebrates there is an additional specialization. The females have sacs within which sperms are retained and kept alive for considerable periods of time. Copulation occurs only once, and thereafter sperms are released from the sacs whenever fertilized eggs are to be laid. The queen bee is an extreme case; she copulates only once and stores the sperms received for the rest of her life, sometimes up to seventeen years.

LARVAE

Development uses energy and materials. If all the necessary foods are supplied in some way or other within the egg, by a parent, or both, development is usually more or less direct. That is to say, when the developing individual reaches the stage of being an independent, self-maintaining organism it is already adapted to a life like that of its adult parents and is recognizably similar to them. Familiar examples are reptiles, birds, and mammals. Reptile and bird eggs contain large stores of food (in the yolk), and this suffices until the young animal hatches. Reptiles hatch as essentially small adults, able to fend for themselves. Most birds after hatching are fed for some time by their parents. Mammal eggs contain almost no food, but the needs of the developing embryo are provided through the mother. For a time after birth all needed food is supplied by the mother in the form of milk.

In most animals, including the overwhelming majority of species of invertebrates, many fishes, and most amphibians, the embryo does not develop directly into an adultlike organism. Free, postembryonic life, no longer dependent on food stored in the egg, is begun in *a form unlike the adult*. The organism in this phase differs more or less from its adult parents in environment, food, locomotion, and other particulars of the way of life. It is a *larva*. A stranger to the earth, perhaps our visitor from Mars again, would never guess that a butterfly is an adult caterpillar, a frog an adult tadpole, or a starfish an adult brachiolaria. Caterpillar, tadpole, and brachiolaria are larvae (Figs. 15-22, 15-18, and 15-21).

Larvae have several different roles in the life histories of animals. In aquatic invertebrates (also notably in parasites) the larva is a means of dispersal. To that extent it is analogous to a plant seed, and indeed it occupies a similar position in the life cycle as a distinctive phase preceding the mature diploid

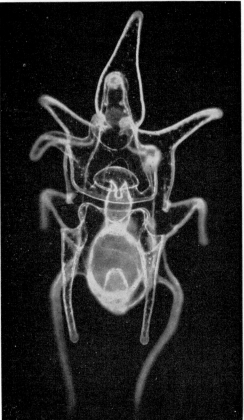

Top, © D. P. Wilson
Bottom, V. B. Schaeffer, from
U.S. Fish and Wildlife Service

15-21 The brachiolaria larva (highly magnified) **and the adult of the starfish** *Asterias.*

organism. Many animals are attached and immobile as adults (zoologists call them sessile): sponges, corals, most sea "lilies" (which are animals, p. 537), oysters, and numerous others. Without exception they have unattached larvae that are scattered by currents in the water in which the larvae float or swim. Even animals that are mobile as adults—starfishes for instance—may be transported much farther as larvae than they could travel in adult form.

Larvae also often represent a special feeding phase in the life cycle. This is particularly true of insects. Most of the feeding and growth may occur in the larval stage.[26] In fact, some adult insects do not eat at all. They are reproductive entirely and in their brief span use up materials and energy acquired while they were larvae. In most insects both larvae and adults eat, but they usually eat different food. Each may rely on a food more available at a particular time of year; for instance, caterpillars may feed on leaves, and butterflies on nectar. In this example, too, all the materials for growth are obtained by the caterpillar. A butterfly does not grow at all, but does acquire energy by eating.

Change from larval to adult form and way of life is called *metamorphosis* ("form changing") (Fig. 15-22). Metamorphosis may be gradual or it may be dramatically abrupt. In grasshoppers the larvae are quite like adults except in proportions and absence of wings. Adult form is acquired gradually through a succession of molts of the external skeleton (p. 350). In dragonflies the larva is aquatic and markedly different from the aerial adult. Metamorphosis occurs during a single molt, involving mostly change in relative development of tissues and organs already present. In most insects, with butterflies as a common example, there is a special, outwardly inactive phase, the *pupa*, between larva and adult. The pupa is enclosed in a case or cocoon, where it undergoes radical metamorphosis. Almost all organs and tissues of the larva are destroyed, and what is essentially

26 This, too, has its analogy in the life cycle of plants, but the analogy is more distant. The gametophyte of a moss is a "feeding" phase, and the sporophyte more exclusively reproductive.

a new organism grows from small cell clumps or buds. Do you see any parallel between this metamorphosis and the phases of the life cycle of *Obelia*?

EVOLUTION OF VERTEBRATE REPRODUCTION

There have been many different lines of evolution, and they have led to many and highly diverse specialized kinds of reproductive structures and processes. Even among the vertebrates are myriad different lines of descent leading to markedly different reproductive systems among recent animals. Of course, too, no species now living are in the lines ancestral to man, nor are they likely to have retained precisely the conditions that did occur in the human ancestry. Nevertheless, comparison of them in the light of phylogeny as revealed by fossils permits highly probable inference as to the course followed in the evolution of human reproduction. In this history there has been a trend toward greater protection and care of the developing embryo and young, and a major transformation connected with the change from water to land life.

In our remote fish ancestors, eggs without shells but with gelatinous envelopes were expelled and fertilized externally. Similar eggs, sperms, and fertilization were retained in the ancestral amphibians, and so was the early, larval phase of the fish life history, but there was a more radical metamorphosis leading to four-legged, semiterrestrial adults. Pairing (but not copulation) probably arose in this evolutionary stage, a male remaining near or on a female while the eggs were being laid and extruding sperm under this stimulus (Fig. 15-18). Transition to completely terrestrial life in early reptiles involved many changes. Fertilization became internal, following copulation. The fertilized egg (a zygote soon becoming an embryo) was enclosed in a protective shell before being laid. Within the shell a membrane (the amnion, Fig. 15-23) developed from the embryonic tissues and formed a fluid-filled sac enclosing the embryo proper, which thus continued to develop in a self-contained aquatic environment. Other membranes (allantois and chorion, Fig. 15-23) formed sacs and surfaces aiding in

Hugh Spencer

15-22 Stages in the life cycle of the swallowtail butterfly, *Papilio*. From left to right: caterpillar larva; pupa (or chrysalis); adult freshly emerged from pupal case; and adult with fully expanded wings.

respiration, in absorption of food within the egg, in storage of waste materials, and in further protection of the whole complex inside of the shell. That is the reptilian condition, retained with variations in the reptiles still living.

In the gradual transition from mammal-like reptiles to true mammals, the eggs were retained during development in the lower (or posterior) parts of the tubes leading from the ovaries to the exterior. These parts of the tubes became enlarged and thickened to form *uteri* (singular, uterus). (In man and some other mammals the two paired uteri have fused into one medial uterus.) The egg shell was reduced and eventually lost. Then the membranes of the embryo (foetus) came in direct contact with the wall of the uterus and began to exchange substances with that wall

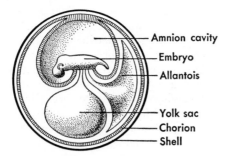

Amnion cavity

Embryo

Allantois

Yolk sac

Chorion

Shell

15-23 The amniotic egg of terrestrial vertebrates.

by diffusion. Oxygen and dissolved foodstuffs were absorbed from the uterus and carbon dioxide and wastes (such as urea, p. 155) given off to it. Finally, this exchange was made most effective by a complex intergrowth of tissues from the embryo and those in the wall of the uterus, forming a *placenta* (Fig. 15-26). In the placenta, capillaries from the maternal and the embryonic circulatory system come into close contact, although normally there is no exchange of blood but only of dissolved substances by diffusion. Special vessels, which become inoperative at birth, connect the embryo with the placenta.

In the meantime special provision for the young after birth was also evolving. Even before the eggs were retained in the uterus, *mammary glands* yielding milk arose in females and provided a rich, balanced liquid diet for the newborn. Finally, in man, even after the child is weaned there is a long period of mental and social training by the parents. (Such training also occurs in many other animals but is, of course, much more prolonged and intensive in man.)

Mammalian reproduction. Sperms develop in large numbers in the testicles and are stored in the coiled tubes of the epididymis and the connecting ducts. The seminal vesicles and prostate gland secrete fluid in which the sperms are transported. Prior to copulation,

The oestrus cycle. In most male mammals mature sperms are produced and sex hormone secretion is intense only at certain times during the year. Sexual desire and behavior are strongly influenced by hormone concentration, and it is only during these periods that the male is ready and willing to copulate. Similarly in most female mammals, eggs mature in ripening follicles once or a few times a year. Simultaneously sex hormone secretion increases and is greatest at about the time when eggs are released from the ovary, the only time when the females are willing, or anxious, to copulate. They are then said to be "in heat." The whole process

the penis becomes stiff and erect by the pressure of blood in its internal tissues. It is then inserted into the female vagina. Frictional stimulation leads to a sudden reflex ejaculation of semen (sperms and fluid) through the urethra in the penis and out into the vagina. The sperms are motile and tend to move from the vagina through the uterus and thence up the uterine tubes. If an egg is encountered in one of the tubes, fertilization is likely to occur (Fig. 15-24).

Eggs develop and ripen (usually one at a time in humans) in small, bubble-like structures, follicles (cf. p. 337; also Fig. 15-25), in the ovaries. When an egg is mature, the follicle bursts, releasing the egg, which normally passes into the funnel-like end of the uterine tube. If there are no live sperms there at the time, the egg disintegrates or passes on down the tube, through uterus and vagina to the exterior. (The egg is so small that its passage is usually wholly unnoticeable.) If the egg encounters live sperms in the uterine tube, fertilization is likely to occur. Development begins in the tube and continues as the embryo slowly passes on down the tube into the uterus. There the embryo becomes embedded in the wall of the uterus, in due course a placenta is formed, and development of the young (gestation) proceeds. After some time (ten days in mice, nine months in humans) intra-uterine development is complete; then the muscular walls of the uterus contract rhythmically, expelling the young through the vagina and then tearing the placenta loose and expelling it (Fig. 15-26).

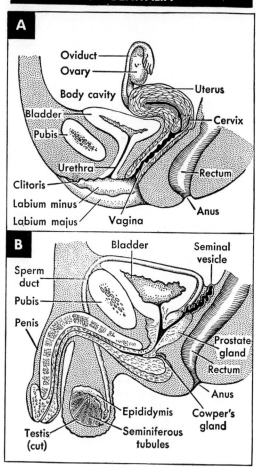

HUMAN REPRODUCTION: I GENITALIA

A

Oviduct
Ovary
Body cavity
Bladder
Pubis
Urethra
Clitoris
Labium minus
Labium majus
Uterus
Cervix
Rectum
Anus
Vagina

B

Bladder
Seminal vesicle
Sperm duct
Pubis
Penis
Prostate gland
Rectum
Anus
Cowper's gland
Epididymis
Seminiferous tubules
Testis (cut)

15-24 Human reproduction: I. Genitalia.

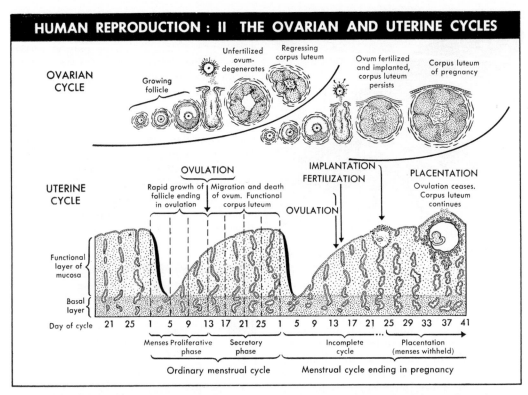

15-25 Human reproduction: II. The ovarian and uterine cycle. The figure outlines the changes that occur in the ovary cycle and in the wall of the uterus (1) during ordinary menstrual cycle, and (2) during menstrual cycle that includes fertilization and ends in pregnancy. (1) The ordinary cycle in the ovary involves the growth of a follicle with its contained egg cell or ovum. When its growth is complete, the follicle bursts, discharging the ovum from the ovary; this event of *ovulation* occurs, on the average, on the 14th day of the cycle. If the ovum fails to be fertilized in the oviduct it degenerates. After ovulation the old follicle undergoes a special development into a *corpus luteum* (yellow body). There is a parallel cycle of change in the wall of the uterus. The uterine cycle is indeed controlled, through hormones, by the ovarian cycle. While the follicle is growing in the ovary, the female sex hormone estrogen is secreted into the blood stream; it stimulates development of a special functional layer (the *endometrium*) of the uterine wall. This layer is richly supplied with blood vessels and is built, so to speak, in anticipation of fertilization and the implantation on it of an embryo to be nourished (Fig. 15-26). After ovulation the corpus luteum that develops from the old follicle secretes another hormone, *progesterone*, which maintains the growth of the endometrium. In the ordinary menstrual cycle (no fertilization), the corpus luteum eventually degenerates, and the endometrium is shed with a loss of blood during a 4- or 5-day period called the *menses*. The whole cycle is renewed as another follicle develops in the ovary and estrogen is again secreted, causing the endometrium to regrow. (2) If ovulation is followed by fertilization the sequence of events is different. The fertilized egg becomes *implanted* in the endometrial layer of the uterus and a *placenta* develops (Fig. 15-26). Following placentation, ovulation ceases because the high progesterone level in the blood (maintained by the corpus luteum, which does not, this time, degenerate) causes the pituitary to stop secreting the gonadotropic hormone that stimulates follicle growth (cf. Fig. 8-7, p. 179): menstruation does not occur (high progesterone level), and the endometrium is retained as a functional part of the placenta. (From Schroeder, as modified by Patten in *Human Embryology*, 1953. Courtesy of Blakiston Div., McGraw-Hill Book Company.)

of build-up and drop in hormone concentration, ripening of follicles and release of eggs, and simultaneous changes in the uterus is called the *oestrus* [27] *cycle*.

In these respects, humans are aberrant

mammals. In men maturation of sperms and secretion of sex hormones is approximately continuous from early adolescence with decreasing vigor into old age. Women have an oestrus cycle, as do other female mammals, but it is unusual in that it goes on continuously with periods of about 28 days from early adolescence until the late 40's or early

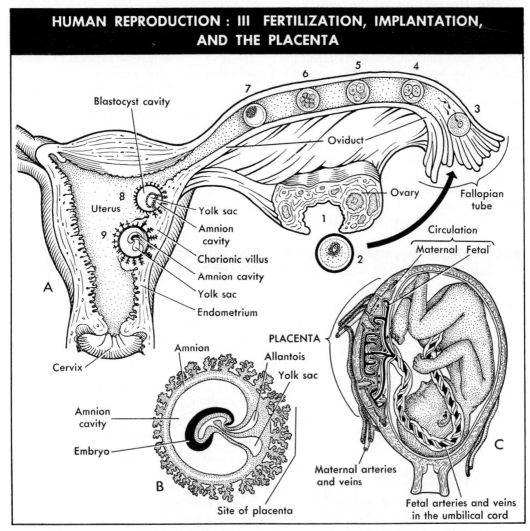

HUMAN REPRODUCTION : III FERTILIZATION, IMPLANTATION, AND THE PLACENTA

15-26 Human reproduction: III. Fertilization, implantation, and the placenta (schematic). *A. 1, 2.* Egg liberated from follicle. Ovary with *corpora lutea. 3.* Egg fertilized in oviduct shortly after entering Fallopian tube (during ovulation the ovary is pressed closely to the Fallopian tube). *4-7.* Cleavage stages. *8, 9.* The embryo implants on the endometrium of the uterine wall; amniotic cavity already clear (*8*); the chorion of the embryo has developed fingerlike villi that burrow deep into the endometrium. *B.* The implanted embryo. The villi of the chorion are the embryo's agents of exchange of nutrients and wastes with the maternal tissues of the placenta. *C.* Advanced fetus in the uterus, showing the fetal circulation in the umbilical cord leading to and from the placenta.

50's except during pregnancies. The main features of the human female cycle are summarized in Fig. 15-25. Fertilization can occur only shortly after release of an egg from its follicle and, although highly variable, that usually happens in women about midway between menstruations.

The Regression of Sexuality

In this chapter we have been concerned mostly with main trends in evolution and with the more usual kinds of reproduction and life cycles. As we have noted (p. 360), there is reason to believe that some device for genetic recombination has occurred in the ancestry of all recent organisms, including viruses and bacteria. In all but viruses, bacteria, and blue-green algae recombination is achieved through a sexual process. Therefore we have stressed reproductive cycles in which fully sexual reproduction, including meiosis and fertilization, is present. Nevertheless, we have noted from time to time that the sexual cycle

is modified or entirely absent in a considerable number of highly diverse organisms. In ancestors of most of these organisms, if not of all, a fully characteristic sexual cycle once occurred, so that they must represent a regression or loss of sexuality. This phenomenon is now to be briefly considered.

Self-fertilization is still sexual, but from an evolutionary point of view, at least, it must be considered as a partial regression of sexuality. Biparental sexual reproduction must be older than uniparental self-fertilization. The latter process necessarily leads to marked reduction of genetic variation, which is the important evolutionary consequence of all kinds of regression of sexuality. In *parthenogenesis*, which occurs in both the higher plants and the higher animals, the sexual apparatus is present and eggs, specialized sex cells, are produced, but these develop without fertilization. Some organisms are parthenogenetic and fully sexual (biparental) in reproduction at different times, sometimes with a fairly regular alternation, as in many aphids

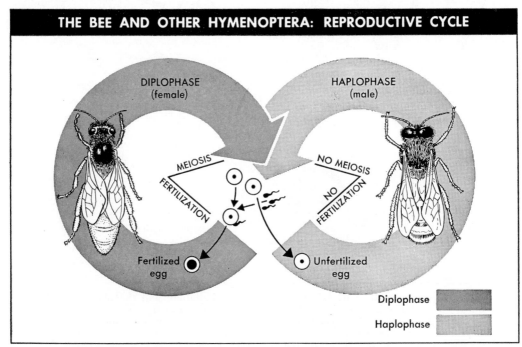

THE BEE AND OTHER HYMENOPTERA: REPRODUCTIVE CYCLE

DIPLOPHASE (female)

HAPLOPHASE (male)

MEIOSIS
FERTILIZATION

NO MEIOSIS
NO FERTILIZATION

Fertilized egg

Unfertilized egg

Diplophase

Haplophase

15-27 The reproductive cycle in the bee and other Hymenoptera. The male develops from unfertilized eggs and is, therefore, haploid. All fertilized eggs give rise to females (diploid). Only a few of these ever become functional females, however; the majority become sterile workers. Since the males themselves are haploid they produce normal haploid sperm without meiosis.

or "plant lice." In bees and many of their relatives males are produced from unfertilized eggs and are haploid, while females arise from fertilized eggs and are diploid, an extraordinary modification of the sexual reproductive cycle that can be diagramed as in Fig. 15-27. Sometimes parthenogenesis is the only method of reproduction, as also exemplified among aphids. Then the cycle resembles the sexual cycle in passing through a gamete (or what was a true gamete in some ancestral form), the egg, but both meiosis and fertilization are lacking. (Why cannot meiosis occur in such a reproductive cycle if fertilization does not?) The two key processes are, so to speak, short-circuited (Fig. 15-27). The effect is the same as in vegetative reproduction: variation is reduced to a minimum because until a mutation occurs *all* the descendants of an individual have exactly the same heredity.

You have seen how frequently both sexual and vegetative reproduction occur in the same kinds of organisms. In the course of evolution it is then possible for vegetative reproduction to be lost so that reproduction is sexual only. This happened in the ancestors of the vertebrates. On the other hand, reproduction may also become entirely vegetative. This has happened to many species here and there, but not to the whole of any large and progressive group,[28] a fact that is certainly significant in relationship to the role of sex in evolution.

When organisms are *well adapted to a uniform and stable environment*, it is advantageous for them to have little genetic variation. (Any mutation or other change increasing variation will be opposed by natural selection, a process discussed in the next chapter.) These are the conditions in which regression of sexuality, which always decreases variation, is likely to occur. When, on the contrary, environments change markedly in the course of time and when a varied environment offers opportunity for diverse new ways of life, groups with high genetic variation are more favorable for survival and progressive change. Then evolution puts a premium on sexual re-

---

[28] The largest group that is wholly asexual (as far as known) is probably that of the blue-green algae, some 2500 living species. Their evolution has been retrogressive rather than progressive in many respects, and they owe survival and abundance to their high resistance to what are, for algae, adverse conditions.

production. In the history of life there has been a balance between the two processes. Sexual regression has frequently prevailed in particular circumstances, but it leads to evolutionary dead ends and strongly limits any further change.

Finally we may inquire why sexual regression is so much more common in protistans and algae than in higher plants or animals, and more common in higher plants than in higher animals. A satisfactory explanation is not yet possible and surely will not be simple, but it seems that these factors may have some bearing: shortness of life cycle, relative simplicity of organism, open as opposed to closed development (p. 336), and relatively greater breadth of reaction ranges. Such characteristics may make adaptation to environmental change possible without a high degree of genetic variation at any one time. The dynamics of these processes involve whole populations of organisms, a subject to which we turn in the next chapter.

Chapter Summary

The generalized reproductive cycle: asexual reproduction—vegetative propagation and spore production; sexual reproduction—the production and union (fertilization) of haploid gametes, forming a diploid zygote that initiates a new generation.

The distribution and significance of sex in organisms: sex as a phenomenon distinct from and added to the basic (asexual) process of reproduction; its evolutionary function in producing genetic recombinations; other mechanisms that produce genetic recombination—in bacteria, in viruses.

The haplophase-diplophase reproductive cycle: haplophase initiated by meiosis and concluded by fertilization; diplophase initiated by fertilization and concluded by meiosis; three major variations on the haplophase-diplophase reproductive cycle.

Reproductive cycles in plants generally: gametophyte and sporophyte as the developed organisms of the haplophase and diplophase, respectively; the reproductive cycles of green protists, algae, mosses, and ferns, showing an increasing evolutionary emphasis on the sporophyte (diplophase).

Reproduction of seed plants: the flower as reproductive organ; sepals and petals, modified leaves, functionally related to effecting pollination; anthers, male sporangia; ovules, female sporangia; ovary, formed by leaflike structures bearing the ovules; embryo sac and pollen tube as much reduced (vestigial) female and male gametophytes; seeds as ovules containing the embryonic sporophyte and food reserves (endosperm and embryonic leaves); fruits as modified ovaries or other flower parts containing seeds.

Reproductive problems inherent in the immobility of plants: (1) getting the sexes together; exploitation of insects as agents for carrying pollen; devices to ensure cross-pollination; (2) dispersal of seeds; adaptations exploiting wind, animals, and insects as dispersal agents.

Reproductive cycles in animals: complete dominance of the diplophase; absence of developed haplophase animal organisms, with rare exceptions like male bees; asexual reproduction in the diplophase of animals; "alternation of generations" in coelenterates entirely *within* the diplophase.

Fertilization in animals: external fertilization in aquatic animals; diverse devices that ensure simultaneous release of male and female gametes; synchronization with the moon; synchronization by mutual excitement in courtship; copulation—internal fertilization—an adaptation to land life.

Larval forms: their function as feeding stages and, especially, as agents of the species' dispersal.

Evolution of vertebrate reproduction: external fertilization in primitive aquatic vertebrates (fish, amphibia); reptilian evolution of penis, internal fertilization, and egg adaptations (membranes, shell) suited to land life; reproductive specialization of mammals—live birth.

Mammalian reproduction: gametes; copulation; fertilization in the oviduct; implantation of the embryo in the uterine wall; formation of placenta—its function in nourishing the fetus; the oestrus cycle in women and other female mammals.

The regression of sexuality: self-fertilization and parthenogenesis; its interpretation as an adaptive abandonment of genetic recombination in organisms already well adapted to a uniform and stable environment.

The Mechanism
of Evolution

PART 5

INTRODUCTION TO PART FIVE

The photograph introducing Part 5 shows a population of seals lying on a rocky coast where, each year, they come ashore for several weeks to mate and rear their young. The scene points up two major features of our present topic, the mechanism of organic evolution: (1) The evolutionary process can be understood only in terms of populations; what evolves, as we shall see, is the pooled hereditary constitution of a population of interbreeding individuals. (2) The mechanism of natural selection—key feature in the mesh of evolutionary causes—focuses on the reproductive process we have previously outlined in Chapter 2.

Seals are descendants of early carnivores that were terrestrial running creatures. Their evolution has been a history of change of habitat and way of life with a corresponding change in bodily structure and function. But in another, more fundamental, view, their evolution has been a history of change in hereditary constitution. In last analysis the evolution of organisms is change in their genetical make-up—a gradual rewriting, so to speak, of their inherited message.

The first task in explaining evolution has already been performed, in preliminary fashion, by Part 4: to discover the causes which introduce variation, or innovations, into the hereditary make-up of organisms. The mechanisms of heredity fail to guarantee a perfect similarity of offspring to parent; mutation and sexual recombination ensure that innovations will continually creep into successive versions of the chromosomal blueprint. The seals in our photograph, for example, all surely differ to some minor extent in their private version of the basic seal-genotype they all possess. There is, however, more to organic evolution than the raw variations that mutation and recombination constantly thrust into the inherited message. For these processes, being completely mechanical and blind to the organism's needs, produce all manner of little changes, very few of which improve the adaptive organization of the living thing. And, of course, one of the most conspicuous features of evolution is the way it has maintained and even increased the adaptation of organisms to their environment.

The second task in explaining evolution is therefore the search for those processes which, given the random hereditary changes of mutation and recombination, mold from them the organized, nonrandom change that fits the organism to new environments or, just as importantly, improves its fitness for the accustomed habitat. Those processes—complex and subtle in their detail—which give this direction and order to evolutionary change are what we collectively refer to as natural selection.

Chapter 16 is concerned with the fundamentals of population genetics; it discusses the nature of natural selection as basically a process of differential or nonrandom reproduction.

Chapter 17 treats those factors in the evolution of populations which cause an increase in life's diversity through the formation of new species.

Chapter 18 returns to the fundamental concept of adaptation; it gives a fuller meaning to the concept of natural selection as involving purely historical processes.

This leaf insect is a not-too-distant relative of the cockroach. Its remarkable resemblance to the leaves that form its background is a product of evolutionary processes, the elementary forms of which are the subject of this chapter. (Photo by Charles Halgren)

CHAPTER **16**

The Elementary

Processes of

Evolution

Individuals, Populations, and Species

THE FOREST AND THE TREES

Not to see the forest for the trees has become a common metaphor for taking a short-sighted view of things, for being tangled up in details and failing to grasp the whole situation. If you look, literally, at a forest and try to understand it, you are likely, and quite rightly, to look first at trees. First questions are, "What is the structure of this particular tree? What is it doing? And how does it do it?" But even as you look at a single tree, you become conscious that it is not living alone. It is affected by surrounding trees and other plants with which it must share the necessities of life: space, water, other materials, and sunlight. Still more important, it reproduces. It is a temporary link in the continuity of its

kind. If (as is usual) its reproduction is biparental, the process of continuity brings together substance and characteristics of different trees in the forest. In a matter of years, or of centuries at most, the one tree you are looking at will be gone, but the forest may endure without significant change.

To understand life it is necessary to see *both* the trees and the forest. So far we have been looking mostly at trees. Preceding chapters have reviewed the biology of individual organisms. Here and there relationships in groups of organisms have been touched on, for there are no really hard and fast divisions of knowledge. Yet even when we discussed continuity and genetics (Chapters 11-15), this was mainly in terms of basic processes as seen in individuals and their offspring.

Now the time has come to look at the forest. We have started to consider diversity, the different kinds or species of organisms. The species are groups. They cannot be understood in terms of individuals only. From here on, most of the rest of this book is devoted to the biology of populations and of communities, which are composed of populations.

THE UNITS OF LIFE

The individual organism. The obvious and basic unit of life in nature is the individual. This is the unit of metabolism, of organization, of responsiveness, and of reproduction and development. Individuals practically always occur in groups and can be understood only in this context (that is the main theme to which we are now turning). Yet whatever happens in nature happens to and among individuals. All processes and developments in groups stem from those in individuals.

There is seldom any difficulty in distinguishing the basic unit, the individual. You know that you are an individual, and you do not hesitate to extend individuality to a dog, an oyster, or a tree. An ameba or other protist is clearly an individual, and all the cells of a multicellular organism, together and not separately, make up an individual. There are some doubtful cases, but these need not confuse the main issue. In a coral colony the various polyps are connected by living matter (p. 7), and in a plant more than one stem and crown may arise from a connected root system. Then there are those interesting animals, such as the Portuguese man-of-war (Fig. 22-5), in which the colony as a whole has a sort of organized individuality distinct from that of the united, differentiated polyps that compose it. These are marginal cases in which individuality is less clear-cut than in a man or a carrot, but they do not invalidate the generalization that life is manifested in individual organisms which are its basic units.

The local population of similar individuals: the deme.

Consider the individuals of a protist, say, *Paramecium* in a pond. All are much alike, they may reproduce for long periods without interbreeding,[1] and they have no social organization. They are about as independent from each other as individual organisms ever are. Nevertheless, the whole population of paramecia in the pond does constitute a naturally defined unit. That population as a whole fills a certain unitary role in the life of the pond. Descendants of any individual in it may spread anywhere in the pond, and, as far as the role of the popu-

lation is concerned, it does not matter what particular individuals or progeny are carrying forward the activity at any time or place within the pond. Moreover, this population in this pond is a unit separable from other, similar populations of paramecia in other ponds in the vicinity.

Coming out on dry land, we may observe a grove of pine trees or a population of squirrels living in those trees. Here, too, there are clearly units of population, definable like the populations of paramecia because the group as a whole has a role that continues, regardless of what particular individuals happen to be there at any given time. Here, however, there is still another factor that helps to define the group: the individuals composing it are all related and they are interbreeding. The future populations of the unit may be derived from any or all individuals now present in this local group. They are less likely to be derived from any individuals of other pine groves or their squirrel occupants.

As another example, we may find among the pine trees a large anthill. Here is a still more sharply defined unit of population. All the ants swarming in the hill are closely related. Usually they include one resident queen and her daughters. Future populations, as long as the colony persists here, will be of the same descent. The population is also more closely knit than those previously exemplified because it has a social organization. The whole population works together as a co-operative unit, with division of labor among the several castes.

A general term for any definable local unit of population, like those of paramecia, pine trees, or ants, is *deme*.[2] The examples have

---

[1] In fact, paramecia and most other protists do occasionally interchange nuclear material, which has the same effect as interbreeding (p. 492). They may, however, serve as an example of the fact that the individuals within a unit of population in nature do not necessarily interbreed. What we say here applies equally well to (the rather few) populations that are strictly and always uniparental in reproduction.

[2] A deme was a population unit, something like a township, in ancient Greece. The word is derived from **demos,** "people." Some purists object to applying a word that used to mean "people" to populations of nonhuman animals or plants—but no one objects to calling them populations, and "population" used to mean "people," too (from Latin **populus**). In modern terminology it really makes no difference what a word meant a couple of thousand years ago. All that matters is how we define it now.

In this book we have used as few strictly technical terms as possible. The technical terms we have introduced are as a rule those universally required and used in discussion of the essential biological principles. The term "deme" is a partial exception to this rule. It was not proposed (in this modern sense) until 1939, and it is not yet in universal use among biologists,

shown that demes can be of several sorts or, at least, that they can be defined by different characteristics. When a deme is defined in part by interbreeding among its individuals, as in demes of pine trees or of squirrels, it can also be called a *genetical population.* (Some authorities use the synonymous term *Mendelian population.*) Social demes are usually also breeding units so that they tend to correspond with genetical populations. This need not, however, be strictly true, as the example of the anthill shows. Few individuals in a social deme of ants ever breed. When they do, they usually crossbreed with individuals from other social demes (anthills) and set up new ones. In the long run, the genetical population thus includes members of a large number of social units. All the anthills over a considerable area may represent the real genetical population, or a genetical deme of a larger and more permanent sort than the social demes.

Do you think the biological concept of demes is applicable to human populations? If so, how would you define various sorts of demes among mankind?

The species: group of similar demes. Adjacent demes often intergrade, and the distinction of any one deme may be quite temporary. It is, in fact, characteristic of demes that they are commonly vague in definition and fluctuating in numbers. A grove of pine trees is distinguished as a deme and a genetical population because its continuity depends for the most part on interbreeding of individuals within the unit. It is, however, more likely than not that pollen from other demes will reach this one and affect its reproduction, and also that some pollen from this deme will spread to others. There is some genetical unity in the deme, but it is not absolute. If pines grow up between this grove and the next, the two former demes may become quite indistinguishable. In a large pine forest, trees in one area are more likely to interbreed among themselves than with

who can be a conservative lot on occasion. Yet it seems to us a convenient and really necessary term for clear discussion of an important biological concept for which there is no other accurate, brief designation either in technical terminology or in common speech.

distant trees in the same forest. There are vaguely separate genetical populations in the forest, but they intergrade so continuously that it would be entirely arbitrary to divide the forest into definitely bounded demes (Fig. 16-1).

Similarly, the squirrels in any one deme are likely on occasion to interbreed with those of surrounding demes. Heredity does pass from one deme to another. Adjacent demes may interbreed so freely as to become essentially one deme: the demes fuse. If all the squirrels in one grove or one part of a forest die out, a deme ceases to exist, but squirrels of surrounding demes may soon occupy the territory, or migrants may give rise to a new deme of the same sort. No essential or permanent change in the squirrel population has occurred. Demes fluctuate and intergrade, but there are larger units of population in nature which tend to be both more permanent and more clear-cut. These are species.

A *species* is a group of organisms so similar in structure and heredity that their demes integrade, may fuse, and may take the place of each other without essential change in the nature and role of the group as a whole. All biologists agree that species are important units in nature and that they correspond more or less with that definition. It is, however, difficult or impossible to frame a really precise, fully meaningful definition which applies without question to all organisms in nature. This is the *species problem*, which will be discussed in Chapter 17. In order to understand the problem and the processes by which species arise, it is necessary first to know more about heredity in populations.

The Genetics of Populations

A deme or any sort of population as it occurs in nature tends to persist for years, centuries, or millennia. It has *continuity*, as we have already emphasized. We have also emphasized that an essential element in that continuity is the passing on of chromosomes, with their genes, from one generation to the next. The persistence of a population without significant change in its characteristics implies that there has been little or no change in its genetical or environmental

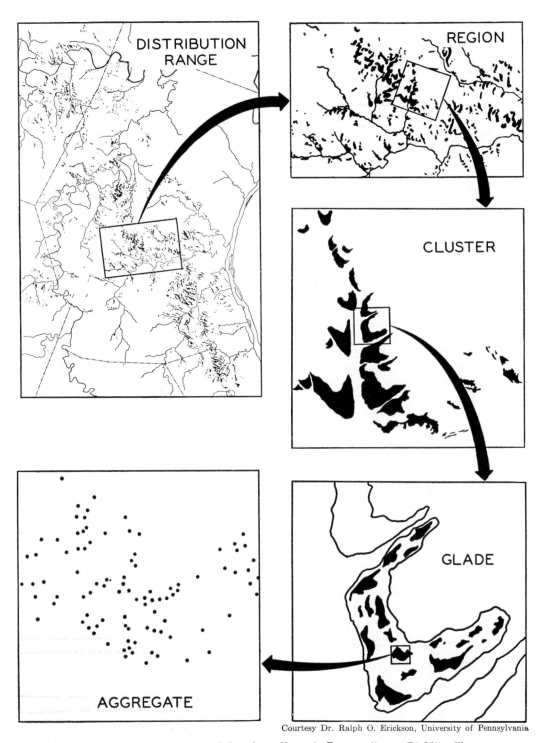

DISTRIBUTION RANGE

REGION

CLUSTER

GLADE

AGGREGATE

Courtesy Dr. Ralph O. Erickson, University of Pennsylvania

16-1 The population structure of the plant _Clematis Fremontii_ var. _Riehlii_. The upper left figure shows the entire distribution; the other figures, as the arrows indicate, show the details of distribution in hierarchical fashion down to an individual aggregate, or deme, in a particular glade.

factors. Change in a population over the generations—in other words, its evolution—must indicate change in genetical or environmental factors, or both. Since changes *directly* due to environmental factors are not heritable, we may for the moment ignore these. Changes in heredity are in the strictest sense the basis of evolution. To understand life and its history it is therefore necessary to know something about the heredity not only of individuals but also of continuously reproducing groups. This is the subject of *population genetics.*

The definition of a species given in the preceding section applies as well to uniparental as to biparental populations. In uniparental populations the genetic situation is comparatively simple and requires little discussion here. Because uniparental offspring characteristically have just the same genetic make-up as their parents, genetic changes in the population as a whole arise only by the appearance of new mutations or the elimination of old ones. Biparental populations are both more usual and more important in the history of life. Their population genetics is also more complicated and more interesting.

VARIATION WITHIN BIPARENTAL POPULATIONS

There is always variation among the individual organisms within a population, and the variation of prime importance for evolution is genetical. Every biparental population that has ever been studied has been found to contain genetic differences among its individuals. *Drosophila* populations in local orchards and woodlands have been intensively studied as examples. All have proved to contain genetic variation, including many of the mutant alleles studied in the laboratory. This is really not surprising in view of what we know about mutation (p. 321). A big enough population of any organism is bound to include mutant alleles at all gene loci (p. 302) in the whole set of chromosomes. The evidence indicates, moreover, that each gene locus may mutate to many more than just two allelic forms. With just two alleles present (A and A_1) three diploid genotypes are possible among the individuals in a population: AA, AA_1, and A_1A_1. With three alleles (A, A_1, A_2)

there are six genotypes possible. (What are they?) The number of possible genotypes increases rapidly as the number of alleles increases. Then, too, we must remember that because of crossing over and chromosome reshuffling at meiosis, each of the possible genotypes at one locus can be combined with any of the several possible at all other loci. The upshot of all this is that *the known processes of mutation and recombination in biparental (sexual) populations guarantee enormous variation within the population as a whole.*

GENETIC EQUILIBRIUM IN BIPARENTAL POPULATIONS

The idea of a population's "gene pool." The genetic variation produced by mutation and recombination is the raw material of evolution. The gradual evolution of a population involves a gradual change in its hereditary constitution. It is useful in this connection to think of what has been picturesquely called the *gene pool* of a population. Were we to count and tabulate all the alleles of all the genes in a population, and pool them, we would have some measure of the population's net genetic make-up. We could then discuss the evolution of the population in terms of the changing ratios of alleles in the population as a whole.

Natural selection is the most important process causing the population's gene pool to evolve. Our main purpose in the rest of this chapter is to show how natural selection works. To clarify this we begin by showing that mutation and the normal processes of sexual reproduction do not *of themselves* bring about long-term evolutionary trends in populations. They simply create and maintain a pool of variations in a state of equilibrium. Natural selection acts on this pool of variation in causing long-term evolutionary change.

Biparental reproduction and genetic equilibrium. Let us set up an imaginary experimental population of *Drosophila* and follow the history of its genetic variation from one generation to the next. Let A_1 symbolize one of the alleles, and A_2 the other. We begin our experiment by introducing 200 *Droso-*

phila (100 males and 100 females) into a breeding cage, where one generation follows another without break so long as we continue to supply food. We cannot wait for mutation to produce variation in our experimental population so we deliberately include both alleles (A_1 and A_2) among the initial flies. Of the 100 flies in each sex, 49 have the genotype A_1A_1, 42 A_1A_2, and 9 A_2A_2. Thus we have an initial population as follows:

100 females			100 males		
A_1A_1	A_1A_2	A_2A_2 $\times$	A_1A_1	A_1A_2	A_2A_2
49	42	9	49	42	9

We allow the males and females to mate at random. Can we predict the relative frequencies of the genotypes that will appear in

successive generations? It is common for people first confronted with this problem to have two impressions: (1) that the less common allele, A_2, will gradually be lost from the population; and (2) that the task of predicting exactly what genotypes will result from indiscriminate matings among so many flies is quite hopeless. Neither impression is correct.

The prediction problem would certainly be formidable if we had to figure out, one at a time, all the matings that could possibly occur and summate their outcomes. Fortunately the problem is much simpler than that. We can treat all the females *as though they were one female* and ask: What kinds and frequencies of eggs will be produced by the population's "composite female"? Treating males simi-

$$100\% = (p+q)^2 = p+q = 1$$

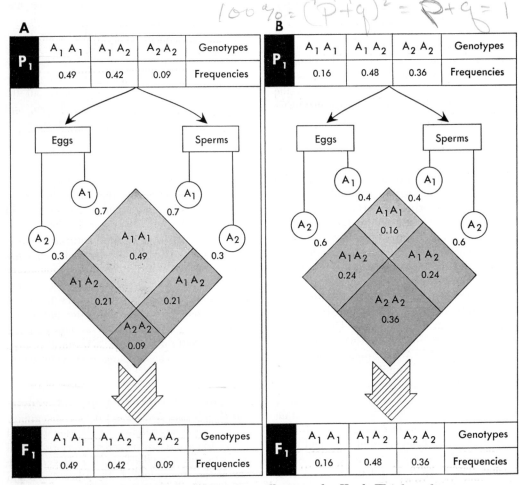

16-2 Genetical checkerboards to illustrate the Hardy-Weinberg law.

TABLE 16-1   *Gene frequencies in an experimental population*

Flies	Gametes A_1	A_2	Totals
49 males are A_1A_1 and produce	490	0	(490)
42 males are A_1A_2 and produce	210	210	(420)
9 males are A_2A_2 and produce	0	90	(90)
The 100 males as a group produce	700	300	(1000)
Ratio of different gametes in the pooled population of sperms as a decimal fraction	0.7	0.3	(1.0)

larly, we can determine what sperms the "composite male" will produce.

Let us begin with the males. Every male produces enormous numbers of sperms, but we can simplify our arithmetic by assuming the number to be 10. This reduction in total numbers does not affect *ratios*, which are our real concern. The 100 males will produce gametes as shown in Table 16-1. The table shows that 3 out of every 10 sperms produced by the total population of males are A_2; 7 out of every 10 are A_1. The ratio between alleles is often conveniently called the *gene frequency*. The frequency of the gene (allele) A_1 in the present population is 0.7. Since the initial females in our experiment had the same genetic constitutions as the males, it follows that in their pooled gametes (eggs) the frequency of A_1 will again be 0.7, and that of A_2 0.3.

The next step in calculating what genotypes will appear in the next generation is to set up the genetical checkerboard shown in Fig. 16-2A. You are familiar with the checkerboard method from Chapter 12. There we used it to predict what genotypes would result from fertilizations made from gamete pools taken from *one* female and *one* male. The method is just as applicable here where we have simply pooled all the gametes from 100 females and 100 males rather than one each.

When we crossed two single heterozygote flies, the gene frequencies in the gamete pool of each parent were of course $0.5A_1:0.5A_2$ (cf. p. 282, Fig. 12-2). In our experimental

population, however, gametes are produced in the ratio $0.7A_1:0.3A_2$. The checkerboard in Fig. 16-2A shows that the zygotes produced by random matings in our population will have genotypes as follows: $0.49A_1A_1:0.42A_1A_2:0.09A_2A_2$. Comparing this ratio with that of the initial parental population, we notice that the two are identical.

A *parental population*
   with genotypes

A_1A_1	A_1A_2	A_2A_2	gene frequency is $0.7A_1:0.3A_2$
0.49	0.42	0.09	

↓

an F_1 population
   with genotypes

A_1A_1	A_1A_2	A_2A_2	gene frequency is $0.7A_1:0.3A_2$
0.49	0.42	0.09	

We must of course conclude that the F_2, F_3, and all subsequent generations would continue to have the same gene frequencies and genotype ratios among individuals. (Why?)

This result may well suprise you. It was certainly not self-evident to the early geneticists. The rule was discovered independently by two men, and it is called after them the Hardy-Weinberg law, one of the most fundamental laws of genetics. The law states that *under certain conditions* (discussed fully below) *gene frequencies and genotype ratios remain constant from one generation to the next in biparental (sexual) populations.* This is true no matter how many alleles there are at each gene locus [3] or what their relative frequencies may be in the initial population. Of course, if the proportion of alleles differs in different populations, the genotype ratios will also differ. Figure 16-2B gives, as further illustration, a checkerboard for a population in which the gene frequencies are $0.4A_1:0.6A_2$. [4]

[3] We have taken only the simplest case of two alleles, A_1 and A_2.

[4] Mathematically inclined students will have recognized before now that our genetical checkerboards are only graphic ways of expanding the binomial expression $(p + q)^2$ where $(p + q) = 1.0$. If we let p = the frequency of the allele A_1 in a population, and q = the frequency of the allele A_2, then the algebraic expansion of $(p + q)^2$ describes the frequency of the three genotypes (A_1A_1, A_1A_2, and A_2A_2) in the population. Taking our experimental fly population (Table 16-1 and Fig. 16-2A) as an example: $p = 0.7$ = fre-

The Hardy-Weinberg law explains one of the most striking and fundamental facts about nature: that, while biparental populations always contain a variety of genotypes, the population as a whole, including its variations, may continue for generation after generation without significant change. Variation, which makes evolutionary change possible, is maintained even when evolutionary change is not occurring.

EVOLUTION: CHANGE IN
THE GENETIC EQUILIBRIUM

Necessary conditions for genetic equilibrium. A useful way of restating the Hardy-Weinberg law would be to say that the relative frequencies of alleles $(A_1:A_2)$ and genotypes $(A_1A_1:A_1A_2:A_2A_2)$ in a population remain in a state of equilibrium through successive generations of sexual reproduction. We have so far simplified our presentation of the genetic equilibrium by omitting reference to several conditions that are necessary if the equilibrium is to remain stable. Equilibrium of the population's gene pool is disturbed if any of the following conditions are not met:

1. The population must be sufficiently large so that chance changes in gene frequency are insignificant.
2. Mutation must either not occur, or have reached its own equilibrium.
3. Reproduction must be random.

All three of these conditions call for explanation and are taken up separately in the succeeding sections.

The indeterminate evolution of small populations. When Mendel crossed two pea plants heterozygous for the flower-color

quency of A_1; $q = 0.3 =$ frequency of A_2. Then it follows:

(1) $\quad (p + q)^2 \quad = p^2 \quad + 2pq \quad + q^2$

(2) $\quad 100\% \quad = A_1A_1 + A_1A_2 + A_2A_2$

(3) $\quad = (0.7 + 0.3)^2 = 0.49 \quad + 0.42 \quad + 0.09$

Line 1 gives the expansion of the binomial; line 2 shows the equivalence of zygote genotypes to the three terms in the expanded binomial; and line 3 shows how the frequencies of zygote genotypes are computed from the binomial. The familiar Mendelian F_2 ratio for a single pair of alleles is only a special case of this same general rule, in which $p = 0.5$.

gene (Cc), he obtained 23.1 per cent (224 out of 929) cc (white) homozygotes in his F_2 instead of the theoretical or ideal proportion, 25 per cent. We noted in Chapter 12 (p. 290) that such departures from the ideal genetical ratios are always experienced in practice. The gametes employed in producing any family are only an *approximate representation*—or *sample*—of the total population of gametes from which they are drawn. This is true whether we are considering the progeny from mating two individual organisms, or the total progeny raised by a whole population of organisms. One hundred sperms taken at random from a population of males in which the gene frequency is 50 per cent A and 50 per cent a will surely contain *approximately* 50 a gametes, but the actual number is quite likely to be 53 or 48 or some other number in the general vicinity of 50. These chance departures from the ideal ratios are called *sampling errors*, and they become increasingly serious the smaller the sample becomes. Conversely they are less serious in larger samples: you will get closer to a 50 per cent incidence of heads the oftener you toss a coin (p. 290).

In the reproduction of large populations of organisms, sampling errors are negligible: the initial ratios of alleles are fairly accurately represented in the large sample of gametes that initiates each new generation. But in small populations a considerable number of errors may accumulate because the sample of gametes that initiates each new generation is small. Thus the equilibrium of the population's gene pool can be changed (can evolve) by purely chance processes. Such evolution is said to be *indeterminate* because, since the changes are due to chance, the genetic equilibrium is as likely to drift one way (for example, toward loss of the allele A) as the other (toward loss of the allele a).

There is much debate among biologists as to the extent and importance of such indeterminate evolution in nature, but there is little doubt it plays a role, perhaps a minor one.

Mutation. Variation at the beginning of our experimental population (Table 16-1, Fig. 16-2A) was created by the deliberate introduction of both alleles $(A_1$ and $A_2)$ into the starting population. In nature new variation is provided slowly by mutation. Even in a population that initially contained only A_1 alleles, A_2 would eventually appear as some A_1 alleles mutated to A_2:

$$A_1 \xrightarrow{\text{gene mutation}} A_2$$

Such mutations occur at all gene loci (A, B, C, etc.) with a frequency that is usually low [e.g., one mutation in a million (10^6) gametes is a typical rate] and a nearly [5] fixed characteristic of the gene concerned.

The genetic equilibrium of a population is defined in terms of the relative frequencies of the alleles it contains; equilibrium in our experimental population was $0.7A_1 : 0.3A_2$. Clearly such an equilibrium cannot be maintained if A_1 is actively mutating to A_2. This process will change the gene frequencies, increasing the proportion of A_2 and decreasing the proportion of A_1 in the population as a whole. Indeed, on the face of it, mutation might seem to you now to be a self-defeating process: while it creates variability in a population containing only A_1, it would destroy variation if it continued until all A_1 was lost by being converted to A_2. It is not, in fact, a self-defeating process because mutant alleles like A_2 are themselves mutable: they can *back-mutate* [6] to A_1. Thus to summarize mutational processes at the A gene locus we must write the following:

$$A_1 \underset{\text{back mutation}}{\overset{\text{forward mutation}}{\rightleftharpoons}} A_2$$

Were it not for the effect of natural selection, mutation would lead to an equilibrium of variation which, of course, biparental reproduction would faithfully conserve, following the Hardy-Weinberg law. The proportion of A_1 and A_2 alleles at such an equilibrium would depend on the relative rates of the forward and back mutations.[7] If the $A_1 \to A_2$ rate were higher than $A_2 \to A_1$, then A_2

would be the commoner allele; if the forward and back rates were the same, then A_1 and A_2 would be equally common alleles in the population. (What, then, would be the ratio of zygote genotypes in the population?)

The reversibility of mutation assures the continual presence of mutant alternatives in a population, and reversibility prevents mutation from causing long-term, or sustained, evolutionary trends. The process of mutation supplies the materials (variations) for the process of evolution but is not evolution itself.

In natural populations alternative alleles (like A_1 and A_2) are always present; both forward and back mutations always occur. But the relative frequencies of the alleles rarely, in fact, attain the exact equilibrium we would expect from knowledge of the forward and back mutation rates. In most populations another factor prevents attainment of the expected equilibrium because it continually favors transmission to the next generation of one of the alternative alleles (say A_1) over the other (A_2). This process is *natural selection*.[8]

Nonrandom (or selective) reproduction. The effect of natural selection on the frequency of mutant alleles in a population can be illustrated by the example of hemophilia. You recall that hemophilia is an inherited disease in man affecting the ability of the blood to clot (p. 144). Hemophiliacs are liable to die from loss of blood because a protective clot fails to cover even the simplest scratch or cut. This disability of the blood is caused by a mutant allele that we will designate H_2. Blood in people with the allele H_1 clots normally.[9]

The mutation $H_1 \to H_2$ occurs at what is, as mutations go, a fairly high rate, about once in every 50,000 gametes. The rate of the back mutation ($H_2 \to H_1$) is not known exactly, but it is much lower than the forward rate. Consequently if the mutational processes at the H gene locus were to reach an equilibrium, hemophilia (H_2) ought to be a common

[5] But cf. p. 324.
[6] Which step is called "back" mutation and which "forward" is a matter of convention. When A_1 is the commoner allele in the population, the step $A_1 \to A_2$ is designated "forward"; $A_2 \to A_1$ is then called the "back" mutation.
[7] Let the forward rate ($A_1 \to A_2$) = u, and the back rate ($A_2 \to A_1$) = v. At equilibrium the frequency of $A_1 = \dfrac{v}{u+v}$.

[8] As we have seen (p. 402), chance may also occasionally prevent the population's reaching equilibrium, especially in small populations.
[9] The precise mode of inheritance and expression of the hemophilia allele involves other complications, but they do not materially affect the points we are making here.

inherited disease in man. In fact, however, the disease is comparatively rare; the ratio of H_2 to H_1 alleles in human populations is about 1:10,000. Clearly H_2 is much rarer than it would be had a mutational equilibrium been reached.

The cause of this departure from mutation equilibrium is not hard to find. Hemophiliacs commonly die while still too young to have reproduced. Even when they survive to sexual

maturity they are less likely to be accepted for marriage, or (if married) are likely to die before they raise as many children as people with normal blood-clotting mechanisms. What does this difference in reproductive competence between normals and hemophiliacs imply in terms of the human population's gene pool?

We can clarify this by *supposing* we had for study a population in which H_1 and H_2

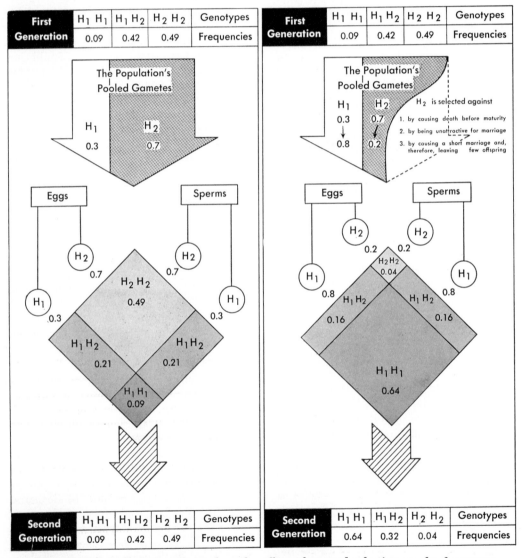

16-3 Genetical checkerboards to show the effect of natural selection on the frequency of a gene in a population.

had reached a mutational equilibrium. Since we do not know exactly what the back-mutation $(H_2 \rightarrow H_1)$ rate is, we cannot be exactly sure what that equilibrium would be, but for purposes of illustration we may assume it to be $0.3H_1 : 0.7H_2$. The mutant allele is commoner because the forward rate exceeds the back-mutation rate: hemophiliacs are common in this hypothetical population.

We would normally set up a genetical checkerboard (Fig. 16-3A) in order to compute what zygote genotypes would appear in this equilibrium population. A checkerboard that assumed that all zygotes were equally competent reproducers would take the values $0.3H_1$ and $0.7H_2$ as the frequencies of alleles in the population's pool of gametes (Fig. 16-3A). On this assumption we would expect zygotes to appear generation after generation with the frequencies $H_1H_1(0.09)$: $H_1H_2(0.42) : H_2H_2(0.49)$. This assumption of *random* (or equally successful) reproduction on the part of the two alleles would, however, be quite unjustified. We have seen that hemophiliacs (carriers of the allele H_2) differ from nonhemophiliacs (carriers of H_1) is being (1) more likely to die before sexual maturity, (2) less likely to marry, and (3) if married, likely to die before raising an average-sized family. Thus *in the sample of gametes that actually initiates the next generation* (those that actually reach the genetic checkerboard, so to speak) *the proportion of H_2 alleles is substantially reduced from the initial value of 70 per cent to something more nearly like 20 per cent* (Fig. 16-3B). Zygote frequencies in the next generation will accordingly be different from those in the first generation: hemophiliacs will be rarer.

This can be summed up in a different way by saying that if the gametes that go to make up a new generation were drawn at random—were a fair sample of the parental population—the ratio of H_1 to H_2 would not change. But because a gamete containing H_2 is less likely to be passed on to the next generation the sample is not a fair (or random) one; it is *biased*, as the statisticians say. Therefore the proportion of H_2 in the population tends to decrease. H_2 would, indeed, be eliminated entirely if it were not continually replenished by mutation.

Natural Selection

THE CAUSES OF EVOLUTION

The evolutionary process, viewed in broad perspective, is characterized by two major features: it produces *diversity* among living things, and it gives rise to their *adaptation*, their fitness to survive and reproduce efficiently in the environments they inhabit. These two features are interdependent: life's diversity is largely a diversity in adaptation. Can we now explain these major features of evolution in terms of the processes revealed by our study of population genetics?

THE CONSEQUENCE OF NONRANDOM REPRODUCTION

The evolutionary changes that result from nonrandom reproduction are clearly adaptive: *the changes are always, necessarily, of such a kind as to improve the average ability of the population to survive and reproduce in the environments they inhabit.*

As it affects populations over successive generations, biparental reproduction involves: (1) mating; (2) production of offspring; and (3) the development and survival of the offspring until they mate in their turn and produce offspring, which also develop, survive, and mate; and so on continuously. In other words, for our present subject reproduction means a complete continuity of life cycles and not only the production of offspring at one stage in the life of one generation. If the process is fully random, it must be random in the three different ways specified. What is more relevant to the present point is the fact that reproduction can be *non*random in the three different ways, and lead to adaptive evolutionary change. We will consider these three sources of nonrandom reproduction separately.

Nonrandom mating. We have encountered earlier (p. 295) the mutant allele (w) which causes white eyes instead of the normal red eyes (W) in *Drosophila*. If in the experimental fly population discussed earlier in this chapter, we had used these alleles causing red and white eyes instead of those causing long and short wings, we would have run into evo-

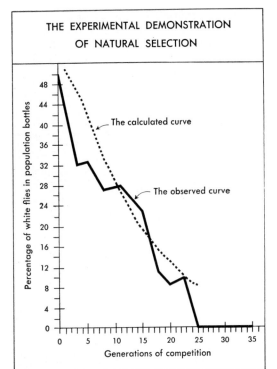

THE EXPERIMENTAL DEMONSTRATION
OF NATURAL SELECTION

The calculated curve

The observed curve

16-4 Experimental demonstration of natural selection due to nonrandom mating. *Drosophila* females discriminate against white-eyed (w) males in favor of red-eyed males. By measuring experimentally a coefficient of their "preference" it is possible to predict the rate at which the gene w (white eyes) will be naturally selected out of a population. Experiments to test the prediction are performed in "population bottles": a population of *Drosophila*, in which the initial proportion of W and w genes is known, is allowed to breed in milk bottles, and the entire population is transferred to fresh bottles with new food at fixed intervals. The proportion of red-eyed (W) and white-eyed (w) flies is followed generation after generation. The figure plots the observed rate, as well as the calculated rate, at which the gene w is eliminated. The agreement is extremely close.

be predicted. Figure 16-4 shows that the experimentally observed evolution of the population follows the predicted course extremely closely.

In one sense the evolution of this population is only a change in frequency of the gene w from 70 per cent to nearly 0. But in another and more important sense it is an evolutionary improvement in the mating (hence reproductive) efficiency of the population as a whole. Nonrandom mating has inevitably caused the evolution of adaptive improvement in the population.

A moment's thought reveals that mating customs, the accepted pattern of courtship, within a species constitute one of the most powerful and direct sources of nonrandom reproduction. Gene mutations that cause deviations from the common, accepted pattern of courtship will be immediately selected against: they will have little chance of entering the next (and therefore *any* subsequent) generation. On the other hand, accepted courtship patterns *can* act not only as a conservative agent, eliminating deviants (like white eyes in *Drosophila*), but also as agents of new evolution. In fishes, birds, and many other animals bright-colored or showy parts may act as a stimulus to the opposite sex, the inherited "password" required before copulation is begun. When, as in some fish, the courtship password is a color spot or a showy tail, almost inevitably larger spots and showier tails evolve. Why? Any new mutations that make the courtship password more readily perceived or more effective are the more likely to succeed in courtship than their longer-established alleles. The new mutant alleles have a favored entree into subsequent generations.

Nonrandom fecundity. The sheer production of more offspring must plainly affect natural selection. If individuals with, say, an allele X_1 regularly produce ten offspring while those with X_2 produce only one, the proportion of X_1 in the population will surely tend to increase. This is, indeed, the most obvious form of natural selection as differential reproduction. Offhand, it might appear that selection would always favor fecundity and that the rise of organisms, such

lutionary change immediately. White-eyed males are unsuccessful in the courtship of both white- and red-eyed females; at least they are much less successful (literally have less sex-appeal) than red-eyed males. As a result the white-eyed allele is quite rapidly lost by the population as a whole. The relative attractiveness of red- and white-eyed males to females can be measured and the rate of elimination of the gene from the population can therefore

as man, which have comparatively few young, would be an anomaly. There is, however, a balance between the factor of fecundity and the factor of survival, next to be considered. If individual chances of survival are low, then selection will indeed favor fecundity. That is true, for instance, of parasites with the hazards of complex life cycles (p. 637), or of many fishes with tremendous mortality among the young. Such organisms have become extremely fecund, often producing literally millions of eggs from one female. If, however, chances of individual survival are high, there may be no selection for fecundity. Indeed there may be selection against fecundity, because the production of many offspring may reduce the chances of their survival, for instance by reducing the effectiveness of maternal care, as in many birds and mammals. If one female produces three offspring all of which survive to breed in their turn while another female produces twenty young only one of which survives to breed, then selection clearly is favoring the genetic characters of the first female. Not only is there an interplay of different factors but also, as in so many aspects of evolution, there are alternative solutions to the same problem: high fecundity, low survival; low fecundity, high survival.

Survival to reproduce. We have seen how mating behavior and fecundity are sources of nonrandom reproduction and of natural selection, and therefore leave their mark on the evolutionary process. They are not the whole story; most organisms have to go through a longer or shorter period of development, growth, and sexual maturation before they ever enter the final reproductive contests, so to speak, which mating and fecundity (the actual reproductive processes) set up. And it is nonrandom success in surviving to and through reproductive age that has given rise to many of the more obvious features of organic adaptation. The ultimate significance of the lion's speed, strength, and cunning is not that these adaptive features promote his survival in the sense of merely staying alive; it is that they promote his survival up to and throughout the period of his

sexual maturity when he can make a contribution to the next generation's gene pool.

In this context one of Darwin's most outspoken critics, Samuel Butler (famous as the author of the utopian novel *Erewhon*) coined a phrase that expresses precisely the evolutionary significance of adaptations that promote survival. He said that the "hen is the egg's device for laying another egg." It seems a splendid irony that Butler's witticism proves to be an excellent statement of the true meaning of natural selection. The crucial issue in natural selection is the leaving of offspring. In terms of our genetical checkerboards, the crucial issue is whether or not an organism succeeds in getting his gametes into those listed on the checkerboard as the source of the next generation. From the point of view of natural selection, what counts about a hen or a lioness is its capacity to produce offspring. Natural selection will never lead to improved survival capacity at the expense of reproductive efficiency. It could well be that a lion might gain in strength, cunning, and longevity from some alleles that lower his fertility or his attractiveness to lionesses, but improved survival at such a cost will never endure in that evolutionary process which our knowledge of population genetics predicts. For such improved survival capacity never gets the genes causing it onto the genetical checkerboard. In terms of the preview of selection in Chapter 2, such a player would be eliminated from the target game.

Survival beyond the reproductive age is extremely rare in nature. What happens to an organism after it has exhausted its possibility of contributing genes to the new generation rarely matters to natural selection. (Once the player has hit the target, he can drop dead for all it matters in the game.) It is true that in some social groups, among insects or men, nonreproducers may help the population as a whole to raise the next generation and so promote significant survival, but that is an exceptional situation. Even in man the ailments that strike increasingly after the age of 45 or 50 testify to the fact that natural selection in our ancestors did not tend to promote survival after reproduction was completed. Medical science is more and more devoted to combating this unpleasant but quite natural consequence of the way we originated.

Survival: the physical environment.

It is obvious that survival of the individual to sexual maturity demands competence to withstand the rigors of the physical environments.

Insects have never been able to become big because of their external skeleton and their mode of respiration (p. 577). Their small size has been a source of danger to them as land animals because it means that their surface is large in relation to their volume. Land animals tend to dry out by evaporation of their water into the unsaturated air which they inhabit, and the danger of death by water loss [a function of surface area (why?)] is proportionately greater the smaller the animal is.

In insect populations those individuals possessing alleles that render the outer coating less permeable to water are more likely to survive and therefore contribute to the next generation than are their brothers and sisters carrying alleles with opposite effects. Insects possess a host of diverse adaptations that are directed at conserving water, and the origin of those adaptations by natural selection is clear enough.

Survival: the biotic environment.

The environment in which an organism must make a living, survive, and raise a family contains important biological as well as physical elements. The organism has to live amid other organisms and the dangers and opportunities they afford. The major feature pervading any community of organisms is its traffic in energy and materials—the scramble to eat and avoid being eaten. This pattern of community life universally imposes natural selection on the community's members.

At the "bottom of the heap" are the plants, confronted with two sources of natural selection due to other organisms. First there is competition for soil room and sunlight arising from the abundance of other plant species constantly showering the ground with seeds, or thrusting in roots and runners from adjacent locations. Secondly, there is the constant threat of being consumed by herbivorous animals of all kinds before the season's crop

of spores or seeds can be produced. These two *selection pressures* will elicit, in the long run, their appropriate adaptive adjustments.

In the desert, plant life is in a most difficult environment, and it comes under special threat of extinction largely because, being scarce to begin with, it is the more likely to be totally destroyed by hungry animal life; here as nowhere else adaptations are developed that discourage the hungry consumer. Thorns abound, as on cactus and euphorbia, and acrid juices, as in sagebrush.

Animals are under a whole complex of pressures in the web of relationships involved in the community's food economy. Most are under pressure to avoid being eaten as well as to find food themselves. Most birds *are* early birds because they have descended from ancestors who caught the worm. Keen vision in the hawk is always at a premium, and for this reason so are all mutant alleles that improve vision. Good eyesight is no less important in mouse or rabbit; alleles in mouse populations that promote quick recognition of the hawk's sinister silhouette floating above make a greater contribution to the next generation's gene pool than alleles that impair this recognition—by no matter how little.

Natural Selection and Adaptive Coloration

THE THEORY OF ADAPTIVE COLORATION

It is a commonplace observation that many animals, insects in particular, tend to be colored or shaped in such a way that they are hard to recognize in their usual surroundings (Fig. 16-5 and illus., p. 395). Grasshoppers are green in the lush grass of meadows and stream banks; other species on the dry prairie grasslands are the same subtle straw color as their parched-out backgrounds. Their relatives, the stick insects, are as elongate and twiglike as their name implies. They are also capable of changing their color to suit their background. The moths of birch and pine trees differ characteristically in their wing patterns, each appropriately matching the surface on which it habitually comes to rest. The pale moth from the birch woods is conspicuous as it rests, mottled white, on the

From *Social Behavior in Animals,*
N. Tinbergen, Methuen Co. Ltd.

Above, warning coloration in the larvae of
the cinnabar moth. Note the conspicuous
cross-banding and the habit of clustering
together.

Above and below, © Douglas P. Wilson

16-5 Protective form and coloration, and warning coloration. *Above, left,* cryptic form as
a protective device in the pipefish (*Entelurus aequoreus*), which rests amidst eelgrass (*Zostera
marina*). *Below,* the topknot, a flatfish (*Zeugopterus punctatus*), resting on a shell-gravel bottom,
provides a striking example of cryptic coloration.

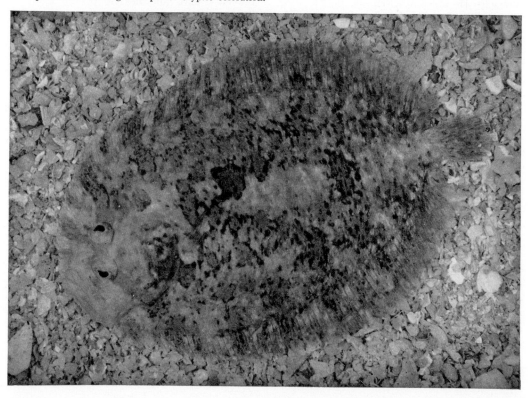

black bark of a pine—fair game for a hungry bird swirling around with eyes peeled for the slightest indication of food. But the moth is nearly invisible in its usual habitat. Although the origin of any or all adaptive characters might be discussed to illustrate the effectiveness of natural selection, adaptive coloration is particularly interesting and will be developed a little further here by way of example.

In the first place, there have been severe skeptics of the theory that coloration is often protective. The fallacies involved in their criticisms merit discussion here because they have far-reaching importance for scientific method, beyond the question of protective coloration. The criticisms have been of three kinds and are treated separately below.

MC ATEE'S CRITICISM

The first line of criticism is as follows: Many animals get eaten in spite of their alleged "protective" coloration; therefore, the fallacious argument goes, "protective" coloration is *not* protective.

McAtee, an American biologist, undertook an extremely laborious and seemingly thorough study of the insect remains inside birds' stomachs. He noted whether the insects were of the type allegedly "protected" or not. He found large numbers of protected individuals and became an outspoken critic of the theory. What are the fallacies in his argument?

To say that a concealing form or protective coloration is not adaptive on the basis of McAtee's data is to imply that the adaptation must be, in some sense, 100 per cent effective. We could then only conclude that no organism is adapted because all eventually die. This is clearly nonsense.

McAtee's data, massive though they were, were quite inadequate to test the theory because he did not measure the relative success achieved by "protected" and "unprotected" forms in avoiding being eaten. Data on the relative abundance of the two types in birds' stomachs must be compared with data on their relative abundance before they are caught. We might find two protected forms in birds' stomachs for every one unprotected form; and such data would still support our theory *if* their relative abundance was, say, four pro-

tected to one unprotected before they were caught. Clearly, then, protected forms are only half as likely to be eaten as unprotected forms, and to this extent they enjoy a considerable adaptive advantage.

THE "REFRIGERATOR FALLACY"

A related fallacy is hidden in the argument that says: Many animals survive well without protective coloration, which, therefore, is not an adaptation because it is not *essential*. This has aptly been called the "refrigerator fallacy" because it amounts to saying: Refrigerators do not constitute an advance in efficient living because our grandparents did very well without them.

Refrigerators are widespread in Western civilization today because once they "arose" (were invented) they proved to be an advantage and were widely adopted. That they are useful does not imply they are indispensable. Protective coloration and indeed all organic adaptation resemble refrigerators in this broad sense: they are useful but not necessarily indispensable.

Let us consider two similar but separate moth populations, each with light wings, in pine woods. They are conspicuous against the dark bark and heavily preyed upon by birds and bats. In spite of heavy predation they survive *as populations* because their output of eggs is large. Indeed the predation is itself a source of heavy selective pressure tending to increase egg output. (Low survival promotes high fecundity, see p. 407.) Suppose, now, that in population 1 (but not in population 2) mutations occur with the effect of *slightly* darkening the wings. What will happen in this population?

Both types of wing present in population 1 are light and easily seen. It would be an error—and a common one—to conclude that, because the mutant wing is only slightly darker and slightly less easily seen, it represents no adaptive improvement. Even if the mutant is overlooked only 1 per cent more often than the normal allele, natural selection will result. In each successive generation the *proportion* of dark-winged forms will increase, even if ever so slightly; eventually the mutant allele will replace its lighter allele entirely. The history of this population shows us that the slightly darker wing is an adaptation: it has arisen by natural selection and it does reduce, even if slightly, the frequency of detection by birds. In the meantime population 2 continues to survive and flourish in spite of possessing lighter wings: it still has them because mutations did not arise to darken them. But its presence and continued survival without dark wings in no way invalidate our understanding of the darker wings in population 1.

WARNING COLORATION:
RULE-PROVING EXCEPTIONS

Some skeptics of the meaning of protective, or cryptic, coloration have pointed to the fact that many successful animals not only lack protective camouflage but get along very well *in spite of* being gaudily colored—of advertising themselves, so to speak. They point to the brilliant colors of many butterflies, the signal red of lady beetles and milkweed bugs. This, at first sight, does seem peculiar: it is one thing, perhaps, to explain the absence of camouflage, as we did above, but it is another to explain the origin of advertisement in animals likely to be preyed upon. The brightly colored animals in nature turn out, however, to be exceptions that prove the rule. Brightly colored insects do well, not *in spite of*, but *because of* their conspicuousness.

Insects like ladybugs (a kind of beetle), milkweed bugs, bumblebees, and wasps are all organisms with features of unpleasant taste, bristly texture, or downright sting that render them unwelcome fare at the table of most predators. The possession of distasteful features profits an animal nothing once it is dead, but, given the additional feature of being noticeable and recognizable, distaste has its obvious merits. The conspicuous *warning* coloration of insects is a sign or message that spells, "This is the color pattern that gave you trouble before." The gaudy creature is left alone. There are more ways of avoiding being eaten than developing camouflage.

The theory of warning coloration *predicts* that local predators recognize and refuse to eat the gaudily colored insects. Several experiments confirm this prediction. Table 16-2 gives data obtained by Carpenter in an ex-

TABLE 16-2   *The adaptive value of warning coloration* *

	Accepted as food by monkey	Rejected as food by monkey	Totals
Warningly colored insect species	23	120	143
Cryptically colored insect species	83	18	101

* The monkey accepted as food 83 per cent (83/101) of all cryptically colored species, but only 16 per cent of the warningly colored species; 87 per cent (120/138) of all species rejected were warningly colored.

periment in which a monkey in West Africa was offered over 200 species of insects, some of which were warningly colored, and some cryptically colored. The predator in some (perhaps all) cases has to *learn* the association between the conspicuous color pattern and the distasteful feature; and he must then retain, as memory, the learned association. This dependence of the entire device on the learning process in the predator accounts for the evolution of a common behavioral feature in warningly colored species: they tend to aggregate and thus display their signals in bulk. By aggregating they increase the chances that the predator will learn his lesson rapidly, and the population as a whole benefits by gaining its ultimate protection with a minimum net sacrifice (Fig. 16-5, upper right).

OTHER KINDS OF ADAPTIVE COLORATION

Besides protective and warning coloration, there are numerous other ways in which the colors of animals can be adaptive. We can do no more here than briefly mention a few of them. Some animals quite acceptable to predators look or act like others obnoxious to the same predators. It is said that they *mimic* (quite unconsciously, of course) the obnoxious species. If a mimic can be mistaken for an unpalatable species, its chances of survival are increased and natural selection will tend to favor and to produce such mimicry. In other instances conspicuous colors may be recognition marks, helping birds of a feather to flock together, or they may be the passwords (p. 406) that make the animal acceptable to a mate. Coloration may be protective not against predation, part of the biotic environment, but against the physical environment. For instance, dark skin is protective against harmful radiation in regions of intense sunshine. Finally, some colors may not, in fact, be adaptive but may be an incidental physiological or chemical corollary of some other adaptation.

The Nature of Natural Selection

CHANGING CONCEPTS OF NATURAL SELECTION

Old ideas about natural selection have become so deeply ingrained that they reappear even in some present-day discussions of the subject. To many of Darwin's contemporaries natural selection seemed to be a brutal struggle for survival in the universal carnage of "nature red in tooth and claw." Such catchwords as "the struggle for existence" and "the survival of the fittest" appear repeatedly even in Darwin's own works, although his views were less extreme than those of many of his followers.

From such concepts there developed a doctrine called "social Darwinism," although it was not supported by Darwin himself. Natural selection was believed to justify as "right" all kinds of cutthroat competition, including war between classes and nations, on the grounds that thus the "fittest" would survive and progress would ensue. The doctrine was completely unjustified, for two reasons. First, this is not a true picture of the way natural selection actually operates. Second, natural selection is not an ethical or moral principle that indicates what is right in human behavior. It is like the law of gravitation, a fact about nature which we must recognize as existing and affecting our lives but which is neither good nor bad in itself.

The question whether natural selection is "right" or "wrong" is ridiculous from a scientific point of view, and there is no reason to discuss it. Questions about what natural selection is and how it operates are legitimate and scientific. The modern concept of natural selection, set forth in earlier pages of this chapter and now familiar to you, has developed from Darwin's, and yet it differs in some essential respects from nineteenth-century ideas on the subject. Natural selection is not struggle, competition, or survival; it is simply nonrandom reproduction.

Of course animals do sometimes fight and plants do compete for space, water, and sunlight. The competition has no bearing on populations and their genetical, evolutionary changes *unless* it leads to nonrandom reproduction. That is the real point about natural selection, and not the winning or losing of a struggle by one individual or another. Competition, struggle, and red-tooth killing often result in nonrandom reproduction, but not always. The concept of competition as a combat or literal struggle is also usually inapplicable to competition as it really occurs in nature (pp. 627 ff.). Moreover, the competitive aspects of nature are not the only ones that result in nonrandom breeding. An animal that gets along best with its neighbors may be precisely the one that has the most offspring. Then selection by nonrandom breeding favors absence of competition. Well-integrated plant and animal communities and, finally, animal social organizations have arisen under the directive influence of natural selection.

CREATIVE SELECTION

Nineteenth-century critics of natural selection (including not only Samuel Butler but also others with more scientific qualifications) objected that its effects would be only negative and noncreative. It could, they admitted, account for the elimination of the unfit but not for the origin of the fit, a more important problem. That objection had considerable force with the older concept of natural selection, centered on the idea of survival or failure to survive. The objection is, however, completely answered by the modern concept, based on population genetics and centered on (indeed, identical with) nonrandom reproduction.

In the light of modern theory it is easy to see that natural selection does have a positive and creative role in evolution. In the first place, the elimination of one allele from a population by selection does not occur unless there is an alternative allele that is, under the existing conditions, superior in terms of effective reproduction. The negative effect of elimination of the "unfit" allele and the positive increase in frequency of the "fit" allele are two sides of the same coin. You cannot have one without the other. In the example discussed on p. 410, selection for darker color literally *created* a moth population better fitted to survive and reproduce in the pine woods.

There is a second, more complex and still more important way in which selection is a creative process. For the sake of clarity we have so far discussed selection for the most part in terms of simple alternatives of alleles at a given gene locus. That is valid as far as it goes, but it is a great simplification of the whole genetic situation in a natural population. The action of any one gene is seldom if ever completely independent. Different genes interact, and even what we study as a single character, such as size or color, may really depend on a large number of different but mutually dependent genes (p. 330). In the last analysis the "fitness" of an individual, that is, its probable reproductive effectiveness, depends on its *whole* set of chromosomes and the co-ordination of all their genes.[10] Moreover, the reproductive effectiveness that really counts is that of the *population*, and this may not be properly specified in terms of individual reproduction alone. There are, for example, many known instances in which a heterozygote is distinctly "fitter" for survival and reproduction than either one of the two corresponding homozygotes in the population. But the highly fit heterozygotes cannot be maintained in the population unless there also regularly appears some proportion of comparatively unfit homozygous individuals. (Why is this so?) Thus natural selection, a process in populations, acts not only on the whole of the apparatus of heredity in individuals but also on the whole genetic structure (especially chromosome and gene frequencies and associations) of the entire population.

If any particular arrangement or association of genes or chromosomes tends to promote reproductive effectiveness of the population, then natural selection will increase its frequency in individuals. Thus selection molds the separate units of heredity into a co-ordinated whole, a process as truly creative (although of course not planned or directed) as the combination of separate bricks into a building.

NATURAL SELECTION IN HUMAN POPULATIONS

It is fitting to close our survey of natural selection with brief reference to human populations. As in all sexually reproducing species, the human population as a whole has abundant genetic variability; it seems, indeed, to be considerably more variable than most other species. Long-continued genetic equilibrium is extremely rare in nature, and we have no reason to believe that our own species has reached such an equilibrium. The biological evolution of man is almost certainly continuing, but (as is true also of most other species) at a rate too slow to be perceptible in a short span of time. Wars and massacres have undoubtedly had some selective effect, but their genetic consequences have probably been almost negligible in comparison with the less spectacular effects of nonrandom reproduction.

Perhaps you belong to a small family. You doubtless know families with more children than yours. Is it possible that there is some genetic difference between your sort of family and theirs? If so, natural selection is in action in a small and local way and without any combat or overt competition! On a worldwide scale, it is a known fact that some genetically distinctive populations of the human species are increasing at a faster rate than others. That is also nonrandom reproduction and must result in evolutionary change for the species as a whole.

As yet there is little detailed knowledge about the human gene pool and especially about the possible genetic basis for factors of intelligence and talent that might be so crucial for the future of mankind. We are also unable at present to judge clearly what the current tendencies of natural selection in man may be, and still less what they may become in the

[10] And also, indeed, on the interaction of the chromosomal mechanism with the cytoplasm of the egg and perhaps other factors outside the chromosomes (Chapter 13).

future. Some statistics for parts of the American population have indicated that those who score higher on certain intelligence tests, who have completed more schooling, or who have higher incomes have, on an average, fewer children. Some alarmists cite those figures as evidence that we are breeding out the most desirable genes (that is, that this nonrandom reproduction, which is natural selection, is reducing their frequencies). That is a possibility and should not be overlooked, but it is not necessarily so. We do not yet know whether the abilities making for greater success in formal tests, in school, or in business are really controlled by genes, in any simple way, at least. We do not know whether genius or more modest special abilities may not depend on some complex of genetic factors more likely to arise from recombination in the population as a whole than from reproduction among the elite. We further do not know whether this particular trend of nonrandom reproduction is present in mankind as a whole, or whether it may not later be reversed where it does now exist. (There is some evidence that it is not universal and also that it is being reversed in some populations.)

Another fact sometimes viewed with alarm is that modern medicine is making it possible for more people with genetic defects (for instance, with a diabetic genotype) to survive and reproduce. This can be interpreted as encouraging the spread of deleterious genes. Yet medical genetics is also increasingly able to counsel prospective parents who are likely to have genetically defective offspring. It is also true that genes deleterious in some respects may be helpful in others,[11] or may be part of a generally desirable genetic system. Aside from these points, the relationship of medicine to natural selection illustrates one of the most important peculiarities of the human species: we will certainly continue to evolve organically, but added to our organic evolution and interacting with it we have a social or cultural evolution. One aspect of this supremely important fact is that adaptations that would necessarily be biological,

[11] There is, for instance, an allele conducive to a form of anemia (sickle-cell anemia) that is lethal when homozygous but that turns out to give high resistance to malaria when heterozygous.

organic, or genetic in other species are often cultural in man. Diabetes in a population of wild mammals can be controlled only by natural selection of the nondiabetic allele. In man it can also be controlled by diet and by injection of insulin. By such a cultural adaptation we may be saving not only the individual but also potentially valuable contributions to human progress.

Chapter Summary

Individuals, populations, species: populations the appropriate unit for study in considering the evolution of life; demes as local populations of similar individuals, and as genetical populations of interbreeding individuals; the species, a group of similar demes.

The genetics of populations: mutation and recombination the two sources of genetic variation in biparental populations; the "gene pool" of variation in the population; the Hardy-Weinberg law, describing the genetic equilibrium of biparental populations; the three conditions necessary for genetic equilibrium concern population size, mutation, and the randomness of reproduction; their failure to hold good as the cause of evolution; evolution as departure from genetic equilibrium.

The indeterminate evolution caused by small population size: the question of its extent and importance in nature.

The determinate evolution caused by nonrandom reproduction which is natural selection (exemplified by hemophilia in man).

Natural selection (nonrandom reproduction) the cause of adaptation and of life's diversity, which is basically a diversity of adaptations to diverse environments; three sources of natural selection: nonrandom mating; nonrandom fecundity; nonrandom survival.

The role of survival in natural selection: survival important only as it bears on reproduction; survival beyond reproductive age never selected for in nature; survival in relation to the physical environment, and in relation to the biotic environment—the pressure to eat and to avoid being eaten.

Natural selection and the theory of adaptive coloration.

Protective colors and forms as typical adaptations evolved by natural selection; former criticisms of this view discussed as misunderstandings of adaptation and of natural selection: McAtee's criticism a failure to appreciate the effectiveness of slight selective advantages; a misconception that adaptations must be indispensable (the "refrigerator fallacy"); the origin of protective coloration in a moth.

Conspicuously colored animals as rule-proving exceptions; warning function of conspicuous colors.

Mimicry of other species in form and appearance.

The nature of natural selection: "nature red in tooth and claw," "struggle for existence," "survival of the fittest" nineteenth-century phrases typifying an older, less accurate understanding of the nature of natural selection; modern emphasis on differential (nonrandom) reproduction rather than on survival as such; natural selection as a creative process; its occurrence and subtlety in human populations.

The Kaibab squirrel is a species distinct from its very close relative, the Abert squirrel. They are now separated by the chasm of the Grand Canyon. This chapter discusses the nature of species and the processes, such as geographic isolation, which lead to new species.
(Photo by Bob Plunkett, R.S.)

CHAPTER 17

Variation, Species, and Speciation

The first reaction of a newcomer to a coral reef or a tropical rain forest is one of confusion. In such places life is most obviously abundant and diverse. The lavishness of nature is overwhelming, and no meaningful pattern is evident at first sight. If perception is not too dulled by familiarity, the same emotion may arise nearer home. A meadow particolored with wild flowers or a swarm of insects around a light has in its own degree the same massing of life and bewildering variety. The diversity of life is a product of the evolutionary process. It is basically a diversity of adaptations to different ways of life—a topic we have already touched upon in Chapter 1. One of the fundamental problems in the study of evolution is how diversity arises. That is the topic of this chapter.

SPECIES: UNIT OF POPULATION DIVERSITY

Were we to look closely at all the individual organisms on a reef, in a forest, or in a meadow we would probably find every individual different in at least some minor respect. And armed with the genetical facts we have already discussed (particularly in Chapters 12 and 16) this would not surprise us. On the other hand, we would be more impressed with the fact that the individual organisms seemed to fall into natural groups of *nearly* similar forms. We might notice the differences among buttercups in the meadow, but we would more certainly recognize their similarity. We would perceive that buttercups form a distinct kind of organism, a natural group of similar individuals—a *species*. The differences that would impress us would be those between species, as between buttercups and daisies. The diversity of life is a diversity of populations, and the species is a significant unit of population.

Intraspecific Variation

Diversity begins at the lowest level, with the fact already repeatedly mentioned that no two individuals are ever exactly alike. No matter how small a unit of population we study, there is always variation among its members. That very fundamental generalization lies at the heart of the diversity of life.

SOURCES OF VARIATION

The sources of variation have all been mentioned in previous chapters. Let us briefly review them as background for the present subject.

The characteristics of organisms arise in the course of their development by the interaction of heredity and environment. Heredity determines a reaction range. The circumstances of development (through the entire life span) determine just where in that reaction range an individual's characteristics will actually be. In the long run the differences that count the most are differences in reaction ranges, and therefore in heredity. If one man or one tree is taller than another solely because of better diet or soil, this may be an important difference between *individuals* but it is not likely to have much significance for the *populations* to which they belong. Being nonhereditary, such variation cannot be passed on to the next generation; it has no continuity in the population. This does not mean that nonhereditary variations within reaction ranges have no biological or evolutionary significance, especially when reaction ranges are wide, as in man. For instance, religion affects attitudes toward reproduction which in turn affect natural selection and human evolution. The fact remains that there is no long-range evolutionary significance unless hereditary differences also become involved. Can you think of ways in which nonhereditary differences could affect the evolution of nonhuman organisms?

Variation due to differences between reaction ranges is of major biological importance and is the source material for evolutionary change and for the diversity of life. Within a population, the variation arises mainly from the shuffling of genes and chromosomes, especially in sexual reproduction. The different kinds of genes and chromosomes involved in this shuffling originated by mutation.

BELL-SHAPED DISTRIBUTION
OF VARIATION IN DEMES

In order to convince yourself of the reality of variation and to learn something of its nature, you should now examine fifty or a hundred specimens from one deme (see p. 396) of some one sort of organism. (If the specimens were collected in a limited area and over a brief period of time they are probably from a single deme.) These may be available in your college's study collections, but they will be more interesting and instructive if you gather them yourself. Among the innumerable possibilities are flowers, leaves (full-grown, each from a different plant of one species); seeds; shells; ants, grasshoppers, beetles, butterflies, or other insects; or field mice (skins, skulls, or both). Whatever you collect, some measurements of size will be possible. Probably also there are characters that can be counted (petals on a flower, scales of a pine cone, ribs on a shell, etc.). Other characters may best be noted in words, perhaps colors and color patterns. These are the principal sorts of observations used in studying variation and classifying diversity.

In your sample some features will be the same in all the individuals. After all, it is characteristic of a deme that the organisms in it are similar. For instance, if you collect simple flowers, all will probably have the same number of petals and other flower parts, although they may not. Other characters are sure to vary in your sample. This is especially true of measurements of size and weight or of counts of such multiple parts as ribs on a shell or scales on a snake or lizard. Observations of such characters may be grouped and tabulated in the form of what is called a *frequency distribution*. Examples of frequency distributions of a usual sort are given in Table 17-1.

These observations can also be presented pictorially in graphs, as in Fig. 17-1. You see that these graphs have definite patterns, which are similar but not identical in the two examples. In both there is a particular range of values, a *class*, that is most frequent. You might say that this class is the fashion among these animals, and it is called by a name for a fashion: it is the *mode*. On each side of the mode the frequencies fall off, with fewer and fewer (and finally, no) individuals in each class.

Most variable characters that can take any one of a considerable number of values in the individuals of a deme tend to have frequency

TABLE 17-1

Examples of frequency distributions

a. A measurement of size. Tail length of individuals from a deme of deer mice.

Measurements in millimeters	Numbers of individuals (frequencies)
52-53	1
54-55	3
56-57	11
58-59	18
60-61	21
62-63	20
64-65	9
66-67	2
68-69	1

b. A count of multiple parts. Number of scales (scutes) along the tails of individuals from a deme of king snakes.

Number of scales	Numbers of individuals (frequencies)
38-40	3
41-43	10
44-46	17
47-49	15
50-52	8
53-55	5
56-58	2

distributions similar to those of Fig. 17-1. This is the most important single generalization regarding variation in demes. The pattern approximates bell-shaped mathematical curves, and especially one particular set of curves known as the normal curve of probability (Fig. 17-1). Some differences from the precise mathematical curve always occur, because nature is not as tidy and regular as mathematicians, but the correspondence of a nearly symmetrical distribution (like Fig. 17-1*A*) may be quite close. This is the basis for some of the essential statistical methods in more advanced and technical study of variation. Some frequency distributions are distinctly lopsided (Fig. 17-1*B*) or may otherwise differ from a normal curve. In advanced analysis these differences are also studied and may reveal important facts about variation in a deme.

It is easy enough to demonstrate as a fact

that variation in demes often has a bell-shaped frequency distribution. In your own sample you can almost certainly find some variation that has this sort of pattern. The fact is interesting, but it does not have much real scientific meaning unless we can link it with biological principles. What does the bell-shaped pattern mean? We know that variation may result either from hereditary differences in reaction ranges under similar conditions or from different environmental conditions interacting with similar reaction ranges. Either or both of these principles may be involved in the bell-shaped distributions.

If organisms with similar or identical genotypes (Fig. 17-2*B*), and hence similar or identical reaction ranges, develop in similar (but not identical) conditions, the pheno-

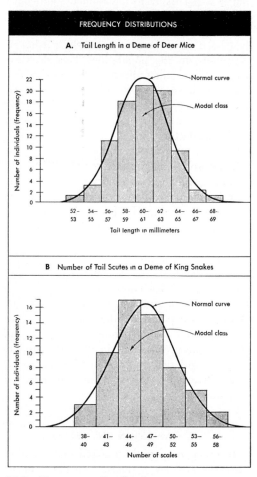

17-1   Frequency distributions.

types will tend to be similar. Most of them will fall into a modal class (the one containing the mode) representing the usual interaction of genotype and conditions of development. Conditions of development producing phenotypes far from the modal class will be comparatively rare. Thus the effects of environment often tend to produce a bell-shaped distribution even apart from hereditary variations. This can be checked by comparing mature leaves from a single plant, actually parts of one individual and identical in genotype. Their variation in size usually has a bell-shaped distribution.

On the other hand, we have seen (p. 307) that characters influenced more or less equally by several or many genes also tend to produce a distribution that you now recognize as like a bell-shaped distribution in a deme. In the experiment previously studied (p. 308), crossing of large and small parents produced a broad, bell-shaped distribution in F_2. In natural populations with the same genes, the same sort of distribution results from interbreeding in a deme and tends to persist through the generations. When a distribution of this pattern (Fig. 17-2A) has a genetical basis, the most probable inference is that this sort of genetical system is involved: one with several or many genes affecting the character being studied.

Thus either environmental or hereditary factors may produce a bell-shaped distribution (Fig. 17-2). In most instances both are involved simultaneously. It is difficult to disentangle the two, but this can be done, approximately, at least. One way is to conduct an experiment like that discussed on p. 308, crossbreeding extreme variant individuals from a deme. If the results are similar to those of that experiment, hereditary variation is present, and further analysis can determine its nature and extent. Another way is to perform selection experiments of the type exemplified by Fig. 17-3. Of course it is impractical to conduct breeding experiments on many of the millions of demes present in nature, and such experiments are wholly impossible for the even more numerous demes now extinct. Still it is possible to get an approximate idea of the amount of truly hereditary variation by statistical anal-

THE BELL-SHAPED CURVE OF POPULATION VARIATION

A

Absolutely Constant Environment; Variation Caused Entirely by Heredity

B

Absolutely Constant Genotype; Variation Caused Entirely by Environmental Conditions

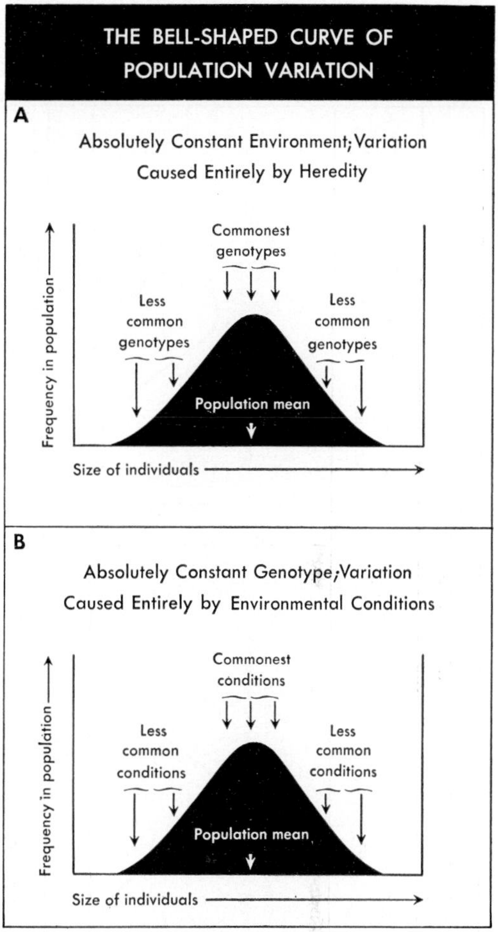

17-2 The bell-shaped curve of population variation. A bell-shaped distribution of phenotypic characteristics (size, weight, color, etc.) in a population may be due theoretically to either (*A*) variation among the genotypes of the population's members, or (*B*) variation in the environmental conditions encountered by the population's members. The bell-shaped distributions of variation encountered in natural populations are nearly always the result of variation in both environmental conditions and individual genotypes.

ysis of variation within demes and between demes living under similar and different conditions.

POLYMORPHISM

Did you ever see a white blackbird? There are such things, and they exemplify another aspect of variation in demes. We have just considered variation that seems to intergrade continuously or that has a sequence of nu-

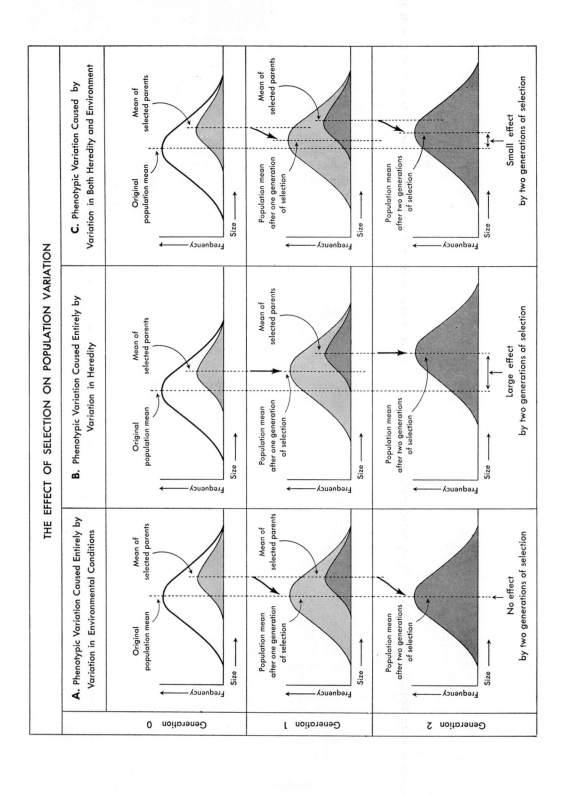

THE EFFECT OF SELECTION ON POPULATION VARIATION

merous classes, usually with bell-shaped distribution. There is also variation with few classes, often strikingly different forms which may occur in varying proportions in different demes. White and black blackbirds are such decidedly distinct forms, and this particular variation has only two classes. Black blackbirds are the rule, and white blackbirds are rare everywhere in nature. Among some other birds a mixture of dark and white forms is usual in demes. There are herons among which demes normally include both gray and white birds, which interbreed. Sometimes there are about three white to one gray, a suggestive approach to the Mendelian ratio for combinations of equally numerous dominant and recessive alleles (p. 402). In some bitterns (relatives of the herons), brown, white, and black (or unusually dark brown) forms commonly occur within single demes. On the other hand, some species of herons are always white and some always colored in the same way.

The natural occurrence of two or more sharply distinct forms in a single deme is called *polymorphism* ("many forms"). Polymorphism is a widespread sort of variation and may occur, in some respect and to some extent, in most demes. It involves not only color but many other characters. For instance, demes of snails may be polymorphic in direction of coiling, some individuals with shells coiled left-handedly and some right-handedly (Fig. 17-4). Most human populations are polymorphic in blood types (p. 422), which do not show but which are sharply distinct biochemically. The number of forms in a deme is usually small: two (colors of some

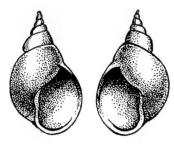

17-4 Polymorphism. Two members of the same snail population; the shell of one has a right-handed coil (the common condition), and the other has a left-handed coil.

herons, direction of coiling in some snails), three (colors of some bitterns), or four (the human A, B, AB, and O blood types). Less commonly many forms may occur; more than 120 distinct patterns have been found in a single species of platyfish (small tropical fish often kept in home aquariums).

What underlies polymorphism? You would not expect it to depend usually or mainly on environmental differences alone. That would mean either that a single reaction range included two or more sharply different phenotypes, or that members of one deme lived in two or more likewise sharply different environments. Either could happen, but both are unusual in nature. In fact, many breeding experiments have been made with the different forms of polymorphic demes, and it has been found that this sort of variation is usually hereditary.

In Chapter 13 you learned that alleles of single genes may accompany striking and sharply distinct differences in particular characters. Such were the characters studied by

---

17-3 The effect of selection on population variation. *A.* When population variation is caused entirely by variation in environmental conditions, selective breeding from one generation to another will fail to change the distribution of population variation. Generation 1, the progeny bred from a select group of large individuals of generation 0, will show (if raised in the same range of environmental conditions) the same distribution of phenotypes that characterized generation 0 as a whole. *B.* The result is different when environmental conditions are constant and the population variation reflects an array of different genotypes in the population. In this case the mean size of generation 1,

bred from selected parents, is considerably larger than the mean of generation 0 as a whole. In fact, it is the same as the mean size of the selected parents. *C.* When both hereditary and environmental variations contribute to the variation of a population's phenotypes, selection does lead to a progeny (generation 1) larger than that of generation 0, but the effect is relatively slight. The mean size of generation 1 is smaller than that of the selected parents. The reason is clear: although he carefully breeds from large individuals, the selector cannot avoid picking some individuals that are large *because of* favorable environmental factors and *in spite of* a relatively poor genotype.

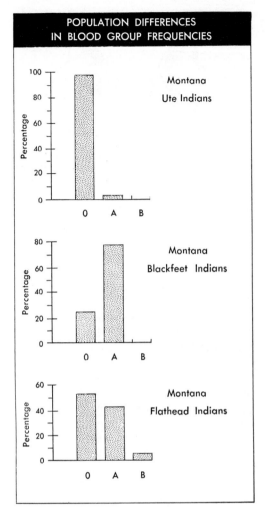

POPULATION DIFFERENCES
IN BLOOD GROUP FREQUENCIES

Montana
Ute Indians

Montana
Blackfeet Indians

Montana
Flathead Indians

17-5 Differences between populations in blood group frequencies. Each of three distinct populations of Montana Indians is characterized by the relative frequency (as percentage) within it of the three blood group alleles O, A, and B.

Mendel, and these are the genes of classical Mendelian experimentation. Polymorphic characters in demes are like the flower colors and seed characteristics of Mendel's peas. They are determined by one or a few genes, each with two or a small number of alleles in various members of the population. They contrast with characters determined by the interaction of larger numbers of genes, which usually have a bell-shaped distribution in demes. This is not an absolute distinction. There is a continuous scale of intensity of

gene action and of single to multiple gene effects on phenotypic characters. Similarly, polymorphic and bell-shaped distributions intergrade in populations. They are, however, distinct in their more extreme or characteristic forms as well as in convenient methods for studying them and in some of their implications for evolution.

DIFFERENCES BETWEEN DEMES

Within a species divided into more or less distinct demes, as most species are, there are two aspects of variation. One is that of variation within any one deme, some features of which have now been mentioned. The other is variation of the species in the form of differences between demes, for two demes are not likely to be precisely similar.

In species with biparental reproduction there is occasionally and often regularly interbreeding between adjacent demes. Offspring from one deme may move into the other, a factor present in both biparental and uniparental species. For these reasons, adjacent demes almost always intergrade and are seldom completely distinct from each other in any characteristic. One deme may have members with larger *average* size than a neighboring deme. Probably some individuals in the first will be larger than any in the second, and some in the second smaller than any in the first. Nevertheless there will be a considerable range of size represented in both demes. If size has a bell-shaped distribution, as it usually does, variation and intergradation of this sort between demes is shown by overlap of the frequency distributions, as in Fig. 17-8.

Adjacent demes often differ and yet usually intergrade in polymorphic characters also. It is rare for the individuals of one deme to be all of one form and those of another, adjacent deme all of a different form. If a character takes two forms, adjacent demes will usually have both forms. If the demes differ in this character, the difference is, as a rule, in the percentages of individuals of each form. Variation of this sort between demes is exemplified in Fig. 17-5. The basis for these relationships is that the same genes and alleles are present in the adjacent demes, but that

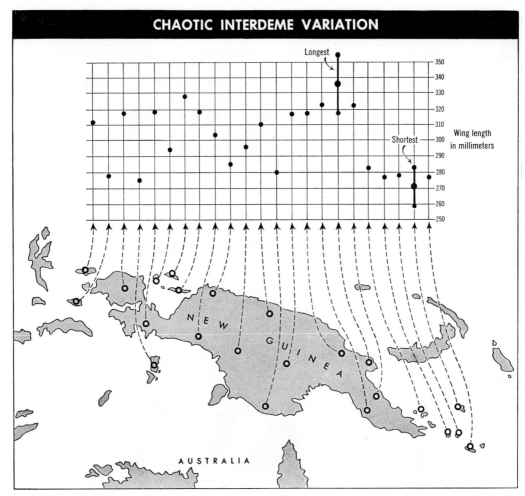

17-6 Chaotic variation in wing length between demes of the cockatoo (*Cacatua galerita*) on the island of New Guinea. The mean wing lengths in 23 demes of the cockatoo are plotted as solid dots on the graph above the map of New Guinea which locates each deme. The variation shown is significant, as indicated by the relatively small ranges of variation (solid vertical bars) in the longest and shortest populations. There is obviously no trend or pattern in the variation between the demes.

some alleles are more frequent in one deme than in another.

Two demes of the same species do not occur in just the same place at the same time.[1] If they did, the demes would quickly fuse and become one. Variation between demes therefore has geographic patterns. The patterns are of great interest because they throw light on many problems such as the genetics of populations, the relationships of populations with

[1] There are a few exceptions, but even in them the occurrence is temporary.

their environments, and the origin of species and other units of classification.

Some geographic patterns of variation are quite irregular. Differences between demes of some species seem to be scattered about in checkerboard or kaleidoscopic fashion, without particular rhyme or reason, as in Fig. 17-6. Of course, there are reasons for this, although the reasons are often difficult to determine. Such irregular patterns seem to have one of two causes, or a combination of the two. They may represent a scattering of small demes

VARIATION, SPECIES, AND SPECIATION   423

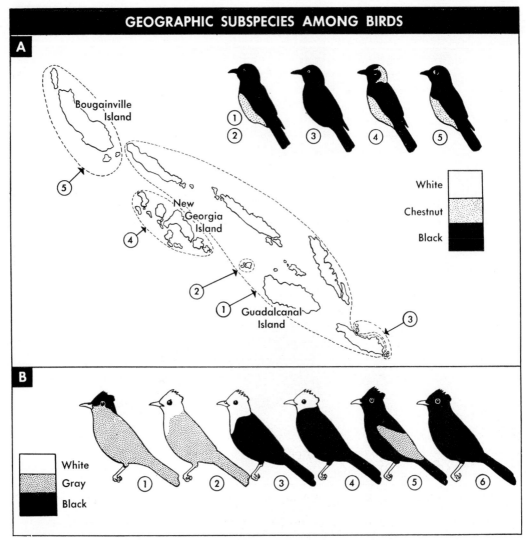

17-7 Two examples of bird species subdivided into distinct subspecies. *A.* Geographic subspecies, and their distribution, of the flycatcher *Monarcha castaneoventris* in the Solomon Islands. Four color patterns (involving white, chestnut, and black) are found among the five subspecies. *B.* Six subspecies of the Asiatic bulbul (*Microscelis leucocephalus*), India through China.

with little interbreeding between adjacent demes. Then each deme may have established its own characteristic mutations and genetic systems, kept distinct by the reproductive isolation of the deme. Or the pattern may represent local adaptation of each deme to irregularly distributed environmental conditions. Then the irregular variation of the populations reflects an irregularly heterogeneous environment. Highly irregular patterns are seldom found unless both factors apply

to some extent: the environment lacks uniformity and there is little interbreeding between some demes or groups of demes. In other words, this is another instance of interaction between the environment and genetical factors, the genetics in this case being that of populations.

It is unusual for each deme to be sharply distinctive or for the differences between demes to be highly irregular. Usually all the demes over a considerable area are closely similar. Such similarity is maintained by interbreeding between demes. Interbreeding over the whole area may, indeed, be so common that in effect the whole regional population is a large unit, a single deme or a complex without distinct division into demes. The large deme or complex of similar demes may constitute the whole of a species. More commonly there are two, several, or many such complexes, their demes also similar among themselves but different from those of other complexes. In classification, the large demes or deme complexes in such a situation are usually designated subspecies (Fig. 17-7). Where two subspecies of one species are in contact, there is usually a zone of intergradation, due to interbreeding, but away from this zone the subspecies may be quite distinct in their characteristics. Figure 17-8 shows an example of this frequent sort of distribution of variation within a species.

Zones of intergradation between demes (or groups of similar demes) are not always narrow and well-defined as in the last example. In fact, a whole regional population may intergrade from one end of its distribution area to another. For instance, southern and northern individuals of a species may be quite different, and yet when the population is followed from south to north there may be no definite line or zone where the change is localized. Or differences may appear gradually as populations are followed from lower to higher elevations (Fig. 17-9) or from wetter to drier situations. Continuity and complete intergradation imply that interbreeding of adjacent demes is usual throughout (why?), and the gradual change is usually correlated with gradients of environmental conditions.[2]

2 The technical term for a sequence of poorly separable demes with gradual, regular change from one area to another is "cline."

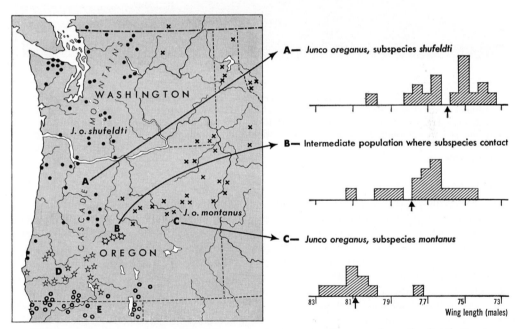

17-8 Intergradation where subspecies come in contact. The map shows the distribution in Oregon and Washington of three subspecies of the small snowbird *Junco oreganus*, and of intergrading populations between subspecies. Each symbol on the map identifies a locality from which samples have been studied. The three subspecies are as follows: **A** (• symbol) = *J. o.* subspecies *shufeldti*; **C** (× symbol = *J. o. montanus*; **E** (o symbol) = *J. o. thurberi*. The ☆ symbol (**D**) represents populations distinctly intermediate between the two neighboring subspecies, *shufeldti* and *thurberi*. The ☆ symbol (**B**) represents intermediate populations between *shufeldti* and *montanus*. Frequency distributions for male wing length are given for *shufeldti*, *montanus*, and the intergrading population (**B**) where these two subspecies meet. Population means are indicated by the arrows on the segmented line.

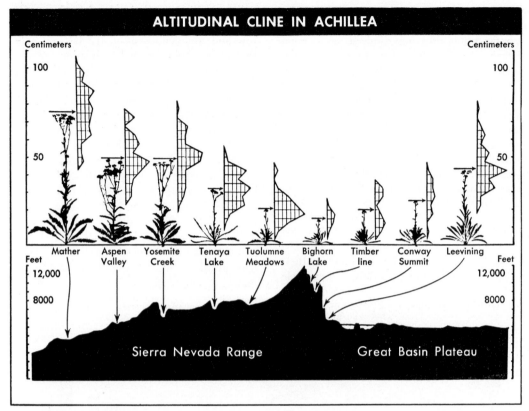

17-9 An altitudinal cline in *Achillea*. The plant species *Achillea lanulosa* occurs at all altitudes in the Sierra Nevada Mountains of California. It shows considerable adaptive intraspecific variation in relation to the different environments at various altitudes. As the figure shows, populations at lower altitudes are taller, at higher altitudes are shorter. Beside the plant representative of each altitudinal population there is a graph showing the distribution of height variation within the population.

Environmental gradients are common in nature. Every mountain range has a gradient from bottom to top, from warmer to colder, and usually simultaneously from drier to wetter, with gradients also in other climatic conditions and in soils. Plains or lowlands have similar gradients from south to north. Gradients of temperature, of salinity, and of light occur in lakes and seas. These gradients in physical environments are often accompanied by gradients in characteristics of the organisms inhabiting them. The gradients may be similar in a number of different species. There are, for example, three famous rules (generalizations with some exceptions) that apply to many mammals and birds:

Within any one species, average size of individuals tends to be smaller in warmer climates and larger in colder climates.[3]

Within any one species, protruding parts such as tails, ears, or bills tend to be shorter in colder than in warmer climates [4] (Fig. 17-10).

Within any one species, colors tend to be darker in warm, moist climates and lighter in cold, dry climates.[5]

There are numerous other rules of this kind that apply to various groups of animals and plants. There is nothing especially mysterious about such rules. They are only special examples of a broader and profoundly important generalization: *Differences between demes*

[3] This is commonly known as Bergmann's rule.
[4] Allen's rule.
[5] Gloger's rule.

tend to be correlated with differences in their environments.

This is not true, or, at least, it is not definitely known to be true of all differences between demes, but it is much more often true than not. The reason for the correlation is that the environment-correlated distinctive characteristics of a deme help to fit the deme for more successful living in its particular environment. This is certainly true in many examples and it is probably always true, although we do not now know the basis of greater adaptation in every instance. Among homeothermous animals (p. 172) heat production and conservation are more efficient in larger than in smaller individuals. That established fact underlies the greater fitness of larger animals in colder climates and explains the first of the three rules given above. The reason for greater fitness of dark-colored animals in warm, wet climates is more complex and is not surely established, although some likely hypotheses have been proposed. Can you think of one? What is a possible adaptive meaning of the second rule given above?

Another way to state the generalization about differences between demes is this: variation among subspecies or local populations of a species is largely adaptive. Most students of the subject agree that nonadaptive variation also occurs in species, and may even be common *within* demes. Within demes, variation involves *particular* characteristics of *individuals*. It is, however, probable that most of the variation represented by differences *between* demes is adaptive. Between demes, variation involves *average* characteristics of natural *groups* of individuals.

Species and Speciation

THE SPECIES PROBLEM

The basic unit of population in nature is the deme. There are still smaller units, such as a family consisting of parents and their offspring. Such units are obviously very temporary. They are distinguishable only for a generation or so. Their distinction and naming are not practical or significant for broader study of the evolution of populations and the

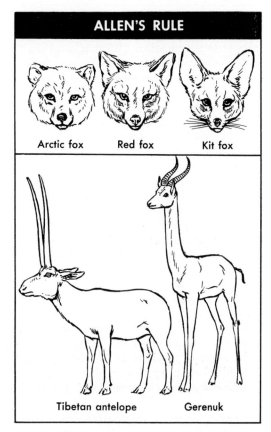

ALLEN'S RULE

Arctic fox   Red fox   Kit fox

Tibetan antelope   Gerenuk

17-10 Allen's rule. *Top.* Three fox species from progressively more southern, warmer distribution ranges: the Arctic fox (*Canis lupis*), the red fox (*C. vulpes*), and the kit fox (*C. velox*). Note the shorter nose and ears in the Arctic fox. *Below.* The gerenuk (*Litocranius*) from Abyssinia and Tanganyika in Africa, and the Tibetan antelope (*Pantholops hodgsoni*). Note the shorter legs and thickset neck and face of the Tibetan species.

diversity of life. The same often applies to demes, which (as you have learned, p. 397) are not likely to persist indefinitely as distinct units. The smallest persistent unit in nature is the *species*.

All organisms are classified into species. All sorts of biologists, from field naturalists to geneticists or biochemists, recognize that a species is a very special sort of thing and one with fundamental significance for the study of life. All biologists think that they have a pretty good idea of what a species is, at least among the particular organisms on which they work. Yet for centuries biologists have been battling and baffling each other about "the species problem." The problem is simply to produce a clear, fully satisfactory answer to the question, "What is a species?"

Millions of words have been written in discussion of the species problem, and the subject is still just as lively today as it ever was. This sounds very distressing and perhaps stupid: all agree that something is absolutely fundamental in their science, but they cannot agree as to exactly what it is. The situation is not really as bad as that, however. Two competent biologists may disagree heartily on the precise definition of a species, but if they look at the same populations in nature they will probably agree nine times out of ten on which groups are and which are not species. They may wrangle over the tenth group, but even then they usually find that they are saying much the same thing in different words. Everyone agrees on some of the characteristics usually defining species, and more often than not there is a strong modern consensus as to the sort of thing a species is.

It is one of the facts of life that an exact definition of a species applicable without question to all sorts of organisms is inherently impossible. It is no waste of time to discuss what species are; on the contrary, that is one of the most important subjects in the whole science of biology. It is, however, a waste of time to try to agree on one, infallible definition of species. In the first place, there are many ways, all useful and important, to approach the subject. A geneticist naturally thinks in terms of breeding, and an anatomist in terms of structure. In the second place, population units tend to be of different sorts among the tremendously varied products of evolution. Why should we expect to find precisely the same sorts of units among, say, yeasts, tapeworms, bees, and primroses? Third, natural populations are not static things that stay put neatly within the confines of rigid definitions. They are constantly changing, splitting up, reuniting, becoming more or less similar to each other, expanding, contracting, acquiring new habits, discarding old structures, and, in a word, *evolving*. The idea that there is somehow a single universal and fixed unit, the species, is a hangover from the primitive belief that just so many distinct

"kinds" of animals and plants populated the Garden of Eden.

We have already given one characterization of species (p. 397): A species is a group of organisms so similar in structure and heredity that their demes intergrade, may fuse, and may take the place of each other without essential change in the nature and role of the group as a whole. A species may not be clearly subdivided into smaller units that can be called demes. Usually it is so subdivided, and then the point is that the demes do not necessarily have evolutionary continuity as distinct units. The species does tend to have long evolutionary continuity and distinctiveness. That, really, is what makes the species such an important unit. The species could also be characterized as a sequence of ancestral and descendent populations evolving independently of others and with its own separate and unitary evolutionary role and tendencies. It is an essential part of the concept that a species is a sort of population, a group, the individuals within which are rather closely related to each other and therefore more or less similar in essential characteristics, although there is always variation among them. The kind and degree of variation are important features of a species. A species is not a group of individuals all of which have the same pattern; that is a nonevolutionary and old-fashioned idea, as will be evident when we discuss classification later on (Chapter 19).

The thing that maintains a species as a unit among biparental organisms is interbreeding. As long as the individuals of a group can interbreed, producing fertile offspring, and as long as they do so with some frequency, the whole group shares in a genetic pool and tends to have the unity and continuity that we have noted as characteristic of species. This does not mean that two distinct species never interbreed. In some groups of organisms hybrids between two closely related species are rather common. The distinction of the species and their integral evolutionary roles are nevertheless maintained if breeding between them is decidedly less common than breeding within each one separately, or if the hybrids are distinctly less fertile than the offspring of parents both of the same species.

Of course there is no absolute distinction between separate demes of one species that interbreed more freely and produce more fertile offspring, and separate species that interbreed less freely and produce less fertile offspring. The two sorts of groups intergrade in nature. The intergradation is part of the process of evolution. That is a reason why a species is not really an absolutely delimited unit and why it is futile to try to define it as such. But if the process goes a little further, until all the hybrid offspring are completely infertile or interbreeding can never occur, then the delimitation has become absolute and no one would seriously question that the two groups are different species.

SPECIATION

The preceding chapter dealt with the genetics of populations and how populations change. Such changes are part of the basis for the diversity of life. Obviously two species, necessarily derived from a common ancestry some time in the past, will not be different unless one or both have changed. It is also obvious that there will not be two species, rather than one, unless there has been another sort of change, a splitting of one group into two. Changes in a continuous population make for differences between earlier and later forms, but they do not increase the number of different populations or species. Another basis for the diversity of life is thus necessarily the process of splitting of a population into two or more. This key process at the crucial level of the splitting of one species into two is called *speciation.*

There has been a great deal of argument as to whether speciation is a sudden or gradual process. Some early evolutionists thought that new species might normally arise as individual "sports" by what they called "saltation," literally, "jumping." De Vries (p. 321), a pioneer geneticist, decided that this fitted in with his studies of mutations. He and some other early geneticists decided that species arose by "big" mutations—those with rather striking phenotypic effects.

A species is not a mutant or otherwise new form or type of organism. It is a group of organisms, a population. The population geneticists, developing the subject beyond the days of De Vries and his contemporaries, found that a single mutation very rarely leads to a new population. Indeed it is usually impossible for it to do so. The mutant form may not breed at all or may breed with other members of the population in which the mutation occurred. If it does breed with them, the mutation may or may not spread in that population. In any case the population continues to be the *same* population even if the mutation does change its characteristics. Speciation cannot occur that way.

There is only one important class of exceptions to the rule that speciation does not occur by saltation or mutation. Chromosome mutations and hybridization resulting in polyploidy (p. 322) can produce individuals that do not interbreed with their parental species but may produce populations among themselves. This has happened often enough among some groups of plants to have had considerable importance in their diversification. It has happened only rarely among animals, and even among plants as a whole it is the exception rather than the rule in speciation. As far as is known, gene mutations never give rise directly to new species among biparental organisms, although they might possibly do so in asexual groups.

Geneticists and other biologists have now returned to the view that was held by Darwin: speciation is usually a gradual process. Demes or groups of similar demes (such as the subspecies of classifiers) often develop somewhat distinctive genetical characteristics. (This may be just a matter of having different allele ratios in their genetical pools.) There is somewhat freer interbreeding within these groups than between them. Usually that is all that happens. The groups continue to be subdivisions of a species and do not become so distinctive as to be considered separate species. Sometimes, however, interbreeding between groups becomes less and less frequent, and its resulting hybrids less and less fertile, or both. If this process continues, the groups eventually become different species, although there is no sharply definable point at which speciation can be said to have occurred.

Kaibab squirrel

Abert squirrel

17-11　The Kaibab and Abert squirrels.

The key processes in evolution down at the level of the populations are thus two: genetic change within populations, and the splitting up of populations by sudden or, much more frequently, gradual decrease of interbreeding between demes or other units of populations. Genetic change within populations was discussed in Chapter 16. Now we turn to processes involved in the splitting of populations.

ISOLATING MECHANISMS

Anything that decreases interbreeding between groups of organisms is called an *isolating mechanism*. Isolating mechanisms are of many different kinds, and some of them are very curious.

The most generally effective isolating mechanism is simply space or geographic separation. Some students believe that speciation

rarely or never occurs (always excepting new polyploid species of plants) unless the groups becoming isolated are in different areas. There may well be exceptions, but certainly spatial separation is usually involved. Sooner or later other isolating mechanisms also arise, even if the effective isolation is purely geographic at first. Two nonmigratory animals a hundred or a thousand miles apart obviously cannot interbreed, and two plants at such distances are most unlikely to do so.[6] If plants or animals of the same species occur fairly continuously in the intervening region, there is still little isolation as far as the whole population is concerned. Individuals at opposite ends of the occupied region cannot interbreed directly, but they can pass on genes to any part of the population in the course of reproduction over a few generations. Often, however, there are spatial breaks in the distribution. Then there is less interbreeding across the gap, and in time the populations on the two sides of it may become different species.

There are rather similar populations of tuft-eared squirrels on the north and south rims of the Grand Canyon (Fig. 17-11). They must originally have come from one population, but in their present positions they seldom or never interbreed because they do not cross the canyon. They have become visibly different. (The northern squirrels have darker underparts and whiter tails.) The difference is not yet very great, but the two populations are usually considered distinct species: Abert squirrels on the south and Kaibab squirrels on the north rim. The distributional break involved in geographic speciation need not be so spectacular as the Grand Canyon. A stretch of grassland between two forests may represent a break between plant and animal populations of the forest. Narrow or wide discontinuities in distribution are abundant, and if they long persist they frequently lead to specific separation between populations on each side of them.

Geographic isolation alone is seldom permanently effective in decreasing interbreeding. Even the Grand Canyon might not entirely prevent the squirrels from interbreeding; some

6 The bare possibility does exist for plants with wind-blown pollen.

might cross, and populations can spread around the ends of the main barrier. (Also in broad geological view, even so tremendous a barrier as the Grand Canyon is only temporary.) In almost all instances of speciation, biological as well as geographic factors eventually decrease interbreeding. It is the biological isolating mechanisms that are strangest and most varied.

Interbreeding between otherwise similar populations in the same region is often reduced simply because they have slightly different habitats in that region. In Florida there are two groups of turtles that do interbreed to some extent and are considered as belonging to the same species, but interbreeding is reduced by the fact that one group prefers to live in lakes and ditches, and the other in running rivers. Anyone who has ever climbed a mountain knows that both plants and animals tend to live at characteristic elevations. Interbreeding between similar populations may be reduced by their preferences for different altitudes.

Interbreeding may also be reduced or even eliminated if animals have different breeding seasons or plants produce pollen at different times. In eastern and central United States there are two groups of common toads, considered distinct species. They can hybridize and occasionally do, producing fertile offspring. The populations as a whole are, however, kept quite distinct by the fact that one breeds early in the season and the other late.

In higher animals, especially insects and vertebrates, sexual isolation is frequently effective. Males and females of different populations simply do not like each other, or perhaps it would be more strictly scientific to say that they do not effectively stimulate each other sexually. Choice of partners may be exercised by males, females, or both. Some experiments with flies (*Drosophila*, again) suggest that the males do not care, but the females rebuff "foreigners." In some tropical fish, however, the males do the selecting. The females have distinctive color patterns, and the males pick out the patterns of their own species and even show preferences for certain particular variants of pattern within their species.

Many animals have elaborate courtship procedures. In these species a female does not breed unless she is properly stimulated by courtship characteristic of the male of her own species. A relatively simple but striking example familiar to most of us is the strutting display of male turkeys (cf. Fig. 15-19 and see illus., p. 221). Some birds go through much more elaborate performances (and so do some men). Even among fishes there may be complex courtship. Male sticklebacks build nests and then induce females to lay eggs in them. Differences in the procedure in different species are effective isolating mechanisms, for a female is persuaded only by the performance of her own sort of male. The following, for instance, are some of the many differences between two species:

The male of one species:	*The male of the other species:*
Builds a nest with separate entrance and exit, hanging on water plants.	Builds a nest with entrance only, on the bottom.
Leads the female to the nest in a series of zigzags, and gets her to enter with a little prodding (cf. Fig. 10-15).	Puts on a special mating play in front of the nest and then forces the female in.

Interbreeding in plants is often restricted by the tendency of pollinating insects to visit only one species of plant on a single foraging trip. This sort of isolation is carried to a high degree in orchids, for instance, which commonly have flowers that attract one species of bee or fly to one species of orchid (p. 375).

The mechanisms so far discussed reduce interbreeding even if the organisms concerned are completely fertile with each other. They are thus of particular importance in early stages of speciation, when the populations are still quite similar and may still be interfertile. Sooner or later another factor enters the picture: genetic isolation, reduction of genetic capacity for reproduction between two populations. Genetic isolation may set in early in the process or may not become significant until long after the species are fully separated, but it does always occur in the long run. The main reason why most of the diverse sorts of organisms do not interbreed is simply that they cannot produce fertile offspring.

Distantly related species usually cannot produce hybrid offspring at all. Their gametes are so different that the chromosomes cannot get together and produce a zygote that will develop. More closely related species may produce hybrid offspring, but continued reproduction between them is nevertheless reduced or impossible. The hybrids may be inferior in survival capacity, or may have reduced fertility or be entirely sterile. Cats and dogs are both carnivores, but they belong to families that have been distinct for scores of millions of years. Their gametes do not produce hybrid zygotes. Goats and sheep belong to the same family but to long-distinct lines in the family. Their gametes form a hybrid zygote that begins to develop but dies before birth. Horses and donkeys are distinct but rather closely related species. Hybrid zygotes develop normally and produce vigorous, long-lived animals, mules, but the hybrids cannot reproduce. Some crosses of closely related kinds of cotton result in fertile hybrids, but reproduction among the hybrids produces a majority of abnormal, short-lived offspring.

Once genetic isolation is fully established, the evolutionary destinies of the two populations are forever separate. They are unquestionably and irreversibly established as distinct species, and the diversity of living things has been increased. The process has been repeated countless millions of times during the history of life, and it has produced the millions of separate species that fill the world of life. The keynote of most evolutionary processes, both those leading to progressive change and those leading to greater diversity, is adaptation, a subject often mentioned earlier in this book and one so important that it now demands a chapter to itself.

Chapter Summary

Species and diversity: diversity of life a diversity of populations adapted to different environments; the species (contrasted to the deme) as the significant unit of population diversity.

Intraspecific variation; its sources.

Variation within a deme: its bell-shaped distribution exemplified; the modal, and the less frequent, classes; approximation of empirical bell-shaped distributions of variation to the normal curve of probability; heredity and environment may each separately cause bell-shaped distributions; both factors contribute to the actual distributions of variation encountered in nature; polymorphism.

Variation between demes: in continuously varying characters like size or weight; irregular patterns between demes; the usual existence of geographic pattern in the variation between demes; geographic subspecies; interbreeding and intergradation of subspecies; interdeme variation correlated with difference of environment: Bergmann's, Allen's, and Gloger's rules.

The species problem: the problem of defining a species; the variety of approaches to a definition; difficulty in giving truly general definition because all species are always evolving; species as smallest *persistent unit* of population in nature; general similarity of species members the result of free interbreeding within the species, whose members therefore share a common gene pool (a common heredity).

Speciation: the evolutionary process whereby one species population splits into two populations which no longer interbreed; speciation not a single step ("saltation") except in the special case of new polyploid plant species; Darwin's view correct—that speciation is gradual; isolated segments of a species population diverge genetically (gene pools gradually change) until interbreeding is permanently prevented.

Isolating mechanisms which prevent interbreeding between populations.

The importance of geographic isolation, especially in initiating speciation (the Abert and Kaibab squirrels of the Grand Canyon).

The evolution of biological isolating mechanisms: ecological isolation (as in Florida turtles); sexual isolation because of periodism or courtship pattern in animals (*Drosophila* and sticklebacks), and habits of the pollinating insects in plants; hybrid sterility the ultimate barrier separating species.

The woodpecker's adaptations equip it both for its narrow specialization of probing insects and for its broad specialization as a flying terrestrial animal. The origin of adaptations is in "natural selection," which includes all the vagaries of the historical process by which life has reached its present condition. (Photo by Allan D. Cruikshank from National Audubon Society)

CHAPTER **18**

The Evolution of Adaptation

Evolution and Human Thought

No other idea brought forth by the natural sciences compares with that of evolution in the profoundness of its impact on human thought. Before a person is old enough to grasp the idea of evolution for himself he has lived in, and has accepted, a strictly human world. All the horizons of his experience have been human: He is the child and grandchild of people, his friends and enemies are people, his life is motivated by human purposes and values and its outcome is measured in terms of human success or failure. This is the world the child understands, in which he feels at home; it is the source of all his confidence, his standards, and the meanings he attaches to things. When he is no longer a child and the ideas of evolutionary biology enter his familiar world, they may

threaten a radical upheaval. Horizons become expanded into wholly unfamiliar and emotionally uncertain realms. They are pushed back in time beyond the already strange world of Greek and Egyptian humanity to a prehuman era. Here is the first real shock— the realization that man is an extremely recent organism, a Johnny-come-lately on an earth inhabited for billions of years by other organisms of which mankind is only a modified descendant. His ancestry traces backwards through reptiles to fishes, and further back (with uncertain detail) through sedentary animals that have kinship with starfishes! Still further back his ancestors were single cells; indeed, ultimately, they were less complex by far than the simplest cell we know today. Then the vista of man's living past ends, for the earliest forms of life arose from the sterile planet Earth. These ideas can be uncomfortable for the maturing person, and they were uncomfortable enough even to many already mature scientists when first proclaimed by Darwin and others.

It is impossible to contemplate the grand sweep of evolution and sense our own true place in nature without experiencing a sense of awe and the truly religious emotions of wonder and humility. It was with such wonder and humility that Darwin closed *The Origin of Species;* his final sentence begins, "There is grandeur in this view of life. . . ."

The grandeur of which Darwin spoke so eloquently elicits many questions from us:

"What has caused evolution?" "Why did it happen?" "What is its purpose, to what end is it directed?" "What is the meaning of evolution, and what is the meaning of that vastly greater world of which man is only a recent and minute fragment?" Few of these questions are scientific [1] in the sense that answers may be given which are capable of being tested by observation. Those questions which are not scientific we cannot follow here, but it is important to recognize them for what they are even if, as scientists, we must lay them aside. The biologist as philosopher cannot escape seeking answers to them, and neither can any thinking person. We all feel the urgency with which they seem to demand an answer. For with the horizons of the more familiar human world so rudely extended and its meaning so strongly challenged, a compelling need arises for a new orientation. It is difficult then to accept the hard conclusion that science, which has been responsible for the dilemma, cannot solve it. It is not the task of the evolutionary biologist, as a scientist and not as a philosopher, to say what the purpose or goal of evolution is, if indeed it has one. He can only observe and infer what has happened and what forces have caused it.

Our reason for raising these nonscientific questions here is simply because they do arise for every thinker about evolution, and because, under the pressure of an emotionally felt need for certain answers, they have often been given pseudoscientific treatment. Even among biologists themselves the scientific and nonscientific issues have been confounded.

The main sources of difficulty and confusion are the facts about apparent *purpose* in organisms and about an alleged *direction* to the course which evolution has followed. People have often drawn comfort, and some still do, from the notion that if man is a mere fragment of the observable universe, he is the pinnacle or goal to which all of evolution has been purposefully directed. As a religious tenet, an act of faith, this view cannot be argued with. But when, as often happens, it is asserted that the facts demand this view,

[1] Which are scientific? Recall our earlier allusion to such problems in Chapter 2, all of which may profitably be reviewed along with your reading of the present chapter.

the assertion assumes the guise of science, and it is wrong.

The facts indicate flatly that there is no single direction to evolution; man may be *one* pinnacle, the end point of *one* direction evolution has taken, but tapeworms, for instance, are the pinnacle of another evolutionary direction. Furthermore, the facts that suggest purpose among organisms and their evolution are the facts about *adaptation* and its origin. Here, as we have already glimpsed in Chapter 2, the immediate purposes of organisms are diverse (food-getting, escape from enemies, etc.), and, insofar as any overall purpose of higher order can be discerned, it is the purpose of survival to reproduce.

In the remainder of this chapter we will examine adaptation and natural selection, bearing in mind that our approach here is to be scientific and is to avoid the strictly philosophical as well as the pitfalls of permitting emotional attitudes to color interpretation of the facts.

The Nature of Adaptations

We have encountered a diversity of adaptations in previous chapters and restrict ourselves here to a brief systematic review and definition of the phenomenon.

A DEFINITION

Like so much else in biology, adaptation proves far from easy to define in a thoroughly exact manner. As in the case of life itself (cf. p. 16), adaptation is better defined by the whole discussion of it here and elsewhere in the book than by any statement condensed within the limits of a sentence. Nevertheless the essential features are covered by stating that *an adaptation is any aspect of the organism that promotes its welfare, or the general welfare of the species to which it belongs, in the environment it usually inhabits.* Individual welfare here means simply the organism's success in obtaining food, avoiding predators, and generally surviving and satisfying its whole range of biological needs. The welfare of the species is not only that of its individual members, but also that of group reproduction, of maintenance or increase of the population. Adaptations are thus the apparently goal-directed features of living things that constantly impress us with the notion that organisms do have purposes, even though we cannot assume for any organisms other than ourselves that these purposes are conscious or that their goals are predetermined beyond the universal goals of survival and reproduction.

THE DIVERSITY OF ADAPTATIONS

Adaptations take any form—morphological, physiological, and behavioral—by which the welfare of the organism or the species is enhanced.

Morphological adaptations are among the most obvious and well documented. Examples are provided by the great structural diversity in insect mouth parts (Fig. 18-1) and the feet and beaks of birds (Figs. 18-2 and 23-24), all of which relate to the efficient functioning of these species in their special environments (compare roach, mosquito, and butterfly mouth parts, and the feet of duck and eagle). Other clear morphological adaptations are the shapes and colors (discussed in Chapter 16) by which animals are protectively concealed. A famous example is that of the leaf butterfly (*Kallima*) of Asia, which at rest is hard indeed to recognize among foliage (Fig. 18-3). Desert plants, possessing water-storage tissues, extremely reduced leaves, and still other features, are spectacularly adapted to the problem of conserving water in arid conditions.

Physiological adaptation, if less obvious, is always present in organisms. The shipworm *Teredo*, which causes so much trouble in the wooden pilings of wharfs and in the hulls of wooden ships, is able to exploit its remarkable habitat because it possesses special enzymes that digest wood. Shrimps that inhabit salt lakes like the Great Salt Lake in Utah have highly specialized powers of regulating their internal osmotic pressures.

Behavior in animals (Fig. 18-4) is almost as conspicuously adaptive as their structure. Termites which, like *Teredo*, are able to live on wood do so not because *they* can manufacture the enzymes necessary to digest it, but because their guts are always inhabited by flagellated protists that can digest the wood for them. Termites, like other insects,

must shed their skin periodically in order to grow. This involves shedding the lining to their hind-gut, and with it they lose their wood-digesting flagellates. The problem this raises—loss of a digestive system!—is overcome by a behavioral adaptation: as soon as they have shed their skins, the termites eat them and thus reinfect themselves with the flagellates they need. Young termites freshly hatched from the egg case acquire the protists they need by the appropriate if indelicate behavior of licking the anus of adult termites.

Behavioral and morphological adaptation is remarkably combined in the moth *Venusia*, which rests each day on the leaves of a tree lily. Its wings are adorned with conspicuous crossbands perpendicular to the body axis. When it comes to rest on the leaf, it always orients its body axis at right angles to the long axis of the lily leaf in such a way that the crossbands of its wings merge into the conspicuous veins running lengthwise down the leaf. If the moth is disturbed, it always resumes its appropriate former position which so effectively conceals it (Fig. 18-5).

BROAD AND NARROW ADAPTATIONS

Adaptations so far mentioned are all both extreme and obvious. Too often in biology there has been a tendency to think of all adaptation in this way. Too often the phenomenon has been regarded as a collection of bizarre curiosities whereby creatures succeed in extremely unusual habitats or in usual habitats in an unusual way. Such a view is in fundamental error. But the correct view of adaptation makes the phenomenon so difficult to define adequately or exemplify fully except at book length. Properly viewed, the entire organism is a bundle of adaptations; it is all adaptation insofar as it is appropriately organized to survive and reproduce in its habitual environment.

We may get a more useful perspective on kinds of adaptation if we classify them as broad and narrow rather than as morphological, physiological, and behavioral. Let us consider the adaptations of a woodpecker on this basis. It shows several obvious *narrow* adaptations to its special way of life; these in-

MORPHOLOGICAL ADAPTATION IN INSECT MOUTH PARTS

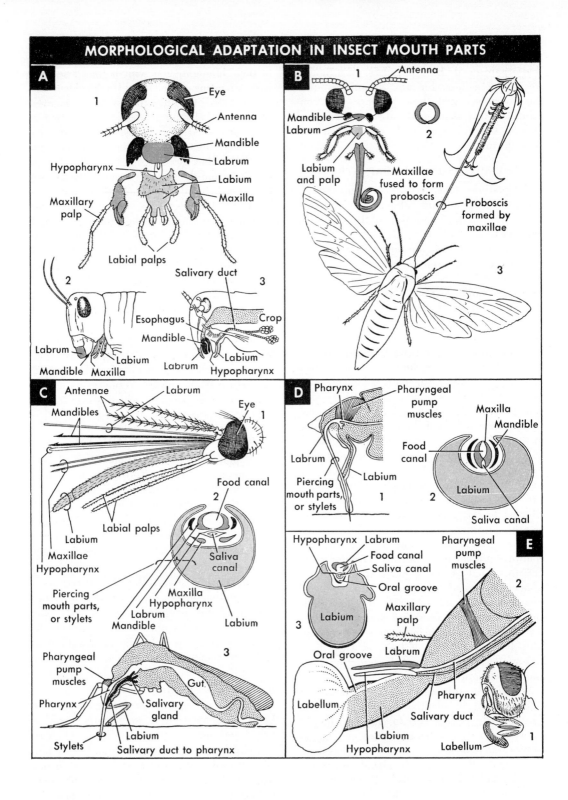

clude its posture, its ability to hop up the vertical face of a tree trunk, its powerful neck muscles which operate the head like a hammer, its large and chisel-like beak, and the long tongue used to probe insects from the crevices it cuts (Fig. 18-6). In all these respects it is adapted to the narrowly defined occupation of extracting insects from tree trunks. But it is also more *broadly* adapted to the bird's way of life generally. Both its wings and its bones, which combine lightness with strength, are adaptations to flying shared by thousands of bird species. Its respiratory system, while similarly specialized to the bird's way of life, nevertheless is to be seen primarily as one of its broadest adaptations. It is shared by all birds, reptiles, and mammals as a fundamental and essential part of the vertebrate organization adapted to life on land. Of still wider adaptive significance is the woodpecker's possession of muscles and nerves intricately organized in relation to each other and to bones in effecting the precisely co-ordinated movements on which its whole life depends. Again, the fact that muscles and nerves are possessed by every

---

18-1 The morphological adaptations of insect mouth parts. The basic insect mouth parts are as follows: (1) a *labrum*, or upper lip; (2) a pair of *mandibles*; (3) a *hypopharynx*; (4) a pair of *maxillae* (technically the first maxillae); and (5) a *labium*, or lower lip (technically a fusion of the second pair of maxillae). *A.* The mouth parts of a primitive biting and chewing insect like a cockroach. The labium and maxillae are used to "manipulate" the food, keeping it in the mouth cavity while it is chewed by the mandibles. The food is salivated through the hypopharynx. *B.* The mouth parts of moths and butterflies are adapted to sucking nectar (honey) from flowers. Superficially these mouth parts bear no resemblance to those of a biting and chewing type. However, as the figure shows, all the same parts are present, although their form has been evolved to suit a very different activity. The mandibles are reduced and functionless; so also are the labrum and labium; the only functionally important element is the proboscis, a long tube formed by the close apposition of the two maxillae. Nectar is sucked from flowers through this proboscis. *1.* The mouth parts of a butterfly dissected. *2.* Cross section through the proboscis, showing how it is formed by the two maxillae. *3.* A sphinx moth sucking nectar from a flower. *C and D.* Many insects have evolved elaborate adaptive modifications of their mouth parts enabling them to *pierce* the surface of other animals or plants and then to *suck* nutritive body juices from their prey. Mosquitoes are one group that pierce the skin of animals and suck their blood; the true bugs (Hemiptera, p. 580 and Fig. 23-13) feed predominantly by piercing plants and sucking juices from the tissues. (Some, however, like the human bedbug, have turned to animals as a source of food.) *C1.* The mosquito's mouth parts. The labium acts as a scabbard in which other mouth parts are housed. The labrum, mandibles, maxillae, and hypopharynx are all elongate and needle-like structures, modified to form collectively an elaborate "hypodermic needle" in which there are two distinct channels. One of these is the hypopharynx down which saliva flows, facilitating the insertion of the mouth parts by a lubricating action. The saliva contains a chemical agent that prevents the victim's blood from coagulating and thus clogging the other delicate channel—in the labrum—through which the blood is sucked up into the pharynx. The sucking is done by a simple structural adaptation of the pharynx itself (*C3*): muscles anchored to the exoskeleton of the head are also inserted on the wall of the pharynx. Their rhythmic contraction and relaxation causes the pharynx to act as a suction bellows. This mechanical adaptation is found in many other sucking insects; it is also shown for the bug (*D1*) and a dipterous fly (*E2*). A plant bug's mouth parts (*D*) are simpler than those of the mosquito. The labium again functions as a sort of protective scabbard for the long needle-like "stylets," formed this time only by the maxillae and mandibles. A comparison of the mosquito and the bug brings out an interesting generalization about adaptations and their evolution. It may be called "the principle of multiple solutions": the fact that different (even though related) organisms are likely to solve a common adaptive problem in different ways. The bug, like the mosquito, pumps a lubricating saliva *down* its piercing mouth parts, and sucks food *upward* in a distinct channel; but the morphological basis of the food and saliva channels is very different in the two cases. In the bug the maxillae are complexly sculptured so that when closely apposed they form two channels, one of which is the food canal and the other the saliva canal. In the mosquito the food canal is in the labrum, and the saliva canal in the hypopharynx. *E.* The housefly and other dipterous (p. 578) flies have evolved a very different set of structural adaptations, which enable them to suck up juices from free surfaces like those of fermenting fruits and decaying foods. *E1* shows the mouth parts (collectively called the proboscis) of a dipterous fly withdrawn under the head. Functionally they could be likened to a vacuum cleaner. At the end of the proboscis is a structure called the labellum; morphologically it is the tip of the labium. Flattened out and covered with capillary grooves, it is well adapted to sponge up fluids from wide surfaces. The necessary suction for the vacuum action is again developed by a pharyngeal pump mechanism.

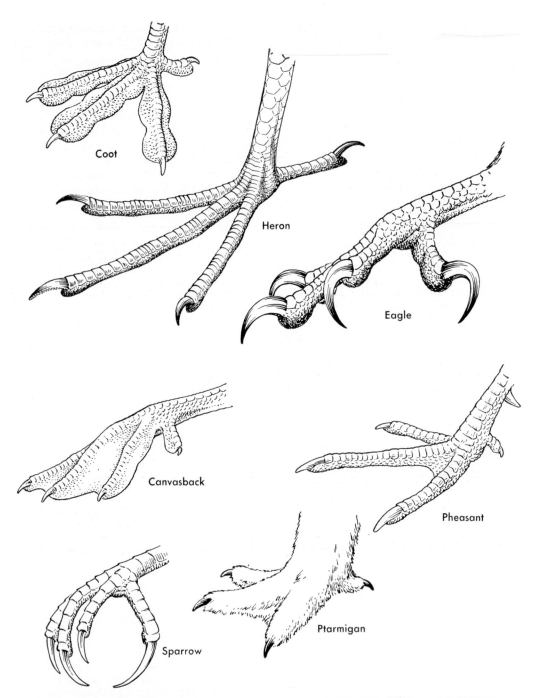

18-2 The adaptive specialization of feet among birds. The *coot* swims or paddles with its feet, which have lobed toes. The elongate toes in front and in back of the feet of the *heron*, a tall and large bird, give it a firm base for walking. The *eagle* is typical of birds of prey in having long talons on each toe with which to grasp its prey. The *canvasback duck* is a swimmer with fully webbed feet. The *pheasant* has feet suited to walking and scratching the ground for food. The *sparrow* is a typical perching bird, with feet suited to grasping a branch (cf. Fig. 10-4). The *ptarmigan*, inhabitant of very cold regions, has its feet stockinged by feathers.

18-3 Kallima, the Indian leaf butterfly.

animal group of higher organization than sponges must not blind us to their adaptive nature. Broadest of all adaptations is the woodpecker's capacity to reproduce itself or, more strictly, to copy the hereditary message which it inherited in turn from its parents. The cellular mechanisms that copy chromosomes are as surely adaptive as the chiseling beak and the long probing tongue; their ultimate biological meaning resides in the contribution they make to a total organization directed at successfully reproducing woodpeckers.

ADAPTABILITY: AN ADAPTATION

A nearly universal adaptation, developed to a greater or lesser degree in different organisms, is exemplified by the response of *Paramecium* to increasing salt concentrations of the water in which it lives. The adaptation concerned is a capacity to adjust or habituate to changed conditions. *Paramecium* is a fresh-water creature whose environment usually contains little salt; in fact, the animal can readily be killed by a sudden and large increase of salt to its water. If, however, the salt is added gradually, *Paramecium* adapts or

18-4 Adaptive behavior. The male of the (marine) fifteen-spined stickleback (*Spinachia vulgaris*) ensures good aeration of the eggs developing in its nest by fanning a current of water over them with its pectoral fins.

habituates to the salt; the concentration necessary to kill it becomes greater. Similar phenomena are known in other organisms, including man, whose ability to habituate to arsenic has been the central theme in many a mystery story. The prospective murderer slowly habituates himself to arsenic and then invites his victim to a dinner of which they both partake; the dinner has been spiced with arsenic adequate to dispose of the guest but innocuous to the habituated host.

18-5 Morphological and behavioral adaptation in the moth *Venusia*. The moth always rests by day on the leaves of a tree lily, with the striations on its wings carefully aligned with the vein striations of the lily leaf.

Habituation to specific toxic compounds is, moreover, only a special example of a much more general phenomenon of somatic adjustment or *adaptability*. Mice or men raised in the lowlands have severe respiratory difficulties at high altitudes where oxygen is scarce. In the course of time their performance improves, however, because the body adjusts to the new stress placed on it by increasing the number of red cells and, thus, the oxygen-carrying capacity of the circulating blood. Many other instances of somatic adaptability are familiar in man: well-exercised muscles respond to the special and prolonged work load by appropriately increasing their size; exposure to a new infective agent elicits manufacture of an appropriate antibody (p. 319); and so on.

Seen in broad perspective, even the capacity of animals to *learn* is itself just another example of the same phenomenon: behavior is appropriately adjusted in the light of past experience in such a way as to heighten the efficiency of living. Thus, whether earlier experience takes the form of unfavorable osmotic conditions, drug intake, low oxygen

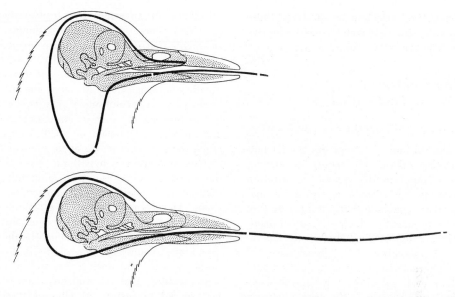

18-6 The adaptive specialization of the woodpecker's hyoid cartilage. The tongue skeleton in all higher vertebrates is a cartilage called the hyoid. In the woodpecker it is enormously long, an adaptive specialization related to the problem of probing insects from deep crevices in trees. The tip of the woodpecker's tongue is equipped with barbs.

content, extra muscle work, or a behavioral problem, the organism possesses the ability to improve its organization for survival efficiency. In all these instances the improvement in adaptation occurs within an individual's life span.

We must therefore distinguish carefully two uses of the verb "to adapt." Looking back over the history of man, we might comment that some of his ancestors *adapted* to life in trees by evolving modifications of forelimb structure (cf. p. 796). In such a comment we are talking about a radically different process from that referred to in a sentence like "Mr. Smith eventually *adapted* to high altitudes and decided to stay in Peru." The adaptation in man's ancestors involved an overhaul of their genetical make-up; it was an adaptive modification of the inherited chromosomal message that specified relatively rigidly the modified structure of limbs. But the process of adaptation in Mr. Smith took place with no change in the chromosomal specifications he received from his parents and transmitted later to his children. The physiological flexibility of Smith's body is guaranteed by his heredity; it is within his inherited reaction range. It is as though his

chromosomes had specified these instructions for his development: "Build a blood system which includes the following special physiological equipment that will permit automatic adjustment of the red-cell content to the precise level appropriate to local conditions."

It is surely unnecessary to emphasize that capacity to learn and to adjust bodily function is in itself an adaptation of the highest order. Were a species population to inhabit a rigorously stable environment, the inherited message could be simplified by specifying a quite inflexible bodily organization appropriate to the enduring conditions. But few, if any, environments are truly stable; the biological environment (pp. 447 and 614) is constantly changing and climatic catastrophes are inevitable. The time eventually arrives for all populations when, in order to survive, they must move, perhaps up a mountain or into more saline waters, or must meet changing conditions where they are. In such circumstances those populations with capacity to adjust somatically (that is, bodily or phenotypically) are at an advantage. Mutational modifications of the inherited message causing development of an *adjustable* body in species meeting changing conditions are favored by natural selection as surely as those mutations that increase simpler fixed adaptive features like protective coloration.

Lamarckism: a Hypothesis That Failed

ELEMENTS IN LAMARCK'S THOUGHT

Virtually no biologists now doubt that natural selection operates in nature, producing adaptive changes in the genetic constitution of populations. Furthermore, the great majority of them conclude that natural selection is the *only* process by which adaptation originates. Only a few retain belief in the operation of Lamarckism (the inheritance of acquired characteristics) as an important supplement or even substitute for natural selection. The issues at stake in the debate between Lamarckians and Darwinians have played such an important role in the history of evolutionary thought that we cannot pass them by completely. Moreover, the Lamarckian hypothesis sometimes presents so strong an intuitive appeal to beginning students of evolution that its shortcomings need special emphasis.

Jean Baptiste de Lamarck was a student of Buffon (p. 26) and was one of the first biologists to attempt to interpret nature in fully evolutionary terms. His name is associated almost exclusively with his hypothesis about the causes of evolution. His views on the subject are complex, involving at least two distinct elements.

First there is an Aristotelian and nonscientific element. Lamarck speaks of animals striving to improve their adaptation to the environment; he regards what Aristotle called an "inner perfecting principle" as a real motive force for adaptive evolution. There is no need to dwell long on this part of Lamarck's thinking: it is manifestly a nonscientific, metaphysical hypothesis, untestable by any observational procedure (cf. p. 21).

There is, however, a distinct hypothesis in his writings that is truly scientific and must be accepted or rejected on the basis of biological fact. This is the famous hypothesis of the *inheritance of acquired characteristics*, to which we have already paid brief attention

(p. 279). It envisages the transmission to each new generation of all those adaptive adjustments that organisms acquire through exercise and experience generally. Lamarck's own example, now hackneyed, was that of the giraffe's long neck. In his view the giraffe's neck was an evolutionary consequence of long-continued exercise in stretching as generation after generation of giraffes strove to reach the succulent leaves at the tops of trees.

This Lamarckian hypothesis has suffered the worst of all fates—it is commonly, and without real justification, regarded as ludicrous. The mental image of a giraffe stretching its neck is certainly comic and unfortunately is forever associated with the Lamarckian hypothesis. But of itself the hypothesis is a good one. It has two commonsense features that recommend it and doubtless served to inspire it. One of these has already been noted (p. 280): it is a fact that in the legal, social, and cultural world of man the improvements acquired by one generation are inherited by the next. The second source of inspiration is similarly an analogy: it is a fact, as we have seen, that organisms can adapt their bodily structure to a limited extent within the span of a single generation. Common sense (which in this case is euphemism for misplaced trust in analogies) sees this somatic adaptability as identical with evolution itself. Common language applies the same verb (to adapt) to both processes. And one of the accepted canons of scientific procedure (simplicity of hypothesis) is apparently satisfied in full measure.

THE INADEQUACY OF LAMARCKISM

All these signposts have proved wrong, however, in this particular case. The Lamarckian hypothesis has foundered on four distinct points. The first objection has already been given in Chapter 12: Lamarckism demands some form of pangenesis (p. 280) whereby hereditary information can be passed backwards, so to speak, from body cells to germ cells. The only mechanisms of hereditary transmission that are known to operate in living organisms preclude pangenesis. Second, enormous effort has been put into experiments designed to demonstrate the occurrence of an inheritance of acquired characteristics, and all such experiments have failed.

The third kind of objection to the Lamarckian hypothesis is curiously the first that was raised against it, and until recently the most often overlooked. There exists in organisms a whole class of adaptations that could never be explained by the Lamarckian hypothesis in any form. Among these are the familiar examples of protective coloration and cryptic form. An insect which so appropriately simulates a leaf in form or color cannot possibly do so by dint of exercise and effort; at least nobody has discovered how to practice becoming green!

The fourth objection, also raised by early evolutionists (including Darwin), relates to acquired characters that cannot possibly be passed on by heredity. The most noteworthy examples are among the neuter or soldier castes in social insects, which do not breed and therefore cannot, under any hypothesis, pass on either their characteristics or the ability to acquire them.

For adaptations inexplicable by Lamarckism, and there are many of them, natural selection is the only hypothesis adequate to explain their origin. Selection has the further merit of explaining all those adaptations that Lamarckism, in principle, *might* have explained. The occurrence of selection in nature is attested by abundant experimental evidence, and it is (most important of all) a theory consistent with the facts both of genetics and of the actual history of life.

The success of natural selection in explaining the factual details of adaptation in life's history is our final topic in this chapter.

Natural Selection as an Historical Process

We have stressed (p. 412) that natural selection is not necessarily a process of competitive combat and strife. Nevertheless, competition, which is usually unconsciously entered, does play an important role in the direction of evolution. Competence to find food and make a living up to and throughout reproductive maturity is an essential part of that more general competence to leave offspring

which is *the* feature of organisms that selection constantly improves.

The natural selection that results from competition for food and a place to live leads to a variety of evolutionary consequences. Broadly speaking, these may be either a narrowing and further specialization in competence, or increased diversification and broadening in competence. Which of these evolutionary effects is realized depends on a variety of circumstances, and also on one's viewpoint—whether, that is, one is viewing (narrowly) the evolution of a single species or deme or (with wider perspective) the net evolution of a whole group of species.

THE OCCUPATION OF NEW ENVIRONMENTS

The pressure to diversify. All species of organisms are adapted to a *particular* environment that is limited, to a greater or lesser extent, in size and resources (food, a place to live, etc.). Sooner or later the reproductive capacity of the species raises the population to a limit that is determined in large part by the availability of resources. This situation creates a selective process in which those individuals able to make use of otherwise unexploited environments and resources are at an advantage: their probability of successfully leaving progeny is heightened by the low competition in the new environment. Thus the theory of natural selection yields a broad prediction that explains that diversity which is one of life's most striking features. When we survey the nearly incredible range of habitats, or environments, exploited by organisms—from hot springs to arctic waters, from ocean floor to mountain streams, deserts, rain forests, and the air above, from the intestines of other animals to the pages of library books—we are viewing the diversity of habitats that have constituted an opportunity for organisms to escape from high competition in other, well-occupied environments.

It is surely unnecessary at this point to labor the fact that, when we speak of "escape from competition," we are not envisaging a deliberate attempt on the part of a squirrel, bird, or bacterium to find a new way of life where the going is easier. The universally present structural devices (p. 377) and behavior patterns that ensure random dispersal of a species cause it constantly (and for the most part quite unwittingly) to sample new environments. Whether the species remains as a resident breeding population, ultimately evolving new adaptation to meet the new conditions, depends on several factors, an understanding of which gives insight into the true nature of the evolutionary process in its broadest perspectives.

Conditions for entry into new environments. To enter a new mode of life a species must be given the *opportunity* to do so in three distinct senses:

First it must have the *physical opportunity* to enter. This is the most obvious of the three conditions and needs little amplification. Conceivably a butterfly species now limited in distribution to South American forests might be competent to exploit some new and so far unused environment in African savannahs, but its evolutionary potential in this respect will remain unfulfilled so long as it lacks physical access to South Africa. The intestines of other animals have been exploited as new environments only by those groups (protists and worms with fresh-water larvae) that have had prolonged physical access to animal intestinal tracts through their presence in drinking water and food.

Prolonged physical access to a new environment does not, however, guarantee its successful evolutionary invasion by a species. A *constitutional opportunity* must develop. We can put this another way by saying that a species has *constitutional access to a new environment* only when it already possesses some minimal adaptation adequate to sustain survival and reproduction while it gains a footing. Once entry is established, selection will steadily raise the level of adaptation to the new conditions. Examples given later in the chapter show that we are not begging the question of how new modes of life evolve by saying that a minimal degree of adaptation must exist before new habitats are entered. It is a commonplace of life's history that the adaptations which permit exploitation of *new* modes of life are only temporary makeshifts initially acquired as adaptation to *old* modes

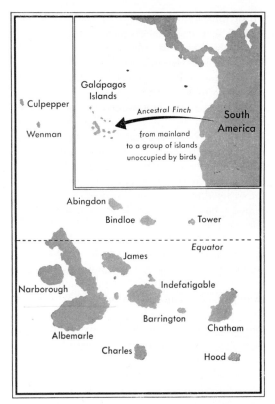

18-7 The Galápagos Islands, home of Darwin's finches.

of life, and subsequently improved or sometimes completely replaced.

Physical and constitutional access are both necessary, but even together they are not in themselves sufficient to ensure invasion of new habitats. The species concerned must also have *ecological access;* the ecological conditions prevailing must be appropriate. Ecological opportunity always means that the competition encountered in the new habitat must be slight enough to permit survival of the new invader during its initial phase, when its adaptation may still be poor.

Much of life's history becomes understandable as exploitation of constitutional and ecological opportunities to enter new environments and thus escape the heavy competition in those that are fully occupied.

Darwin's finches: an adaptive radiation. The role that ecological opportunity plays in determining evolution is well illustrated by the history of a group of small land birds, the Geospizinae (or Darwin's finches), on the Galápagos Islands (Fig. 18-7). These islands are a compact group lying about 600 miles off the coast of Ecuador. They were visited by Darwin when he was serving as a naturalist aboard the exploration ship H.M.S. *Beagle* in 1832. Observations on these islands strongly influenced Darwin's later thought about evolution.

The biologist's interest in the Galápagos stems from the fact that they are *oceanic islands* thrust up from the ocean floor. They have had no connection with the mainland at any time in their history. Coming into existence late in the history of life, they initially constituted a completely unoccupied environ-

ment, and a remarkable ecological opportunity for the land organisms already existing on the South American mainland. The nature of the present flora and fauna gives away completely the story of how the islands were initially colonized by life. The groups now present on the Galápagos are an extremely spotty sampling of those present on the mainland. In the absence of a land connection with the islands, only a few kinds of organisms have ever reached them. Their successful immigration was an extremely rare event brought about by the chance movement of winds and debris floating along where currents chanced to drive them. As soon as vegetation became established on the islands, immigrant animals were free to enter any of the several new

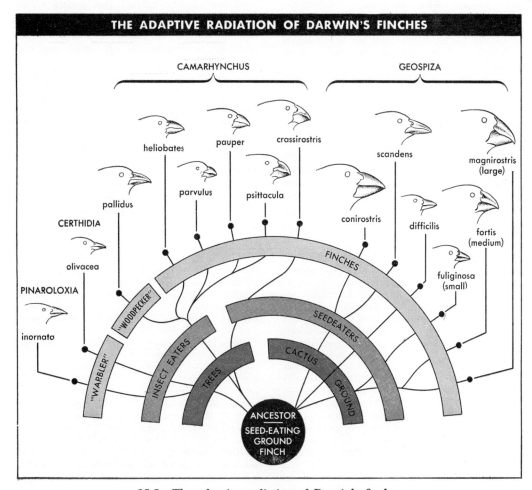

THE ADAPTIVE RADIATION OF DARWIN'S FINCHES

CAMARHYNCHUS   GEOSPIZA

heliobates   pauper   crassirostris

scandens   magnirostris (large)

parvulus   psittacula

pallidus   conirostris   difficilis   fortis (medium)

CERTHIDIA

olivacea   FINCHES   fuliginosa (small)

PINAROLOXIA   "WOODPECKER"   SEEDEATERS

inornata   "WARBLER"   INSECT EATERS   TREES   CACTUS   GROUND

ANCESTOR
SEED-EATING
GROUND
FINCH

18-8   The adaptive radiation of Darwin's finches.

18-9 Camarhynchus pallidus. The adaptive radiation of Darwin's finches has produced one species that is essentially a woodpecker. It has mastered this way of life by evolving, not the morphological specializations (Fig. 18-6) of the familiar woodpecker, but a behavioral substitute. It uses cactus thorns instead of a long tongue to probe insects from trees.

environments they encountered and to which they had constitutional access.

All the small land birds of the Galápagos today are descendants of a small finch (sparrowlike) from the South American mainland (Fig. 18-8). Since its arrival this finch has evolved into at least fourteen distinct species, each of which specializes to some extent in exploiting the resources of the islands. The evidence indicates that the ancestral finches were ground birds feeding mainly on seeds and other vegetation. Of the fourteen species that evolved from this stock, three are still ground finches feeding on seeds [*Geospiza magnirostris* (large), *G. fortis* (medium), and *G. fuliginosa* (small)], two are mainly cactus finches (*G. scandens* and *G. conirostris*), and one (*G. difficilis*) combines ground and cactus feeding. All the others have become tree finches, the majority of which (*Camarhynchus* species) are insectivorous. Within these broad categories (ground, cactus, and tree finches, some vegetarian and others insectivorous) still further specialization has developed. In both *Geospiza* and *Camarhynchus*, the species differ markedly in beak size and structure; this relates to the size of food they capture and eat. One of the tree finches (*C. pallidus*) has become essentially a woodpecker. It lacks the long tongue (Fig. 18-6) that is an adaptation of the true woodpeckers but substitutes a remarkable piece of behavior. After chiseling with its beak, it snaps a cactus spine and probes its insect prey from the crevice it has chiseled (Fig. 18-9). Another of the tree finches (*Certhidia*) has become to all intents and purposes a warbler.

The difference in evolutionary future between the initial finch immigrants to the Galápagos and their brothers and sisters on the mainland is striking (Fig. 18-10). All the

18-10 Evolutionary opportunity, or access: prerequisite to adaptive radiation. *A* and *B*. Conditions for adaptive radiation: *A*. Habitat (or niche) 1 is filled by species A (consider it to be a bird like the ancestral ground finch which colonized the Galápagos). Competition within the species constitutes a perpetual pressure on the population to diversify, to exploit new and unoccupied niches. The species can diversify only when it has physical, constitutional, and ecological access to (opportunity to enter) the new habitat. (*a*) Such is the case for species A with respect to habitats 2, 3, and 5. (*b*) Although species A has physical and constitutional access to habitats 4 and 6, it lacks ecological access: these niches are already occupied by the well-adapted species B and C. (*c*) Species A (a bird) has ecological and physical access to habitat 7 (say that of a cat), but it lacks constitutional access! (*d*) Species A could, constitutionally and ecologically, enter habitat 8, but it lacks physical access: habitat 8 is on another island. *B*. The consequences of these opportunities are as follows: (*e*) Three new species (A₁, A₂, and A₃) evolve as the original species A exploits the combined evolutionary opportunities afforded to it. (*f*) Habitats 4 and 6 are never entered because, in its transitional stage of incomplete adaptation, A cannot compete with the well-adapted occupants B and C. (*g* and *h*) Habitats 7 and 8 remain unoccupied. *C* and *D*. Galápagos versus mainland. The figures compare schematically the evolutionary opportunity afforded the same species of finch on the South American mainland and in the Galápagos Islands. For the most part, the adaptive radiation of the finches in the Galápagos has been limited only by the constitutional opportunities the initial ground finches possessed; having gained physical access to the islands, they had virtually unlimited ecological opportunities.

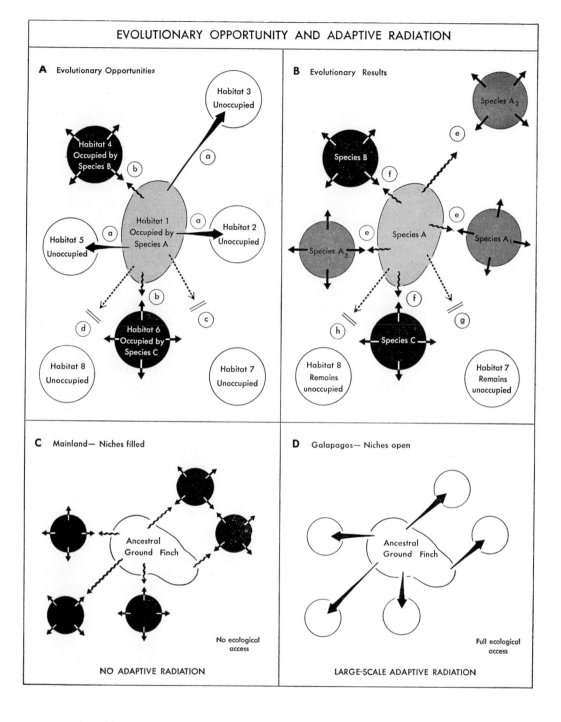

EVOLUTIONARY OPPORTUNITY AND ADAPTIVE RADIATION

A Evolutionary Opportunities

Habitat 3 Unoccupied

Habitat 4 Occupied by Species B

Habitat 1 Occupied by Species A

Habitat 2 Unoccupied

Habitat 5 Unoccupied

Habitat 6 Occupied by Species C

Habitat 8 Unoccupied

Habitat 7 Unoccupied

a b c d

B Evolutionary Results

Species A₂

Species B

Species A

Species A₁

Species A₃

Species C

Habitat 8 Remains unoccupied

Habitat 7 Remains unoccupied

e f g h

C Mainland— Niches filled

Ancestral Ground Finch

No ecological access

NO ADAPTIVE RADIATION

D Galapagos— Niches open

Ancestral Ground Finch

Full ecological access

LARGE-SCALE ADAPTIVE RADIATION

Galápagos finches of today have departed so far from the original ancestor that we can no longer identify it among the mainland finches. But we are sure of this: not one of the mainland finches (including the ancestor of the Galápagos birds) has been able to undergo the extensive adaptive diversification that occurred on the Galápagos, in spite of having identical physical and constitutional opportunity to do so; *the mainland birds lacked the ecological opportunity* created by the vacant habitats on the Galápagos (Fig. 18-10).

The evolution of new species on the Galápagos Archipelago was further enhanced by the island nature of the new territory. Island-to-island movement of small birds like the finches is extremely limited, though adequate to ensure the population of all the islands in time. The geographic isolation of each new island population promoted the initial breaking up of the finch population into new species (cf. p. 430). The various species specialized to some extent to local conditions but ultimately spread all over the archipelago. The result has been that most of the islands now support a number of species. Roughly the same ecological opportunities existed on most of the islands. On all of them openings existed, for example, for large, medium, and small vegetarian ground finches. These openings were filled on all the islands, although not always by the same species. Even among the Galápagos finches themselves we can discern how local differences in ecological opportunity from island to island have affected the history of individual species. Thus *Geospiza conirostris* is principally a cactus-feeding finch, as on the island of Tower (Fig. 18-11), where *G. magnirostris* is present as the successful large vegetarian ground finch. *Magnirostris* has, however, failed to reach the island of Hood, where *conirostris* again appears. In the absence of competition from *magnirostris*, *conirostris* on Hood has exploited both cactus and large ground-finch habitats; in doing so it has evolved the larger beak that is the characteristic adaptation of the large ground-finch way of life. Figure 18-11 illustrates other, similar consequences of unusual local opportunities.

The evolutionary phenomenon exemplified by the Galápagos finches is a very general one called *adaptive radiation*. The descendants of an ancestral species that was itself adapted to a typically restricted way of life have *radiated* out into a diversity of new habitats. Adaptive radiations have characterized the evolution of life throughout its long history. Whenever for one reason or another a group of organisms has been confronted with a diversity of new ecological opportunities (unfilled environments to which it has physical and constitutional access), radiations have occurred. Some radiations, like those of the Galápagos finches, are trivial in extent even if beautifully clear in understood detail. Other radiations have taken place on a more massive scale with far-reaching importance for the history of life in general.

MAJOR ADAPTIVE RADIATIONS

The total evolutionary opportunity afforded the Geospizinae on the Galápagos Islands was limited in two ways. First, the diversity of open habitats (*ecological opportunities*) was limited; the range of vegetation types was restricted. Second, vegetarian ground finches have limited *constitutional opportunities*; many ways of life, for instance those of cats or of large rodents, remained open on the Galápagos, but the finches had no access to these ways of life because they lacked teeth and unspecialized forelimbs. Cats and rodents themselves did not exploit those opportunities on the Galápagos because they lacked physical access; they did not cross the sea barrier between South America and the islands. Evolutionary opportunity of far greater scope and significance has been created when organisms with fewer constitutional limitations have been confronted with a wider range of ecological opportunity.

A major adaptive radiation of great importance in our own history followed the first conquest of land by vertebrates. The earliest vertebrates to emerge even temporarily on the land were fishes that (1) could breathe air to a limited extent with lungs that were extremely crude by modern standards, and (2) could walk or wriggle in still cruder fashion with the aid of slightly modified fins (Fig. 31-4). The evolution of these minimal constitutional prerequisites took place as part

	CENTRAL ISLANDS	SMALL OUTLYING ISLANDS		
		TOWER	HOOD	CULPEPPER
LARGE GROUND FINCH	*magnirostris*	*magnirostris*		*conirostris*
CACTUS GROUND FINCH	*scandens*	*conirostris*	*conirostris*	*difficilis*
SMALL GROUND FINCH (ARID ZONES)	*fuliginosa*	*difficilis*	*fuliginosa*	*difficilis*
SMALL GROUND FINCH (HUMID WOODS)	*difficilis*	The outlying islands lack the moist woodland habitat occupied by *difficilis* in the central islands		

18-11 **The exploitation of local evolutionary opportunities by *Geospiza* species** on the Galápagos Islands. Several of the small outlying islands (Fig. 18-7) have never been colonized by some species from the central islands. *G. magnirostris* is an example: it has failed to reach Hood and Culpepper. Its absence on these islands left open the large-ground-finch niche to which *G. conirostris* had physical and constitutional access (cf. p. 444 and Fig. 18-10). On Hood *conirostris* has evolved a larger beak than elsewhere and occupies both the large-ground- and cactus-ground-finch niches; on Culpepper it has a still larger beak and occupies the large-ground-finch niche. On the central islands *G. difficilis* is a small ground finch of humid woodlands, a habitat absent on the arid outlying islands. On these islands *difficilis* has succeeded only where *fuliginosa* (the common arid-zone small ground finch) is absent and it has had, therefore, the ecological opportunity to enter the new niche.

of a strictly fish radiation and is a point to which we shall return below. What is important here is the fact that, once able to colonize the land to any extent, the vertebrates had clear sailing from then on: being the first large terrestrial animals, they met with no competition. Amphibians, reptiles, and mammals successively emerged through subsequent geological periods. The reptiles were the first really competent land vertebrates; equipped with an improved reproductive apparatus they could move inland away from water and exploit the rich array of wholly unoccupied land habitats. The reptile radiation was a grand one; it produced herbivorous forms in rich assortment, a diversity of carnivores, a host of flying reptiles, and even forms that successfully returned to water, making a good living in spite of fish competition.

Two special points should be noted in connection with the reptilian radiation. First, it removed the *ecological opportunity* that was earlier open to the emerging fishes that were becoming amphibious. The fact that fish once evolved into land vertebrates but can no longer do so has proved puzzling to many people. How could fish have accomplished the feat 300 million years ago if they cannot do so now? The answer is simple enough: the evolutionary step from water to land involves a poorly adapted transitional stage, neither fully aquatic nor fully terrestrial, that was extremely unlikely to be successful once efficient competitors were already established on the land. No fish today would, to put it crudely, stand a chance.

The second special point concerns the history of mammals. It is clear from the fossil record that one branch of the early reptilian radiation produced animals that later gave rise to mammals. Indeed, mammals of a sort were in evidence throughout the prolonged (130 million years) heyday of the reptilian dinosaurs, but they were of restricted variety and abundance. For reasons still obscure (p. 774) *almost* all the reptiles became extinct about 70 million years ago. With their passing, all the ways of life they had formerly filled became available. Into these now open environments the mammals, which had survived the great dying (p. 774), were now free to radiate.

As in the earlier great radiations, the evolution of mammals was rapid and divergent. Forms appeared that paralleled most of the earlier reptilian adaptive types: herbivores, carnivores, flying forms, swimmers, and so forth. The history of the mammals themselves has involved a whole series of still later, more restricted radiations, some of which are discussed in later chapters.

THE EVOLUTIONARY LOTTERY

Multiplicity of evolutionary directions. The direction which evolution takes is determined wholly by the combination of *physical, constitutional,* and *ecological* opportunities inherent in the prevailing circumstances. Far from having a single direction, the early evolution of land vertebrates had, for instance, as many different directions as there were ecological opportunities for reptilian structure to exploit. The multiplicity of directions in which a group of organisms evolves is like a lottery. Each new piece of evolutionary change is undertaken with no insight into its later consequences; it is a gamble in which the evolving organisms unwittingly stake their future. Maintaining this analogy, we can survey some of life's diversity and recognize at what stage various groups picked losing and winning tickets.

Tickets with a limited future. Two broad examples will illustrate how features of an organism that were adequately adaptive in their day subsequently turned out to restrict further evolution.

Arthropods (p. 569), ancestral to crabs and insects, emerged as one of the products of the first great adaptive radiation of animals. Their success was achieved in large part by their acquisition of a skeleton. The fact that their skeleton was external (p. 228) set few limitations to their early evolution, and to this day they remain a conspicuously successful group of animals judged on the basis of number and diversity. But in comparison with the vertebrates they drew a poor ticket in the lottery of the first great radiation. The size of all arthropods is severely restricted by growth problems inherent in their possessing an external rather than an internal skeleton. For this reason alone arthropods are forever debarred from the higher way of life open to the larger vertebrates whose much bigger brains are capable of more complex functions.

Such flatworms (p. 530) as found low competition and easier living in the internal organs of other animals entered an evolutionary blind alley. Once committed to parasitism, they became subject to a highly specialized pattern of natural selection. The parasitic way of life leads to loss or nondevelopment of features like sense organs and a nervous system, which are prerequisite for successful entry into almost every other type of environment. We do not know of a single species of organism that ever committed itself to parasitism and subsequently escaped to occupy a nonparasitic environment.

Tickets with no future: extinction. Temporary evolutionary success has often been achieved, as it has by parasites, through the acquisition of adaptations to a highly specialized and restricted environment. The dangers inherent in such evolutionary ventures are not only in the restrictions they commonly impose on future evolution; they include the danger of absolute extinction. Obviously, organisms survive only so long as they remain adapted to some environment. All environments are subject to change, and all species are therefore called upon sooner or later to find a new habitat to which their present organization is adaptive, or else to evolve appropriate adjustments to the new conditions. In these circumstances narrow specializations prove to have been poor tickets in the evolutionary lottery. The narrower the specialization by which an organism temporarily succeeds, the fewer are the opportunities that will later be open to it as changing conditions close the old way of life.

Winning tickets: evolutionary progress. Man shares a common ancestry with other mammals, with reptiles and fishes, with arthropods, and even with parasitic flatworms. Like all of them, he is descended from animals that underwent that first great adaptive radiation which produced the animal phyla. Part of his ancestry traces through the later radiation of fishes (first vertebrates), through the still later radiation of reptiles, and so on.

The obvious evolutionary advance that man represents when compared with all his relatives—close and distant—is the product of the same lottery process in which so many organisms staked all and often lost their future. No special forces have guided man on the evolutionary pathway; he simply happens to be the child of a long line of organisms that drew winning tickets in every successive adaptive radiation. All the adaptations acquired by his ancestors have proved, in hindsight, to be broad enough not to constitute an evolutionary blind alley.

Essential parts of our present broadly adaptive organizations are our respiratory system and basic mode of locomotion. We owe their origin to the happy accident that some Devonian fishes (the crossopterygians, or crossopts, p. 588) hit upon them, under pressure of selection in oxygen-poor swampy water, as adaptations to strictly fish problems. The lungs permitted the creatures to supplement their gills as respiratory structures of little use in stagnant water, and their crude fin-legs permitted temporary excursions overland to new ponds. Both features proved to be more than valuable adaptations in the radiation of fishes; they conferred upon those particular early fishes constitutional access to environments then unoccupied. The sequence of causes here is clear: crossopts did not evolve lungs *in order to* become land vertebrates; they became land vertebrates because the ticket they drew in the lottery of fish radiation happened to be a winner.

Among man's most significant physical adaptations of later origin is the structure of his hands. The complexity of manipulations he can execute is an essential foundation to his whole culture. Complex manipulation is a prerequisite to human tool making and all that this implies for human society. And yet our hands evolved in relation to a highly specialized problem, the grasping of tree limbs, which arose in an ancient mammalian adaptive radiation long before man as such evolved (see p. 796).

HISTORICAL MAKESHIFT VERSUS DESIGN

The complexity of organic adaptations sometimes strains our credulity as to the adequacy of natural selection to explain them. The task of molding something as complex as the human ear seems too much for natural selection if we look upon the ear as an invented and completed thing. But the adequacy of selection to bring about this result is evident if we follow the actual historical development. Selection accounts for this development at every step, but in a most devious way, which no pure conjecture could conceive.

The ear is—almost literally—a patchwork of ducts, bones, and membranes (Fig. 18-12) that in earlier vertebrate history were variously employed in a surprising diversity of functions, many of which had nothing to do with sound reception. The Eustachian tube (Fig. 18-12) was originally a gill slit serving the respiratory needs of our fish ancestors. The three bones that transmit vibrations from the eardrum to our inner ear also had a history just as incidental to their present function. One of them (the stapes, Fig. 18-12) was at different times in its career a skeletal element in the throat and later a convenient prop to the jaw apparatus of the first biting vertebrates (p. 584). The other two bones (incus and malleus, Fig. 18-12) were part of the reptilian jaw of 200 million years ago. The present function of all three ear bones is due to a fortuitous combination of circumstances. First, their earlier roles happened, quite incidentally, to bring them into close proximity to a pressure-sensitive organ (the future inner ear) in the brain case. While functioning in their former capacity of jaw components, the bones happened, willy-nilly, to transmit sound (pressure) waves to this organ. Second, suc-

THE EVOLUTIONARY HISTORY OF THE MAMMALIAN EAR OSSICLES

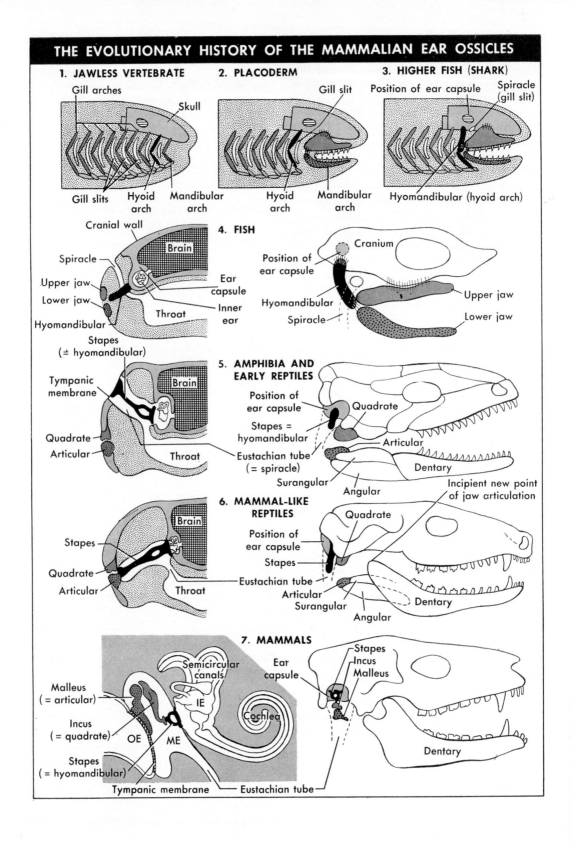

cessive adaptive improvements in the vertebrate jaw structure made all three bones nonessential in their initial functions. Released in this way from one kind of selection, their future was determined by the ever-present premium on efficient sense organs and the natural selection this creates; they became exclusively devoted to a function that was previously incidental and of minor importance.

Natural selection is always restricted in what it can accomplish by the opportunities with which it is confronted. Earlier in this chapter we discussed opportunities for selection arising from ecological accidents—encounters with unoccupied environments. Now in the history of the ear we have exemplified

---

18-12 Evolutionary history of mammalian ear ossicles. *1.* The evolutionary history of the mammalian ear bones begins with the earliest jawless vertebrates (Agnatha, p. 582). In these "fish" the wall of the throat, or pharynx, is perforated by gill slits and is supported, between the slits, by a series of skeletal elements, the *gill arches*. The first two of these are called the mandibular and hyoid, respectively. *2.* The jaws of all later vertebrates represent an evolutionary transformation of the first—mandibular—arch. This is first seen in the Placoderms (p. 584), in which the jaws are quite separate from the cranium, or brain case, and are attached to it only by ligaments. *3* and *4.* In later fishes, like the shark, the second (hyoid) arch has been moved forward, its upper element (the *hyomandibular*) being used as a brace to the jaw apparatus. At one end the hyomandibular attaches to the brain case at a point close to the ear capsule, the bony cavity in which the inner ear is housed; at its other end the hyomandibular connects with the point of jaw articulation which thus becomes firmly braced to the skull. In the hyoid arch's evolutionary movement forward, the first gill slit has been forced into a position above the jaws, near the ear capsule, and has been reduced to a vestigial condition no longer functional in respiration. It is now called the *spiracle*, and is clearly visible behind the eyes in our photograph of a ray (close relative of the shark) in Fig. 23-16. A highly schematic cross section through one side of the skull and throat is given in *4, left.* Note how the jaw articulation is braced to the skull by the hyomandibular at the ear capsule, and how the spiracle opens to the exterior above the jaws. *5.* Figures comparable to those in *4* exemplify the jaw-ear relations of Amphibia and early reptiles. The principal innovation is that the upper jaw has now fused with the cranium; it is not a separate element, as it was in fishes. The main evolutionary consequence of this reorganization was the liberation of the hyomandibular from its earlier function as a brace to the jaws. Its proximity to both the spiracle and ear capsule has been exploited in a radical transformation of function. It has come to lie *in* the spiracle, which is now called the Eustachian tube. The tube is closed off at the exterior by a tight membrane, the tympanic membrane or eardrum. Sound waves that fall on the membrane cause it to vibrate, and these vibrations are transmitted to the inner ear by the hyomandibular, which is now called the stapes. The stapes, lying in the Eustachian tube, attaches at one end to the tympanic membrane, and at the other end to a membrane that covers an opening (the oval window, Fig. 9-9) into the inner ear; it is an efficient mechanical device to communicate sound vibrations from the surface of the skull to the auditory sense organ located deep in the head. The jaws themselves now comprise many bones. The lower jaw, for instance, is made up of four bones, including the *dentary* (bearing the teeth) and *articular*, which as its name implies, is the bone that articulates with the upper jaw. The articulating bone of the upper jaw is the *quadrate*. (In *5, 6,* and *7,* for simplicity, only the articular and quadrate bones are given the characteristic shading that identifies their history with the whole of the lower and upper jaws in the earlier figures *1, 2, 3,* and *4.*) *6.* The condition of the mammal-like reptiles (actual ancestors of the mammals) is substantially the same as that of the Amphibia and earlier reptiles. However, two items of change point the way to the ultimate condition of the mammals. First, the Eustachian tube and tympanic membrane have shifted, the membrane now being very close to the point of quadrate-articular articulation. Second, the jaw itself is beginning to develop a new point of articulation with the skull: the end of the dentary bone is curved upward and is beginning to make contact with the cranium at a point in front of the original quadrate-articular joint. *7.* In mammals the new articulation of the dentary bone to the skull is complete. Indeed the lower jaw consists solely of the dentary; the other former jawbones have assumed new functions or have been "lost." The articular has been transformed into an ear ossicle, the *malleus*. The quadrate has become a third ear bone, the *incus*. Sound is now transmitted from the tympanic membrane to the oval window of the ear capsule by a chain of three bones: malleus, incus, and stapes. Thus, as in the history of the hyomandibular, the liberation of articular and quadrate from jaw function was accompanied by their opportunistic utilization in a new function—that of sound transmission. In this history there was, doubtless, no sharp point of functional switchover. Indeed there surely was an historical period when the bones concerned, although still functioning in the mechanics of jaw movement, nevertheless served to transmit sound vibrations to the nearby ear mechanism. Their ultimate transformation to an *exclusively* auditory role was an exploitation of an anatomical opportunity—the accident of their location near the ear capsule and the Eustachian tube.

a distinct kind of evolutionary opportunity that arises from anatomical accidents like the physical proximity of jawbones and inner ear.

The history of our ear is thus a general warning: In seeking to uncover the forces responsible for present-day "design" in organisms, we waste time when we seek a single "creative" agent in any way conscious of its goal. Our task is rather that of unraveling an historical succession of transient organic needs (which constitute selection pressures) and transient opportunities to meet these needs. By the time we are through unraveling the history of a contemporary adaptation like the human ear, our intuitive feeling that it must have been designed is gone. Formerly regarded as an architectural masterpiece, it will now seem more like those improvisations with pulleys, tilting buckets, and string-tied joints which imaginative cartoonists delight in creating! But *this* improvisation works, and under the blind but firm control of natural selection it works better in each successive stage of its evolution.

Natural Selection and the Inherited Message

We have repeatedly emphasized the fundamental problems posed for the biologist by the fact of life's complex organization. We have seen that organization always requires work for its maintenance, and that the universal quest for food is in part to provide the energy needed for this work of maintaining organization. In Chapter 1, and again in Chapter 11, we stressed the fact that all organizations are in a sense improbable, or nonrandom, things, that they demand information or instructions for their development and maintenance. We can restate this simply by noting that *any* energy expenditure is not sufficient to develop and maintain order: a bull in a china shop performs work, but he neither creates nor maintains organization. The work needed is *particular* work; it must follow specifications; it requires information on how to proceed.

Our whole treatment of the subject of genetics from Chapters 11 through 14 was presented in this light. We envisaged embryological development as the creation of a complex adult organization, and the study of heredity proper as the search for the inherited information that specified how the work of development must proceed. This search led us to the nucleus and its chromosomes, which proved to be the carriers of the inherited specifications ultimately responsible for the organization of the living system.

In showing that the organization of living matter is controlled by the presence of information in the chromosomes, genetics provides only the beginnings of a full explanation. Like the Martian inspecting the automaton (p. 310), we need to know not only where the information is (chromosomes) and how it is decoded by the organism, but *how it got there*. The answer to this final question lies of course in the historical processes of evolution we have now reviewed.

The processes of mutation are always introducing new instructions into the inherited message; genetic recombination is always reshuffling, to a limited extent, the variations on the inherited message that exist among the many individuals of a population. Most of the variants thus produced in the chromosomal instructions are disadvantageous; they are a garbling of an otherwise clear and appropriate set of inherited specifications. As such, however, they never persist long in the succession of generations, for their very inappropriateness guarantees their reproductive inefficiency. Natural selection keeps the population's inherited message in good repair. But it does more than that. *Some* of the novelties in the message *happen* to specify a more appropriate organization—a better-adapted organism—than did the original message. As a result of natural selection this more appropriate information ultimately becomes the prevalent form of the inherited message throughout the population. Thus natural selection is the agent which *created* the message in the first place as the appropriate set of specifications which guarantee the adaptive organization of living things.

Chapter Summary

Evolution and human thought: impact of the idea of evolution on human values and orientation; emotionally felt need for certain answers to nonscientific questions; danger of mistaking nonscientific for scientific answers, especially in connection with problems of purpose and direction in evolution; purpose and adaptation.

Nature of adaptations: the diversity of adaptations—morphological, physiological, and behavioral; broad and narrow adaptation (exemplified by woodpecker); adaptability itself an adaptation (exemplified by Paramecium's adaptation to salt and human adaptation to toxicity and high altitudes).

Lamarckism:

Elements in Lamarck's thought: inner perfecting principle and the inheritance of acquired characteristics; its "commonsense" appeal; the false analogy between somatic adaptation of the individual and the evolution of adaptation.

Inadequacy of Lamarckism: its demand for pangenesis; failure of experiments to demonstrate it; its failure to account for insect coloration, and its failure to account for the adaptive evolution of neuter insects; everything explicable in principle by Lamarckism also explicable by natural selection.

Natural selection as an historical process: the occupation of new environments; pressure to diversify generated by intraspecific competition; conditions for entry into new environments: physical, constitutional, and ecological opportunities.

Adaptive radiation as diversification: Darwin's finches; colonization of Galápagos Islands by ancestral seed-eating ground finch; absence of other small birds and consequent ecological opportunities for ancestral finch; its radiation into 14 different species occupying different ecological niches; comparison of evolutionary history of ancestral finch on the mainland and on the Galápagos; special ecological opportunities on individual islands.

Major adaptive radiations: adaptive radiation of first (reptilian) land vertebrates; lack of ecological opportunity for modern fish to conquer the land; opportunities created for mammals after the widespread extinction of reptiles.

The evolutionary lottery: the opportunistic and blind nature of natural selection; adaptive radiation compared with a lottery: "tickets with a limited future"—evolution of adaptive features that set restrictions on further evolution; "tickets with no future"—evolution of overspecialization leading to extinction; "winning tickets"—evolution of adaptive features that permit progressive evolution (exemplified by evolution of fish adaptations permitting conquest of land).

Historical makeshift versus "design": evolution of the mammalian ear as example of the lack of design in adaptive structures.

Natural selection the agent that maintains and creates the information in the inherited message of the chromosomes.

The Diversity of Life

INTRODUCTION TO PART SIX

The introductory photograph to Part 6 shows a rich assortment of organisms in a drop of sea water. Greatly magnified, it shows several diatoms—photosynthetic protists—as well as crustaceans and the larvae of echinoderms. Diverse as it is, the life in this drop of the sea cannot begin even to suggest the over-all variety that confronts the biologist when he turns—as he must—to study the total array of different organisms that evolution has brought into existence. The truly immense diversity of life, attested to by the existence of well over a million species alive today, is almost bewildering. But our bewilderment gives way to understanding as we perceive two general themes running through the rich variety of life.

The first theme is that the diversity of species is basically one of mode of life: species differ in the adaptations they have evolved to diversified environmental opportunities.

The second theme that brings order into the array of different organisms is the fact that they are all related to each other, some to greater, others to lesser, extent. Organic reproduction, under the control of heredity, is basically a conservative process. The adaptive innovations and diversity that have come about in life's evolution have rarely obscured, or transformed beyond our recognition, a basic and ancient pattern of organization. The trained observer can perceive these ancient organizations that underlie the more special adaptations wrought by natural selection. And to this extent he can recognize the line of evolutionary descent by which an organism has come to its present condition. The elucidation of evolutionary relationships lies at the heart of the natural classification of organisms by which life's diversity is most effectively rendered into understandable order.

Chapter 19 describes and discusses the evolutionary principles that underlie the process of classification. Chapters 20, 21, and 22 survey the major groups of organisms from the viewpoint of evolutionary affinity. A whole chapter (23) is devoted to those three groups—mollusks, arthropods, and vertebrates—which represent the culmination of evolutionary change in three distinct directions in the animal kingdom.

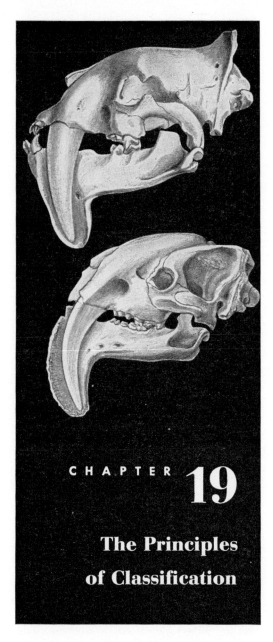

The sabertooths are long-extinct animals that evolved extraordinarily long canine teeth and an extension of the lower jaw which has the appearance of a shield for the saberlike canine. The two skulls shown look much alike, but they are only very distantly related; their characteristics are not an inheritance from a common ancestor. The upper skull is that of a North American placental mammal (Eusmilus sicarius) of the Oligocene (c. 40 million years ago). The lower skull belongs to a South American marsupial (Thylacosmilus atrox) of the Pliocene (c. 10 million years ago). A principal task in classifying organisms is to distinguish such similarities from more fundamental similarities reflecting a common ancestry. (Drawing by Charles Halgren)

CHAPTER **19**

The Principles
of Classification

Principles of Classification

Variation within demes and species and the nature and origin of species, as discussed in Chapter 17, are fundamental aspects of the diversity of life. Still they leave us far from real comprehension of that diversity. Even if all species were clearly delineated, we would

end up with a couple of million units, among living organisms alone. We could not possibly grasp so many different items or see meaningful relationships among them. We need to arrange the units in a more comprehensive, orderly way. In short, we must *classify* them. The most meaningful classification must rest on principles that are biologically significant. The next step, then, is to consider what principles best apply to the problems of classification.

RESEMBLANCE AND DIFFERENCE

Probably the most obvious thing about the diversity of life is that some organisms are more and some less alike. Two daisies are so much alike as to be hard to distinguish. A daisy and an aster are still a good deal alike, but they are easy to distinguish. They are both very different from a pine tree. Red and gray squirrels are rather similar, but they are increasingly unlike cats, frogs, fishes, or earthworms.

To make a classification of organisms all you have to do is to group together those that are alike and put those that are different into other groups. That sounds simple, but as soon as you try to do it in a really clear and systematic way you begin to run into serious difficulties.

The first problem is that there are different degrees of resemblance, and these degrees evidently should be taken into account. A red squirrel is more like a gray squirrel than like a cat, more like a cat than like a frog, more like a frog than like a fish, more like a fish than like an earthworm, and more like an earthworm than like a daisy. It is not too hard to meet that difficulty. The solution is simply to establish groups of different scope, like this:

ORGANISMS: everything that is alive, including daisy, earthworm, fish, frog, cat, gray squirrel, and red squirrel.

ANIMALS: no daisies, but including earthworm, fish, frog, cat, gray squirrel, and red squirrel.

VERTEBRATES: no earthworms, but including fish, frog, cat, gray squirrel, and red squirrel.

TETRAPODS (four-limbed vertebrates): no fishes, but including frog, cat, gray squirrel, and red squirrel.

MAMMALS: no frogs, but including cat, gray squirrel, and red squirrel.

RODENTS: no cats, but including all kinds of squirrels (also rats, porcupines, and so on).

SQUIRRELS: divided into red and gray squirrels, among others.

This is a *hierarchy*,[1] an arrangement of groups of decreasing scope, one within another. A great many different hierarchies are possible. The example we have given happens to correspond with one now in general use, but there is nothing absolute and fixed about it. Many other arrangements could be made that would be just as natural and just as useful as long as students agreed on them and understood what was meant by them.

The next and more serious problems arise from the fact that organisms resemble each other in different ways. A possible sort of classification, one that dates from antiquity if not from prehistory, is according to ways of life. Plants, for instance, can be arranged as aquatic, herbaceous, shrubby, or arborescent; or animals as swimming, walking, or flying. (Those groups do not exhaust the possibilities, but they will do as examples.) Such a classification might also bring in re-

1 From the Greek for "sacred rule." Obviously the word has greatly changed in meaning since ancient times. It came to be applied to the various ranks or orders of church officials, and then to any series or arrangement in which each step has authority over or includes all those below it in the sequence.

semblances and differences of habitat: swamp or alpine plants, marine or desert animals, and so on. Classifications of that sort, according to habit and habitat, are meaningful and useful. They are, in fact, in wide use today, especially in the study of ecology, or communities and their relationships with environments (see Chapters 24-27). Nevertheless they have rarely been used for the general, basic classification and naming of organisms.

Even in antiquity it was apparent to some students that classification by habit and habitat often brings together organisms that are different and separates those that are alike in some fundamental way. A yucca is shrubby and a Joshua tree is arborescent, but even a casual observer feels that somehow they resemble each other more than a yucca resembles most other shrubs or a Joshua tree most other trees (Fig. 19-1). Alligators and otters have many similarities in habits and habitats which lizards and weasels do not have, yet in some more basic way an alligator is surely more like a lizard, and an otter more like a weasel.

Doubtless you already know that organisms are ordinarily classified on evidence derived, in large part, from their anatomy and physiology. Perhaps you are a little impatient with us for not coming right out and saying so without preamble. The reason is that classification by anatomy and physiology is not a simple and clear-cut matter. It is not practical or, indeed, really meaningful to base classification on some such procedure as this: a gray squirrel has 10,001 anatomical and physiological resemblances to a red squirrel, 8346 to a cat, 3921 to a frog, 2754 to a fish, and 172 to a daisy. The figures used for example certainly are not correct. We have no idea what the correct figures are or how you could find out for certain; that is one reason why classification is not really based solely on anatomical and physiological resemblances.

Cacti and many South African euphorbias are succulent, spiny, flowering plants physiologically adapted to very arid conditions. Cactus fanciers call both groups "cacti." That is unconscious use of classification by habit and habitat, but anatomical and physiological resemblances between the two groups are also

19-1 The yucca plant and the Joshua tree. The superficial similarity between the yucca (*left*) and the Joshua tree (*right*) is less than that between the skulls of marsupial and placental sabertooths (illus., p. 459). Nevertheless they are closely related, as the morphology of their flowers shows.

real and numerous. Botanists ignore those resemblances in classifying the plants and separate the euphorbias sharply from cacti, placing them in a different family along with many other plants, such as the poinsettias, which no one would think of calling cacti. Similarly, the Tasmanian wolf (now possibly extinct) was called a "wolf" because it is very like one in appearance and habits (Fig. 19-7). It does have many anatomical and physiological resemblances to wolves. It has other, much less obvious resemblances to kangaroos. Nevertheless, in zoological classification it is grouped with the kangaroos and widely separated from the true wolves.

Classification by anatomy and physiology requires that characters be selected and interpreted. The fact that the ovary is superior in spiny euphorbias and inferior [2] in cacti is considered more important than the fact that

2 The technical botanical terms refer to the higher or lower position of the ovary in the flower, not to its better or worse qualities!

both have spines. The fact that Tasmanian "wolves" have pouches and marsupial bones while real wolves do not is emphasized in classification, and the fact that both are four-footed running animals with flesh-cutting teeth is given secondary importance. What characters are selected, what meaning is assigned to them, and finally what classification is devised depend on the way in which the characteristics of organisms are interpreted. They depend on a decision as to one of the most profound questions of biology and of philosophy: What is the nature of a systematic unit among organisms and how do the characteristics of such units originate? The principles on which classification is based arise from answers to that question.

THE NATURE OF SYSTEMATIC UNITS

The form of classification of organisms still in use today is conventionally dated from the middle of the eighteenth century. It is dated especially from the book *Systema Naturae* by the Swedish botanist Linnaeus (1707-1778), which appeared in 1735 and went through many editions. This dating applies, however, only to the *form*, the terms and names used. There have been two revolutionary changes in the *principles* of classification since Linnaeus. The result is that, although a classification of plants or animals today *looks* almost the same as one of two centuries ago it *means* something altogether different.

In Linnaeus' day classification was based on the philosophical doctrine that species are fixed, unchanging units. That doctrine was heavily reinforced by the reigning theological dogma, common at that time to all Western religions (Hebraic and Mohammedan as well as Christian), that the units were created as such by God. Some slight change within a species was admitted as possible, on the example of the various races of domesticated animals. There were also a few biologists who considered the evolution of new species possible. These ideas, however, had not yet had any real influence on systematics. The systematists' task then was simply to recognize the units of divine creation. The units were presumed to be sharply distinct, like cats, dogs, sheep, pines, or maples, and to pose no "species problem." Linnaeus did not express any doubt that the 4235 species of animals listed by him were actually the "kinds" of the Creator and subject to no further revision by human systematists.

For most systematists of Linnaeus' day a species had its characteristics because it was created just so. This implies a pattern, one for each species. Deviations from that pattern, so evident in nature as variation within species, were considered accidental and irrelevant. In fact, the varying individuals belonging to a species were held to be of no particular importance for systematics. The essential thing, the ultimate or transcendental reality of a species, was believed not to be material and tangible but a pattern, a divine idea, a *type* or, as then often designated, an *archetype* ("primeval pattern"). The way for a systematist to look at organisms, then, was supposed to be to ignore individuals, to brush aside variation and all characteristics of populations as such, but to abstract an idea of what the individuals have in common. That abstraction was the type or archetype of the species.

The same concepts were applied to groups of wider scope than species. (Remember that we are still talking not about modern systematics, but about the eighteenth century, a necessary preliminary to understanding the present, different principles.) Carnivorous mammals included numerous species. The Carnivora, as a group, were therefore not a "kind" as a unit of creation. Nevertheless, all Carnivora were thought to have certain characters common to all included species. Those common characters were also supposed to reveal an archetype, one broader than the specific archetypes, involving fewer but (in some way not too clear) more fundamental characters. Thus there was a whole series of "ideas," of divine patterns, becoming increasingly detailed and explicit. This would be analogous to your wishing to have some sort of vehicle built for you. The idea "vehicle" is the broadest archetype, like the idea "organism." Then you decide to have a wheeled vehicle for use on roads, a narrower archetype like "animal." Next is the idea of an automobile with internal-combustion engine, narrower still, like "mammal." You decide on a make, again narrower, like "carnivore," then on a particular model, thus coming down to the minimal archetype, the basic unit of manufacture or creation, like the species "dog."

These were the classical principles of systematics, the ones with which the science was established. The first revolution occurred when it was learned that species are not separate and unchanging creations but that they have evolved, one from another, in the long course of the history of life. This concept of species, and of all systematic groups made up of species, is profoundly different from the special-creationist concept. Species are now known not to be fixed units, but to be changing things, in continual flux over immense periods of time. Hence the "species problem," because you cannot give a fixed definition to units that change and grade one into another.

Even more important than the new concept of evolving species was the discovery that relationships among species are not abstractions, reflections of metaphysical archetypes. Species are related to each other in the fully material sense that one descends from another and several or many have descended by the processes of organic reproduction from the same ancestral species. Conformance with a broader archetype was no longer the principle for grouping species into larger units of classification. Instead, the principle became, and still is today, that all species in any systematic grouping are of common ancestry.

Revolutionary change in the principles underlying classification made no difference in the form and, at first, little difference in the practice of classification. Pre-evolutionary classification grouped organisms according to the anatomical and physiological characters common to all within the group, interpreting these characters as physical manifestations of a metaphysical archetype. Evolutionary classification established groups in just the same way and, indeed, took over most of the groups already established by Linnaeus and other nonevolutionary biologists. The only real difference was that the characters in common were now considered as physically inherited from the common ancestry of the whole group.

Classification as it was practiced by the evolutionary systematists of the later nineteenth century and, indeed, as it is still being practiced by a few systematists today did not do away with the pre-evolutionary archetype. As far as it really affected classification, the archetype was simply relabeled and differently interpreted. Each species had a type, now an individual specimen, supposed to be a sort of standard, a model, in a sense really an embodied archetype. Other individuals were compared one by one with type specimens and placed in the species the type of which they most nearly resembled. The fact that they were never *exactly* like the type was simply a nuisance. Variation in species was not an integral part of the species concept, but an imperfection of nature that had to be put up with by the poor systematist.

Higher groups, including several or many species, also continued in practice to have archetypes in more or less veiled form. The groups were defined by characters in common, abstracted patterns quite like archetypes even though considered as somehow representing the characteristics of an ancestor. The equivalence has been most frankly recognized by some systematists, who have assigned to each group an abstract *morphotype* ("form model"), with which imperfect, varying real individuals were measured for conformity. "Morphotype" is thus only a later synonym for the old-fashioned archetype. A few students have even proposed a theory of evolution in which the groups of classification arise by the sudden appearance of their morphotypes.

Although classification soon became evolutionary in principle after publication of Darwin's *Origin of Species* (1859), it remained largely pre-evolutionary in practice. It was still *typological*, as in Linnaeus' day. It continued in practice, regardless of stated principles, to picture the diversity of life as a series of idealized types, with individuals merely embodying the type patterns more or less adequately.

The second major revolution in principles of systematics since Linnaeus is the change from a typological to a *population* concept of the nature of systematic units. The turning point cannot be associated with one man and date, as that of evolutionary systematics can with Darwin and 1859. Some earlier students, including Darwin, grasped at least the rudiments of a systematics of populations rather than of types. Full comprehension, however, required the discovery of Mendelian genetics and then the development of population genetics on that basis. Systematics clearly based on populations and explicitly nontypological is mainly an achievement of the second quarter of the twentieth century. In fact, this revolution in systematics is still going on. New implications and applications of the population concepts are still being found, and there are diminishing numbers of typological systematists who do not accept or cannot grasp the change occurring in their science. It is because this change in principles is so recent and still going on that we have carefully traced the changes in systematic concepts since

Linnaeus. You belong to the first generation of students of biology to whom the biology of populations can be made familiar from the start.

The following, then, is the modern, fully evolutionary concept of systematic units:

A systematic unit of organisms in nature is a population or a group of related populations. Its anatomical and physiological characteristics are simply the total of those characteristics in the individuals making up the population. The pattern of characteristics is neither a real individual nor an idealized abstraction of the characters of an individual. It is a frequency distribution of the different variants of each character actually present at any given time. Species are populations of individuals of common descent, living together in similar environments in a particular region, with similar ecological relationships and tending to have a unified and continuing evolutionary role distinct from that of other species. In biparental species, the distinctiveness and continuation of the group are maintained by extensive interbreeding within it, and less or no interbreeding with members of other species. Demes and subspecies are subdivisions of species, more local in distribution, less isolated genetically, and without established and distinct continuing evolutionary roles for each such unit. Systematic units more inclusive than a species are groups of one or more species of common descent.

The best and the only *direct* evidence that an individual belongs to a particular species is not the anatomy or physiology of the individual as such, but the observation in nature that the individual is living with the specific population and functioning as a member of that population. Such direct evidence is not available in practice for organisms that have been removed from the context of nature—that are specimens in collections rather than parts of living populations. Fully direct evidence is also lacking for fossils. It is also usually impossible to obtain entirely direct evidence that a group of species is of common descent and hence is properly classified as a higher systematic unit. In all these cases pertinence to a systematic unit must be judged by indirect evidence. There are many kinds of indirect evidence, anatomy and physiology among them.

The one other point to make here is that use of anatomy, for instance, as *evidence* that an organism belongs to a particular species does not mean that a species as a systematic unit is *definable* in anatomical terms. A species or other systematic unit is defined in terms of populations and their biological, evolutionary relationships. These relationships have anatomical consequences, among others, from which they may be inferred. If two people look exactly alike, that is evidence that they are, or may be, identical twins. But they are not twins because they look alike; they look alike because they are twins. Similarly, typological systematics maintained that organisms belong to the same systematic unit because they have the same anatomical pattern. Modern systematics has learned that they have the same anatomical pattern (to the extent that they really do) because they belong to the same biological, evolutionary population or groups of populations. The systematist is not engaged in classifying anatomy or any other sort of evidence. He is engaged in using the evidence to classify populations of organisms.

The Interpretation of Form and Descent

The resemblances between a yucca and a Joshua tree (p. 461) are somehow more important than the fact that one is a shrub and one a tree. The differences between a Tasmanian "wolf" and a true wolf (p. 461) are likewise in some way more important than the fact that they are four-footed carnivores similar in appearance and habits. "More important" means, in this connection, more reliable indications of phylogenetic relationships and hence primary bases for modern classification of these organisms. The resemblances of yucca and Joshua tree are old and fundamental characteristics inherited from the common ancestry of the two sorts of plants. The differences between them are of relatively recent evolution and do not contradict close relationship. Botanists classify these plants as different species of the same

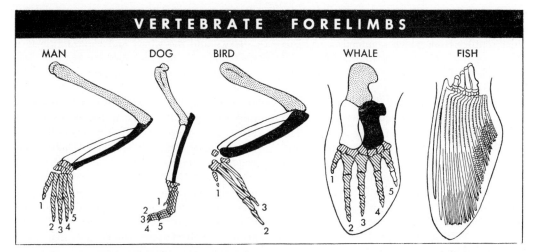

MAN DOG BIRD WHALE FISH

19-2 Vertebrate forelimbs. Homologous bones in the limbs of man, dog, bird, and whale are indicated as follows: stippled, humerus; white, radius; black, ulna; upper crosshatching, carpals; lower crosshatching, metacarpals, and phalanges (finger bones). Numbers refer to digits (or fingers).

genus. In the example of the Tasmanian and true wolves, it is the differences that are phylogenetically old and the resemblances that are more recent and less fundamental. Zoologists place these animals in widely different major groups of mammals. (Among the marsupials and the placentals, respectively.)

In such examples the decisive factor is whether resemblances between organisms have or have not been inherited from a common ancestry. Interpretation and application in classification depend on some historical, evolutionary principles and processes, which must now be reviewed.

HOMOLOGY

Homology is correspondence between structures of different organisms due to their inheritance of these structures from the same ancestry. Such structures are called *homologues* and are said to be homologous.[3]

[3] From the Greek for "agreement." Biological use of these terms stems mainly from a publication in 1843 by the eminent British anatomist Richard Owen. Like all biologists of those and earlier times, Owen recognized that some similarities between parts of organisms are more fundamental than others, and he proposed to call the more fundamentally similar parts "homologues." The then current explanation as to why the similarity is more fundamental was that the parts correspond with an archetype of a higher order (p. 462). Even Owen, who never explicitly accepted the truth of evolution, later (in 1866, after publication of "The Origin of Species") admitted that inheritance is the "most intelligible" explanation of homology.

If the bones of a man's arm and a dog's foreleg are compared (Fig. 19-2), the number and arrangement are remarkably similar. The resemblance also extends to the way the limbs arise embryologically and, in greater or less degree, to the arrangement in them of muscles, blood vessels, and nerves. The only reasonable explanation is that the limbs are homologous. Although in man they are now used differently, one mainly for manipulation and the other mainly for locomotion, the limbs were inherited from the same ancestry. The differences between them have arisen since the lines of descent leading to dogs and to men separated. From fossil (paleontological) evidence, we know that the separation occurred about 70 to 75 million years ago. It happens that evolution of the forelimb has not been particularly rapid either in men or in dogs, and in spite of the long lapse of time it is still clearly evident that not only the limbs as a whole but also the various bones in them are homologous.

If, now, comparison is made with the wing of a bird, the similarity is less striking (Fig. 19-2). Nevertheless it can be established beyond any doubt that man's arm, dog's foreleg, and bird's wing are all homologous, and even that some homologous bones are present in all three. The evidence involves anatomical and embryological comparisons and, still more convincingly, fossils of early mammals (from which men and dogs later evolved), of ancient birds, and of the still older reptiles from which mammals and birds arose. Separation of the reptilian ancestries of mammals and birds occurred not less than 200 million years ago, but a fundamental genetic resemblance has not been obliterated.

Let us now add the front (pectoral) fin of a fish to the comparison (Fig. 19-2). The resemblance is even slighter, and this is not surprising because we are now comparing animals whose nearest common ancestry is more than 300 million years in the past. The fish's fin is still certainly homologous with the forelimb of bird, dog, or man, but it is no longer possible to designate homologous individual bones in the limb with any assurance. Extremely ancient fish fins are known from which both modern fish fins and the limbs of air-breathers have evolved, but the separate lines of evolution have undergone changes so profound that the homologies of the bones have been practically obliterated.

The degree of homology in the examples given is the basis for phylogenetic inferences which, in turn, are involved in the classification of these organisms. Men and dogs are more nearly related to each other than either is to a bird. Men, dogs, and birds are more nearly related than any is to a (modern) fish. Homology is the anatomical evidence for degrees of relationship among organisms. The problem, then, is to distinguish between resemblances that are homologous and those that are not.

HOMOPLASY AND ANALOGY

Anatomical features that resemble each other but that are not inherited from the same feature in a common ancestry are called *homoplastic,* and this phenomenon is *homoplasy.*[4] Thus correspondences in anatomy between two plants or between two animals are either homologous or homoplastic. If they are homologous, they are evidence of relationship or genetic affinity. If homoplastic, they are not such evidence. The terms are, of course, interpretive. They express an opinion or a deduction from the available evidence. The use of comparative anatomy in classification

depends on this decision whether anatomical resemblances are homologous or homoplastic.

If we add the wings and legs of insects to the comparisons previously made, they provide clear-cut, sure examples of homoplasy (Fig. 19-3). The front leg of an insect has an anatomical correspondence with the front limb of a dog or man (with his upper limb or arm). It is, however, certain that the limbs of insects and mammals evolved wholly independently and were not inherited from an ancestry common to the two. Insects and mammals did have a common ancestry, but this was extremely remote, more than 500 million years ago, and the limbs of the two groups evolved after their ancestries had separated. The limbs are not homologous, but they are to some extent homoplastic.

The homoplastic forelegs of insects and the arms of men do not function in the same way. If an insect and a dog are compared, however, there is a resemblance in function, for in both the limbs are used mostly for walking. When structures that are not homologous have a functional resemblance they are *analogous* and are called *analogues.*[5] The wing of an insect is to some extent homoplastic and is completely analogous with the wing of a bird (Fig. 19-3). It is certainly not homologous.

Homoplastic structures are usually also analogous. It is a rule of evolution that resemblance in structure not due to inheritance from a common ancestry is correlated with similarity of function. Homoplasy usually results from similar *adaptations* of organisms of different ancestry. Like almost all biological rules, this one has exceptions but is true in the great majority of instances. Structures may, indeed, be analogous without having any noticeable degree of anatomical resemblance. The gills of a fish and the lungs of a mammal are anatomically so different that they would hardly be called homoplastic, but both are organs of respiration and are in that respect analogous. The homologue of the lungs in fishes is the swim bladder (Fig. 19-3).

[4] "Same-forming" (but not same inheritance).

[5] "Things proportionate to each other." The technical meaning in biology is different from and more precise than the Greek word or the meaning of "analogy" in everyday speech.

HOMOLOGY, HOMOPLASY, and ANALOGY

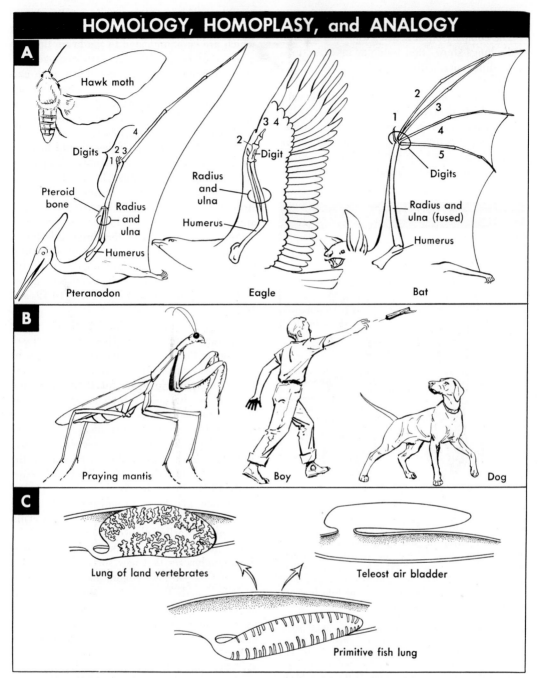

A

Hawk moth

Digits { 4 2 3 1

Pteroid bone

Radius and ulna

Humerus

Pteranodon

3 4 2

Digit

Radius and ulna

Humerus

Eagle

2 3 1 4 5

Digits

Radius and ulna (fused)

Humerus

Bat

B

Praying mantis

Boy

Dog

C

Lung of land vertebrates

Teleost air bladder

Primitive fish lung

19-3 Homology, homoplasy, and analogy. *A, B.* The wings and legs of insects bear a *homoplastic* relation to those of vertebrates. The wings in *Pteranodon* (extinct flying reptile), eagle, and bat are *homologous.* The wings of insects and vertebrates are *analogous:* they perform similar functions. The forelimbs of man and praying mantis are not only *homoplastic* but *analogous:* both are used to "manipulate." The forelimbs of man and dog, which are homologous, are not fully analogous: the dog's forelimb, nearly exclusively, serves locomotion. *C.* Lungs and **air** (**or** swim) bladders in fishes are homologous but not analogous.

The comparison of a fish's kills and a mammal's lungs shows that homologous structures may differ markedly both in anatomy and in function. In most living fishes the swim bladder is a simple closed sac filled with gases which decrease the specific gravity of the fish and help it to maintain a favorable depth in the water—a sort of internal water wings. It has nothing to do with breathing. In one group of fishes it has become even less

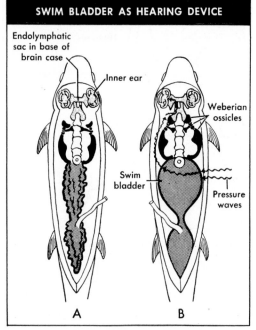

SWIM BLADDER AS HEARING DEVICE

19-4 The swim bladder of fishes as a hearing device. The swim bladder in modern bony fishes evolved first as a lung (p. 451). In some later fishes it has been transformed into a hydrostatic organ used to adjust the net specific gravity of the fish. In some of these later (teleost, p. 587) fishes it has been exploited to serve still another function: hearing. Bony processes of the vertebrae closest to the skull have evolved into a chain of *Weberian ossicles*. They function in a manner analogous to that of the ear ossicles in land vertebrates (Fig. 9-9): pressure waves striking the taut membrane of the swim bladder are transmitted mechanically by the Weberian ossicles to an endolymphatic sac in the base of the brain case, which communicates with the endolymph of the inner ear. *A.* The swim bladder shown collapsed to illustrate how the chain of Weberian ossicles is attached. *B.* The swim bladder inflated and the ossicles pressing on the endolymphatic sac.

lunglike and acts as a sort of sounding board or resonating chamber, the vibrations of which are communicated to the brain through a series of bones. It is, in fact, analogous to an eardrum (fishes do not have real eardrums), although still homologous with the lungs. This extraordinary development can be seen in goldfishes, as well as many other fresh-water fishes (Fig. 19-4).

It is odd enough that fishes should hear by means of a structure homologous with part of our breathing apparatus. It is at least as peculiar that *we* hear by means (in part) of structures homologous with parts of the jaw apparatus of reptiles, including our own reptilian ancestors. Two of the three little bones that transmit vibrations from our eardrums to our inner ears are homologous with the bones that form the joint between upper and lower jaws in reptiles (Figs. 18-12 and 19-5).

One of the most fascinating things about comparative anatomy, phylogeny, and classification is that homologous structures can be so very different both in form and in function. From the point of view of their evolution, this means that structures can and often do change radically both in appearance and in the way they work. Such radical changes are known, logically enough, as *transformations*, and they have been rather common in the history of life (Fig. 19-5). They are especially likely to be involved in the origin of major new groups of organisms, such as the rise of mammals from reptiles or of flowering from nonflowering plants.

The widespread occurrence of transformations emphasizes that new sorts of organisms, new organs, or new adaptations evolve from what is already there. A good engineer should be able to design a better reproductive apparatus than a magnolia flower, a better means of walking than a salamander's leg, or a better sound receptor than an opossum's ear. The point is that these structures were not designed. They evolved on the basis of mutations affecting earlier structures that functioned differently. And even though they are not perfect, they do work. They have been molded by and have stood the test of millions of years of natural selection.

THE IRREVOCABILITY OF
EVOLUTION

The fact that evolutionary change occurs on the basis of what is already there—that is, of the results of all previous evolution—has extreme and widespread consequences. It makes evolution *irrevocable*. What has already happened before any given time necessarily affects and limits what can and does happen next. The future cannot change the past; what is past is irrevocable. Evolutionary change never wholly eradicates the effects of previous evolution. The most radical transformation does not wipe out influences of the previous condition of the structure transformed. If the little mammalian ear bones had not been part of the reptilian jaws they would certainly not have the relationships that they do, in fact, have. If any of our ancestors, back to 1 billion B.C. or earlier, had been different from what they were, we too would be different in some respect and to some degree.

There is also another side to the principle of irrevocability. If the past cannot be wholly lost, neither can it be fully regained. Nothing quite like an earlier form of life ever evolves again, for the simple reason that time does not double back on itself. If there is a sequence of ancestral and descendent organisms $a \rightarrow b \rightarrow c$, then b evolved from a and would have been different if a had been different in any respect. Evolution cannot be reversed: b cannot evolve again from c, because c is different from a and cannot possibly give rise to quite the sort of organisms that arose from a. This aspect of the irrevocability of evolution is usually called the "irreversibility of evolution," [6] and it is not always recognized that it is just a special case of the more general principle. Failure to grasp the broader principle has also led to misunderstanding of the meaning of the irreversibility of evolution. Some biologists formerly supposed, for instance, that if animals had grown larger in the course of their evolution they

[6] You will also find it called "Dollo's law" in most books on evolution. Actually it is not a law, properly speaking, but a principle. Also, Louis Dolo (1857-1931), an eminent Belgian paleontologist, was not the first to state or discuss the principle, and we now know that his statement of it was inadequate.

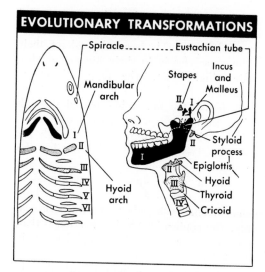

EVOLUTIONARY TRANSFORMATIONS

19-5 Evolutionary transformation of the primitive vertebrate gill arches. The evolutionary transformation of two of the primitive vertebrate gill arches into the mammalian ear ossicles has already been illustrated (Fig. 18-12). The present figure illustrates the ultimate transformation of the remaining gill arches into several other features of the mammalian skull and pharyngeal region. For simplicity the mammal (man) is compared with a contemporary shark, which retains ancestral features of the gill arches but is not, of course, itself an ancestor of the mammals. The gill arches in the shark are numbered I through VI, and the mandibular and hyoid arches are named. The arches have been transformed in the mammal into the following structures: (I) the lower jaw and two of the ear ossicles (incus and malleus); (II) the third ear ossicle (stapes), the hyoid cartilage (tongue skeleton), the styloid process of the skull, and the styloid ligament; (III) the thyroid cartilage, which is part of the skeleton of the larynx; and (IV) the cricoid cartilage and epiglottal cartilages of the larynx.

could not have smaller descendants. In fact, an evolutionary trend like that toward larger size can be and frequently has been reversed. The real point is that, although the descendants come to be of the same size as remote ancestors, they still are very different organisms. Even the genetic mechanism determining size is almost certain to be different.

The principle of irrevocability is of great importance in systematics. An example should make its relevance clear. Land vertebrates, such as reptiles and mammals, arose remotely from aquatic forms, fishes. Some reptiles and mammals, such as the whales, became aquatic and fishlike in habits. Their evolution reversed the way of life, but of course this did not make them fishes again. The effect of irrevocability can be seen throughout their anatomy, as clearly in their flippers as elsewhere (Fig. 19-2). The flipper functions like a fish's fin, but it is quite different because, unlike the fin, it has passed through a stage when it was a leg. That is one aspect of irrevocability. However, even though the flipper has become finlike, it has not lost the effects of its land-living ancestry, and the bones in a whale flipper are still plainly homologous with those in the leg of a land mammal. That is the other aspect of irrevocability. The application to classification is that, even though a whale is more fishlike in habitat, habits, and general appearance, it is more closely related to land animals than to fishes. It is classified as a mammal.

CONVERGENCE AND PARALLELISM

The example of whales and fishes shows that organisms may be alike in living conditions and appearance, even though they are of quite different ancestry and relationships. Such resemblances may arise between organisms even more distantly related. Spending an evening in a southwestern garden, a visitor was astonished to see what were apparently large numbers of hummingbirds gathering

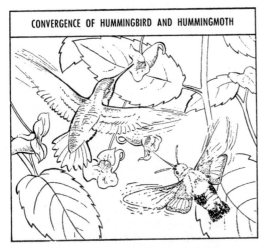

CONVERGENCE OF HUMMINGBIRD AND HUMMINGMOTH

19-6 Hummingbird and hummingmoth: convergent evolution. Wholly unrelated, the bird and the moth have converged in form, flying habit, and feeding procedure in their common exploitation of the nectar in flowers as a food source.

nectar in the dusk. A closer look showed that they were not hummingbirds but hummingmoths, insects almost identical with the birds in actions, size, and superficial appearance (Fig. 19-6).

The evolutionary development of resemblance between organisms whose ancestors were less alike is called *convergence.* (What relationship does this have to homology and homoplasy?) Convergence is a common phenomenon in nature. The previously noted resemblance between cacti and some euphorbias (p. 460) is convergent, and so is that between Tasmanian and true wolves (p. 461). The wolves are part of a large-scale convergence. In Australia, an island continent, the isolated evolution of marsupials has produced kinds convergent toward many different nonmarsupial (placental) mammals of the rest of the world. There are not only native "wolves" but also native "mice," "cats," "anteaters," "moles," and "sloths," as well as the squirrel- and flying squirrel-like phalangers and the groundhog-like wombats. These are not related to true wolves, mice, cats, anteaters, moles, sloths, squirrels, and groundhogs but are products of convergent evolution (Fig. 19-7).

It is well for the systematists that evolution is irrevocable, for otherwise convergence would commonly be mistaken for community of ancestry. Such mistakes have been made in the past and probably a few are still being made, but by and large modern systematics has sorted out truly related from merely convergent organisms. The fact that convergent forms did have ancestors less similar means that they cannot become identical. Traces of the ancestral dissimilarities persist and can be recognized for what they are. No one studying specimens with a view to classifying them would really mistake a hummingmoth for a hummingbird or a euphorbia for a cactus.

In such examples the separate ancestries of convergent forms were so different that the convergent nature of the resemblance is obvious with a little study. Things become more difficult if the ancestries were not very different, and still more so if the ancestries were related and evolution in the descendent lines has simply followed more or less the same

CONVERGENT EVOLUTION OF PLACENTAL AND MARSUPIAL MAMMALS

PLACENTALS

MARSUPIALS

Wolf
(Canis)

Tasmanian
wolf
(Thylacinus)

Ocelot
(Felis)

Native cat
(Dasyurus)

Flying
squirrel
(Glaucomys)

Flying
phalanger
(Petaurus)

Ground
hog
(Marmota)

Wombat
(Phascolomys)

Anteater
(Myrmecophaga)

Anteater
(Myrmecobius)

Mole
(Talpa)

Mole
(Notoryctes)

Mouse
(Mus)

Mouse
(Dasycercus)

19-7   The convergent evolution of placental and marsupial mammals.

course. This sort of evolution intergrades with convergence and is not clearly distinguishable, but it is usually given a different name: *parallelism*. Parallelism is even more common than convergence. Moreover, close parallelism may be practically impossible to distinguish from close community of ancestry unless the actual ancestors have been found as fossils. It was, for example, long assumed that the American and Old World porcupines are closely related and that their spininess is homologous and part of the evidence for that relationship. Later work raises a strong possibility that this is a case of parallelism, that the common ancestor was really very remote and was spineless. If this is so, the spines (and a number of other resemblances) have evolved independently in the two groups and are homoplastic, not homologous. The fossil evidence is still insufficient and the question remains open, but most systematists now think that parallelism is involved in the history of porcupines. In recent years it has become apparent that parallelism has occurred far more widely among all sorts of organisms than was formerly recognized. This is one of the major problems of systematics today.

The cause of convergence is known; indeed you have probably already thought of it in the light of what you have learned about the factors of evolution. Plants or animals of different origin become adapted to similar habitats and habits or, in general, ways of life. Cacti and cactuslike euphorbias are both water-storing desert shrubs. Tasmanian and true wolves are both running predators preying on other animals of about the same size and habits. Adaptive similarity involves similarity also of structure and function. The mechanism of such evolution is natural selection; in fact, of all evolutionary phenomena, convergence seems to be most rigidly controlled by natural selection. Differences persist in convergent forms because they arise from different bases. Structures adapted to the new activities and conditions are likely to be different to start with and may not even be homologous. Mutations, materials for natural selection, are also likely to be different in the two groups.

Parallelism is also largely a matter of similar adaptation under the control of natural selection. The ill-defined difference between convergence and parallelism, however, involves factors that make parallel forms more similar than convergent ones. The term "parallelism" is usually applied to evolving organisms that were rather similar to begin with and that were related closely enough for some of the same mutations to arise in them. Very close parallelism is usual only between groups that are, in fact, related. The resulting resemblances may then be misleading only as to the degree and not the fact of relationship.

DIVERGENCE

If you try to predict the future of two evolving groups of organisms there are plainly three possibilities: the groups can become more similar (convergence); they can evolve in much the same way, so as to remain about equally similar (parallelism); or they can become less similar (divergence). It is obvious that divergence is extremely common. Indeed, it is the universal rule for directions of evolution and is necessarily the basis for the whole of the diversity of nature. Within a species there is fluctuating, reversible divergence as demes or other subdivisions of the species develop differences from each other. As soon as speciation occurs, two (or more) species arise from one (p. 429), and divergence between the two becomes essentially irreversible and tends to increase as times goes on.[7]

Special examples of divergence are unnecessary, because it is illustrated by the manifest differences between any two species or organisms. The pattern of divergence recurs in all groups of organisms. It is the basic element reflected in classification. When we

[7] It is conceivable that two parts of a specific population might permanently cease to interbreed without developing any readily visible differences. Some such instances are known; they are called "sibling" or "cryptic" species. They are comparatively rare, and in every example some differences have been found by detailed new study, even though the differences may be so slight as to have been missed by earlier systematists. Sibling species evidently do not persist very long without developing more clear-cut differences and hence ceasing to be sibling species.

list the species of a genus, we are (if our classification is successful and correct by modern principles) listing populations that have diverged from a single ancestral population. The genera of a family, the families of an order, and so on, are also the representatives and results of divergence of increasingly long standing and on an increasingly large scale.

The frequent occurrence of convergence and parallelism do not at all contradict the fact that divergence is universal in evolution. There can be neither convergence nor parallelism unless there has been previous divergence. Furthermore, in comparing any two groups of organisms of near or remote common ancestry it never has been found that they are completely, in every respect, convergent, parallel, or divergent. In some respects the two have always retained some ancestral features unchanged; in some features they are always divergent; in others they may or may not be convergent or parallel.

The Practice of Classification

Classification consists mainly of three operations: (1) recognizing and describing related smaller and larger groups of organisms according to the principles of populations and of phylogeny; (2) fitting these groups into a formal hierarchy; and (3) providing names for the various groups. Only the first of these operations involves the direct observation and interpretation of nature. The second and third are equally necessary in order to put the results of the first into meaningful form and to supply the names by which we can think and talk about those results. The second and third operations are, however, necessarily subjective and more or less arbitrary. The third, nomenclature, involves completely artificial, legalistic symbolic devices.

THE SYSTEMATIC HIERARCHY

The hierarchic principle has been introduced on p. 461. By general consent, a particular form of hierarchy, modified from that of Linnaeus (p. 462), is now in general use, and a special term is applied to each recognized level or category:

Kingdom
 Phylum (plural, phyla)
  Class
   Order
    Family
     Genus (plural, genera)
      Species (identical in singular and plural; "specie" means "coin" and has no application in biology)

There is no reason in nature why the hierarchy should have seven steps. Groups of almost any inclusiveness could be recognized, for in nature there is no fixed size inherent in the facts. A hierarchy might have five basic steps or fifty, and fixing on seven is only a matter of usage that has grown up among systematists. In fact, with the tremendous increase in the number of known kinds of organisms, most specialists have found that seven steps are not enough for their purposes and have supplied additional steps by prefixing "super-," "sub-," and "infra-." [8]

A full classification of a human subspecies, with the names applied to the groups at the various levels, shows how the system works:

Kingdom Animalia
 Phylum Chordata
  Subphylum Vertebrata
   Superclass Tetrapoda
    Class Mammalia
     Subclass Theria
      Infraclass Eutheria
       [Cohort Unguiculata—optional]
        Order Primates
         Suborder Anthropoidea
          Superfamily Hominoidea
           Family Hominidae
            Subfamily Homininae
             Genus *Homo*
              Subgenus *Homo* (*Homo*)
               Species *Homo sapiens*
                Subspecies *Homo sapiens sapiens* [9]

[8] "Sub-" categories are in general use at all levels. The others are less generally used, especially "infra-." Some botanists use "division" in place (approximately) of "phylum." A few other categories and terms are used by some students or in certain groups of organisms, but are not fully standardized. Most common are "cohort," sometimes inserted between "class" and "order," and "tribe," sometimes inserted between "family" and "genus."

[9] Whites of European descent belong in this subspecies, by the accident that Linnaeus happened to belong in it. All living humans belong in the same species, but there are other subspecies.

SAMPLE AND POPULATION

A species is a special sort of category in nature and in evolution, and therefore also in classification. It is a population which may be subdivided in various ways but which has an essential internal unity and continuity in evolutionary role, in geographic and ecological distribution, in genetical relationships, and in physical, phenotypical characteristics. It has some degree of external discontinuity, sometimes relative but tending to become absolute, from any other species. Groups higher in the hierarchy than species are less unified and continuous, because they generally include more than one species. Groups lower than species are less clearly bounded because there is less or no discontinuity between them within the species. The species, then, is the fundamental population unit of classification.

Classifying a species involves determination of the characteristics of a population. How would you go about this? The procedure can be compared with what you would do if, for example, you were a wholesaler who planned to buy the output of a large apple orchard. You would need to know what the whole crop is like, and you would be sure that the apples would vary considerably in size, color, ripeness, and other characteristics important to you. Surely you would not pick one apple and base your price and plans on the idea that the apple (a *type*) is sufficiently representative of the whole lot. Obviously, too, it would not be practical for you to examine every one of tens of thousands of apples in the orchard. (In systematics, examination of all individuals of a species is usually not merely impractical but downright impossible.) What you would do would be to take a sample of perhaps a hundred apples, being careful that the selection was at random so that it covered the range of variation fairly well and was not loaded with the better or poorer apples. If you really knew your business, you would know methods (derived from the science of statistics) for deciding how many apples you need as an efficient sample for your purposes. By related methods you would estimate from the sample the average quality of the crop and its variation, and you would calculate how close your estimates are likely to be to the actual characteristics of the whole crop (the population).

That, in principle, is the modern procedure for determining (or more strictly speaking, for estimating) the characteristics of a species or smaller natural population unit in systematics. To be sure, some systematists still use the older and now clearly inadequate one-apple (typological) method, but their number is decreasing rapidly. In systematics, too, you often cannot obtain the most efficient sample. Sometimes you may even have to be content with one apple (specimen). Even so, you think of it as a sample of a varied population, not as a type to which other apples will or should conform. You still can tell from it something about the population, although you know that your estimates are rougher, less reliable, than if you had a better sample.

HIGHER CATEGORIES

Placing species into genera, genera into families, and so on upward in the hierarchy is not based on inferences from samples about populations. The basic population units, the species, are successively combined in increasingly larger groups according to interpretation of their evolutionary relationships, in other words, their phylogeny. In principle all the species of one genus have evolved from one ancestral species, all the genera of one family from one ancestral genus, and so on. Of course we do not yet know the phylogeny of all organisms with high probability and in sufficient detail to produce a definitive, final classification on which everyone can agree. Classification is constantly changing in some respects as we learn more about phylogeny, and experts often disagree about details of phylogeny and classification.[10]

10 Experts who tried to produce "objective" classifications, based wholly on the resemblances between organisms and not on their phylogeny, disagreed still more, because they had to give priority to some characteristic or other and had no sound principles (such as that of phylogeny) for assigning priorities.

Even when phylogeny is adequately known and there is no disagreement about it, classification in higher categories does not automatically follow. Suppose the phylogeny of five living species were as shown in Fig. 19-8. All five arose from one species, so it is "correct" to put them in one genus; that is, this is consistent with their real relationships. It is, however, equally "correct," in the same sense, to put them in two, three, four, or five genera, as shown in the figure. The same sort of choice arises for any of the higher categories from genus to kingdom. It is completely impractical to express *all* the intricacies of phylogeny and relationships in a classification simple enough to be understandable and usable. All that can be done is to assure that the classification is *consistent* with a reasonable theory of phylogeny. Many different arrangements may be equally consistent with the same phylogeny. Choice is a matter of usage and personal taste. Since reasonable stability is desirable, conservative systematists hold that a classification in general use should not be changed unless new study shows that it is probably inconsistent with phylogeny.

NOMENCLATURE

Systematists come in for a good deal of derision because they call a rose by another name or stutter *Rattus rattus rattus* when they mean plain "rat." It is true that there are people who like to make things sound mysterious and difficult, but systematists have been forced into a complex and stuffy nomenclature whether they like it or not. There are millions of species that must be named, not to mention all the other groups up and down the hierarchy. No everyday language has enough names to go around. Innumerable sorts of plants and animals simply do not have common names. This applies, naturally, to all extinct organisms, but also to many still living. Worse yet, the common names that are available are usually vague in application, often misleading, and almost always are applied indiscriminately to different groups that the systematist must distinguish. In New Mexico, alone, there are 13 species of wild roses.

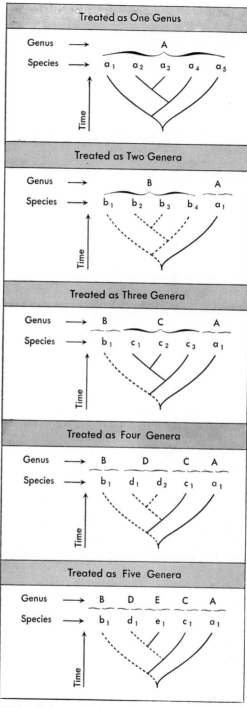

19-8 Valid alternative groupings of five species into genera. The lines show the pattern of evolution through time. In each case all species in a genus have a common ancestor at a more recent time than they have with species in other genera.

In the Old World there are more than 560 species and subspecies of rats of the genus *Rattus*, and hundreds more called "rats" that do not even belong to that genus!

A less impelling but still important reason for not using common names is that these are different in every language. What is a "squirrel" in England becomes an *écureuil* when you cross the English Channel, an *ardilla* if you cross the Pyrenees, an *Eichhorn* across the Rhine, and hundreds of other names here and there around the world.

The systematists had to invent an artificial system for naming organisms, and fortunately they agreed to use the same names everywhere, regardless of native language. This is one useful holdover from the days when all scholars wrote in Latin. Linnaeus wrote Latin, and naturally he also named plants and animals in Latin. Innumerable scientific names are also derived from Greek, and in modern usage they may be derived from any language or from none, just made up. However, they are always latinized and treated as if they were Latin words. This is not too barbarous, for the Romans did the same thing, especially with Greek words. Biologists now write in English, German, Russian, Japanese, or whatever language they prefer, but they still use Latin or latinized names for groups of organisms. The name of any group from a kingdom down to a genus is a single capitalized word (see the examples on p. 477). Names of genera are usually printed in italics, but those of higher groups are not. The name of a species is (usually) two italicized words: the name of the genus followed by a name (not capitalized) [11] peculiar to the species. The name of the human species is *Homo sapiens*, not just *sapiens*; that is why the nomenclature is called *binomial* ("two-named"). For subspecies, a third italicized word (not capitalized) is added to the name of the species.

It frequently happened that different workers applied different names to the same group or the same name to different groups. Frequently, also, some systematist has decided that two or more groups that had different names should be combined into one, or that a group with one name should be split into two. Even after systematists had agreed in principle on a system of nomenclature, such duplications and changes tended toward chaos. Finally international congresses and biological unions drew up codes of nomenclature designed to solve these problems and to settle on one name for each group and a different name for each. The codes are complex and appeal more to the legalist than to the biologist, who is likely to regard them as a necessary evil. The codes depend heavily on the *rule of priority*. The valid name of a group is the first published name applied to it (if it was published after a fixed date and if it complied with certain requirements). If the same name has been given to two groups, the name belongs to the group to which it was first applied, and the other group must have a different name.[12] Priority sounds both simple and sensible, and it has worked out in most instances. However, in a good many cases the working of the rules is neither simple nor sensible. An international commission considers such cases when they are brought to its attention. The commission is empowered to suspend the rules if necessary to preserve a stable, widely known name that might become invalid under the rule of priority.

The nomenclatural codes require that there be designated type specimens for species, type species for genera, and type genera for families. The use of the term "type" in this connection is unfortunate, because it recalls the old typological systematics from which it was inherited. Confusion results because the terminology suggests that the nomenclatural type is somehow typical or a standard of comparison. Modern biology and systematics recognize no "types" in that sense. The types required by the codes of nomenclature are only legalistic devices, of no real biological significance, used in order to specify what groups of real organisms the names are tied to. In that usage *nomenclatural* types are essentially aids in stabilizing nomenclature.

[11] Botanists formerly capitalized specific names derived from proper nouns and some others, but this is no longer required by the rules of botanical nomenclature, and it is banned by the zoological rules.

[12] Except that a group of plants and one of animals can have the same name; botanical and zoological nomenclatures are entirely separate, although they follow the same general system.

A Classification of Organisms

The following classification is not meant to be learned as such. Examination of it gives an over-all picture of the tremendous basic diversity of life. Beyond that, it will serve for reference and orientation when mention of some particular group is made. All phyla are listed, as well as most classes. When classes are not listed, either the phylum is small and has a single class or the arrangement of classes is not yet satisfactory. A few phyla and subphyla that are *relatively* unimportant in the modern world are named in lighter type. Groups that are totally extinct are indicated by the symbol † preceding the name. It is noticeable that very few phyla or classes are extinct. There are, of course, very numerous extinct smaller groups (between orders and species), and most of the phyla and classes include known extinct smaller groups.

For each class or phylum at least one genus is named by way of example. As far as possible the examples are organisms often available for demonstration or dissection. They include most of the genera used as examples in this book.

Kingdom Protista (Protists)

PHYLUM SCHIZOMYCETES, bacteria: *Bacillus, Escherichia, Azotobacter, Clostridium, Pneumococcus*

PHYLUM MASTIGOPHORA, flagellates

Class Phytomastigina, plantlike flagellates: *Euglena, Volvox, Chlamydomonas, Cryptomonas*

Class Dinoflagellata, dinoflagellates: *Ceratium, Peridinium, Gymnodinium, Gonyaulax, Ceratodinium, Noctiluca*

Class Zoomastigina, animal-like flagellates: *Trypanosoma, Polytoma, Chilomonas, Astasia, Oikomonas, Mastigamoeba, Hexamitus, Calonympha*

PHYLUM SARCODINA: rhizopods, *Amoeba* (and see Fig. 20-4); forams, *Globigerina;* radiolarians, *Lychnaspis*

PHYLUM SPOROZOA: *Plasmodium*

PHYLUM CILIOPHORA

Class Ciliata, ciliates: *Paramecium, Stentor, Stylonichia, Euplotes, Epidinium* (and see Fig. 20-6)

Class Suctoria: *Podophrya*

PHYLUM MYXOMYCETES, slime molds: *Lycogala*

Kingdom Plantae (Plants)

PHYLUM MYXOPHYTA, blue-green algae: *Anabaena, Nostoc, Oscillatoria* (and see Fig. 20-13)

PHYLUM CHLOROPHYTA, green algae

Class Chlorophyceae, grass-green algae: *Ulothrix, Oedogonium, Spirogyra, Closterium*

Class Charophyceae, stoneworts: *Chara, Nitella*

PHYLUM CHRYSOPHYTA

Class Xanthophyceae, yellow-green algae: *Vaucheria, Tribonema, Botrydium*

Class Chrysophyceae, golden-brown algae: *Synura, Dinobryon*

Class Bacillariophyceae, diatoms: *Navicula, Pinnularia, Tabellaria, Actinoptychus*

PHYLUM PHAEOPHYTA, brown algae: *Ectocarpus, Laminaria, Fucus*

PHYLUM RHODOPHYTA, red algae: *Porphyra, Batrachospermum, Nemalion, Lithophyllum*

PHYLUM MYCOPHYTA, fungi

Class Phycomycetes, tube fungi: bread molds, *Rhizopus;* water molds, *Saprolegnia;* white rusts and downy mildews, *Albugo;* chytrids, *Chytridium*

Class Ascomycetes, sac fungi: bread molds, *Neurospora;* yeasts, *Saccharo-*

myces; blue and green molds, *Aspergillus, Penicillium;* powdery mildews, *Microsphaera;* cup fungi, *Sclerotinia;* morels, *Morchella*

Class Basidiomycetes, club fungi: mushrooms, *Psalliota;* toadstools, *Amanita;* bracket fungi, *Fomes;* smuts and rusts, *Puccinia*

(*Fungi imperfecti:* Under this name botanists place a large number of disease-producing fungi, such as those causing athlete's foot or beet leaf spot. They are probably ascomycetes and basidiomycetes in which the sexual cycle has been lost or is unknown. This is not, strictly, a unit of classification but a catchall for fungi that have not been classified.)

PHYLUM BRYOPHYTA

Class Hepaticae, liverworts: *Marchantia, Riccia, Conocephalum*

Class Anthocerotae, hornworts: *Anthoceros*

Class Musci, mosses: *Sphagnum, Andreaea, Mnium, Funaria, Pottia*

PHYLUM TRACHEOPHYTA, vascular plants

Subphylum Psilopsida

Class † Psilophytales: † *Rhynia,* † *Psilophyton*

Class Psilotales: *Psilotum, Tmesipteris*

Subphylum Lycopsida: lycopods
† *Lepidodendron,* † *Sigillaria, Lycopodium, Selaginella*

Subphylum Sphenopsida: † *Calamites, Equisetum*

Subphylum Pteropsida, ferns and seed plants

Class Filicineae, ferns: *Ophioglossum, Cyathea, Polypodium, Aspidium, Azolla*

Class Gymnospermae, gymnosperms: † seed ferns, † *Neuropteris;* † cycadeoids, † *Cycadeoidea,* † *Williamsonia;* cycads, *Zamia, Dioon;* ginkgos, *Ginkgo;* † cordaites, † *Cordaites;* con-

ifers, *Pinus, Abies, Tsuga, Taxus, Sequoia, Metasequoia, Araucaria;* joint firs, *Ephedra*

Class Angiospermae, angiosperms, flowering plants

DICOTS: magnolias, *Magnolia;* snakeroot, *Aristolochia;* eucalypts, *Eucalyptus;* oaks, *Quercus;* elms, *Ulmus;* maples, *Acer;* beeches, *Fagus, Nothofagus;* peaches, *Amygdalus;* cacti, *Cereus;* blackberries, *Rubus;* peas, *Pisum;* nightshades, *Solanum;* sages, *Salvia;* mustards, *Brassica;* dandelions, *Taraxacum;* ragweeds, *Ambrosia*

MONOCOTS: grasses, *Panicum, Stipa;* sedges, *Cyperus;* lilies, *Lilium;* tulips, *Tulipa;* yuccas, *Yucca;* palms, *Sabal;* orchids, *Cypripedium, Ophrys, Cryptostylis*

Kingdom Animalia (Animals)

PHYLUM PORIFERA, sponges

Class † Pleospongiae: † *Archeocyathus*

Class Calcispongiae, chalky sponges: *Scypha*

Class Hyalospongiae, glass sponges: *Hyalonema*

Class Demospongiae, horny sponges; bath sponges, *Spongia*

PHYLUM COELENTERATA, coelenterates

Class Hydrozoa: *Hydra; Obelia; Gonionemus;* Portuguese man-of-war, *Physalia, Velella*

Class † Stromatoporoidea: † *Clathrodictyon*

Class Scyphozoa, jellyfishes: *Aurelia, Chrysaora*

Class Anthozoa: corals, *Astrangia, Madrepora;* sea anemones, *Metridium, Dahlia*

PHYLUM GRAPTOLITHINA, † graptolites: †*Didymograptus*

PHYLUM CTENOPHORA, comb jellies: *Cestum*

PHYLUM PLATYHELMINTHES, flat-worms

    Class Turbellaria, planarians: *Dugesia*

    Class Trematoda, flukes: *Fasciola, Polystomum, Schistosomum*

    Class Cestoda, tapeworms: *Taenia*

PHYLUM MESOZOA: *Rhopalura*

PHYLUM NEMERTEA, ribbon worms: *Lineus*

PHYLUM NEMATODA, roundworms: *Ascaris, Trichina*

PHYLUM NEMATOMORPHA, horsehair worms: *Paragordius*

PHYLUM ACANTHOCEPHALA, spiny-headed worms: *Gigantorhynchus*

PHYLUM KINORHYNCHA: *Echinoderes*

PHYLUM TROCHELMINTHES

    Class Rotifera, rotifers or wheel animalcules: *Asplanchna*

    Class Gastrotricha: *Chaetonotus*

PHYLUM BRYOZOA, bryozoans, sea mosses, or moss animals

    Class Endoprocta: *Urnatella*

    Class Ectoprocta: *Plumatella, Bugula*

PHYLUM BRACHIOPODA, brachiopods or lampshells

    Class Inarticulata: *Lingula*

    Class Articulata: *Laqueus, Terebratulina*

PHYLUM PHORONIDEA: *Phoronis*

PHYLUM CHAETOGNATHA, arrow worms: *Sagitta*

PHYLUM MOLLUSCA, mollusks

    Class Amphineura: chitons, *Chiton*

    Class Gastropoda, gastropods: snails, *Helix*; whelks, *Buccinum, Ocenebra*; slugs, *Arion*; limpets, *Patella*; nudibranchs, *Archidoris*; sea hares, *Tethys*

    Class Scaphopoda, tooth-shells: *Dentalium*

    Class Pelecypoda, pelecypods: clams, mussels, *Venus, Anodonta, Mya, Pecten, Chlamys, Tridacna, Pholas, Teredo, Solen, Mytilus*

    Class Cephalopoda, cephalopods: squids, *Loligo*; octopuses, *Octopus*; nautilus, *Nautilus* (and see Fig. 32-1)

PHYLUM ANNELIDA, annelids, segmented worms

    Class Polychaeta, polychaetes, sandworms: *Neanthes, Nereis, Aphrodite, Chaetopterus*

    Class Oligochaeta, oligochaetes: earthworms, *Lumbricus*

    Class Archiannelida: *Polygordius*

    Class Hirudinea, leeches: *Hirudo*

    Class Gephyrea: sipunculid worms, *Sipunculus, Echiurus, Priapulus*

PHYLUM ARTHROPODA, arthropods

    Class Onychophora: *Peripatus*

    Class † Trilobita, † trilobites: † *Triarthrus*, † *Neolenus*, † *Ogygopsis*, † *Isotelus*, † *Calymene*

    Class Crustacea, crustaceans: brine shrimps, *Artemia*; † *Barrella*; † *Hymenocaris*; water fleas, *Daphnia*; copepods, *Cyclops*; cirripeds (barnacles), *Balanus, Lepas, Sacculina*; wood lice, *Armadillaria; Caprella*; euphausids, *Euphausia*; prawns, *Leander*; lobsters, *Homarus*; crabs, *Cancer*

    Class Arachnida: † eurypterids, † *Pterygotus*, † *Carcinosoma*, † *Hughmilleria*; spiders, *Eurypelma, Theridion*; scorpions, *Vejoris*; king crabs, *Limulus*; ticks, *Dermacentor*

    Class Chilopoda, centipedes: *Lithobius*

    Class Diplopoda, millipedes: *Julus*

    Class Insecta, insects: cockroaches, *Periplaneta*; grasshoppers, *Melano-*

plus; dragonflies, † *Dunbaria, Libellula*; bugs, *Cimex, Halobates*; butterflies, *Papilio, Colias*; flies, *Musca, Drosophila*; beetles, *Calosoma*; ants, *Pogonomyrmex*; bees, wasps, and allies, *Bombus, Vespa, Coccophagus*

PHYLUM ECHINODERMATA, echinoderms

Class † Cystoidea, † cystoids: † *Caryocrinites*

Class † Edrioasteroidea, † edrioasteroids: † *Edrioaster*

Class † Blastoidea, † blastoids: † *Pentremites*

Class Crinoidea, crinoids, sea lilies: *Antedon*

Class Asteroidea, starfishes: *Asterias*

Class Ophiuroidea, serpent stars, brittle stars: *Ophiura*

Class Echinoidea, sea urchins: *Strongylocentrotus*

Class Holothuroidea, sea cucumbers: *Cucumaria*

PHYLUM CHORDATA, chordates

Subphylum Hemichordata, tongue worms (acorn worms): *Balanoglossus*

Subphylum Tunicata, tunicates: ascidians, *Ciona*

Subphylum Cephalochordata, lancelets: *Branchiostoma* (amphioxus)

Subphylum Vertebrata, vertebrates

SUPERCLASS PISCES, aquatic vertebrates, fishes

Class Agnatha, agnaths, jawless fishes: † *Cephalaspis*, † *Kieraspis*, † *Pteraspis*; lampreys, *Petromyzon*

Class † Placodermi, † placoderms: † *Climatius*, † *Diplacanthus*, † *Coccosteus*, † *Dinichthys*, † *Pterichthyodes*

Class Chondrichthyes: sharks, *Squalus*; rays, *Raja*

Class Osteichthyes, bony fishes: † *Cheirolepis*; sturgeon, *Acipenser*; trout,

Salmo; perch, *Perca*; anglerfish, *Photocorynus*; crossopterygians: † *Osteolepis*, † *Eusthenopteron*, † *Holoptychius*, † *Diplurus, Latimeria*; lungfishes: † *Dipterus, Epiceratodus, Protopterus* (and see Fig. 23-18)

SUPERCLASS TETRAPODA, land vertebrates, tetrapods

Class Amphibia, amphibians: † labyrinthodonts, † *Diplovertebron*, † *Eryops*; salamanders, *Ambystoma, Necturus*; frogs, *Rana*; toads, *Bufo*; tree toads, *Hyla*; caecilians (Apoda), *Gymnophis*

Class Reptilia, reptiles: † cotylosaurs; turtles, *Aromochelys*; † ichthyosaurs, † *Ichthyosaurus*; † plesiosaurs; rhynchocephalians, *Sphenodon*; lizards, *Gerrhonotus, Crotophytus*; snakes, *Thamnophis*; † thecodonts; alligators, *Alligator*, and crocodiles, *Crocodilus*; † pterosaurs, † *Nyctosaurus*, † *Pteranodon*; † dinosaurs, † *Coelophysis*, † *Ornitholestes*, † *Tyrannosaurus*, † *Brontosaurus*, † *Anatosaurus*, † *Stegosaurus*, † *Ankylosaurus*, † *Triceratops*; † mammal-like reptiles, † *Dimetrodon*, † *Cynognathus*

Class Aves, birds: † *Archeopteryx*; † *Aepyornis*; † *Hesperornis*; kiwis, *Apteryx*; † *Diatryma*; pigeons, *Columba*; chickens, *Gallus*; owls, *Micropallus, Otus*; woodpeckers, *Centurus*; flickers, *Colaptes*; flycatchers, *Myiarchus*; finches, *Geospiza, Camarrhynchus, Certhidia*

Class Mammalia, mammals: marsupials, including opossums, *Didelphis*, and others (see Figs. 19-7 and 23-27). † Mesozoic placentals, † *Deltatheridium*, † *Zalambdalestes*. Primates, including: † *Notharctus*; *Loris*; monkeys, *Cebus, Cercopithecus, Macaca*; apes, *Gorilla* and others (see Fig. 32-14), † *Australopithecus*; men, † *Pithecanthropus, Homo*. Anteaters, *Myrmecophagus*. Rodents: rats, *Rattus*; mice, *Mus, Peromyscus*; hamsters, *Cricetus*. Carnivores: † Creodonts, † sabertooths; dogs, *Canis*; cats, *Felis*; seals,

Phoca. Cetaceans: whales, *Orcinus;* porpoises, *Phocaena.* Ungulates: condylarths; † uintatheres; † titanotheres; elephants, *Loxodonta,* and others (see Fig. 32-10); horses, *Equus,* † *Miohippus,* and others (see Figs. 2-5 and 32-11); deer, *Cervus, Odocoileus,* † *Megaceros;* pigs, *Sus;* sheep, *Ovis;* cows, *Bos*

Chapter Summary

The principles of classification:

Resemblance and difference between species; their recognition the elementary act in classification; the hierarchy of groups in classification; possibility of different hierarchies; accepted system based on anatomical and physiological characters; the problem of selecting significant characters in classification; its relation to the nature of systematic units.

Modern classification still Linnaean (1735) in form, but justified by principles radically different; twofold revolution in post-Linnaean systematics: (1) advent of evolutionary thought and rejection of concept of archetypes or divine patterns; the recognition that species are related in material sense of common ancestry; but early evolutionary systematics still typological—concept of morphotype; (2) second revolution, the replacement of a typological by a population concept of systematic units; the systematic unit as a population or group of populations related in the material genetic sense; the nature of evidence in systematics.

The interpretation of form and descent:

Homology: structural correspondence between organisms due to inheritance from common ancestor (exemplified by vertebrate forelimbs); contrasted with homoplasy and analogy; homoplasy as structural correspondence not caused by common ancestry; analogy as functional correspondence (exemplified by wings and legs in insects and vertebrates).

Transformation: radical evolutionary change in structure and function (exemplified by the history of fish lungs and swim bladders, and the mammalian ear mechanism).

Irrevocability in evolution: past structural evolution never wholly eradicable; old structure never wholly regainable; past evolution as a commitment setting conditions, or limits, for future evolution (exemplified by aquatic mammals).

Convergence and parallelism: convergence as evolution of resemblance between organisms whose ancestors were dissimilar (exemplified by hummingbirds and hummingmoths, and by the history of Australian mammals); parallelism a comparable and commoner phenomenon, involving ancestors less remotely related than in convergence; distinction ill-defined but useful; the evolution of similar adaptations the cause of convergence and parallelism.

Divergence: opposite of convergence and parallelism; its universality; the basic element of evolution reflected in classification.

The practice of classification: three basic procedures·

(1) Treatment of species: sample and population; the special status of the species group in systematics; more clearly bounded than the higher categories in the hierarchy; use of adequate population sample for characterization of the species.

(2) Treatment of higher categories: based on inference of phylogeny; existence of alternative acceptable treatments; consistency with phylogeny the only criterion of acceptability.

(3) Nomenclature: the practical need for an elaborate nomenclature; the binomial system; rules of nomenclature; priority rule; nomenclatural types (not to be confused with archetypes).

CHAPTER 20

Protists and Simple Plants

At the end of Chapter 19 is an outline, a very summary one, of one way in which living things can be classified. It is relegated to a chapter appendix, not because it is unimportant but because it is reference material. It cannot be read with pleasure, and memorizing it, although possibly useful, would not make you particularly wise. It is, however, important as a guidebook or a road map to country that you will be exploring in the next four chapters. We have now covered some of the principles underlying the fact that living things are and have long been of such an amazingly large number of different kinds. Next to be considered is what those different kinds are, how they resemble each other, and how they differ, and what roles they play in the drama of life. The technical names of all the groups to be discussed and a formal representation of their relationships

are provided in the appendix to Chapter 19.

We shall be dealing mainly with the major subdivisions of each kingdom of living things, the large groups called *phyla* (singular, *phylum*).[1] Some individual examples will of course be mentioned, but it is not necessary (or possible) in a study of the basic *principles* of biology as a whole to enter into much detail as to the anatomy, physiology, and other peculiarities of many of the extremely numerous kinds of organisms. In some of the more important and more familiar phyla some of the lesser included groups, especially the *classes*, will be separately discussed. Further detail in this more descriptive and taxonomic part of the broad science of biology is the special province of the systematic biological subsciences: protistology,[2] botany, and zoology.

The Protists

Few people have ever seen even one representative of the most abundant organisms in the world. The great majority of them are too small to be seen clearly, if at all, with

1 Botanists frequently call the major groups "divisions" instead of "phyla" (footnote 8 of Chapter 19), but it is also justified and is better in a general biology to use the same terms for the classification of all forms of life.

2 The kingdom Protista, as will be further mentioned, is not universally recognized as distinct from the plant and animal kingdoms, and its study, protistology, is commonly divided between botany and zoology, in elementary systematics courses, at least.

the naked eye (Fig. 3-7). They include a few giants as much as 2 centimeters in diameter, or even a bit more, but almost all of those present in our usual environments are between about $\frac{1}{10}$ and 200 μ in diameter.[3] They are therefore nearly or completely invisible as individuals, as you can readily understand if you convert those sizes into more familiar terms.[4] Sometimes they pile up in such numbers that it is obvious that *something* is there, but only a microscope can reveal the fact that the something consists of uncounted millions or billions of tiny organisms. In nature such a situation occurs, for instance, in the red tides that sometimes sweep an ocean shore. The red tides are caused by concentrations of up to 40 million red protists (generally species of *Gonyaulax* and of *Gymnodinium*) per cubic meter of water. Such red tides may be dangerously destructive because the microscopic organisms are poisonous to many fishes and also to man. In the laboratory, bacteria entirely invisible as individuals become easily visible as groups when they are cultured in large colonies (Fig. 20-1).

The fact that there is a whole world of life smaller than the eye can see has had a profound influence on human thought and history. Most of the organisms that cause human diseases belong in this microscopic realm. In the long millennia before their existence was suspected it was impossible to have a rational idea of the causes of disease, and irrational ideas became deeply embedded in human thought. They are not yet fully eradicated. This gap in the possibility of observation was also partly responsible for the fallacious notion of spontaneous generation (see p. 261). More widely still, the invisible protists have indispensable parts in the operation of nature, in the intricately intermeshed cycle of life. Life itself could not be understood, even in a superficial way, until these tiniest of its manifestations were discovered.[5] The for-

[3] For the length of a micron, symbolized as μ, see p. 45.
[4] Cf. p. 45, where a scale of magnitudes is given.
[5] You may object that it is not necessary to see an object in order to know that it exists, and that is true. No one has ever seen an electron, nor is likely to, but electrons surely exist, and a good deal is known about them. It is similarly true that we would have to postulate

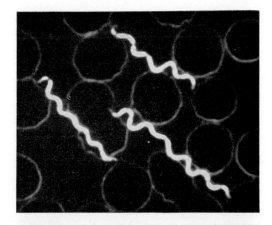

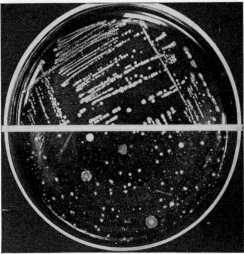

Above, Carl Strüwe; below, C. E. Clifton, Stanford University

20-1 Bacteria. *Above,* spirochetes, the pathogenic (disease-causing) agents of relapsing fever in blood (×1100). *Below,* bacterial colonies growing on plates of agar jelly. The figure is compounded from photographs of two agar plates. In the top one the bacterial cells used to make the inoculation—used, that is, to start growth of the large colonies now visible—were streaked across the jelly with a needle. Individual bacterial cells left on the jelly started each of the hundreds of round colonies that now lie along the paths of the needle. In the bottom half-plate the cells used in the inoculation were first suspended in water, which was then spread uniformly over the plate. Each of the colonies now visible grew from a single cell.

the existence of microorganisms even if we could not see them, and the existence of some of them was indeed postulated before they were seen. (How would you go about determining their existence and characteristics without using a microscope?) Nevertheless, general acceptance and understanding followed the visual demonstration.

tunate man who made the discovery of protists was Anton van Leeuwenhoek, a minor Dutch official and amateur biologist, who lived from 1632 to 1723. His must have been one of the most exciting experiences anyone ever had! He saw a whole new world more truly than did Columbus or any other explorer. Think of him the next time you look at a drop of pond water under a microscope.

CHARACTERISTICS OF PROTISTS

We have had occasion to mention protists before (p. 54, for example), and you already know that they are the one-celled or, better, noncellular organisms, that is, those not made up of separate, differentiated cells at any time in their lives. Such a definition seems clear-cut, but nature has a way of not falling into such conveniently definable categories. Some protists have hard cell walls, perform photosynthesis, and are generally quite like plants. Others are motile, eat plant or animal food, and are generally animal-like. On that basis some could be, and often are, called plants and some animals, but that does not solve the problem. Some act like plants part of the time and like animals part of the time. Some seem intermediate between a plant and an animal. Others do not seem to be much like either plants or animals. Calling them neither plants nor animals but protists, as we do here, does not solve the problem, but it is a convenient and also an enlighteningly different way to look at the matter.

It is usually relatively easy to distinguish even the most animal-like protists from the "true" or multicellular animals. Moreover, the difference between multicellular animals and multicellular plants is fairly clear-cut. Everyone knows that a tree is a plant and a dog is an animal. The distinction is not always as easy as that, but it is almost always possible. (We shall return to the comparison of plants and animals in more detail in Chapter 22.) It is in the comparison of protists with "true" or (generally) multicellular plants that a sharp line of distinction becomes impossible. There are some organisms (among the algae and the fungi) that are one-celled but that seem to be closely related to typically multicellular plants and that are therefore best classified as plants rather than as protists.

There are a few organisms (especially the slime molds) that have suggestions of the beginning of multicellular differentiation but that can be only distantly related to any unquestioned plants or animals and that are therefore classed as protists.

The protists apparently represent a variety of organisms not now very closely related to each other or to anything else. These are age-old branches from the tree of life that split off before true or typically multicellular plants or animals had arisen. They have not followed any of the main paths of complication and differentiation seen in the usually larger true plants and animals. Nevertheless, many of them have become highly specialized within their own sphere. They include the bacteria, the flagellates and their allies, the slime molds, and three more animal-like phyla commonly grouped together as Protozoa ("first animals").

Bacteria

GENERAL CHARACTERISTICS

The most striking physical characteristic of bacteria (Fig. 20-2) is their extremely small size. They are the smallest indisputably living things; only some viruses (which hardly meet usual definitions of living organisms, see p. 43) are smaller. The smallest bacteria are about 0.1 μ in diameter. There are viruses larger than that. A giant among bacteria may be as much as 60 μ long by about 6 μ in transverse diameter. With bacteria of usual size, between these extremes, it takes about 1,000,000,000,000 (more simply written as 10^{12}) to weigh 1 gram.

With ordinary (light) microscopes, organisms of such almost inconceivably small size are barely visible. It can be seen that some are spherical, some elongated or rod-like, and some variously spiral. They commonly occur singly or heaped up more or less at random in highly populous colonies, but in a few species the individuals stick together in chains. Further study with the electron microscope has shown that bacteria have a rather rigid cell wall outside the cell membrane itself, which is a plantlike characteristic. They also have at least one and usually many hair- or whiplike flagella so delicate that they are commonly not seen in classroom preparations of bacteria. Their flagella give bacteria some limited power of movement.

Until comparatively recent years bacteria were thought to lack a nucleus. Indeed, there was reluctance among some biologists to regard the bacterium as a cell. Now, however, it is clear not only that the bacterium has a well-defined membrane and wall but that it does possess a nucleus. It still remains to be proved, however, how fundamentally similar this nucleus is to those of other, better-known cells. Bacteria reproduce by simple cell fission. Claims, still unconvincing, have been made that a normal mitosis occurs. We noted in Chapter 15 (p. 360) that there is some genetic recombination among bacteria by methods in part, at least, quite different from the sexual process characteristic of higher organisms.

The most extraordinary thing about bacteria is that these microscopic, morphologically simple objects are extremely complex in molecular composition and structure. They carry out all the really basic processes of life. They do not differ fundamentally from other organisms, up to man or to a higher plant, in the complexity and general nature of their transformations of matter and energy. They testify to the unity of life and to the common basis from which, in the course of evolution, the extraordinary diversity of living organisms has developed.

SELF-FEEDING AND OTHER-FEEDING

Bacteria themselves are highly diverse. They differ in size, shape, living places, and reactions to various stains used in studying them. The most significant differences among them are in their requirements for energy and materials from their environments. Some of them require carbon only in the form of carbon dioxide (CO_2) and can synthesize all their many and elaborate organic molecules from that simple basis. In that respect they resemble the green plants. Among these bacteria are some that can derive all the needed energy for synthesis and other purposes from inorganic chemical sources, notably sulfur or simple inorganic compounds of nitrogen.

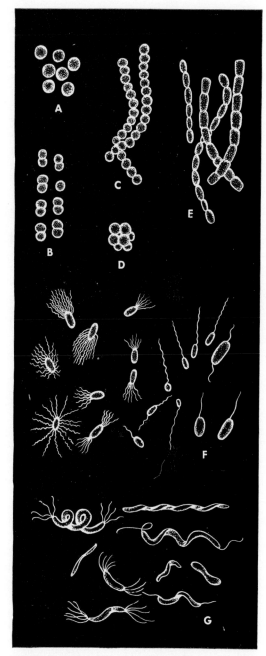

20-2 A diversity of bacterial cell types. *A-D,* cocci (singular, *coccus*) are round cells that may grow singly, in pairs, or as long chains. *E*. Bacilli (singular, *bacillus*) are rod-shaped. They, too, may grow singly as well as in chains. *F*. Many bacteria are flagellated. *G*. Spirilla (singular, *spirillum*) are helical cells.

Others derive energy from light by way of pigments closely allied to the chlorophyll of green plants. Like the latter, they are *photosynthetic* (p. 111). The details of the process are, however, different from those in green plants. For one thing, photosynthesis in green plants produces free oxygen (O_2) as a by-product, but photosynthesis in bacteria does not.

Both bacteria and green plants with such simple demands on the environment are known as *self-feeding*.[6] Most bacteria, the nongreen plants, and all animals cannot synthesize from CO_2 all the carbon compounds they require. They must obtain complex organic compounds from the environment, and those compounds must result from prior metabolic processes of other organisms. They are therefore designated as *other-feeding*.[7] The other-feeders normally utilize complex organic compounds not only as a source of materials but also as a source of energy, in place of inorganic molecules or of radiation.

Among the bacteria especially, the distinction between self-feeding and other-feeding is not so sharp as it seems at first sight. Some bacteria can be either self-feeding or other-feeding, depending on what is actually available in their environments. Both self-feeders and other-feeders have quite diverse and, for each kind, quite specific requirements. Some of the other-feeders can get along if they take in just a few organic compounds. On this basis they can proceed with the necessary synthesis of all else needed within the cell. Others have more limited powers of synthesis and must take in a more varied supply of raw materials. Most of the known bacterial mutations affect the power to synthesize one organic compound or another.

There has been much discussion as to whether the self-feeders or the other-feeders are more primitive. It seems simpler to be able to get along on CO_2 and a few inorganic materials. It also seems logical to conclude that, since other-feeders must derive food from other organisms, they cannot have arisen

first. Yet the self-feeders must really be the more complex of the two groups from another point of view. They synthesize all the sorts of compounds found in other-feeders, and this must involve more intricate internal chemistry than obtaining many compounds ready-made. That would suggest that the other-feeders, if they could find suitable food somewhere, would be more likely to be primitive. On the other hand, as we have elsewhere (p. 112) mentioned, a common trend in mutation and, by inference, in evolution has been loss of the capacity to synthesize certain compounds. Then emphasis is increasingly placed on other-feeding. Extreme other-feeders, with most elaborate dietary demands, would thus seem to be most specialized and least primitive.

The fact seems to be that even among the lowly bacteria no recent organisms are truly primitive. They have been on earth as long as any other living things. They clearly have not changed as much as our own ancestors did, for instance, but they have all certainly changed a great deal. Evidently some of the changes were toward increased self-feeding, and some toward increased other-feeding. The speculative question as to which (if either) really came first will be considered later (pp. 737 ff.).

BACTERIA AND THE ENVIRONMENT

Bacteria are highly versatile organisms. Their activities are limited by their small size and the fact that their locomotion is slight and apparently unoriented. They are further limited by the fact that they must be in a liquid medium, usually water, to carry out their vital processes, including reproduction. Some can float in air or meet other dry environments for considerable periods without being killed, but under such circumstances their vital processes are virtually suspended. Active life is not resumed until or unless they again reach a liquid environment. The few photosynthetic bacteria of course require light, but all bacteria are sensitive to radiation, especially ultraviolet radiation, which kills most of them on relatively brief exposure. Hospitals take advantage of this fact and kill air-borne bacteria with ultraviolet lamps.

Within these general limitations bacteria

[6] The technical term is "autotrophic," from Greek roots which mean "self-feeding." The technical term seems to have no particular advantage over the equally short and precise popular synonym.

[7] Heterotrophic.

occur practically everywhere, even in places where other forms of life are rare or absent. They are particularly abundant in the waters of the earth, from the greatest depths of the ocean up to high mountain streams, and in damp soils. Many can thrive without free oxygen (which is required by all animals and many plants). Indeed, some are definitely harmed by oxygen.[8] Others tolerate or require oxygen.[9] Different kinds of bacteria can live and reproduce at temperatures from 0°-75° C. Quick-frozen bacteria can survive almost indefinitely at temperatures far below 0° C., and some pass through a stage which can briefly survive boiling (100° C. at sea level), but they do not reproduce in such extreme conditions. Each kind has a temperature at which it grows best. These optimal temperatures range from 12° to 60° C. for different species.

USEFUL BACTERIA

The great majority of bacteria are useful in the sense that their activities are essential for the continuous maintenance of living communities. Indeed, the whole scheme of life as it has evolved depends on bacteria. This is true especially because bacteria are the principal (but not the only) organisms of *decay* and virtually the only organisms capable of *nitrogen fixation*.[10]

When a plant or animal dies, much of the material in its body is in organic compounds that cannot be directly utilized by green plants. Many of these compounds are quite stable and do not tend to break down into simpler, usable materials by inorganic processes under usual conditions. Nitrogen, for instance, is mostly in the form of proteins, amino acids, and other compounds more elaborate than the nitrates required by most green plants. Carbon occurs in the same compounds and also in fats and carbohydrates, not as the CO_2 required by green plants. If the compounds in dead plants and animals were not somehow broken down, by now some crucial materials for green plants would all be locked up in the remains of the dead, and life would have become extinct ex-

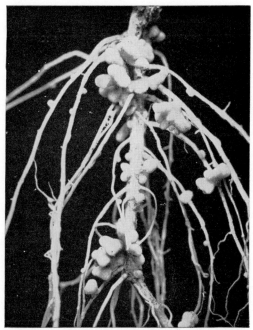

Hugh Spencer

20-3 Bacteria-containing nodules on the root of a pea plant.

cept, perhaps, for a few self-feeding bacteria. (Why?)

This is where the bacteria of decay demonstrate their usefulness. Decay is simply the breaking down of organic compounds by bacteria (and by some nongreen plants). An essential part of the process is the successive breaking down of proteins into amino acids and then of amino acids into ammonia. Other bacteria then oxidize the ammonia to nitrites, and still others oxidize the nitrites to nitrates, available as the principal nitrogen source for green plants.[11]

Some bacteria, to be sure, go too far with the breaking-down process and produce free nitrogen, which cannot be used by green plants. This loss is, however, compensated by still other bacteria that fix nitrogen. They are able to use free nitrogen, which constitutes nearly 80 per cent of the atmosphere, in the synthesis of their own proteins. By further metabolism and decay those nitrogen compounds eventually become available to other

8 These are called anaerobic ("not air living").
9 They are aerobic ("air living").
10 Some blue-green algae can also fix nitrogen.

11 Plants can also use ammonia and, in some cases, amino acids as the immediate source of nitrogen.

organisms. The nodules on the roots of many plants of the pea family (legumes) contain colonies of bacteria that obtain energy from the carbohydrates of the host plant and utilize part of that energy to fix nitrogen (Fig. 20-3). Soils that have become depleted of nitrates, and therefore have become infertile for green plants, can be restored by planting nodule-bearing plants such as clover or alfalfa. (The cycles of energy and materials involving bacteria are further considered in Chapter 24.)

BACTERIA AND DISEASE

Although most bacteria are useful in the broad sense that they help to keep the cycles of life going, many kinds are parasites. They are responsible for most of the infectious diseases in man and other animals and for many, but fewer, diseases of plants. Bacteria may invade any part of the body of any larger organism. If the bacteria produce substances, *toxins*, poisonous to the host, disease usually ensues. As far as is known, all the bacterial toxins are, or include, proteins. Some are excreted by the living bacteria,[12] and others are part of the bacterial cell, liberated after death of the bacterium.

Disease-producing bacteria must have arisen far back in the history of life. The survival of other organisms has depended on their evolving one or more of a triple set of defenses: resistance to invasion by bacteria, resistance to their survival or multiplication in the host, and resistance to the effects of their toxins. What are some of the natural means of defense in man? Why, in the long struggle between disease-producing bacteria and their hosts, have both survived, without complete victory for either? Since the discovery that bacteria are among the causes of disease, man has contrived artificial means of

[12] This explains the fact that there is one extremely serious disease due to bacteria that does not involve invasion of the victim by the responsible agent. Botulism is caused by eating food in which a certain bacterium (**Clostridium botulinum**) has been living. This kind of bacterium excretes a toxin that is probably the strongest poison known in its effects on man and other mammals. Eating even a microscopic amount of this toxin is usually fatal. Yet the bacteria that produce it are common in soil and we regularly come in contact with these without any ill effects.

strengthening all three lines of defense. What are some of these means?

Animal-like Protists

Several major groups, phyla, of protists are particularly like animals and are often, indeed, classified as animals. They are the phyla Sarcodina, Sporozoa, and Ciliophora of the classification on p. 477. Those who prefer to classify them as animals rather than as protists generally unite all of them [13] in a single phylum, Protozoa. That name means "first animals" and refers to the belief that they preserve something of the characteristics of the earliest organisms that could, by any possible definition, be considered animals. This may be true in an extremely broad sense, but again we must note that all "protozoa" now living have surely undergone profound evolutionary changes. It is unlikely that they are like the truly first animals in detail.

The most animal-like features of these groups of protists are, first, that they eat plant or animal food, ingesting it in chunks into the protist body, and, second, that most of them are quite active. Within their small worlds they move about, scouring their surroundings for nourishment. Often there is even a sort of purposiveness in their movements, or, it would be better to say, an orientation: they tend to move toward food or better environmental conditions and away from obstacles or poor living conditions. Thus they do exhibit the rudiments of animal-like behavior. Moreover, as we shall see, the more complex among them have simple or rudimentary organs that are also more animal-than plantlike.

All of them are small, some as little as 2 µ in diameter, as small as many bacteria. A few, the largest of all protists, reach 3 or 4 centimeters in largest dimension. Most of them range from 100 to 300 µ, too small to see clearly if at all with the naked eye but a comfortable size to study with a light microscope. They have visible nuclei and chromosomes, and when they divide they go through essentially the same process of

[13] And usually also the phylum Mastigophora of our classification.

mitosis[14] (p. 268) as the cells of higher plants and animals. Whatever may prove to be true of bacteria, in these protists the usual apparatus of heredity is fully established. They reproduce by fission, and this does introduce an element in their heredity not present in the same degree, at least, in multicellular organisms. The young protist generally starts out in life not only with a full set of parental chromosomes but also with its bodily structure and material directly derived from the parent. In most groups of these protists there also occurs from time to time an exchange of nuclear material between two individuals. This does not lead forthwith to reproduction, but over a sequence of generations it has the same genetic consequences as sexual reproduction in multicellular organisms. (See p. 492.)

THE AMEBA AND ITS KIN

An ameba is about as simple as a fully developed organism can be, and it is famous on that account (Fig. 20-4). It has become a living symbol of the primitive, as in the common expression of evolution "from ameba to man," although it is improbable that anything quite like an ameba ever did really figure in our ancestry.

An ameba is a lump of protoplasm, without top or bottom, front or back, and with little evidence of organelles or special differentiation except for the nucleus. Some species have within the granular cytoplasm a small, clear sphere that looks like a bubble but is really full of a watery solution. This sphere pulses and then collapses, expelling the water. This extremely simple structure is actually an organ of excretion and of control of osmotic pressure. It gets rid of some waste products and also of excess water. Freshwater protists tend to take up more water than they lose through the cell membrane by osmosis. (Why? See p. 154.) By forcibly expelling water the ameba solves the problem of how not to swell up to the bursting point.

Although we call this mechanism "extremely simple," it is well to note that even here biology has unsolved mysteries. No one

[14] Some marked variations do occur; in some the spindle develops within the nuclear membrane.

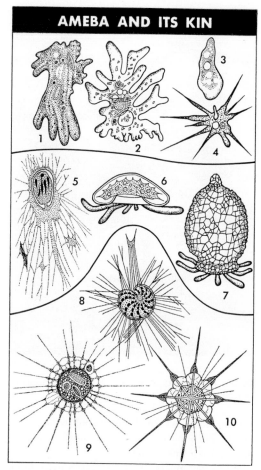

AMEBA AND ITS KIN

20-4. Ameba and its kin: the Sarcodina. *1-4.* Members of the order Amoebina, showing different forms of pseudopodia. *1. Amoeba proteus* ($\times 40$); *2. Amoeba dubia* ($\times 40$); *3. Vahlkampfia limax* ($\times 280$); *4. Amoeba radiosa* ($\times 170$). *5-7.* Members of the order Testacea, all of which possess a shell, or test, of chitinous material, which in some species (*6*) is heavily thickened, and in others (*7*) is supplemented by addition of foreign particles. The animal can withdraw completely inside the shell, or may extend pseudopodia all over it (*5*). *5. Gromia ovoidea* ($\times 25$); *6. Arcella discoides* ($\times 34$); *7. Difflugia urceolata* ($\times 100$). *8. Polystomella crispa* (order Foraminifera) ($\times 15$). Note the long filamentous pseudopodia. *9. Actinosphaerium eichhorni* (order Heliozoa) ($\times 27$). Pseudopodia filamentous. *10. Acanthometron elasticum* (order Radiolaria). Note the siliceous spikes.

yet knows for certain how the contraction and expulsion are produced, or just what products are excreted in this way rather than through the cell membrane. It is significant that ma-

Carl Strüwe

20-5 The empty cases of various Foraminifera, greatly magnified.

rine protists, which do not tend to take up excess water by osmosis (why not?), usually do not have this device.[15]

When an ameba is active, it moves by a streaming motion of the cytoplasm (p. 225). That motion pushes out one or more irregular bulges in the direction toward which it is moving, and pulls in bulges at the opposite end.[16] If food is encountered—the food is frequently another protist—the bulges surround it, and it is taken into the body in a sac surrounded by a membrane. Digestive enzymes are secreted into the cavity thus formed, the products are absorbed through the membrane, and any undigested remnants are expelled from the protistan body.

There are a great many protists more or less similar to the ameba in structure and function; tens of thousands of species of this

---

[15] However, it is also true that a few marine protists do have it, and a few fresh-water protists do not. Can you think of a hypothesis to explain these facts? Can you design an experiment to test your hypothesis?

[16] The bulges are technically called "pseudopods," which means "false feet."

---

phylum (Sarcodina), living and fossil, have been described. The most varied and perhaps the most interesting are the Foraminifera [17] (or forams, for short) most of which secrete limy shells. The shells, when suitably magnified, are often of great beauty and amazing complexity (Fig. 20-5). It is especially remarkable that such intricate structures, characteristic for each species and fixed by heredity, can be built by what looks like a completely structureless blob of living material. Evidently there is more structure in protoplasm than we have yet succeeded in finding. Forams, most of which are marine, are so abundant in the seas that much of the bottom ooze is made up of their shells. Forams are also common as fossils. They are good indexes of the age of rocks and can readily be recovered when a well is bored in rocks originally laid down in the sea. For these reasons their study is useful in the petroleum industry, and they are the principal object of the science of micropaleontology. Forams have made an even greater contribution: much of the petroleum itself has probably been derived from their soft organic parts through the ages, although other organisms have also contributed.

SPOROZOA

The phylum Sporozoa especially well illustrates two characteristics that are widespread among the animal-like protists: many of them are parasites, and many have complicated reproductive cycles.

Many of the parasite sporozoans cause severe disease. They vie with the bacteria in the amount of misery they have caused man and other animals. The combination of parasitism and a complex reproductive cycle is well seen in the sporozoans that cause malaria. While living as parasites in mosquitoes, the malarial sporozoans have a sexual process, followed by multiple fission. Introduced into the human blood stream by a mosquito bite, they reproduce asexually and periodically. The cycle is completed when the biting mosquito acquires individual sporozoans from

---

[17] Foraminifera ("hole-bearers"), so called because their shells are usually pierced by many tiny holes.

the human blood. The details are shown in Fig. 25-5.

CILIATES

The ciliates (Fig. 20-6) are so called because they have numerous tiny hairlike projections, or cilia (singular, cilium), which beat rhythmically and drive these protists through the water in which they live. They are by far the largest and most complexly organized protists. *Paramecium*, one of the most abundant ciliates, occurs almost everywhere in fresh water, although, curiously enough, the way in which it colonizes isolated streams or pools is unknown. It has become a famous laboratory "animal." It is easy to propagate and to study under a microscope; the range of length is about 100 to 300 μ. Its behavior is complex for a protist (p. 235), and its genetics is especially enlightening, in part be-

---

20-6 Ciliates. Note the distinction between macronucleus (*MN*) and micronucleus (*mn*) which is visible in some of the figures. The macronucleus is often a long chainlike structure, as in *1* and *2*. *1. Spirostomum ambiguum* ($\times$40), a large freshwater ciliate. Note the oral groove curving inward on the right side of the figure; the large area, shaped like an inverted hatchet and unstippled in the figure, is the contractile vacuole. *2. Paramecium bursaria* ($\times$100). The dots in the cell are symbiotic green protists. *3. Cycloposthium bipalmatum* ($\times$210), a parasitic ciliate from the gut of horses. The cilia are compacted together into robust paddle-like processes called cirri. The elongate structure to the right of the macronucleus is a skeletal rod. Note several contractile vacuoles lying near the macronucleus. *4. Stentor mulleri* ($\times$48), which lives in a case it secretes. The large cilia around the "top" of the animal set up feeding currents in the adjacent water which bring microorganisms into the oral groove and mouth (cf. Fig. 10-11). *5. Ellobiophrya donacis* ($\times$600), attached by two armlike processes to the gill bar of the mussel *Donax*. Recall how pelecypods feed (Fig. 6-2); the gill of a mussel is a rich hunting ground for a ciliate that feeds on microorganisms! As in *Stentor*, the ring of cilia sets up local currents that lead to the mouth. *6. Stylonichia mytilus* ($\times$140), a ciliate that uses its cirri (cf. *3* in this figure) as highly co-ordinated leglike structures: it literally walks (*6b*) on the bottom of ponds or on leaf surfaces under water. *7. Vorticella* sp. ($\times$80), a ciliate with contractile stalk that quickly pulls the main cell body away from a source of stimulation. *7b*. A free-swimming individual budded off from the colony. *7c*. Detail of the cell. The ring of cilia around the oral groove (leading deep into the cell) creates a feeding current.

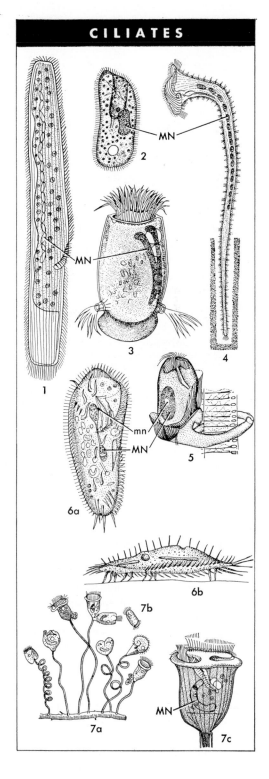

CILIATES

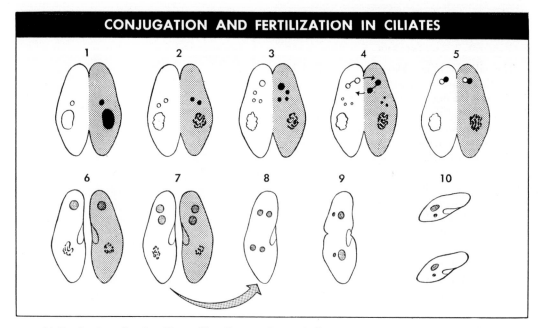

CONJUGATION AND FERTILIZATION IN CILIATES

20-7 Conjugation in ciliates like *Paramecium*. *1.* Two paramecia come in contact at the oral-groove region; technically, they are said to conjugate. *2.* The micronucleus (diploid) in each cell divides, undergoing the first of two meiotic divisions, and the macronucleus begins the process of degeneration which continues throughout subsequent stages of conjugation and is complete by about *7. 3.* The micronuclei have completed the second meiotic division; three of the four haploid nuclei produced by meiosis begin to degenerate, and the fourth undergoes a mitotic division to produce (in each cell) two gamete nuclei. *4.* One gamete nucleus in each cell migrates into the other cell. *5.* Nuclear migrations complete. *6.* The two micronuclei in each cell now fuse, completing fertilization; the conjugating cells fall apart. *7.* The diploid zygote nucleus divides mitotically once. Degeneration of old macronucleus is now complete. *8.* (We will now follow only one of the two formerly conjugating cells.) The micronucleus divides again; the four nuclei space out, two at either end of the cell. *9.* The cell divides in the oral groove region, producing (*10*) two new paramecia each with two nuclei. One nucleus in each cell undergoes further development into a macronucleus.

cause it goes through a rather odd sexual process called *conjugation,* shown diagrammatically in Fig. 20-7.

The ciliates dramatically illustrate how much structural and physiological differentiation can occur in a small space and how far from true simplicity even a protist may be. Although there is no division into cells,[18] they have well-developed structures, organelles, analogous to the organ systems of multicellular animals. In various ciliates there are locomotory systems (the cilia), the operation of which is finely co-ordinated; "muscular" systems of contractile fibers; reactive co-ordinating and conductive tracts analogous to an incipient nervous system; an alimentary

canal with "mouth," "gullet," and "anus"; excretory organelles; stiffening plates analogous to a skeleton; and other organelles. Such organisms are evidently far from primitive, and they show how far evolution can go without taking the crucial step to multicellular structure (Fig. 20-8).

Flagellates

The flagellates and their allies [19] (Fig. 20-9) deserve special emphasis because they are transitional between strictly plantlike and strictly animal-like organisms and because they also illustrate a possible transition from

[18] The ciliates usually do have two or three distinct nuclei of different sizes.

[19] Phylum Mastigophora ("whip-bearers"). "Flagellates" means the same thing but is derived from Latin instead of Greek.

protistan to multicellular structure. Again it is evident that no flagellate living today can preserve in detail the characteristics of the ancient protists ancestral to multicellular organisms. It is, however, probable that the flagellates are less modified from that remote ancestry than are any other present-day protists. Sponges (p. 524) and numerous true plants, especially among the algae, have cells or life stages that are almost indistinguishable from flagellates. Moreover, some flagellates form colonies in which there may be some functional differentiation and also a degree of co-ordination among the individuals. It then becomes a mere matter of definition whether we consider such an aggregation as an advanced colonial union of individual protists or as a rudimentary grouping of cells in an individual of a higher order. *Volvox*, already encountered on p. 56 and in Fig. 3-14, is an example.

In the absence of any fossil record of the actual transition from protists to multicellular organisms, it is impossible to be sure; the subject is highly speculative. At present, however, the consensus is that multicellular plants and sponges, at least, were derived from colonies of protists somewhat like flagellates. The multicellular animals other than sponges may well have had a similar origin, but that is not the only possibility. We will return to the problem when we discuss the multicellular animals (p. 551).

Flagellates are so called because almost all of them have one or a few long whiplike appendages, the flagella (singular, flagellum). They drive or pull the protist along by lashing (p. 225). The body usually is more definite and fixed in form than in amebas and commonly has some differentiation of organelles, although much less than in the ciliates. One of the most interesting facts about flagellates is that their various kinds have just about every sort of nutrition and associated physiology that is conceivable for organisms of their size. Some (*Euglena* and *Volvox* are common examples) contain chlorophyll, perform photosynthesis, and are generally much like plants, among which they are frequently classified. Others ingest chunks of plant or animal food and are

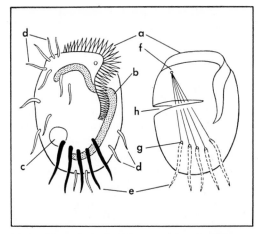

20-8 The neurofibrillar system of ciliates is an analogue of a nervous system. *Euplotes* is another ciliate (cf. *Stylonichia*, Fig. 20-6) which uses cirri in highly co-ordinated locomotor movements. It can be shown by experiment that the co-ordination of the cirri is controlled through the nervelike neurofibrils that supply them. *Left*, a general view of *Euplotes*. *Right*, view of experimental incision that severs the neurofibrils to five major cirri. The cut completely destroys their co-ordination; equally severe cuts elsewhere in the cell which fail to sever the fibrils do not destroy cirral co-ordination. *a*, band of cilia down oral groove to mouth; *b*, macronucleus; *c*, contractile vacuole; *d* and *e*, locomotory cirri; *f*, the motorium, a brainlike center from which the neurofibrils lead out to granules (*g*) at the base of the five major cirri; (*h*) experimental incision.

thoroughly animal-like in nutrition. Many are organisms of decay, absorbing molecule by molecule through the cell membrane the breakdown products from the remains of other, dead organisms. (*Euglena* can do this, too, when it is not being a green "plant.") Many are parasites and cause serious diseases, although some are relatively innocuous. The trypanosomes, which cause African sleeping sickness and some other diseases, are flagellates.

Flagellates are very abundant in the sea and there share with the diatoms (p. 497) basic roles in the turnover of organic materials. The producers of red tides previously mentioned (p. 483) are flagellates. So are the commonest of the organisms causing "phosphorescence" in sea water. One of these has the appropriate name of *Noctiluca*, the "night-shiners." (See Figs. 20-10 and 20-11.)

Betwixt and Between

The flagellates refuse to be pigeonholed consistently as either plants or animals. We have met that problem by recognizing that they may be either plantlike or animal-like in physiology and that in phylogeny they probably split off from a protistan ancestral stage earlier than multicellular plants or animals. Two other groups of organisms are even harder to pigeonhole: the slime molds[20] and the blue-green algae.[21] In some stages, at least, they are multicellular, but they do not

[20] Phylum Myxomycetes (p. 477).
[21] Phylum Myxophyta (p. 477).

have the same kind of anatomical and physiological differentiation seen in most unquestioned plants or animals. Their classification is almost completely arbitrary. Many authorities call both groups "plants." Our *arbitrary* compromise is to call the slime molds "protists" and the blue-green algae "plants" along with the other, more fully plantlike algae. (See p. 497.)

SLIME MOLDS

At one stage in their life history, slime molds (Fig. 20-12) are noncellular organisms with flagella and might well be classified as animal-like flagellate protists. Later, those

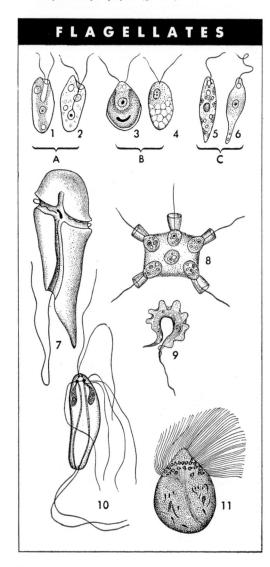

FLAGELLATES

20-9 Flagellates. *1. Cryptomonas ovata*, photosynthetic; *2. Chilomonas paramaecium*, a nonphotosynthetic form closely related to *Cryptomonas. 3. Chlamydomonas monadina* ($\times$610), photosynthetic; *4. Polytoma uvella* ($\times$870) nonphotosynthetic, closely related to *Chlamydomonas. 5. Euglena pisciformis* ($\times$195), photosynthetic. *6. Astasia klebsii* ($\times$300), closely related to *Euglena*, but nonphotosynthetic. (See p. 112 and footnote 12 in Chapter 5 for comments on these three pairs of flagellates.) *7. Ceratodinium asymmetricum* ($\times$600), a dinoflagellate from brackish waters. It possesses two flagella, one of which beats within the confines of a groove running around the cell wall. *8. Protospongia haeckeli* ($\times$320), a simple colony of eight collarflagellate cells embedded in a common matrix. (See p. 552 for comment on the resemblance between *Protospongia* and the ancestors of sponges [Porifera].) The collar flagellates feed by trapping debris and microorganisms on their collars, which are like perpetually moving flypaper: the collar maintains a surface streaming that brings trapped food down the collar to the cell surface proper, where it is engulfed in a food vacuole. This is also how sponge cells trap and ingest food. *9. Trypanosoma giganteum* ($\times$400), a parasitic flagellate from the blood of fish. Other trypanosome species attack man and livestock, causing sleeping sickness. The flagellum runs alongside the cell, and an "undulating membrane" of protoplasm is stretched between the cell and the flagellum, much as a soap film can be stretched between wires. *10. Hexamitus intestinalis* ($\times$2000), a parasitic flagellate from the gut of frogs and other vertebrates. *Hexamitus* is of interest as one of the few flagellates having more than one nucleus per cell. The nuclei are pear-shaped bodies near the top of the cell. (The two long rodlike structures running down the cell connect the granules at the base of each flagellum; their function is unknown.) *11. Calonympha grassii* ($\times$630), a symbiotic flagellate from the gut of termites. (See p. 435 for comment on the significance of these and related flagellates to the termites in whose gut they live.)

that survive lose the flagella and become thoroughly amebalike. In both the flagellate and ameboid stages they reproduce extensively by simple fission, with mitosis of the nucleus, which is haploid (p. 271) in these stages. Eventually many of the ameboid individuals clump together. Then the separate cell membranes usually break down, and the result is a single mass of protoplasm with hundreds or even thousands of nuclei. This mass moves about and ingests food like a

gigantic ameba; it may reach a diameter of 25 centimeters or more.

So far the slime mold's life cycle is like that of a protist, at first solitary and later colonial in a peculiar way. The colonial mass (plasmodium) may undergo an extraordinary differentiation that is plantlike, at least superficially. From the basal mass stalks grow upward, and bulblike expansions develop at the ends of the stalks. The remaining basal cells or nuclei, those in the stalk and those coating the bulbs, do not further reproduce. They die, just as the somatic cells (p. 281) of higher plants and animals die while the germ cells continue the race. In the slime molds, the inner nuclei of the bulb fuse two by two in a sexual process, resulting in diploid nuclei. Meiosis (p. 272) then occurs and haploid spores are formed. The spores are scattered, and, with luck, each may produce an individual of the flagellate stage as the cycle continues.

Are such organisms animals or plants, protistan or multicellular? The alternatives

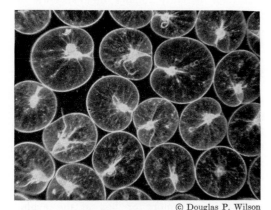

© Douglas P. Wilson

20-10 *Noctiluca scintillans* ($\times 60$), a large phosphorescent flagellate of the ocean's surface waters.

© Douglas P. Wilson

20-11 *Ceratium tripos,* **a marine dinoflagellate.** A flagellum can be seen "in motion" at one o'clock in the figure. *Ceratium,* like *Ceratodinium* (Fig. 20-9, item 7) and other dinoflagellates, maintains one flagellum in motion within a groove on its body wall.

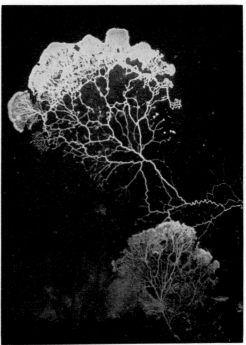

Hugh Spencer

20-12 **The plasmodium of the slime mold** *Physarum* (approximately natural size).

are not clear-cut, and the question hardly makes sense. Perhaps the most likely phylogenetic answer is that the slime molds evolved from protists that somehow struck off on a peculiar line of specialization of their own, not like that followed by any other organisms.

BLUE-GREEN ALGAE

In spite of the name, only about half the blue-green algae (Fig. 20-13) are blue-green.

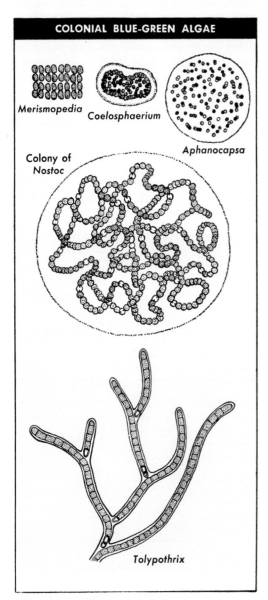

COLONIAL BLUE-GREEN ALGAE

Merismopedia

Coelosphaerium

Aphanocapsa

Colony of Nostoc

Tolypothrix

20-13   A variety of blue-green algae.

The others are highly varied in color: blue, green, yellow, red, and intermediate hues. Some are unicellular (the name seems more appropriate here than when applied to characteristic protists). Most of them consist of clumps or colonies of attached cells, with little or no differentiation. Probably the most characteristic form is a filament made up of cells attached end to end. In all of them the cell or the whole colony has a mucilaginous outer wall. The cells contain nuclear material and their heredity implies the existence of genes, but the presence of definite chromosomes and nuclei has not been established. Reproduction is vegetative or by fission, and no evidence of a sexual process has yet been found.

These characteristics are suggestive of the bacteria, especially when it is remembered that some bacteria also tend to be grouped in filamentlike strings. It has been suggested that the blue-green "algae" are in fact advanced, colonial bacteria or (and this may be only another way of saying the same thing) that they are extremely primitive algae, which have remained more or less at the evolutionary level at which algae arose from protists. The latter opinion seems to be the consensus among botanists. It is, however, also possible that the simplicity of the blue-green algae is to some extent secondary. If, as seems to be true, some bacteria have a sexual process, the absence of such a process in the blue-green algae is not likely to be original. (Why not?) And secondary loss of sex in protists and plants has been rather common (p. 391).

Blue-green algae are another group that are extremely abundant in the seas. The Red Sea may have been so named because of the presence of red "blue-green" algae. They also abound in lakes, streams, and the soil. Some species grow in especially difficult environments: hot springs, heavily mineralized waters, antarctic pools, and other places where they (and often some bacteria) may be the only forms of life. How would you account for the fact that such structurally simple organisms as bacteria and blue-gree algae may exist in places where complex, higher plants and animals cannot live?

Algae, the Grass of the Waters

We have emphasized the fact that photosynthesis is the basic dynamic process of life. That may not always have been true, but therein lies a different tale (p. 737). It is true now that practically all the energy of living things is first made available to them by photosynthesis, which is also one of the key processes in building up organic compounds. We naturally think of photosynthesis in terms of green fields and forests. Yet it is true now and evidently has always been true that most of the photosynthesis so important in the economy of life occurs in water, especially in the vast reaches of the sea. Many protists are involved in this tremendous and ceaseless activity, and so are those betwixt-and-betweens, the blue-green algae. However, most of the photosynthesis in water—and that means most of it on earth—is performed by the many kinds of primarily aquatic true green plants: the algae (singular, alga).

Algae are symbolically the grass of the waters not only in the sense that they are the principal energy-fixers of the "meadows of the sea," but also in the sense that they are the original food source for most of the untold billions of aquatic animals. This greatest of all food sources has hardly been touched by man as yet. The only significant human use, and even it is only a small fraction of human food consumption, is indirect: the eating of fish and to still less extent of other seafood. Now that human population has outrun land food production over large areas, experiments are under way for the cultivation and more direct utilization of algae. The results are not very significant as yet, but it can be confidently predicted that these efforts will assume great importance if the world population continues to increase rapidly.

Some algae are as small as some bacteria. Others are more than 200 feet in length. Most of them are multicellular, but some are unicellular. The unicellular algae are not classified as protists because they seem to be related to or even derived from multicellular algae. They are, it seems, cells that get along alone but that are of essentially the same kind as those in their multicellular relatives. The vegetative parts of algae have little differentiation of tissues or organs. In many, all the vegetative cells are practically alike. Others do have some distinctions of size, shape, and function among their cells but without differentiation of such organs as roots or leaves or of such tissues as the vascular, tubelike, sap-conducting bundles of cells that occur in land plants. For this reason the algae are included among the *nonvascular* [22] plants, as opposed to the *vascular* plants, which include most of the familiar land plants. The reproductive structures of algae, in contrast with their vegetative parts, may be highly differentiated and complex.

Most algae are fully aquatic. Others grow in soil, where they are abundant, or in such odd places as inside or among the tissues of other plants, but always in damp or wet situations. Almost all have pigments of the chlorophyll family and are photosynthetic, but a few have lost the pigment and have become organisms of decay.

In popular language the main groups of algae are usually characterized by their predominant color: blue-green, green, yellow-green, golden-brown, brown, and red. As we have already noted for the blue-greens, however, colors are not infallible means of recognizing the groups. More fundamental are details of anatomy, especially in reproductive structures, and of the life cycle. The essentials of reproduction in algae and their widely diverse life cycles have already been discussed in Chapter 15.

Although there is a tendency to lump all the algae together, botanists believe that they represent at least five main groups each of which arose independently from protists. A phylogenetic classification (see Chapter 19) should, then, recognize each of these groups as a primary subdivision of the plant kingdom.[23]

Algae include the familiar seaweeds and the green scum of still ponds. Among other groups peculiar in various ways are the diatoms, lichens, and stoneworts. *Diatoms* (Fig. 20-14) are tiny plants, usually unicellular but occasionally in small, colonylike aggregations. They secrete unique skeletal structures

[22] See note 1 on p. 137.
[23] See the classification on pp. 477-81. The algae of popular speech are the phyla Myxophyta, Chlorophyta, Chrysophyta, Phaeophyta, and Rhodophyta of our classification.

20-14 Diatoms. *Left,* a variety of diatom cell walls from New Zealand waters, to show diversity of form (×67). *Right,* the genus *Actinoptychus* (×130), photographed with polarized light.

made of silica (SiO_2, the same compound as that of rock crystal), sometimes complex and with a delicate beauty. Diatoms are especially important because despite their small size they are often so amazingly abundant as to be the main photosynthetic organisms over wide areas, especially in the sea but also in lakes and streams. The whole productivity of the oceans, from the tiniest animals up to the great whales, depends largely on diatoms.

Lichens (Fig. 20-15) are familiar to many as the scale-like, varicolored patches on rocks or tree trunks. Those who have been in the far north know another lichen as "reindeer moss," which is not really moss. A lichen is a composite of two quite distinct kinds of plants intergrown in close, obligatory association. A fungus forms a dense web of threads within which grows an alga. The fungus obtains organic food from the alga, and the alga obtains water and dissolved salts from the fungus. Neither plant can grow alone under natural conditions, but together they can live on bare rocks, in arctic climates, and in other situations where few or no other plants can survive. They are pioneers that often play an important role in the first steps of breaking down rocks into soils. Their association is an excellent example of symbiosis, a way of living happily together discussed elsewhere (p. 632). (Lichens are frequently classified with the fungi because of the prominence of the identifiable fungus partner.)

Stoneworts (Fig. 20-16) are of relatively little importance in the total economy of nature, but they are worthy of mention because they are the most complex algae. They look like a sort of abortive attempt to evolve a higher type of plant.[24] They have "roots," branching "stems," "leaves," and strangely marked "seeds." The structures named in quotation marks are not anatomically like the true roots, stems, leaves, and seeds of higher plants, but they do serve similar purposes and show a remarkable degree of differentiation for an alga. Stoneworts also secrete lime in the cell walls and may locally contribute to the formation of marl and limestone.

[24] For this very reason some students do not classify them as algae but set them aside in a group of their own.

20-15   Lichens. *Left*, a foliaceous (or leafy) lichen on a rock. *Right*, the genus *Cladonia* growing tightly on the surface of a fallen tree.

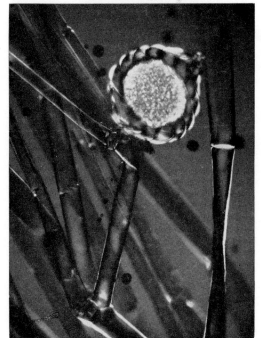

20-16   The stonewort *Nitella*, with a fruiting body or "seed" ($\times 23$).

Fungi

The great majority of algae and of other true, multicellular plants have chlorophyll and perform photosynthesis. This is true to such an extent that "green" and "plant" are words almost automatically associated. However, one large and important group of plants do not perform photosynthesis: the fungi (Fig. 20-17).[25] Everyone has seen some parts of fungi, and many fungi grow to considerable size, but they are for the most part hidden organisms. The basic unit of their structure is a threadlike element, or *hypha* (Figs. 6-5 and 20-17). The hypha consists of an elongate cylindrical wall containing a mass of cytoplasm and hundreds of nuclei which are not separated by cross walls. The mass of hyphae that constitutes a fungal growth is collectively referred to as a *mycelium*.

[25] They are often distinguished as "nongreen plants," although as a matter of fact there are a few green fungi, as you know if you have seen a green-molded piece of bread. The green pigment is, however, not chlorophyll. There are also a few "green plants" (members of groups mainly photosynthetic) that have no green pigment. It is so difficult to make a universally valid generalization about things as versatile as organisms, or to characterize their groups by names valid for all members of the group.

20-17 A variety of fungi. *Left,* a bracket fungus (*Fomes*) growing out from a tree trunk. *Right,* *Amanita muscaria,* a poisonous mushroom. *Left,* the mycelium of the mold *Penicillium chrysogenum,* showing individual hyphae. Penicillin is produced by the fungus. *Right,* cells of brewer's yeast (*Saccharomyces cereviseae*) in the process of budding.

The mycelium of *molds* visibly spreads on old food (Fig. 6-5) in damp, dark places, and sometimes on the surfaces of other plants or even of animals. *Yeasts* are familiar to the housewife, although what she sees is a mass of organisms rather than the small individuals. Structurally, yeast are atypical fungi, for they consist not of hyphae but of single cells (Fig. 20-17).

Mushrooms are delicacies; toadstools are a recognized danger. (That is not a scientific distinction; "toadstools" are mushrooms that are poisonous or believed to be so.) *Bracket fungi,* sometimes also called "conks," form spongy-looking but hard shelves on stumps and tree trunks. Farmers can readily see the *smut* or *rust* that may infect their grain and ruin a crop. All those easily visible organisms are fungi—masses of tightly packed hyphae —but hundreds of other kinds are hidden. Even among the readily visible fungi what are seen are often only reproductive structures. The vegetative mycelium lies hidden in the soil or inside the tissues of a host plant or animal. It is the often-hidden vegetative part of the fungus within the plant and animal tissues that is harmful to the host. (How?) When the spore masses appear, as in smuts and rusts, the damage is already done to the host. The mushrooms we eat are immature reproductive parts growing up from a mycelium buried in decaying organic matter.

All fungi are other-feeders (p. 111). Many of them require as organic food only a simple sugar and can carry on all the other necessary syntheses from there. Some have highly specific requirements for more complex organic foods. In any case all must absorb through cell membranes a carbohydrate, at least, that has been synthesized by some other organism. They are all either parasites or organisms of decay, absorbing food from the living bodies or dead remains of other organisms.

Fungi reproduce asexually by spores (p. 359), which may be as small as 1 μ in diameter, although they are usually several times that size. Such tiny objects float freely in air, and the air around us is rarely without a multitude of them. If they land on a suitable medium, the spores develop into vegetative bodies, which in turn develop anew the spore-bearing organs, often elaborate in shape and structure. Thus almost any piece of bread left exposed to air develops mold; damp shoes and luggage made of parts of dead animals become mildewed; a compost heap sprouts mushrooms—all developed from the ubiquitous air-borne spores. Most fungi also have sexual processes, and their life cycles may be quite complex (Fig. 20-18).

The most widespread and destructive diseases of plants are caused by parasitic fungi, which do many millions of dollars of damage every year to crop plants, vegetables, and trees. Even when the plant is not killed outright, it may be stunted, its productivity reduced, or its fruit blotched or scabbed so as to be unmarketable. Diseases caused by fungi

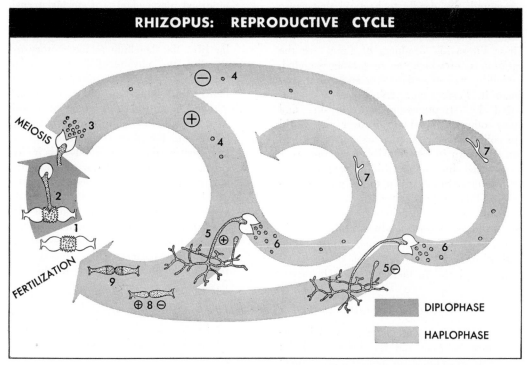

RHIZOPUS: REPRODUCTIVE CYCLE

DIPLOPHASE

HAPLOPHASE

20-18 The reproductive cycle of the bread mold *Rhizopus*. The diplophase is of minor significance, consisting only of the zygote and the sporangiophore with its terminal sporangium that produces haploid spores (meiotic products). *1.* Zygote. *2.* Sporangiophore, grown out of zygote, with terminal sporangium. *3* and *4.* Haploid spores which are of two mating types, ⊕ and ⊖. (The term "mating type" is used where there is neither morphological nor physiological distinction between the "sexes" other than that ⊕ will only mate with ⊖, and ⊖ will only mate with ⊕.) *5.* New mycelia (two mating types) germinated from the spores. *6* and *7.* Spores and a new generation of vegetatively propagated mycelia. *8.* Two hyphae (technically progametes at this stage), one from a ⊕ mycelium and the other ⊖, come in contact and (*9*) produce gametes at their tips; fertilization consists of a fusion of the two gametes.

are less common in animals than in plants, but they do occur. Athlete's foot, "ringworm" (which is due to a fungus and not a worm), and San Joaquin fever are human fungal diseases.

Although some fungi do untold damage from our human point of view, many others are highly useful from the same point of view. Brewing and all the industrial operations involving fermentation depend on yeasts, which have the attractive property of metabolizing sugars into alcohol and carbon dioxide. Bread raised with yeast utilizes the same reaction, but here the carbon dioxide bubbles in the dough are desired, not the alcohol. (What becomes of the alcohol?) A number of fungi, especially molds, synthesize compounds poisonous to competing organisms and particularly to bacteria. Some of these compounds are deadly to bacteria that cause human diseases but are only mildly if at all toxic to the human hosts of the bacteria. These life-saving products of fungi are the *antibiotics*, of which the first to be isolated, penicillin, was named for the mold that produces it, *Penicillium*. It has now been followed by streptomycin, aureomycin, and many others. Explorers all over the world are collecting soil samples from which fungi can be grown in laboratories. Each fungus is then tested for the antibiotic properties of its products. Some prove to be no more effective than others already known. Some turn out to be as injurious to humans as to the invading disease-producers. But one in many becomes a new weapon in the fight against disease—and our debt is increased to the fungi and to their intricate chemistry.

Chapter Summary

The protists: their size, diversity, and importance for man and for life as a whole; their unicellular, or noncellular, nature; their systematic status as little-changed descendants of ancient groups in existence before multicellular organisms.

The bacteria: their extremely small size; the bacterial cell: its nucleus, its great diversity in chemical and physiological respects.

Self-feeding and other-feeding bacteria; the question of which is the more primitive condition.

The universality of bacteria in all environments.

Useful bacteria; their role in decay and in nitrogen fixation; harmful bacteria: their role in disease; toxins.

Animal-like protists, the "Protozoa."

The Sarcodines: ameba and its kin; general form; the contractile vacuole and its functions; the food vacuole; pseudopodial locomotion; Foraminifera.

The sporozoans, parasitic protists with complex life cycles.

The ciliates: their form; possession of cilia; relatively large size; complex behavior; sexual process of conjugation; complexity of structure for a unicellular organism.

The flagellates: their importance as little-modified descendants of forms transitional between plant and animal; and transitional between uni- and multicellular life; the flagellum as locomotory organelle; the physiological diversity of flagellate types; their ubiquity, abundance, and importance in food chains.

Two phyla difficult to classify as plant or animal, as protist or multicellular: the slime molds and the blue-green algae.

Myxomycetes, the slime molds: their life cycle, involving unicellular and colonial stages; their fruiting bodies and spores.

Myxophyta, the blue-green algae: their diverse colors; unicellular and colonial forms; the problematic nature of their nuclear material; viewed as possible descendants of bacteria and as ancestors of true algae; their ubiquity—in the sea, fresh water, and soil.

Algae, "grass of the waters": photosynthetic organisms—simple plants; primary food source for the majority of animals; possibility of human exploitation as energy source.

Their wide range in size; unicellular and multicellular forms; their nonvascular nature; the complexity of their reproductive structures; their aquatic environments.

Types of algae: seaweeds; the green scum of ponds; diatoms; the algae in lichens; stoneworts.

Fungi: as nongreen (nonphotosynthetic) "plants"; the hypha as the unit of their structure.

Types of fungi: molds; yeasts; mushrooms and toadstools; bracket fungi; the mycelium often hidden in soil or parasitized tissues.

Fungi as other-feeders; their reproduction; the ubiquity of fungal spores; their possession of sex.

Fungi as agents of destruction and disease; useful fungi: yeast in bread and alcohol production; penicillin and other antibiotics.

Flowers like those of the day lily shown here characterize the most complex of plants, the angiosperms. The angiosperms and other, more primitive land plants are the subject of this chapter. (Photo from American Museum of Natural History)

CHAPTER 21

The More Complex Plants

If you were asked to bring in examples of plants, it is unlikely that you would come up with any of those discussed in the last chapter. Fungi are, indeed, abundant all around you, but mostly as spores too small to see or else as developed plants largely hidden in the soil or in other organisms, living or dead. Algae may be even less accessible to you unless you live near a pond or seashore. Some algae, to be sure, almost certainly are present somewhere near you, but most are so inconspicuous that you are hardly aware of them. In their active phases of growth and reproduction, at least, the algae and fungi must be in water or near it. If they are entirely immersed in water they may nevertheless grow to great size, as the giant kelps and some other seaweeds. Parts that do grow out into the open air, where you live and are most likely to see them, are limited in size. A few

fungi, among the mushrooms or the bracket fungi, may have exposed parts as much as 50 centimeters in diameter, but the vast majority of fungi are much smaller. It is the true land plants, those that push up freely from the soil into the air, that are most conspicuous in our own environment. Fungi and algae have never become land plants in the fullest sense of the words.

The Conditions of Land Life

Every living cell must obtain water and other materials by absorption through the cell membrane, and such materials must be constantly available throughout the whole of an active organism. Protists are not long active unless wholly immersed in water. As long as that condition is met, there is no special further difficulty; processes of molecular diffusion suffice to distribute materials in the tiny body. The multicellular fungi and algae also get along if each cell is in contact with external water, which must of course also contain in solution the materials needed by the cells of the particular organism. Difficulties arise when some cells are internal—out of direct contact with the environment—and especially if some parts extend into the air, distant from a source of water and dissolved materials. Then in a relatively simple plant like an alga or a fungus, water must be passed along from cell to cell by osmosis and diffusion. The processes are slow and are ineffective over any considerable distance inside the plant. (See Fig. 7-4.)

That is a first barrier to any great extension of a plant into the air. It has been overcome most completely by the plants that have developed vascular tissues. These tissues, in some ways analogous to the circulatory systems of animals, make possible the prompt supply of needed solutions to cells far from an external source of water.

A differentiation of organs accompanies, or indeed even preceded, development of a vascular system. A land plant needs water and minerals (in solution) from below, from the soil, and it needs sunlight and CO_2 from above. Below there develops a specialized absorptive system, the roots, and above there develops a specialized photosynthetic system, the leaves.[1] Between roots and leaves is the stem, a structural element containing the central conduits of the conductive system.

Another requirement for land life is especially associated with the stem. In water an organism may simply float, and in soil it lies among the mineral grains. There is no special requirement for support. A stem or other structure extending into the air must support itself and anything attached to it, such as fruits or a crown of leaves. Thus all the true land plants have specialized supporting tissues. In plants growing to any considerable height, the support must be particularly strong and rigid; their stems are woody.

Still another limitation imposed by land life has to do with sexual reproduction. Gametes are, in effect, protistlike organisms that cannot long survive exposure to air. In an aquatic environment one or both of the gametes that are to unite can simply be shed into the surrounding medium. This is impossible in air. Conquest of this difficulty has involved a long series of specializations in land plants, culminating in the angiosperm seed (pp. 368 and 511).

[1] It is true that some land plants lack true roots or true leaves. These, however, are specializations in which the functions of roots or leaves have been taken over by other parts. In the course of evolution everything that could happen has happened, and so almost every generalization has an exception.

Liverworts, Hornworts, and Mosses

Among living plants the bryophytes (Fig. 21-1)—the liverworts, hornworts, and mosses [2]—represent a group that might be called amphibious. They do not have well-developed vascular systems and are thereby restricted in size and in possible range of land environments, but they are considerably advanced over the algae in adaptation to the land. The better-developed among them do have structures superficially similar to roots, stems, and leaves.

Some bryophytes are aquatic, although none is marine. A few manage to live in arctic wastes and arid deserts. Those hardy species can survive cold and dryness by suspending vital activities until warmth and moisture come along, when they revive and make up for lost time. Bryophytes grow most luxuriantly, however, in moist, shady places and in bogs. The low, tangled vegetation of mosses often holds water like a sponge, so that even on dry land they make for themselves what is practically an aquatic habitat. They reach a height of a few tens of centimeters at most (usually much less) and are rarely solitary. Usually they form an extensive, dense mat, a little world in itself, inhabited also by bacteria, algae, fungi, worms, insects, and snails.

You already know something of the reproduction and life cycle of the bryophytes (p. 369). The conspicuous green plant is the gametophyte. The sporophyte, with little or no chlorophyll, is in most cases a virtual parasite on the gametophyte. Only in hornworts is the sporophyte partially independent of the gametophyte. Although so remarkably hardy in revival after drying, bryophytes require moisture for sexual reproduction: the sperm must swim in order to meet and fertilize the egg.

In comparison with the vascular plants, the bryophytes seem primitive and at a distinct disadvantage. Without true vascular tissue, they cannot rise high in the competition for light. They must be wet at some time if the usual life cycle is to be completed. The gametes are highly vulnerable. Yet the bryo-

[2] The phylum Bryophyta ("moss plants"). For the classification of this and other plants referred to in this chapter, see p. 478.

American Museum of Natural History and
Hugh Spencer (center photo)

21-1 Bryophytes. *Top,* a liverwort, *Conocephalum conicum. Center,* sporophyte capsules of the moss *Pottia truncata. Bottom,* a mat of *Sphagnum* moss.

phytes have survived and are still abundant. One reason is that there are some situations for which they are really better adapted than other plants. A peat bog, characterized especially by the moss *Sphagnum,* is such a place. Another reason is that they are tough. If they cannot compete for the good things of life they manage, like the poor, to make do with what they have. If they cannot rise into the sunshine, they get along with more modest photosynthetic demands in shade too deep for most green plants. They are often pioneers, spreading into places not yet reached by other vegetation. When, in part through their own activities, conditions have been improved, other plants move in and the pioneers may be crowded out. Such is the usual fate of pioneers, plant or human.

Ferns and Early Vascular Plants

All the groups of plants that are still to be dealt with have vascular tissue (p. 59). All had the evolutionary potential to rise into the air and become upstanding growths. All have followed, to varying degrees, an evolutionary path nearly opposite to that of the bryophytes. In the bryophytes, as you know, the gametophyte became the principal or sole vegetative stage in the life cycle. That development was quite successful in a limited sort of way, but it seems to have run those plants into an evolutionary blind alley from which no radical further progress is possible. In the vascular plants the gametophyte became reduced until in the latest and most progressive groups it is microscopic and transient. The female gametophyte became a well-protected parasite on the sporophyte, and the sporophyte is in all vascular plants the principal, and usually the only, vegetative, photosynthetic phase in the life cycle.

Plants that had reached only the early phases of these important changes were at first spectacularly successful in covering the land with vegetation. Later most of them were supplanted by plants with more specialized reproduction, by means of seeds. A few relics of earlier groups live on, however, and one such group, that of the ferns, has survived in considerable abundance.

PSILOPSIDS [3]

The earliest known vascular plants belong to this group, for which there is no common name in English. It is nearly extinct, with only two relict genera surviving (*Psilotum*, Fig. 21-2, and *Tmesipteris*). It was a varied group early in the history of vascular plants, but was soon almost entirely replaced by more progressive forms. The whole anatomy tends to be almost diagrammatically simple. There are no true roots, a subterranean part of the stem serving the same needs. Some psilopsids have small, simple leaves, while others are leafless; in the leafless plants the aerial part of the stem carries on the necessary photosynthesis. Gametophytes are as yet unknown for the ancient psilopsids, although they must

[3] Subphylum Psilopsida.

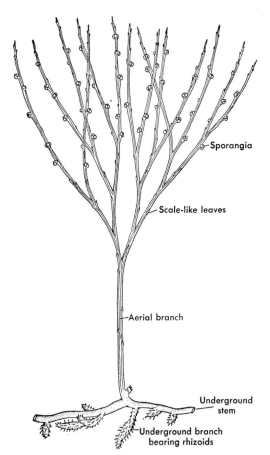

21-2   The sporophyte of *Psilotum*.   (From Smith, *et al.*, *A Textbook of General Botany*, © The Macmillan Company)

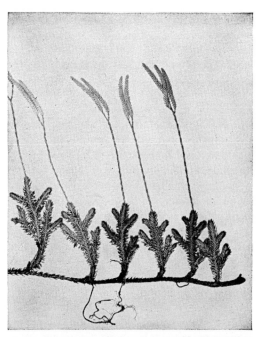

21-3   The sporophyte of the club moss or lycopod *Lycopodium clavatum*.   Note the upright branches with minute leaves (sporophylls) on which the sporangia are borne; the conelike structure formed by the sporophylls collectively is called a *strobilus*. (From Smith, *et al.*, *A Textbook of General Botany*, © The Macmillan Company)

have had them. In the surviving forms the gametophytes are small, colorless, and subterranean.

LYCOPODS [4] (CLUB MOSSES)

The lycopods are another group now represented only by relicts, four genera in this instance, but with fairly numerous and widespread species (Fig. 21-3). Most of the living lycopods are low herbs, although some of the vinelike species may reach as great a length as 20 meters. In their time of glory, in the coal forests of the Carboniferous (p. 763), some lycopods were great forest trees, 1 to 2 meters in diameter and 30 to 40 meters high.

Lycopods have true, although sometimes poorly developed, roots as well as differentiated stems and leaves. Their anatomy in general is more complex than in the psilopsids. They show another advance over both the psilopsids and the nonvascular plants. Some

[4] Subphylum Lycopsida.

produce two distinct kinds of spores (microspores and macrospores, p. 369) one of which develops into a male and the other into a female gametophyte. The gametophytes are tiny but independent organisms, sometimes photosynthetic, sometimes colorless and living on organic debris in the soil.

A few fossil lycopods had another remarkable advance in mode of reproduction. The eggs developed in a well-protected case on the female gametophyte and were retained there even after they had been fertilized and had begun to develop into an embryonic sporophyte. The result was similar to a seed. It is unlikely that the seed plants evolved from these particular lycopods, but they show clearly how such a momentous change could take place.

SPHENOPSIDS [5] (HORSETAILS)

Living sphenopsids all belong to one genus, *Equisetum*, with only about 25 species (Fig. 21-4). They are nevertheless locally abun-

[5] Subphylum Sphenopsida.

American Museum of Natural History

21-4 Terminal part of the sporophyte of *Equisetum sylvaticum* (wood horsetail) with strobili containing sporangia.

dant and are usually easy to find around bogs or in sandy soil near streams. They are commonly known as "scouring rushes" because the stems contain gritty silica and were useful for cleaning pots and pans in the days before soap operas and the products they advertise. Our native species are rarely over a meter tall, although some tropical equisetums reach much greater heights. The equisetums, too, are relicts of a group that was at its height in the ancient coal forests and then included large trees.

Nothing like a seed is known in any sphenopsids, and the spores are rarely, if ever, differentiated into microspores and macrospores. Otherwise in degree of differentiation and in life history the sphenopsids are quite like lycopods (or ferns). They are, however, quite different in appearance and in details of anatomy. The stems are vertically ribbed and jointed, with a whorl of leaves at each joint. In the living genus the leaves are small, and photosynthesis occurs mainly in the stems, which are of course green. In some extinct species the leaves were large and were probably the main photosynthetic organs.

FERNS [6]

From primitive psilopsids three major groups of plants evolved with divergent complication in their anatomical and functional differentiation but with little change in major features of reproduction or life cycles. All three reached their climax about the time of the Carboniferous coal forests. We have seen that two of those groups, the lycopods and the sphenopsids, greatly declined thereafter but still have a few living survivors. The still more ancient and originally ancestral psilopsids also straggled along even when overshadowed by their more exuberant descendants. The third of the progressive divergent groups, that of the ferns, also declined [7] in

[6] Class Filicineae.
[7] The decline of the ferns was not so great as is sometimes stated, because they were never so dominant as was once believed. Early students of paleobotany thought that ferns were the commonest plants of the Carboniferous, and you may still see that time referred to as an "Age of Ferns." It is now known, however, that many plants of that age formerly believed to be ferns because of their fernlike foliage were really seed plants (see p. 512).

21-5 Ferns. The majority of ferns are relatively small, herblike plants like the Christmas fern (*left*). A few, however, have evolved the arborescent (tree) habit like these tree ferns in New Zealand (*right*).

importance but is still so abundant and varied that its members cannot be called unsuccessful or relicts (Fig. 21-5).

The reproductive and life cycle of ferns is similar to that of the vascular plants just described; it has been discussed in Chapter 15 (see p. 371). In some respects the ferns are even less progressive than some of the ancient lycopods. Lycopods and ferns do not represent successive evolutionary steps, but are divergent groups that arose at about the same time and have remained at about the same level. The gametophyte in ferns is small, but is usually an independent, photosynthetic plant. The eggs are fertilized where they are formed, on the damp underside of the gametophyte, but the sporophyte develops directly from the zygote, without the appearance of a seedlike, protected embryo. Sperms are still flagellated cells that must swim through an external watery medium if they are to encounter and fertilize the eggs. In this respect ferns are no better adapted to land life than are mosses. Ferns are also comparatively unprogressive in that only a few of them have differentiated microspores and macrospores.

Vegetative reproduction is common in ferns.

Although few nonbotanists have ever noticed the gametophyte of a fern, the leaves, at least, of the sporophytes of various species are familiar to everyone. The leaves may be only a few centimeters in length, but in some tropical climbing ferns they may reach the astonishing length of 30 meters or more. Some ferns have simple leaves, but in most the leaves are divided into leaflets, which may in turn be subdivided. Thus arises the lacy appearance so characteristic of the most familiar fronds of ferns.[8] The spores are borne in sporangia on the underside of the fronds. These are quite evident as little brown dots in many of our native ferns. Some species have some of their fronds without spores, and in some species the spores develop on specialized parts unlike the vegetative fronds.

The stems of ferns have a well-developed vascular system, and true roots are usually present. In the familiar species of our temper-

[8] Specialists in the study of ferns sometimes call the whole leaf a frond; if it is divided into leaflets these are called pinnae, and if the pinnae are further subdivided their parts are called pinnules.

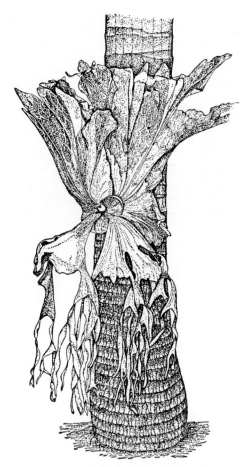

21-6 The epiphytic staghorn fern growing on a palm stem. (From Brown, *The Plant Kingdom*, Ginn, 1935)

and variety toward the humid parts of the tropics. They culminate in wet tropical forests in a great profusion of forms, which include not only herbaceous species, similar to most of ours, and tree ferns, but also creepers, vines, and striking epiphytes. (Epiphytes, p. 631, are plants that grow on other plants, using them as attachment, but they draw no nutrition from the host and are not parasitic.) In rain forests such epiphytic ferns as the staghorn (Fig. 21-6) contribute to the aerial gardens that grow profusely on upper trunks and branches of the tall forest trees. In these situations the forest floor is dark, with so little light that few photosynthetic plants can live there. The epiphytes of the aerial garden are too small to compete for sunlight except by using the tall successful competitors themselves as a base and thus growing far up where they can share the light.

A few ferns are aquatic. In these species there is a differentiation of microspores and macrospores, and separate female and male gametophytes consequently develop. Can you think of any reason why this separation of the sexes is associated with aquatic life?

The Seed Plants: Gymnosperms

Abundant as they are, the ferns still do not represent completely successful adaptation of plants to land life. The gametophytes, particularly, are highly vulnerable to environmental conditions. The sperms still require environmental water, even if only a film of it, if they are to fertilize the eggs. The most sensitive and vulnerable stages in the life cycle were eliminated in the plants that evolved *seeds*. In them, as you will recall (pp. 372-73), the partially developed male gametophyte becomes a *pollen grain*, which is often highly resistant to drying and can float for long periods in the air without dying. The female gametophyte is entirely parasitic and lives its whole life protected in the tissues of the parent sporophyte. The male gametophyte completes its development and the zygote also forms within these parental tissues. The zygote then develops further into an embryonic sporophyte, which is enclosed in protective tissue and provided with food before it is freed from the grandparental plant. Then

ate zone the stems are usually horizontal, on or in the soil, with simple roots (occasionally absent) extending into the soil from the prostrate stem. In more uniformly warm climates many ferns have large, vertical stems or trunks which may grow to great heights and develop bark: such are the *tree ferns*, common in the tropics but not extending far into regions of cold winters. The tree ferns have better-developed root systems than the herbaceous species, but even in these the roots are less extensive and complex than in most seed plants.

As you might expect (why?), ferns are most abundant in warm, moist, shady situations. Some manage to grow in cold and in arid climates, but they increase in numbers

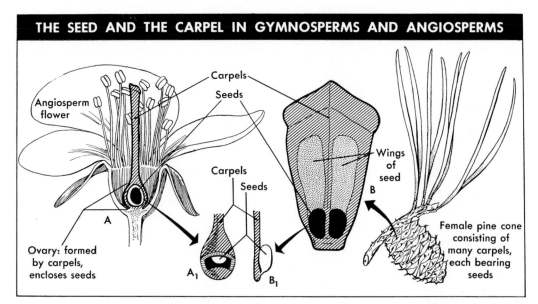

21-7   The seed and carpel in gymnosperms and angiosperms. In the angiosperm (A) the carpels form an ovary in the cavity of which the seed is *enclosed*. In the gymnosperms (B) the carpel is a flat, primitively leaflike structure bearing the seed *nakedly* on its surface. A_1 and B_1, wholly schematic representations of the relation of seed to carpel in angiosperm and gymnosperm, respectively; the ovary wall is cut away in A_1 to show the seed inside.

it is by some agency moved off to start a new, independent sporophytic generation.

Associated with the evolution of seeds is also the most extensive and effective development of root and stem systems and tissues and of leaves. These factors have made the seed plants incomparably the most abundant and widespread of land plants. In most terrestrial environments they have nearly, although not completely, ousted and replaced all the groups of nonseed plants. Some seed plants have become aquatic, but the group is far from dominant in fresh water and is almost absent in the seas. Why has there been no significant tendency for seed plants to replace the far simpler algae in aquatic environments?

In the first seed plants to evolve, protection of the seeds was not yet perfected and flowers had not yet appeared. Spores, egg cells, and seeds developed in organs sometimes of considerable complexity but without the still higher degree of organization seen in a true flower. The seeds arose on leaflike structures (technically known as carpels or sporophylls) which did not enclose them; thus the seed was comparatively naked, and the plants with such seeds are called *gymnosperms* (from

Greek roots for "naked seeds").[9] Plants with flowers and with seeds encased in an ovary (whose tissues are in fact the carpels, or sporophylls, which bear the seeds) are *angiosperms* ("enclosed seeds") (Fig. 21-7).

The gymnosperms, first seed plants on the scene, early (mainly in the latter part of the Paleozoic, see p. 736) underwent an extensive adaptive radiation. Numerous groups became divergently adapted to various environments and ways of life without, as a rule, much fundamental progressive change in basic characteristics. Some of the main branches of this basic radiation have become extinct, probably through competition with more progressive or efficient plants: the seed ferns, cycadeoids, and cordaites. Others survive but are so diminished in numbers, diversity, and geographic distribution that they are today mere relics: the cycads, ginkgos, and joint firs.[10] Only one main branch of the early

[9] The nakedness of the seed is, however, comparative only; it does have other protective coatings.

[10] But the so-called joint firs, most familiar to us as "Mormon tea" (a species of **Ephedra**) seem never to have been abundant, and they may not have arisen in the basic gymnosperm radiation.

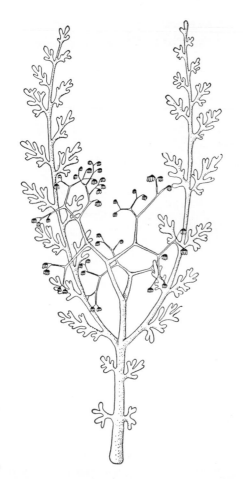

gymnosperm radiation has continued to the present in great abundance and diversity, although even it is past its heyday: the familiar conifers.

SEED FERNS

The coal forests of the Carboniferous period (p. 763) were dominated by shrubs and trees with fernlike leaves (Fig. 21-8). It was long assumed by paleobotanists that all these plants were, indeed, ferns. Slowly, however, the suspicion grew that some of them might be gymnosperms. At first this conclusion was based on minor anatomical peculiarities of the stems and leaves. Finally it was confirmed by finding fossils in which gymnospermous seeds were actually attached to "fern" fronds. The difficulty was one that often arises in the study of fossil plants. Roots, stems, leaves, and reproductive cells and organs may all be found, but usually not in direct association. The paleobotanists' problem then is to decide which leaf goes with what type of wood, which seed or spore with which leaves, and so on. Some of the fernlike Carboniferous vegetation has turned out really to belong to ferns, plants with spores and no seeds. Much of it, however, belonged to plants with seeds, and those plants are now generally called seed ferns.[11] The name is not wholly apt, because the plants may better be considered gymnosperms with fernlike leaves than ferns with seeds. The group is, however, more or less intermediate between early ferns and the more advanced gymnosperms.

The seeds of the seed ferns usually grew singly and, so to speak, openly rather than in the conelike structures so characteristic of most gymnosperms. They were attached along a frond or leaf stalk in various ways, not unlike the varying attachments of spore cases on fern leaves. The whole plant is evidently primitive as gymnosperms go, and it is not surprising that the seed ferns, although early abundant, were soon replaced by more progressive groups and are now wholly extinct.

21-8 Seed ferns (or pteridosperms), most primitive of gymnosperms. *Top,* drawing of a seed fern's sporophyll-bearing clusters of sporangia. *Bottom,* photo of fossil seed-fern foliage. (Drawing from Smith, *et al., A Textbook of General Botany,* © The Macmillan Company; photo from Chester A. Arnold)

11 The accepted technical name of the group is Pteridospermae.

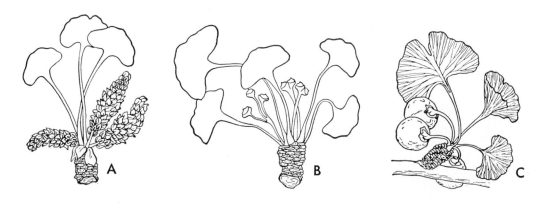

21-9 *Ginkgo biloba*, the maidenhair tree. The two sexes occur as separate trees. *A.* Branch of male tree with mature male strobilus. *B.* Branch of female tree with young ovules (female sporangia). *C.* Mature seeds. *D.* Ginkgo trees. (Drawings from Smith, *et al., A Textbook of General Botany,* © The Macmillan Company; photo from U.S. Forest Service)

mous seeds, rather like those of seed ferns. The wood and some other parts are more like those of conifers. The ginkgos are an ancient main branch of gymnosperm radiation, and they were once spread over most of the earth. Only a single species has survived, mainly in the form of cultivated plants in China.[12] It is a striking, woody, branched deciduous tree that has recently been spread all over the world by man. It is now familiar along American streets and in parks, although few people who know it are aware of its long and romantic history. It is a tough plant, vying with the plane trees in its ability to survive in the poisonous, sooty air of large cities. How do you suppose it happens that a plant that had become virtually, if not completely, extinct in nature thrives in cultivation?

Ginkgos share with cycads a primitive feature lost in all other living gymnosperms and in angiosperms: they still have motile, flagellated sperms. The pollen, which is as you recall a partly developed male gametophyte, lands on the structure enclosing the egg cells. There the pollen develops further and produces sperms that swim to meet and fertilize the egg cells, much as in moss or

GINKGOS

The living maidenhair tree, *Ginkgo biloba,* is a famous living fossil (Fig. 21-9). The foliage is larger but otherwise much like that of a maidenhair fern, whence the popular name, but the plant bears true gymnosper-

12 It used to be said that there are no living wild ginkgos, but recent reports have it that some are still growing wild in a limited area in China. It is possible, however, that those trees have escaped from cultivation.

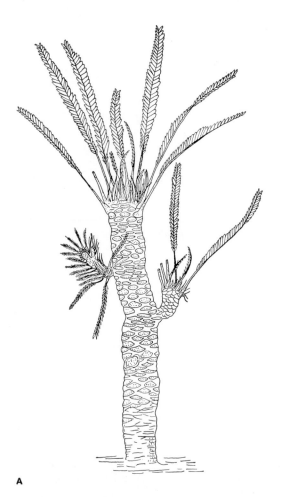

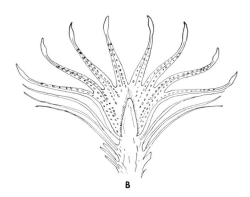

B

C

A

D

21-10 Cycadeoids and cycads. *A.* The extinct cycadeoid *Williamsonia sewardiana* (Jurassic age, about 150 million years ago; cf. Table 30-1). *B.* The so-called "flower" of the cycadeoid *Cycadeoidea.* The figure represents a median section through the flower; the central conical structure bore ovules, and the surrounding corolla-like structure bore "stamens" at the points marked by the circular scars. The cycadeoid "flower" is not historically related to those of true flowering plants. *C.* A living cycad (*Dioon edule*) in Mexico. Note its palmlike character (see p. 515). *D.* The male cone, or strobilus. *E.* A single sporophyll from the male strobilus, bearing several microsporangia containing pollen. *F* and *G.* Sporophylls from the female strobilus, each bearing two ovules—*F*, young, and *G*, older.

E

F

G

Drawings from Chester A. Arnold. Photo at center right from Chamberlain, *The Living Cycads,* U. of Chicago Press; lower four photos from Smith, *et al.,* *A Textbook of General Botany,* © The Macmillan Company

ferns. In these primitive gymnosperms, however, the distance to be swum is very small,
and the swimming is indoors: it is in a chamber enclosed by the tissue around the eggs.
In other living gymnosperms and in angiosperms there is no motile sperm, and a pollen
tube develops in the way already described
(p. 370). It is probable that the ancient, extinct seed ferns, cycadeoids, and cordaites,
had motile sperms like the surviving ginkgos
and cycads. Can you think of a possible explanation for the fact that sperms are still
motile in all the most progressive animals but
have become nonmotile in the most progressive
land plants?

CYCADEOIDS AND CYCADS

The extinct cycadeoids and the relict cycads
are closely similar in general appearance and
structure (Fig. 21-10). Their reproductive
organs are, however, quite different. They
were probably closely related in origin but
long followed partly divergent and partly
parallel lines of evolution. They have short,
stumpy, palmlike stems, rarely reaching a
height over 2 or 3 meters and usually much
less. Most of them are unbranched; some are
simply branched. The foliage is also palmlike,
and the cultivated plants, often raised in tubs
in conservatories, are usually mistaken for
palms. (Real palms are not gymnosperms,
but actually advanced angiosperms.)

The cycadeoids [13] were common and widespread around the middle of the Mesozoic
(see p. 778) but became extinct soon thereafter, geologically speaking. In them the male
(sperm-producing) and female (egg-producing) organs were united in a single, complex structure, resembling a flower (Fig.
21-10). Some students have maintained that
these structures were, indeed, the forerunners
of flowers. The detailed anatomy, however, is
not so flowerlike, and the consensus now is
that the evolution of these pseudo flowers and
of the true flowers of the angiosperms took
place independently. This seems to be an unusually good example of parallel evolution
(p. 470).

[13] Technically the Cycadeoidales. Many works
on biology or botany call them "Bennettitales,"
but that name is invalid under the technical
rules of nomenclature.

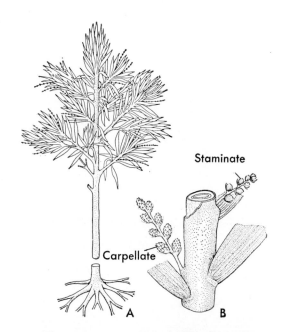

21-11 The cordaites. *A.* Cordaites. The whole
plant, but part of stem omitted. Note the separate
branches bearing cones (or strobili). *B.* Portion of
major branch showing two minor branches bearing
staminate (male) strobili and carpellate (female)
strobili. *Below,* photograph (×4) of the fossil seed
of a cordaites, *Cordianthus ampullaceus.* (Drawing
from Smith, *et al., A Textbook of General Botany,*
ⓒ The Macmillan Company; photo by Chester A.
Arnold, U. of Michigan)

THE MORE COMPLEX PLANTS   **515**

21-12 Conifers. *Top left*, mountain hemlock (*Tsuga mertensiana*) in Washington State. *Lower left*, the monkey puzzle tree (*Araucaria araucaria*). *Right, Sequoia gigantea* and other conifers in Yosemite Park, California.

Cycads[14] are still rather widespread in places with warm climates, including Florida, but they are nowhere abundant, and they comprise relatively few genera and species. They are at least as old as the cycadeoids and have survived far longer, but they were probably never so abundant as the cycadeoids in their prime. Cycads are most readily distinguished from cycadeoids by the fact that pollen and egg cells are produced in separate,

conelike structures. In this respect the cycads resemble the conifers.

CORDAITES[15]

The cordaites (Fig. 21-11), now long extinct (since early Triassic, p. 736), were another common group in the Carboniferous coal forests. They were tall trees with long, straplike leaves. Pollen and egg cells were produced in separate structures, somewhat like

[14] Cycadales.

[15] Technically, Cordaitales.

21-13 The cones of white pine. *Left,* a branch bearing female (carpellate) cones of three successive years: oldest at bottom, youngest at tip of branch. *Right,* a branch bearing several male
cones. (From Smith, *et al., A Textbook of General Botany,* © The Macmillan Company)

simple cones. The special interest of cordaites
is that they may have given rise to the conifers, although if so the separation must have
occurred early in cordaitean history and
among primitive members of the group.

CONIFERS [16]

The only really common living gymnosperms are the conifers, many of which are
certainly familiar to you. They include the
pines, firs, spruces, cedars, hemlocks, cypresses, redwoods, junipers, and many others;
there are about 450 living species. All of them
are woody perennials (living for several or
many years), and most of them are trees,
although some are shrubs. They include the
largest and oldest of all living things: se-
quoias and redwoods (two closely related
species) up to 10 meters in diameter, 100
meters in height, and 4000 years or more in
age (Fig. 21-12). Conifers are the dominant
trees over much of the temperate zone and
often form great forests made up of only one
or a few species. In spite of this wide and
dense distribution, it is evident that conifer
forests are most common in relatively unfavorable situations: dry, cold, and windy,
or with poor, sandy soil. In the most favorable situations angiosperm forests are more

usual. Have you encountered other instances
of the survival of a comparatively old group
in generally less favorable environments?

Most conifers have narrow, needle-like or
scale-like leaves (Fig. 21-13). A few have
broad leaves, and a few have reduced leaves
and perform photosynthesis mostly in the
stems. Most of them are *evergreen,* and the
whole group is sometimes called the evergreens. Evergreens do shed their leaves, as do
all trees, but they do not shed them all at
once and so always have some green leaves
in place. However, some *deciduous* conifers
shed their leaves all at once at the onset of
the cold or dry season. Among conifers familiar in this country, larches and tamaracks
are deciduous. There are also some evergreen
angiosperms (do you know any?), and the
contrast evergreen-deciduous does not completely coincide with gymnosperm-angiosperm.

Conifers have separate male and female
cones (Fig. 21-13).[17] A pollen tube develops
(p. 370), and the sperms are nonmotile and
without flagella. As in the angiosperms, they
are reduced to a minimum. Each sperm (two
arise from each pollen grain or in each male
gametophyte) consists merely of a haploid
nucleus in the pollen tube.

---

[16] Coniferales ("cone-bearers"), but, as you
have seen, some other gymnosperms also have
cones or something quite similar.

[17] In some, however, the cone has been secondarily modified so as to be hardly recognizable
as such; the juniper has "berries," for instance,
which have evolved from cones and are not true
berries.

Conifer pollen usually has small winglike projections; dispersal of the pollen so that it reaches female cones and fertilizes their egg cells depends entirely on the wind. The seeds, also sometimes with a wing, may be dispersed by wind or simply by falling, rolling, and bouncing. They are frequently dispersed by rodents, which carry them away and store them but fail to eat all they take. It is interesting that the ancient cordaites had winged pollen and seeds and certainly were dependent on wind for the dispersal of both. There were no rodents, and probably no other small seedeaters, when the cordaites and the earliest conifers lived. Some angiosperms have wind dispersal of pollen and seeds. It is, however, among the angiosperms that the most elaborate or specialized means of dispersal by animals, especially insects but also birds and mammals, occur (p. 374). The spread of the angiosperms, their modernization and increasing dominance over the older gymnosperms, broadly coincides with the evolution of special groups of insects, birds, and mammals. That is surely not pure coincidence. What are some of the evolutionary concomitants of this interdependence of broadly different groups of organisms?

Conifers as a group are abundant enough, but they are past their prime, and many kinds of conifers are extinct or are relicts. Araucarias (Fig. 21-12), for instance, familiar in cultivation as the "monkey puzzle tree," were once world-wide but now occur only in a limited part of South America and in Australia and the southwestern Pacific islands. To us they seem highly exotic, but the famous petrified forest of Arizona consists largely of ancient members of the araucaria group. Even more remarkable is *Metasequoia*, known as a fossil from many parts of the world.[18] Its remains are common in the United States. It was long believed that *Metasequoia* had been extinct everywhere for tens of millions of years, but in 1944 a living *Metasequoia* forest was found in a remote part of China. This resurrected fossil is now being grown

[18] Paleobotanists used to confuse it with **Sequoia.** The needles of **Metasequoia** and **Sequoia** are similar in some species, but the relationship is not really very close. The needles are differently arranged, and **Metasequoia** is deciduous while **Sequoia** is evergreen.

in cultivation by a number of people in the United States, but it is not yet common here.

The Flowering Seed Plants

The plants with flowers, the angiosperms, are far and away the most successful of land plants today. This is true by any reasonable criterion: individual abundance, numbers of species (probably about 175,000), area covered, or total metabolic activity. They are also by far the most important to man. Much the greater part of our food is of angiosperm origin, directly or indirectly. Almost all of our own food plants are angiosperms: cereals, vegetables, fruits, and the rest. Likewise, almost all our food animals live mostly or entirely on angiosperms, so that when we eat them we are still eating angiosperms at one or two removes. Most of our ornamental plants are angiosperms, although here the conifers do play a considerable role. Of course all our flowers are angiosperms. Conifers are at present a more important source of wood and other forest products, but angiosperm forests are also productive. Man's existence, like that of all animals, depends on the plant kingdom, and man is one of the species that depends most heavily on the angiosperms. (It is only fair to add that our most obnoxious weeds are also angiosperms.)

The angiosperms arose later than other groups of plants of comparable scope. They probably evolved early in the Mesozoic (p. 736), but were not dominant until toward the end of that era. The expansion of the angiosperms coincided with the decline or extinction of most groups of gymnosperms, and undoubtedly this is an indication of cause and effect. Angiosperms represent the highest level of plant evolution up to now. It would be rash to predict that no higher will occur, but it seems impossible to imagine what that higher might be. They are highest not in extending their dominance over all, for far older groups continue to be dominant in some environments, but in living in environments farthest removed from the ancestral sea and in being most successful in those particular environments. There is a parallel here to animal evolution. Among animals old groups (mollusks, fishes) continue

Left, American Museum of Natural History; right,
U.S. Dept. of Agriculture

21-14 Angiosperms. *Left,* tulip, a monocotyledon. *Right,* cotton plant, a dicotyledon.

to dominate in the water, but the highest animals in an evolutionary sense are younger groups in more recently occupied environments.

The essential features of the physiology, structure, and reproduction of flowering plants have been mentioned in previous chapters (see especially Chapter 15). In general physiology they are much like other green plants. In structure they present variations on the same themes as other vascular plants. In reproduction, they are typical seed plants with the addition of the carpel-covered seed and the flower. The sequence in the present chapter has involved comparison with and approach to the culmination of land plants in the angiosperms. All that pertinent material should be reviewed but need not be repeated here.

The incredibly extensive array of the angiosperms runs in size from the barely visible duckweeds to great trees exceeded only by a few conifers among all living things. Comparatively few angiosperms are aquatic, but some are. (Can you name some?) On land they grow practically everywhere that any life exists. A few are parasites, although they are not disease-producers in the ordinary sense. (A hay-fever victim allergic to angio-

sperm pollen may quibble at that statement if he likes.) Some are organisms of decay, but the vast majority are photosynthetic. A few are in part carnivorous (Venus's-flytrap and sundew, Fig. 10-1). Angiosperms provide most of the food for man and (nonaquatic) beast, but many are deadly poisonous to both. Their flowers may be microscopic in size or several feet across. They are of almost every imaginable shade. Some of them even have color patterns invisible to our eyes, although none of them is pure black. (Why not? Incidentally, the quest for a black tulip or a black rose, never actually achieved, is a favorite theme in literature.) They give off scents ranging from what is to us an unbearable stench to perfumes more impelling than *Mon Nuit,* thus demonstrating that man is not the measure of all things. The "unbearable stench" is as attractive to some insects as *Mon Nuit* is supposed to be to the human male.

In somewhat more systematic vein, angiosperms are divided into *monocotyledons* and *dicotyledons* (Fig. 21-14).[19] The bulk of an angiosperm seed is made up of one or

[19] These rather cumbersome names are usually shortened to "monocots" and "dicots."

two leaflike structures (cotyledons) packed with food,[20] especially starch, with which the young plant begins its development. Monocots have one such organ and dicots have two. The distinction is obvious on comparison of a grain of corn (a monocot seed) with a peanut (a dicot seed). In monocots the veins in the leaves are usually parallel; in dicots the veins are usually netted. In monocots the vascular tissue is scattered in bundles throughout the pith; in dicots the bundles form a cylinder around the pith. Some authorities think that monocots are a more specialized group, derived from early dicots. Others think the two groups are of equal antiquity and represent a basic split that developed among the earliest angiosperms.

Familiar monocots include: grasses, sedges, cattails, lilies, onions, tulips, palms, and orchids. Dicots are considerably more numerous. They include: magnolias, carrots, peas, mints, morning-glories, nightshades, potatoes, mustards, squashes, dandelions, and sunflowers, as well as almost all the broad-leafed shrubs and trees. (Also spinach, poison ivy, and gardenias.)

[20] Sometimes food reserves are also present as endosperm (p. 371).

Most of our important angiosperm food plants have been cultivated since prehistoric times, although many varieties of them have been developed recently. Even early man exercised rigorous selection, so that the older cultivated plants have been changed, sometimes beyond recognition, from their wild ancestors. For instance, one of the most disputed problems in genetics and botany has to do with the wild plants from which pre-Columbian Indians evolved corn (or maize). The word "evolved" is used advisedly. The ability of man to develop new strains, even wholly new species, of cultivated plants is convincing evidence that nature has done likewise, though more slowly and less systematically from the human point of view. Much has been learned about evolutionary principles from experiments with such plants. Knowledge of evolution has, in turn, assisted efforts to develop desirable new cultivated plants. Cultivated plants are often referred to as *cultigens.*

The bulk foods of most agricultural communities have always been those rich in starch and, in different parts of the world, have usually been monocot seeds (such as corn, wheat, or rice) or dicot tubers (such

TABLE 21-1

A summary of characteristics of the major groups of plants

(+ indicates that the stated character is the usual or the ancestral condition for the group; 0 indicates usual or ancestral absence of the stated character)

Group	General way of life	Dominance of: Gameto-phyte	Sporo-phyte	Roots, stems, leaves	Vascular tissue	Seeds	Flowers
Algae	Aquatic (secondarily in other moist situations); photosynthetic	Variable		0	0	0	0
Fungi	Aquatic and moist situations; non-photosynthetic; parasites and organisms of decay	+ *	0	0	0	0	0
Bryophytes	Semiterrestrial, mostly in moist situations; photosynthetic	+	0	0 †	0	0	0
Ferns (also psilopsids, lycopods, equisetums)	Terrestrial; photosynthetic	0	+	+	+	0	0
Gymnosperms	Terrestrial; photosynthetic	0	+	+	+	+	0
Angiosperms	Terrestrial; photosynthetic	0	+	+	+	+	+

* The terms "gametophyte" and "sporophyte" are not strictly applicable to many fungi.
† Leaves and stems of bryophytes (some authorities prefer to speak of them as scales and stalks) only superficially resemble those of vascular plants. The rootlike structures bear little resemblance to true roots. Nevertheless, there is definite organ differentiation.

as potatoes, yams, or cassava). A really fascinating exercise, unfortunately one we cannot follow up here, is to chart agricultural food supplies among primitive peoples throughout the world and to trace the history of the plants down into our modern economy.

Table 21-1 summarizes some of the characteristics of the major groups of plants.

Chapter Summary

Problems raised by land life, the condition for the more complex plants: acquisition of water and nutrients; their transportation inside the plant (the significance of vascular systems); differentiation of root and shoot systems; mechanical problem of support in air as against water (significance of supporting tissues); problem of getting the sexes together (significance of flowers).

Bryophytes: liverworts, hornworts, and mosses; their poorly developed vascular systems; restricted exploitation of land—predominantly moist habitats; dominance of gametophyte; dependence on water for fertilization; modest photosynthetic demands.

The early vascular plants: evolution of sporophyte dominance with a vascular system.

Psilopsids: most primitive vascular plants, formerly abundant; roots absent; simple leaves; small subterranean gametophyte in the surviving genera, *Psilotum* and *Tmesipteris*.

Lycopods: club mosses; abundant in Carboniferous; few surviving forms; true roots present; microspores and macrospores; tiny gametophytes; ancient lycopod evolution of seedlike structures.

Sphenopsids: horsetails; abundant in Carboniferous; then included tree forms; one surviving genus, *Equisetum*; leaves in whorls around the stem; no differentiation of macro- and microspores.

Ferns: third main line of evolution from primitive psilopsid vascular plants; small independent gametophyte; dependence on water for fertilization; organization of the sporophyte—roots and leafy shoot systems; sporangia; most successful in warm, moist climates; diverse types: tree ferns, epiphyte ferns, and aquatic ferns.

The seed plants: fern descendants; ultimate plant adaptation to land life; the ferns' incomplete mastery of conditions of land life (vulnerability of gametophyte to desiccation); the seed as evolutionary solution to the problem; retention of female gametophyte in (sporangial) tissues of parent sporophyte; growth of male gametophyte and of zygote also *within* sporophyte tissue; seed as old sporangium containing embryonic sporophyte and food reserves; further evolution of root and shoot system in seed plants.

Gymnosperms: seed plants with seeds borne naked on the supporting sporophyll, or carpel; their extensive radiation in Paleozoic; subsequent decline.

Seed ferns: long-extinct seed plants.

Gingkos (maidenhair tree): motile, flagellated sperms, a primitive feature; sexes on separate trees.

Cycadeoids and cycads: palmlike appearance; cycadeoids abundant in Mesozoic but subsequently extinct; their evolution of flowerlike structure, an example of parallel evolution; surviving cycads in warm, moist areas; separation of male and female cones.

Cordaites: abundant in Carboniferous; ancestors of conifers?

Conifers: only common surviving gymnosperms; predominant today in unfavorable situations; needle- or scale-like leaves; evergreens; separate male and female cones; nonmotile sperms; wind dispersal of pollen and seeds, a primitive condition contrasted with that of angiosperms, in which insects and other animals are exploited for pollen and seed dispersal; various modern conifers.

Angiosperms: flowering seed plants; sporophyll encases young seed in an ovary; most successful of land plants today; importance in human economy; first appearance in early Mesozoic; dominance by end of Mesozoic; abundance and diversity in size, appearance, and habitats; monocots and dicots.

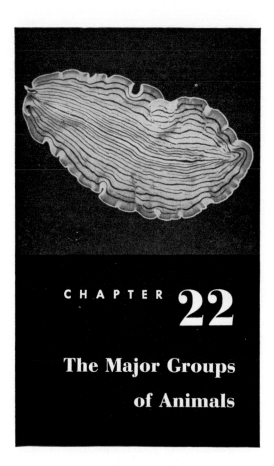

This is a flatworm, Prostheceraeus vittatus, *of the phylum Platyhelminthes. Lowly as flatworms are, they have been the subject of important discussion in attempts to elucidate evolutionary relationships among major groups of animals.*
(Photo © Douglas P. Wilson)

CHAPTER **22**

The Major Groups of Animals

WHAT IS AN ANIMAL?

This chapter starts with a question that everyone thinks he can answer, but one that is often answered wrong. Obviously dogs, cats, and cows are animals. To many people an ant is something else, perhaps a "bug" rather than an animal. Of course you know by now that an ant is an animal. So are sponges, corals, worms, clams, and a vast array of other organisms. When it comes to the protists, as you already know, there is no complete agreement as to which are "really" animals and which are plants (p. 484). The solution of calling them neither plants nor animals was found workable but rather unsatisfactory. The distinction between some of them like *Chlamydomonas* (p. 494) and undoubted plants is not really clear-cut (p. 494), nor is there a sharp way of excluding others, like *Stylonichia* or *Euplotes* (Fig. 21-8) from the

category "animals." The best answer to "What is an animal?" is not in terms of description at all. It is this: An animal is an organism that belongs by descent and common ancestry to any of the phyla that biologists agree to call "animals." It is, however, possible to make descriptive generalizations about characteristics found more often in animals than in plants. Resemblances and differences between animals and plants have been mentioned frequently in preceding chapters. Now we need only to summarize and review some of the more important and widespread contrasts:

Metabolism. Most plants are photosynthetic. All those that are not were probably derived from photosynthetic ancestors. Animals probably also had photosynthetic ancestors among the protists, but no animals, as such, are photosynthetic. All derive food from other organisms.

Mobility. Most plants are attached and nonmotile as developed and independent organisms, and are dispersed in specialized reproductive phases, such as spores or seeds. Many animals are also attached (sessile) as adults, but most animals are mobile throughout life and all have at least a mobile phase in development.

Structure and organization. Most animals have a fixed structure to which new elements are added only at limited, usually early, phases of development. Most plants have less fixed patterns, with new elements added at almost any time or periodically throughout life. Tissue and organ differentiation in animals is often more definite and more complex than in plants. Individual plant cells usually have rigid walls; animal cells usually do not. Plant cells are vacuolated when mature; animal cells usually are not.

Maintenance. In most animals the cells are either surrounded by sea water or are in a fairly constant internal environment that resembles sea water in being rich in sodium chloride (common salt). Devices for the maintenance of a constant internal environment are less evident in plants, and the internal fluids are usually low in sodium chloride.

Responsiveness. Most animals are far more responsive than any plants. With relatively few exceptions, animals have nerves and muscles, markedly unlike any plant tissues. Almost all plants lack special receptors, and the rare special receptors that do occur are few and simple. Most animals have special receptors, and these are usually numerous and complex.

Reproductive cycles. Most plants have a sexual cycle with some development of the haplophase between meiosis and fertilization. In animals development of the haplophase is highly exceptional.

Any significant contrast between two groups of organisms points up the fact that the groups have different roles in the complex interrelationships of populations in nature. Plants and animals, as a whole, clearly do have different roles, even though their characteristic roles may be modified or lost in some particular kind of plant or animal. *The most basic difference is in acquisition or synthesis of foods.* The other important differences are all more or less closely related to this one. The fact that animals are characteristically more mobile certainly has something to do with their getting food from other organisms rather than manufacturing it from raw materials. Differences of animals from plants in structure, maintenance, responsive-

ness, and even in reproduction all seem to have had some original relationships to mobility. Try to work out some of these relationships in more detail.

The Major Animal Phyla

The classification on pp. 477-81 places animals in twenty-one phyla, not counting the more animal-like protists, which are often considered another phylum under the name "Protozoa." Some systematists recognize more phyla, and some, fewer. For instance, the two classes of Bryozoa may have had different origins and are sometimes called separate phyla. On the other hand, brachiopods and bryozoans have some fundamental resemblances and may have had a common origin sufficiently recently to justify uniting them in a single phylum.

The great majority of known animals, both living and extinct, belong to only eleven of the twenty-one phyla of our classification, those named in heavier type on pp. 477-81. The other ten phyla are mostly rare and of no great importance at the present time, and nine of them are little known as fossils. Rotifers (phylum Trochelminthes) are now very abundant, to be sure, but they are not highly diversified, they are not key figures in the activities of life as a whole, and they have no fossil record. Graptolites (phylum Graptolithina) are totally extinct, known only as fossils. They were very abundant in some ancient seas, but they do not loom large in the history of life. It is also probable that we would not consider them a separate phylum if we understood their relationships, which are highly speculative at present.[1] That is also true of some or most of the smaller living phyla: if we knew their ancestries and the changes involved in their origins we would probably place them in other, larger or better-known phyla. The ctenophores (phylum Ctenophora), for example, may be an off-shoot of the Coelenterata, and the mesozoans (phylum Mesozoa) may be unusually degenerate Platyhelminthes.

The best way, and indeed the only adequate

[1] A current view is that they may belong in the phylum Chordata (subphylum Hemichordata, see p. 537), which would be rather exciting if true—but the evidence is poor and ambiguous.

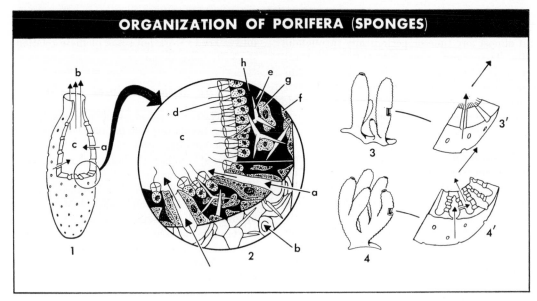

22-1   Porifera.   *1.* The gross structure of a simple sponge like *Olynthus*. Water, laden with micro-organisms that are captured as food, enters minute pores (*a*) all over the body surface. Passing through (*c*), the body cavity, it leaves by the "mouth," or osculum, at (*b*). *2.* A portion of the wall of the sponge enlarged to show cellular detail. (*a*) Entrance pore formed by a single cell which lines the channel all the way into the body cavity (*c*); (*b*) pore, surface view; (*d*) collar cells that line the body cavity; (*e*) skeletal spicule; (*f*) external covering cell; (*g*) an amebocyte (an ameba-like cell) embedded in the jelly-like matrix (*h*) which fills most of the space between the external cover-ing cells (*f*) and the layer of collar cells (*d*) that lines the body cavity. Maintenance of the flow of water into the pores, through the body cavity, and out the osculum is the major activity of all sponges: the flow is maintained by the beating of the flagella of the collar cells. Microorganisms in the water are trapped on the collar (cf. Fig. 20-9) and ingested by the collar cells. Some of the food so captured is transported elsewhere in the sponge by the amebocytes constantly moving about the jelly matrix. All the water passing through the sponge enters by many pores but leaves by the one opening (osculum). It is thus under considerable pressure, and its velocity carries it (depleted of food and oxygen and therefore useless to the sponge) far away from the animal. *3* and *4.* Views of successively more complex sponges and parts of their body wall. Sponge evolution has consisted pri-marily of adding complications to the body wall such that the incoming currents of water pass through a succession of chambers lined with collar cells. The functional significance of this is the sponge's ability to "handle" more water and maintain greater pressures to the exhalant current.

way, to learn the characteristics of the various phyla of animals is not from books. As far as possible you should first see them alive in their natural surroundings or, failing that, in aquariums and zoos. You should then examine preserved specimens, models, and dissections in museums or classroom collections and should dissect some examples yourself. De-tailed descriptions and anatomical terminol-ogy can be found in works cited in the bibliography at the end of this book. This is not a textbook of zoology or anatomy, and we do not propose to describe the various phyla in detail. Concrete examples are pro-vided by the accompanying illustrations.

Beyond that, you need at this point only such brief characterization of the more important phyla as will help to fit them into the broad biological scheme of things. The next chapter will discuss somewhat more fully the three phyla that are now dominant, most varied and complex, well illustrative of certain bi-ological principles, and in many respects most interesting to us humans.

PORIFERA

Sponges (Fig. 22-1) resemble protistan [2] colonies in that the separate cells seem to lead semi-independent lives within the or-

[2] Protozoa. Animal-like protists were de-scribed in Chapter 20. Their evolutionary rela-

ganization as a whole. Nevertheless, the cells are of a few well-differentiated kinds with different functions, and there is some simple coordination of their activities. All sponges are aquatic, and most of them are marine. Their way of life is not very exciting: they are sessile and do little more than maintain a current of water inflowing through many small pores around their sides and outflowing through a larger opening, usually at the top. They feed on microscopic particles carried along by the current. Fossil remains suggest that sponges have been numerous since early in the history of life, and that they have not changed a great deal for some hundreds of millions of years. You may wonder why in so long a time sponges (and some other lowly organisms) have not evolved into anything distinctly more elaborate. The answer is similar to that of the elderly lady who was asked whether she had done much traveling, and who replied that she had not needed to travel because she had been *born* in Boston. Sponges have not gone places, evolutionarily, because they were already there. When life was young they were already well adapted to a widely and continuously available way of life. (See also Fig. 22-2.)

American Museum of Natural History

22-2 The sponge *Hippospongia canaliculata*. This is a colony of sponges; note the many exhalant oscula.

COELENTERATA

Coelenterates [3] are characterized by a sac-like digestive cavity with a single opening, which is surrounded by tentacles with stinging cells (Fig. 22-3). All are carnivorous and snare food in their tentacles. The prey ranges from microscopic animals of many sorts to relatively large crustaceans, worms, or fishes. Like sponges, coelenterates are exclusively aquatic, and they are even more predominantly marine, although there are a few freshwater types, such as *Hydra*.

The coelenterate's body may assume one of two basic forms: the *polyp* and the *medusa*. These two body forms are only variations on a basically similar pattern (Fig. 22-3), and are related to different modes of life. The polyp, an elongate cylinder, is sedentary; the medusa, flatter and bell-like, is free-swimming. Polyps and medusas may alternate

in the life cycle of one kind of coelenterate, but usually one form or the other is dominant or exclusively present. When the medusa is present in the life cycle, it is asexually budded off from the polyp, and is the stage that effects sexual reproduction (gamete production). The free-swimming medusa also guarantees dispersal. In the evolution of coelenterates there has been a recurrent tendency for the polyp stage to become colonial. The polyp commonly reproduces other polyps by budding (p. 359); incomplete separation of budded polyps produces a complex organism composed of many recognizably distinct but connected polyp units.

Coelenterates are highly diverse. Among the different sorts are:

Hydroids: usually small and soft-bodied, with solitary or colonial polyps predominant, but medusas often also present in the life cycle. *Hydra* and *Obelia* are both hydroids (Fig. 22-4).

Siphonophores: floating colonies with differentiated polyps; the Portuguese man-of-war (Fig. 22-5) is an example.

Jellyfishes: medusas, with a polyp generation reduced or absent (Fig. 22-6).

Sea anemones: [4] relatively large, solitary, soft-bodied polyps (Fig. 22-6).

tionships to other groups are discussed later in this chapter.
[3] Phylum Coelenterata. The Greek roots mean literally "hollow guts."

[4] Of course they have nothing more to do with real anemones than that someone thought they looked like flowers.

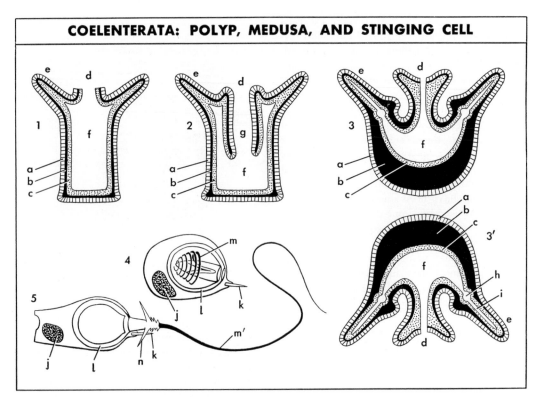

22-3   The basic organization of Coelenterata. *1* and *2*. *Sedentary polyps:* (*1*) the simpler type present in hydroids; (*2*) more advanced type found in sea anemones, with gullet (*g*) leading to the digestive cavity (*f*). *a*, ectoderm; *b*, jelly-like layer between the ectoderm and endoderm (*c*); *d*, mouth; *e*, tentacle; *f*, digestive cavity; *g*, gullet. *3. Free-swimming medusa,* the body form predominant in the jellyfishes, and present as a motile sexual phase in the life cycle of the hydroids (Fig. 22-4). The medusa is essentially an inverted polyp in which the jelly-like layer (*b*) is extensive and the mouth (*d*) is much drawn out. *3* shows the medusa inverted to facilitate comparison with the polyp; *3'* is the actual medusoid orientation. The letters *a* through *f* have the same reference as in *1* and *2*; *h* is a circulatory canal that passes along the outer perimeter of the medusa; *i* is the extension of the circulatory canal into the tentacles; *h* and *i* are continuous with the digestive cavity (*f*), whose water content is circulated through them. *4* and *5*. All coelenterates are characterized by stinging cells or *nematocytes* on their tentacles. *4* shows the nematocyte before it is discharged, and *5* after it is discharged. *j* is the nucleus of the nematocyte cell; *k*, the receptor bristle which, when touched, relays the stimulus to the nematocyte capsule (*l*), which contracts, everting the long, previously coiled (*m*) filament (*m'*); *n*, barb at the base of the filament. The nematocyte cell is thus a self-contained receptor-conductor-effector system (cf. p. 187). Its function is to impale prey which are then gradually forced into the mouth.

"Corals": a few solitary and a great many colonial polyps that form hard calcareous supports or skeletons. "Coral" is a popular term applied to almost all coelenterates that happen to have skeletons. They occur in a number of different groups without closer relationships than that they are all coelenterates (Fig. 22-6).

The coelenterates are another ancient phylum that has become more diversified and

has changed in many minor ways but in no really fundamental way for several hundred million years. The fossil record of "corals" is particularly rich, but, oddly enough, quite a few fossil jellyfishes are known. (Why is that odd?)

It is an interesting and disputed problem whether polyps or medusas are more primitive, that is, whether the first coelenterates fully organized as such were free-swimming

Life cycle of *Obelia*

Life cycle of *Aurelia* (jellyfish)

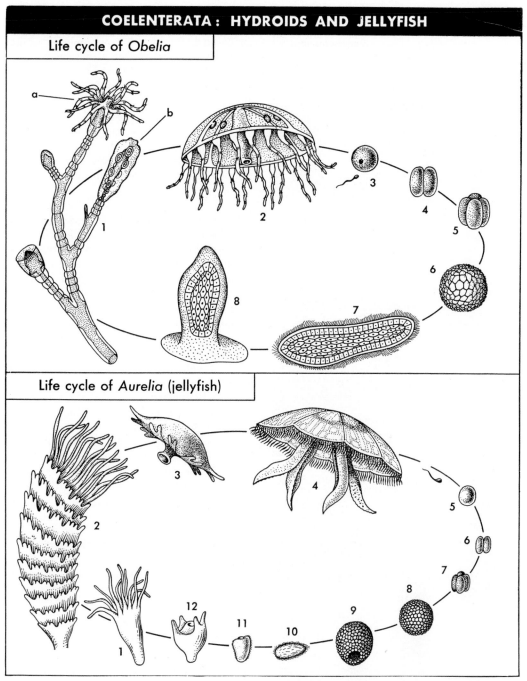

22-4 The polyp and medusa play typically distinct roles in the life cycle of coelenterates. *Obelia*, a hydroid: the principal stage is the polyp, which, by asexual budding, becomes a branched colony. Some members (*a*) of the polyp colony are feeding units equipped with tentacles. Others (*b*) are reproductive polyps which continuously bud off medusas (*2*). The free-swimming medusa serves to disperse the species; it is sexual, producing (*3*) gametes. *4-6*. Successive stages in the development of the ciliated larva (*7*), which ultimately settles (*8*) to initiate a new polyp colony. In *Aurelia*, jellyfish, the medusa is the dominant body form. The polyp (*1*) is a small transient stage that actively buds off (*2*) young medusas (*3*), which when fully developed (*4*) are quite large animals (6 inches in *Aurelia*). *5*. Gametes liberated by the medusa. *6-9*. Stages in the development of the ciliated larva (*10*), which becomes (*11-12*) a polyp.

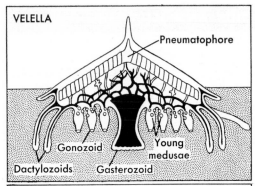

VELELLA

Pneumatophore

Gonozoid

Young medusae

Dactylozoids

Gasterozoid

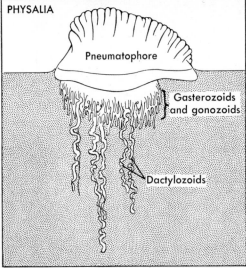

PHYSALIA

Pneumatophore

Gasterozoids and gonozoids

Dactylozoids

Photo © Douglas P. Wilson

or attached. The two forms are about equally old as known fossils. There are good arguments on both sides, but our opinion is that characteristic coelenterate structure arose in relationship to sessile life and that the earliest true coelenterates were therefore either polyps alone, or alternately polyps and medusas. Among reasons for this conclusion are the facts that coelenterates are radially symmetrical (p. 546) and hermaphroditic (footnote 9, p. 637). Both these features are commonly characteristic of sessile organisms.

PLATYHELMINTHES [5]

In popular speech almost any elongated, wiggly animal without prominent legs is called a "worm." Early zoologists thought that most worms were related and put them in a phylum Vermes (Latin for "worms"). Now we know that "worm" refers properly to an *adaptive body form* that occurs in many groups of animals fundamentally different in structure and origin. Even as a body form, "worm" includes a number of different adaptive types. Of the twenty-one phyla of our classification, the worm body shape is a basic adaptation for ten: Platyhelminthes, Mesozoa, Nemertea, Nematoda, Nematomorpha, Acanthocephala, Kinorhyncha, Phoronidea, Chaetognatha, and Annelida. Six other phyla, although not basically wormlike, include groups or forms that have become more or less wormlike: Ctenophora, Trochelminthes, Mollusca, Arthropoda,

[5] The name means simply "flat worms."

22-5 Siphonophores are highly evolved coelenterates whose bodies are essentially colonies of polyps that have undergone extensive specialization or division of labor. A large polyp (*pneumatophore*, in the figure) forms a float which buoys up the rest of the colony; all siphonophores are floating oceanic organisms. Another polyp (in *Velella*) or several other polyps (in *Physalia*) specialize as feeding units, *gasterozoids*. Other polyps, *gonozoids*, are devoted entirely to reproductive activity. Finally, some have become very long fingerlike processes (*dactylozoids*) devoted entirely to attack; they are heavily endowed with nematocysts. The upper two figures are schematic representations of the organization of two genera of siphonophores, *Velella* and *Physalia*. The lower figure is a photograph of the Portuguese man-of-war, *Physalia*, with a fish it has captured in its dactylozoids.

22-6 Coelenterates.
Right, white coral, *Madrepora oculata*, from the Bay of Biscay. *Below*, the medusa *Gonionemus murbachi*. Note on the tentacles the opaque knobs which are clusters of nematocysts.

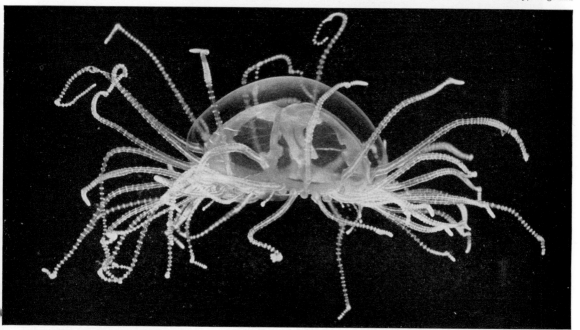

Sea anemone, *Dahlia*. Note the mouth in the center of the tentacles.

Jellyfish, *Chrysaora*.

Sea anemone, *Metridium sessile*.

Echinodermata, Chordata. Many so-called worms (cutworms, inchworms, apple worms, etc.) are insect larvae. Blindworms or slow-worms are legless lizards. The worm shape has evolved so often that it is clearly associated with some of the most successful and advantageous ways of life, but it seems nevertheless to be a dead end of evolution. None of the most progressive and dominant animals

are wormlike (as adults, at least). The platyhelminthes (illus., p. 522, and Fig. 22-7) or flatworms are, as the name implies, flattened from top to bottom, which makes many of them somewhat ribbon- or tapelike. Indeed, tapeworms are platyhelminths, and so are flukes (Fig. 25-4), which are also common parasites. Like many other internal parasites (see Chapter 25), these have lost organs and tis-

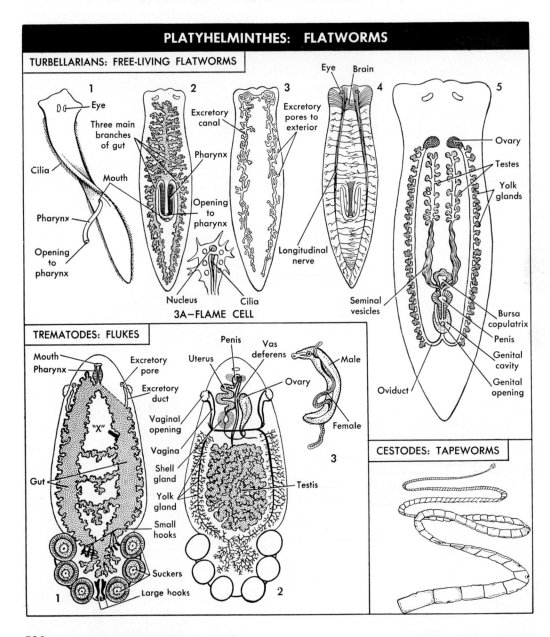

PLATYHELMINTHES: FLATWORMS

TURBELLARIANS: FREE-LIVING FLATWORMS

1 — Eye, Cilia, Pharynx, Opening to pharynx

2 — Three main branches of gut, Mouth, Pharynx, Opening to pharynx, Excretory canal

3 — Excretory pores to exterior

3A—FLAME CELL — Nucleus, Cilia

4 — Eye, Brain, Longitudinal nerve

5 — Ovary, Testes, Yolk glands, Seminal vesicles, Bursa copulatrix, Penis, Genital cavity, Genital opening, Oviduct

TREMATODES: FLUKES

1 — Mouth, Pharynx, Gut, "X", Suckers, Large hooks, Excretory pore, Excretory duct, Vaginal opening, Vagina, Shell gland, Yolk gland, Small hooks

2 — Penis, Uterus, Vas deferens, Ovary, Testis

3 — Male, Female

CESTODES: TAPEWORMS

sues that occurred in their ancestry. Basic characters of the platyhelminths are better preserved in such nonparasitic forms as the planarians, already familiar to you. Look up "planarian" in the index and review what has been said about these flatworms. Most free-living flatworms resemble coelenterates in having a digestive cavity with only one opening, but in other respects they are more complex and more like higher animals: they are fully motile and bilaterally symmetrical, with sensory receptors including eyes (which do not, however, form images), specialized excretory and reproductive organs, and a fairly complex nervous system including even a brain of sorts. The group must be very old,

but fossil flatworms are extremely rare and poorly preserved.

NEMATODA

Nematodes [6] or roundworms differ superficially from flatworms in being literally rounder and less flattened, and they differ more fundamentally in having a digestive tube with two openings—mouth as entrance and anus as exit (Fig. 22-8). Nematodes are incredibly numerous and occur practically everywhere there is any life at all, from the

[6] Phylum Nematoda, from the Greek word for "thread." The name would be more appropriate for the horsehair worms, which do have a similar name: Nematomorpha (p. 479).

22-7 Platyhelminthes. The most primitive flatworms are free-living (nonparasitic) *Turbellaria*, the planarians. *1* and *2*. They are flat and ribbonlike. Many still move by the primitive method of beating cilia. The alimentary system is a blind cavity, like that of coelenterates. The mouth is in the middle of the body on the under surface; a long muscular pharynx is protrusable from it. *3*. The flatworms show the "first" specially developed excretory system. It is a series of blind-end ducts that connect with a pair of principal excretory canals running the length of the body. These canals vent to the outside by a series of excretory pores. At the blind end of each excretory duct is a specialized cell (a "flame cell," *3A*), which is evidently the active secretor of nitrogenous wastes into the duct. It is ciliated; its cilia beat actively within the cavity of the duct. *4*. The nervous system consists of a simple "brain," two longitudinal nerves (p. 210), and a network of other fibers. *5*. The reproductive system is extremely complex and one of the most interesting features of the phylum. The phylum, as a whole, is hermaphroditic: individual animals carry both male and female organs. This feature is undoubtedly a major reason why the flatworms have been so successful in exploiting the parasitic way of life: all the trematodes and cestodes are parasites (cf. p. 637). Eggs, shed by the ovaries, pass down the long oviducts to the common genital cavity; on their way they receive yolk material (nutrients) from the extensive yolk glands. The multiple testes vent their sperm into the large seminal vesicles, where they are stored before copulation. Like the hermaphroditic flowering plants, flatworms rarely, if ever, self-fertilize; copulation occurs with a mutual exchange of sperm. The muscular penis of each animal inserts sperm into the partner's *bursa copulatrix*. When eggs are later laid, the fertilizations which take place involve sperm (ultimately from another animal) released by the *bursa*

copulatrix—not sperm from the animal's own seminal vesicles. *Trematoda*, flukes, are exclusively parasitic flatworms. *1* and *2*. Major features of the anatomical organization of *Polystomum*, a trematode parasitic in the bladder of frogs. It attaches to the host by six powerful suckers and two series of hooks. The mouth, as in other trematodes, is shifted toward the anterior end. The alimentary canal is only a strong, muscular, sucking pharynx and blind gut typical of flatworms. There are two excretory ducts. The reproductive system (*2*) is fundamentally similar to that of planarians, but with added complications. Its most significant point is the extent of its development, characteristic of parasites (p. 636): it comprises the larger part of the animal's body. The huge testis leads through a duct (the *vas deferens*) to a muscular penis that is extruded through the genital opening during copulation, when the penis of each animal enters one of the two special vaginal openings of the mate. Eggs are shed by the single ovary. In passing along the complex oviduct the eggs first receive yolk from extensively branched yolk glands; next they receive sperm (from the vagina); later they receive a covering from the shell gland; finally, after temporary storage in the uterus, they are shed to the exterior. Trematodes have a curious duct (marked "X" in *1*) which connects the yolk glands with the gut; it probably serves to avoid waste by relaying excess yolk into the animal's gut, where it is digested. *3*. A very few trematodes, like *Schistosomum* (a parasite of the human bloodstream), have evolved separate sexes, but they spend their lives in permanent embrace, effecting in a roundabout way the advantages of their former hermaphroditism, so important to a parasite (cf. p. 637). *Cestoda*, tapeworms, are illustrated briefly here by *Taenia solium* (the tapeworm of man), and in more detail in Fig. 25-3.

1

a
d
e
g
b
f

2

c

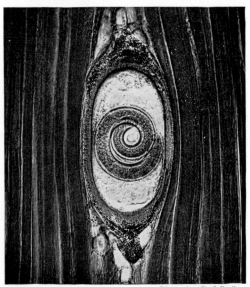

Photo by Carl Strüwe

equator to the arctic and from mountaintops to the deep sea. An acre of soil often contains three billion or more nematodes, and you are likely to turn up a million at a time with a spade in your garden. Moreover, nematodes live as parasites in innumerable other animals and also in many plants. Fifty or so species parasitize man; you have probably been a host to them at some time and may well be right now. Some are practically harmless and others, such as hookworm and trichina, cause serious diseases. *Ascaris*, the commonest nematode parasitic in man, is often unpleasant but seldom disabling or fatal (see Chapter 25 on parasitism and parasites). There is little good to say about nematodes from the human point of view. Nematodes are among the great successes of the impersonal forces of evolution. They teach nothing about how to win friends, but they are fine examples of one way to get along in the world.

BRYOZOA [7]

Almost all bryozoans are colonial, the colonies encrusting shells and rocks or forming mats or branching fans (Fig. 22-9). The colonies build supports of limy or horny material, and the individuals live in small cups in the skeletal framework. To that extent they resemble many corals, and they also have tentacles around the mouth, but there the resemblance to any coelenterates ends. Even

[7] "Moss animals," from the fact that their colonies may look somewhat like moss (but not very much like!). In some books they are called Polyzoa ("multiple animals") because they are colonial.

22-8 Nematoda. *1.* Schematic representation of a dissected *Ascaris* (female), the threadworm parasitic in human intestines. The internal organs are few and simple: *a*, mouth; *b*, alimentary canal; *c*, anus; *d*, nerve ring around pharynx; *e*, major ventral nerve cord; a dorsal nerve (crosshatched) is also visible; *f*, ovary; *g*, genital pore. *2.* The threadworm *Gigantorhynchus gigas* on the gut wall of the pig. (*Gigantorhynchus* is nowadays placed in a closely related though separated phylum, the *Acanthocephala*. The group is, for convenience, represented here with the nematodes, of which they were, in fact, once considered a class.) *Below*, a photograph ($\times$ approx. 100) of *Trichina spiralis*, the threadworm responsible for trichinosis, embedded in muscle.

© Douglas P. Wilson

22-9 Bryozoa. *A.* Organization of an individual
member of a bryozoan colony. Note that the whole
mouth region with its tentacles can be withdrawn,
by retractor muscles, within the cuticle. The *avicularium* shown is a modified individual animal that
plays much the same role in the economy of the
colony as do dactylozoids in siphonophores; its
"jaws" snap shut on moving obstacles (like small
larvae) that touch it. *B.* Part of a colony of the
fresh-water bryozoan *Plumatella. Above*, a photograph (×1.2) of the marine bryozoan *Bugula tur-
binata* hanging from a rock.

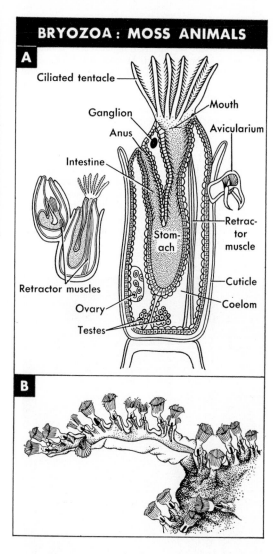

BRYOZOA: MOSS ANIMALS

A

Ciliated tentacle
Ganglion
Anus
Mouth
Avicularium
Intestine
Retrac-
tor
muscle
Stom-
ach
Retractor muscles
Ovary
Cuticle
Coelom
Testes

B

the tentacles are really different because in
bryozoans they have no stinging cells and do
not capture food directly. Their cilia create
a current that carries microscopic food particles into the mouth. The internal anatomy
is far more complex than in coelenterates. The
digestive system is a complete tube, doubled
into a U so that the anus is near the mouth,
an arrangement correlated with life in a cup
without a rear exit. There are nervous and
muscular systems, and most bryozoans have
a true coelom (see p. 545).[8] Bryozoans are
another group that is exclusively aquatic and
mainly marine, although fresh-water bryozoans are fairly common. They occur in all
seas and are especially numerous on coral

reefs, where they add materially to the stony
matter. Fossil bryozoans, including many reef-
dwellers, are more abundant and diverse than
the living forms.

BRACHIOPODA

Brachiopods[9] are animals enclosed in two
approximately equal shells. To that extent

[8] The more abundant group (Ectoprocta) of
bryozoans has a coelom and has the anus outside the ring of tentacles. A much rarer group
(Endoprocta) has no coelom, and the anus is inside the ring of tentacles. These differences are
considered so important by some students that
they classify the two groups as distinct **phyla.**

[9] Phylum Brachiopoda ("arm-footed"). The
name is based on an elaborate mistake. The
structures carrying the tentacles were compared
with arms and were supposed to have something
to do with walking. They really have no functional resemblance either to arms or to feet,
but the name is as good as any other or, indeed, better because all zoologists use it for
this group.

22-10 Brachiopoda. *1.* A brachiopod, *Lingula*, in its burrow; *a*, with stalk (*c*) relaxed so that the animal (*d*) can set up feeding currents; *b*, animal withdrawn in burrow, with bristles (*e*) fringing the edge of the shell. *2.* Generalized schematic view of brachiopod organization. *a*, stalk; *b*, mouth; *c*, intestine; *d*, digestive gland; *e*, ovary; *f*, coelom; *g*, dorsal shell; *h*, ventral shell; *i*, lophophore, bearing the tentacles. Note also the shell-closing muscles, which can be seen passing obliquely behind the intestine (*c*). *3.* Plan showing path of feeding currents to the mouth (*m*). *4.* Brachiopod hanging from rock by stalk; this habit is commoner in the brachiopods than that of *Lingula* (*1*). *5* and *6.* General views of the fossil brachiopod *Terebratula* to show the relation of the dorsal and ventral shells to the posterior and anterior ends of the animal. *Below*, photograph of a brachiopod opened to show the lophophore bearing tentacles.

Ralph Buchsbaum

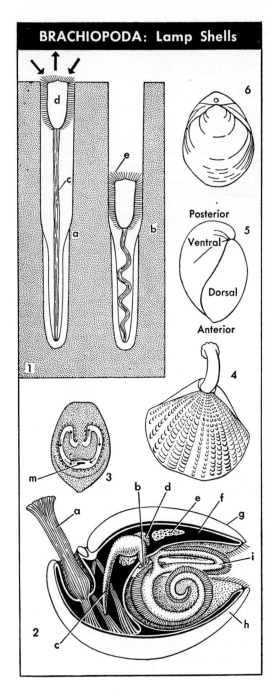

they resemble clams (phylum Mollusca), but the resemblance is superficial. In clams the shells are lateral, on the right and left sides of the body. In brachiopods they are dorsoventral, on the top and bottom of the body. This involves a difference in symmetry (Fig.

22-10). The internal anatomy is also quite different in the two groups. Brachiopods are more complex than any phylum previously discussed, with a coelom and well-developed nervous, muscular, digestive, circulatory, excretory, and reproductive systems. The most conspicuous peculiarity is a firm internal support, a pair of spirals or other more or less complex form, bearing tentacles. As in bryozoans, the tentacles (or, strictly speaking, tiny hairlike cilia on the tentacles) set up feeding and respiratory currents. Brachiopods are noncolonial. The individuals usually become attached by a fleshy stalk that protrudes through the hind end of the lower shell. They are exclusively marine and always have been. The survivors are not very abundant and diverse, but they are mere remnants of a great host, occurring literally by the millions as fossils in rocks of many ages.

MOLLUSCA [10]

As will be explained later in this chapter, the various phyla, especially as we see them today, do not really represent an evolutionary progression. It is, however, clear that three of the phyla, each in its own way, have gone farther than the others. Each represents a culmination of evolution in complexity of structure, in co-ordination of functions, and in diversity and success of adaptations. The great culminating groups are the mollusks, arthropods, and vertebrates. The next chapter is devoted to these three phyla. Here we need only to mention them as belonging in this conventional sequence of the major phyla, and to note that the mollusks include such familiar animals as the snails, clams, and squids.

ANNELIDA

The annelids [11] are another group of worms (Fig. 22-11), but worms very different indeed from the flatworms or roundworms. Annelids are also literally round worms, built on a cylindrical, tubular plan, with mouth at one end and anus at the other. The cylindrical surface is, however, modified by rows of bristles and often also by more complex appendages. Most strikingly, these worms are made up of numerous segments, visible ex-

ternally as ringlike bulges and separated internally by partitions. The digestive tube and principal lengthwise blood vessels and nerve cords run right through many or all segments. Other organs, such as nerve ganglia, circular blood vessels, and excretory tubes, are repeated in several or many segments. Earthworms (of which there are many species) are the annelids best known to most of us. Specialized for life in moist soil, they literally eat their way through the ground, passing the dirt through the alimentary canal (Fig. 6-6, p. 125). Organic matter is digested from the soil, and the residue is ejected from the anus in the form of the familiar worm casting. Their reworking of the soil is so extensive that Darwin doubted whether "there are any other animals which have played such an important part in the history of the world." Do you agree? If not, what animals do you think have played a more important part?

Although earthworms are so readily obtained that they are the usual examples of annelids in biology courses, most of the annelids are marine and look and live quite differently from earthworms. They live almost everywhere in the sea, sometimes free-swimming but often in burrows or tubes. A few annelids are true parasites, and one group, the leeches (Class Hirudinea) is semiparasitic, living on the blood of vertebrates, including man. Parasitism is, however, less common among annelids than among other worms. You need not be such a worm fancier as Darwin to agree that some of the plumed, brilliantly colored marine annelids (the polychaetes) are handsome and fascinating.[12]

ARTHROPODA [13]

This is, almost beyond comparison, the largest of all phyla, plant or animal. Among other groups, it includes the crustaceans, spiders, and insects. No other phylum of organisms is anywhere near so diverse, and

---

[10] The name, derived through French from Latin, implies that the animals are soft-bodied. In fact, most of them have shells, and the bodies within the shells are no softer than those of most other animals, but as with other systematic names the appropriateness of the derivation makes no difference now.
[11] Phylum Annelida, from a French word derived in turn from the Latin for "ring," because the body seems to be divided into a series of rings.

[12] Admiration for these beautiful worms is reflected in the names given some of them, such as **Aphrodite** (but its popular name is less enticing: "sea mouse"). By the way, the scientific name of the quahog or common hard-shelled clam (mollusk), more attractive to the palate than to the eye, is **Venus mercenaria.**
[13] The arthropods ("jointed feet").

22-11 The polychaete annelids. *Left,* although the annelids are likely to be most familiar through the common earthworm, the group to which it belongs (*Oligochaeta*) is much less abundant and typical of the phylum Annelida than are the *Polychaeta,* which are marine. The simplest and most typical polychaetes are free-swimming, like *Nereis* shown here. They are carnivorous, possessing stout jaws. Their most characteristic feature is the bristle-bearing, paddle-like parapodia ("feet equivalents") borne on each segment. Used principally for locomotion, the parapodia are also excellent respiratory structures, combining large surface area and a rich blood supply.

Many polychaetes, including the peacock worms, *Sabella favonina* (*above*), are sedentary animals that live in tubelike cases they themselves secrete. They set up currents of sea water along elaborate tentacles that lead to their mouth; and from the sea water they extract microorganisms and debris as food.

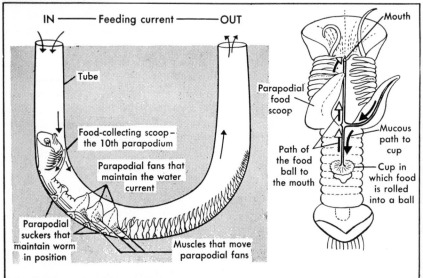

Chaetopterus pergamentaceous is a polychaete (in photo, removed from its tube) which has evolved extensive specializations for its tube-living existence. It lives in a U-shaped tube through which it sets up a feeding current of water propelled by many parapodia that have fused into three sets of special "fans." Parapodial suckers grip the tube, keeping the animal in position. Two special food-collecting parapodia on the 10th segment protrude, like scoops, into the feeding current. Food particles in the current are here entangled in mucus (acting like "flypaper"), which is moved by cilia *backward* to a cup-shaped organ where they (food particles) accumulate into a ball that is then moved *forward* along the groove all the way to the mouth.

none except the vertebrates is so complex in structure and behavior. The arthropods will be discussed more fully in the next chapter.

ECHINODERMATA

The echinoderms [14] are relatively complex animals (Fig. 22-12) with a (usually) complete digestive tube, coelom, and specialized excretory, reproductive, nervous, and circulatory systems, although the last two are simpler than in most animals otherwise so complex. In spite of belonging in these respects among the "higher" phyla, they resemble the coelenterates in being radially symmetrical (Fig. 22-12). At least, most adult echinoderms seem to be so. In fact, their larvae (p. 557) are bilaterally symmetrical, and there are traces of bilateral symmetry even in the adult, but the over-all shape of most adults is radial, usually with five rays, as in common starfishes. Another unique feature of echinoderms, in addition to the true circulatory system (which is very poorly developed), is a well-developed water circulatory system. This contains sea water filtered through a special sieve plate. In many echinoderms the water circulatory system is connected to numerous "tube feet," operated by hydraulic pressure and used in slow locomotion and for grasping (Fig. 22-12). Almost all echinoderms have hard, limy plates in the skin, and in some, such as the sea urchins, these may be immovably united into a hard, protective box. (Sea urchins also have movable spines jointed to the outside of the box.) All echinoderms are marine.

The echinoderms well illustrate how a single ancestral body plan may become diversely adapted in radically different ways. Although the internal anatomy is for the most part essentially similar, the main groups of living echinoderms are extraordinarily different in appearance and habits:

Crinoids or sea lilies: body enclosed in a rigid box, with branching, flexible arms extending from around mouth and anus; body usually sessile, attached by a stalk; no tube feet; food microscopic organisms and debris (Fig. 22-13).

Starfishes: body star-shaped, or five-sided, stiff but flexible; free but moving by slow crawling; tube feet strongly developed; feeding usually on clams and other relatively large invertebrates, which may be digested by everting the stomach around them (Fig. 22-13).

Brittle stars, serpent stars, or ophiurans: somewhat similar to starfishes, but with long, slender arms which lash about rapidly in locomotion or in seizing prey (Fig. 22-13).

Sea urchins: body in a rigid box; armless but spiny; slowly moving by means of spines and tube feet; feeding mostly on seaweeds and dead organic matter (Fig. 22-13).

Sea cucumbers: elongate, leathery, sausagelike bodies; no arms or spines; limy plates tiny and scattered in skin; tentacles around mouth; feeding on small animals or organic material in mud or sand (Fig. 22-13).

The echinoderms have an exceptionally fine fossil record, extending over several hundred million years and including very numerous groups, some markedly different from any living today. It is especially noteworthy that most of the oldest forms are sessile, although among living echinoderms only crinoids are sessile, and not all of them are. What bearing may this have on the radial symmetry of echinoderms? (If you cannot see any bearing now, you will when you have read the rest of this chapter.)

CHORDATA [15]

Most of the chordates are vertebrates—the familiar fishes, amphibians, reptiles, birds, and mammals. They are another of the culminating groups to be discussed in the next chapter. Three major groups of chordates (Fig. 22-14) are not vertebrates. The Hemichordata ("half-corded") or "acorn worms" are indeed fully wormlike in body form, and yet they have what seems to be a short

[14] "Prickly skins," a name appropriate for sea urchins and extended to their relatives.

[15] "With a cord," because these animals have at some stage in their lives a stiffening rod, called a notochord, along the back.

equivalent of a notochord and also some other chordate characteristics (such as dorsal nerve cords and gill slits, see p. 542). The Tunicata ("with a tunic," from the stiff outer coating of the adults) look even less like vertebrates as adults, in which stage most of them are sessile, superficially spongelike creatures (Fig. 22-14) and some are colonial. Even the adults do have some vertebrate characteristics, and some of the larvae pass through a stage in which they are very much like tiny fishes. The Cephalochordata ("head-corded," because the notochord extends to the extreme tip of the head, which it does not in vertebrates), or

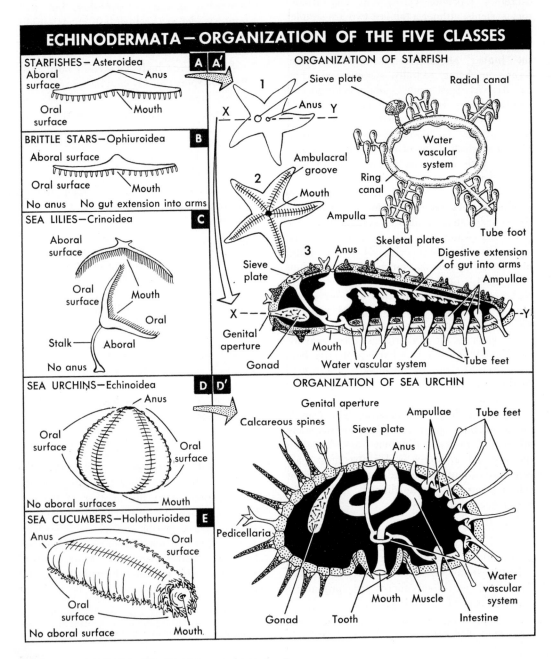

ECHINODERMATA—ORGANIZATION OF THE FIVE CLASSES

lancelets, are quite fishlike in appearance throughout life. They have most of the basic vertebrate characters but lack vertebrae as well as a true brain and some other vertebrate features. The common form, usually available for observation or dissection, is amphioxus (the technical name of which is *Branchiostoma*). The three groups of nonvertebrate chordates are particularly mentioned and illustrated here because, as we shall soon see, they cast some (rather feeble) light on the knotty problem of the origin of the vertebrates.

Adaptive Radiation versus the Ladder of Life

The ancient Greeks were wonderful people and are rightly honored in all histories of science, and yet sometimes a horrid suspicion arises that we would understand life better today if some of their philosophical notions had been forgotten. It was apparently the Greeks who started the idea that organisms form a "ladder of life," with simplest organisms at the bottom and all others fitting in a sequence on up to the top. (Who do you suppose was put at the top? *You* were.) The ladder of life became orthodox biological theory long before evolution, as we now understand it, was even thought of. The evo-

lutionists took it over, some of them just because it was what "everybody knows" and some because they thought it was the pattern of evolution.

Many of the steps in evolution must have proceeded from the simple to the complex. That is practically a physical as well as a biological necessity for many early and some later steps. It has therefore been argued that an arrangement of living organisms from simple to complex is, or at any rate closely resembles, the actual course of evolution. But that is a *non sequitur* that is likely to lead (and has led) to serious error and misunderstanding. Even today the old, mistaken notion of a ladder of life underlies much biological thinking and teaching. Some biologists still think of the phyla of animals as an "evolutionary series," with some dead ends and side branches, to be sure, but still on the whole one main sequence. Students are likely to study the "evolution of the vertebrates" by dissecting a dogfish, a frog, and a cat.

Some phyla must have arisen earlier than others, and some probably arose from others. It is also true that you can learn something about vertebrate evolution from dogfish, frog, and cat. The trouble is that thinking about the phyla or those vertebrates primarily as forming an evolutionary sequence gives in some essential respects a false picture of how

---

22-12   The echinoderms. *A* and *A'*. Starfishes, Asteroidea. The true dorsal and ventral surfaces of the bilateral larva (p. 547) are completely obscured in the adult, and it is convenient to recognize oral and aboral surfaces instead of the usual ventral and dorsal. *1* and *2* in *A'* show the aboral and oral surfaces, respectively. The arms lie on five axes radiating from the mouth; these five axes are recognizable throughout all the echinoderms. Along the oral surface of each arm runs a so-called ambulacral groove in which the tube feet lie. The tube feet are extensions of the water vascular system which connects with the external sea water via the sieve plate. The sieve plate is connected by a duct to a tube (ring canal) encircling the alimentary canal; from this circular vessel ducts lead along each arm. From these main ducts in the arm pairs of tube feet penetrate the body wall. The tube feet are effective walking organs (ambulatory, hence the name of the groove in which they lie), insofar as they are kept inflated by pressure on the sea water within; this pressure is maintained by the ampullae. *A*. Side view

of the starfish. *B*. Side view of brittle star. There is no anus, and the gut is entirely restricted to the central mass; it does not enter the five arms, as in starfishes. *C*. Side views of (1) free-swimming sea lily, and (2) stalked, sedentary sea lily. *D* and *E*. Side views of sea urchin and sea cucumber. As in *A'2* the ambulacral surfaces bearing the tube feet are shown diagrammatically as crosshatches along the length of the radiating axes from the mouth. In both these groups the aboral surfaces are entirely wanting: their organization may be visualized by imagining the tips of the five arms in a starfish being drawn backward (away from the mouth) and brought to a point. *D'* shows further detail of the sea urchin. Note how the arm of the water vascular system that bears the tube feet is curled upward to the anus. Compare *D'* with *A'3*. Around the mouth sea urchins have strong calcareous teeth moved by muscles. The pedicellaria (*D'*) are jointed jawlike structures used in attack and defense. Compare them with the avicularia of Bryozoa (Fig. 22-9); the pedicellaria are not, however, degenerate individuals.

Sea cucumber, *Cucumaria frondosa.*

22-13 Echinoderms.

Starfish, *Asterias.* Note the white sieve plate in the left photo, and the tube feet in the far right photo of the oral surface of a single arm.

Below, a fossil sea lily, *Eucalyptocrinus crassus.* From the Silurian of Indiana.

Below, left, brittle stars, *Ophiothrix fragilis; right,* Echinus esculentus, sea urchin crawling on aquarium wall. Note tube feet at the upper right corner.

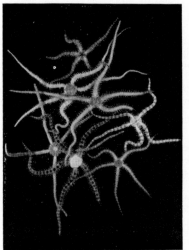

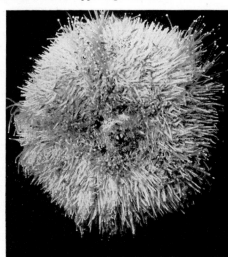

evolution has really occurred. A truer picture is not so simple, but simplicity is no virtue unless it is also true.

Think a little more about the dogfish, the frog, and the cat. They are all living today. Therefore no one of them can be ancestral to any other one. At most the dogfish might be in some respects something like one of the ancestors of a frog, and a frog something like the ancestor of a cat. It is true that mammals (including cats) arose by way of reptiles from amphibians (and frogs are amphibians), and amphibians arose from fishes (and a dogfish is a fish). A shrewd anatomist would, however, suspect at once that a frog is not much like the amphibian ancestor of a mammal, or a dogfish much like the fish ancestor of an amphibian. Fossils, the only evidence that can be really conclusive on these points, show that the suspicion is certainly justified. The fishes ancestral to amphibians were radically different from a dogfish. The amphibians ancestral to reptiles and, through them, to mammals were radically different from a frog.

What, right now, is the significance of the differences between the three contemporaneous animals, dogfish, frog, and cat? It is not that they are steps in a ladder of life, each "lower" form being (or even representing or resembling) the ancestor of the next, "higher" form. The significance is that each of these animals follows a decidedly different way of life from the others. Whether we consider one lower, higher, simpler, or more complex than another (points that could be endlessly disputed and that are largely matters of verbal definition), the differences among them are plainly adaptations to living in different ways and in different environments. A cat can no more dart about chasing fish beneath the waves of the sea than a dogfish can climb a tree and rob bird nests.

How the differences in adaptation arose, as a matter of history, is a different question entirely. It would make no difference in the facts of diverse adaptation if the cat ancestry had given rise to fishes instead of the other way around. (As a matter of fact, somewhat catlike forms did give rise to some that are more or less fishlike in their way of life. Do you know what these are?) An animal that climbs trees is not inherently "higher" than one that swims in the ocean. It happens that fishes evolved before mammals, as we know from fossils. Some fishes remained in their ancestral habitat, the sea, and eventually evolved into dogfishes, among many others all quite different now from the ancient ancestral fishes but broadly similar in adaptive type. Other fishes acquired legs, left the ancestral habitat, and eventually evolved into cats, among many other animals now radically unfishlike. That is the history as it actually occurred. It has profound influence on just when and how the differences between dogfishes and cats arose, but it does not in the least alter the fact that the differences are adaptations to different ways of life.

Perhaps the fundamentals will be made clearer if you bring a pigeon into the series for dissection. There was no mammal stage in the ancestry of the pigeon, and no bird stage in the ancestry of the cat. The differences are purely and simply adaptive to different ways of life, which historically happened to be acquired at about the same time by different groups of organisms.

The same considerations apply to the differences between the phyla of animals—major groups that represent the most basic diversity of the animal kingdom. Some phyla are simpler than others. Sponges are certainly simpler than most other animals, but that does not necessarily mean either that sponges are older or that other animals arose from sponges. (The most competent authorities are reasonably sure that they did not.) In other instances, degrees of simplicity cannot be determined. Whether an earthworm or a starfish is simpler is a question that hardly makes sense when their very different anatomies are compared. The fundamental point is that the various phyla are basically different and that the differences arose as adaptations, that is, are related to different ways of life assumed by the early members of each phylum.

In dealing with great, long-lived groups like the phyla, the basic adaptive differences are obscured and the whole situation is much complicated by diversity within each phylum. The more successful phyla have themselves become greatly diversified, and it has often

THE INVERTEBRATE CHORDATES

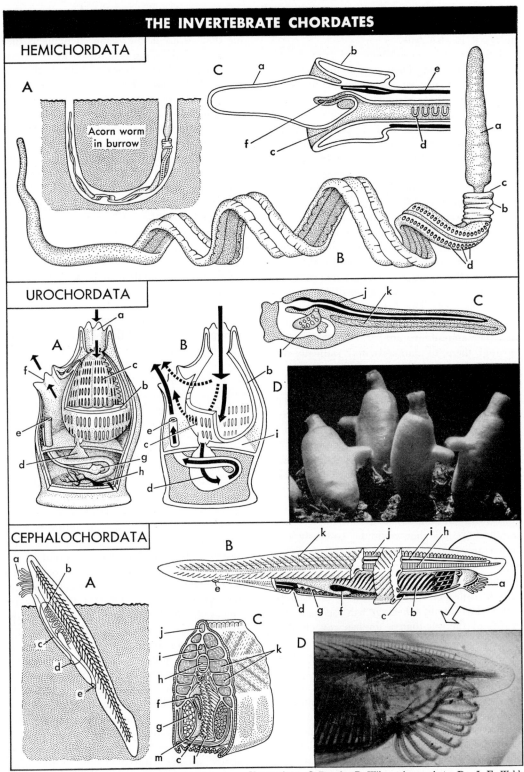

HEMICHORDATA

Acorn worm in burrow

UROCHORDATA

CEPHALOCHORDATA

Upper photo, © Douglas P. Wilson; lower photo, Dr. J. E. Webb from *The Proceedings of the Zoological Society of London.*

happened that members of a phylum (phylogenetically defined) have acquired ways of life widely different from that basic for the phylum. Another problem arises from the fact that many animals, even some whole phyla, have become parasitic. Parasitism is a peculiar way of life which involves not only special new adaptations but also frequently the loss of organs and tissues of fundamental importance to nonparasites, such as the digestive system. You can seldom be sure whether a parasite is simple because it has lost complications or because it never had them. Secondary simplicity can also appear in animals that have greatly decreased in size, that have become sessile or attached, or that have made some other changes in their way of life.

It is quite clear that the animal phyla do not form a single ladder, or even just two or three ladders in which one phylum after another arose in succession. The conclusion is reinforced by historical evidence (see Chapter 30) that there is relatively little difference, geologically speaking, in the ages of most of the phyla. A picture truer than that of a ladder would be a fan (Fig. 22-15), with the phyla as ribs of the fan diverging from

a remote base as they spread by evolutionary change into different adaptive relationships and potentialities. What remains of the old idea of evolutionary sequence among the phyla (and what made it seem plausible to earlier students) is simply two points. First, some phyla did probably arise from early members (which are unknown in all cases) of other phyla, from which they inherited some complexities to begin with. Second, some phyla have changed more radically than others since they first arose, or since their common ancestry with other phyla.

Basic Characters of the Animal Phyla

You now have a passing acquaintance with the more important phyla, taken individually. For broader understanding of animals and their diversity, the next step is to acquire an over-all view of the differences and resemblances among the phyla. Then, on this basis, something may be said about the origins and relationships of these major groups of animals.

Since the characteristics of the phyla are related to their ways of life, it might be sup-

22-14   The invertebrate chordates. *Hemichordata: Balanoglossus*, the acorn—or tongue—worm. *A.* Whole animal in U-shaped burrow in sand. *B.* External features: *a*, burrowing proboscis; *b*, collar; *c*, mouth; *d*, gill slits. *C.* Detail of the head region: *a-d* as in *B*; *e*, dorsal nerve cord; *f*, notochord extending forward from roof of pharynx into the proboscis. The animal is a filter feeder; water and mud enter the mouth and are filtered of food at the gills; excess water passes out of the gills and oxygenates them at the same time. *Urochordata* (Tunicata): *Ciona*, a sea squirt or tunicate. *A.* View of whole animal with body wall cut away to show internal organization: *a*, mouth (or incurrent siphon) through which the feeding and respiratory current of water (see arrows) enters; *b*, wall of much-enlarged pharynx, which is perforated by numerous gill slits (*c*); *d*, stomach; *e*, anus; *f*, excurrent siphon by which water current leaves animal; *g*, gonad; *h*, heart. *B.* The pharyngeal region of the alimentary system; *b*, *c*, *d*, and *e* are as in *A*. The inhalant and exhalant siphons are walled off (*i*) by a membrane from the body cavity proper (stippled). The cavity so formed (unstippled, above *i*) is the *atrium*. The feeding current entering the inhalant siphon is filtered through the pharynx wall; the food passes on

(solid arrow) into the alimentary system; the filtered water passes (broken arrows) into the atrium and leaves by the exhalant siphon. *C.* Schematic representation of the sea-squirt larva. It is bilaterally symmetrical, elongate, and free-swimming. It is mainly interesting because of its bearing on the origin of vertebrates (see Fig. 22-23). Note its dorsal nerve cord (*j*) and notochord (*k*); *l*, pharynx with gill slits. *D.* Photograph of sea squirts. *Cephalochordata: Branchiostoma*, or amphioxus. *A.* Whole animal half-buried in sand or mud bottom, where it lives a semisedentary existence as a filter feeder like the other invertebrate chordates; *a*, cirri surrounding mouth; *b*, gill slits in pharynx; *c*, atrium; *d*, opening of atrium to outside; *e*, anus. *B.* The animal as though dissected from the side; *a-e* as in *A.* The pharyngeal gill slits, as in the tunicates, open into an atrium (*c*) that vents to the outside (*d*); *f*, liver; *g*, gonad; *h*, notochord; *i*, nerve cord; *j*, fin rays, supporting the dorsal fin; *k*, segmental muscles. *C.* An enlarged section through the pharyngeal region; *c* and *f-k* as in *A* and *B*; *l*, endostyle, a gutterlike groove in the base of the pharynx along which the filtered food moves into the intestine; *m*, coelom. *D.* Photograph of head and mouth region.

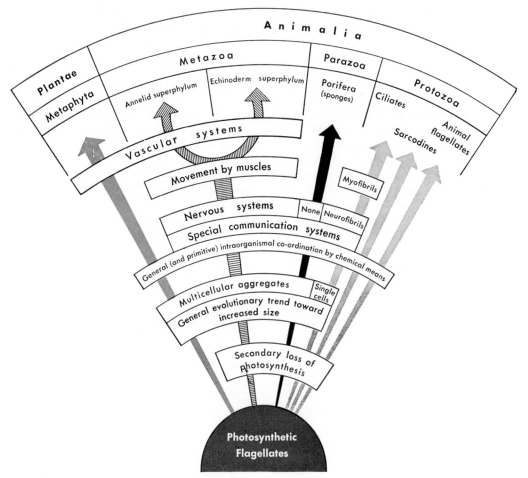

22-15 The radiation of phyla. See Fig. 22-21 for detail of metazoan superphyla.

posed that they reflect adaptation to widely different physical environments. For instance, some phyla might be marine in origin, others fresh-water, and still others terrestrial. This is not the case. *Most of the animal phyla certainly arose in the sea, and all of them may have.* Three minor phyla (Mesozoa, Nematomorpha, Acanthocephala) are exclusively parasitic and of uncertain origin. All include parasites of marine animals, and they may well have originated in the sea. Flat-worms (Platyhelminthes), nematodes (Nematoda), and rotifers (Trochelminthes) are more common in fresh water or damp soil (especially nematodes) than in marine waters, but all do include marine species. All the other phyla seem clearly to be of marine origin.

Most phyla include both marine and fresh-water species.[16] Although both environments are aquatic, they may involve radically different physiological adaptations (see p. 86). Several phyla, notably the nematodes and annelids, are abundant in damp soil, an environment not greatly different from fresh water in its physiological restrictions. *Only three phyla include strictly terrestrial groups,* animals capable of carrying on all their life activities in the open air: Mollusca (the fully

[16] The exclusively marine nonparasitic phyla are: Graptolithina, Ctenophora, Kinorhyncha, Phoronidea, Chaetognatha, and Echinodermata.

terrestrial forms are the land snails), Arthropoda (insects, spiders, and some others), and Chordata (reptiles, birds, and mammals). These, too, include many marine and freshwater animals, and they are evidently of marine origin. Some of their lines of evolution became adapted to the most stringent of all physical environments, the land, where life is so difficult that no other phyla have been able to cope with it. Yet the groups that did become terrestrial underwent no *major* change; no new phyla emerged. It is significant that the three phyla that did conquer the terrestrial environment are also extremely successful in aquatic environments and are much the most varied and, in many respects, the most progressive of all the phyla.

The basic differences among phyla include striking anatomical features related to processes such as nutrition, internal transport and maintenance, organ differentiation, co-ordination, and locomotion. All these features are closely interrelated. They add up to a different over-all structural and functional pattern for each phylum. Let us briefly review some of these characteristics in the eleven major animal phyla.

TISSUE LAYERS [17]

The Porifera have no distinct differentiation of tissue in embryo or adult. In the coelenterates there are only two reasonably distinct tissue layers (endoderm and ectoderm, p. 342) in development and in the adult, although scattered cells or an irregular intermediate mass may be present between the layers. The nine other major phyla have three layers (endoderm, mesoderm, ectoderm, p. 344) more or less clearly involved in development, with marked differentiation of tissues and organs within each of the embryonic layers.

DIGESTIVE SYSTEM [18]

The Porifera have no special digestive organs. Microscopic bits of food are carried along by currents set up by flagellated cells, and these are engulfed and digested within the cells. The Coelenterata have a central cavity with only one opening, into which food is

17 See p. 344.
18 See p. 124.

conveyed from the tentacles. Digestion is partly in the cavity, stomachlike, and partly within cells lining it, spongelike. The digestive system of the Platyhelminthes also has only one opening, and digestion is also partly in the cavity and partly in its lining cells. The cavity is, however, much more complex than in coelenterates, with intricate branching throughout the body. Digested products are thus available near all other tissues in spite of the absence of a special transport system (p. 140). The other eight major phyla have a digestive tube open at both ends, so that food enters one end and residues and wastes leave the other. The tube may be almost completely simple or may be markedly differentiated into different regions or organs. In parasitic members of these phyla the digestive system is often reduced and may be lost.

COELOM [19]

Porifera, Coelenterata, and Platyhelminthes have no cavity between the digestive cavities and body wall. In Nematoda there is such a cavity, but it does not have a special lining and so is considered a pseudocoel (or "false coelom") rather than a true coelom. The other seven major phyla have a true coelom, with cellular (mesodermal) lining.

SKELETAL SYSTEM

The majority of multicellular animals have evolved skeletal systems to support their mass of otherwise flabby tissue, to permit locomotion, and in some cases to serve as protection. The nature of the skeleton varies greatly in different groups, but comparison of these variations throws little light on the relationships between phyla. In groups like the mollusks and brachiopods the skeleton takes the form of an external, largely calcareous "house"; in others (coelenterates, bryozoans, etc.) it is external and either calcareous or protein in nature. The arthropods generally have external skeletons made in part of protein, but their skeletons are elaborately jointed, permitting locomotion. In vertebrates the skeleton is, of course, bony and internal— a derivative of mesoderm tissue. Echinoderms also have mesodermal skeletons, but their

19 See p. 344.

skeletons are functionally external and are calcareous, with no real resemblance to bone.

CIRCULATORY SYSTEM [20]

Porifera, Coelenterata, Platyhelminthes, Nematoda, and Bryozoa have no special circulatory systems. In them cell layers must be thin (they are usually only one or two cells in thickness) and in contact with or near body fluids or the digestive cells. Otherwise the separate cells could neither obtain adequate food by diffusion nor dispose of waste products. Brachiopoda, Mollusca, Annelida, Arthropoda, Echinodermata, and Chordata have vascular circulatory systems, correlated with development of thicker and more complex cell layers and masses.

SEGMENTATION

Three phyla, Annelida, Arthropoda, and Chordata, are characterized by some occurrence of successive segments in the length of the body during development. In annelids many of the segments are closely similar. with repetition of various visceral organs in them. The arthropod segmentation was about as in annelids to begin with, but early became much modified by fusion or reduction of segments, with decreased repetition of organs. Chordate segmentation arose independently and was primarily related to locomotion. It is most evident in some muscles, nerves, and bones (notably the vertebrae) and is obscure or absent in other tissues and organs.

SYMMETRY

Most animals are more or less symmetrical in external form, at least. Among those most clearly symmetrical, some have a central axis and are radially symmetrical around this axis, much as a wheel is symmetrical around its axle. Other animals (such as you) have bilateral symmetry: the two halves are more or less mirror images of each other on each side of a central plane. Even animals that seem to have some other system of symmetry or none at all usually are found to have basic radial or bilateral symmetry when their development and ancestry are studied. Coiled snails, for instance, are not symmetrical in

20 See p. 141.

adult form, but their ancestors were surely bilateral, and they are still bilateral in early development. The coiling arises by unequal growth of the two originally symmetrical sides.

The fundamental significance of symmetry is clearer if body form is also considered in terms of asymmetry, or directional differentiation. The differentiation of directions in animal form is related to locomotion or, more broadly, to orientation with respect to the environment. In a spherical body all directions from the center are the same. Among adult organisms such a form occurs only in a few protists. They float freely in water, buoyed up so that direction of motion or of gravity has no significance in their way of life. For almost all organisms, the directions *up* (away from gravity) and *down* (toward gravity) are significant. All multicellular organisms have some degree of bodily differentiation corresponding to up and down. If this is the only distinct directional differentiation, body form tends to be radially symmetrical. This is especially true of sessile (attached) organisms. The direction of attachment (which usually is downward) is functionally distinct from the direction straight away from the attachment into water or air. Other directions, around and away from the up-down axis, are all about the same as far as the organisms' needs and reactions are concerned.

Animals that move under their own power usually have a habitual direction of movement, and this involves another functional differentiation of direction into forward and backward and of form into fore and aft. Fore-aft, or anterior-posterior, and up-down, or dorsal-ventral, differentiation makes for symmetry only in the direction from side to side: bilateral symmetry. Since most animals are motile, or had motile ancestors at not too distant a date, most of them are bilaterally symmetrical, or they are anteroposteriorly and dorsoventrally *asymmetrical*.

Among the major phyla, the Porifera and Coelenterata have basic up-down differentiation and tend to be radially symmetrical. Sponges may become quite irregular in form, but in most coelenterates the radial symmetry remains beautifully clear. The Echinodermata usually have radial symmetry, but their larvae are bilateral and some trace of bilateral symmetry is present even in adults. It is probable that the remote ancestors of the echinoderms were motile and bilateral but that the early echinoderms themselves were

RADIAL AND BILATERAL SYMMETRY

sessile. Then a secondary radial symmetry developed because of the attachment of the adults. Although many later echinoderms became detached and slowly motile, they retained the secondary radial symmetry. All the other animal phyla (other than Porifera, Coelenterata, and Echinodermata) were bilaterally symmetrical in original plan, and most of their members clearly retain that symmetry.[21] (See Fig. 22-16.)

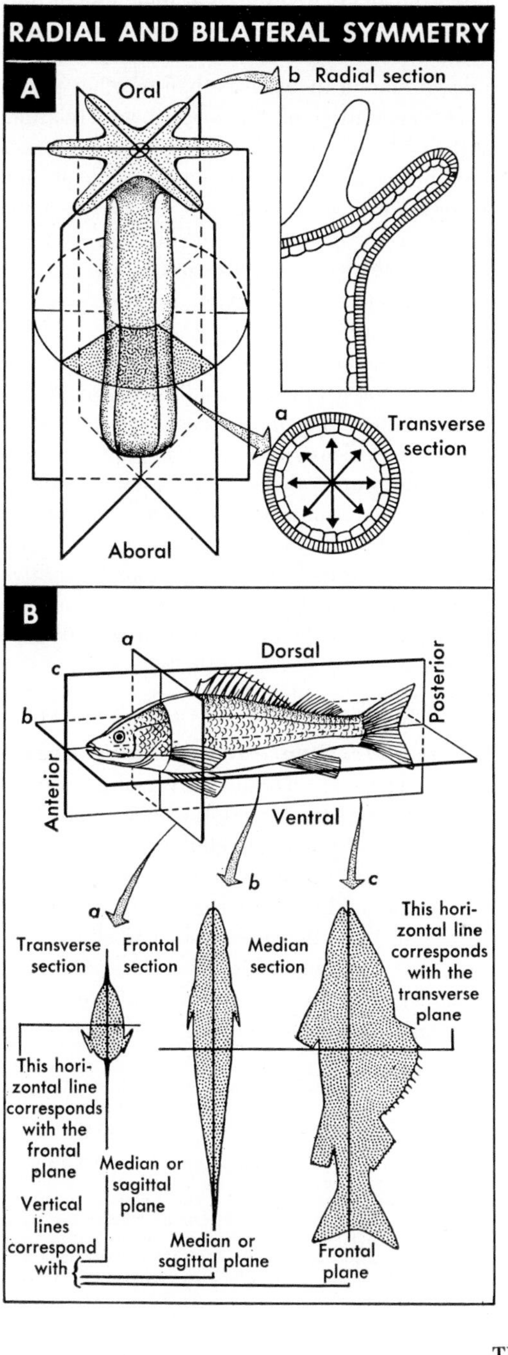

LARVAE

Many animals have larvae (see p. 384) that differ markedly from the adults. Some sorts of larvae are characteristic of particular phyla, and some cast light on relationships between phyla, as will be discussed in the next section of this chapter.

SUMMARY

Table 22-1 and Fig. 22-17 summarize some of the outstanding characteristics of the eleven major phyla. The characters listed are not necessarily present in all the living members of each phylum but are believed to be primitive for the phylum, to have occurred in its earliest and ancestral members.

[21] That the Bryozoa and Brachiopoda are bilaterally symmetrical but are sessile may seem to contradict our explanation of the adaptive origin of symmetry. Their bilateralism is inherited from motile ancestors, and they retain it because of a peculiarity of their attachment, which is not at the end of an up-down axis (as in coelenterates) but at one end of a previously developed fore-aft axis (Fig. 22-10).

22-16 **Animal symmetry.** *A. Radial symmetry,* exemplified by a coelenterate polyp like *Hydra.* The significant axis is the oral-aboral (mouth-to-base) axis; *a,* a transverse section which shows perfect symmetry in all radial directions; *b,* a radial section. *B. Bilateral symmetry,* exemplified by a fish. The upper figure shows the three planes (*a,* transverse; *b,* frontal; *c,* median or sagittal) in terms of which symmetry is discussed. A *transverse section,* obtained by cutting in the transverse plane, shows bilateral symmetry; it is symmetrical on the two sides of the median plane. It is not symmetrical up and down, that is, on the two sides of the frontal plane. A *frontal section* (cut through frontal plane) also shows bilateral symmetry about the median plane, but not about the transverse plane. A *median section* shows no symmetry about either the transverse or frontal planes.

Origins and Relationships
of the Animal Phyla

We earlier compared the animal phyla to the ribs of a fan (p. 543 and Fig. 22-15). Of course this is just a figure of speech, and you should guard against thinking that an analogy of that sort is precisely valid in all details. If the phyla were *exactly* like the ribs of a fan, spreading equally and all from the same point, there would be no point in talking about the relationships between any particular phyla. (Why?) In fact, although the origins of all of them are extremely and comparably remote (all near the base of the fan), some did branch off a little later than others, and some have diverged less than others. Thus some groups of phyla seem to be more nearly related among themselves than to other phyla.

Determination of the origins and relationships of the phyla is one of the most interesting, but also one of the most difficult and at present most speculative, of phylogenetic problems. After hundreds of millions of years of separate evolution, the phyla are now so distinct that clues to their relationships are very obscure. Fossils help a little, but not much.[22] The earliest members of each phylum were extremely ancient, small, soft-bodied animals that have not in any case been preserved as fossils. At least, no fortunate paleontologist has yet found them. The earliest known (fossil) representatives of each phylum are already quite distinct from those of any other phylum. Nevertheless, they are more primitive than living forms, and so they add to the clues provided by the structure and, especially, the development of living animals.

PROTOZOA: [23] UNICELLULAR ANIMALS

Flagellates: ancestral cellular organisms. There is virtually universal agreement among biologists that multicellular organisms have evolved from unicellular ancestors. Indeed, this conclusion is hard to resist on logical grounds alone. Agreement is almost as universal that the ancestral unicellular organisms were something very closely akin to modern flagellates. The group of now-living flagellates has, in other words, departed less

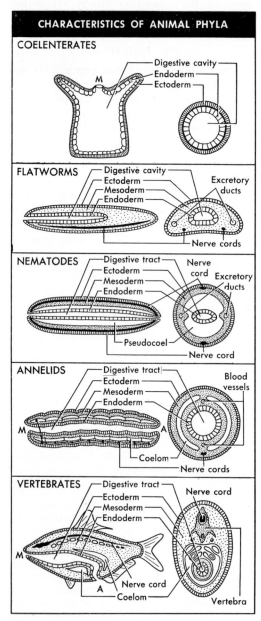

CHARACTERISTICS OF ANIMAL PHYLA

COELENTERATES — Digestive cavity, Endoderm, Ectoderm, M

FLATWORMS — Digestive cavity, Ectoderm, Mesoderm, Endoderm, Excretory ducts, Nerve cords

NEMATODES — Digestive tract, Ectoderm, Mesoderm, Endoderm, Nerve cord, Excretory ducts, Pseudocoel, Nerve cord

ANNELIDS — Digestive tract, Ectoderm, Mesoderm, Endoderm, Blood vessels, M, A, Coelom, Nerve cords

VERTEBRATES — Digestive tract, Ectoderm, Mesoderm, Endoderm, Nerve cord, M, A, Nerve cord, Coelom, Vertebra

22-17   Characteristics of the animal phyla. M = mouth; A = anus.

[22] Note that it is strictly the origin of phyla on which fossils throw little light. Evolution (of classes, etc.) within phyla is, in many cases, very fully documented by fossil evidence. See especially Chapters 30, 31, and 32.

[23] Sometimes, as we have noted before (pp. 54 and 484) it is useful to treat all single-celled organisms as protists; at other times, as now, it is convenient to treat them as primitive animals or plants, as the case may be. Protists that evolved along lines characteristic of animals are often placed in the phylum Protozoa ("first animals").

TABLE 22-1 Some characteristics of major phyla of animals

Phylum	Embryonic cell layers	Digestive system	Coelom	Circulatory system	Segmentation	Symmetry	Larvae	Other features of adults probably primitive for phylum
Porifera	Indistinct	No special organ					Peculiar to Porifera	Sessile. Cellular ingestion of microscopic food from flagella-produced currents.
Coelenterata	Two	Pouchlike; one opening	None	Absent		Radial	Peculiar to Coelenterata	Sessile. Food capture by tentacles with stinging and grasping cells.
Platy-helminthes					Absent		Trocho-phorelike *	Motile. Flattened, wormlike. Passive or immobilized animal food.
Nematoda			Pseudocoel				No true larva	Motile. Cylindrical, wormlike. Soon becoming parasitic, or including some parasites.
Bryozoa								Sessile but bilateral. External skeleton. Early becoming colonial. Flagellated tentacles.
Brachiopoda		Tubular; two openings	True coelom			Bilateral	Trocho-phore *	Sessile but bilateral. Dorsal and ventral shells. Noncolonial. Flagellated tentacles inside shell.
Mollusca	Three			Present				Motile, creeping on ventral foot. Shelled (but primitive form of shell uncertain).
Annelida					Present and similar in the two phyla			Motile. Cylindrical, wormlike. Bristle appendages.
Arthropoda							None or secondary	Highly motile. Jointed legs. External skeleton.
Echino-dermata					Absent	Secondarily radial	Pluteus and pluteuslike †	Sedentary or sessile. Noncolonial. Heavy protective skeleton.
Chordata					Present, different from annelids and arthropods	Bilateral	Pluteuslike, † none, or secondary	Highly motile. Internal skeleton aiding propulsion.

* See p. 554.   † See p. 557.

from the truly ancestral single-celled organisms than has any other group.

This important conclusion is based on the following lines of evidence:

1. Subsequent to its origin, life must have passed through a phase when it was predominantly if not exclusively self-feeding by photosynthesis (p. 740). The flagellates are the only group of persisting protists that includes photosynthetic members and can be considered as *representing* ancestors. (Other photosynthetic protists—bacteria—are excluded as ancestors on other grounds; see the following paragraph.)

2. The flagellates are the smallest and structurally the simplest of the protistan groups that can be admitted as potential ancestors. Bacteria, blue-green algae, and viruses are all excluded as ancestors of "higher" organisms because all lack the chromosomal-mitotic system of hereditary transmission that characterizes later organisms. The other animal-like protistan groups (see below) are all more readily interpreted as derivatives of flagellates than as ancestors of them. And they are unlikely ancestors of later animals.

3. All animals, including the multicellular groups, retain a flagellum at some stage of the life cycle—usually as the male gamete.[24] This seems to be a true relict of the ancient and ancestral mode of cellular locomotion.

We noted in Chapter 20 that algae and other higher plants are probable descendants of photosynthetic flagellates. Photosynthesis has been abandoned in favor of the animal mode of other-feeding by many flagellates (p. 112). It seems very probable that multicellular animals evolved from animal-like flagellates, or by later loss of photosynthesis in some flagellated multicellular organism. Before turning to the evolutionary relationships of multicellular animals, which is our main concern, let us look further into the single-celled animals derived from flagellates.

Sarcodines: exploitation of an opportunity. The Protozoa are grouped into five

[24] The same is true of plants in general; a gamete flagellum was lost late in the evolution of land plants. You recall that it is still present in moss, fern, and some gymnosperm gametes.

classes by zoologists: Flagellata, Sarcodina, Sporozoa, Ciliata, and Suctoria. The Sporozoa (all parasites) are closely allied to and probable descendants of sarcodines. Suctoria (Fig. 22-18) are certain descendants of ciliates. We noted main characteristics of these groups in Chapter 20. Here it is of interest to note the evolutionary trends involved in the origin of the two major lines of descent from flagellates.

The evolution of the sarcodine line (ameba, forams, radiolarians) from flagellates nicely illustrates two common evolutionary principles discussed earlier (Chap. 18): overlapping functions and opportunism. Pseudopodia evidently arose first as useful supplementary feeding devices in animal flagellates.[25] Some still-living flagellates exemplify transitional stages that must have occurred in the evolution of pseudopodia. *Oikomonas* (Fig. 22-18) is an animal flagellate in which pseudopodia are developed on a localized area of the otherwise firm cell surface, and engulf solid food particles. *Mastigamoeba* (Fig. 22-18) is a form that retains a flagellum but develops pseudopodia all over its surface. The evolution in flagellates of a highly mobile cell surface primarily for feeding purposes created an opportunity for further evolution— of *a new mode of locomotion*. Exploitation of this evolutionary opportunity gave rise to the sarcodines, characterized by ameboid, or pseudopodial, movement (p. 224). It is noteworthy that many sarcodines (forams, for instance) produce flagellated gametes, reminders of the ancestral mode of movement.[26]

Ciliates: a sterile solution to a general problem. The ciliates, like other protozoan groups, are characterized by their mode of locomotion. Theirs is a less radical departure from the ancestral flagellate mode. Instead of the one to four flagella typical of most flagellates, they have a large number of motile whips (cilia) usually distributed over the

[25] Why are pseudopodia useful to primitive other-feeding protists?

[26] In what kinds of environments would pseudopodia be more efficient organs of locomotion than flagella? How about movement through tissues of other animals? Is it possible that the evolution of ameboid movement created still further opportunities for highly successful sarcodine parasitism of other animals? Sporozoa are probably sarcodine derivatives.

whole body surface. Again several surviving protozoa suggest transitional stages in the evolution of ciliates from flagellates (Fig. 22-18). The Suctoria (Fig. 22-18) are highly specialized, sedentary descendants of ciliates that lack cilia as adults but are fully ciliated as embryos, like their ancestors. (We have noted the great structural complexity of ciliates. They are the only protistan group in which the young may be so much simpler than adults that an actual development is recognizable.)

The ciliate-suctorian line of flagellate descendants is interesting in another, more significant, respect. It exemplifies a widespread evolutionary tendency to increased size. Ciliates in general are enormously bigger than flagellates and sarcodines, a point illustrated by Fig. 22-19, showing symbiotic flagellates in a ciliate, and parasitic sarcodines on another ciliate. Ciliate size increase is interesting because its particular mode—enlargement of the single cell—is an evolutionally sterile alternative to another mode of size increase adopted by other flagellate descendants. This is the point we now turn to more fully.

ORIGIN OF MULTICELLULAR ANIMALS

We know nothing about the *exact* line of descent whereby multicellular animals evolved from flagellated protists. We can, however, profitably take note of two "problems"—or sources of natural selection—that were in part responsible for the evolution of multicellular

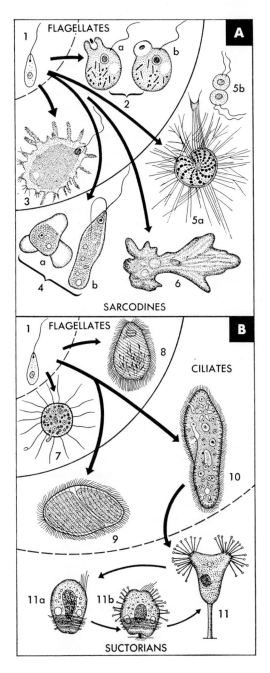

22-18 **Protozoan descendants of flagellates.** *A.* Flagellate-sarcodine relations. *1.* A flagellate. *Oikomonas* (*2*) and *Mastigamoeba* (*3*) are flagellates utilizing pseudopodia for feeding. *4, 5,* and *6.* Sarcodines revealing their flagellate ancestry: *Naegleria* (*4*), alternately pseudopodial and flagellate; *Polystomella* (*5*), a foraminiferan sarcodine with flagellated gametes (*5b*); *Amoeba* (*6*), with the pseudopodia (originally a flagellate feeding device) now the organs of locomotion. *B.* Flagellate-ciliate relations. *1.* A flagellate. *7* and *8.* Flagellates approaching the ciliate condition: *Multicilia* (*7*) an interesting flagellate with (a) pseudopodia as feeding device, (b) many flagella, and (c) more than one nucleus—the latter two characters being ciliate-like; *Holomastigotoides* (*8*), from termite guts, shows huge numbers of flagella organized in rows, like cilia. *9* (*Opalina*) and *10* (*Paramecium*) are ciliates, but (*9*) still lacks the differentiated macro- and micronucleus characteristic of true ciliates. *11. Acineta* is a suctorian and, as such, a ciliate descendant, as is evidenced by its macro- and micronuclear organization and the temporarily ciliated larva (*11a*) which eventually settles down (*11b*) and develops the stalk and suctorial tentacles of the adult.

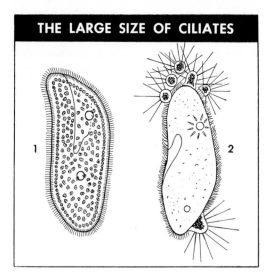

THE LARGE SIZE OF CILIATES

22-19 The large size of ciliates. *1.* Symbiotic green flagellates in *Paramecium bursaria*. *2.* Parasitic sarcodines on *Paramecium*.

animals. They give proper perspective to the history of multicellular animals.

Size. One source of natural selection causing evolution of multicellular life is related to size. Organisms as small as flagellates have relatively little control over their own movement. It is true that they can change direction and even orient to external stimuli like light (p. 236), but for the most part they go where currents or water turbulence take them. The larger the animal, the greater is the force it can exert against currents and turbulence. Insofar, therefore, as controlled direction of movement is advantageous—and clearly it is in many instances—natural selection will favor larger organisms. Nor is this the only source of selection for increased size. (Can you think of some others?)

The problem of increase in size has been solved in two different ways by descendants of flagellates. One solution is that found in ciliates: the single cell increases its bulk. However, this type of solution is limited by the amount of cytoplasm a single nucleus can successfully control. One aspect of ciliate evolution has been an unsatisfactory (or at least evolutionarily sterile) "attempt" to meet this problem. Some ciliates have evolved a special *macronucleus* which is essentially a sac containing many nuclei spread along much of

the cell's great length (Fig. 20-6). This ciliate solution to the size problem has, however, proved something of a blind alley: it does not permit the association of differentiated nuclei with differentiated (or specialized) parts of the whole animal. Possibilities for further evolution have consequently been limited.

The other way in which flagellates responded to selection for increased size suffered no such limitation; the development of multicelled aggregates is potentially nearly unlimited in size. Of the two solutions, only the multicellular one created the opportunity for further, more elaborate evolution.

Locomotion and internal co-ordination. As the multicellular animal increased in size, several new problems arose: (1) the inadequacy of flagella for the locomotion of really large animals; and (2) the demand for efficient communication and co-ordination between cells and organs as these became increasingly further separated. At least two distinct lines of descent from flagellates are represented among modern multicellular animals, the two subkingdoms [27] Parazoa and Metazoa (Fig. 22-15). These two lines are characterized by different solutions to the larger animals' problems of locomotion and co-ordination.

The subkingdom Parazoa contains only the single phylum Porifera (sponges). The sponges have almost certainly evolved from protists closely allied to the still-surviving collar flagellates (like *Protospongiae*, Fig. 20-9), which still show a tendency to evolve colonial cell aggregates. The sponges' solution to the inadequacy of flagella for locomotion of big animals has been simple: sponges have sidestepped the problem altogether, and adopted a sessile life. They draw in water (by flagella) and feed in protistan fashion on microorganisms.

The further problem of co-ordinating parts of the multicellular animal is accordingly not so acute in sponges as it is in those other multicellulars, the Metazoa, which have maintained and further elaborated autonomous lo-

[27] The kingdom Animalia is sometimes subdivided into three subkingdoms: (1) the unicellular Protozoa; (2) the Parazoa; and (3) the Metazoa. See Fig. 22-15.

comotion. In sponges internal communication is not only poorly developed but has taken a form that, like ciliate size, is an evolutionary blind alley.[28] Much of the internal communication is effected by mobile ameboid cells that act as messengers of sorts, slowly moving through the jelly-like matrix in which sponge cells are embedded.

The Metazoa have evolved from a line of multicellular flagellate-descendants in which the problems of movement and co-ordination were met in entirely different fashion—one that, again, has proved the more fruitful of the possible alternative solutions. In Metazoa movement is effected one way or another through the agency of contractile cells, muscles. And hand in hand with evolution of muscle, other cells have specialized as nerves for rapid transmission of signals over long distances. Evolution of rapid co-ordinated movement has been impossible for sponges, much as modern civilization would have been impossible if we had continued to depend on runners for message transmission.

It is important to bear in mind when considering the origin of the Metazoa that they represent only one of several lines of adaptive evolution that early flagellates were forced into by selection. Emergence of the Metazoa as the dominant animal subkingdom has been dependent on two successive steps. At each step several different solutions of the adaptive problem were possible. At each, the ancestors of the Metazoa happened to attain the solution that, as events proved, made possible the most progressive later evolution.

THE RELATIONSHIPS OF
COELENTERATES TO FLATWORMS

In the latter part of the nineteenth century zoologists were quite sure that the coelenterates had a key position in the evolution of animals and that this position was well understood. The coelenterates were supposed to have arisen from hollow, globular protistan colonies. If one side of the globe pushed in so as to come into internal contact with the other side, you would have a pouchlike, radially symmetrical body with two layers

28 Compare the number (diversity) of phyla that have evolved from early Parazoa and early Metazoa. How would you explain the enormous difference?

of cells in its wall, which is the basic pattern of coelenterates. The coelenterates were then supposed to have given rise to flatworms by development of bilateral symmetry and of intermediate, mesodermal cells. From flatworms the other animals could have arisen in sequence by evolution of an anus, a coelom, and other progressive complications (Figs. 22-15 and 22-17).

That view is still held by many zoologists—perhaps a majority—and it is still commonly taught in courses on biology, zoology, or evolution. It may very well be correct. The fact that the theory is old and has become traditional is no reason to think that it is wrong. The nineteenth-century zoologists were right more often than not, and they laid a firm basis for present knowledge. If we sometimes emphasize their failings more than their successes, that is not because they failed more than they succeeded but because where they failed is where there is the most work for us to do. *On the other hand, we must remember that a traditional theory is not necessarily correct, and we must keep other possibilities in mind.*

There are grounds for suspecting the traditional theory of the origin of metazoan phyla through the coelenterates. That theory was really suggested by and heavily dependent on two other theories that have had to be profoundly modified, if not discarded altogether: the theories of the ladder of life (p. 539) and of recapitulation (p. 352). Coelenterates are more complex than protists and simpler than flatworms. Therefore, it was concluded, they must be the link (or the rung on the ladder) between protists and flatworms. We now know that the conclusion does not necessarily follow. Coelenterates could just as well be secondarily simplified or a divergent line that had nothing to do with the origin of flatworms. It was argued that, when some other animals go through the two-cell-layer *gastrula* stage in development, they are recapitulating the adult coelenterate stage in their ancestry. We now know that development does not recapitulate *adult* ancestral stages. *Moreover, the actual mode of development of the gastrula-like form,* which is much better evidence than static comparison at any one stage in life, *occurs in quite diverse ways among coelen-*

terates and is not really much like the process in other animals.

Besides the traditional view, there are at least three other possibilities as to coelenterate relationships:

1. The coelenterates may have arisen independently from protists, like the sponges, and may not have *any* close relationships with other animals. That is a possible view, but it ignores some highly suggestive evidence of coelenterate relationships, at least with the flatworms: both groups lack an anus; coelenterates do have traces of tissue between ectoderm and endoderm, suggestive of flatworm mesoderm; corals are not perfectly radial (they have some bilateral symmetry in their partitions); a third phylum we have previously ignored—the Ctenophora—has some resemblances to coelenterates and some to flatworms. This evidence of relationship between the phyla is explained in the traditional theory by saying that flatworms have evolved from coelenterates.

2. Recently it has been argued that, in the absence of fossil evidence, the facts can just as well be read in the opposite direction; that is, the facts are consistent with the view that coelenterates evolved from flatworms. This is a highly debatable point, and we have reviewed this possibility—indeed, the whole vexed question of coelenterate relationships—only as an example of phylogenetic inference and the special difficulties it involves when fossil evidence is lacking.

3. A third alternative [29] to the traditional view seems to us a more nearly true—and necessarily vaguer—theory of coelenterate and flatworm relationships. Coelenterates probably arose from the very early and primitive Metazoa that were ancestors of the annelid superphylum (see below). Those motile, bilateral ancestors may have given rise to coelenterates by becoming sessile and radially symmetrical. It is tempting to note that some coelenterate larvae are essentially solid, somewhat elongate multicellular masses that move by cilia. (Why must we qualify this evidence as a "temptation"?)

[29] Our third alternative to the traditional theory is perhaps only a more cautious version of the second.

Laying aside the difficult question of coelenterate affinities, we can be more confident about the flatworms (Platyhelminthes). They are surely members of the annelid superphylum (see below) and retain some features that are in all probability truly primitive for that superphylum and perhaps for all later Metazoa. Their lack of the following features is surely primitive: (1) a circulatory system; (2) an anus; and (3) a body cavity (coelom).

(1) We have earlier noted (p. 140) that increasing size in multicellular organisms raises transport problems. As usual, the problem has been met in more than one way. Some early Metazoa hit on the solution of a circulatory system, and this permitted the subsequent evolution of all later phyla other than modern flatworms. The flatworms have adopted an alternative blind-alley solution, flattening of the body surface and branching of the gut.

(2) All "higher" phyla than platyhelminthes have also acquired an anus, permitting one-way traffic of food in the alimentary canal and hence regional specialization within the canal for separate digestive functions. Without one-way traffic in the gut, assembly-line specialization of digestive processes is impossible.

(3) The body cavity (coelom) in higher Metazoa serves several functions but is primarily significant in permitting free and lubricated movement of the internal organs suspended in it.

Metazoa that have evolved these three features lacking in flatworms fall into two major groups, or superphyla: the annelid superphylum, and the echinoderm superphylum.

THE ANNELID SUPERPHYLUM

If you look again at Table 22-1 you will see that four of the major phyla (Bryozoa, Brachiopoda, Mollusca, and Annelida) are indicated as having larvae called "trochophores." These larvae differ a good deal in different species and phyla, but they also have fundamental resemblances. They are all free-living and bilateral, with a complete, regionally differentiated digestive tube. They all also have a ring of beating hairs or cilia situated anterior to the mouth. The ring looks somewhat like a wheel, and that is why the larvae are called *trochophores* ("wheel-bearers").

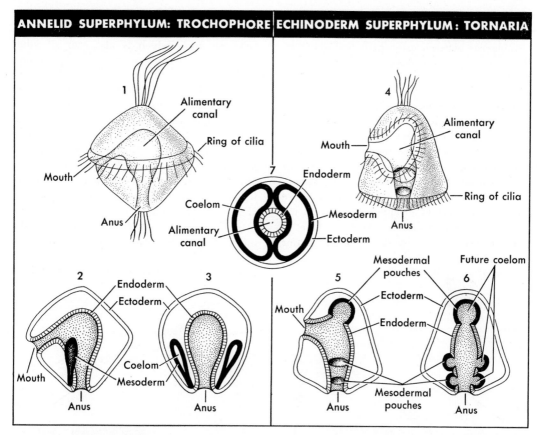

ANNELID SUPERPHYLUM: TROCHOPHORE | ECHINODERM SUPERPHYLUM: TORNARIA

22-20 The two superphyla: larval forms, and the origins of mesoderm and coelom. *1* and *4.* Side views of trochophore and tornaria. The major differences are in the pattern of cilia bands. *2.* Median section of the trochophore to show the relation of the tissue layers, and how the mesoderm arises as a mass (black) from special cells near the ectoderm-endoderm transition in the anal region. *3.* Transverse section of the trochophore, showing the coelom arising as a split within the mesodermal mass. *5* and *6.* Median and transverse sections of the tornaria to show how the mesoderm (black) arises as pouches from the gut wall. The cavity of the pouches is the future coelomic cavity. *7.* Generalized transverse section for both superphyla to show relation of mesoderm and coelom to endoderm and ectoderm.

There are other resemblances in early development in these phyla, irregularly distributed and varied in their members and yet suggesting that ancestors of the phyla did all develop in the same way. Differentiation usually starts with the first cleavage, and even in the two-celled stage (p. 340) each cell is destined to give rise to different tissues and organs in the course of later development. The mesoderm arises by cell cleavage between endoderm and ectoderm, and the coelom later develops as a space within the mass of mesoderm (Fig. 22-20).

The evidence is not conclusive, but it does strongly suggest that the four phyla with trochophore larvae arose from the same very remote ancestry. If so, that ancient common ancestry also had trochophore larvae. This does not tell us what the adult ancestor looked like. Presumably it did not look much like a trochophore.[30] The adult ancestor must, however, have developed from a trochophore and have incorporated some trochophorelike anatomical features.

[30] Many zoologists used to think it did look like a trochophore, and some charts of phylogeny still illustrate a trochophore as the ancestor of these phyla. That is based on the clearly wrong older interpretation of the "biogenetic law," the belief that ontogeny literally repeats phylogeny (see p. 352).

Arthropods do not have trochophore larvae. However, there are other developmental resemblances between arthropods and annelids. Even among adults there are strong indications of relationships between these two groups. These are the only two phyla for which the evidence of relationship is strong and clear, and there is really no doubt that they did have a common ancestry. Moreover, the annelids seem, on the whole, to have changed less, and the ancestors of the two groups were more annelidlike than arthropodlike. Among the arthropods the trochophore stage in life history disappeared early in the course of their evolution. Later in some of the groups of arthropods different, newer kinds of larvae evolved, such as the wormlike larvae of many insects.

Some flatworms have larvae that resemble trochophores except that the digestive system lacks an anus, which is also true of adult flatworms. A coelom is also lacking in flatworms, but there is a mass of mesoderm that arises much as in annelids. The difference depends essentially on whether or not a space opens up in the mesoderm mass. The consensus is that flatworms probably are related to the phyla with trochophore larvae, a group of phyla sometimes called the *annelid superphylum*. Most zoologists think that the striking peculiarities of the flatworms, such as absence of anus and of coelom, are explained by their ancestry's branching off from the other phyla before these characteristics had evolved.

The annelid superphylum includes at least

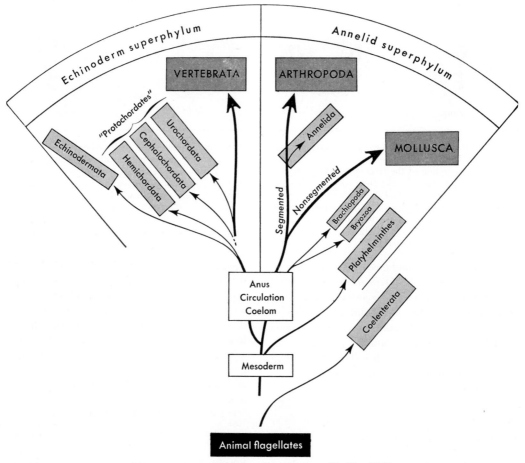

22-21   The superphyla of animals.   Cf. Fig. 22-15.

the major phyla Platyhelminthes, Bryozoa, Brachiopoda, Mollusca, Annelida, Arthropoda, and probably also some of the lesser phyla. It is speculative but reasonable to imagine that there was an ancestral group, now long obscured in the mists of time, that split or radiated into at least four basically different branches. One of the diverging, descendant groups evolved into flatworms. Another soon split again and evolved into bryozoans and brachiopods. The third evolved into mollusks. The fourth evolved into annelids, and the most primitive annelids split into two major groups, one of which evolved into later annelids and one, with more radical change, into arthropods.[31] (See Fig. 22-21.)

THE ECHINODERM SUPERPHYLUM AND THE ORIGIN OF VERTEBRATES

We are vertebrates ourselves, so it is not surprising that the origin of the vertebrates has long been of particular interest to zoologists. There are now no real doubts as to the origins and relationships of the various classes *within* the subphylum Vertebrata (as will be shown in the next chapter). These origins are clearly revealed by fossils, but fossils cast no clear light on the remoter origin of the very first vertebrates. The oldest known fossil vertebrates are extremely primitive as vertebrates, but they have no suggestive resemblances to any phylum other than the Chordata, of which the vertebrates are a subphylum.

You recall (pp. 537 and 542) that besides the Vertebrata there are three other surviving subphyla of Chordata: Hemichordata, Tunicata, and Cephalochordata. They lack vertebrae and some other characters of the earliest, as well as of recent, vertebrates, but they seem surely to have had a common origin with the vertebrates. They must have branched off

from the vertebrate ancestry at a very remote time, before the vertebrates had originated as such. It would be expected that they would by now have evolved many peculiarities of their own, characters such as never occurred in the ancestry of the vertebrates, and this seems indeed to be true. However, the mere fact that they are different, ancient branches from the same ancestry means that they might also have retained some features of that ancestry which have been lost in the vertebrates. This, too, seems to be true. There is also reason to believe that the nonvertebrate chordates have, on the whole, changed less than the vertebrates. It is the development of some members of these groups that seems at present to give the most likely clues to the origin and relationships of the chordates in general, and therefore also of the vertebrates.

Vertebrates have no floating larvae. This developmental stage probably occurred in their remote invertebrate ancestors, but as in arthropods it has been lost in the course of evolution. In the vertebrates that do have larvae (some fishes, most amphibians), the larval stage is a new evolutionary development, not inherited from invertebrate ancestors. The hemichordates, however, still do have floating larvae that somewhat resemble trochophores but differ in several ways. The striking difference is that the hemichordate larva has a twisted ring of cilia that encircles the mouth, instead of a single ring anterior to the mouth as in trochophores.[32] The hemichordate larva is extraordinarily like the larva of an echinoderm; it was, indeed, mistaken for an echinoderm when first discovered.[33] This is strong, but not conclusive, evidence that hemichordates and echinoderms have inherited their larval stages from the same very ancient marine invertebrate ancestry. Since the hemichordates seem to be an offshoot of the vertebrate ancestry, the vertebrates, too, are probably derived from the same ultimate source as the echinoderms. Because the hemichordate and echinoderm larvae are different from trochophores, the chordate-echinoderm ancestry

---

[31] There is no fossil record of the nematodes, and the living forms are so profoundly modified that they have no clear trace of broader relationships. It is possible that they are another branch of the annelid superphylum, affected by early adaptation to semi- or wholly parasitic habits. Rotifers (Trochelminthes, p. 479) are probably members of the annelid superphylum strongly affected by great reduction in size. Some adult rotifers are rather like trochophore larvae. Several other minor phyla may also belong to this superphylum, but they are too profoundly modified or too poorly known for clear evidence.

[32] The hemichordate larva is called a tornaria.
[33] Echinoderm larvae are called bipinnaria or pluteus.

probably early became distinct from the ancestry of the annelid superphylum. Chordates and echinoderms may, then, be considered as members of a second superphylum, sometimes called the *echinoderm superphylum* (Figs. 22-21 and 22-22).

There is some other evidence of relationships between echinoderms and chordates and of their distinction from the annelid superphylum. In both echinoderms and chordates the early cleavages of the zygote usually produce cells that are still undifferentiated, each capable of developing into a whole adult if separated (see p. 340). In echinoderms and some chordates the mesoderm and coelom also develop in the same way, a way quite different from that of the annelid superphylum (p. 555). Pockets or folds arise from the endoderm of the developing digestive tract. The spaces in the pockets become the coelom, and their walls become mesoderm (Fig. 22-20). Development is much modified in most vertebrates, but this feature is probably primitive for chordates as a whole. Finally, it is interesting that echinoderms and chordates share a common biochemical feature: their phosphagen (p. 130) is identical—creatine. The common phosphagen in the annelid superphylum is, on the other hand, arginine.

Many other theories as to chordate and vertebrate origin were advanced in the latter years of the nineteenth and earlier years of the twentieth centuries, when this subject was most actively studied. The principal alternatives to the echinoderm theory were that chordates arose from annelids or from arachnids. Both theories were based mainly on comparisons of adult forms specialized in quite diverse ways, and both demanded profound structural transformations which are not impossible but for which there is no good evidence. Few, if any, zoologists now support those theories, and the theory of echinoderm-vertebrate affinities, inconclusive as it is, holds

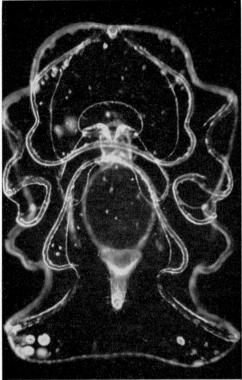

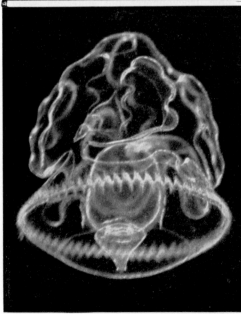

Both photos © Douglas P. Wilson

22-22 The larvae of an echinoderm and a hemichordate. Both photographs are of living specimens, magnified. Note in the lower figure the waves of beating cilia. *Above*, echinoderm (sea cucumber) larva. The view is facing the mouth. The wavy bands of cilia are clear, as is the alimentary canal. *Below*, hemichordate (tornaria) larva, viewed obliquely from the right side. The mouth is obscured at the right by the lower ring of cilia, but the arching alimentary canal is clear, as is the anus, immediately below the lower ring of cilia.

the field by default, at least. It should be emphasized that the view now generally accepted does not envision the transformation of an echinoderm into a chordate—the descent of the Chordata from the Echinodermata, as such. It is believed that the two phyla arose by strongly divergent evolution from some group of animals now long extinct and of unknown *adult* structure, but with early developmental stages and larvae similar to those of echinoderms. From that remote ancestry the echinoderms evolved as sedentary, sessile, or sluggish animals.

Indeed, there is strong suggestive evidence that the sedentary habit may have been characteristic of the whole superphylum in some early stage of its evolution. One of the most characteristic chordate features (the pharynx perforated by gill slits) is a likely adaptation to sessile life. In fact, two of the three surviving nonvertebrate chordate groups employ the perforated pharynx as a feeding device (Fig. 22-14). One of these groups, the tunicates, is even today predominantly sedentary. The other group, the Cephalochordata (amphioxus), although capable of swimming, burrows in sand, tail down, and lives an effectively sedentary life, drawing in water and filtering microorganic food through its pharyngeal slits.[34] The evolution of the chordate (and therefore vertebrate) pharynx is certainly easily understood as an adaptation to the sedentary habit. How, then, can we explain the emergence of vertebrates—most spectacularly motile of animals—as descendants of early sedentary chordates?

Some modern tunicates give a hint as to the likely mode of vertebrate origin. Like other sessile animals, they rely heavily on motile larvae to disperse the species. The motile larvae of tunicates (Fig. 22-23) are elongate, bilaterally symmetrical forms that are like a simplified caricature of a vertebrate. Most significant is their possession of an elongate *notochord* lying, as in vertebrates, dorsal to the gut. It serves the function of a skeleton for simple fishlike locomotion. Many zoologists now consider it very probable that vertebrates evolved as *neotenic*

[34] The chordate pharyngeal slits persist, of course, in fishes as gill slits with a respiratory function.

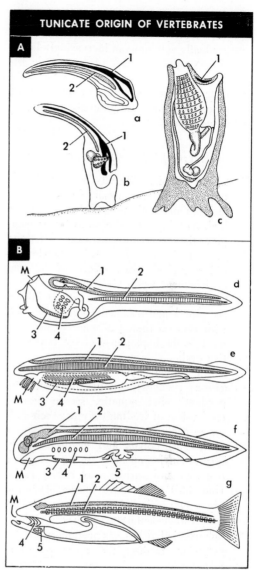

TUNICATE ORIGIN OF VERTEBRATES

22-23 The theory of the tunicate origin of vertebrates. *A.* Younger (*a*) and older (*b*) larvae of a tunicate, metamorphosing into the sedentary adult (*c*). *B.* The larval tunicate (*d*) compared with the basic organization of (*e*) a cephalochordate (*Branchiostoma*), (*f*) the larva of a cyclostome (agnathous fish, p. 582), and (*g*) a mature fish. In all four organisms note the similarity in (*1*) dorsal nerve cord; (*2*) skeletal notochord; (*3*) the endostyle, the gutter at the base of the pharynx which in higher vertebrates (including the adult of the cyclostome, *f*) becomes the thyroid gland; (*4*) pharyngeal gill slits; and (*5*) the heart. Note also the principal point that the larval tunicate is motile and bilaterally symmetrical, thus making plausible a transition from the sedentary primitive members of the superphylum to the motile vertebrates.

tunicates (note 11, p. 354). The theory envisages the motile larva of some sedentary tunicate gradually assuming an increasingly larger and more important part of the whole life cycle. Eventually it became, in this view, capable of its own reproduction and sloughed off, so to speak, the ancestral adult stages adapted to the sedentary habit.

Chapter Summary

What is an animal? Difficulty of definition in protists; major animal characteristics include: metabolism—nonphotosynthetic; high mobility; definite adult form; complex tissue and organ differentiation; general absence of rigid cell walls and cell vacuoles; maintenance of internal environment (with high sodium chloride content); high sensitivity (specialized receptors) and responsiveness, associated with nervous tissue; absence of development in the haplophase of the reproductive cycle.

The major animal phyla:

Porifera: sponges; colonies of semi-independent cells; aquatic, sessile forms; mechanism of feeding current; their failure to evolve greater complexity.

Coelenterata: polyps and medusas; body form: single opening to gut cavity; tentacles and carnivorous habit; polyp (budding) and medusa (dispersal) in the life cycle; colonial habit common; diversity of coelenterates: hydroids, siphonophores, jellyfishes, sea anemones, corals; polyp or medusa the more primitive form?

Platyhelminthes: flatworms; lack of exact zoological meaning for the word "worm"; body form: flat, with one opening to body cavity; bilateral symmetry; receptors in head region; nervous system; complex reproductive and excretory systems; parasitism common.

Nematoda: threadworms: anus present; parasitic, ubiquitous, and abundant.

Bryozoa: "moss animals"; colonial habit; skeleton; ciliated tentacles and feeding currents; U-shaped gut; aquatic, mainly marine; abundant as fossils.

Brachiopoda: "lamp shells"; two shells housing animals; contrasted with clam; bearing tentacles; noncolonial; abundant as fossils.

Mollusca: snails, clams, squids (treated in Chapter 23).

Annelida: segmented worms; earthworms, their soil-eating habits and importance for agriculture; marine annelids; free-swimming and tube-living forms; leeches, parasitic annelids.

Arthropoda: "jointed-feet" animals; crustaceans, spiders, and insects (treated in Chapter 23).

Echinodermata: "prickly skins": sea lilies, starfishes, brittle stars, sea urchins, and sea cucumbers; body form: radial symmetry, water vascular system, tube feet, skeleton; marine; abundant as fossils.

Chordata: animals "with a cord," the notochord; fishes, amphibians, reptiles, birds, and mammals; and less familiar, invertebrate forms: Hemichordata—acorn worms, Tunicata—sea squirts, and Cephalochordata—amphioxus; their possession of notochord, dorsal nerve cord, and pharyngeal gill slits.

Adaptive radiation of animal phyla: fallacious Greek idea that organisms form a simple ladder of life, with man at top; complex organisms descendants of simpler organisms, but dogfish, frog, and cat, for instance, not an evolutionary sequence; no now-living form an ancestor of another now-living form; fish, frog, and cat as specialists in different environments; the animal phyla, similarly, not a simple evolutionary *sequence;* for the most part specialists (as groups) in different environments; phyla as products of an early adaptive radiation; animal phyla best thought of as a fan rather than a ladder; *some* evolutionary sequences among phyla, but now largely obscured.

Basic characters of the animal phyla: the marine origin of most or all phyla; exploitation of fresh-water habitats by many phyla; only three phyla (Mollusca, Arthropoda, Chordata) now strictly terrestrial; no new phyla evolved on land; anatomical features important in understanding the phyla:

Tissue layers: two or three.

Digestive systems: one or two openings; degrees of differentiation of organs.

Coelom: true and false coeloms.

Skeletal systems: exo- and endoskeletons.

Circulatory systems: vascular or nonvascular.

Segmentation: some occurrence in Annelida, Arthropoda, and Chordata.

Symmetry: radial and bilateral.

Larvae: forms cast light on relationship between phyla.

Origin and relationships of the animal phyla:

Protozoan evolution: flagellates, ancestral cellular organisms; sarcodines, flagellate descendants that exploited feeding mechanism for locomotion; ciliates: evolved larger unicellular size, an evolutionarily sterile mode of size increase.

Origin of multicellular animals: evolution of size increase by formation of multicellular aggregates, a fruitful alternative to the pattern of ciliate size increase; locomotory and co-ordination problems inherent in increased size; Porifera as exemplifying sterile solution to co-ordination problem; muscle and nerve as key to evolutionary success of Metazoa.

Relationships of coelenterates to flatworms: exemplify difficulty of historical analysis in absence of fossil evidence.

The annelid superphylum: Bryozoa, Brachiopoda, Mollusca, Annelida, Arthropoda; trochophore larvae characteristic of all these phyla except Arthropoda; differention starts with first cleavage; origin of coelom as split in mesoderm.

The echinoderm superphylum: origin of vertebrates; status of invertebrate chordates; hemichordate and echinoderm larvae, and evidence of their affinity; other evidence—cleavage of egg, origin of coelom as pouches from gut, phosphagens; vertebrates as neotenic tunicates.

CHAPTER **23**

Mollusks,

Arthropods,

and Vertebrates

The vertebrates—exemplified here by the codfish (Gadus) are the most complex of the three great phyla, mollusks, arthropods, and vertebrates, which represent end points of three distinct lines of evolutionary progress. (Photo © Douglas P. Wilson)

Some tourists whiz through the desert assuring each other in boredom that there is nothing there. A lounger on the beach may not spare a moment to glance at a boy toying with a crab or a shell. Yet the desert is full of life and movement for anyone willing to sit still and look, and the boy is unwittingly illustrating dramatic contrasts and resemblances in the play of life. One of the finest values of biology is that it reveals profound meanings in apparent commonplaces. The greatest poetry is not written in garrets or printed in books. It is all around us in the living world. To read it we need only to pause, to observe sympathetically, and to learn a little about the long history and the incessant activities of life.

Let us look more closely and with more understanding at the boy, the crab, and the shell. The contrasts seem obvious enough. The

shell is perhaps that of a marine snail that lived in the water of the sea or burrowed in the sandy bottom. Its feeble sensory equipment can give it only a rudimentary perception of the world. Its motions are almost painfully deliberate. The crab is a species of the shore, in and out of the water but not out for long at a time. It scuttles with nervous activity constantly and seemingly with awareness, and yet it is hardly intelligent in seeking whatever animal food, living or dead, it can tear and devour. The boy was born to mastery of the land. His body is bursting with energy; his keen senses picture the fascinating world in tremendous detail; his brain is the greatest marvel in the universe.

The resemblances between the boy, the crab, and the shell require a little more thought, but there are, as you know, profound likenesses in all living things. These three are of course made up of cells with nuclei, chromosomes, and the rest. The syntheses and other metabolic processes are much the same within their cells. All are animals and must eat other organisms—all three could, indeed, live on the same food if the boy's mother was willing. In all three the food is taken in through a mouth and digested in a stomach, and wastes are similarly ejected in the three. All have nerves, muscles, glands, gonads, and other, similar organs and tissues. All three are, in short, complex and advanced animals. They share something else which, paradoxically, depends on their differences:

all of them represent culminations of the evolutionary processes. They exemplify the three phyla that have reached greatest complexity of structure, highest co-ordination of functions, and most manifold diversity of successful adaptations. It is the distinctive characters, the differences that so obviously exist between them, that make each of them in its own way such a high point in the expanding evolution of animal life. It will be interesting and enlightening to learn a little more about each of the major groups to which they belong: the mollusks, arthropods, and vertebrates.

Mollusks

On a smaller scale and within the limitations imposed by one ancestral anatomical plan, the mollusks illustrate the same sort of fanning out into adaptive diversity that is seen among the phyla of animals. They comprise five main subdivisions, classes, three of which are extremely diverse within themselves. The classes are so different and so old that it is hard to generalize about the phylum and impossible to say what the very first mollusks were like. The chitons, Class Amphineura, are on the whole the simplest mollusks, and zoologists are inclined to think that they are the most primitive. It is, however, probable that much of their simplicity is secondary, an evolutionary consequence of their becoming virtually sedentary animals. For instance, their lack of well-differentiated heads and special sense organs is more likely due to degenerative loss than to primitiveness. Other mollusks (unless obviously degenerate) have differentiated heads with sense organs, and it is probable that this is a basic feature of the whole phylum, present in the earliest ancestral true mollusks. Nevertheless, the simplicity of the chitons does make them clear illustrations of some other basic molluscan characteristics (Fig. 23-1).[1]

[1] Chitons are not common fossils, and they appear in the known fossil record later than the apparently more specialized classes Gastropoda, Pelecypoda, and Cephalopoda. Their later appearance need not imply later evolution: it could be due to their lack of preservation and human discovery in early rocks. The evidence does, however, suggest that all classes, including the Amphineura, arose at about the same time by rather rapid divergent evolution from an ancestry not closely like any of the known classes.

Mollusks are especially characterized by the development of a muscular region or organ behind the mouth. This serves for crawling locomotion in many mollusks and is called the *foot*. Above it is the soft mass of viscera. Practically all the organ systems found in any animals are present in most mollusks: digestive (sometimes with a unique rasping device, the *radula*), circulatory (with a heart), respiratory (usually with complex gills, *ctenidia*), excretory (with "kidneys"),[2] nervous (often with brainlike ganglia and sometimes with well-developed eyes and other sense organs), muscular, and reproductive. Above and surrounding the viscera is a *mantle* of specialized tissue, usually including glands that secrete one or more shells (Fig. 23-1).

The most important groups of mollusks are the classes Gastropoda (snails and their relatives), Pelecypoda (clams and relatives), and Cephalopoda (squids, octopuses, the chambered nautilus, and relatives).[3] Each of these groups has great diversity of specific adaptations evolved from a basic ancestral adaptation that is different in each class. The two other classes, equally distinctive but less diverse and relatively unimportant, are the Amphineura, already mentioned, and the Scaphopoda, or tooth shells (Fig. 23-2).

GASTROPODS

The deliberateness of a snail's gait is notorious. Nevertheless, snails are motile, and their slow crawling in search of food is an essential part of their way of life. Also characteristic is protection by a single shell with one opening. The early larva is bilateral, but in metamorphosis the viscera are twisted in a loop. This brings the anus from its original

[2] The term "kidney" is applied rather loosely to excretory organs in different Metazoan groups. The molluscan kidney has no evolutionary relationship (no homology) with the kidney of the vertebrates (echinoderm superphylum). The molluscan kidney is clearly a much elaborated version of the simple excretory tubules (nephridia) found in other members of the annelid superphylum.

[3] The gastropods ("belly-footed") because a snail or slug seems to crawl on its belly. The pelecypods ("hatchet-footed") because the foot of some clams is a little like a hatchet in outline. The cephalopods ("head-footed") because what is the foot in other mollusks has developed into tentacles around the mouth in the head region, and these tentacles may also be used in locomotion.

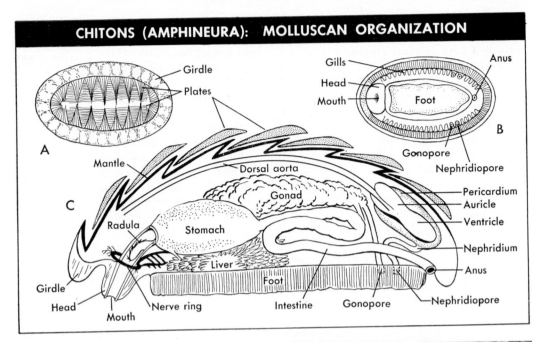

© Douglas P. Wilson

23-1 Chitons (*Amphineura*) as an example of molluscan organization. See p. 563 for major features of molluscan structure. The Amphineura, though typical of Mollusca in most respects, are atypical in: (a) the absence of special organs on the head; (b) the multiplicity of gills (themselves atypical ctenidia) in the mantle cavity; and (c) the multiplicity of plates on the mantle. The coelom is represented by the pericardium, in which the heart lies. The photograph is a dorsal view of a chiton attached to a rock.

position behind mouth and foot to a point above the mouth. However this peculiarity may have evolved, it is highly practical for an animal that lives in a house with only one door and that crawls about feeding on the bottom. After the twisting, the visceral organs of one side fail to develop, and further lopsided growth usually gives a spiral turn to the mantle and to the shell secreted by the mantle.

Gastropods (like all mollusks) were originally marine, and most of them still are. Some, however, have become almost fully terrestrial, although sensitive to dry air and commonly found only in moist locations. The terrestrial gastropods have lost their gills and have instead a lunglike cavity in the mantle that enables them to extract oxygen from air. Among the numerous fresh-water snails some have gills and some "lungs." Those with gills are of marine origin, while those with "lungs" had terrestrial ancestors and have returned to the water. That they did not regain their long-lost gills is a good example of the irrevocability of evolution (p. 469). It is paralleled by the return of air-breathing mammals, whales, to the remotely ancestral sea, where they retained lungs and did not regain the lost gills of their fish ancestors. (The gastropod lung is an evolutionary modification of the mantle cavity.)

Gastropods have evolved into a tremendous

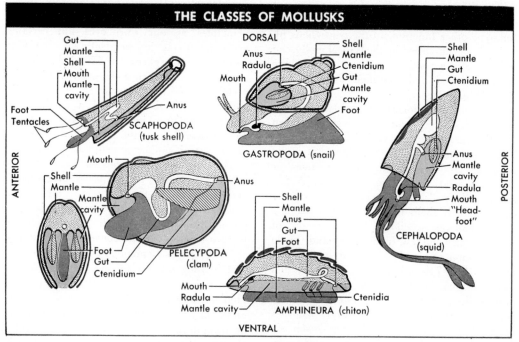

23-2 The classes of mollusks.

array of different forms, usually beautiful and often bizarre. Wherever you live, you are familiar with some of them, especially if you have had opportunity to collect sea shells. A museum display of gastropods is one of the most impressive evidences of the diversity of life. One curiosity is that some gastropods have lost their shells. Among them are the unlovely garden slugs and the really beautiful marine nudibranchs (Fig. 23-3). These forms also illustrate the irrevocability of evolution: their viscera still show the twisting and lopsidedness that went with development of a shell in the ancestors. It is not clear what evolutionary forces were responsible for loss of the shell. But its loss is clearly the ultimate cause of some later evolution of protective devices substituting, so to speak, for the shell's function of protection. Some shell-less gastropods that feed on coelenterates have evolved the remarkable ability of digesting all the victim's tissues except embryonic stinging cells. These cells are borrowed, eventually appearing in the gastropods' soft skin, where they mature, conferring protection on their former predator! Such gastropods are brilliantly colored. Might this

have adaptive meaning? (Cf. p. 411.) Other shell-less gastropods, easy meat to predators, have acquired ability to squirt out a colored solution as a sort of smoke screen when disturbed.

PELECYPODS

Pelecypods have retained bilateral symmetry and have two shells or valves, usually nearly symmetrical, one on each side of the body; hence the name "bivalve" is often applied to them. They were primitively motile, and most of them still are, but they usually lead rather sedentary lives and are even less speedy than snails. They seldom move far from where the larva settles down, and some, like oysters, become permanently attached. In keeping with their more sedentary lives, pelecypods have lost the differentiated head region and usually have fewer and simpler receptors than gastropods. However, many have "eye spots," simple light receptors, in the mantle along the opening between the shells.

Like so many other sedentary animals, the pelecypods feed by filtering microorganisms from their watery medium. Their mode of filtering illustrates, once again, the way evolution of organisms exploits for new purposes structures already available, evolved initially for some other function. In the pelecypods filtering is accomplished by the typical molluscan gill, initially a respiratory structure but here much enlarged and modified as a feeding sieve (Fig. 6-2).

In diversity of forms (Fig. 23-4), pelecypods are less spectacular than gastropods, but still they are extremely varied and abundant. The great majority are marine, but some occur in fresh water (fresh-water clams or river mussels). None are terrestrial. A few swim fairly well; scallops (*Pecten*) swim by clapping their shells together. Burrowing is a more common specialty. Many species of marine clams burrow in mud or sand, as do our common edible clams (*Venus* and *Mya*). Others (like *Teredo*) burrow in wood and cause serious damage to wooden boats and pilings. Some (like *Pholas*) burrow in solid rock. The astonishing giant clams (*Tridacna*) of the South Pacific, which may reach six feet in diameter, burrow in living coral reefs.

CEPHALOPODS

It is a literary tradition to play up the horror and menace of octopuses.[4] This is a bit hard on shy creatures which have seldom if ever seriously harmed a man. They, and even more particularly their relatives the squids, are also among the most complex and in almost any sense highest products of evolution (Fig. 23-5).

"Active" is the keyword for the cephalopods. They are all free-living and, on occasion, fast-moving, forms. Squids have a large mantle cavity with muscular walls and a funnel-like tube (sometimes called a "siphon") through which water can be ejected rapidly by contraction of the walls. The animal moves swiftly by the principle of jet propulsion. If the tube is turned backward, the squid darts forward in pursuit of prey (Fig. 23-6). When it is the pursued rather than the pursuer (which seems to be the more frequent situation), it turns the tube forward and darts backward. In conjunction with its active life, the squid has a remarkably large and complex brain, as brains go among the

[4] You may call them "octopodes" or "octopi" if you prefer.

invertebrates. It also has elaborate image-forming eyes, which work on just the same principles as our own eyes but certainly evolved entirely independently, a classic example of convergence (p. 470).[5] Another remarkable convergence between squids and vertebrates is that squids, alone among invertebrates, have developed a cartilaginous internal skeleton, including a skull-like protective case around the brain. Only traces of the ancestral molluscan external shell remain.

The fact that cephalopods have tentacles with suction disks is familiar to everyone. In octopuses the tentacles serve for slower clambering about (octopuses have jet propulsion, too), and in all cephalopods the tentacles seize prey and convey it to the sharp, shearing jaws. Cephalopods are predaceous, that is, they actively pursue, kill, and devour other living animals such as fishes or crabs (but not humans!). Have you ever meditated on the fact that characteristics we admire, such as brain development, keen senses, and skillful co-ordination, are more likely than not to be best developed in predaceous animals, while animals that lead quiet, respectable lives seem to have little else to recommend them?

Besides squids and octopuses (several genera and species of each), there is just one surviving genus of a markedly different group of cephalopods. This is the nautilus (genus *Nautilus*). The animal lives in a coiled shell divided into chambers by partitions. From time to time as the animal grows, it moves to a new chamber and seals off the old one. The nautilus is a relic of the past, the last survivor of formerly very abundant groups of animals that played a major role in the history of life for tens and hundreds of millions of years.

[5] The convergence of their eyes with those of vertebrates has given cephalopods a curious place in the history of evolutionary thought. In the early nineteenth century Lamarck's evolutionary hypothesis had not yet found a secure place in biology. In 1830 the French naturalist Saint-Hilaire engaged in a now-famous debate with the great and much abler French zoologist Cuvier, who was a firm disbeliever of evolution. Saint-Hilaire staked the case for evolution in part on the resemblance between cephalopod and vertebrate eyes. Cuvier, a great student of mollusks, had no trouble in demonstrating that vertebrate and mollusk eyes were quite unrelated in any sense (evolutionary or otherwise); and evolutionary thought suffered a serious setback from Saint-Hilaire's unfortunate choice of evidence.

23-3 Gastropods. *Left,* garden snails (*Helix*) on a twig. Their mantle cavity has become a functional lung. *Below right,* a nudibranch gastropod (*Archidoris britannica*) which has no shell, no mantle cavity, no ctenidium. The animal respires by the cluster of gills that surround the anus (at right in photo).

The whelk (*Buccinum*), a predatory marine gastropod. A long proboscis (with terminal mouth) protrudes between the tentacles.

Above, the sea hare, *Tethys*. The foot region is developed into two large "parapodia" that enable it to swim. A herbivorous tidal-zone gastropod.

Below, the shell-less garden slug (*Arion*) with freshly laid eggs.

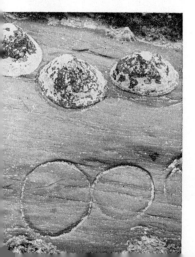

Left, limpets (*Patella*) on a soft slaty rock which shows scars left by limpets which have died.

Above, left, the giant clam (*Tridacna*) of coral reefs, with coral growing on one of the valves. *Above, right,* the queen scallop (*Chlamys*) escaping from a starfish buried in the sand. Scallops swim by opening and closing the valves, producing a jet-propulsion effect.

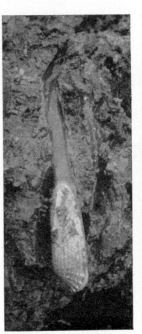

All photos © Douglas P. Wilson except top left,
American Museum of Natural History

Above, mussels (*Mytilus*) attached to rock by byssal threads they secrete. They are being attacked by the predatory gastropod *Ocenetra,* which drills through the mussel shells with its radula. *Right, Pholas,* a pelecypod that burrows into solid rock, using the edges of its valves as a drill. *Far right, Solen,* the razor shell, with its foot extended.

23-5 Cephalopods. *Above, left,* the cuttlefish (*Sepia*) is a very active swimmer. Note the large eyes. (See note on p. 566.) *Above, right,* the common octopus (*Octupus vulgaris*), showing the suction disks on its tentacles. *Right,* the chambered nautilus (*Nautilus pompilius*), with shell cut away to show the animal in the last, largest chamber.

The nautiloids, closer relatives of the nautilus, were the first cephalopods to evolve. They swarmed in ancient seas and had many different forms (Fig. 32-1). Next to arise were the ammonoids, which resembled nautiloids in having chambered shells but differed in (among other things) having more complicated partitions between the chambers. The last of the ammonoids became extinct some 70 million years ago.

Arthropods

No one knows how many species of arthropods there are in the world. The number is at least a million, and estimates run as high as 10 million. Arthropods have been brought up from the deepest sea bottoms that have been dredged. They have been encountered by airplanes flying miles above the earth. They are everywhere that life exists at all. They fly, swim, hop, crawl, and just sit still. There is probably no species of organism that is not on occasion eaten by one arthropod or another. Arthropods are, in turn, eaten by many other animals. They are man's chief competitors for food and all sorts of organic materials. They include the worst of pests, but they are also essential links in maintaining the verdure-clad world as it is.

In basic structure the arthropods are somewhat like annelids (p. 535), and there is no doubt that the two phyla had a common origin something over 500 million years ago.

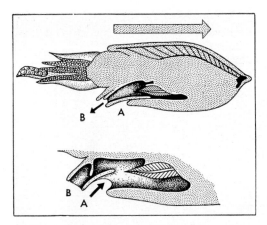

23-6 Cephalopod locomotion. *Upper figure,* animal moves in direction of stippled arrow; water is propelled as a jet (*B,* solid arrow) from the mantle cavity through the siphon. *Lower figure,* mantle cavity being recharged with water between the siphon and the mantle cavity wall. Note the valve actions. The siphon, which is muscular, can be directed backward (reverse position in the figure) so that its jet propels the animal forward.

Among the more important differences are these:

> The external coating or *cuticle* of arthropods is harder and serves mechanically as an external skeleton (see p. 228).
>
> Arthropods have legs divided into distinct, movable segments or joints (hence the name of the phylum).
>
> Arthropods have muscles in definite groups mechanically related to specific movable parts. The muscles of annelids form relatively simple sheets throughout the body.
>
> Arthropods generally have fewer segments, and there is a tendency for the segments of some regions, notably in the head, to fuse and to become strongly differentiated in structure.
>
> Arthropods have distinctly developed jaws. (These open from side to side instead of up and down as our and other vertebrate jaws do.)
>
> Their nervous system is usually more highly developed than in annelids and is accompanied by elaborate sensory receptors, including those in the antennae and eyes.

Most of these arthropod characteristics improve or elaborate their reactions to stimuli in the environment. Their advantage over other invertebrates is largely in the efficiency and adaptability of their behavior. The vertebrates, and notably man, also owe their dominance in great part to their adaptable and efficient behavior. In arthropods the behavior is relatively inflexible in a given species, but is modified genetically in the course of evolution. Vertebrate behavior has, as a rule, a larger element of flexibility in the individual (see Chapter 10). We are likely to consider our own kind of behavioral adaptation as "better" or "higher." Arthropods are, however, from ten to a hundred times more numerous than vertebrates in species, incomparably more abundant in individuals, and divergently adapted to an even wider range of environments and habits. They easily hold their own against all the attacks of man and of other animals. Which is the more successful phylum?

Our classification (p. 479) recognizes seven classes of arthropods (Fig. 23-7). One of these (Onychophora) includes only a few rather obscure living animals, about seventy species, mostly in the Tropics.[6] The class (with the genus *Peripatus*) is of great interest because it is not fully arthropodlike and has some distinctly annelid characteristics; hence it tends to link the two phyla. Otherwise it is unimportant. The trilobites (Class Trilobita) are abundant, important fossils (illus., p. 733) and interesting forerunners of the crustaceans, but they have long been extinct and need not further detain us now (see p. 755). Centipedes (Class Chilopoda), the "hundred-legs" (they may in fact have over three hundred legs but thirty to seventy are more usual) and millepedes (Class Diplopoda), "thousand-legs" (an exaggeration) are rather common, but still of minor importance in the phylum as a whole (Fig. 23-9). The outstanding classes are those

6 It is frequently stated that this group is known from fossils in the pre-Cambrian (see p. 743), which would make it among the oldest of all animal fossils. This is wishful thinking. It is wholly uncertain whether the fossils in question belong to the Onychophora or are of the stated age. Fossils likely to be Onychophora are known, but of an age after well-developed arthropods are abundant as fossils.

of the crustaceans, the spiders (and relatives), and, above all, the insects.

CRUSTACEANS [7]

All of us are familiar with some crustaceans (Fig. 23-8), if only because we eat them with pleasure: lobsters, crabs, shrimps, crayfish, prawns. We have only those five common names for them, but there are literally thousands of species of these larger, free-living crustaceans, many of them edible by humans. They are the decapods or "ten-legs" among the crustaceans in general. Most of them are marine, but they are also numerous in fresh water, and some crabs can survive considerable periods in the air as long as they do not dry out. All are carnivores or scavengers, eating a wide variety of small living animals and any sort of dead animal matter.

Decapods are most familiar to us, but they are not the most numerous of crustaceans or the most important in the economy of nature. Those distinctions must be assigned to the small, even microscopic crustaceans that swarm by countless billions in all seas and most bodies of fresh water. Krill, the principal food of some of the largest whales, is composed of crustaceans (genus *Euphausia*) under an inch in length. Others, still smaller, abound in salty (example, *Artemia*) or fresh (example, *Daphnia*) ponds. More diversely specialized crustaceans well exemplify a broad *adaptive radiation* (see p. 447).

Ostracods are very small crustaceans that secrete, in addition to the usual arthropod cuticle, two protective shells, much like miniature clam shells.

Some of the *copepods* are free-living, important fish food ("brit"), but many are parasitic on or in worms, other crustaceans, echinoderms, and chordates.

Barnacles are sessile as adults, within complex limy cups secreted by the animals. A shell-less relative, *Sacculina*, parasitic on crabs, is a classic example of extreme degeneration.

Isopods and *amphipods* are small, buglike crustaceans, marine, fresh-water, or living in

[7] "With a crust or shell"; all arthropods have tough "crusts," but this is perhaps most evident in crustaceans.

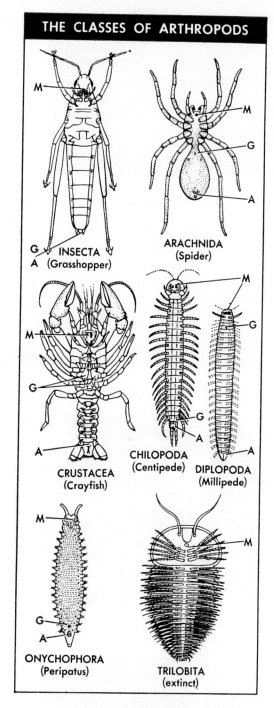

THE CLASSES OF ARTHROPODS

INSECTA (Grasshopper)

ARACHNIDA (Spider)

CRUSTACEA (Crayfish)

CHILOPODA (Centipede)

DIPLOPODA (Millipede)

ONYCHOPHORA (Peripatus)

TRILOBITA (extinct)

23-7 The classes of arthropods. M = mouth, G = genital opening, A = anus. Note significant differences between classes in the location of the genital opening. (The location of the genital opening and anus in the trilobites is unknown.)

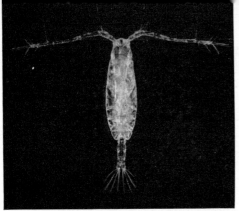

23-8 Crustaceans. *Left*, a copepod (*Acartia clausi*) in dorsal view (×88). *Right*, a decapod, the crab *Cancer magister*, from Alaska.

Far left, another decapod, the common prawn *Leander serratus* (×⅔). *Left*, the sow bug or wood louse (*Armadillaria vulgare*) is one of the few crustaceans that have become terrestrial.

Below, barnacles, *Balanus perforatus* (approx. natural size).

Below, *Caprella aequilibra* is a delicate, slender-bodied crustacean living among seaweeds in the tidal zone (×6).

Below, the goose barnacle, *Lepas fascicularis* (×½).

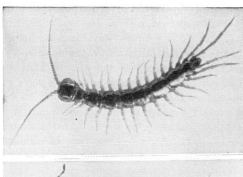

23-9 Chilopods and diplopods. *Above*, a centipede (chilopod). Note one pair of legs per segment. The centipedes are carnivores feeding mostly on other arthropods. *Below*, a millepede (diplopod). Note two pairs of legs per segment. The millepedes are herbivores.

damp places on land: "sow bugs," "pill bugs," "wood lice," "beach fleas," and so on. They are entirely distinct from true bugs, lice, or fleas, all of which are insects.

One of the principles of evolutionary change particularly well illustrated by crustaceans is the regional specialization and differentiation of parts. Primitive crustaceans probably had many segments, most or all of them with appendages that were closely similar throughout. Such a very primitive condition is unknown among any true crustaceans, but it is closely approached in the older, extinct trilobites, closely allied to crustaceans and possibly ancestral to them. (Some authorities include trilobites in the Class Crustacea.) In such a crustacean as the lobster (Fig. 23-10) no two of the nineteen pairs of appendages are exactly alike, and those of different regions are highly differentiated in form and function, as indicated in Table 23-1.

It is an evolutionary generalization (open to exceptions, as such generalizations always are) that, when ancestral organisms have numerous parts similar in structure and function (like the appendages of trilobites), the parts in their descendants tend to be reduced in number and specialized in different places for different functions (as in the lobster appendages).

TABLE 23-1

The appendages of the lobster

Segments	Appendages
1	None.*
2-3	Antennae, different in form on the two segments. Sense organs.
4-9	Jaw parts, different on each segment. Chewing and handling food.
10	Large pincers. Offense and defense.
11-14	Legs, all different, the first two pairs with small pincers. Walking, grasping.
15-19	So-called "swimmerets." They aid in slow forward swimming but are more involved in circulating water to the gills, in mating, and in carrying the eggs and young.
20	Broad plates. Swimming backward. (They are snapped forward under the body, an action that makes the whole animal dart backward.)
21	None. (The segment as a whole is a flat plate that assists the appendages of the 20th segment in the backward darting motion.)

* The possible first segment in the lobster is so reduced or fused with those following that its existence is sometimes doubted, but this segment occurs in primitive crustaceans and there may be traces of it in the lobster.

ARACHNIDS [8]

The arachnids (Fig. 23-11) are another group, like the octopuses, that have been given a largely undeserved bad name. It is true that most spiders and ticks are poisonous, but only a few are dangerous to man, and most of us are rarely under the slightest menace from them. Most spiders are beneficial to man because they prey on insects considered undesirable with better cause. Mites and ticks, also arachnids, do deserve a bad name from our point of view, for they include unpleasant and dangerous external parasites of man and domestic animals and are intermediate hosts for organisms producing some serious diseases. Daddy longlegs or harvestmen are another group of arachnids,

[8] Class Arachnida, from the Greek for "spider."

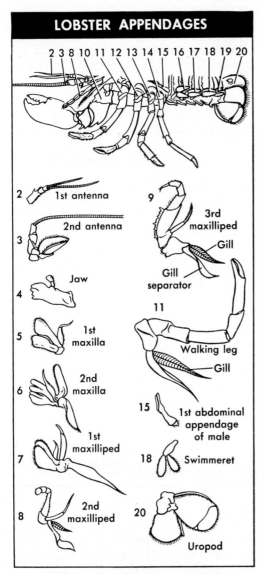

LOBSTER APPENDAGES

2 3 8 10 11 12 13 14 15 16 17 18 19 20

2   1st antenna

3   2nd antenna

4   Jaw

5   1st maxilla

6   2nd maxilla

7   1st maxilliped

8   2nd maxilliped

9   3rd maxilliped — Gill — Gill separator

11   Walking leg — Gill

15   1st abdominal appendage of male

18   Swimmeret

20   Uropod

23-10 The appendages of the lobster. The numbers in the figure refer to the number of the segment bearing the appendages shown.

entirely harmless and indeed helpful from our point of view.

Most people think of arachnids as insects or bugs (which are, strictly speaking, a group of insects). Arachnids are really quite different and are easily distinguished by the fact that they have four or five [9] pairs of

[9] There are really six pairs of appendages in most arachnids, but the first pair, at least, and usually the first two pairs, are so modified that they do not look or function like legs.

legs, while insects have three pairs. This is what systematists call a diagnostic or key character. It is a handy way to spot whether a particular animal is an arachnid or an insect. But an animal is not classified as an arachnid *because* it has four or five pairs of legs rather than three. It is classified in the Arachnida because it has the same ancestry as other arachnids and a different ancestry from insects over some hundreds of millions of years, as attested by all the varying characteristics of the two groups and by large numbers of fossil representatives of both. It happens that legs were early reduced to three pairs in insects and not in arachnids, so that is a convenient way to tell them apart. Among some other animals, such as the centipedes, closely related forms may have quite different numbers of legs or appendages. In contrast, extremely distantly related animals may have the same number of appendages: some protists have four, as we do!

Another living arachnid looks offhand completely unlike a spider, scorpion, or tick: the horseshoe or king crab, genus *Limulus* (Fig. 23-11). The broad protective dorsal shield (carapace) does look rather crablike, but examination of the legs (five pairs) and internal anatomy reveals indubitable phylogenetic resemblances to spiders and differences from crabs. This animal is an evolutionary relict, a famous conservative. It has changed very little in the last 200 million years or so. Still older relatives, the eurypterids (Fig. 31-1), are an extinct group of more scorpionlike arachnids that long played an important role in ancient seas. They included the largest of all arthropods, over six feet in length.

INSECTS

No one needs to be told that insects are the most successful and diverse of invertebrates. In fact, no other group of organisms of any kind, protists, plants, or animals, can begin to compare with them in diversity. At least half and probably a much larger proportion of all the species of all organic kingdoms living in the world today belong to this one class. What we have said about the importance and dominance of the Phylum Arthropoda (p. 569) is true mostly because it includes the Class Insecta.

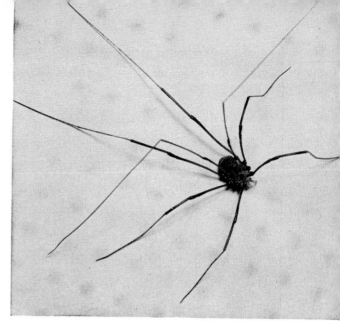

Above, a house spider (*Theridion*) with egg sacs on the back of a leaf. *Below*, the dog tick (*Dermacentor*) transmits the infective organism causing Rocky Mountain spotted fever in man. *Bottom*, a scorpion.

Above, harvestmen, or daddy longlegs, feed on small insects.

23-11   Arachnids.

Ventral (*left*) and dorsal (*right*) views of *Limulus polyphemus*, the king crab.

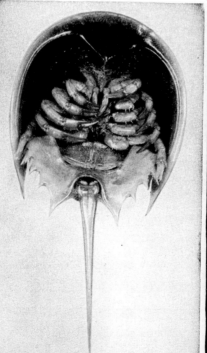

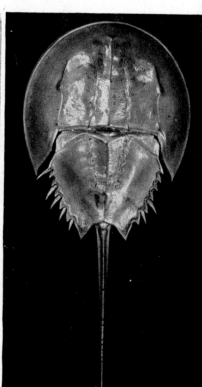

THE GRASSHOPPER: INSECT ORGANIZATION

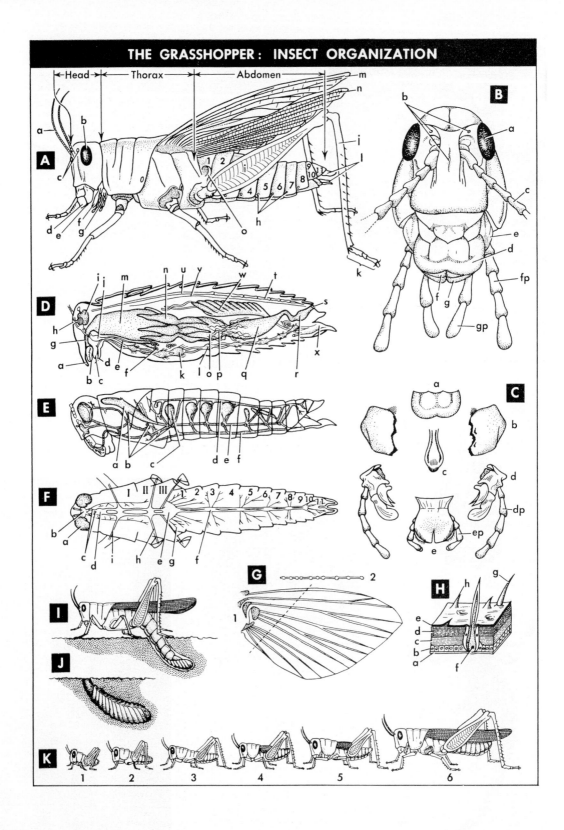

There is just one strong restriction on the distribution of insects. If we lived in the sea, we would be much impressed with their fellow arthropods the crustaceans, but we would consider insects a rare and unimportant group. Insects arose as terrestrial animals. That was the most fundamental adaptive feature in the origin of the class. Many of them have subsequently adapted to life in fresh water, commonly in the larval stages only. A few pass their larval stage or even their whole lives along the shore between tides and in salty pools. There is perhaps only one (genus *Halobates*) that can be considered fully a creature of the open oceans, and it is a water strider that really lives in the air, not the water, which is the floor of its world.

One other restriction on the adaptive range of insects is a matter of size. Multicellular organisms cannot function below a minimum size which is extremely small to our eyes, to be sure, but which looks large in comparison with a bacterium or many other protists. The smallest insects (which are parasites in the eggs of other insects) are about 0.2 millimeters (that is, only about $\frac{1}{125}$ inch) in length. Most insects are at least 2 millimeters long. On the other hand, there is a mechanical

and physiological upper limit for the size of insects. The weight and the stress of muscles and motions are borne by an external skeleton. There is a limit to the total weight a given kind of skeleton can support. At the limit the skeleton itself either becomes too heavy to move or too light to stand up without collapsing under the weight of the rest of the body. This limit is very much higher for an internal than for an external skeleton; that is one of the advantages that mammals and other vertebrates have over insects. The respiratory and vascular systems also impose limits on the size of insects. They are very efficient for small animals but probably could not adapt to any considerable increase in bulk. Few insects are more than about 40 millimeters long, and the upper limit is around 275 millimeters (less than a foot) for body length. Some moths have a slightly greater wingspread, up to about a foot. A few ancient insects known as fossils had a wingspread of over two feet, but the body bulk was not as large in proportion.

A favorite theme of science fiction involves insects as large as men or larger. Aside from the fact that this is mechanically and biologically impossible, do you think it would make

---

23-12 The grasshopper: organization of a typical insect. *A.* External anatomy of female grasshopper. Note the division of the body into three major parts: head, thorax, and abdomen. *a*, antenna; *b*, compound eye; *c*, ocelli (supplementary light-sensitive organs); *d*, labrum (upper lip); *e*, mandible; *f*, maxilla; *g*, labium (lower lip); *h*, spiracles (breathing apertures for entry of air into tracheal system); *i*, femur of the third leg; *j*, tibia of leg; *k*, tarsal segments of leg; *l*, ovipositor; *m*, forewing; *n*, hindwing; *o*, tympanum (the organ of hearing). The eleven abdominal segments are numbered. *B.* Details of the head: *a*, compound eye; *b*, ocelli; *c*, antenna; *d*, labrum; *e*. mandible; *f*, maxilla; *fp*, maxillary palp; *g*, labium; *gp*, labial palp. *C.* Mouth parts: *a*, labrum; *b*, mandible; *c*, hypopharynx; *d*, maxilla; *dp*, maxillary palp; *e*, labium; *ep*, labial palp. *D.* Internal anatomy (tracheal system omitted): *a*, labrum; *b*, mandible; *c*. hypopharynx; *d*, labium; *e*, salivary duct; *f*, salivary gland; *g*, esophagus; *h*, ocellus; *i, j*, supra- and subesophageal ganglia, forming the brain; *k*, third thoracic ganglion of nerve cord; *l*, first abdominal ganglion of nerve cord; *m*, crop; *n*, gastric pouch (or cecum); *o*, stomach; *p*, Malpighian (excretory) tubules; *q*, intestine; *r*, rectum; *s*, anus; *t*, heart; *u*, aorta (main blood vessel

leading to head region); *v*, diaphragm (separates section of body cavity containing heart from rest of body cavity); *w*, ovary; *x*, vagina. *E.* Respiratory (tracheal system): *a*, thoracic air sac (reservoir of air); *b*, spiracles (air-entry apertures); *c*, first of several abdominal air sacs; *d, e, f*, dorsal, lateral, and ventral tracheal trunks. *F.* The nervous system in dorsal view: *a*, eye; *b*, supraesophageal ganglion; *c*, connective nerves (pass around esophagus) to *d*, the subesophageal ganglion; *e*, third thoracic ganglion on the pair of ventral nerve cords; *f*, first abdominal ganglion; *g, h, i*, nerves to third, second, and first legs. The three thoracic segments are identified in Roman numerals, the eleven abdominal segments in Arabic numerals. *G.* The wing of a generalized insect, to show the distribution of veins on it: *2* is a cross-sectional view corresponding with the dashed line on *1*. The veins carry tracheae whose walls are thickened, forming a supporting structure for the wing membrane. *H.* The body covering of a generalized insect: *a*, a basement membrane; *b*, epidermis; *c, d,* and *e*, collectively, the exoskeleton; *f*, cell at base of *g*, a movable bristle; *h*, fixed spine on exoskeleton. *I.* Female laying eggs (ovipositing) in ground. *J.* The egg mass. *K. 1-5*, successively older young grasshoppers or nymphs; *6*, adult.

23-13 A variety of insects.
Above, a green and orange stinkbug (Pentatomidae) from Barro Colorado Island in the Panama Canal Zone. *Left,* the Luna moth (order Lepidoptera, butterflies and moths): adult male. *Center left,* a dragonfly (order Odonata, dragonflies and damsel flies): adult resting. *Below,* the common housefly (order Diptera, flies, mosquitoes): a model.

Below, mosquitoes (order Diptera): an adult female sucking blood (*left*); and the larvae respiring at the surface of a pond (*right*).

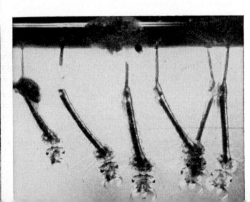

Above, a lubber grasshopper (order Orthoptera, roaches, crickets): female laying eggs.

Top left, a cicada wasp (order Hymenoptera, bees, wasps, and ants), with a cicada it has stung. *Above*, boll weevil (order Coleoptera, beetles).

Above, left, the human body louse (order Anoplura, lice), carrier of typhus fever. *Above, right*, a bumble-bee (order Hymenoptera) with pollen packed into special "pollen baskets" on its hind legs. *Below*, ants (order Hymenoptera); adult workers and pupae.

our war with the insects easier or harder? Lion hunting is more exciting and dangerous than mouse hunting, but are mice easier to exterminate? In fact, is not the small size of insects, and the accompanying small food requirement of any one of them, a reason why they are so extremely numerous and diverse and are often such pests from our viewpoint?

Most insects are small and nonaquatic. Aside from these limitations insects have a bewildering variety of forms and follow almost every imaginable way of life, including many that would be inconceivable if the insects did not demonstrate them to us. They all have some features in common (Fig. 23-12), characteristics that must have been involved in the evolutionary origin of the class. Among the most striking of these are:

The head consists of six segments, thoroughly fused and practically inseparable in the adult. Appendages of one segment have become sensory antennae. Other appendages have become complex mouth parts.

The thorax, central section of the body, is distinctly separate from head and abdomen and consists of three segments, each with a pair of legs.

The abdomen has eleven or fewer segments, (usually) without appendages, and the posterior segments are specialized for reproduction.

Respiration is by tracheae (p. 135); the circulatory system is open, without capillaries or veins; oxygen transport by blood is unimportant because the tracheal branches carry oxygen directly to nearly every cell in the body.

Simple and compound eyes occur, as well as many other receptors in antennae and elsewhere. The nervous system is complex, with two large ganglia or "brains" in the head and a double ventral cord.

Many insects lack wings altogether, and it is probable that wings never occurred in the ancestors of some of them, such as the silverfish and springtails. Thus wings were not involved in the origin of the class, but they certainly evolved early in its history. The great majority of insects have wings, and most of the wingless forms (lice, fleas, wing-less ants, etc.) had flying ancestors. Insects commonly have two approximately equal pairs of wings, and this condition was probably primitive. In many insects, notably the beetles, the front pair has become a protective cover. In flies (called Diptera, or "two-wings," on this account) the hind pair is greatly reduced in size and is a balancing, not flying, organ.[10] Another characteristic that is widespread but not universal in insects is the occurrence of feeding larvae, with gradual or sudden metamorphosis into the adult. We have already referred to this complication in the life history (p. 385; see also Fig. 15-22).

Specialists on insects (entomologists) divide the class into about twenty-five living orders, the number being variable because it is a matter of taste and opinion whether some related groups should be considered separate orders or suborders of one order. A dozen or more wholly extinct orders are also known. Some faint idea of the stunning diversity of insects is suggested by Fig. 23-13. Among the more numerous and familiar groups of insects are: the roaches and grasshoppers; termites (or "white ants," but they belong to a different order from true ants); dragonflies; May flies; lice; bugs [11] and aphids; caddis flies; moths and butterflies; true flies; fleas; beetles; and ants, wasps, and bees.

The diversity of insects involves not only the enormous number of species and other groups but also the fact that two or more sharply distinct forms may occur within a single species or, indeed, deme. This phenomenon, which also occurs in many other groups of organisms, is called *polymorphism* ("many forms"). The different forms may characterize different stages in the life history, for instance, the wormlike larvae and flying adults

10 In another group, so little known as to have no popular name (technical name: Strepsiptera), it is the front pair of wings that is reduced. In this group the wings occur only in males. The females are parasites in other insects, from which they protrude their hind ends for fertilization by the flying males. The young, both male and female, go through two distinct parasitic larval stages. Many insects go through life histories even more curious and complicated than this. One could spend a limetime (many have!) enumerating the strange and intricate lives of insects.

11 Although in daily speech we are likely to call any insects, and even some noninsects, "bugs," bugs strictly speaking are the members of a single order of insects, the Hemiptera.

of butterflies and many other insects. Polymorphism may also correspond with functional differentiation in a social organism, as in the castes of ants and other social insects (Fig. 25-7). The phenomenon is most striking, however, and is most strictly defined as polymorphism when it depends neither on age nor on function. For example, among our common sulfur butterflies (genus *Colias*) most of the females are yellow, but a considerable number of them (up to 20 per cent or more in some places) are white. Why do these white sulfur butterflies not constitute a subspecies or other systematic group? What is the relationship between polymorphism and the genetic variation that occurs in all populations? Can you think of any other kinds and find other examples of polymorphism, in coelenterates, for instance? In fishes? In mammals? In mankind?

The Vertebrates

You learned in the preceding chapter that the phylum Chordata is usually subdivided into four subphyla, three of which include a relatively small number of peculiar marine animals. The other subphylum, Vertebrata ("with vertebrae"), is another of the great culminations of the evolutionary processes. It is in many respects the most important and most progressive of all groups of organisms. Vertebrates are much less diverse and less abundant than insects. Their role in the total metabolic turnover of the living world is far less than the parts played by several groups of plants and also less than those of some other animals. The vertebrates are, nevertheless, highly diverse and abundant, and they do have important ecological roles. Moreover, as a whole they are characterized by the highest development of reception of environmental stimuli and the greatest flexibility and widest repertory of reactions. The vertebrates include man, who is in those respects and some others incomparably the most progressive of all organisms and who is, even from the point of view of other organisms, much the most potent force on earth today. While rightly patting ourselves on the backs as the supreme animals, however, we must not forget that the vertebrates in-

clude other groups that are also dominant and are evolutionary culminations in their own ways and in different adaptive spheres, notably the bony fishes, the perching birds, and the rodents.

THE ANCESTRAL VERTEBRATES

Some idea of what the first vertebrates were like can be obtained by making comparisons among living vertebrates.[12] Similarities between the most diverse species, for instance, between a lamprey (p. 584 and Fig. 23-15) and a man, are almost sure to have been inherited from the earliest vertebrates. In such a comparison we need not worry much about the misleading effects of convergence and parallelism (p. 470), because the evolution of the two groups has in fact been so divergent that they are unlikely to have any similarities that are not homologies (p. 465).

Still, the comparison leaves us with a very incomplete picture. For the many characters that are decidedly different in man and lamprey, which was the condition in the early vertebrates, or was it distinct from either? For instance, men have jaws and lampreys do not. The human skeleton is bony and that of a lamprey is cartilaginous. Our skin is dry and hairy; lamprey skin is smooth and slimy. What were the early vertebrates like in these respects? The evidence of early fossil vertebrates provides answers to many questions of that sort. The fossils indicate, for example, that early vertebrates were more like the lamprey in lacking jaws, more like man in having bony skeletons, and not like either one in type of skin, which was covered with scales or plates. It is true that lampreys are on the whole a good deal more like the earliest vertebrates than men are. This fact is also a help in attempting to reconstruct the vertebrate ancestry, but plainly it does not follow that lampreys (or any other recent animals) are in all respects primitive.

Here are some of the known facts and most

12 We are talking now about the first vertebrates, not the first chordates, which preceded the first vertebrates and some of which were ancestral to vertebrates. As you learned in the preceding chapter (p. 557), there is some evidence of what the larvae were like in the earliest chordates, but inferences as to the adults are equivocal and disputed. For the vertebrates there is more and better evidence.

probable inferences about the earliest verte-brates:

They were aquatic. (Some biologists think that they originated in fresh water. This is quite uncertain, but they soon spread to both fresh and salt water.) They were motile, highly active, bilaterally sym-metrical, swimming animals with fishlike bodies.

They had an internal skeleton, which in-cluded a flexible rod, the *notochord*, down the back. Around the notochord a seg-mented, jointed series of bones, the *verte-brae*, developed. A notochord is present in all chordates, which are named for that feature. In most later and higher vertebrates the notochord is present in the embryo only, and in later stages of life is entirely replaced by the vertebrae. There were also internal fin supports and bony plates in the skin as well as a rigid skeletal support, the *skull*, around the brain and the sense organs of the head.

The early vertebrates had powerful muscles, especially a segmented series of V-shaped muscles along the sides of the body, used in locomotion.

The mouth was a simple opening with-out jaws. The early vertebrates probably fed on microorganisms and on organic mat-ter in mud and sand.

The pharynx (the part of the alimentary and respiratory canals immediately be-hind the mouth cavity) had a series of paired lateral openings, *gill slits*, through which water, taken in through the mouth, passed outward over the gills, which were the respiratory organs.

The rest of the alimentary canal was a relatively simple tube, perhaps somewhat twisted or looped but with little regional dif-ferentiation. There was a well-developed liver, and kidneys were also present.

Reproduction was bisexual, the sexes being different individuals. The females laid eggs, and fertilization was external.

There was a complex, closed circulatory system with capillaries. The red blood (with hemoglobin in corpuscles) was pumped by a heart with a single series of chambers.

The nervous system was already more

highly developed than in any other animals. Its most striking feature was the hollow *spinal cord* above (dorsal to) the notochord and the anterior expansion of this nerve tube into a *brain*, already relatively large and well differentiated into several parts.

Sense organs were also well developed, including lateral-line organs (see p. 202), image-forming eyes essentially like those of all later vertebrates, and ears, which, how-ever, were organs of equilibrium rather than of hearing. (In most higher vertebrates they are both.) There were only two semi-circular canals (p. 203) in the ear, rather than the three in almost all later vertebrates. (The *very* earliest vertebrates may have had only one.)

It was from such beginnings that the whole array of vertebrates developed: lamprey, shark, trout, frog, snake, sparrow, man, and the rest. The vertebrates may be arranged in eight classes, the first four of which are aquatic and are popularly known as fishes: Agnatha, Placodermi (the only extinct class), Chondrichthyes, and Osteichthyes. The four mainly nonaquatic classes are: Amphibia, Reptilia, Aves, and Mammalia (Fig. 23-14).

AGNATHS [13]

The first vertebrates were agnaths or jaw-less fishes (Fig. 23-14), which had all the ancestral characteristics just discussed but which occurred in a multitude of specific forms. They were abundant and highly di-versified in the early days of vertebrate his-tory and then dominated the realm of fishes for a relatively short time (although, even so, for some tens of millions of years; see Chapter 31). The living lampreys (Fig. 23-15) and hagfishes are relicts of that extremely ancient group. They have the basic characters listed above, except that they have no bone tissue. In addition to the loss of bone they have become highly specialized in some re-spects, notably in their feeding habits and in their elongate, eel-like bodies, a body form that did not occur (as far as known) in any of the earliest vertebrates in spite of the fact that they were otherwise quite diverse in shape. Lampreys have larvae that feed, as

[13] "Jawless."

THE CLASSES OF VERTEBRATES

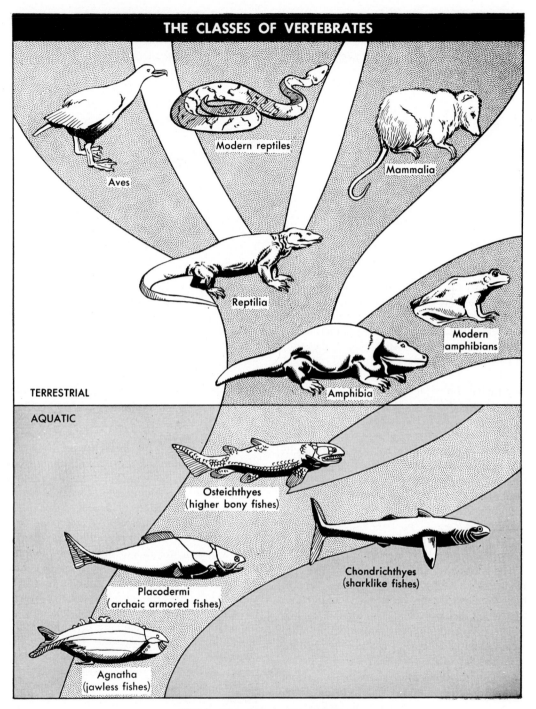

Modern reptiles

Aves

Mammalia

Reptilia

Modern amphibians

Amphibia

TERRESTRIAL

AQUATIC

Osteichthyes (higher bony fishes)

Chondrichthyes (sharklike fishes)

Placodermi (archaic armored fishes)

Agnatha (jawless fishes)

23-14 The classes of vertebrates.

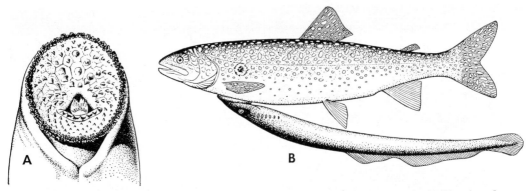

23-15 Lampreys, contemporary Agnatha. *A.* Head of a lamprey, showing the sucking funnel that surrounds the mouth. Note the hooklike teeth on the sucker, and the rasping tongue in the mouth. *B.* Lamprey attached to a fish it is parasitizing. Note the circular mark on the fish's flank—the scar of an earlier attack.

most of the early agnaths probably did, by sucking up mud containing microorganisms and organic debris. After metamorphosis they develop a round, sucking funnel lined with teeth. With this organ they attach themselves to living fishes, rasp a hole in the skin, and suck blood. (A few lampreys do not eat at all after they metamorphose into adults; they merely breed and die. This seems to be a recent evolutionary change; indeed, it may still be going on.) Hagfishes, which are not known to have larvae, also have a sucking funnel with which they eat their way right into and through the bodies of other fishes, usually attacking fish already disabled or dead. There are both fresh-water and marine lampreys. All the hagfishes are marine. (See also Fig. 31-2.)

PLACODERMS [14]

The survival of a few agnaths like the lampreys and hagfishes is probably due to their having developed a peculiar adaptation, the funnel and rasp, and associated habits in which they had no competition from other fishes. Most of the early jawless fishes had no such special adaptation and were probably mudsuckers, extracting nourishment from contained organic matter in the mud. They were soon replaced by fishes with jaws, which clearly are more effective than mere jawless openings for securing most kinds of food.

Jaws evolved from a pair of hinged gill supports (Fig. 18-12), a remarkable example of evolutionary transformation (p. 453). The earliest fishes with jaws are classified as *placoderms.* The placoderms early became extinct and were replaced by more modern sorts of fishes, with more complex and still more efficient jaws. We shall have occasion to mention placoderms again in connection with the history of life in the sea (Chapter 31).

CHONDRICHTHYANS [15]

Two groups of higher fishes evolved independently from placoderms at about the same time and, between them, soon replaced the placoderms. The reason for this early and basic subdivision of higher fishes into two main groups (classes) is that one—the Chondrichthyes—was *originally* specialized for life in sea water, and the other—Osteichthyes (the next class to be discussed)—for life in fresh water.[16] In the millions of years since the groups arose, a few chondrichthyans have wandered into fresh waters, but only a few and more or less haphazardly. The group is still fundamentally marine. On the other hand, the osteichthyans, while continuing to dominate the fresh waters, early spread secondarily into the sea and are now also by far the dominant marine fishes, even though

[14] "Plate skins," because many of them had bony armor plates (but so did most early agnaths).

[15] "Cartilage fishes," because their skeletons are entirely cartilaginous.

[16] Many books on zoology still say that the chondrichthyans were an older, more primitive group and that the osteichthyans evolved from them. This is an old theory conclusively disproved by fossils.

23-16 Chondrichthyes, cartilage fishes. *Above,* the West Indian shark (*Hyporion brevirostris*). Note the five conspicuous gill slits. *Left,* the spotted ray (*Raia maculata*). The functional gill slits are on the ventral surface, not visible in the photograph; but note the spiracle, which is a functionless gill slit (cf. p. 453 and Fig. 18-12), immediately behind the eye.

their competition has not wiped out all the chondrichthyans.

The principal chondrichthyans are the sharks and the rays (with their relatives, the skates) (Fig. 23-16). Their original physiological adaptation is seen in the fact that they meet the problem of osmosis in salty water in a markedly different way from the osteichthyans and that their way is decidedly more efficient. In the osteichthyans the internal osmotic pressure, Δ, is less than that of sea water, and much metabolic energy is required to keep enough water in the body (see p. 86). Chondrichthyans retain large amounts of dissolved urea in the body fluids—a peculiar specialization, for such concentrations of

urea would be fatal to most animals. Together with the inorganic salts usual in such fluids, the dissolved urea raises the internal Δ to approximately that of sea water, so that marine chondrichthyans, unlike other marine fishes, are in osmotic equilibrium with their environment. In discussing the adaptations of various groups of organisms, we are likely to refer to anatomical characteristics, because these are easier to observe. Osmotic regulation in the chondrichthyans is a good example of the fact that physiological adaptations are just as numerous and may be even more important.

Of course the chondrichthyans do also have characteristic anatomical features. The most obvious and universal among them is the one they are named for: the completely cartilaginous skeleton. That (contrary to some earlier opinions) is a specialization. Another specialization is that the eggs have heavy, leathery shells and that fertilization is internal. The males have modified posterior paired (pelvic) fins with structures called *claspers* that aid in injecting sperms into the females. A feature that is probably primitive in comparison with osteichthyans is the absence of lungs or *swim bladders*.

The oldest chondrichthyans are sharks, and of course sharks are still common today, changed in many details but still of the same adaptive type: elongated, streamlined, swift-swimming predators. These and other characteristics of the group are well seen in the so-called dogfishes, usual laboratory animals, which are small sharks. Later in origin and now also abundant are the skates and rays—broad, flattened forms, most of which live on the sea bottom where they devour various invertebrates.[17]

17 There is also a third main group of fossil and recent chondrichthyans, that of the chimaeras and their relatives, rather uncommon and of minor importance. They have peculiarities related to eating hard-shelled mollusks (among other things).

OSTEICHTHYANS [18]

Most osteichthyans (Fig. 23-17) have retained and some have even intensified the development of bone in the skeleton. In only a few of them, represented today by the sturgeons and spoonbills, has the bone retrogressed markedly so that the skeleton is largely of cartilage. The gill slits, each of which opens separately to the exterior in the chondrichthyans, open into a chamber covered by a (usually) bony plate or flap, the *operculum* (Fig. 6-12). Primitive osteichthyans had lungs as well as gills. Like the internal Δ, which is nearer that of fresh water than of salt water, the lungs were probably an adaptation to fresh-water life, providing a supplementary means of respiration when oxygen dissolved in the water became deficient. A few living osteichthyans have retained the lungs as such. These *lungfishes* (Fig. 23-18) survive as relicts in Australia, South America, and Africa. In most osteichthyans, however, the former lung has lost its respiratory function and has become a swim bladder (see p. 467), a gas-filled sac which

18 "Bone fishes," because in contrast with the chondrichthyes most of them have retained bony skeletons.

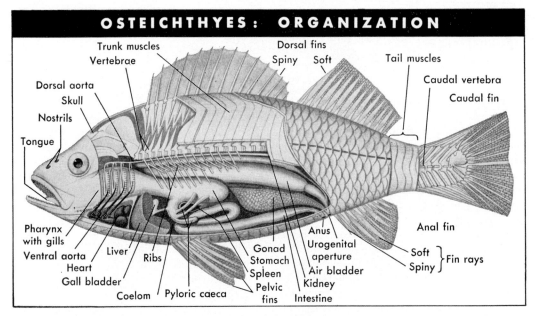

OSTEICHTHYES: ORGANIZATION

Trunk muscles · Vertebrae · Dorsal aorta · Skull · Nostrils · Tongue · Dorsal fins Spiny Soft · Tail muscles · Caudal vertebra · Caudal fin · Pharynx with gills · Ventral aorta · Heart · Gall bladder · Liver · Ribs · Coelom · Pyloric caeca · Gonad Stomach Spleen Pelvic fins · Anus Urogenital aperture Air bladder Kidney Intestine · Anal fin · Soft Spiny } Fin rays

23-17 The organization of a bony fish (Osteichthyes). (The pyloric caeca are digestive pouches of the gut.)

23-18 Contemporary lungfishes. *Above, Neoceratodus,* the Australian lungfish. *Below, Protopterus,* the African lungfish. The modern lungfishes are river dwellers that can surface and gulp air into their lungs; they can survive in water too foul (low in oxygen) to support other fish, which are entirely dependent on gills for respiration.

modifies the buoyancy of the fish as a whole and helps to maintain its position in the water. Some fishes that live on the bottom have lost the swim bladder (in the adults, at least). Can you think of a possible adaptive relationship between their habits and loss of the bladder? Do you think they live on the bottom because they have no swim bladders, or have no swim bladders because they live on the bottom? Or is neither statement correct as it stands?

The earliest osteichthyans were heavily armored, covered with bony scales coated with a hard enamel-like tissue. A few modern fishes, such as the gars, have retained the armor, but in most of them it has evolved into more flexible scales in which the harder tissues have degenerated. Some fishes (most of the eels, for example) have lost the scales altogether.

The osteichthyans, and especially the great group (usually classed as a superorder) called *teleosts*,[19] are the dominant aquatic animals today. They have become adapted to almost every aquatic environment, from the unchanging cold darkness of the deep sea to dashing mountain streams. One species or an-

other eats practically everything that is edible by any aquatic animal. Some are sluggish, but they include some of the most swiftly moving of all animals. Their diversity in form is really astonishing; Fig. 23-19 gives just a hint of the extraordinary shapes among them. More than 20,000 species are known. The individual abundance of some single species is also remarkable. It is estimated that there

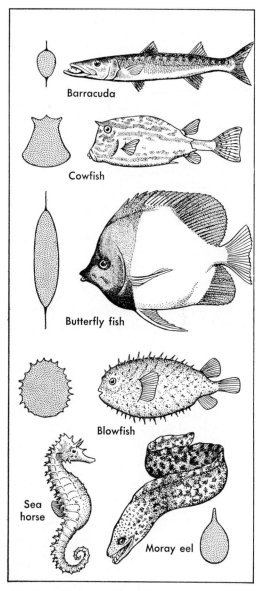

23-19 A diversity of body forms in bony fishes. The stippled silhouettes represent transverse sections through the various fishes.

[19] "Perfect bones," the implication being that they are the most perfected or progressive of the bony fishes.

are at least a trillion (1,000,000,000,000) herrings in the Atlantic Ocean.

The rarest of all the surviving osteichthyans are of special interest: the crossopterygians,[20] or crossopts for short. These animals were abundant in the earliest days of osteichthyan history when, with their allies the lungfishes, they were the dominant fishes. Thereafter they became less and less common, and until 1939 everyone thought they had been extinct for about 75 million years. Then a single specimen [21] of a living crossopt (*Latimeria*, illus., p. 753) was caught off the east coast of South Africa, a discovery almost as extraordinary as finding a living dinosaur.[22] The most important thing about the crossopts is not this survival, extraordinary as it is, but the fact that amphibians and through them all the vertebrates of the land and air evolved from early crossopts.

AMPHIBIANS [23]

It is characteristic of evolution that the amphibians did not evolve from late, specialized, progressive or perfected osteichthyans, such as the teleosts, but from primitive forms that lived near the beginning of osteichthyan history. It has usually been true that when a radical adaptive change occurs and a new major group arises, it originates from primitive and not from advanced members of the ancestral group. With progressive adaptation to any one way of life, there often comes a time when the adaptation seems to become irrevocable—a special aspect of the irrevocability of evolution in general (p. 469). Then change to a radically different way of life becomes, if not impossible, at least extremely improbable.

[20] "Fringed fins," from the structure of the paired fins.
[21] More have since been caught, in the vicinity of Madagascar.
[22] But not quite. The dinosaurs have been extinct (as far as we know) for about the same length of time. But the surviving crossopt lives well down in the waters of the sea, the region least known to us of all the habitats of living things. Dinosaurs could not have become submarine forms without changing into something quite different from a dinosaur. The denizens of all recent habitats where dinosaurs could have survived are well known, and dinosaurs are not among them. Reports to the contrary have turned out to be fiction, hoaxes, or just plain mistakes.
[23] "With a double life," because some of them are aquatic as larvae and terrestrial as adults, or because some adults are literally amphibious.

In the fish-amphibian transition, for instance, the presence of lungs in primitive fishes was a crucial factor. Lungs enabled the osteichthyans to get a start in life in waters that were sometimes deficient in oxygen. Later their general and increasing efficiency enabled them to spread into waters, especially those of the sea, that are continuously well oxygenated. Then the lungs lost their respiratory function and evolved (not, of course, by any plan or wish) other functions that made the fish still more efficient in the water but that made it practically impossible for any descendants of theirs to take to the land. There are few complete absolutes in nature, and even the loss of the respiratory lungs may not have made it absolutely impossible for later fishes to have evolved some other way of obtaining oxygen from air. In fact, there are a few teleosts that can clamber about on land for short periods. None of them has become really terrestrial, and it does seem that their commitment to the water (where, incidentally, they are getting along very well) is practically irrevocable. The historical fact is that land vertebrates did evolve on the basis of lungs and other features present in the most primitive osteichthyans but absent in the more specialized and successful of later fishes.

Since lungs were already present in fishes, it was not their appearance that marked the beginning of vertebrate conquest of the land. It was, instead, the change of the paired fins into legs. In other respects the first amphibians were still almost completely fishlike. Probably, too, they spent most of their lives in the water. But they could, if need be, come out on land and waddle along to some other pond of water. They lived only in fresh water, and only there would they have had any advantage at all over fishes. Such slight advantage started their descendants on the way to becoming fully terrestrial. (See Fig. 31-4.)

Among modern amphibians (Fig. 23-20) the salamanders, although specialized or degenerate in many respects, have most nearly retained the ancestral habits, fishlike body form, and even a fishlike undulatory movement of the body as a whole. They go through a larval stage that resembles the adult

23-20 Modern amphibians. *Above*, the common tiger salamander, *Ambystoma tigrinum*. The adult is about 8 inches long, an inhabitant of moist woodlands and streams. *Right*, *Necturus maculosus*, the mud puppy, an inhabitant of streams. The adult, attaining a length of 12 to 17 inches, retains bushy external gills.

Below, a tree frog, "spring peeper" (*Hyla crucifer*). The animal is small (up to 2 inches) but possesses a loud "voice" amplified by the distended vocal pouch acting as a resonator.

Photos above, Isabelle Hunt Conant; photos below, Hugh Spencer

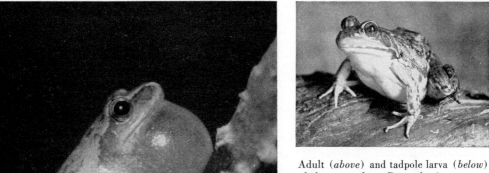

Adult (*above*) and tadpole larva (*below*) of the green frog, *Rana clamitans*.

rather closely except that, among a few other details, the larvae have gills that are lost when metamorphosis occurs. The larvae of frogs and toads, familiar to everyone as tadpoles, are also fishlike, perhaps even more so because they lack legs. Their metamorphosis is more radical, and an adult frog or toad is completely unlike a fish, or indeed unlike anything on earth except a frog or toad. The adult anurans [24] (let us call them that so as not to keep on repeating "frogs and toads") are among the most aberrant and specialized of all the vertebrates. The most obvious specializations are that they have no tails (that is one of our most obvious specializations, too, but of course we did not get it from the anurans), and that the hind legs are tremendous leaping mechanisms. Besides these more obvious points, anuran anatomy, physiology, and habits are replete with other aberrant features. In particular, they are radically unlike the amphibians that were ancestral to the fully terrestrial vertebrates and therefore can show us little about that ancestry. On the other hand, their very aberrancy gives them a way of life in which they have few serious competitors and which makes them the only group of amphibians that was very successful in the long run.

Besides the salamanders and anurans, there is another, small and relatively unimportant group of living amphibians: the Apoda or Caecilians.[25] They are blind (or practically so) and entirely limbless, and most of them burrow in wet soil. Some of them are so like earthworms in appearance and habits as to provide a remarkable example of convergence between members of two widely different phyla.

REPTILES [26]

Even though a few kinds of amphibians came to occupy ecological positions in which they continue to have modest success, amphibians are anomalous animals. During parts of their lives they are ecologically or adaptively fishes. In this respect they are superior to true fishes only in being less rigidly and

permanently confined to the water. They have succeeded and survived only because ability to leave the water when occasion demands has survival value. But as land animals they are still tied to the water. At the least (with partial exceptions of no importance in the broad picture), they must return to the water to breed, and water is still the obligatory habitat of the young.[27] On land, then, Amphibia must usually be at a disadvantage in comparison with animals able to live their whole lives there. It was inevitable that most amphibians would become extinct, given the evolutionary possibility of the rise of fully terrestrial vertebrates or, more objectively, given the fact that such vertebrates did evolve.

It was the reptiles that became the first fully terrestrial vertebrates. They evolved from amphibians, or another way of putting the matter would be to say that the name "reptile" and classification in the class Reptilia are applied to a branch of early amphibians that became fully terrestrial and to the highly diversified descendants of those first fully terrestrial vertebrates. In agreement with a generalization already familiar (p. 588), the ancestors of the reptiles were early, primitive amphibians, not any later forms resembling those that now survive.

The key adaptations were in the modes of reproduction and respiration. The eggs, laid on land,[28] have leathery or limy shells that impede fatal loss of water by the embryo. Fertilization is internal (male and female copulate). The eggs (Fig. 23-21) contain a large amount of food (yolk), and full development, with no larval stage, occurs before the young hatch. The newly hatched young are already essentially like adults in form and activities,

[24] "Untailed."

[25] "Apoda" means "footless." "Caecilian" is from the generic name of one of them, ultimately from the Latin word for "blind."

[26] The name is old, ultimately derived from the Latin for "crawl."

[27] Some modern Amphibia are also tied to the water by the inadequacy of their lungs as respiratory organs. Air is inadequately forced into them by the weak bellows action of the floor of the mouth cavity. The frog's skin, supplied with blood vessels, is its principal respiratory organ and, as such, must be kept moist. It is uncertain whether this dependence on the skin for respiration characterized ancestral Amphibia. It could well be that it is an evolutionary novelty in later Amphibia which were restricted to moist places anyway and simply exploited the skin as a potential supplement to inefficient lungs.

[28] In some reptiles, the eggs are retained in the mother during development, and the young leave her body as they hatch. How does this differ from the birth of the young in man and other mammals?

although of course they later grow and, as a rule, change in proportions.

In several respects the respiratory mechanism of reptiles shows marked advance over that of Amphibia. The lungs are more efficiently ventilated by movement of ribs by muscles, inflating and emptying the lungs like a bellows. Other improvements in respiration hinge on structural changes in the respiratory system, especially the heart (Fig. 7-7). A partition (incomplete and still therefore "imperfect") arose in the ventricle of the heart, separating nonoxygenated blood from other blood freshly oxygenated, returning from the lungs. There can be little doubt that acquisition of the improved circulation familiar in modern reptiles was part of the early reptilian evolution as true land vertebrates.

There were of course other anatomical and functional changes throughout the body, barely perceptible in the first reptiles but becoming more pronounced in many of their descendants. Among these was a tendency for the limbs to become larger and more powerful, better able to support the body free of the ground.

The reptiles expanded and diversified into many different habitats throughout the land (except in its coldest climates), and some even returned to the sea and competed with (and also consumed) fishes. Their dominance during the Age of Reptiles and their later decline are dramatic parts of the history of life, to which we will later return (Chapter 31). Systematists recognize about fifteen orders of the Class Reptilia, living and extinct. Only four now survive (Fig. 23-21). Even among these four, one is on the verge of extinction, represented only by a few individuals of a single species, *Sphenodon punctatum*, on islands off the coast of New Zealand.[29] The other three living orders are still fairly abundant and are familiar to everyone: turtles and tortoises (Chelonia),[30] crocodiles and alligators (Crocodilia),[31] and lizards and

snakes (Squamata).[32] Lizards and snakes are the most abundant living reptiles. There are around two thousand living species of each, and they occur in many habitats from the high seas (sea snakes) to the desert. Different as the legged, swift-running lizards and the legless, crawling snakes seem, they are rather closely related. Snakes are descendants of an early group of burrowing lizards. There are still some burrowing lizards, of later origin, that have also become legless and snakelike. Does that make them snakes? Why (or why not)?

BIRDS

The two latest and most progressive classes of land vertebrates both (but entirely separately) evolved from early reptiles. The birds, Class Aves,[33] are a group in which one key characteristic opened up a whole new realm of life. This characteristic is, of course, flight. The oldest known fossil birds (*Archaeopteryx*, "ancient wing") were still almost reptilian except in one respect: they had feathered wings (Fig. 23-22). If the change had stopped there, however, birds would never have reached the great diversity and wide success which makes them one of the great climaxes of evolution and which is reflected in their classification as a class. In such a case we would probably consider them simply an order of flying reptiles, which, indeed, is how we do classify another group that developed flight from reptilian ancestors: the pterosaurs ("winged lizards"), a long-continued but comparatively unsuccessful group which finally became extinct, perhaps from competition with the birds.

Along with and after their acquisition of wings, birds evolved other characteristics associated with intense and sustained activity, keen perception, and rapid and varied reactions. They have high and steady metabolic rates, with precise control of the internal environment. Along with the mammals, they are the only organisms that maintain a constant temperature (that is, are homeothermous, see p. 172). Feathers serve not only for flight but also as insulation (Fig. 23-23). As in mammals, the heart is four-chambered; it is completely divided into what are essentially two

29 **Sphenodon** looks just like a lizard and is, indeed, related to lizards, but its internal anatomy shows that it belongs to an order, Rhynchocephalia ("beak-headed") that split off from the lizard ancestry before lizards, as such, had evolved (Fig. 23-21).
30 From the Greek for "tortoise."
31 From the Latin (and earlier Greek) for "crocodile."

32 Latin for "scaly."
33 Latin for "birds."

23-21 Modern reptiles. *Left,* the common garter snake (*Thamnophis*).

Right, the tuatara of New Zealand (*Sphenodon punctatum*), a "living fossil"; it is the sole living representative of an ancient group of reptiles, Rhynchocephalia (see p. 591 and Fig. 31-9).

Below, the American plated lizard (*Gerrhonotus*) with its eggs. These lizards (about a foot long) live in fallen timber.

Above, musk turtles (*Aromochelys odoratus*) (about 5 inches long) inhabit rivers and lakes. Note their webbed feet.

Below, the salt-marsh crocodile (*Crocodilus palustris*) of southern Asia reaches a length of 12 feet.

separate hearts. This represents the final step in proper "plumbing" of the circulatory system in relation to lung respiration (p. 147, Fig. 7-7). Bird senses, especially those of vision, equilibrium, and hearing, are particularly acute. Their brains are large and are peculiarly specialized (see p. 214). Their behavior, although in considerable part stereotyped or instinctive, is often very complicated.

Ancient birds, even some considerably later than *Archaeopteryx*, retained simple teeth inherited from the reptiles. Today, when there is nothing scarcer than hen's teeth, no bird has had teeth for tens of millions of years. Instead, the birds have beaks of bone covered with horn. Beaks serve not only for obtaining food, but as instruments for many purposes, from knot tying to wood boring. In their basic anatomy birds are remarkably stereotyped. If there were no other reasons, the stringent mechanical necessities of flight would keep them so. But within the limits of the basic stereotype they are fascinatingly diverse. The many forms of their beaks, most of which are clearly adaptive, illustrate this fact (Fig. 23-24). The feet, too, have numerous adaptive patterns (Fig. 18-2). And everyone knows and enjoys something of the diversity of bird colors and patterns, the biological significance of which (when known) is in some cases protective, by blending the bird into its background, and in others social, serving for recognition by other members of the group or as a stimulus to the opposite sex.

The systematics of recent birds (Fig. 23-25) has been worked out in better detail than for any other animal group of comparable scope—not that all is yet well understood about this group that is so attractive to both amateur and professional zoologists. There are some 8600 living species, about half of them belonging to the single order of perching birds (Passeriformes, "sparrowlike"), which includes among many others the kingbirds, larks, swallows, crows, wrens, thrashers, thrushes (among which is the American robin), vireos, warblers, blackbirds, and sparrows. Other large and familiar orders are those of the herons and their allies (Ciconiiformes, "storklike"); ducks, geese, and swans (Anseriformes, "goose-

ARCHAEOPTERYX AND PIGEON

23-22 Comparison of *Archaeopteryx* and pigeon to illustrate some major features in the evolutionary specialization of modern birds. *1*. Teeth are present in *Archaeopteryx*, but absent in the pigeon. *2*. The brain case of birds is larger than that of reptiles and the early *Archaeopteryx*. *3*. In the "hand" of *Archaeopteryx* three of the digits are still clearly present and separate. *4*. The immense development of the sternum to anchor the large flight muscles is characteristic of modern birds. *5*. In the modern bird the pelvic girdle is much enlarged and firmly fused to the spinal column. *6*. The tail is much reduced in the modern bird.

like"); the predaceous birds such as the hawks (Falconiformes, "falconlike"); partridges, turkeys, and their many allies (Galliformes, "chickenlike"); gulls and their kin (Charadriiformes, "ploverlike"); owls (Strigiformes, "owl-like"); and woodpeckers (Piciformes, "woodpeckerlike")—that is only a hint of the diversity of this great group. Modern classifications recognize 25 to 30 different orders of living birds.

As you would expect, the birds most truly distinctive in anatomy and physiology are those that no longer have the ancestral adaptation to flight, kinds like the penguins (which still do fly, but fly under water) or the ostriches. Since flight is the key character of the class, how would you explain the fact that some birds cannot fly? That is a very difficult question indeed, although it is possible to find a reasonable answer. Here are some easier questions: What is the largest bird? The smallest? How does the size range compare with other animals? Are the sizes of birds related to their ways of life?

MAMMALS [34]

The final and (to us, at least) the supreme class of vertebrates arose from the reptiles not with the appearance of any key characteristic, such as flight, but by long-continued gradual change in many ways. On the whole the changes made for greater mechanical, physiological, and reproductive effectiveness in ways of life similar to those of the diversified reptiles of the Age of Reptiles. Thus mammals now occupy much of the range that was once the domain of the reptiles, although they have gone further than the reptiles ever did and although a few special kinds of reptiles still live successfully along with the mammals. Thus the mammals contrast with the birds, which by a new key adaptation

[34] Class Mammalia, named for the presence in the females of milk glands or mammae.

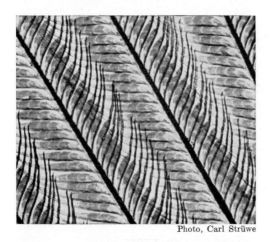

THE STRUCTURE OF FEATHERS

1
2
3
4
5

Photo, Carl Strüwe

23-23 Feathers, one of the key structural adaptations of birds. *Above, 1. Contour* feathers cover the animal and, by establishing its smooth contours, contribute to its streamlining; they also contribute to its insulation. The much elongated contour feathers of the wings provide the effective flight surfaces of these organs. *2. Down* feathers are adaptively important in providing excellent heat insulation, a property exploited by man in the making of sleeping bags and comforters. The down feathers, like the hair of mammals, are an important part of the body temperature control system. *3.* The small, elongate *filoplumes* (drawn at a much enlarged scale relative to the others figured) lie between the other feathers and are of uncertain function. *4.* The bristles around the mouths of birds like the whippoorwill and flycatchers are modified feathers. *5.* The structure of a contour feather. A central *shaft* runs along the middle (cf. the contour feather in *1*) and supports the wide, flat *vane* of the feather. The vane itself consists of parallel *barbs* on each side of the shaft. The barbs in their turn support *barbules* on their sides. The barbules are provided with *hooklets* which engage the edge of barbules in the next row. Through the action of the hooklets, which can slide freely along the barbule edge they engage, the whole system of barbs and barbules is bound into a flexible wide-surfaced vane. In down feathers the barbules do not engage each other. *Below*, photograph showing the detailed structure of the vane of a contour feather from a hummingbird.

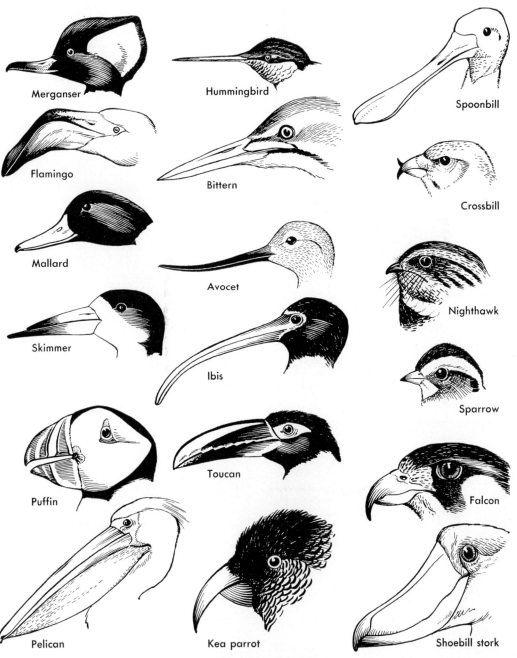

Merganser

Hummingbird

Spoonbill

Flamingo

Bittern

Crossbill

Mallard

Avocet

Nighthawk

Skimmer

Ibis

Sparrow

Puffin

Toucan

Falcon

Pelican

Kea parrot

Shoebill stork

23-24 A diversity of bird beaks.

23-25 A variety of modern birds. *Above,* terns (order Charadriformes) are marine birds that dive for their fish food. *Above, right,* the blue jay (order Passeriformes), a relative of the crow, is an inveterate egg robber.

Above, the kiwi (order Apterygiformes) a flightless bird of New Zealand, has hairlike feathers that do not form a useful vane. Its sternum lacks a well-developed keel. *Below,* this female marsh hawk (order Falconiformes) is about to alight. Like all its relatives, it is a bird of prey.

Above, a Canada goose (order Anseriformes) sitting on its eggs in a nest of reeds. *Below,* the great blue heron (order Ciconiiformes), a relative of the storks and ibises, feeds on fish, frogs, and small mammals.

entered and exploited a whole new realm of life.

The reptiles ancestral to mammals were of course very different from any living today. Here again and perhaps more than ever the comparison of recent animals is merely confusing as to the real evolutionary changes. A picture of mammalian origin from anything like a snake, lizard, crocodile, or turtle is ludicrously wrong. The reptilian ancestors (Fig. 31-9) of the mammals were both more primitive and more mammal-like than any later reptiles, much as the fishes ancestral to amphibians were more primitive and more amphibianlike than later fishes. In fact, the contrast is even greater because fishes somewhat amphibianlike (especially the lungfishes and *Latimeria*) have survived, but the whole great group of mammal-like reptiles became extinct soon after the rise from it of the mammals. Since the process was gradual, some characteristics of the mammals arose in animals nominally classified as reptiles, and some did not arise until after nominal mammals existed. The line between mammal-like reptile and mammal is arbitrary, a convenience of classification. Nevertheless the characters that did come to stamp the mammals and that underlie their great success in the world are real enough. Among them are these:

Warmbloodedness (homeothermy), as in birds, and external insulation, also as in birds but by hair [35] rather than feathers— both characters (independently developed in the two classes) are, again, related to higher metabolism and more precise and sustained internal regulation.

Complex differentiation of teeth and development of a new joint between the lower jaw and the skull (Fig. 18-12). The two characters seem to be related and together to involve greater efficiency in utilization of food. Whatever may have been the factors in their origin, they did certainly lead to remarkable later diversity and efficiency of feeding in mammals. Reptiles (and indeed all vertebrates except mammals) have several different bones in the lower jaw. Mammals have only one.

In the change-over, some of the reptilian bones were incorporated in the ear (see p. 453), which thus also became markedly different in mammals.

Limbs more upright, more beneath the body, which thus comes to be carried higher off the ground. Changes in the limbs tended in general to make for more rapid and efficient locomotion. Associated were changes in the joints, with increased mechanical precision, and in the manner of growth of the long bones (see p. 349).

Increased (although still not complete) separation of respiratory and alimentary passages (Fig. 23-26). Completed separation of chambers of the heart (p. 147). Further improvement (over reptiles) in efficiency of lung ventilation by acquisition of a diaphragm (Fig. 23-26). All three features improve continuity and efficiency of respiration and thus are other concomitants of sustained metabolic maintenance.

Increased protection and sustenance of young, both before and after birth, and hence greater reproductive efficiency. Fertilization and embryonic development are internal, and the embryo is nourished by the mother, through a placenta (p. 389, Fig. 15-26) in most mammals.[36] After birth the young continue to receive parental care and are fed on mother's milk.

Greater individual modifiability of behavior, or wider behavioral reaction ranges. Increased comparative size of the brain and especially of its cerebral cortex (p. 214). In the earliest mammals, and even in some of the stupider living mammals, the brain is not notably better than in some reptiles. Nevertheless most mammals did eventually evolve brains much larger than in any other organisms.

In the obscure earliest history of the mammals there were several major groups clearly not ancestral to any living forms. We need not discuss them here (but see p. 781). Practically all the mammals of the Age of Mammals and down to today are marsupials or placentals. The exceptions are the monotremes [37]

35 Recall other mammalian specializations (physiological) that contribute to their homeothermy (p. 172).

36 See below for exceptions in the monotremes and marsupials.
37 "One-holes," because the anus and urinogenital openings are not separate externally, another resemblance to reptiles.

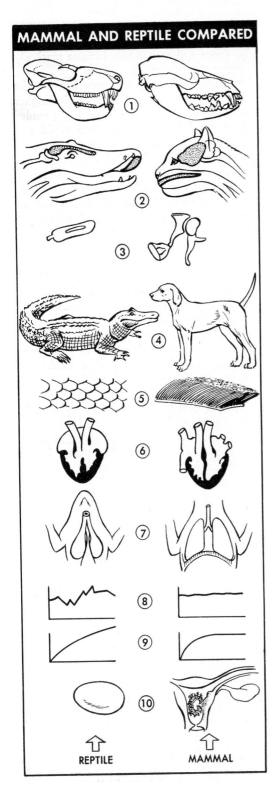

① ② ③ ④ ⑤ ⑥ ⑦ ⑧ ⑨ ⑩

REPTILE   MAMMAL

of Australia and adjacent islands, fascinating and famous because they lay eggs and yet give milk (Fig. 23-27). They are, throughout, a strange blend of characters otherwise reptilian, characters otherwise mammalian, and characters highly peculiar to themselves. They represent, not really an ancestral stage in evolution of the mammals, but a line of descent that branched off from the mammalian ancestry at some very remote time. They have become extremely and aberrantly specialized in their own way, but have also retained some ancestral characters lost in other or true mammals. Opinions differ as to when the monotremes branched off. It may well have been in a stage nominally reptilian; then it might be more indicative of their relationships to consider them as surviving mammal-like reptiles rather than to call them mammals. The point is not very important. There is little question as to their general relationships; only the degree is in real doubt.

The marsupials and placentals are clearly groups of common origin among the mammals. It was formerly believed that the marsupials were an older group and ancestral to the placentals, but on present evi-

23-26 Mammal and reptile compared. *1.* Skull: the mammal has a larger brain case and complex cheek teeth; its jaw consists of only one bone (the dentary) while the reptile's consists of several. *2.* Brain: the mammal's forebrain is greatly developed over that of the reptile (cf. p. 214). Palate: the respiratory and alimentary passages are separated by a bony palate (heavy outline in the figure) in the mammal. *3.* Ear ossicles: the two additional ossicles in the mammal are transformations of two extra jaw bones in the reptile (cf. p. 453). *4.* Posture: the mammal's limbs are rotated under the body, which is thus kept off the ground—a contribution to the control of body temperature. *5.* Skin: the mammal's skin is covered with hair—another contribution to body-temperature control. *6.* Circulation: in the mammal the lung and body circulations are kept separate by a complete partition of the ventricle—an improvement in efficiency of respiration. *7.* Diaphragm: the thoracic cavity of the mammal is completely separated from the rest of the body cavity by a diaphragm—an improvement in efficiency of lung ventilation. *8.* Body temperature: uncontrolled in the reptile, controlled in the mammal. *9.* Growth: continuing throughout life in the reptile; limited in the mammal. *10.* Reproduction: eggs, no care of young, no milk in the reptile; placental reproduction, parental care of young, milk in the mammal.

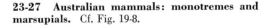
Above, a kangaroo with young in its pouch.

23-27 Australian mammals: monotremes and marsupials. Cf. Fig. 19-8.

Above, a wombat, with a way of life and gross appearance similar to those of the American woodchuck. *Below*, the duck-billed platypus, a monotreme.

Australian News and Information Bureau

dence this is highly improbable. They simply diverged from a common ancestry, and many of the peculiarities of the marsupials probably are specializations that evolved in that group, and not characters formerly present in the ancestry of the placentals. The most striking of such peculiarities is that the developing embryo receives little or no nourishment from the mother while in the uterus. It is born in very immature form, crawls into a pouch on the mother's belly, hangs onto a nipple, and there completes development. You probably know that marsupials include kangaroos, wombats, and other exotic mammals of Australia (Fig. 23-27), "land of marsupials." Marsupials, mostly opossums, are, however, also abundant in North and South America and were formerly even more abundant, especially in the southern continent (see p. 725).

Placentals are the mammals in which the fetus is nourished (through a placenta, hence the name) within the maternal uterus until development is far advanced. Although not as diverse as they were a few million years ago, placentals (Fig. 23-28) are still the dominant land vertebrates and have been throughout the Age of Mammals. A modern classification divides them into twenty-seven orders, of which, however, only sixteen have living representatives. Some species belonging to the more abundant of these orders are already quite familiar to you and well illustrate the remarkable adaptive radiation that has occurred among placentals in the last 70 million years or so: shrews and moles (Insectivora, "insect eaters") bats (Chiroptera, "finger-wings"), armadillos (Edentata, "toothless"), rabbits (Lagomorpha, "harelike," see illus., p. 3), squirrels, porcupines, mice, and a host of other rodents (Rodentia, "gnaw-

23-28 A diversity of modern placental mammals. *Left,* African leopard (*Felis pardus,* order Carnivora). *Above,* a deermouse (*Peromyscus* sp., order Rodentia).

Below, left, mole (*Scapanus latimanus,* order Insectivora) in its underground burrow. *Below, right,* South American anteater (*Myrmecophaga,* order Edentata). Note the elongate snout.

Below, left, African elephant (*Loxodonta,* order Proboscidea) is a herbivorous mammal. *Below, right,* the porpoise (*Phocaena,* order Cetacea), a relative of the whale, is found in all the oceans of the world.

Bats (order Chiroptera) are the only true flying mammals. Flying squirrels (order Rodentia) do not really fly; they glide.

ers"), whales (Cetacea, "whale-like"), cats and dogs (Carnivora, "meat-eaters"), elephants (Proboscidea, "with a trunk"), horses (Perissodactyla, "odd-toed"), and pigs, camels, sheep, and cows (Artiodactyla, "even-toed").[38] Placentals burrow, fly, climb, run, and swim. They eat worms, fruit, insects, grass, seaweed, squids, crustaceans, bark, cocktail canapés, and each other. They live in the open sea, in tropical treetops, on Arctic ice floes, in apartment houses, and in sandy deserts. Can you add to this list of habits and habitats and make it more systematic?

In terms of numbers, both of species and of individuals, the outstanding placentals are the rodents. On land they swarm practically everywhere, and some are amphibious (although none are completely aquatic or marine—the only possibility they seem to have overlooked). In only one respect do they really fall short of being the dominant mammals and the climax of vertebrate evolution, but that is an important respect: they are not as smart as we are.

That is our excuse for calling the order to which we ourselves belong Primates (Latin for "the tops"). Not that all primates (Fig. 23-29) are particularly intelligent. Some living primates are below the average intelligence for mammals and so, judging by the outer form of the brain known for a few of them, were the oldest primates. The order arose among the most primitive of placentals, from early Insectivora, and seems at first to have had little to distinguish it beyond the use of the forefeet as hands and increasing co-ordination of visual perception and manual response. Yet somehow these primitive creatures had the potentiality to evolve the highest intelligence ever reached by any organisms. "Potentiality" in this application is not explanatory. We only know, after the fact, that they could because they did. Just what there was about them at the time that made possible that later development is not fully clear.

The earliest primates, which were abundant

[38] Remember that the name of a systematic group does not need to be, and often is not, appropriate for all its members. Some insectivores do not eat insects; some edentates (notably the armadillos) have teeth; some carnivores do not eat meat; and so on.

and lived pretty much all over the world except in Australia and South America, were prosimians ("pre-monkeys"). Some prosimians (lemurs, "bush babies," tarsiers, etc.) still survive in modified and more or less specialized form in Africa, Madagascar, and southeastern Asia. From early prosimians three other major groups evolved. The New World monkeys, Ceboidea, or ceboids in the vernacular, arose in and are still confined to Central and South America. The name "ceboid" means "cebuslike." *Cebus* is the genus of common South American capuchin monkeys. Marmosets, howlers, and others also belong to this group. Throughout the warmer parts of the Eastern Hemisphere (except Australia) lived and live the Old World monkeys, Cercopithecoidea. This name of the whole group of Old World monkeys derives from the generic name (*Cercopithecus*) of the commonest African monkeys. Rhesus monkeys (much used in experimentation), baboons, mandrills, and others belong to this group. Originating somewhere in that vast area of the Old World and soon spreading throughout it was the climax group of the primates, the Hominoidea ("manlike"). Formerly much more diverse, this group now includes the gibbons, apes (orangutan, chimpanzee, and gorilla), and man.

Chapter Summary

Mollusks, arthropods, and vertebrates: widely different animal phyla; those phyla of greatest complexity, co-ordination of function, and diversity of adaptation; three great pinnacles of animal evolution.

Mollusks: the five classes, exemplified by Amphineura:

Gastropods: slow gait; shell; marine origin; terrestrial forms with lungs; their adaptive diversity.

Pelecypods: bivalves; mostly sedentary habit and loss of sense organs; filter feeders; their adaptive diversity.

Cephalopods: complexity; active, fast-moving mollusks; their jet propulsion; complex brain and image-forming eyes; predatory nature; history and diversity.

Arthropods: their immense numbers, diversity,

23-29 Some modern primates (see also Fig. 32-14). *Top left,* the tarsier (*Tarsius tarsier*) is the only surviving member of an ancient and primitive group of prosimian primates. Note the large eyes rotated forward (cf. p. 794). *Above,* a capuchin monkey (*Cebus apella*) of South American forests. Note the long tail which in South American monkeys may be used as a "fifth limb." *Center left,* the crab-eating macaque (*Macaca irus*) is a South Asiatic form often used in biological research. *Left,* the mandrill (*Mandrillus sphinx*) is another African monkey. It lives on the ground and walks four-footed like a dog.

and ubiquity; arthropod characters; the seven classes, exemplified by:

Crustacea: familiarity of the decapods; the diversity of other crustacean types; evolutionary specialization of crustacean appendages, exemplified by lobster.

Arachnids: an undeserved bad reputation; useful as well as harmful species; four or five pairs of appendages; diagnostic characters; *Limulus*, a living fossil.

Insects: their success and diversity, comprising at least one-half of all living organisms, but no marine types; primarily terrestrial, but have secondarily invaded fresh waters; factors responsible for restricting their size: the exoskeleton, respiratory and circulatory systems; insect organization described and exemplified by the grasshopper; winged and wingless insects; adaptive modifications of wings in beetles and flies; feeding larvae; polymorphism.

Vertebrates: a subphylum of the Chordata; the most progressive and important of all animal groups, but less abundant and diverse than insects; their great awareness of their environment and complexity of behavior; ancestral vertebrates; their characters, especially the following: aquatic, probably fresh-water, forms; notochord; vertebrae; skull; musculature; jawless mouth; gill slits in pharynx; simple alimentary system; bisexual reproduction with external fertilization; closed circulatory system with single heart; dorsal, hollow nervous system; relatively large brain; well-developed sense organs.

The eight classes of vertebrates:

Agnaths: earliest vertebrates; jawless fish, exemplified today by lampreys and hagfishes; the funnel and rasp.

Placoderms: first vertebrates with jaws; jaws as modified gill supports; their extinction.

Chondrichthyans: cartilage fish; originally and still a marine group; sharks and rays; urea and osmotic regulation; internal fertilization.

Osteichthyans: bony fish; originally freshwater forms, now both fresh-water and marine; their bony skeleton; operculum;

early acquisition of lungs; modern lungfishes; modification of lung to swim bladder; bony armor of early forms, and scales in modern forms; the teleosts, most successful of the bony fish; diversity of bony fish; the survival of *Latimeria*.

Amphibians: their origin from early osteichthyans; role of lungs and limbs in origin of amphibians; modern amphibians: their locomotion, larvae, metamorphosis, specialization, and divergence from early forms.

Reptiles: the restriction of amphibians to watery environments; reptiles as descendants, and first true land vertebrates; key adaptation: shelled eggs and internal fertilization; lung ventilation, partitioning of ventricle; the adaptive radiation of reptiles; the four surviving orders.

Birds: descendants of early reptiles; *Archaeopteryx*; bird adaptions to land life, permitting sustained high activity; development of body-temperature control; improved respiration and circulation; development of brain and sense organs; loss of teeth; specialization of beaks and feet; the classification of modern birds; flightless birds.

Mammals: descendants of early reptiles; "supreme" class of vertebrates; their occupation of former reptilian ways of life; contrast with birds, who exploited different ways of life; major mammalian characters, contrasted with those of reptiles: body-temperature control, evolution of teeth, more upright limbs and more rapid locomotion, improvements in respiration and circulation, protection and sustenance of young (including evolution of placenta and milk glands), elaboration of nervous system and behavior. PRIMITIVE MAMMALS: monotremes and marsupials.

PLACENTAL MAMMALS: represented by twenty-seven orders; rodents as most abundant (individuals and species) order; the primates of special interest because of their relation to man; their origin from insectivores; co-ordination of hands and eyes as creating potentiality for evolution of higher intelligence; diversity of modern primates.

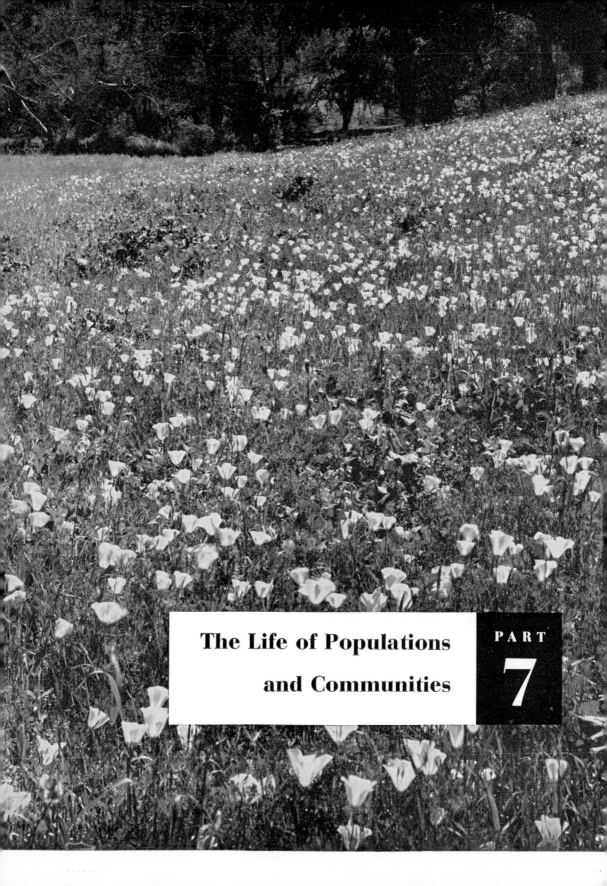

The Life of Populations

and Communities

PART

7

Where there is one poppy there will be more. In fact, there will be a whole population of them, as in the photograph introducing Part 7. Associated with the poppies will be populations of other species—grasses, trees, insects, mice, hawks, and the rest—which collectively form an integrated community. One of the most striking facts of life is that individual organisms do not, because they cannot, live a wholly solitary existence. They are bound together by one cause or another—by sex, by social ties, by sharing common needs satisfied only by a particular habitat, and, above all, by dependence on one another for shelter and food. This interdependence of organisms dominates the entire subject of ecology, the study of organism-environment relationships; it raises problems and demands explanatory principles of its own, which are the topics of Part 7.

Throughout this section of the book we will be examining communities and their constituent populations as unit living systems much as in some earlier parts we considered the individual organism as a unit living system. But this approach—of treating populations as units of life—is of course not wholly new to you; in Part 5 on the mechanism of evolution we had to begin (Chapter 16) with populations as entities whose genetic constitution (gene pool) is the fundamental unit subject to evolutionary change.

Chapter 24 is concerned with what we could well call the "metabolism of communities." It treats of the sources and cycles of materials used by the community as a whole; it shows how many of the most general features of community structure are necessary consequences of the physical laws governing energy transfers. It will be recalled from Chapter 1 that the traffic in energy is one of the major themes giving structure and meaning to the life of the community as a whole.

Chapter 25 shows how the various populations within a community interact; it is concerned with the structure and organization of mature communities and how these are determined by the interaction of the constituent populations.

Chapter 26 discusses those factors, such as food supply, predation, and competition, which control the birth, growth, mature stability or fluctuation, and ultimately the death of populations as units. The chapter also briefly touches on the similar growth and change that characterize the life history of the community as a whole.

In Chapter 27 the principles of community biology are applied to the special case of man; he is considered as a subject of biological study especially in respect to his impact and dependence on natural communities.

"The sunlight that each day drenches the forest is the ultimate source of all the energy expended in the whole living community." (Quotation from Chapter 1; photo from Redwood Empire Association)

CHAPTER 24

The Flow of Energy and Materials

THE WEB OF LIFE

A contemporary of Darwin's suggested that the glory of England was due to its old maids. This is the argument: The sturdy Britons were nourished by roast beef from cows, which ate clover, which was pollinated by bumblebees, which were attacked (in their nests) by mice, which were kept under control by cats, which were raised by old maids. The argument has become quaint with the passage of time, and perhaps it was always a little farfetched. It is, however, still valid in pointing out that these, or any, organisms do not live alone. All form parts of a *community* in which the existence and activities of each species and individual are affected by others.

You need not go so far afield to illustrate the interdependence and interactivity of living things or to observe that not only the organisms themselves are involved in inter-

action but also many other things outside and around them. Within a few hours or less you will be hungry, a signal that the energy and materials of your tissues need to be renewed. Perhaps you will eat a hamburger and thus transfer to yourself energy and materials previously acquired, transformed, and stored by another animal. That animal got them from plants, perhaps from grass. The grass, in its turn, acquired materials from the air and from water and solutions in the soil. The energy used in syntheses in the grass and stored in the products came from the sun. The substance of your body has come, mostly through the medium of other organisms, from the air, water, and watery solutions of the earth. All your energy was derived, through the same intermediaries, from atomic energy generated in nuclear reactions some 93 million miles away, which, incidentally, is an excellent distance at which to be from nuclear reactions. (Are there any substances in your body that were not derived from other organisms? Is there any of your energy that was not?)

Even without bringing in bumblebees or old maids, it is easy to see that many other factors influenced the passage of materials and energy from earth and sun to you. The grass was rooted in soil. The properties of the soil that determined the possibility and the amount of growth of grass depended on many things: composition of rocks in the crust of the earth; weathering, erosion, and deposition; climate; movement of ground water; activities of earthworms, bacteria, and innumerable other organisms within the soil; effects, past and present, of plants at the given locality; and so on, through a list too long to make complete. And not only the soil affected the grass. Its growth was also directly influenced by sun, wind, rain, temperatures, insects, rodents, grazing animals, and many other things. The presence of the grass also depended on a long sequence of prior events, such as the development and growth of seeds through generation after generation, the origin of this species of grass and the long evolution of its ancestry back to the beginning of life, and indeed the still older origin of the planet on which life could and did arise.

There is nothing particularly new to you in all this, although you have perhaps not looked at it in just this way before. You already knew that plants synthesize organic from inorganic materials and that animals must acquire organic materials from other organisms. You also knew that all species of organisms have arisen by evolution, even if you had not thought that the eating of a hamburger was a result of the whole history of the earth and its inhabitants. You would not get through your meals in time if you stopped to realize that each bite has been influenced by a vast community of organisms and by the complex circumstances under which they lived, but you are well aware that organisms do live in communities and are affected by their environments.

In turning to discussion of communities in which numerous and diverse organisms live together, we find, again, that we are not taking up a completely new and separate topic, but are simply looking more closely at a particular aspect of the living world, all aspects of which are inseparably related to all others. Everyone has some idea of the existence of communities in nature and of relationships of organisms and environments, and up to this point such general knowledge has been assumed. To organize and extend such common knowledge, we shall now consider first the environment, basic relationships between organisms and environment, and some consequent fundamentals of community organization. Those are the subjects of this chapter. Chapters 25-27 will continue the discussion of living together in communities, including the human community and its interactions with its environments. The next section of the book (Part 8, Chapters 28-29) also has much to say about communities and environments but from another point of view, that of spatial or geographic distribution and association.

Environment

The word "environment" has been used repeatedly in previous chapters without being defined. As good a definition as any is that environment is the totality of extrinsic things and conditions affecting an organism. As so often happens with definitions, this one becomes blurred when it is applied to specific instances. The main trouble is that the word "extrinsic" needs defining itself. We do not want it to mean simply "external." Previously mentioned (p. 124) was the odd fact that the inside of your own stomach is (geometrically, at least) external to you. Yet we would not maintain that the gastric juices are part of your environment except, possibly, in the different sense of the *internal* environment. On the other hand, we would say that a parasite in stomach, intestine, or in the fully internal blood stream is environmental; it is extrinsic to the essential structure and contents of you as an organism. This is a special case, but it serves to stress the concept of environment construed broadly as everything that influences an organism which is not an *intrinsic* part or condition of that organism.

In this broad sense the environment includes several distinct but simultaneous and (of course) interacting phases. It includes, first, the nonliving aspects of the place where an organism lives—its *physical environment*. It includes, too, all the living things that affect the organism—its *biotic environment*.

THE PHYSICAL ENVIRONMENT

All organisms live in water or in air. (Even those that live within the soil are effectively surrounded either by water or by air.) That is the most fundamental feature of the physical environment. The conditions of life are very different in water and in air, and most organisms are confined to one or the other. It is, to be sure, easy to think of exceptions, but they are such exceptions as tend to prove the rule. Many plants live in both environments at once, with roots in water and stems and leaves in air, but the different parts are adapted to the different environments. Many animals spend part of their lives in water and part in the air, as do the numerous insects with aquatic larvae, but the organism is quite different when in one environment than when in the other. Many can temporarily leave one environment for the other, as a fish can jump into the air or a man plunge into the sea. More impressively, there are whole hosts of plants and animals, especially along the shore, that regularly undergo alternation between the two environments. Yet in almost all these plants and animals, one element is vital for the organism and the other is only briefly endured. Can you think of other exceptions to the generalization that the physical environment of most organisms is usually water or air but not both?

Radiation and climate. Organisms that live in air are profoundly affected by weather and climate, and aquatic animals are similarly affected by such factors as temperature. One of the most important factors in such conditions is *radiation*. Radiation important to living things is mainly in the form of electromagnetic waves from the sun. Radiation that we call "light," because our eyes (and those of most other animals) are sensitive to it, is most intense (Fig. 9-2). (Do you think that is a coincidence?) Organisms are also sensitive in other ways to solar radiation of shorter (ultraviolet) and longer (infrared, or heat rays) wave lengths.

The importance of solar radiation cannot be overstressed because (with insignificant exceptions) it supplies all the energy available for all the processes of life in all organisms. This is the income from which all the life activity on earth must be budgeted. The influence of radiation in any particular local environment follows from this basic fact. Green plants, primary converters of solar energy into vital energy, grow only where solar radiation is received. The amount of their activity is limited by, and is roughly proportional

to, the average amount of radi... environment. The activities of ... isms are, in turn, limited by those of ... plants from which, directly or indi... practically all their energy and mater... must come.

Environments with little or no solar radiation have no green plants. They are inhabited only by animals, some nongreen plants (mostly fungi), and certain protists (especially among the bacteria). These organisms in lightless environments necessarily depend on organic foods that are somehow brought in from elsewhere, from environments that do receive solar radiation. Offhand you might think that environments without solar radiation would be quite limited: caves, for instance, which do have an interesting, sparse population but are of no great importance. Actually, however, such environments are more extensive than any others. They include the soil, below its most superficial layer, and the vast reaches of the sea below the depths to which daylight penetrates.[1] Where does the food of soil organisms come from? Of deep sea organisms?

Less solar energy is converted directly into vital energy than is expended in changing and maintaining the *temperature* of the environment. Expenditures of solar energy have been calculated (by C. Juday) for Lake Mendota in southern Wisconsin, as shown in Table 24-1.

TABLE 24-1

Expenditure of solar energy

Expenditure	Percentage of solar energy received
Reflected or otherwise lost	49.5
Absorbed in evaporation of water	25.0
Raising temperatures in the lake	21.7
Melting ice in the spring	3.0
Directly used by organisms	0.8

[1] Radiation is gradually absorbed and scattered as it passes through water, and there is no sharp line where radiation ceases in the sea. Its penetration varies greatly. In very clear water light may still be evident at a depth of 2000 feet. Radiation in the sea is, however, seldom significant below about 600 feet, and deeper waters have few or no living green plants. Red algae in general reach lower depths than any other plants.

...ne figures are quite different in other environments, but everywhere only a small fraction of radiation is used directly by green plants, and a much larger part goes to warm the water or air. (In the example of the lake much of the energy "lost," in the sense of not heating the water at least, heats the air

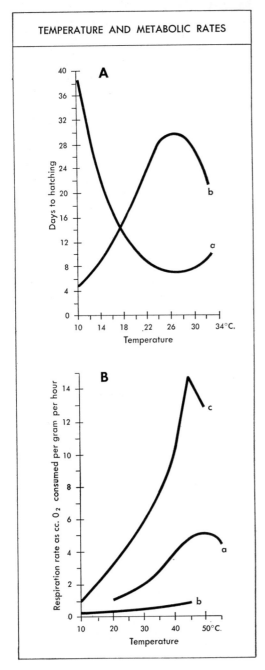

TEMPERATURE AND METABOLIC RATES

A

Days to hatching

b

a

10   14   18   22   26   30   34°C.
Temperature

B

Respiration rate as cc. O₂ consumed per gram per hour

c

a

b

10   20   30   40   50°C.
Temperature

above it.) Maintenance of environmental temperature is another necessity for life as we know it, which can exist only in the range of temperatures that is, in fact, maintained on earth by solar radiation (see p. 15). Metabolic activities are very strongly influenced by the temperature of organisms (Fig. 24-1), and in all plants and most animals the internal temperature depends largely on that of the environment. (What are the exceptions?) Specific adaptations of plants and animals are also related to the averages and ranges of temperatures in particular environments. You know, for instance, that orange trees require sustained warmth but apple trees thrive in regions with low winter temperatures, and that polar bears live only in the cold north and boa constrictors only in the tropics.

As the figures for Lake Mendota exemplify, enormous amounts of solar energy are also expended in the evaporation of water. This, too, is profoundly important for living things. In fact, without it life would be possible only in the sea. Evaporation maintains the *humidity* of the atmosphere and is the key process (the power-input phase) in the *water cycle* (Fig. 24-2). Involved are *rainfall* by condensation of evaporated water in the atmosphere and consequent maintenance of streams, lakes, and water beneath the surface of the ground (ground water). The cycle thus provides the whole of the fresh-water environ-

---

24-1   Temperature and the rate of metabolism. *A.* The effect of temperature on the rate of development in the insect *Sitona:* (*a*) the number of days required to complete egg development at different temperatures; (*b*) the reciprocal of curve *a*, thus representing the velocity of development. Note how the velocity increases with rising temperature up to about 29° C. At higher temperatures the velocity decreases: 29° C. is the *optimum* temperature. *B.* The effect of temperature on the rate of respiration in flies: (*a*) in the larval stage; (*b*) in the pupal stage; (*c*) in the adult fly. The rate of metabolism, as measured by the rate of oxygen consumption, is very different in the three stages of the life cycle, but in all of them it increases with rising temperature. The curves for the larval and adult stages again show the existence of an *optimum* temperature; above the optimum the rate of metabolism decreases again. How would you expect the optimum temperature to relate to the distribution of the species in nature?

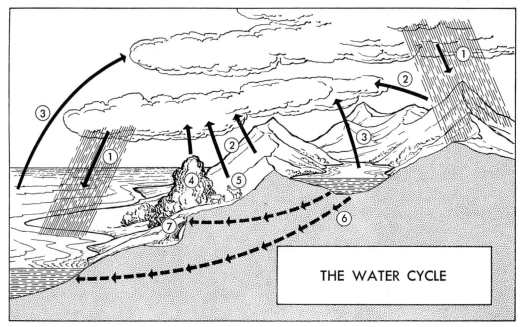

24-2 The water cycle. *1.* Precipitation as rain or snow. *2.* Immediate return to the atmosphere through evaporation from the ground. *3.* Evaporation from standing bodies of water: lakes, oceans. *4.* Transpiration from plants. *5.* Transpiration from animals. *6 and 7.* Drainage from high to low land and, ultimately, to the ocean.

ment and also all the enormous quantities of water required by land organisms. No farmer needs to be told that water supply is a crucial factor in the activity of plant life, and the contrast (in both plants and animals) between a well-watered New England hillside and a dry Arizona desert is well known.

Movement of water or air is another feature of the physical environment. All these factors ramify and interlock; both in water and in air movement helps to determine the distribution of temperatures, and air movement is a crucial element for rainfall. Winds and currents also influence organisms more directly in many ways. Innumerable land plants, among them the conifers and many grasses, are wind-pollinated (see p. 372). The animals in swift-flowing streams can remain there only by anchoring themselves somehow or by making headway against the current. Most animals in flowing fresh water have eggs that sink to the bottom, below the current, although many marine animals have floating, drifting eggs. What would eventually happen if trout eggs, for instance, floated? The fact that some animals have floating eggs or

larvae and some plants wind-borne seeds also suggests another important effect of water and air currents: the geographic spread of organisms, a topic to which we will return (Chapter 29).

Microclimates and niches. Great care is taken in gathering the weather data on which descriptions of climates are based (climate is just weather over a longer period). Temperature is measured in a shady, ventilated, elevated shelter, away from heat reflections or cold pockets of the ground, pavements, or walls. Wind velocity is taken where gusts and eddies do not disturb. The recorded humidity is taken distant from the ground or any local factors that might influence it. But these are not really the conditions under which we or other organisms live. The weather, and hence the climate, of our immediate surroundings may be quite different from that recorded by the Weather Bureau.[2] For an

[2] Someone has said that records are made only of conditions never actually encountered. The remark is nearly true, but it is unfair. Records of all microclimates could hardly be made, and they are largely influenced by the idealized climate of the official record.

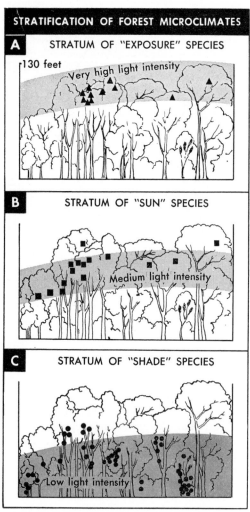

STRATIFICATION OF FOREST MICROCLIMATES

A STRATUM OF "EXPOSURE" SPECIES

130 feet

Very high light intensity

B STRATUM OF "SUN" SPECIES

Medium light intensity

C STRATUM OF "SHADE" SPECIES

Low light intensity

24-3 The stratification of forest microclimates. The existence and ecological significance of differences in *microclimates* is well illustrated by the vertical distribution in forest of epiphytic (p. 631) ferns, orchids, and bromeliads that grow on the trees' branches. Each epiphytic species has its particular requirements for temperature, moisture, and light. The marked vertical gradients in these environmental factors result in an equally pronounced stratification in the distribution of the various epiphytic species. The figure shows the vertical distribution of three groups of bromeliad (p. 703) species in a South American rain forest: one of these groups (*A*) occurs only in the highest levels of the forest, where its demand for extremely high light intensities is met; *B* demands moderate light intensity; and *C* is a group of species that requires shade and high humidity.

organism a few inches under the soil the temperature is usually different and always less variable than for one on the surface. The climate on the floor of a forest is decidedly cooler, less sunny, more humid, and less windy than the climate in the tops of the trees (Fig. 24-3). Organisms in a region generally have small climates, *microclimates*, of their own, which are quite diverse and more or less different from the idealized regional climate.

Similarly, particular organisms do not really live in a regional environment, such as a "forest environment," but in small environments of their own. Animals burrowing in the mold, running along the ground, lurking under bark, or flitting through branches certainly have very different personal environments, both physical and biotic. The microenvironment of a particular species is its *niche*.[3] Every regional environment has a large number of different niches. The environment, indeed, is not precisely the same for any two individuals, but it tends to be closely similar for members of the same species at the same stages in their lives. It is not the same for any two kinds of organisms in a community. Every species has its own niche. Even two microorganisms of different species living side by side in the soil are influenced somewhat differently by their inorganic and organic surroundings, and hence have different niches. How many niches can you distinguish in a community known to you? Are there any possible niches that are not in fact occupied by organisms?

The particular, detailed conditions of an organism's microenvironment are intricate and subtle and may defy adequate analysis. Tapirs, although land animals, always live near water. The reason appears to be that they always defecate while standing in water and become constipated when no water is nearby. As to why they stand in water to defecate, no one knows. Any species is likely to present equally baffling, although seldom quite so bizarre, problems of environmental relationships.

[3] The word is French but is anglicized with the pronunciation "nitch" (not "neesh"). Some ecologists tend to confine the term to the physical environment or to think of it as the place where life is lived. However, it is also common and probably preferable usage to apply it to the whole of the microenvironment.

The substratum. Some organisms, from protists to whales, spend their whole lives suspended in water, and some spend much of their lives (although none spends all of it) suspended in air. Nearly all plants and the majority of animals, however, rest on a bottom of some sort from which they project into water or air. They may be firmly attached, like a tree or a coral, or may be highly motile, like a man, but they are in contact with some surface most or all of the time. The surface to which they are attached or on which they move is their *substratum* ("underlayer").[4] This, too, is a part of the physical environment that strongly influences the organisms on it. The plants of clay, sand, and rocky substrata are usually strikingly different. So, frequently, are the animals of sandy and of rocky stretches even in the same region. The shore life of mud flats, sandy beaches, and rock pools has even greater contrasts. The influence of the substratum is partly mechanical. Burrowing animals, for instance, will generally be found in a soft substratum, and sessile animals are more common on a hard substratum. The chemistry of the substratum, and of the environment in general, is also of vital importance.

The chemical environment: soil. Thanks to its constant and often rapid and turbulent motion, the composition of dry air is much the same almost everywhere: by volume about 78 per cent nitrogen, 21 per cent oxygen, and 1 per cent carbon dioxide.[5] Variations affecting organisms are those of water content, already mentioned (p. 612), and local concentrations of gases near volcanoes and industrial plants.

Soils and waters are markedly varied in their chemistry, and their differences profoundly affect organisms. Probably the most obvious difference is that between sea and fresh water, some of the effects of which have been discussed (pp. 86-87). Fresh water does have large amounts of mineral salts in dilute solution, and sea water is not the strongest possible (saturated) solution. But some salt lakes are saturated, and have few and peculiar organisms in consequence. Every gradation between fresh water and salt lakes exists, and differences in salt content are reflected by the presence of different plants and animals and sometimes by the same organisms' assuming different forms. What is the relationship of these facts to the principle of the reaction range (p. 334)?

Soils have a special interest because the lives of nearly all land organisms, including man, depend largely on soil. The bulk of a soil is composed of grains of minerals, especially a mixture of silica (the mineral of common sand) and clays. The mixture is formed by disintegration and decomposition of underlying rocks, or from silts and other sediments washed in by streams or blown by the wind. Among the particles of the soil are spaces, generally from a third to a half of the volume of the soil, occupied by air or water. Water in the interstices of soil is the source of most of the great amounts of water required by land plants. It is also a complex solution from which are drawn many of the other materials incorporated in all sorts of land organisms.

Soils well illustrate the fact that the contrast between physical and biotic environments is not absolute. These aspects of the environment also interact. Soil is penetrated by roots, which change it both physically (for instance, by loosening up its packed particles) and chemically (for instance, by withdrawing mineral salts from it). As plants die, parts of their organic materials are incorporated in the soil. Those organic materials, as well as parts of living plants in the soil, provide food for incredibly huge numbers of bacteria, algae, fungi, nematodes, earthworms, and other organisms. These soil organisms further modify the physical and chemical characteristics of the soil and add their excretions and dead bodies to its contents. Soil is thus itself a populous and complex com-

[4] Of course, the substratum is usually either the surface of the ground or the bottom of a body of water. However, a few animals, such as the insects called "water striders," live in the air with the surface of water as their substratum. That is one reason why it is useful to employ the mildly technical term "substratum." It sums up the situation simply without recourse to such an expression as "air-water-lithosphere interphases."

[5] Plus relatively very small amounts of rare gases such as neon and helium, which man has learned to extract and to turn to his own uses but which are of little or no importance to any other organisms.

munity in which the inorganic and the organic interact endlessly and inextricably.

THE BIOTIC ENVIRONMENT

By definition, the biotic environment of an organism includes all the living things that affect it. The living things that affect any one organism are certain also to affect each other, directly or indirectly. They are likely, also, to exist within a circumscribed area at any one time. They are, in short, a community in themselves or a part of a larger community. Discussion of the organization of communities and of relationships in them is therefore, from another point of view, a discussion of biotic environments. That is the main subject of this and several following chapters.

Here at the outset one major distinction may be made among the various members of a community viewed as the biotic environment of any particular organism in it. There is a fundamental difference between the environmental relationships of members of different species and those among members of the same species. The members of different species have different roles; they occupy different niches. They constitute an *interspecific* ("among species") *environment*. Members of the same species have, if not quite the same, at least more closely similar roles and niches. For any individual of the species they are its *intraspecific* ("within species") *environment*. Their activities are interrelated and organized in a way unlike the relationships among different species. The fact that they have interbred (if biparental) or have expanded by descent from the same individual source (if uniparental) ensures also a special biological relationship that may further entail (among animals) special social relationships.

The community as a whole has interspecific organization, relationships among the various activities of its numerous species. Within the community the members of a particular species have intraspecific organization. A fundamental feature of the interspecific community organization is the acquisition, transformation, and passing on of materials and energy among the diverse organisms of the community. This organization involves a sort of community metabolism, which is the sum of the metabolisms of individual organisms and of environmental factors related to their metabolism.

Cycles of Materials

THE CARBON CYCLE

All organic compounds contain carbon (p. 73). Carbohydrates and fats, compounds of carbon, hydrogen, and oxygen, are the principal (but not the only) forms in which energy is stored in organisms and passed on from one to another (p. 110). The flow of carbon in communities is therefore one of the essential features of their metabolism.

The great reservoir of carbon in nonorganic form and the source of almost all the carbon incorporated in organisms is the carbon dioxide, CO_2, in the atmosphere and dissolved in the waters of the earth. The usual first step in the utilization of carbon as a material in living things is photosynthesis by green plants (Chapter 5). The carbon thus becomes part of simple carbohydrates, and later syntheses in the same plants transfer part of it into polysaccharides, proteins, fats, and other complex organic compounds. Animals eat plants, and the organic compounds are digested and resynthesized (Chapter 6). Other animals eat the meat-eating animals, with still more digestions and resyntheses. Thus carbon is transferred from one organism to another through a shorter or longer, sometimes very long, sequence. In the course of the sequence, and even within any one organism of the series, the carbon atoms are constantly shifted from one kind of molecule to another. But as long as it is a vital part of an organism the carbon is in some organic compound of greater or less complexity.

Eventually most of the organic carbon becomes a part of CO_2 again and is returned to the inorganic realm of water and air. This return phase is an essential part of the cycle that has kept life going since early in its history, as the available carbon has continuously circled from air and water through plants and animals and back to air and water again. Some of the return is fairly direct. CO_2 is an end product of respiration in both plants and animals (p. 98), and the respired CO_2 passes at once into the water or air of the organism's immediate environment, where it is available to start the cycle all over again.

Much carbon remains in the tissues of organisms when they die, or is eliminated by animals in waste products that are still fairly complex organic compounds, not usable as a carbon source in photosynthesis.[6] If this carbon were not somehow converted into CO_2, life would have come to an end by now. All the available carbon would be locked up in organic but nonliving form. Here is the role of the organisms of decay or putrefaction, most of which are bacteria or fungi. They attack and digest the organic materials of dead plants and animals and of excretions, reducing them to the simpler and energy-poor compounds with which the various cycles of materials and energy begin. After their work is completed, most of the carbon of organic compounds has become CO_2 again.

There are some other ways in which organic compounds can be finally broken down. Most familiar is fire or slower combustion (oxidation). When wood is burned, for instance, the carbon of its cellulose and other materials is removed from the organic compounds as CO_2. But combustion, aside from that now caused by man,[7] is not a continuous and widespread process in nature. It would not suffice to keep the carbon cycle, or other organic cycles, going. This is an extremely important principle: the continuity of organic cycles through final breakdown of organic compounds into raw materials for renewed synthesis by green plants depends on the activities of living things. That is certainly true now and has clearly been true during most of the history of life. Can it, however, have been true at the very beginning of life?

Some carbon is withdrawn from the cycle for long periods, if not permanently. Not all the organic compounds of dead organisms have decayed; some have been incorporated in the crust of the earth as coal, petroleum, and natural gas. By burn-

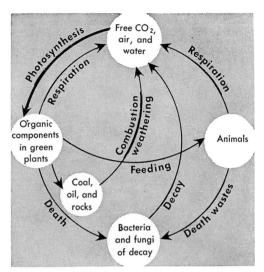

24-4   The carbon cycle.

ing these, man makes their carbon again available for the organic cycle. Before man, there was little return of this stored carbon, even though some of it was liberated by combustion and by bacteria. An even larger amount of carbon is locked up in limestone, the principal mineral of which has the composition $CaCO_3$. Much, but by no means all, limestone is a result of the activities of life. Coral reefs provide a clear example of life-made limestone. The carbon of limestone may be released as CO_2 by natural processes, such as the action of weathering and natural acids, but much limestone is now deep in the earth, where its carbon will not be available for a very long time, if ever.

The most striking features of the whole carbon cycle are summed up in Fig. 24-4.

THE NITROGEN CYCLE

Nitrogen is no less essential to life than carbon. It is, as you know (p. 74), part of all amino acids and proteins. Its cycle (Fig. 24-5) is similar to that of carbon and goes on at the same time, but there are some distinctive features.

Nitrogen makes up the greatest part of the atmosphere, but green plants can use little or no atmospheric nitrogen (N_2) in their syntheses—a marked contrast with carbon, which (as CO_2) is mainly derived from the air by green plants. Green plants require nitrogen as

[6] Urea, for instance, an abundant animal excretion, contains carbon. It is $CO(NH_2)_2$. Uric acid and some other excretions contain still larger percentages of carbon. Urea is utilized by some algae but not, of course, in their photosynthesis.

[7] How was coal and wood combustion initiated before the evolution of man, and how is it initiated today apart from man?

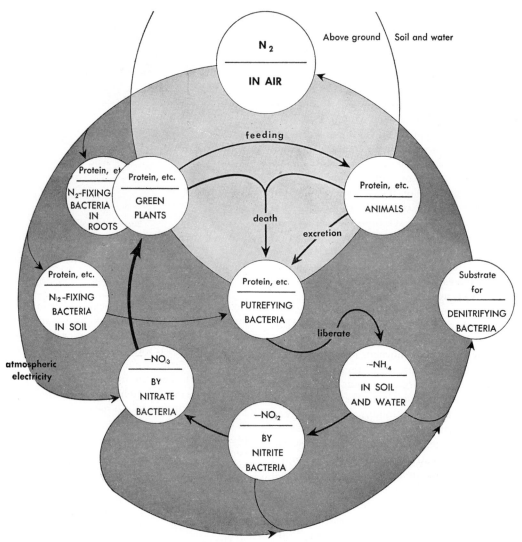

24-5 The nitrogen cycle.

ammonia (NH_3) or in the form of nitrates (compounds containing NO_3), and these are obtained from solution in the soil. Atmospheric nitrogen can be converted into such compounds by lightning (or other discharges of atmospheric electricity), but this is a minor source. The important source is the *nitrogen-fixing bacteria*, which can utilize N_2 directly in the synthesis of amino acids and proteins. Some nitrogen-fixing bacteria live independently in the soil and some live in nodules in roots of other plants, especially the legumes, members of the pea family. In either location, their death frees nitrogen compounds, which can be utilized by other plants, and particularly green plants.[8] The nitrogen of green plants, thus acquired either from ammonia and nitrates in the soil or from nitrogen-fixing bacteria, may be passed on to animals that eat plants, and then from animal to animal, as carbon is.

As with carbon, too, nitrogen is excreted by animals (in urea, for instance) and also remains in the tissues of dead organisms. Again, it is mainly bacteria that return this

[8] There is evidence also that legume roots secrete nitrogen-containing compounds directly into the soil while they are still alive.

locked-up nitrogen to the cycle. Bacteria of decay produce ammonia from proteins and other nitrogenous compounds. Other bacteria, *nitrifying bacteria*, oxidize ammonia to nitrites (salts of nitrous acid, e.g., KNO_2), and still others perform further oxidation to nitrates (salts of nitric acid, e.g., KNO_3). Thus inorganic nitrogen compounds directly utilizable by green plants are restored to the soil.

Another distinction of the nitrogen cycle from the carbon cycle is that it does not necessarily or regularly involve a phase during which the nitrogen is in the atmosphere. Such a cycle as nitrates in soil → green plants → nitrifying bacteria → nitrates in soil, and so on, can continue indefinitely without the nitrogen's ever occurring as a gas, N_2, in the air. An N_2 phase may occur in a cycle, however, and when it does the return of N_2 to the atmosphere is brought about by *denitrifying bacteria*. They break down nitrates (and some other compounds) and liberate N_2. Whatever nitrogen does not simply remain in the atmosphere and does in fact continue the cycle is then returned to the soil by the action (mainly) of the nitrogen-fixing bacteria, which we met on our last time around the circle.

It may be a little misleading to speak of *the* carbon cycle and *the* nitrogen cycle. You can see that the pattern of flow, even simplified as it is in Figs. 24-4 and 24-5, does not have a single, circular course that carbon or nitrogen necessarily follows. The patterns are more complex, each with a number of different paths that the two elements may follow in a cyclic manner. The simplest course for nitrogen is soil → plants → bacteria → soil, and so around again and again. What is the simplest cycle for carbon?

Consideration of all the organic cycles shows that green plants and putrefactive bacteria *must* be present if life is to continue indefinitely with a cyclic flow of materials and energy. Animals are unnecessary. In the total metabolism of life they are a side issue or an extra step that complicates the process without really contributing to it. From *this* point of view, at least, should not we animals be a little more humble?

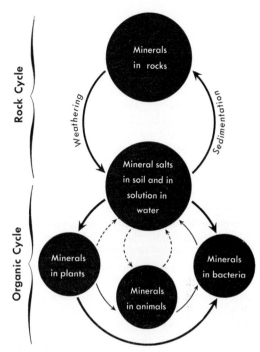

24-6 The mineral cycle.

MINERAL CYCLES

You learned in Chapter 4 that the principal inorganic materials that become incorporated in living things are water, carbon (generally as CO_2), oxygen, nitrogen, and a variety of mineral salts. The carbon and nitrogen cycles have now been especially considered. Analogy with these cycles and what you have learned elsewhere in this and previous chapters are sufficient for you to work out the essentials of the water and oxygen cycles. (The water cycle is also summarized in Fig. 24-2.) The mineral cycles have some features of special interest and merit a diagram (Fig. 24-6) and some additional comments. Before reading these comments, review pp. 71-75, on the inorganic materials of life.

With few and unimportant exceptions, the inorganic sources of all the mineral elements necessary to organisms are salts in solution in water, whether in the soil or in bodies of water. (Even so-called fresh water is in fact a dilute solution of many mineral salts, among other things.) The salt-solution phase is a part of two great cycles in nature, cycles that interlock through this phase. One, the *rock cycle*, is inorganic in essence, although it is strongly influenced by organisms, and organisms may even have direct parts in it. The mineral salts of the earth came originally, and more are still coming, from the crust of the earth. They are formed and liberated from rocks of the crust mainly by processes summed up as "weathering," disintegration, and decomposition under the influence of air, water, and organisms. The soluble salts arising among the products of these processes then enter another of nature's cycles, the *water cycle*. With the water, they move through soil, streams, and lakes and eventually into the sea. As they pass through this cycle, perhaps with long stops during the trip, they are available to organisms in all the environments of life. Most of them eventually reach the oceans, where much salt remains indefinitely. Some of the mineral salts do complete a cycle and return to the crust of the earth through the processes of sedimentation.[9] They are incorporated in limestones, silts, salt beds, and other sedimentary deposits that become parts of the earth's crust. These, in turn, may weather, and their mineral salts may begin the cycle again.

In the organic cycle of the mineral salts, plants, animals, and bacteria may all acquire salts from the inorganic solutions of their environments, although this activity is most extensive in plants. All may also return salts directly to the inorganic worlds of soil and water; plants are least active in this respect. Animals also acquire salts from plants and from other animals eaten as food. Putrefactive bacteria and other organisms of decay acquire salts from dead plants and animals and, as in all organic cycles, form the last organic link in the longest, most complex sequences.

Transfers of Energy

THE FIRST LAW OF THERMODYNAMICS

When you run a hundred-yard dash, or when you merely move your hand, you are expending energy. The steady beat of your heart and the flicker of a thought through your mind also expend energy. You know that even a plant standing motionless in a field is continually using energy in the syntheses within its living cells. The utilization and transfer of energy as fundamental features of the living world have already been stressed in Chapter 5, where our emphasis was on the cell and the individual organism. Here we are concerned with energy transfers again—this time in relation to whole populations and communities of organisms.

Two generalizations about energy—the capacity to perform work—may be recalled from Chapter 5 (p. 91): (1) Energy may be *potential* or *kinetic*. A boulder on a hilltop has potential energy that becomes kinetic ("pertaining to motion") when it rolls downhill. (2) Energy assumes many different forms [mechanical, chemical, electrical, radiant (light), thermal (heat)], and may be transformed from one kind into another (Fig. 1-5).

Transfers and transformations of energy are governed by the laws of thermodynamics. *The First Law of Thermodynamics* relates to the conservation of energy. Whenever transfers or transformations of energy occur, there is neither gain nor loss in the total energy involved in the transaction.[10]

The significance of the First Law of Thermodynamics may be re-emphasized in chemical terms because chemical-energy transfers are especially important for living things. Every substance contains potential chemical energy. Chemical reactions by which substances are changed also change the total amount of potential energy in them. If the products of a chemical reaction contain less potential energy than the reactants from which they were derived, kinetic energy (as heat or light) is released. A familiar example is the burning of charcoal, or any other form of carbon:

$$C + O_2 \rightarrow CO_2 + \text{Energy (Heat and light)}$$

[10] Everyone knows nowadays that matter can be turned into energy, as in an atomic bomb. That sort of reaction does not occur in living things, and anyway is not a real exception to the law. It demonstrates only that matter itself is a form of energy. The only connection with life is that the sun's radiation involves the transformation of matter to radiant energy.

[9] They do not to any considerable extent go through the return phase of the water cycle, which takes place by evaporation and does not carry along appreciable amounts of minerals.

In such an *exergonic* reaction (p. 95) the kinetic energy released is exactly equal to the loss of potential chemical energy in transforming carbon and oxygen into carbon dioxide: Potential energy of reactants (C and O_2) = Potential energy of products (CO_2) + Kinetic energy liberated (Heat and light). *Energy was neither lost nor gained in the transaction.*

If, on the other hand, the substances resulting from a reaction contain more energy than those that went into the reaction, then energy must be supplied from somewhere (*endergonic* reaction, p. 95), or the reaction will not occur. You are familiar with some reactions of this sort, notably the series of reactions of photosynthesis summarized as:

$$6CO_2 + 6H_2O + Energy \rightarrow C_6H_{12}O_6 + 6O_2$$

CO_2 and H_2O, compounds comparatively poor in energy, are transformed (in part) into carbohydrates, compounds comparatively rich in energy. The extra energy was acquired from sunlight.

THE SECOND LAW OF THERMODYNAMICS

The Second Law of Thermodynamics is equally important in the processes of life but is somewhat harder to grasp. One way of putting it is to say that, as energy is transferred from one substance to another or transformed from one form to another, less and less of the total energy is utilizable in further transfers and transformations. Although the *total* amount cannot change, *the amount that can perform work of any sort, chemical, mechanical, or other, becomes steadily smaller*. The *usable* energy in a sequence of transfers tends to run down, and the whole process will come to a stop unless there is a continuing input of energy from somewhere.

The laws of thermodynamics have literally vital consequences for the activities of living things. In the cycles of *materials*, such as carbon or nitrogen, nothing is lost or necessarily becomes unusable. All the materials that start the cycle are (or, at least, can be) returned to their original form after going through the cycle, and then they are ready to start around again. There is no reason why the process should not go on forever without addition of anything from outside.

This is fundamentally not true of energy.

In every organism, energy transfers occur through many chemical reactions, and chemical energy is also transformed into other sorts of energy, such as heat, motion, or (but this is comparatively unimportant in organisms) light. In accordance with the First Law of Thermodynamics, the total activity can involve only the amount of energy that the organism receives. An organism cannot generate any *new* energy. In accordance with the Second Law, much of the energy received is made unusable by the activities of the organism. The energy received cannot be destroyed (that would violate the first law), but it is *dissipated*, scattered in such forms (mainly as heat transferred to the environment) that it can no longer be used by that organism or by others.

Thus organisms pass on to others less energy than they received. When a herbivore eats a plant, it receives chemical energy, but the energy received is much less than the energy that the plant received from the sun. A carnivore, in turn, acquires chemical energy by eating a herbivore, but it receives from the herbivore much less energy than the latter received from the plants it ate. When, finally, the organisms of decay end the sequence, they pass on the materials of life in forms that are utilizable by other organisms, but they practically complete the dissipation of energy in the community. In fact, the flow of *energy* in a community is not a cycle at all. It is a one-way sequence in which vital energy, like all energy, follows the Second Law and becomes continuously less available.[11]

Since communities do keep going, and have for over a billion years, obviously energy is continually coming in to them from some outside source. You well know the source: the sun. The sun, too, is subject to the Second Law. Some time all its energy will no longer be in usable form. Then life on earth will no longer be possible, but the event is billions of years in the future, so far away that some other catastrophe may wipe out the earth's life long before then. As to where the energy

[11] Some authors of popular books claim that life does not follow the Second Law, and draw pseudo-profound philosophical and even religious conclusions. Such authors have not thought the problem through.

of the sun came from to begin with, the
only honest *scientific* answer at present is,
"We do not know."

Food Chains and Pyramids

FOOD CHAINS AND WEBS

It has been shown that there is a flow of
materials and energy in a community, cyclic
for materials and one-way for energy. Both
are transferred from one species of organism to another, and that is a, or *the*, basic
feature of a community as an organized association of different, interacting species. The
sequence of species through which the materials and energy pass is called a *food chain*.
A food chain necessarily starts with photosynthetic green plants or green protists, since
they are the organisms that acquire energy

from nonorganic sources. (There are exceptions, see p. 111, but they are of little significance in the over-all picture.) The shortest
food chains involve green plants and organisms of decay. Even in so simple a sequence,
several species may be involved: a green
plant, one or more species of fungi, and several species of bacteria.

More complex food chains involve animals.
One was exemplified at the beginning of this
chapter: grass → cattle → man. (Is this a
complete chain?) The second link in such a
chain is a plant-eating animal. Later links, before those of final decay, are animal-eating
animals. The sequence among animals can include numerous links, for instance: insect →
spider → frog → fish → otter. To be complete,
any such chain must always have photosynthesis at the beginning and decay at the end,
so that the general form of most chains is this:

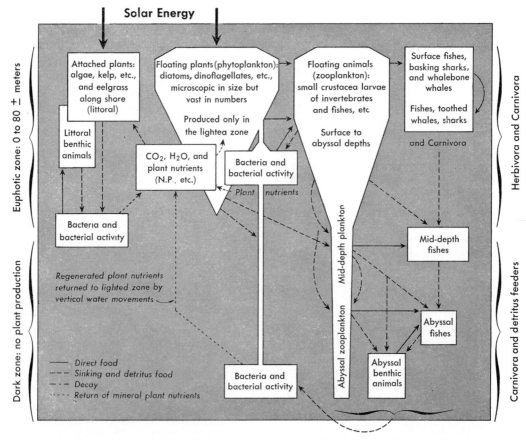

24-7 The food web of the major ocean community. The arrows indicate the direction of
energy and material transfers within the community.

photosynthetic organism → herbivore → carnivore → organism of decay. The two middle steps do not necessarily occur in a chain, and the last two steps may each include several successive links. What other chains can you think of with at least four links?

In a natural community the flow of materials and energy is really much more complicated than is suggested by any one food chain. Practically all species of organisms may be consumed by more than one other species. Also, most animals eat more than one species of organism, although quite a few "prefer" a single item of diet. A single kind of plant may provide food for several species of insects, a number of birds, rabbits, several kinds of rodents, and deer, not to mention many fungi and bacteria that consume it, alive or dead, or worms living on the mold from its leaves. Each of these many species also, in all probability, derives food from several other species of plants. Each in its turn may be food for several species. A rodent, for instance, may include this particular plant among a dozen species that it habitually eats, and the rodent may be eaten by an owl, hawk, weasel, badger, coyote or other carnivore. It may, indeed, be eaten by another rodent, and this introduces still another complication: a single species does not necessarily confine itself to one position in a food chain. Quite a few animals, of which you are one and a rat is another, are about as likely to play the role of carnivore as that of herbivore. There are so many branchings and cross-connections among the food chains of any community that the whole situation is rather a *food web* than a series of readily distinguishable chains. Figure 24-7 suggests something of the web pattern, but still is greatly simplified. No one has ever worked out the complete pattern in all details for any natural community.

If you think of what you had for dinner last night, you will see that each item of your food made you part of a large, widespread food web. What are some of the other connections in this web?

THE PYRAMID OF ENERGY AND MASS

In spite of the real and tremendous complication of food webs, the partial chain of plant → herbivore → carnivore does sum up much of the food flow in any community.[12] Each link in the chain has available for its activities less energy than the previous link; that follows, of course, from the laws of energy just discussed. The total energy of the plants in a community is always more than that of the herbivores, and the energy of the herbivores is more than that of the carnivores. The total amount of actual living substance, its bulk or mass, also tends to decrease from one link to another. This decrease in mass is not a rigidly necessary result of physical law, like the decrease in energy, but it is an extremely probable result and does seem to be true of all natural communities. There are several reasons for this, among them the facts that total energy and total mass tend to be proportional and that some material is lost from the chain in each link. Some, for instance, is lost by respiration and some skips directly to the end of the sequence when organisms decay instead of being eaten. If you raised sheep for food and ate nothing else,[13] it is fairly obvious that in order to keep you going the total weight of your flock of sheep would have to be continuously much greater than your own weight. That is about the simplest possible example of the generalization that in a community the total mass represented by species later in food chains is less than that in earlier links.

Thus, in its mass and energy, a community is like a pyramid. It is largest at the bottom, that is to say, at the beginning of the food chains. Each successive step in the sequence of food utilization is smaller than the last (Fig. 24-8).

THE PYRAMID OF NUMBERS

A concept related to the pyramid of mass and energy and sometimes confused with it (although it is quite distinct) is what animal ecologists call "the pyramid of numbers." If

[12] The following discussion also applies in principle to the final, decay stage of the chains, but with the complication that organisms of decay derive food from all previous links and not only (in fact, least of all) from carnivores.
[13] This is not as fanciful as it may sound. Some people, in Patagonia for instance, do live on a practically 100 per cent diet of sheep. No dietary deficiency normally develops if everything but skin and bones is eaten.

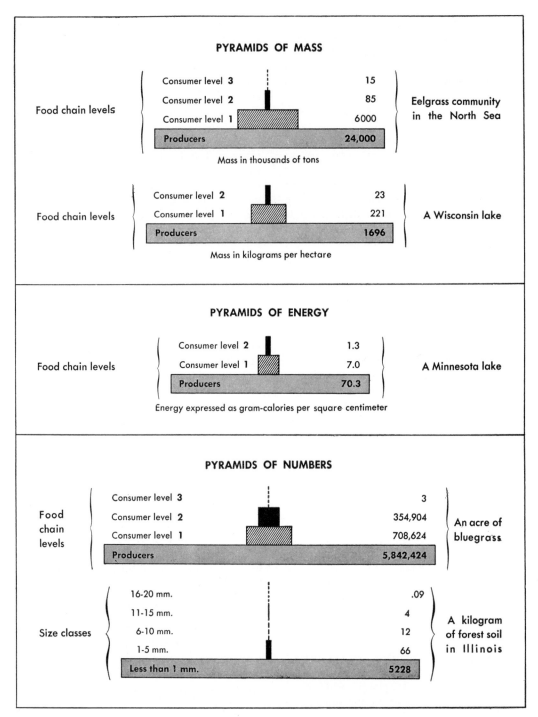

24-8 Pyramids of mass, energy, and numbers of organisms in a community. See pp. 620-21. "Producers" are the plants, primary converters of environmental resources into living material. "Consumers" are animals. The three levels represent the hierarchy of predation in the community: consumer level 3 feeds on consumer level 2; consumer level 2 feeds on consumer level 1; and consumer level 1 feeds directly on the producers.

a census is taken of animals of different sizes, smaller animals are generally found to be more numerous than larger ones (Fig. 24-8). You can probably verify this from your own experience. In any natural community known to you, what is the comparative abundance of animals of the sizes of insects, squirrels, and cats or dogs?

The pyramid of numbers depends in some instances and in part on the pyramid of mass. Predaceous animals, those that pursue and kill prey, generally eat animals smaller than themselves. Since the predators are higher in a food chain than their prey, according to the principle of the pyramid of mass the *total* bulk of the predators is considerably less than that of their prey. Therefore the predators are usually both larger and fewer than their prey. The pyramid of numbers also frequently applies, however, regardless of predator-prey relationships or of the positions of the animals in food chains. A large animal requires more food (of whatever sort it may be) than a small one, and so may have to monopolize more territory if it is to survive. Furthermore in any given area there is food for more small than large animals. Large animals are also able to and usually do range more widely than small animals. A larger animal simply does occupy more space; think how many mosquitoes could and sometimes do occur in space the size of an elephant! [14]

Do you think that the pyramid of numbers applies to plants? If so, why? (Remember that no two green plants are successive links in a food chain.)

BUDGETS: THE LIMITATION OF LIFE

The principles of cycles of materials, of energy transfers, of food chains, and of mass and energy pyramids have important implications for the abundance and activity of the life of the earth as a whole and of living things at any one place and time. It has been shown that practically all the energy and much the greatest part of the materials in all living things must pass through green plants. They are the basic source of foods, but they are also the bottleneck of life's activities. The total activity of life, the flow of energy through all living organisms, can proceed no faster than the fixing of that energy by photosynthesis. Photosynthesis can proceed no faster than the inflow of radiant energy from the sun. As a matter of fact, photosynthesis is very much slower. Only a small fraction of sunlight that reaches the surface of the earth is transformed into chemical energy by photosynthesis. The available data are highly inexact, but the figure must be well under 1 per cent.[15] Whatever the precise figure may be, it represents all the energy available for all the living things on earth.

The great difference between summer and winter activity in natural communities of the Temperate and Frigid zones exists because more solar energy is received in summer. Much of the influence is indirect, caused by changes in temperature and precipitation, which are in turn affected by differences in radiation from the sun. However, another direct factor is that in winter less energy is available for photosynthesis.

Limitations of vital activity by the budget of available materials are also strong and may be more obvious in particular localities. On land the most apparent limitation is often in the water budget, as water supply is highly variable and water is the material needed in largest quantities by all living communities. The comparative scarcity of life in the sun-drenched desert is obviously not due to deficiency of solar energy but to limitation of water. In general the amount of green vegetation, and therefore of total life, in a land area tends to be proportionate to the water supply available to plants. The most common budget limitation in the soil is in nitrates (principal source of nitrogen, p. 74) and phosphates (essential mineral salts, p. 75). Agriculturalists well know that on heavily farmed land these are the principal materials that have to be renewed by fertilization. Differences in natural supplies of these ma-

[14] Another reason sometimes given for the pyramid of numbers is that smaller animals have a higher "reproductive potential," but this probably has little bearing. Larger animals do usually reproduce more slowly, but still the rate is sufficient to supply the largest population that could possibly live in any available area. As far as the reproductive potential is concerned, elephants have been in Africa long enough to be as numerous there as ants—but there is not food or room for that many elephants!

[15] See p. 609. The value at Lake Mendota was 0.8 per cent.

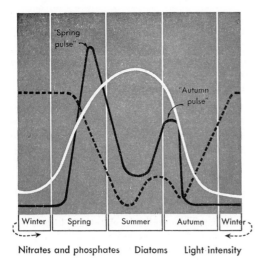

"Spring pulse"

"Autumn pulse"

| Winter | Spring | Summer | Autumn | Winter |

Nitrates and phosphates   Diatoms   Light intensity

24-9 Seasonal fluctuation in diatom abundance in the North Atlantic. *Winter:* Surface waters are cold and poorly illuminated. Under these conditions diatom growth is inhibited, and, as a consequence, the concentration of nitrates and phosphates in the surface waters increases. It is normally reduced when the growth incorporates them into protoplasm. *Spring:* Surface waters warm up and light intensity increases. These optimum conditions for photosynthesis, combined with high concentrations of nitrates and phosphates, lead to a spectacular "spring pulse" of diatom growth. *Summer:* The diatom population declines for two reasons: (1) they are consumed in huge numbers by herbivorous animals; and (2) the concentration of necessary nitrates and phosphates declines during the summer. This limitation of essential minerals itself has two causes: (1) it has been subject to removal through the earlier diatom growth, and (2) it has not been renewed from the depths of the ocean. The main source of return of nitrates and phosphates is the dark, deep ocean bottom where bacteria-caused decay is high and photosynthesis is nonexistent. Actual return of the minerals to the main zone of life—the surface—depends on their upward movement from the bottom. The complex distribution of temperature conditions in the summer ocean prevents the upward movement and thus temporarily contributes to a nitrate-phosphate limitation that in turn contributes to the decline of the diatom population. *Autumn:* The temperature conditions of the ocean change, permitting a renewal of nitrates and phosphates from the depths. This "autumn pulse" in the diatom population is, however, never as great as the spring pulse because temperature and light intensity have fallen, thus limiting the rate of photosynthesis. *Winter:* Growth continues to decline in the winter because of the light and temperature conditions, and consequently the nitrates and phosphates accumulate to the high concentration that will again make possible a huge "spring pulse."

terials are also reflected in different abundances of land life.

In aquatic environments there is practically no limitation of water budget, but other materials, especially, again, nitrates and phosphates, may be stringently limited. Great quantities of these materials are washed into the sea from the land, which is why marine life is particularly abundant along shores and off the mouths of rivers. Farther out to sea, nitrates and phosphates are rapidly used in upper levels of the water, where photosynthesis occurs. The return of nitrates and phosphates to the cycle by decay is more active at deeper levels, as dead organisms sink through the water and are decomposed by bacteria. They may be returned to the sunlit surface waters by rise and diffusion from deeper water or by the upwelling of deep currents along coasts. There is, for instance, such a zone of upwelling along the coast of Peru, marked by an extraordinary richness of marine life. Combined limitations of energy and material budgets are particularly well illustrated by fluctuations in abundance of diatoms (see p. 497) in the North Atlantic (Fig. 24-9). Since diatoms, in spite of their small size, are the most important photosynthetic organisms of the open sea, the whole rich life of the ocean community changes with their fluctuation.

Chapter Summary

The web of life: the interaction of living things everywhere; transfers of energy and materials in a community.

Environment: the totality of extrinsic things and conditions affecting an organism; the complexity of environment; physical and biotic environment.

Physical environment: all environments either aquatic or aerial.

Radiation and climate: solar (electromagnetic) radiation the most important; as ultimate energy source for the community; as controlling the temperature of environments; history of total solar energy falling on Lake Mendota; as cause of evaporation of water and hence power input to drive water cycle; water and air movements; their effects on organisms.

Microclimates and niches: the diversity of microclimates in a general climatic zone (exemplified by microclimates in forest); the diversity of niches in a habitat like a forest (exemplified by bark and soil insects).

The substratum: its physical diversity—clay, sand, rock, shore, etc.

The chemical environment: remarkably uniform composition of air; highly diverse aquatic and terrestrial environments; fresh and salt water contrasted; chemical differences between soils; interaction of physical and biotic environments in soil.

Biotic environment: as all living things affecting an organism; inter- and intraspecific environments.

Cycles of materials:

The carbon cycle: the central roles of photosynthesis and respiration; role of decay organisms; temporary withdrawal of carbon from cycle—incorporation into coal, natural gas, petroleum and limestone; its ultimate return to cycle from these sources.

The nitrogen cycle: the relative unimportance of atmospheric nitrogen; nitrogen-fixing bacteria; the importance of nitrates as mode of incorporation into life from physical environment; the passage of nitrogen from plants to animals; return to soil by excretion and death; role of bacteria in the soil.

Mineral cycles: organic and rock cycles.

Transfers of energy: potential and kinetic energy; First Law of Thermodynamics: conservation of total energy during energy transfers; Second Law of Thermodynamics: dissipation of useful energy during energy transfers; absence of a cycle of energy comparable to materials cycle.

Food chains and community pyramids:

Food chains and webs: transfers of energy and materials as *the* basic feature of a community; food chains, beginning with photosynthesizers; subsequent links of the chain as "other-feeders"—fungi, bacteria, animals; interactions of food chains producing food webs.

Pyramid of energy and mass: greatest mass and energy in primary (photosynthetic) link of food chain; progressively less in successive links (a consequence of the Second Law of Thermodynamics).

Pyramid of numbers: smaller animals more numerous than larger ones.

Community budgets: the limitation of life; photosynthesis the bottleneck to whole community's energy input; limitations on solar energy; limitations on nitrates and phosphates in soil and aquatic environments. and of diatoms in ocean.

CHAPTER 25

Population and Community Interactions

The hermit crab makes use of an old snail shell as a house; the sea anemone feeds on leftovers from the hermit crab's meal. Such interactions between species are the subject of this chapter. (Photo © Douglas P. Wilson)

Living things and their environments influence each other. No organism is ever for even an instant of its life independent of the requirements and the advantages of the conditions in which it lives. None lives without constantly influencing its surroundings. You cannot possibly think of an organism to which both these generalizations do not apply, and you need not go outside your own daily life to find examples of them. The influence on you of your physical environment is evident enough, for instance, every time you breathe. Wherever you live, it must also be clear to you that you and your fellow men have influenced your physical environment. The mere fact that you live in a house is an example, and it is equally true although perhaps less obvious that the simple act of breathing influences the environment in your immediate vicinity, modifying its chemical composition, humidity, and temperature.

No less universal are mutual and reciprocal influences between organisms and their biotic environments. That is the same as saying, from a different point of view, that these influences occur among the members of a community. When you ate a hamburger, you completed a food chain, and food chains are among the most widespread interactions in communities. A farmer and his field of corn may, to be sure, be viewed as links in a food chain, but their direct interaction is not that of food and its consumer. The farmer further interacts with insects that attack his crop and with people who buy it. Farmers and corn live together and benefit reciprocally, for the farmers perpetuate the corn and provide the best conditions for its life, while the corn (indirectly, as a rule) supports the farmers. Farmers and insects are competitors. Farmers and corn merchants co-operate in a social organization. The fact that these examples involve humans does not put them in a class by themselves. On the contrary, it demonstrates that biological interactions involving man are of the same sorts and subject to the same principles as those in nonhuman communities. Reciprocal benefit, competition, co-operation, and other relationships take innumerable forms, but all are widespread in nature. What sorts of interactions are exemplified in the maintenance of the glory of England by spinsters (p. 607)?

Here it is useful to bring up again and to

stress a distinction already briefly made (p. 614) between inter- and intraspecific biotic environments. Some interactions in communities take place between different species, and others occur among the members of a single species. All are interrelated and are parts of a single whole, the life of the community, but interspecific and intraspecific interactions do have importantly different aspects and principles. Both will be considered in this chapter: first some of the interspecific reactions, especially competition, symbiosis, and parasitism, and then some of the intraspecific reactions, especially aggregation in its many forms, including the fascinating and important subject of societies.

Niches and Competition

RELATIONSHIPS AMONG NICHES

In some of the driest deserts of Arizona grows the gigantic cactus *Cereus giganteus*, commonly called "saguaro" (or "sahuaro," in either case pronounced sah-*wah*-roh). Although it is not a widespread plant and is absent from most American deserts, it is so striking and picturesque that paintings, decorations, and cartoons have made it the recognized symbol of the Southwest. There are two birds, a flicker (*Colaptes chrysoides*) and a woodpecker (*Centurus uropygialis*) that cut round openings in the spiny, ridged stems of saguaros and excavate recesses for nests in the softer internal tissues. They make more holes than they keep in use, and often an unused flicker or woodpecker hole is occupied by elf owls (*Micropallas whitneyi*), dainty little creatures no larger than sparrows. An elf owl rarely nests anywhere else.

The saguaros, living only in deserts and only in particular parts of those, have their special niche (p. 612) among plants. They provide, in turn, one aspect of the niches of desert flickers and woodpeckers. These birds, in their turn, excavate the homes of elf owls, and these homes are one of the defining characteristics of the elf-owl niche. The interdependence of all these organisms is evident, and so is the fact that their roles in the community are quite different; they have, in fact, different niches.

Another owl, slightly larger than an elf owl but still small as owls go, also nests in woodpecker holes in saguaros: the saguaro screech owl (*Otus asio gilmani*). A saguaro screech owl and an elf owl may be found in adjacent holes on the same cactus plant. Here, you would be inclined to say, are two species occupying the same niche, but it is not so. The elf owl feeds mainly on small insects, such as beetles, ants, or crickets. The screech owl likewise eats some insects, especially the larger grasshoppers and locusts, as well as scorpions, but also includes in its food mice and other rodents that are seldom attacked by elf owls. There are other differences in their activities, such as the fact that the screech owls raise their young earlier in the year than do elf owls. In short, despite the identity of their homes and the similarity of their habits, these two species of owls do have distinctly different total relationships to their environment or different roles in their community, which is a way of saying that they occupy different niches.

The desert scene illustrates a principle that operates equally in any community: each species in an established community has a distinctly different niche. Known exceptions occur when one species invades the territory of another, but the duplication is then temporary. There may be other exceptions, and some naturalists think there are, but none has been definitely proved and in any case they would be exceptions to what is plainly the general rule. The reason for the rule is *competition*. Equal sharing between different species is unknown in nature. If two species really have the same niche and hence the same requirements for their continued existence, they always compete for those requirements and sooner or later one of them wins out. Hence the principle involved can be stated in another way: two species do not long live together if one of them can fully utilize an aspect of the environment necessary to both of them.[1]

Competition need not extend to all environmental necessities, and it seldom does. Elf owls and screech owls do not seriously compete for woodpecker holes. Different species

[1] In this form the principle is technically designated as the principle of ecological incompatibility.

of fishes in the sea do not compete for water. There is plenty to go around, and there are plenty of woodpecker holes in the desert.[2] Species may compete for only one crucial thing and share everything else quite amicably. Still they cannot long exist together if they continue to compete for *anything* that is vitally essential to them.

Environmental requirements of two species in the same community may be so different that there is no real overlap. Then there is no question of competition. Saguaros and woodpeckers affect each other in many ways. Aside from the fact that woodpeckers live in saguaros, both are parts of some of the same food chains: saguaros → insects → woodpeckers. (Woodpeckers may also obtain water from saguaros, but this is uncertain.) Yet the niches are so different that the idea of competition as a relationshp between them simply does not arise. There is, on the other hand, close similarity or wide overlap in the niches of screech owls and elf owls. A factor becomes crucial when the competition for the same thing would eliminate one or the other. It must be this factor that limits the population of each, and thus keeps them down to the point where they do not compete for those things that they do, in fact, share.

This crucial factor is to be sought among the things that are different in the overlapping niches of two species. With the two desert owls, the crucial factor is evidently food. Even in food, there is some overlap because some kinds of insects are eaten by both. In times of abundance, this does not matter. In times of scarcity, when competition is fiercest and one or the other would eventually go to the wall, they can eat different things: especially small insects for the elf owls and larger rodents for the screech owls. So the competition is relieved and does not become lethal. Among the most closely similar and most frequently competing species of a community there is always (as it seems) some such safety valve. Birds may merrily share the abundant foods of late summer, and then, when the supply dwindles and competition really begins to tell,

they will take to different foods or will migrate to different regions. There are many such escapes from lethal competition. What others can you think of?

THE NATURE OF COMPETITION

Almost anything needed from the environment may be the object of competition. Plants compete for water or sunshine, sometimes for mineral salts—whatever is in shortest supply at a given time and place. In the desert each mesquite bush is surrounded by a zone of completely bare soil from which it has ousted competitors for water. In the forest a dense growth of seedlings thins out progressively as a few more vigorous trees pre-empt the sunshine and others die in their shade. In the sea one species of photosynthetic organisms may locally drive out another as it wins in competition for nutrient nitrates or phosphates.

Among animals food is the usual object of competition. That lies back of the fact that the food habits of animals are so extremely diverse and frequently so specific, characteristics that reduce competition for food between different species. Animals may, however, compete for things other than food. They may also compete for water in a dry environment, or for desirable nesting places or shelters.

We are inclined to think of competition in terms of athletic events or of struggles in which one side goes after the other and tries to beat it. Such events do occur in nature. When a coyote chases a rabbit there is a race, with food as a prize if the coyote wins and life if the rabbit does. Ants stage epic struggles, real pitched battles between large opposing forces. Jays drive other birds away from food. But such face-to-face combat is decidedly *not* characteristic of competition in nature. The usual competition is not a matter of one species trying to take something away from another, but a passive process in which each seeks to utilize what the other needs. A plant in getting its water supply does not attack other plants, and a deer eating foliage may not have any contact with the other herbivores with which it is in fact competing. In this, the usual biological sense of the word, are coyote and rabbit really competing?

[2] There are, in fact, enough holes so that they are regularly occupied by still another species of bird, a flycatcher (**Myiarchus tyrannulus**), and casually by many other desert animals, including lizards and snakes.

Competition frequently occurs among organisms similar to each other, with overlapping niches, and often phylogenetically related. It may, however, occur just as frequently between species that have some one requirement in common but that otherwise lead completely different lives. Man's most severe competitors for food are the insects. Competition between rabbits and sheep caused a crisis in wool growing in Australia.

COMPETITION AND EVOLUTION

If two species compete strongly, the frequent but not inevitable outcome is that one of them becomes extinct. This is not the only cause of extinction, but it has been a widespread cause during the long history of life. A large-scale example occurred when North and South America became reunited from one to several million years ago (see p. 726). Each of the previously separated continents had its own distinctive species of mammals, including rodents, carnivores, and herbivorous ungulates (hoofed mammals). North American species invaded South America, and in the ensuing competition all the ungulates, all the carnivores, and a great many of the rodents native to South America became extinct.

Competition has also played a less macabre part in evolution. As it occurs within species, that is, among the individual members of a single species, it is one of the forces inducing change through natural selection (p. 412). That may be the major evolutionary role of competition, but it is not our main concern just here, where we are primarily discussing interspecific relationships. Both within species and between species, in a continuous process in which the distinction is not perfectly sharp, competition has been a force tending to develop and maintain differences among populations. It has been instrumental in the occupation of particular niches and in the multiplication of the number of niches in communities. Once a niche has been occupied, it becomes a conservative force tending to keep the population there, impeding its change or its spread into other niches.

It is easy to see how competition works as an evolutionary force both to change species and to prevent their changing (Fig. 25-1). If two similar species compete strongly, the tendency of natural selection will be to increase the differences between them. Variants in each species least like the other species will have least competition and hence are

25-1 **Evolutionary effects of interspecific competition.** The adaptive radiation of the tree finches (*Camarhynchus* spp.) and ground finches (*Geospiza* spp.) of the Galápagos Islands has been discussed in Chapter 18. The finches also provide excellent examples of the evolutionary effects of competition between ecologically similar forms. *C. parvulus, C. pauper,* and *C. psittacula* are closely related insect-eating tree finches. Their beak size reflects the size of insects they eat. *C. parvulus* has the smallest beak. Variations in its size are plotted here as frequency distributions. (Cf. Figs. 17-1 and 17-2.) The *parvulus* graph on all three islands is stippled; the graph for a competing species is given in white (unstippled); in the figures for the islands of Charles and Albemarle the graph given in broken line is a representation of the *parvulus* graph for Chatham, given for comparison. On Chatham *C. parvulus* is the only species of the three that is present. On Charles it is in competition with *C. pauper,* which feeds on slightly larger insects than *parvulus* does. The competition from *pauper* on this island has caused a local evolutionary decrease in the size of the *parvulus* beak. The effect of competition has been to cause a specialization on still smaller insects by *parvulus,* thus minimizing the competition. On Albemarle island competition is from *C. psittacula.* The evolutionary effects of interspecific competition between *G. fuliginosa* and *G. fortis* on Charles and Chatham are clear.

likely to be more successful in rearing offspring. Over the generations, the species will come to occupy more distinctly separate niches. On the other hand, in a well-integrated community with numerous occupied niches, variants of any species farthest from the usual (or modal, pp. 417 and 419) adaptation to its niche are most likely to encounter competition from the occupants of other niches. The trend of selection will be adverse to these variants and will favor maintenance of the status quo.

Interspecific Interactions: Symbiosis

All the members of a community live together—that is part of the definition of a community. Indeed, so widely ramifying are the interactions of organisms that it can well be maintained that all living things on earth are living together, members of the grand total community of life which is subdivided into innumerable, intergrading local communities. A barnacle on a whale, a hermit crab in and a sea anemone on a snail shell, or a dog and its fleas exemplify particularly intimate ways of living together. Such special and closer associations of individuals of different species, within the looser association of the community as a whole, are given a special name: *symbiosis* (Fig. 25-2), which simply means "living together." [3]

The three examples given in the last paragraph embody different relationships between the symbiotic animals. Presumably a whale does not mind a few barnacles on its hide and is neither helped nor harmed by their presence. The barnacle, on its side, gets nothing out of the association except a free ride. Whale and barnacle are simply messmates who run around together, eat perhaps at the same table, but take nothing from and give nothing to each other. That is *commensalism* ("being at table together"). Hermit crab and sea anemone, without taking thought or having altruistic motives, are nevertheless helpful to each other. The sea anemone, with

[3] Many biologists apply the term "symbiosis" only to associations that are beneficial to both parties—to what we call "mutualism." The usages adopted in this book seem more convenient, accord better with the meanings of the words, and are also backed by authority.

its many stinging cells, protects the crab. Sometimes it also obviates the necessity for the growing crab to leave its protective shell and seek another to fit by actually remodeling the shell. The crab seeks out food and tears it to shreds, and the sea anemone lives on such bits as come its way. The relationship is mutually beneficial, and so it is called *mutualism* (illus., p. 626). The dog's fleas benefit; the pup is their food as well as their home. But their unwilling host receives only annoyance or disease in return. That sort of symbiosis is *parasitism* ["eating beside (at the expense of) another"].

COMMENSALISM

Distinctions between mere association in a community, commensalism, mutualism, and parasitism are not clear-cut. All sorts of intermediate relationships occur, and it is evident that one sort of relationship has often evolved into another. All the closer associations probably evolved from looser communal relationships. In commensalism one of the associates usually does derive some benefit. Whether the partnership is completely unimportant to the other (making it commensal), more or less helpful (therefore mutualistic), or harmful (parasitic) may be practically impossible to determine or may be a matter of definition or point of view.

Suppose we run briefly through a few more examples usually labeled "commensalism." You will note that one partner generally derives food, protection, transportation, or a combination of these from the other. You decide what the effect is on the other partner. Besides the barnacles that live on whales, there are barnacles that live only on those barnacles that live on whales. Some species of cockroaches habitually live in human habitations and eat overlooked bits of human food. They annoy good housekeepers, of course, but do they do any real harm? There are several small fishes that usually live among the tentacles of coelenterates (especially siphonophores, p. 528, and sea anemones), apparently immune to attack by the stinging cells, which are capable of killing other fishes and yet for these fishes provided protection and probably also some food. There are some little crustaceans (a species of isopods, p. 571) that live

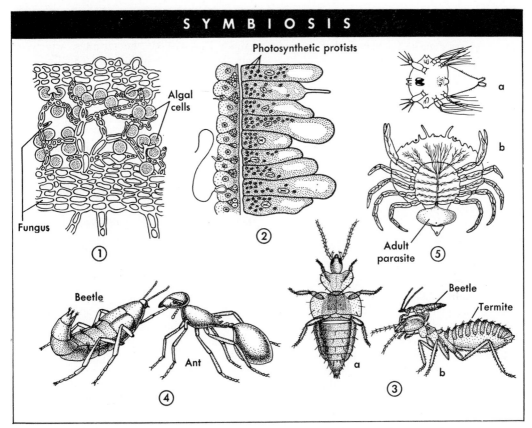

SYMBIOSIS

Photosynthetic protists

Algal cells

Fungus

① ② ③

Adult parasite ⑤

Beetle

Ant

④

Beetle

Termite

a

b

25-2 A variety of symbiotic relationships. *1. True mutualism:* a lichen (p. 632) consisting of fungal hyphae (nonphotosynthetic) and photosynthetic algal cells. Neither member of the mutualistic union ever grows separately in nature. *2. Mutualism:* photosynthetic protists in cells of *Hydra:* the *Hydra* gains carbohydrates, and the protist gains water, nutrients, and "shelter." *3. Commensalism:* a staphylinid beetle (*a*), which lives in the colony of a termite as a tolerated scavenger; (*b*) the beetle riding on the head of a termite; it scavenges food fragments as they are passed from one worker to another. *4. Social mutualism:* a beetle that is not only tolerated but actually reared and protected by ants for the sake of its secretions. *5. Parasitism:* (*a*) the larva of a crustacean, *Sacculina*, a relative of the barnacles; (*b*) the adult *Sacculina*, a parasite of crabs, is reduced to a mere pouch of (reproductive) tissue that bulges out between the abdominal segments of its host.

in the mouths of fishes (menhaden), where they pick up bits of the fishes' food as it goes by. Sessile algae may grow on almost any support in the water, but at least one species grows only on the shells of certain living turtles. Would you say that the growth of Spanish moss or of orchids on a tree is commensalism? (Spanish moss, orchids, and many other plants that grow attached to a plant of different species are not parasites; they derive only support, not food, from the attachment.) [4]

4 Such plants are called epiphytes—plants that are "upon (other plants)." Although usu-

MUTUALISM

Few, indeed, are the plants or animals that are not inhabited by other plants or animals or by protists. You yourself, clean and healthy as you doubtless are, are certainly a host to many bacteria and other protists on your skin and throughout your alimentary canal. Such relationships run the whole gamut, or indeed two gamuts, from being completely unimportant to the host to being quickly deadly, on one hand, or being essential to the host's

ally confused with parasitism by nonbotanists, the relationship is basically different from true parasitism.

life, on the other. The association is frequently beneficial to both, and often this mutualism has gone so far that neither species can survive without the other.

Many photosynthetic protists (mostly flagellates, p. 492) live in the tissues of animals. The chemical exchange involved must be elaborate and is not well understood, but it is known that in many such instances the host benefits from oxygen released by photosynthesis in the guest, and the guest derives CO_2 produced by respiration in the host. In Chapter 1 (p. 10) you encountered an example in the protists that live in reef corals and give them their color. On the same reefs photosynthetic protists also live in and brilliantly color the mantle edges of various mollusks, notably of the giant clam *Tridacna*. This relationship is widespread. The hosts may be animal-like protists (protozoans), sponges, coelenterates (not only corals; green hydras are colored by algae in their tissues), flatworms, or mollusks.

Mutualism is common among plants. Lichens (Fig. 25-2), which seem to be single plants and are even classified as if they were, are actually intimate, mutualistic associations of, in each case, an alga and a fungus. The fungus, nonphotosynthetic, derives food from the alga. The fungus helps to maintain the water supply necessary for growth of the alga. Most of the higher green plants have fungi that grow around or actually within their roots. Some of these fungi may be harmful to the host, but many are beneficial. It has been shown that pines and some other plants die if deprived of their root fungi, even though the exact nature of the benefit to the host is seldom clear. The benefit is obvious from nitrogen-fixing bacteria in root nodules of peas and their allies (p. 487).

The wood-eating termites [5] live on cellulose, a food that they cannot digest. It is digested by protists (species of flagellates, again) that swarm in the digestive tracts of the termites, and the termites obtain their food from the protists. These termites cannot live without their internal protists, and the protists (a distinctive species in each species of termites) cannot live without the termites, which obtain the wood on which they feed.[6] Cows and some other herbivorous mammals also acquire some food indirectly from cellulose, which they cannot themselves digest, but they are not wholly dependent on this process, as are wood-eating termites. Bacteria in the cows' alimentary canals digest some of the cellulose in grass or other forage, and the cows, in turn, later digest some of the bacteria. Most or all mammals, including man, normally have large numbers of bacteria in their intestines. Some of the bacteria seem to be helpful in synthesizing vitamins that are then absorbed by the mammalian host.

There are also many mutually beneficial associations in communities that involve no such prolonged intimacy as the examples already given. The widespread dependence between flowering plants and insects that feed on them and also pollinate them (see Chapter 15) is one of the most important communal relationships in nature and is plainly mutualistic. Still more peculiar and less widely important examples include the birds that feed on ticks on mammals, and the ants that care for aphids (a group of insects) and receive a sweet secretion in return. The latter relationship suggests that of man and milk cows, and indeed the association of man with all his domestic animals and cultivated plants can be described as at least loosely mutualistic. What are the benefits given and received by man and pigs? Horses? Dogs? Wheat? Seedless oranges? Roses?

PARASITISM

The nature and extent of parasitism. Almost everyone, including many a biologist, feels a certain repugnance for a tapeworm or a louse. Parasites are disgusting, and the fact that some of them attack us makes them all the more so. But the scientific approach does not assign praise or blame to actions that are neither good nor bad but merely natural. Nor, in fact, is it logical and sensible to do so. Why should our killing a cow for

5 Man is most concerned with termites that have the destructive habit of eating what was, before their attacks, sound wood, but the fact is that most species of termites do not have this diet. Some cockroaches, relatives of termites, eat wood that is digested by internal protists as in termites.

6 See p. 435 for adaptive behavior of termites related to their dependence on mutualistic flagellates.

food be proper or praiseworthy, while a tapeworm that derives food from the same cow without killing it or harming it seriously is contemptible? From the point of view of food chains and the general flow of materials and energy in a community, there is no essential difference between the herbivores and carnivores that devour plants and animals and the parasites that also derive their food from those same plants and animals. If parasitism were defined solely as living at the expense of other organisms, then the whole animal kingdom, including man, would have to be called parasitic. Even if "parasitism" is more precisely confined to particular ways in which species interact, the term is not always clearly distinguishable from other relationships. A weasel kills a rabbit and sucks its blood. A fly alights and sucks blood from a rabbit without killing it, and then the fly goes on its way. A louse spends much of its life on a rabbit, taking blood when so inclined. A protist lives in the blood stream of a rabbit, within the fluid that feeds it. Which of these are parasites?

It is worth while to distinguish parasitism from other relationships of foods and their consumers because it is a special case, or rather a large number of special cases with something in common. The distinguishing features are that a parasite is an organism that lives on or in another living organism for a considerable part of its life cycle, that derives its food from its host, and that is more or less harmful or, at best, not beneficial to the host.

The extent of parasitism and the diversity of parasites are astonishing. Very few living things are free of parasites. Perhaps the only organisms not subject to parasitism are a few that are, you might say, the last word in parasites themselves. Many parasites do have parasites of their own. As Swift put it, "A flea hath smaller fleas that on him prey, and these have smaller still to bite 'em, and so proceed *ad infinitum.*"

From a parasite's point of view you are a habitat providing a large number of niches. The whole outside of your body is a parasite's paradise, and there are species specialized for particular niches there. Some lice, for instance, live in the head hair, and quite different lice live in pubic hair. The niches inside are more numerous. Almost every part and tissue is a potential habitat for one parasite or another. There are innumerable parasites of the alimentary canal. Others live in the lungs, blood, nerves, muscles, glands, or elsewhere.

There are insects that begin life as parasites inside the eggs of other insects. There is a species of insects [7] in which the larval females are parasites in other insects, and the larval males are parasites in the parasitic female larvae of their own species. In several species of animals, including some annelids, crustaceans, and fishes, the adult males are parasites on the adult females.

Parasites are very numerous among protists. Among plants, most of the major groups —including even the highest, that of the flowering plants—have some parasites, but parasitism is particularly common among fungi. Several comparatively small phyla of animals are wholly parasitic (p. 543). The most noteworthy animal parasites are many species of flatworms, nematodes, and arthropods, including some crustaceans, innumerable insects, and many arachnoids (especially ticks and mites, p. 573). Almost all other phyla have at least a few partly parasitic species. True parasitism is, however, extremely rare among vertebrates; indeed, it is practically nonexistent aside from a few partially or doubtfully parasitic fishes.[8]

Besides being of so many kinds, parasites are extremely numerous in individuals. A census is impossible, but some biologists believe that *most* of the organisms now living are parasites. Whether we like it or not, parasitism includes many of the most successful ways of life and is one of the most important and widespread characteristics of all communities.

[7] **Coccophagus scutellaris,** a small wasplike insect.

[8] Lampreys and hagfishes (see p. 584) are often called parasitic, but this is a marginal case hardly distinguishable from ordinary predation. As already mentioned, a few fishes, such as the deep-sea angler **Photocorynus,** have truly parasitic males, but the females are not parasitic. Cuckoos that impose the care of their young on other birds are "parasites" of a sort. Can you think of possible relationships between humans that might be classed as (social) parasitism?

Conditions and adaptations of parasitism. External parasites, living on but outside organisms, exist under the peculiar condition that their substratum is alive. Yet they are in the outside world and subject to many of the same influences of the physical environment as their nonparasitic associates. Most external parasites, such as fleas, lice, or ticks, are relatively little modified structurally in adaptation for parasitism; they are usually semi-independent animals that can live on their own for short periods, at least, or can freely move from one host to another.

Internal parasitism, on the other hand, involves life in environments that are totally different from those of free and independent organisms. The peculiar conditions of life within other organisms pose problems that are met by many special and, to our eyes, strange adaptations. For one thing, the mere fact that they do live within other organisms —and must leave room for their hosts' vital activities, too—means that they must be comparatively small. Some tapeworms may be as much as sixty feet long, which is not exactly tiny, but still their bulk is far less

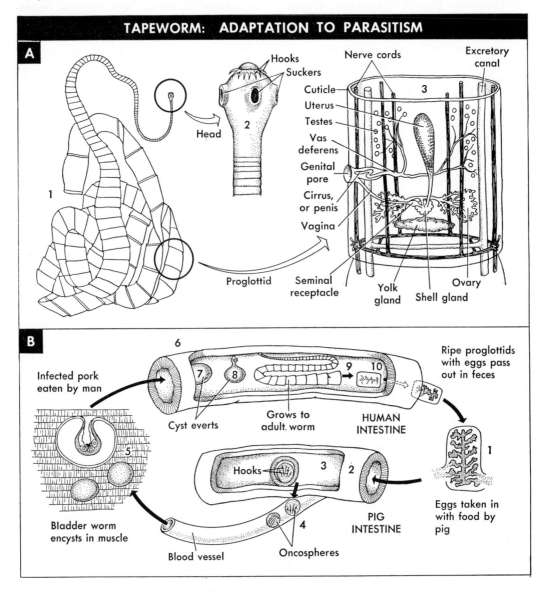

TAPEWORM: ADAPTATION TO PARASITISM

A

Hooks
Suckers
Head
Nerve cords
Excretory canal
Cuticle
Uterus
Testes
Vas deferens
Genital pore
Cirrus, or penis
Vagina
3
Proglottid
Seminal receptacle
Yolk gland
Shell gland
Ovary

B

Infected pork eaten by man
6
7 8
9 10
Ripe proglottids with eggs pass out in feces
Cyst everts
Grows to adult worm
HUMAN INTESTINE
5
Hooks
3 2
1
Eggs taken in with food by pig
Bladder worm encysts in muscle
Blood vessel
Oncospheres
4
PIG INTESTINE

than that of their hosts. Most parasites really are tiny, and a great many are barely visible with a microscope.

The host unwittingly provides an internal parasite with food, shelter, and a more or less stabilized environment. A tapeworm in a mammal, for instance, is bathed in predigested food that need only be absorbed through the tapeworm's body wall. The parasite is also sheltered from all rigors of the outer world. Some structures and processes useful in free life are of no use to such an internal parasite. It is a tendency in evolution that what is not useful is likely to disappear. Disappearance is not invariable or always prompt, and its causes are disputable, but the reality of the tendency is well established. Tapeworms do not need and do not have special sensory organs, a clearly developed brain, or a digestive system, although all these occur in their free-living relatives, and all must have occurred in ancestors of the tapeworms. Simplification and loss of some organs is almost universal in thoroughgoing internal parasites. This tendency is usually labeled "degeneration." On the other hand, it might be considered a positive adaptation to a way of life in which the lost characteristics are of no use and might be disadvantageous. Which point of view do you find more explanatory?

Parasites live under conditions that also require adaptations clearly positive and not degenerative in nature. The tapeworm in a mammal's gut lives in a medium of readily available food, but one also rich in digestive enzymes which pose a serious threat to its existence. The tapeworm has evolved a thick cuticle (absent in free-living relatives) resistant to digestive enzymes. The constant danger of being totally evacuated from its host's gut when it defecates is overcome by the hooked head (Fig. 25-3) that anchors the parasite to the gut wall. But the principal condition of internal parasites that demands special and positive adaptation is the fact that they must be able to move from one host to another. An adult individual need not do so, but sometime in the life cycle a change of hosts must occur. In the course of the cycle the organisms must be adapted not only to the environment of the adult parasite but also to quite different environments. Tapeworms and other internal parasites have evolved complex life cycles. Commonly the stages are a free-living, aquatic embryonic or larval stage, one or more larval stages parasitic in intermediate hosts, and a final adult stage in a host of a different species. The final host usually acquires the parasite by eating the intermediate host. The commonest tapeworms

---

25-3 The tapeworm: adaptation to parasitism. *A.* The structure of *Taenia solium*, the pork tapeworm of man. *1.* The adult worm found in human intestines; with head (or scolex) and hundreds of individual body segments, or proglottids. *2.* Detail of head, showing a ring of hooks and three of the four suckers, all of which are used to maintain the worm within the host's intestine. *3.* An individual proglottid. Proglottids are continuously being budded off from the unsegmented region immediately behind the scolex. Each proglottid matures a complete set of reproductive organs essentially the same as those of a trematode (cf. Fig. 22-7); both male and female organs are present in each proglottid. Copulation may occur between proglottids within an individual worm (resulting in self-fertilization) or between different worms. The uterus, in which fertilized eggs are stored, has no pore to the outside; as the proglottid matures, it becomes almost entirely filled with an ever-expanding uterus full of eggs. Such a mature proglottid is eventually budded off the worm and shed to the outside in the host's feces. There the proglottid bursts, liberating eggs. The adult tapeworm shows several special adaptations to parasitism:

(a) a heavy, enzyme-resistant cuticle; (b) absolutely no alimentary system—food is absorbed directly from the nutrient-rich environment of the host's gut. *B.* The life cycle of *Taenia* also has several features adaptive to its parasitic habit. In general all these relate to increasing its reproductive potential. First there is the previously mentioned habit of continual asexual reproduction—the production of new young proglottids. *1.* The eggs liberated to the ground from the burst proglottid enter the hog's intestine (*2*) with its food. By the time the eggs are eaten, they have developed into an embryo (onchosphere) armed with six hooks. *3.* Once inside the hog's intestine, the armored larvae burrow (*4*) into blood and lymph vessels, ultimately reaching voluntary muscles, where they encyst (*5*) and undergo further development into a second larval stage. This stage has a young scolex inverted within its bladderlike body; it is commonly called a "bladder worm." When infected pork is eaten by man, the cysts (*7*) germinate in the human intestine (*6*); the young scolex is everted (*8*) and develops further into an adult worm (*9*) that reinitiates the cycle by liberating proglottids (*10*).

in humans are two species that have domestic livestock as intermediate hosts; one occurs in cattle, the other in hogs. They may be acquired by eating rare beef or pork. Another human tapeworm, a monster that may grow to lengths of over sixty feet, has two intermediate hosts and is acquired by man from raw or underdone fish, especially pike and pickerel but also trout and others. We think

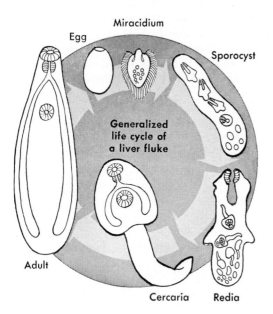

Generalized life cycle of a liver fluke

Egg
Miracidium
Sporocyst
Adult
Cercaria
Redia

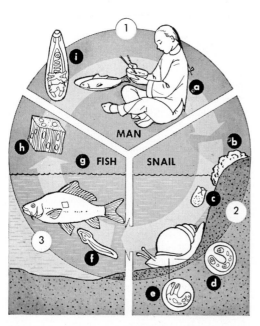

1
MAN
FISH   SNAIL
2
3

a b c d e f g h i

of such parasites as characteristic of oriental countries, where sanitation is poor and raw fish and other poorly prepared foods are eaten. As a matter of fact, this worst of all human tapeworms is especially common in parts of Europe and has been spreading in the United States.

Flukes (Fig. 25-4) and the protists that cause malaria (Fig. 25-5) further exemplify complex life cycles in internal parasites. The life cycle of such parasites involves very specific co-ordination with the habits and biochemistry of particular hosts, and often of two or more hosts in succession. One consequence is that any one egg or larva has an exceedingly small chance of encountering the right hosts at the needed times and of living to become an adult. This hazard is countered by the fact that adult animal parasites usually have extensive reproductive systems (sometimes they seem to consist of little else) and produce countless millions of eggs. Successful completion of a parasite's life cycle is usually so improbable that only one in millions makes it.

Indeed, in reviewing positive (rather than degenerative) adaptations to parasitic way of life, we become impressed with the fact

25-4 **The life cycle of the Chinese liver fluke** (*Clonorchis sinensis*). The trematode (Fig. 22-7) liver flukes show some adaptations to parasitism basically similar to those of the tapeworm: the life cycle involves more than one host (man, snail, and fish), and there is much asexual budding, which bolsters the total reproductive potential. *Top figure*, the succession of developmental stages in the life cycle. The adult liberates eggs that hatch as miracidium larvae. The miracidium becomes a sporocyst that buds, internally, a large number of redia larvae. The rediae in turn bud, internally, a large number of cercariae. The cercaria larvae develop into adult liver flukes. *Lower figure*, the succession of hosts. *1*. Man: (*a*) Eggs are liberated in human feces (*b*), reaching fresh-water ponds, where the miracidium larvae (*c*) swim about and, on contacting a snail, enter it. *2*. Snail: Within the snail the miracidium develops into a sporocyst (*d*) that, in turn, liberates rediae (*e*). The rediae enter the snail's liver; here they themselves produce more rediae, some of which eventually produce cercariae (*f*). *3*. Fish: The cercariae leave the snail and swim free in the pond, eventually entering a fish in whose muscles they encyst. The infective cycle is completed when the fish is eaten by man; the cysts germinate and the adult fluke parasitizes man.

that the most universal adaptations relate to problems of successful reproduction. Asexual reproduction—either as simple cell fission in protists, or as budding in more complex parasites like tapeworms and flukes (Fig. 25-4) —is more prevalent in parasites than in any other animal group. Real dangers arise if the parasite is committed to sexual reproduction while in the host. If chances are often poor that a larval parasite will encounter any suitable host, they are even poorer that it will encounter one harboring a potential mate for the parasite. It is a striking fact that the only animal phylum regularly hermaphroditic —the Platyhelminthes—has been more successful than any other in the parasitic way of life. Many Crustacea are parasites, and of these the most successful are relatives of the common barnacles (p. 572). They belong to a group (the Cirripedia) that is primitively sedentary and hermaphroditic.[9] In parasitic Crustacea in which the sexes are separate it is common for individuals of opposite sex to join together permanently in their free-swimming larval stage. The female then becomes attached to a host, and the male—a midget—remains attached to the female near her genital opening.

Is parasitism an easy way of life? Parasitism seems to involve "problems" that are "solved" by such adaptations as alternation of hosts and extreme fecundity. Is that a clear, scientific way of putting the matter? Who or what posed the problems, and who or what solved them?

Parasitism is a highly successful way of life in itself, but it is a blind alley as far as any further evolutionary change is concerned. The specializations and the degenerations (if you wish to call them that) fitting a parasite for life in its peculiar environment make it completely unfit for life in any other environment. They also tend to make further adaptation to anything but a still narrower parasitic niche highly improbable if not downright impossible. It is unlikely that any free-living organisms have evolved from parasitic ancestors.

9 Cf. p. 372 and the fact that the majority of plants are hermaphrodites, and sedentary. Do you think the early evolution of barnacles as sedentary animals may have had any bearing on their later evolution as parasites?

Parasitism and disease. An organism living inside another is an alien in the body. Such aliens may be helpful collaborators (mutualism, p. 631), but they are likely to cause trouble. They absorb foods and other substances needed by the body of the host. Their movements or even their passive presence is likely to upset the operation of nerves, muscles, and other organs of the host. Moreover, and most important of all, they are distinct biochemical systems with proteins and other substances that are foreign to the specific chemical and regulatory system of the host and that may act as poisons for the host. It is small wonder, then, that parasites are the causes of a great many diseases, and especially of the *infectious diseases*. These are the diseases caused by "germs" or "microbes," names applied to all disease-producing (*pathogenic*) parasites of microscopic size. Of course larger parasites may also cause diseases, and many diseases are not caused by parasites at all. Can you name some?

Most germs are viruses and parasitic protists, especially bacteria, but also many of the other protists. We have noted several times earlier (pp. 43 and 316) the problem of deciding whether viruses are organisms— whether they are alive. This is in the last analysis merely a matter of definition. They are at least objects that interest the biologist! They undergo reproduction and they mutate. They consist of protein and nucleic acids (p. 316). These—their only known properties—suggest they are closely akin to the genetical material of higher, certain organisms. It has often been suggested that viruses are the most primitive of living organisms, but nowadays most biologists lean toward a different view. It seems more likely that their extreme simplicity of viruses is an end point of parasitic evolution, that they represent the "bare bones" of the reproductive mechanism of parasitic organisms. We noted in Chapter 15 that evidence now indicates genetic material may migrate from one bacterial cell to another. What would happen if genetic material (protein or nucleic acid, or both) migrated from the cell of one kind of bacterium into another kind and there parasitized the reproductive mechanisms of the host bacterium? The migrant material might then be indistinguishable from a virus! Research in this field is currently very active, and we can look forward to a surer knowledge of the evolutionary status of viruses in the near future. In the meantime the consensus associates the simplicity of viruses with their parasitism rather than with their supposed primitiveness.

Among the human diseases caused by viruses are smallpox, chicken pox, yellow fever, influenza, and infantile paralysis (poliomyelitis or "polio"). _Rickettsia,_ a group of parasitic organisms or pseudo-organisms

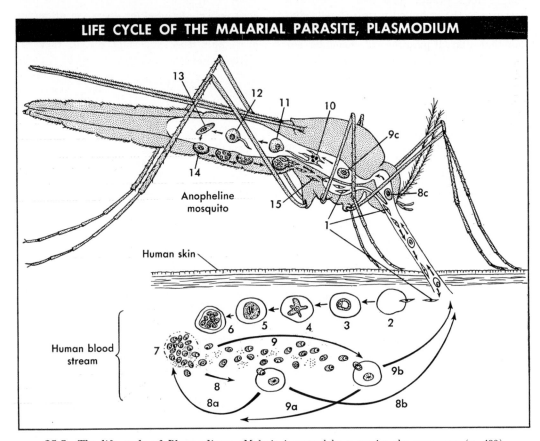

LIFE CYCLE OF THE MALARIAL PARASITE, PLASMODIUM

Anopheline mosquito

Human skin

Human blood stream

25-5   The life cycle of _Plasmodium._   Malaria is caused by a protist, the sporozoan (p. 490) parasite _Plasmodium._ Characteristically for a parasite, the life cycle involves more than one host and much asexual propagation. _1._ The _sporozoite_ stage is a convenient starting point. These elongate cells occur in the salivary glands of the mosquito. When the insect bites man, it salivates in order to lubricate the incision and introduce a chemical agent that prevents coagulation of the blood (Fig. 18-1). The sporozoites infect (_2_) the victim's red blood cells. In the blood cells the parasite undergoes a development (_3, 4, 5_) before asexual reproduction (_6_), which produces large numbers of _merozoites_ (_7_). These merozoites infect other red blood cells (_8, 9_). Their subsequent history may follow one of two courses: First, they may undergo (_8a, 9a_) another asexual reproduction, producing still more merozoites. This asexual cycle takes 48 hours; it is synchronized in the huge number of blood cells involved; at its completion the liberation of merozoites is accompanied by a liberation of toxins that cause the cyclic (every 48 hours) recurrence of fever in the host. Second, some merozoites, on infecting new blood cells, may develop (_8b_ and _9b_) into _macrogametocytes_ (_9b_) or _microgametocytes_ (_8b_). These cells, sucked up by a biting mosquito, enter its stomach (_8c_ and _9c_). The microgametocyte liberates four to eight microgametes (_10_), and the macrogametocyte becomes a _macrogamete_ (_11_). Fertilization (_12_) occurs in the stomach of the mosquito, and the motile zygote (_13_) enters the gut wall, where it becomes an _oöcyst_ (_14_). The oöcyst eventually ruptures, liberating large numbers of sporozoites that migrate (_15_) through the mosquito's body fluids and reach the salivary glands (_1_). The cycle is then complete.

larger than viruses and of disputed nature also, causes typhus, spotted fever, and several other diseases. Bacteria cause the great majority of infectious diseases, among them scarlet fever, pneumonia, tuberculosis, diphtheria, bubonic plague, cholera, gonorrhea, syphilis, whooping cough, and undulant fever (brucellosis). Animal-like protists cause, among other diseases, malaria, several forms of trypanosomiasis,[10] including African sleeping sickness, and amebic dysentery. Fungi cause athlete's foot, "ringworm" (which is not a worm), a serious lung infection with various names including San Joaquin fever, and other diseases. Among the larger animal parasites that commonly produce human diseases in the United States are tapeworms, hookworms (which are nematodes), and trichinas or beef and pork worms (also nematodes). All these groups also have species that cause diseases in other animals and in plants. Human diseases are mentioned because they strike close to home and provide comparatively familiar examples.

In the face of this long, gruesome list, which could be greatly extended, it may seem contradictory to say that really successful, well-established parasites rarely cause serious diseases. Such is the fact, and it illustrates one aspect of the dynamic balance of nature. If a host dies quickly after infection by a parasite, the parasite also dies. Species of parasites are usually highly specific, living only in one or a few species of hosts or, what is still more restrictive, in a definite sequence of host species in the round of the life cycle. If infection regularly causes early death of the host, the host species will almost certainly become extinct, and then so must the parasite species. Even widespread illness as a result of infection of a host species may cause extinction of both host and parasite, for the host species may be placed at a serious disadvantage in comparison with its competitors and predators. Therefore when a host-parasite relationship continues for any long period, a balance is necessarily reached. The host

species of a well-established parasite usually is not seriously damaged by the parasitism.

Balanced host-parasite species are in fact extremely common. Most organisms, including man, are hosts to innumerable parasites that do them no good but that also do them no great harm. There are two main factors in the development of this balance. A species of parasite becoming adapted to a host tends to evolve in such a way as to cause less serious disturbance; the parasite becomes *less virulent*. How would natural selection effect such a change? At the same time the host tends toward greater success in resisting disturbance; it develops *resistance* or *immunity*. Individual resistance to disease is one of the stabilizing mechanisms of the body. Immediate reaction to infection in man and many other animals is attack on the parasites by some of the white blood cells (p. 145). A reaction of longer range is the formation of *antibodies* (p. 319) (including *antitoxins*), chemical substances that disable invading parasites or that counteract the disease-producing poisons (*toxins*) released by the parasites. Antibodies may remain in the host's body for a long time, even a whole lifetime, and while they do, they confer some degree of immunity on the host against the particular sort of infection that originally produced the antibody. There is also good evidence (especially in plants but also in animals) that host organisms may have or can build up racial resistance or immunity to an infectious disease. Unlike immunity by means of antibodies, which depends on prior infection of each individual, such resistance is hereditary. Can it be explained by natural selection? [11]

If host-parasite interactions do tend to become balanced in time, why are there many serious diseases among humans and other organisms? There are several reasons. One is that all species could produce larger popula-

10 From **Trypanosoma,** the genus that includes these various pathogenic species. Trypanosomiasis is common in parts of tropical America, but the disease generally called "sleeping sickness" in the United States has nothing to do with African sleeping sickness and is a virus disease.

11 Discussion of the artificial control of human infections cannot be included in this work on general biology. Pertinent topics, on all of which you surely already have some information and can readily obtain more, would include: prevention of infection; injection of antibodies or their stimulation by injection of toxins and vaccines; specific drugs such as Salvarsan and quinine; antibiotics from **Penicillium** and other fungi (and their synthetic equivalents).

tions than their environments could support. Disease that weeds out individuals, especially among the very young and very old, without reducing the average numbers and vigor of the breeding adults does not necessarily endanger survival of the species as a whole and may even be beneficial to it. Nevertheless it is not beneficial to the parasites or the individual hosts killed, and in such a situation natural selection does often tend toward slow reduction in the severity of the disease.[12] Furthermore, parasites mutate, and mutation may produce newly virulent diseases that persist until the extinction of parasite, host, or both, or until establishment of a new balance. Parasites balanced with one host may spread to others with which they are not balanced and in which they cause severe disease. This condition may persist indefinitely if parasitism in a second kind of host is only occasional and is not essential in the parasites' life cycle. Can you find examples and think of other reasons for persistence of virulent disease?

Intraspecific Interactions

Members of the same species living together in a community necessarily affect each other. Relationships corresponding with food chains (for example, predator-prey) and with parasite-host interactions between species are slight or absent within species.[13] Competition, aggregation (more or less analogous with commensalism between species), and cooperation (analogous with mutualism) are at least as common within as between species, but they tend to take different forms and have different evolutionary results in the two cases.

[12] This is a distinction from the predator-prey relationship in which there is also a balance favorable to both species (p. 654). By definition a predator kills its prey, and selection does not tend to lessen severity of attack on the individuals affected.

[13] In fact, it is not altogether uncommon in nature for animals to eat others of their own species, and we have mentioned the rare occurrence of species in which males are parasitic on females. Nevertheless, it is impossible for either predation or parasitism on other members of the species to be the usual way of life of a species as a whole. Why is this impossible? Have you heard the story of the islanders all of whom made a living by doing each other's laundry?

Species in the same community compete if their niches overlap in some essential and exhaustible environmental requirement (p. 628). The result is that each species in a stable community has its own niche, and vital overlapping tends to be eliminated. All members of a single species live (approximately) within the same niche. Obviously, intraspecific competition may be particularly strong, but it is equally obvious that its effect is not to move each individual into a separate niche. Each niche has a number, usually large, of places that may be occupied by individuals without lethal interference among them. Competition is for these individual places in the specific niche. The winners are, as a rule, those individuals most precisely and efficiently adapted to the niche. This is one of the processes that leads to natural selection (p. 629). It is the one most stressed by Darwin, but in the modern concept it is only one of many selective forces. What are some of the others?

In its simplest form, the net effect of intraspecific competition in the community is merely to eliminate surplus population and to assign to each survivor its own place, or what the Germans call *Lebensraum* ("living space"). That minimal effect is universal. A gardener thins out seedlings as they grow. You have only to watch the annual growth of herbs in a field or the slower growth of trees in a forest to see the same process occurring in nature. The same sort of process occurs among all groups of animals. Even fully mobile species are thinned out to the numbers that can be supported by available materials and energy.

Among animals with more complex behavior, especially arthropods and vertebrates, *territoriality* is common. Each animal has a smaller or larger territory that is somehow "home" to it. It may spend all its time there, or, if it does stray far afield, it returns periodically to home territory. Often the territory centers around a literal home, such as a hive, nest, or burrow. The competitive background of such behavior is particularly evident in the many species in which the home territory is actively defended. You must have seen birds or chipmunks aggressively driving away trespassers on their preserves. Not only some birds and mammals but also some lizards, fishes, crabs, and others defend territory. This is one of the many deep-seated biological tendencies that are still present, even in their primitive forms, in man, although there integrated into a far more complex network of intraspecific interactions. "An Englishman's home is his castle"—it is defended territory.

Few animals exclude absolutely all other members of their species from their personal territories. They generally admit at least a mate and perhaps also their infants, and defend the territory from other groups. The many ants in a single anthill fiercely attack trespassing outsiders, whether of their own species or another. The howling monkeys of tropical America live in bands and defend their territory from neighboring bands, although the defense is more likely to be a howling contest than a physical encounter. Does this sort of phenomenon also occur among humans? How has *intra*specific competition been related to the evolution of territoriality? Can territoriality be regarded as an adaptation benefiting the individual family? The species?

AGGREGATION AND CO-OPERATION

Group defense of territory introduces, in relatively complicated form, other widespread kinds of relationships among members of a species. "Birds of a feather flock together." Members of a species usually tend to occur together, to be *aggregated*, and within such groups complex interactions in addition to competition may develop. In plants and in many animals, especially those with comparatively simple behavior, the aggregation is passive. Individuals do not seek out each other's company, and there is little or no differentiation of roles within the group. Even so, the aggregation as such has biological significance and survival value for the species. If nothing else, it facilitates interbreeding in biparental species.

Animals with more complex behavior are, to be sure, often solitary in habits. They live alone or briefly with a mate, and relationships within the species are dominantly competitive. What birds or mammals, for instance, do you know of which this is true? However,

an opposite tendency has appeared over and over again in the course of evolution. In many species, individuals live in groups. They may actively seek each other out, and in any case they do actively maintain their aggregation. Many species of fishes gather into large schools or shoals (Fig. 25-6), which move about in a body and may maintain their unity as a group over long periods of time. Some birds live in flocks all the time, and many others live in family groups on defended territories during nesting season and then gather into large flocks when the young take flight. "Prairie dogs" (really a genus of ground squirrels) live in "towns," which frequently have a population of hundreds and which may continue over many generations. Bison, cattle, sheep, horses, and other ungulates, both wild and domestic, gather into herds and flocks.

The size of such an aggregation is limited by the available food and, sometimes, space. Competition within the group is one of the factors preventing overpopulation and determining which individuals shall survive. But the relationships within the group as a whole are not predominantly competitive. They are at least tolerant, and they are usually co-operative to some degree. Membership in the group and tolerance of or co-operation with others is advantageous to each individual. Decrease of competition *within* the group is advantageous in *external* competition both with other groups of the same species and with other species. Shoaling is protective for small fishes, and it helps to promote breeding. (Herrings, for instance, shoal at mating time.) Sentinels in prairie-dog towns give warning cries at the approach of possible danger, and the signal is passed quickly to the whole population. Predators seldom successfully attacked the solid front of a bison herd.

The formation of mutually tolerant and co-operative groups has been not a universal, but nevertheless a frequent and a highly successful, trend in evolution. The widespread occurrence of that trend should be strongly emphasized. It flatly contradicts the idea that the process of evolution is one of unbounded individual competition in "nature red in tooth and claw." It is particularly important for a

Jim Jernigan from Gendreau

25-6 A school of fish (*Notemigonus crysoleucas*).

true understanding of the evolution of man, the biological basis of human society, and the possible future of our species.

DIVISION OF ROLES AND
THE RISE OF SOCIETIES

In most protists and plants and in a good many animals all individuals of a species are so nearly alike that differences hardly matter. They all play the same role among their *con-specific* ("belonging to the same species") as-sociates and in their community. In species with individually separate sexes (some plants and most animals), the sexes have different roles in reproduction, at least. That difference is often accompanied by marked differences in size, color, pattern, physiology, and behavior, especially in higher animals, with correspond-ing differences in roles even beyond the es-sentials of reproduction. Males and females may even belong to quite different food chains, as in mosquitoes, with males eating the juices of green plants and females eating mammalian blood. In groups that defend territory, de-fense is usually by the male, even though the territory may be shared with a female.

In co-operative groups there is a further evolutionary tendency for differentiation of roles, not necessarily on a sexual basis. Even in loosely organized animal aggregations there is often an order of dominance or a "social scale" in which each individual has its place. The more dominant animals often take the lead in group activities; they are likely to have first whack at food; the more dominant among the males may monopolize the more desirable females. This dominance sequence is called the "pecking order," be-cause it is readily seen in who pecks whom in a flock of fowls, in which dominance has been extensively studied. If you observe a flock of hens, you will almost surely find that there is one hen that pecks all the others and one hen that is pecked by all the others but never pecks back. Throughout the pecking order, each hen pecks those of lower status and is pecked by those higher in the order. Such dominance is established com-petitively, but once it is established it reduces competition and tension in the group. After the group is organized into a pecking order, less pecking goes on. Each hen, or each member of the sequence of whatever species, learns to know its place and gives way to its "betters" without further fuss.

Not all groups are organized into a pecking order. For instance, ants, which live in very rigidly organized groups, have none. There may, nevertheless, be a distinct division of roles in such groups, as the ants also exemplify. Sometimes the division is temporary. In a prairie-dog town or in a roving band of baboons, some individuals generally act as sentinels while the others go about their business, but sentinel duty rotates. Army ants on the march follow a leader, but the leadership shifts rapidly, each leader remaining at the head of the column for perhaps only an inch of the advance. On the other hand, there is often also a more or less permanent division of labor. When army ants are moving their base, the workers always carry the young and the soldiers always protect the line. When a grazing herd is attacked, in most species it is the mature males that wheel into the first line of defense.

Differentiation of roles in its many forms makes a group more than merely an aggregation. It introduces organizations within the group and makes it a *society*.

Societies

"Society" is again a word that is loosely used and difficult to define. It has half a dozen different colloquial usages, which are doubtless familiar to you. Even as a technical biological term it is used in different ways in different subdivisions of the science and by different writers. We shall confine the term to animals, although botanists do sometimes apply it to plants. A society differs from other aggregations of animals in being composed mainly or entirely of members of one species, in having a degree of permanence, usually extending over the whole of a life cycle or over successive generations, and in having some measure of internal organization with differentiation of roles. It differs from a family in that the organization may include but is not confined to the roles between two parents or between parents and offspring. Still, the distinction between "aggregation" or "family" and "society" is not absolute. It is evident that various societies have gradually evolved from aggregations and from families, and that the distinction must therefore be somewhat arbitrary, without a clear-cut line or moment when the group suddenly becomes a society.

In our definition of societies we include only those that have, indeed, evolved from families or other aggregations of clearly distinct individuals. A roughly, but only roughly, analogous development has also occurred rarely by evolution of colonial organisms, in which the whole colony arises from a single zygote and the resulting individuals retain organic continuity. Usually the polyps in a coelenterate colony, for instance, are virtually identical, with none of the individual differentiation of roles essential to the definition of a society. Sometimes, however, as in the coelenterate Portuguese man-of-war (*Physalia*) there is a strong differentiation of roles with polyps in the colony specialized for different functions, such as capture of prey, digestion of food, and reproduction (Fig. 22-5). Colonies of that kind have occasionally been called "societies" ("organic societies"). Biologically, however, the whole colony is better considered as an individual organism in which differentiated organs have been evolved in an unusual way: from the colonial polyps. The organic continuity is that of an individual, and the whole organic unit arises from a single zygote, like an individual. The difference from a society of separate individuals is radical, and the chief reason for mentioning these coelenterates here is to point out that they do *not* have a bearing on the evolution of societies as we have defined the term "society."

Groups that can loosely, at least, be called true societies have evolved independently in different kinds of organisms and in different ways. All have features in common, and something can be learned of each from any other. In some respects it is hard to distinguish them clearly. Nevertheless, they often represent separate and divergent evolutionary trends, and it is to be emphasized that what is true of one is not necessarily true, or even particularly comparable, in another. That caution applies especially to comparison between the most complex forms of animal societies: those of the social insects and of man.

INSECT SOCIETIES

Everyone knows that some insects have complex societies (Fig. 25-7). That is true at the present time of all termites and ants and of some bees and wasps. Although termites are antlike and are often called "white ants," they are not closely related to ants but more nearly to cockroaches. Societies arose separately in ancestors of the termites and of the ants, and were so successful that only social groups survive. There are still solitary, nonsocial bees and wasps, and various species even now demonstrate most of the intermediate stages between that condition and such advanced societies as in the honeybees. The bees and wasps are younger groups than the termites and ants, and their still incomplete socialization arose later. Societies have thus arisen repeatedly and at various times by parallel evolution among different groups of insects. All insect societies have their distinguishing features, but they also share many characteristics because they have arisen in basically similar animals and have tended to follow more or less similar lines of evolution.

All known insect societies have in common the fact that *they are extended and specialized families. All have evolved from a family unit of parents and offspring.* Many female insects merely lay their eggs where they have some chance of survival and give the offspring no further care. That is doubtless the primitive condition. Some female insects make protective chambers and stock them with food on or in which the eggs are laid (Fig. 10-18). No direct care is taken of the larvae hatched from the eggs, but food is there for them. Still other female insects stay with the eggs until they hatch and then protect and feed the larvae until they can shift for themselves. These varying degrees of parental care, observable especially among different species of

25-7 Termites, social insects. The royal cell of a termite from British Guiana. The queen (reproductive female), who has an enormously enlarged abdomen, lies in the center of the chamber. The king (reproductive male) is in the left foreground. The smaller individuals are workers and soldiers.

25-8 Termite castes. *Left,* an immature sexual form; *center,* a worker; *right,* a soldier with large mandibles.

wasps at the present time, strongly suggest that all insect societies arose through much the same stages. The decisive step in the rise of insect societies was evidently that in which the female parent and young remained together for a time as an interacting family group.

Final steps in the rise of true societies among insects occur when the young stay with each other and their mother as they mature, taking over the task of feeding and protecting further broods of young and finally also feeding the mother. In these stages there are at least three distinct social roles in the group, and the roles are generally played by individuals different in structure and appearance. The male usually has no part other than fertilizing the female, and generally dies or at any rate leaves the group after that act. The reproductive female or queen has the primary role of laying eggs from which the other members of the social group develop. Often the queen starts a new group and rears the first brood of young, but sometimes even her first brood is reared by offspring of an older queen. The workers differ from the queen in size and structure and usually do not or cannot reproduce. Thus there are three basic castes, as they are called: males, queens, and workers. In ants and termites (but not in bees or wasps) there are often other castes,

especially soldiers, which are large and protect the group with formidable weapons (Fig. 25-8).

Caste determination is a complex subject, not yet fully understood. In most (but apparently not all) ants, bees, and wasps the males are haploid, developing from unfertilized eggs (Fig. 15-27). Queens, workers, and (in ants) soldiers, are diploid and are genetically females. The differences are usually determined by the amount or kind of food provided for the larvae, but in some species there is evidence of determination by the genetics of the zygote or by characteristics of the egg. In termites the males are diploid and the females haploid. Workers and soldiers may be either male or female genetically, although they rarely reproduce. The younger animals serve as workers and may grow up to be soldiers. Sometimes growth of certain individuals is arrested, apparently by something in the food, and such individuals remain workers throughout life. In all the social insects caste is determined by a complex interplay of genetical and developmental factors.

The important point is that the social role of any of these insects is determined either in the egg or in early developmental stages. Moreover, the behavior appropriate for each caste is *not learned* and is subject to *little modification.* Its elements are hereditary, and heredity confines its variations within quite narrow limits. The number of distinct possible roles is small, generally three and rarely over four.

Insect societies are well designated as *integrated*. The individual has no choice of role, and changes in roles or increases in their complexity are matters of slow evolutionary change, if they occur at all. A social insect has practically no chance of surviving if separated from its own social group. The group as a whole stands or falls depending on how well it copes with environmental demands and crises. The individuals are organically separate, but they are inseparably united in the social group. Typically, they are all sisters (plus usually one mother) in any one functioning social unit. They are bound together also by deep behavioral and physiological patterns. They recognize members of their own unit (probably never as individuals) chiefly by smell, and they kill or drive out strangers. They often exchange secretions which form an actual chemical bond among them—a curious phenomenon called trophallaxis.

HUMAN SOCIETIES

A human society has certain factors in common with insect societies. It also is a group of individuals living together and reacting more or less as a unit toward other groups and with respect to many of the forces of evolution. There is some complexity of organization within the group, and different individuals have different roles. Beyond those broad resemblances, the two kinds of societies are fundamentally different, and the parallel so often drawn between them should be viewed with reserve or even suspicion. The biological basis of human society is of course to be sought among human ancestors and relatives, especially the mammals, and not among animals like the insects, which have been evolving in a strongly different direction for hundreds of millions of years.

In human societies, too, the family is basic and persistent, but not to the same extent or even in the same sense as in insects. In all mammals the mother and her suckling young, at least, remain together and so form a sort of primitive social unit. Yet a group in which differentiation of roles is no more than into father, mother, and young is not yet a society. A mammalian society is not an expanded family, but is an aggregation of adults (with their children in the persisting but subordinate family units) with some differentiation of roles other than that of male and female in their reproductive capacities. In mammals other than man the differentiation of roles seldom goes beyond dominance or leadership of some individuals over others. In civilized human societies, with their butcher, baker, and candlestick maker, the differentiation may become almost incredibly complex. A recent official classification of occupations in the United States lists 40,023 different occupations—and it is clearly not complete.

Heredity and development have some but comparatively little influence on determination of human social roles. Being male or female, constitutionally weaker or stronger, more or less intelligent have a bearing of course, but nevertheless leave a tremendous range of possibilities for everyone. Moreover, the precise role followed is always learned, and consequently there is a flexibility of role and choice wholly absent in insect societies. The human individual is comparatively independent and self-reliant, prospering best in an accustomed social group but able to survive (temporarily, at least) without it, able to change his role within usually broad limits, and able to transfer from one group to another. All normal members of the society are able to reproduce. The lack of differentiation in this respect, so different from the insect society's situation, takes away from the family any really *essential* biological role in the organization of society beyond the function of producing and, to some extent, training the young. This further sharp contrast with insect societies is not contradicted by the fact that within a human society, without regard for differentiation of social roles, the family remains as an essential institution with profound psychological involvements and repercussions in most aspects of life.[14]

14 The clan system exemplifies a psychological ramification of family sentiment in the delimitation of larger social units. The clan is thought of as an expanded family, although this may be more a legal fiction than a biological fact. Even in such cases, and the many other complicated meshings of family with other social

Most mammalian social differentiation, including that of human societies, tends to override the immediate parent-child relationship of the included family units. In this and in other respects such societies are *associative* rather than integrated as in insects. They evolve from aggregations of individuals and families rather than from the single family unit. Above all, the roles are less rigidly determined and potentially (at least) more varied and changeable.

One of the important consequences of these facts is that there is little inherent limitation in the size or the complexity of human social units. In insects such units can be no larger than the number of progeny produced by one (or sometimes a few) females and cannot achieve even remotely comparable complexity.

The flexibility of human societies in contrast with the rigidity of insect societies reflects and depends on the similar contrast in the behavioral patterns of the individuals involved (Chapter 10). This is another example of alternative solutions of evolutionary problems. Both kinds of societies are biological adaptations with high survival value, and both have been outstandingly successful in their quite different ways. Institutions and organizations within the framework of human societies may also be viewed as biological adaptations meeting, by different and generally more complex means, the same broad kinds of basic needs as are met within insect societies. Typically human organization depends on the biologically versatile, all-purpose human individual; ant organization depends on the biologically restricted, specialized, and almost depersonalized insect individual. Sociology has a biological basis and can be studied from a biological point of view, but it is a complex and highly special subject beyond the scope of general biology.

Chapter Summary

The interaction of the organism and its physical environment; interaction with the biotic environment; interorganismic rela-

tionships—competition (inter- and intra-specific) and co-operation.

Niches and Competition:

Relationships among niches (exemplified by the birds inhabiting saguaros); competition as the cause of specifically different niches; principle of ecological incompatibility; nature of competition; competition among plants for light and soil space; competition among animals for food, water, and breeding facilities; competition only rarely of the active type.

Competition and evolution: a cause of extinction (exemplified by history of South American ungulates); a cause of adaptive diversification of species (exemplified by Galápagos finches).

Interspecific interactions: symbiosis—its three categories:

Commensalism: close association between two species of a nearly neutral type (exemplified by barnacles and whales, fish and siphonophores, etc.)

Mutualism: interspecific association with mutual benefit (exemplified by photosynthetic protists in several animals; lichens; nitrogen-fixing bacteria in legumes; termites and ciliates, etc.

Parasitism: interspecific association with unilateral benefit of parasite at expense of host; the ubiquity of parasitism; examples; conditions and adaptations of parasitism in external parasites; in internal parasites—the loss of organs, especially sense organs; the acquisition of specializations, especially in reproduction (exemplified by tapeworm and other parasites); parasitism and disease; parasites as agents of infectious diseases; viruses and bacteria in particular; immunity and resistance; antibodies; evolutionary tendency to loss of virulence of infectious diseases.

Intraspecific interactions:

Competition within the species; as evolutionary force—one major source of natural selection; territoriality.

Aggregation and intraspecific co-operation: aggregations in fish, birds, mammals; co-operation as decrease of competition within group; its adaptive value to the group in competition with other groups.

units, it is obvious that the part played by the family in social structuring is very different in men and ants.

Division of roles and the rise of societies: division of reproductive roles in sex; dominance hierarchies, and their social utility; other role specializations, especially in insect societies.

Societies: problem of exact definition; distinguished from simple aggregations and families, although evolved from aggregations or families:

Insect societies: especially well-developed in termites, ants, bees, and wasps; all are evolutionary elaborations of the family as a unit; characterized by fairly rigid caste differentiation, and innate rather than learned behavior patterns; as *integrated* societies, bound together by behavioral and physiological patterns.

Human societies: similarities to and differences from insect societies; mammalian societies as *associative* societies, evolved from *aggregations* rather than from single family; complexity of role differentiation; flexibility of behavior; importance of individual; insect (integrative) and human (associative) societies as alternative solutions to common biological problem.

CHAPTER 26

Change in Populations and Communities

Populations and communities, wherever they may be, are dynamic groups living in (and forming part of) environments that are also dynamic. They change constantly, from hour to hour, season to season, year to year, and epoch to epoch. The rhythm of day and night is reflected in the activities of all communities. Here in the Temperate Zone we are all familiar with the dramatic cycle of the seasons: the fall of leaves, migration of birds, disappearance of insects, and general closing down of nature's business in the autumn, the quiescence of winter, the rebirth of spring, and the bustling activity of summer. This is a cycle that tends to return annually to the same condition, but it does not do so exactly. One rare day in June may be much like another a year hence, but as the years pass they bring slower changes.

The gardener finds tent caterpillars and other pests more abundant some years than others. The New Englander sees the pastures of his boyhood overgrown with shrubs or merging into the surrounding woods. The old swimming hole in the Midwest may now be a marsh or a prairie. The sod of the high plains, turned by courageous but sometimes injudicious pioneers, too often gives way to tumbleweeds and to desolate dust bowls which yet, with renewed rain, slowly recover a carpet of green. In the Southwest, the ruins of large prehistoric Indian dwellings show where thousands of men once lived in wooded country and in fertile, watered valleys where now is a desert. The student who traces the longer history of the earth finds still greater changes. Turtles, alligators, and fishes once swarmed where now extend the dry sagebrush flats of New Mexico, and the sands of barren dunes lie buried beneath fertile fields in the Mississippi Valley.

All these changes and many more are essential parts of the processes of life. The principles of change are no less important for an understanding of living communities than are the principles of organization examined in the last two chapters. Change, then, is the theme of this chapter. Changes in the make-up of a community, in the census figures of species and individuals, are a matter of the appearance, rise, fall, and disappearance of specific populations. We shall therefore approach the subject from the point of view of the growth and decline of populations. Next we will consider some of the cyclic and periodic changes of communities, and finally the slower processes by which one kind of community gives way to another.

The Rise and Fall of Populations

BIRTH, DEATH, AND SURVIVAL

The size of a population is apparently determined by quite simple facts of life, birth, and death. If more organisms are born than die, the net result is an increase, and if more die than are born, a net decrease occurs. The factors that determine birth and death rates are not so simple; in fact, they are very intricate. The situation is also complicated and made more interesting by the fact that the size and composition of the population is not determined by birth and death rates alone but also by how long individuals survive, that is, by *when* death occurs. A simple problem will demonstrate that fact. Suppose that in some species 1000 individuals were born and the same number died each year. Would there be a change in population from one year to another? What would be the size of the population at any one time if each individual died at the age of one year? If each died at the age of ten years? In the latter population, what percentage of individuals would be seven years old?

The problem is, of course, oversimplified by the assumption that all individuals die at the same age. This is not really true of any species. Some individuals drop out at all ages from birth to death. The percentage of individuals that die at a given age—the death rate for that age—also changes markedly through the life span. Usually the death rate is high among the very young and the very old and reaches a low point somewhere in between. This is as true of man as it is of most other organisms. The human death rate is high in the first year, drops to a low in the early teens, and then rises slowly at first (until about 60) and then with increasing rapidity. That fact of life as it is really lived contrasts with the fact that all normal organisms of the same species are usually *capable* of living for about the same length of time, a life span characteristic of the species.

There is, as would be expected, some hereditary variation in potential life span. By and large, however, all members of a species born with a stock of genes usual in the species, without disabling mutations or other accidents of heredity, would tend to "die of old age" at about the same time. The mechanism runs down of itself after a certain length of time. Earlier death, which is more the rule than the exception, is a premature failure due to an environmental incident such as competition, infection, predation, or accident.

Thus are contrasted the potential or physiological life span built into the organism and the almost always shorter actual span that it manages to achieve. Man's biblical allotment of three score and ten years is an estimate of potential span, too low an estimate for most humans. The potential span in *Homo sapiens* is the longest among mammals [1] and is longer than in the vast majority of other animals. In spite of frequent stories and news reports to the contrary, probably no birds, amphibians, or fishes have as long a potential life span as man. A few species of turtles may have as long a span, or perhaps a little longer. Almost all invertebrates have comparatively short spans, from a few weeks to a few years, but some coelenterates and some large crustaceans may live almost as long as man. Most plants also have short spans; the countless annual plants are so called because their potential life is one year. Trees and many shrubs, however, commonly have spans counted in centuries, and a few run into thousands of years, up to about 4000 for the sequoia. At the other end of the scale, the potential span for some protists may be a matter of hours or even minutes.[2]

[1] The common belief that elephants may live longer than men is wrong. The highest authentic record for an elephant is 69 years. The maximum for man is unknown, since extreme claims are unsubstantiated by evidence and are usually tall tales. There are a few, but very few, apparently authentic records of 110 to 120 years. Undoubtedly correct claims to ages from 100 to 110 are fairly numerous.

[2] Of course the problem arises (which is only one of definition) whether a protist becomes two new individuals when it reproduces by division. The same sort of problem of individual age span arises with vegetative reproduction in general. For instance, some Southern Hemisphere beeches (**Nothofagus**) send up a ring of new trunks from the root system around the original trunk, and these may continue for hundreds of years after the central trunk has died. Is this survival of the individual?

A clear and convenient way to represent the incidence of death in a population is by a *survivorship curve* (Fig. 26-1), which shows the percentage of individuals still living at various times after birth. If most individuals lived out their potential life spans, the curve would be nearly horizontal until that span was reached and then would drop precipitously (Fig. 26-1*A*). If, on the other hand, most individuals die early in life and the survivors of that critical period have comparatively low death rates, the curve drops rapidly at first and then levels off (Fig. 26-1*B*). The first situation, practically speaking, does not occur in nature. The second seems to be fairly common. Probably more common, however, are survivorship curves intermediate between the two extremes (Fig. 26-1*C* and *D*).

Human survivorship curves are of the intermediate type (Fig. 26-1*C*), but differ greatly in precise form in accordance with nutrition, sanitation, and medical care in a particular population. Where the level of public health is high there is an approach to type *A*, and where it is low the approach is to type *B*. There is little evidence that any of the great advances in public health and medicine have increased the *potential* life span. They have greatly improved the chances that individual lives will more nearly achieve their potential span. One of the effects of that change is to increase the percentage of older people in the population. In the United States and most other Western countries the last fifty years have been generally characterized by a declining birth rate.[3] The net result of these two factors has been that the percentage of Americans aged 20 to 45 (hence in the ages when most reproduction occurs and in the ages of most productive work) has remained fairly steady, while the percentage of younger people, under 20, has decreased and that of older people, over 45, has correspondingly increased. What influence of this change can you see in your own community? In the national political and economic scene?

MALTHUS AND THE GROWTH OF POPULATIONS

All populations, both natural and human, have tremendous capacity for increase. Elephants are notoriously slow in reproduction, but it is certainly conservative to estimate that, if all their young survived, the population would more than double every fifty years. A single couple that lived 100,000 years ago (and that is a short time in the history of natural populations) thus *could* have an astronomically enormous number of descendants today—a number represented, *at the very least*, by 4 followed by 602 zeros! That many elephants would fill the visible universe, so we are obviously leaving something out when we say that so large a number of descendants is possible. It would be possible *if* all elephants reproduced at the stated rate and all offspring reached their potential life span. The result, in itself, forcefully demonstrates that such survival is absolutely impossible. Yet the example merely supposes that the population doubled in fifty years. In numerous invertebrate species one female may lay more than two million eggs per year. If all eggs developed and survived, the population would increase a millionfold every year—and would fill the universe during the lifetime of one generation of elephants.

If unchecked, the size of all populations would increase at fantastic rates. Their numbers would literally multiply each year, and

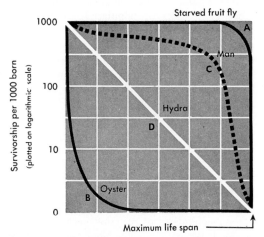

26-1 Survivorship curves. The survivorship curve for fruit flies (*A*) applies only to their life span under the unnatural conditions of starvation in the laboratory.

[3] Since World War II it has begun to climb once again, but it still has not reached its earlier height.

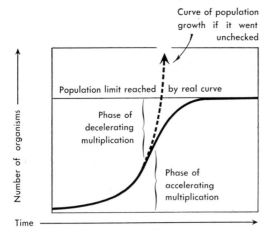

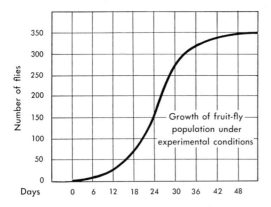

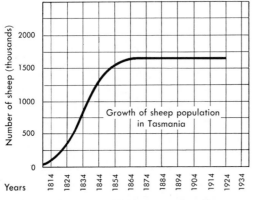

26-2 Curves of population growth. *Top,* generalized growth curve showing how multiplication ultimately decelerates to reach a population limit. *Middle and bottom,* specimen growth curves for actual populations—one of fruit flies in bottles, and the other of the sheep population of Tasmania.

the growth of the population in absolute census figures would be a curve that rapidly shot up sky-high (Fig. 26-2). The increase must be and is always checked. The environment can contain and support only so many individuals of a given species. When a population starts to grow from a few individuals in an environment favorable to it, its size does shoot up at first, but then it begins to run against the barrier of the capacity of the environment. Population increase then slows down, and finally the population size is stabilized at a figure at or below environmental capacity (Fig. 26-2). Increase in the carrying capacity of the environment may be quickly countered by further population growth. Decrease in capacity leads to higher death rates and so to a decline in population. The result is a tendency for populations to be as large as possible under existing conditions or, you might say, to live up to their income. Yet organisms usually keep on reproducing at rates that would rapidly raise the populations above capacity level if all the offspring survived and bred. The obvious corollary is that all offspring do not survive and breed. Only a small fraction of them do under usual conditions. The others necessarily are eliminated by competitors, within or outside their species, and hence by starvation or by enemies, diseases, and other fatalities.

An English clergyman and economist named Thomas Robert Malthus pointed out those grim facts of population limitation a long time ago (in 1798, to be exact). Malthus applied the principle to man and concluded that famine, pestilence, and war are inevitable brakes on increase of human populations. Darwin noted that the Malthusian principle applies even more clearly to most organisms other than man. He saw that the inevitable decimation of offspring is a possible mechanism for evolution by natural selection. There is no serious doubt that Darwin was right on that point and that Malthusian or Darwinian selection is an important process in evolution, although we now consider that other mechanisms of selection occur and may be at least equally important, as we have stressed several times.

Malthus' conclusions as applied to man were decidedly unpleasant. We all have an ingrained human (but not scientifically sound) tendency to disbelieve what is unpleasant to us. It is not surprising, then, that it has become an article of faith for many, including some politicians, theologians, economists, and even biologists, that the Malthusian principle does not really apply to man. Indeed, events during the last 150 years in some progressive countries have seemed to give the lie to Malthus. In those countries, of which the United States is an outstanding example, populations have increased greatly because birth rate exceeds death rate and survival has been lengthened. Yet the standard of living, instead of dropping to minimum subsistence level, has risen notably. The explanation is of course that the extent and efficiency of production have been raised and that population growth, although large, has lagged behind increase in production. In other words, for some human populations the capacity of the environment has enlarged faster than the population. This has encouraged belief that the solution to human population problems is simply to go on increasing production as fast as possible. Unfortunately for so optimistic an outlook, it is a biological fact that that solution can work only temporarily and locally.

There are physical limits to the amount of food that the earth can possibly produce for any one species, including man. No matter how much of the earth's surface is brought into production for human use and how efficiently it is managed, the limit of environmental capacity is still there and cannot be removed. We are only temporizing with the Malthusian principle, not evading it. Eventually population must be balanced, and birth rate cannot continue to exceed death rate. That is the inevitable conclusion from biological principles. Whether the balance is to be by decrease of birth rate or increase of death rate, and at what level of subsistence and crowding the balance is to be achieved— these are economic and political problems of great magnitude and urgency. They concern the biologist not so much as a biologist but, like everyone else, as a citizen. What do you think about them?

Limiting and Balancing Factors

Apart from its controversial aspects, the Malthusian principle is certainly correct to the extent that for every species there are factors that limit population growth and determine population size by a balance of reproduction, death, and survivorship. Most of these factors are inherent in the interactions studied in the last two chapters. Here they can be reviewed briefly from this different point of view.

MATERIALS AND ENERGY

All life is ultimately limited by the usable energy received from the sun (p. 609). Remember that the percentage that can be directly used by life is always small. This is true not only because of the low efficiency of photosynthesis, but also because still larger amounts of energy go to keep the earth livable, especially to maintain the temperatures of its surface, water, and air and to run the water cycle on which all land organisms are dependent. If the energy now used in these ways were to decrease significantly, living populations would automatically decrease. Materials available for organisms in any community are also limited, and no population can live beyond its budget.

FOOD CHAINS

Each link in a food chain is dependent on the links before it (p. 620). Population size at any point in a food chain is therefore limited by the sizes of populations in all previous links. The connection is particularly evident when, as often happens, fluctuations of population size in one species are accompanied by fluctuations in another that feeds on the first. An example will be given when we discuss periodic changes in communities (p. 663).

PREDATION

Population size in food chains is influenced in two directions. The population of a food species limits the population that feeds on it, and at the same time the fact of being eaten affects the population of the food species. In parasitism there is necessarily a balance between the numbers of parasites and the damage done to the hosts (p. 639). The plant-herbivore balance is closely analogous to that of host-parasite, as the herbivore does not necessarily kill the plant on which it feeds. Reciprocal balance of populations is especially evident in the relationship called predation, in which the individual used as food is killed. The predator population necessarily has less bulk than the prey population (except in very temporary instances) and usually is much less numerous. Increase in prey population usually increases predators, but increase in predators tends in turn to decrease the prey population. This interaction can produce very complex results in the populations, but one of three reactions or a combination of them usually ensues, two of which are illustrated in Fig. 26-3. Increasing predation may wipe out the prey population, after which the predator population either also becomes extinct or turns to other prey. This is obviously a short-range reaction that cannot persist in a balanced community. Increased predation and decrease of prey may be followed so promptly by decrease of predators that the prey survives, becomes more abundant with lessened predation, and then predators and predation increase again, and so on. This cyclic relationship can persist indefinitely, but it is delicately balanced and may lead to extinction of the prey or to a more stable situation. In a stable balance, certainly common in nature and probably the rule in established communities, predators consume just about as many of the prey as to keep the prey population at or below the limit of environmental capacity. It can be said that predators are simply cropping excess production of the prey.

In stably balanced prey-predator populations, predation is often actually beneficial to the prey as a group, even though it destroys individuals. That fact and the unforeseen and disastrous possibilities of ignorant interference in natural communities are dramatically illustrated by the history of deer on the

PREY-PREDATOR RELATIONSHIPS

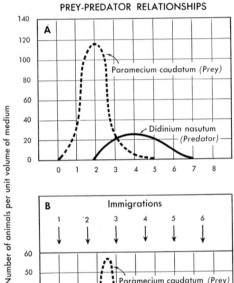

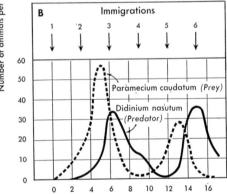

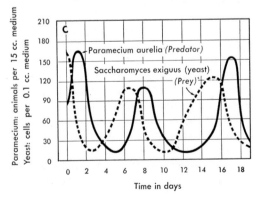

26-3 Prey-predator relationships. *A.* The simpler case: The prey population (*Paramecium*) continues to grow until predation by the ciliate, *Didinium*, commences. The predator population grows until the prey is exterminated; the prey population—now without resources—itself declines to extinction. *B* and *C.* Two cases of prey-predator oscillations: The relationship here is in general the same as in *A*; however, the declining prey population causes the predator population to decline, and thus relieves pressure on the prey before it reaches extinction. The prey population, under temporary reprieve, again begins to grow; but as it does so, the predator—now with renewed resources—grows also. The system can persist for many cycles in this oscillatory state. (In *B* the prey population is protected against extinction by the regular addition ["immigrations" *1* through *6*] of small groups of individuals.) (Gause's data)

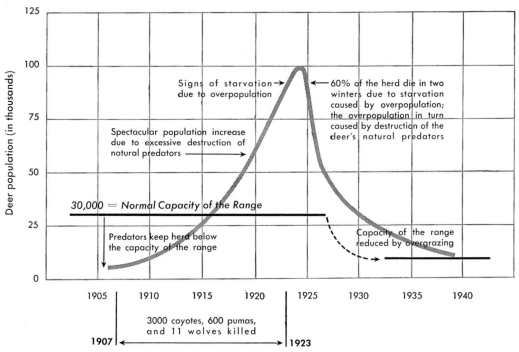

26-4 The history of the Kaibab deer. (See illus., p. 649.) The gray line is the graph of population numbers of the deer.

The following labels appear within the figure:

Deer population (in thousands)

Signs of starvation → due to overpopulation

← 60% of the herd die in two winters due to starvation caused by overpopulation; the overpopulation in turn caused by destruction of the deer's natural predators

Spectacular population increase due to excessive destruction of natural predators →

30,000 = Normal Capacity of the Range

Predators keep herd below the capacity of the range

Capacity of the range reduced by overgrazing →

3000 coyotes, 600 pumas, and 11 wolves killed

1907 ← → 1923

Kaibab Plateau in Arizona (Fig. 26-4). Before 1907 the plateau had a healthy deer herd with a stable population kept well below the capacity of the vegetation (which thus also was healthy and stabilized) by heavy predation of pumas, wolves, and coyotes. With the idea of benefiting the deer by removal of their "enemies," a campaign of extermination was waged against the predators. The deer population did, indeed, increase enormously, from about 4000 in 1907 to some 100,000 in 1924. The peak population was far beyond the capacity of the range, and in the next two years more than half the deer starved to death. Thereafter the deer population continued to decline more slowly and by 1939 was down to 10,000, living up to the capacity of the range, now seriously damaged by over-cropping. With the range still deteriorating, starvation continued to kill more deer than the predators had.

COMPETITION

The immediate cause of death of most of the Kaibab deer after removal of predators was starvation, but the starvation resulted

from excessive *intraspecific* competition for a limited food supply. The frequent result of close *interspecific* competition is the decline and ultimate extinction of one of two competing populations. Experiments have shown patterns of population change that underlie such events in nature (Fig. 26-5). Population growth of the successful competitor is slowed down, but eventually the population reaches the size it would have had without competition. The losing competitor's population starts to grow normally, but soon slows down and then gradually declines to extinction.

DENSITY

The Kaibab deer illustrate another population factor not hitherto discussed: that of density of population, or the number of individuals concentrated in a given space. At their highest population total, the density of the deer led to intense competition for food and to starvation. There were too many deer in the available area. A little thought shows that in all such situations, environmental limitation is more a matter of density than of total population. It has repeatedly been found for a great variety of organisms that increased density slows population growth, eventually stops growth entirely, and when

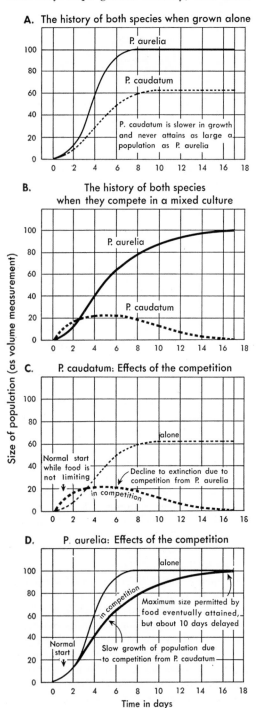

A. The history of both species when grown alone

P. aurelia

P. caudatum

P. caudatum is slower in growth and never attains as large a population as P. aurelia

B. The history of both species when they compete in a mixed culture

P. aurelia

P. caudatum

Size of population (as volume measurement)

C. P. caudatum: Effects of the competition

alone

Normal start while food is not limiting

Decline to extinction due to competition from P. aurelia

in competition

D. P. aurelia: Effects of the competition

alone

in competition

Maximum size permitted by food eventually attained, but about 10 days delayed

Normal start

Slow growth of population due to competition from P. caudatum

Time in days

extreme (as for the deer) leads to reduction in the size of the population (Fig. 26-6). Usually density affects the population through the amount of food available. This may be so even when not obvious. In experiments of growing flies under crowded conditions, it was found that crowding reduces the number of eggs laid by a female. Other experiments demonstrated that the density effect was really due mainly if not entirely to food supply; the crowded females were undernourished and laid fewer eggs in consequence. Another frequent reason why heavy densities often react unfavorably on populations is that they promote the spread of diseases.

Other studies suggest that there is for most species a range of densities in which the population does best and that either lower or higher densities impair maintenance and growth of the population. There are several factors involved in this phenomenon. Certainly any organisms can become overcrowded, and generally then limited in population. Undercrowding, occurrences in densities too thin for population maintenance, is less obvious. Widely dispersed individuals may not find mates. There is often some defensive strength in concentration of numbers (p. 641). Highly social groups usually do not function well if the social unit is either too large or too small. A dense population alters the temperature, the humidity (if in the air), and the chemistry of its environment by muscular activity, respiration, excretion, and other processes. A great concentration may actually poison the environment, as when too

26-5 An experimental study of interspecific competition. The experiments concern competition between two species of *Paramecium*—*P. aurelia* and *P. caudatum*—grown in the same culture vessels. They compete for food and other requirements. *A.* The growth of both species when grown separately under conditions similar to those in which they later compete. Note that *aurelia*'s growth is more rapid; and its stable population size (about 100 units) is greater than that (about 60 units) of *caudatum*. *B.* The history of the two species in competition. *C* and *D.* Comparison of each species, grown alone and in competition. *P. caudatum* is eliminated by the competition from *aurelia*; competition slows the population growth of *aurelia*, but it eventually attains its normal population size (about 100 units). (Gause's data)

many fish are kept in one aquarium, but there is also evidence of density ranges that condition the environment favorably for the species. Goldfish grow better in water conditioned by other fishes than when living alone in clean water. In higher animals there are also psychological factors, innate or learned "preferences" for lower or higher densities. What are some of the influences of density in human populations?

Periodism

By "periodism" we mean a tendency for changes in populations or communities to recur. The recurrence may be inexact and at irregular intervals, or it may be quite precise and regular, in which case it is usually called *cyclic*. There are many cycles in the environmental rhythms of nature, and some of these affect organisms so strongly that they seem to be built into the very fabric of life. Most obvious, and for that reason among the most important, are the daily and yearly cycles arising from the earth's motion as a planet.

DAILY CYCLES

A day is too short a cycle to be commonly accompanied by important changes in composition of communities or sizes of populations, but in almost all communities there is a strongly pronounced daily rhythm of activity. In green plants, photosynthesis occurs only during the daylight hours. Most animals are more active during some hours than during others of the twenty-four. In some, the presence of light stimulates activity either directly or through the sense of vision. The higher temperatures prevailing through the day tend to increase activity. On the other hand in very hot environments, as in many deserts, the heat of the day is so intense as to retard activity or even to cause death. There many animals rest in shade or burrow by day and are most active at night. Other animals escape predators by hiding during the day and coming out at night, an evolutionary development countered by the evolution of some nocturnal predators.

Most mammals are nocturnal (more active at night), although there are many excep-

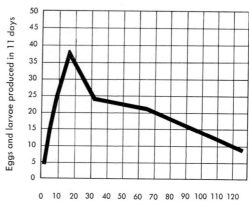

Grams of flour per pair of beetles

26-6 Experimental demonstration of an optimum population density in flour beetles. It is not surprising that egg productivity of the beetles increases as their food allotment is increased from 0 to about 18 grams of flour per pair; but note that further allotment of flour, surprisingly, leads to a decline in productivity. There is an *optimum* density of beetles in the flour. (Thomas Park's data)

tions. This fact may have something to do with their evolution from the reptiles, which, again with many exceptions, are mainly diurnal (most active by day). It may even have been a factor in evolution of mammalian homeothermism, which enables mammals to be active in cooler environmental temperatures. It almost certainly is related to the fact that most mammals lack color vision, which requires more light than is usually present at night and thus is generally absent in nocturnal animals. (Our own color vision ceases to function in dim light, as you have doubtless noticed.) The mammals most familiar to us are the relatively few diurnal species, and it is a revelation to observe the wealth of mammalian and other animal life abroad at night in woods or deserts. Even closely related species may differ in this respect. Flying squirrels are nocturnal, and ordinary squirrels, which may live in the same trees, are diurnal. Whole classes may be distinguished by their usual daily rhythms. Mammals seem to be fundamentally and predominantly nocturnal, but birds are even more predominantly diurnal. Nevertheless nature abounds in exceptions, and there are some thoroughly nocturnal birds. What are they? Man is a mammal, of course, and yet is

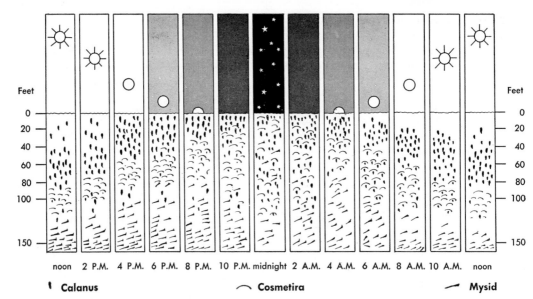

noon	2 P.M.	4 P.M.	6 P.M.	8 P.M.	10 P.M.	midnight	2 A.M.	4 A.M.	6 A.M.	8 A.M.	10 A.M.	noon

ᛌ Calanus   **⌒ Cosmetira**   **⌒ Mysid**

26-7 Daily periodism in the vertical migration of marine plankters (types of planktonic organisms). The figure illustrates the cycle of up-and-down movement of three animals; their movement is doubtless related to the similar daily migration of the plant plankters on which they feed. It seems likely that the plant migration (mostly diatomaceous) is related to attaining an optimum light intensity.

naturally [4] diurnal, in spite of the fact that he may be active far into the night, especially when in large groups—another density effect. What are some adaptations to diurnal and to nocturnal life?

Most communities include both diurnal and nocturnal species, and a few animals are equally active day and night. Activity in a community goes on around the clock, but usually different species are active at different times. You might almost say that there are in any one place different communities by day and by night.

Daily cycles of activity are also very prominent in insects and other small terrestrial invertebrates constantly endangered by their tendency to dry out. For them the significant point is the increased desiccating power of the air during the warm dry midday period.

[4] This is sometimes disputed with evidence that newborn infants have no daily periodism and only learn to be diurnal as they grow older. Nevertheless human vision is definitely adapted to daylight. Also man's closer relatives are among the most diurnal of mammals. The increasing diurnality of infants, although perhaps hastened and reinforced by learning, is an innate maturation process. Human activity at night is learned behavior and is made possible only by artificial light.

Insects are probably primitively nocturnal animals like mammals, although for different reasons. The nocturnalism of cockroaches (truly ancient and primitive insects) is well known. The evolution of later insects has involved a tendency to be active in daylight, doubtless in part because of their increasing association with flowers.[5] Most insects still, however, restrict activity to the less dry periods near dawn and sunset. Full diurnalism (with activity at midday) is common only in two of the most highly evolved insect orders, Hymenoptera (bees and wasps) and Lepidoptera (butterflies). Moths are also Lepidoptera but retain nocturnalism. Do you think there might be any evolutionary connection between the differences in color and time of activity between moths and butterflies in general? Could you frame a hypothesis about possible long-term evolutionary causes of why flycatchers and bats are crepuscular (dawn and dusk) animals? How might you test such an historical hypothesis with data on now-living organisms?

[5] There are a few nocturnal flowers, significantly drab in color and highly scented. Moths are probably their main visitors.

Daily cycles are prominent in the sea (Fig. 26-7). Most noticeable is the fact that countless millions of small floating animals concentrate near the surface at night and sink to deeper levels during the day. Along with them, there is a movement of more active animals that feed on them, larger animals that feed on *those* animals, and so on. The cyclic movement is undoubtedly correlated with intensity of light, but no more profound explanation seems to be available as yet. There is a similar but deeper daily up-and-down movement of the "scattering layer," a vast aggregation of something or other that occurs widely in the oceans at depths usually between 1000 to 1500 feet. The "something or other" is probably animals of some sort or sorts, but no one knows what animals. Such are the abysmal mysteries that exist so close to us.

The timing of daily activity in animals has proved so significant in their over-all adaptation to the rhythm of environmental change that many have evolved internal timing devices, or clocks. These internal clocks, measuring intervals of 24 hours' duration, can be synchronized with the external cycle of physical conditions. Evidently the animal always recognizes dawn as the one reliably timed event in the day. Perception of dawn serves to set the zero hour on the internal clock, which then supplements external signals (light intensity, temperature, humidity, etc.) as an indicator of the time of day most appropriate for a particular activity. In a few animals like the bee and the shrimps described earlier (p. 208) these timing devices have evolved to the point where they have been reliably exploited for elaborate new functions like celestial navigation. Evolution of clocks has occurred in other animals besides insects, and even in plants.

LUNAR CYCLES

Cycles of animal activity that follow the phases of the moon are less common or less often noticed, but they do exist. There is a great deal of folklore about influence of the moon on crops or on human physiology, but there is as yet little sound evidence that these supposed moonlight cycles are real.

Some evidence has recently been obtained suggesting presence of lunar rhythms of metabolism in carrots and potatoes, so we had better wait before passing final judgment on the folklore! Doubtless there is some minor psychological influence, as men and coyotes tend to give vent to their emotions more freely under a full moon. And it does seem possible that the 28-day menstrual rhythm in women is an evolutionary relict from early mammalian ancestors with rhythmic, synchronized periods of heat (p. 382). The best-established lunar cycles in nature are, however, due mostly to the tides and hence only indirectly to the moon. Of course they affect animals of the seashore more than any others. A famous example is the grunion, a fish of the California coast, which swarms to the beaches and lays eggs exactly at high tide on the second, third, and fourth nights after the spring tide (Fig. 26-8). Palolo worms (marine annelids) also swarm and breed at definite phases of moon and tide (different times in different places); with them the duration of moonlight, as well as the tide, may be a factor. Many other (probably most) organisms of the intertidal seashore zone show lunar or tidal rhythms of one sort or another.

ANNUAL CYCLES

The intense seasonal cycle of the Temperate Zone is familiar to you in many of its aspects, and we have referred to it before (pp. 357, 649). The major change from summer to winter involves sharp decrease of activity for most perennial plants and many animals. Some animals merely tend to stay home and move about less. Others go into a sort of coma, more profound than sleep and accompanied by much lowered metabolism, a phenomenon called *hibernation*. Adult annual plants and many animals, especially insects, die, and the species passes the winter in a relatively inactive life stage, as seeds, eggs, or pupae (p. 385). Summer residents among migrant animals, mostly birds, move out, and different winter residents move in. A few permanent residents are active summer and winter, but even with the addition of winter residents the number of active species and individuals is much smaller in winter. The

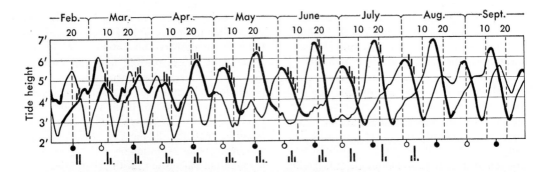

26-8 Tidal and lunar periodicity. The lower figure is a photograph (by flash) of a remarkable phenomenon exhibited by the grunion (*Leuresthes tenuis*) on the southern coasts of California. The grunion wriggles out of the waves at the highest point during the highest (night) high tides of the lunar cycle. Momentarily stranded on the wet beach between waves, the females wriggle down into the sand tail-first. (Females with only their head protruding from the sand are visible in the photograph.) In this position the female lays her eggs while the male, curled around her body, ejaculates sperms which reach the eggs, traveling over the female's wet flank. Both male and female return to sea with the next wave that covers them. The entire grunion population's egg-laying is thus synchronized, being restricted to the two periods of highest tides in the lunar cycle. Furthermore, although there are two high tides each 24 hours, the grunion restrict their activity to the high water that occurs at night. The eggs, buried in the sand, hatch as young fish in time to go to sea with the next set of very high tides about two weeks later. *Upper figure*, occurrence of grunion egg-laying in relation to tidal and lunar cycles at La Jolla, California. The heights of high tides (in feet) about 24 hours apart have been connected by smooth lines. The two tides each day yield the two series of curves; tides occurring in darkness are indicated by the heavier line in the graph. Grunion activity is shown by short vertical bars above the curves. Moon phases are shown below. (The black circles indicate new moon, and the white circles full moon.) The vertical bars under each set of high tides show relative intensity of individual "runs" on successive nights. (Courtesy of Dr. Boyd Walker)

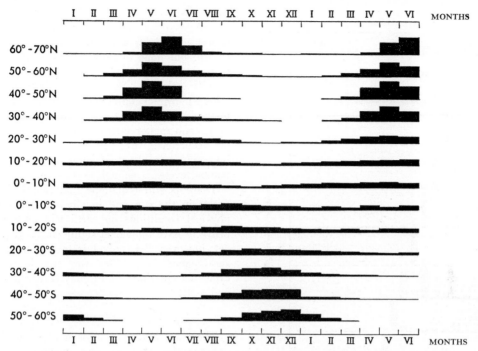

26-9 The annual cycle of breeding activity of the English sparrow at different latitudes. Near the equator there is virtually no annual cycle; breeding is distributed nearly at random. To the north and to the south pronounced cycles develop but, of course, with a 6-month phase difference.

species that do remain active are in different environments in the different seasons, and their food and other habits must change accordingly (Fig. 26-9). In your own region what are some of the species that are (*a*) perennial but dormant in winter, (*b*) annual, (*c*) migrant summer residents, (*d*) migrant winter residents, and (*e*) permanent residents active all the year?

Radical seasonal changes characterize land environments in the Temperate and Frigid zones. In fresh-water environments, especially lakes, of the same zones the changes may be equally or more striking, especially where ice locks the waters. There are, however, seasonal changes in most other environments as well, including those of the tropics and the open sea.

In the tropics there is little change in temperature from month to month, but usually a decided change from day to night. The environmental cycle usually present and most strongly affecting organisms is an alternation of rainy and dry seasons. Inhabitants of the tropics often call the rainy season "winter" (although it is no colder than "summer"), and the dry season "summer." It is, however, the dry season in which vital activity is lower and which therefore is biologically more analogous with the temperate winter. Deciduous trees in the tropics shed their leaves at the beginning of the dry season. In the rain forests, the so-called "jungles," seasonal changes are slight, and there is no well-defined dry season. In any case, the contrast of seasons is less marked than in the Temperate Zone, and community activities are more sustained throughout the year.

Activity is still more evenly sustained in tropical seas, but even there many species have well-defined breeding seasons, as do the palolo worms of the reefs (p. 659). Outside the tropics, most seas have more strongly defined seasonal cycles dependent in part on water temperature and in part on solar radiation. You have already met an example of that rhythm (p. 624).

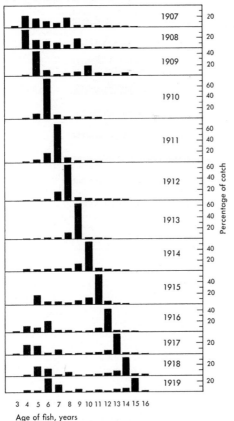

Percentage of catch

26-10 Population periodism in the herring. 1904 was clearly a good year; it is the principal contribution to all catches through 1916, when another good year class (1910) began to become prominent.

OTHER ENVIRONMENTAL CYCLES

Many have studied the curious and intricate subject of cycles in nature and in human affairs. Aside from the obviously real and influential daily, lunar, and annual cycles, many others have been listed. Perhaps the best-established is the sunspot cycle, which averages about 11 years but is really quite variable, sometimes as short as 8 years or as long as 16. There is evidence that the sunspot cycle may influence weather on earth, and therefore it would seem logical to suppose that it would influence living communities. Such influence has been claimed repeatedly, but more critical study has tended to reject the claim. For instance, an eminent student of cycles has found evidence in the widths of tree rings for eight different cycles of more rapid or slower growth, from about 6 to 23 years in length, but none of these cycles corresponds with the sunspot cycle. In fact, none corresponds with any known cycle in climatic or other environmental conditions. Critics of the method claim that any recurrent series of events, no matter how irregular and random the recurrences are, can be arbitrarily fitted into an artificial set of simultaneous mathematical cycles if enough cycles are used.

There is still real hope that the study of cycles in the sun and in climatic and other physical conditions on earth will eventually prove to have biological significance. At present, however, it is only fair to say that such significance is dubious for any inorganic cycles except those of the day, lunar month, and year.

POPULATION PERIODISM

There are innumerable periodic changes in communities that involve intervals longer than the yearly cycle. Many of these fluctuations, probably the majority, are unpredictably irregular and episodic rather than recurring at approximately equal intervals in a truly cyclic way. Even in a community that tends to go year after year without evident change in its composition and organization, the equilibrium is not static. There are usually dynamic and intricately interrelated fluctuations in populations, in numbers of individuals of each species. A community that is in fact in equilibrium is not marked so much by a constant yearly census level as by fluctuations that tend nevertheless to center around a long-term average and that rarely decline to extinction or expand much beyond the capacity of the environment.

It is a matter of common observation that in most communities there are good years and bad years for particular species or for the community as a whole. That fact is, for instance, well known to commercial fisheries, for which there happen to be particularly good statistics (Fig. 26-10). Some of the fluctuations seem to be completely irregular, and others vary from vaguely to quite obviously cyclic rhythms. Cyclic rhythms among land animals have been especially studied in fur

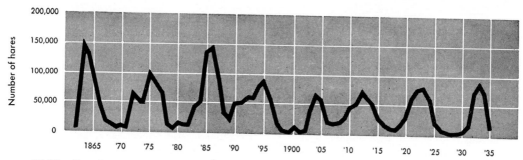

26-11 Population periodism in the varying hare of Canada and Labrador. The cycle reaches its maximum about every ten years.

bearers of northern Canada and Labrador, for which there are also good records extending as far back as 1750. The abundance of varying hares fluctuates strongly with a rhythm that is somewhat irregular but tends to have a cycle of about ten years (Fig. 26-11). Populations of lynxes, which are predators on the varying hares, have cycles that closely follow those of the hares. Foxes in Labrador have equally cyclic changes in population but with a shorter cycle, about four years.

Such fluctuations in populations may have widespread secondary effects. In 1863 central Asiatic sand grouse suddenly appeared in Europe, and there were later invasions at approximate intervals of eleven years, with a tendency for every second invasion (at twenty-two–year intervals) to be larger. The invasions were related to a population cycle in the Gobi Desert, with migrations occurring at peaks of overpopulation.

Irregular fluctuations can often be directly ascribed to some environmental cause. Great reduction of the house sparrow population of the Shetland Islands in 1926-28 is known to have resulted from epidemic [6] disease, and periodic decrease in populations of a species of British sea urchins in 1917 and 1929 followed unusually cold winters. As we have

[6] "Epidemic" comes from ancient Greek roots meaning "among the people," and some writers therefore insist that such diseases in nonhuman animals should be called "epizootic" ("among animals"). In view of the facts that we are not ancient Greeks and that everyone applies such terms as "population" (which means number of people) to plants and animals, the objection is overpedantic, to say the least. Recall that we, with other biologists, apply the word "deme" (same Greek root) to a local population of any organism.

noted, correlation of *cyclic* population changes with climatic or other physical cycles remains a possibility but is not established at present. It is now believed that the principal causes of regular population cycles are biological reactions within the communities themselves. The varying hare cycle of the Hudson Bay region (Fig. 26-11) is believed to involve mainly population density, overcrowding with reduction in population from epidemics and other high-density effects, followed by rapid reproduction at abnormally low densities, which in turn builds up in a few years to overpopulation again. The lynx cycle is a secondary effect of the hare cycle, caused by changes in food supply of the lynxes.

GEOLOGICAL PERIODISM

Still longer periodic changes in population and communities, seldom regular enough really to merit the name of "cycles," involve the geological processes that change the face of the earth and therefore the environments in which organisms live. This again is an intricate affair, for the activities of communities themselves are a part of these geological processes. The time involved may usually be reckoned in dozens of years, at shortest, or in hundreds, thousands, or millions of years. As an example, from a geological point of view all lakes are temporary. No sooner are they formed than their disappearance begins, by erosion of outlets and eventual draining and by sedimentation and biological processes that fill them. A community in any one lake is therefore necessarily temporary (although it may endure for some hundreds of thousands of years in extreme instances) and must change as the environment does. As another example, bare rock weathers to soil (another geological process in which organisms are very actively involved), and again the community changes with this environmental change. Through the long, long span of earth history, mountains have repeatedly risen and been worn down again; seas have advanced over the lands and later withdrawn; glacial epochs have alternated with milder periods; deserts have spread and disappeared. All these and many other geological events have profoundly affected the living communities of the earth.

Succession

Another way to speak of the kinds of geological changes mentioned in the preceding paragraph is to say that they are examples of *physiographic* [7] *succession*. A physiographic succession is accompanied by an orderly sequence of changes in communities, and there is thus also *community succession*. A community succession may occur without any really noticeable physiographic change, but often the two proceed together. They are, indeed, difficult to disentangle because communities are also geological forces involved in physiographic succession.

EXAMPLES OF COMMUNITY SUCCESSION

Consider what is likely to happen to a lake in northeastern United States (Fig. 26-12). The open waters of the lake have a community including protists, algae, small aquatic animals, and fishes, among other things. In shallower water near shore are pond lilies, cattails, and other comparatively large plants that grow (so to speak) with their feet in the water and their heads in the air. Silt and soil wash in and are piled up by waves, and dead vegetable matter accumulates. The lake becomes shallower, with marshy margins.

[7] "Physiography" originally meant "the description of nature," but somehow the term came to be largely confined to the geological description of the face of the earth. Geologists nowadays seldom refer to physiography as a branch of their science and speak instead of "geomorphology," the "science of earth forms." Biologists continue to use the outmoded term "physiography." It is true that "geomorphological succession" is quite a mouthful, but otherwise it is the preferable term and will probably be adopted by biologists eventually, which is why we mention it.

The former shoreward rim of the lake becomes damp land on which grasses, herbs, and willows take root. The filling and the succession of new communities progress toward the center of the lake until finally open water and the aquatic community disappear. In the meantime the marshy marginal soil continues to build up as humus and silt accumulate. Eventually oaks sprout here, and finally the whole site of the vanished lake is occupied by a beech and maple forest, which follows the oaks.

Similar successions where lakes once were can often be followed over periods of thousands, even tens of thousands, of years. Changes are recorded in layers of silt, peat, and humus that fill the lake basin. Changes in vegetation can be followed in great detail by study of the different kinds of pollen deposited in the various layers.

Community succession is not confined to lakes or to the Temperate Zone. It occurs wherever physiographic or climatic changes take place. A coral reef grows toward the surface, its rich community changing as the species of shallower water immigrate and become more populous. Waves grind coral rock to sand and pile the sand up in shifting dunes barely above the tides. Vines take root, bind the sand in place, and contribute to it the humus of their dead tissues. Low trees, resistant to winds and spray, grow in the accumulating soil, to which they contribute in turn. Finally a copse of tall trees develops in the richer soil, and a more protected land environment is thus gradually formed. Or perhaps the climate becomes progressively drier in a region where a pine forest flourishes. The pines, starved for water, die, and scrubby junipers grow in their place. Still drier conditions see the junipers replaced by sagebrush and greasewood. Finally there may be a cactus and thornbush desert where once a forest stood.

In all these examples, plants are stressed because they are in most instances the clearest indicators and the biological keys of the situation. In each situation, however, the association of plants is accompanied by a characteristic association of animals, and the two together make up the community.

CONVERGENCE AND CLIMAX

Let us return to northeastern United States and consider what happens to a bare rock exposed near the lake where we followed a community succession. The first living things to get a foothold on the rocks are small, scaly lichens (p. 499). The lichens hasten the mechanical decomposition and chemical disintegration of the rock surface. In them dust lodges and humus begins to develop. More luxuriant lichens arise, and then moss and ferns. Soil develops along with increasing vegetation, and shrubs spring up. As the process continues, trees begin to grow, perhaps pines first while the soil is still rather rocky and comparatively poor in organic matter. Oaks follow, and in their shade appear seedlings of beech and maple, which grow up to overshade the early trees. Finally a beech and maple forest flourishes where once was bare rock, and it spreads and joins the beech and maple forest that grew up where a lake was earlier.

Different beginnings and different community successions led to the same result: the beech and maple forest community. The two successions *converged* and gave rise to the same kinds of community, or even to parts of identically the same community. Successions in the same region starting, say, on bare silt left by a flooding stream or on a cut clay bank would involve different sequences of communities, but would also tend to converge, culminating in beech and maple forest. That forest is the usual culmination or *climax* of community succession in the region. Once it is established, there is little tendency for further progressive change in the community. With the usual and incessant fluctuation of populations, the forest community persists until some further physiographic or climatic change or some interference by man starts a new community succession.

Most regions have a type of *climax community* with which all the community successions of the region usually end and which then tends to persist there. Of course the climax is not always a beech and maple forest (although that is a common climax over much of northeastern United States), or even a forest of any kind. In many mountains the climax is a spruce and fir forest. A frequent climax on Western plateaus and other uplands is ponderosa pine forest. Mesquite communities are the climax in many more arid regions. (Mesquite is a thorny shrub belonging to the pea family.) The climax over most of the high plains east of the Rockies is grassy prairie. The nature of the climax is ultimately determined more by climate [8] than by any other factor. Local differences in climate are fairly common even within a single region, so that regions often have more than one climax in different, more limited localities. Both grassland and forest climaxes are common in some regions.

What is the usual climax community in your part of the country? Has man disturbed or destroyed that community in places? If so, has the disturbance started a new community succession? Is there a tendency for abandoned fields and clearings to follow a succession back to the original climax?

CLIMAX AND CHANGE

Here is a question that probably arose in your mind as you read about climax communities: If the community in each locality tends toward a fixed climax in time and if this has been going on for millions of years, why are there any further changes in communities? Why are not all communities everywhere set and static at their climaxes?

A climax community tends to persist, it is true, but it tends to persist only as long as no internal or external disturbance affects the community and there is no essential physiographic or climatic change in its environment. In fact such disturbances and changes are frequent, and in the long run they are sure to happen. Inevitably, always and everywhere, the climax community does eventually change. New successions lead to new climaxes, or change is so continual that a stable climax can hardly be designated. These facts have raised some doubts as to the general validity and usefulness of the concepts of convergence and climaxes. The doubts are not very serious if we remember that convergence and climaxes are not defined as universal and eternal. Con-

---

[8] The climate's ultimate effect on the community may be felt through its primary effect on soil.

SUCCESSION AND THE OBLITERATION OF LAKES

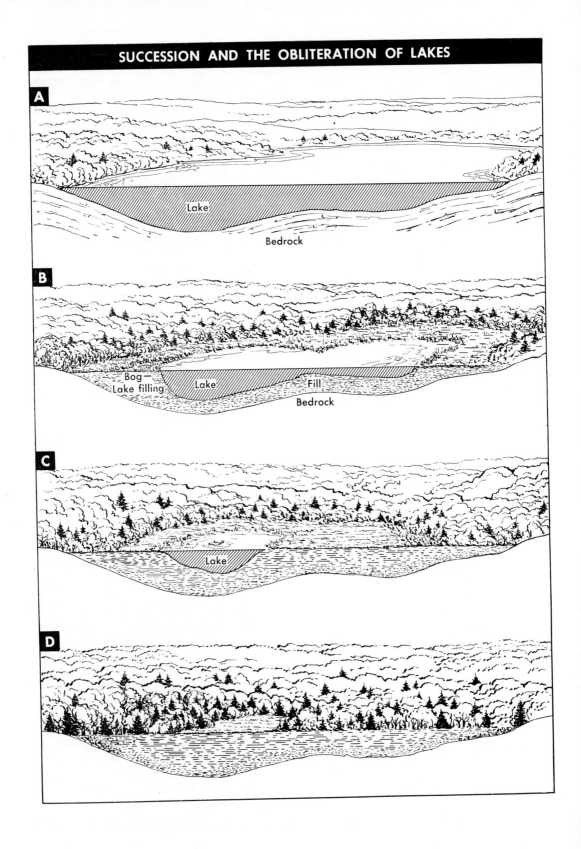

A

Lake

Bedrock

B

Bog—
Lake filling   Lake   Fill

Bedrock

C

Lake

D

vergence is a frequent tendency, and climaxes often do plainly exist and tend to persist for periods long in terms of human life, even though they always do change finally. The concept of climax as a stable condition in nature does have validity, but only in a limited and short-range way because nature is not static.

Physiographic changes, such as the filling in of lakes, do not always tend toward climax communities. New lakes are formed, too (otherwise all would be gone by now), and in them the succession starts again. Erosion lays bare sands, clays, and harder rocks on which succession also begins from the start. Floods kill the established communities and, again, leave tracts where new communities and new successions arise. In broader view, new land rises from the sea and old land sinks into it. Mountains are worn down to plains, and, as they wear away, their communities also go through a succession, but one that goes rather from one climax to another than in sequence to a fixed climax. Not so long ago (ten thousand years or so) almost the whole northern half of our continent was buried in ice, and new successions have occurred since then, not only in the glaciated areas but in almost all others as the climates changed.

Disturbances within communities are also frequent. Forest and prairie fires (which antedate man, although he is responsible for most of them nowadays) wipe out whole communities. Population changes in climax or other well-established communities tend to fluctuate around an average, but they do not always do so. Great increases may actually change the environment and the community as a whole, as that of the Kaibab deer did (p. 655). Decreases may go on to extinction, with a consequent long or permanent change in the composition of the community. New

species frequently enter a community from elsewhere. Inevitably they change the interactions in the community, and they may profoundly change its whole nature.

Moreover, communities evolve not only by the extinction of species in them and the incursions of new species, but also by evolution within their populations. The species of which a community is composed are not themselves static units. Over the generations each one of them changes, and so necessarily does the community of which it is a part.

In the last few thousand years something new has been added, a species of animal that has intruded in almost all the communities in nature and has changed them more rapidly than any other influence and more profoundly than most. The next chapter considers the community of that species and its influence on communities throughout the earth.

Chapter Summary

The kinds of population and community change: daily, seasonal, yearly, and epochal; understanding of change begins with analysis of rise, growth, and fall of specific populations.

Rise and fall of populations: birth, death, and survival; survivorship curves; the growth curve applied to populations; limit of population growth set by environmental factors; the Malthusian principle; its bearing on evolution; its bearing on human populations.

Limiting and balancing factors: materials and energy as limiting factors; ultimately limited by the amount of solar radiation; food chains; population size limit of each link in food chain set by population size of next lower link; predation; the interaction of population size in successive

---

26-12 Vegetation succession in the obliteration of lakes. *A.* Initial conditions: lake surrounded by hardwood (beech-maple) forest; a few conifers, like larch or tamarack (bog forest), near the edge of the lake. *B* and *C.* Accumulation of humus from lake plants (water lilies, cattails, pickerelweed, etc.) forms a marginal marsh or bog invaded by sedges and sphagnum moss; then blueberry, wintergreen, and similar plants; then willows, poplars, and other trees;

later by tamarack, yew, dogwood, and maple. *D.* This succession of plants, as the lake fills with humus, ends when the surrounding beech-maple forest takes over entirely. The stage shown in *D* has not yet reached this climax; the filled lake is still surrounded by the tamaracks (larches), and other members of the bog forest, which are ultimately succeeded by the hardwoods. (Modified by Lobeck, after Dachnowski)

links of food chain; prey-predator cycles; the possibility of extinction in prey-predator cycles—and of equilibrium; artificial disturbance of the prey-predator balance (exemplified by the Kaibab deer); effects of competition and density; the existence of optimum density.

Periodism: cyclic population changes.

Daily cycles of activity in organisms: correlated with cycle of light and temperature in day and night; reptiles as examples of diurnal animals, and mammals as nocturnal; daily cycles in insects, which were primitively nocturnal; daily cycles in the sea; the evolution of 24-hour clocks.

Lunar cycles: the menstrual cycle in women; the lunar cycle of the grunion, and of the palolo worm.

Annual cycles: hibernation; seasonal migrations; seasonal breeding.

Other environmental cycles, such as 11-year sun-spot cycle; population periodism; its irregularity (exemplified by fishes); varying hares and lynxes; the problem of causes; geological periodism.

Community succession: exemplified (1) by the filling of a lake and the succession of vegetation types culminating in beech-maple forest, (2) by the history of a coral reef, and (3) by succession from pine forest to desert; convergence of successions to a common climax; the familiar climax vegetations of North America; tendency for stability of a climax; environmental changes that disturb a climax and renew succession.

Amazonian Indians, fishing with bow and arrow, are so clearly dependent on the immediate environment that one quickly perceives that they have—like the fish they hunt—an ecology open to analysis. And so have all the other races of man. (Photo from UNESCO Courier)

CHAPTER 27

The Human Species and Communities

MAN AND NATURE; MAN IN NATURE

Let us take a quick tour of the world, beginning at home. You are reading these lines in a human community, probably in a town or city where little or nothing remains of the natural community that existed there before man came. Somewhere nearby are fields where the original communities have also been eradicated and replaced by rich, new communities partly (only partly) of man's choice. From those fields and from other communities, near and far, even from the opposite side of the world, ships, trains, trucks, and planes bring foods and other materials into your community. Power, fuel, and water are also poured into the community from nearer or more distant sources.

A first hop to a rain forest in the Amazon Basin offers a major contrast. Here you may find small, naked, reddish-brown people, quite different in appearance from your neighbors at home (illus., this page). Some of them hack out small clearings along the edge of the forest where they plant cassava, corn, or other crops. Some gather wild fruits and vegetables and hunt the birds, mammals, and other animals of the forest. They use no power but their own; they find fuel and water where they may be. But even they are almost certain to have beads, knives, fishhooks, and other things that originally came from distant lands unknown and unimaginable to them. Another great hop may take you to central Asia, where squat, powerful, weather-beaten brown nomads live in felt houses, travel on horseback, and tend flocks of sheep. In southern Asia and its islands yellowish or tan farmers slosh through their wet rice fields. In an African savanna you will see magnificent, tall, shining black people, living in well-organized villages and owning large herds of cattle. At a village perched on the Norwegian coast you may see fishermen (who do look just like some of your neighbors at home) setting out to gather a crop from the sea.

Nowadays, even if we have never left home, all of us are familiar with those scenes and a thousand others over the varied surface of our planet. Taken together, they illustrate biological facts and principles of profound human significance. Human interest is likely to center on the people in the scenes and to notice their differences first. The human species is endlessly varied, and among its variations are sets of characteristics by which we distinguish local groups and races, analogous to the demes and subspecies of plants and animals. Next, however, is the fact of unity in that diversity. All men are more alike than different, biologically. All groups intergrade and all can interbreed (a fact we may not have had time to note on our hurried trip). Mankind is one species.

Each human community is found to be intimately associated with, indeed really to be a part of, a broader biological community in which there are also many other species of animals and plants. The biological communities differ in different places, and the human communities are adjusted to those differences. The human communities, too, reflect environmental conditions and have local adaptations. Yet, now that we are in the second half of the twentieth century, human communities everywhere interact in ways more extensive and intensive than was usual in earlier biological communities, and they have drawn the biological communities also into a world-wide network of interactions. Everywhere we see that man has changed the environment. He has modified all the biological communities in which he lives. The effects seem slight in the Amazonian forest and are tremendous in your home town, but they exist everywhere that man is or has been. Many of the changes are constructive, from the human point of view at least. They have oriented nature for the benefit of its dominant species. Other changes are decidedly destructive from almost any point of view. They have reduced the capacity of the environment to support our own or other species, and they constitute a serious man-made problem for man.

In taking up these themes of the present chapter, we are drawing together threads that have run through what has been said before. The science of biology is integral, and all of it has a bearing on human life. Logical compartition of different biological "subjects" or of the biology of man and of nature is neither possible nor desirable. The particular aspects now to be considered—man as a species of organism and as a biological element in communities—derive especially from the broader groundwork of Part 5 and of previous chapters of this Part 7. The present themes also impinge on much else, on, for instance, the political and emotional problems of racism and segregation, the economic and technological problems of food supply and industry, and problems of, in the broadest way, man's modification and utilization of his environment— problems economic, social, political, technological, and psychological, all at once. Discussion of all these problems and proposals for their solution must be left to other books and other courses. They all do have biological aspects, and it is their more strictly biological basis that is to be reviewed here.

Homo sapiens: *the Systematics of Man*

After what has been said, it is unnecessary to stress again the fact that man is an organism, subject to all the principles that apply to other living things. It is also a thoroughly familiar fact that man is an animal of the phylum Chordata, class Mammalia, and order Primates. Systematists are unanimous in considering man the only now-living member of a family Hominidae and in placing all living men in the genus *Homo*, the name of which is simply the Latin word for "man." Our present concern is with the systematics of the present human population, by itself, rather than with the phylogenetic inferences that place man among his relatives in the whole system of animal classification.[1]

The principles of systematics in general (see especially Chapter 19) apply to all organisms and therefore also to man in particular. Here, however, their application is complicated by the fact that man is unique in many respects. Man is the most widespread of all species and has an unusually high degree of what was originally local differentiation. He is the most mobile of all species, and that mobility has always blurred and has now thoroughly mixed the regional differences usual in a widespread species. On top of that, man's more strictly biological characters are not only overlaid by but also inextricably interwoven with cultural factors wholly absent

[1] Chapter 32 gives a fuller background to the systematic position of man among the primates.

in most species and only barely incipient in any other species of animal.

ORIGIN AND NATURE OF RACES

It is entirely obvious that mankind includes numerous different groups that are physically different (Fig. 27-1). Chinese, American Indians, and Scandinavians are groups within which there is great variation, but there are also consistent differences between any two of these groups. A member of one can almost always be distinguished from a member of another. Interbreeding can and does take place between the groups, but it is far less common than breeding within one group. If, however, the whole sequence of peoples through Europe and Asia and over into the Americas is taken into consideration, it is impossible to draw a fixed line, either geographically or between populations, and say, "Here, precisely, is where the Scandinavian physical type leaves off and the Chinese begins, or the Chinese ends and the Indian starts."

That kind of situation is common in species other than *Homo sapiens*. It is, indeed, the rule for populous, widespread species of either animals or plants. There is every reason to believe that the biological phenomenon is exactly the same in man as in any other species. Small local populations, demes, tend to have gene frequencies somewhat different from those of adjacent demes, partly as a random result of mutation and sexual reproduction and partly as a result of natural selection under local conditions. Nevertheless there is gene exchange among demes, and groups of demes tend to have genetic features in common that distinguish them, on the average, from other, more distant groups. When such groups of demes become fairly distinctive, they are usually designated as subspecies. Subspecies intergrade and fluctuate. They are not permanent or absolutely definable evolutionary units. Differences between them are real, just as there are real differences between your family and the family next door, but the distinctions do not necessarily persist over many generations, and the subdivision of a species into a definite number of subspecies is largely an arbitrary procedure.

The major races of mankind as usually designated, such as the Mongolian or Caucasian races, are exactly like the subspecies of other species of animals. They have all the characteristics of subspecies mentioned in the last paragraph (see also p. 425). In fact they are subspecies, or perhaps (for reasons soon to be mentioned) it might be better to say that they *were* subspecies. The word "race" has been so abused for political and ideological reasons that some well-intentioned persons have denied the fact that such subdivisions really occur. Of course they do, and perhaps it would avoid unscientific emotionalism if we called them "subspecies" instead of "races." That would emphasize the biological facts that races or subspecies are not fixed and separate units but are arbitrary and shifting subdivisions of the species and that there is no possible way to designate them as "higher" or "lower," "primitive" or "advanced." They are simply regional populations all with the same status within the species.

Subspecies have intermediate demes that can hardly be assigned with assurance to one subspecies or another. So do human races. Subspecies include demes and groups of demes that could, as a matter of taste or preference, be distinguished by name or considered separate subspecies. So do human races. Subspecies are practically always differentiated on a geographic basis; their differences are differences between the populations of different regions. That also was surely true of races. Even now it is evident that the various races evolved by differentiation of populations in different parts of the earth. In the early days of human history populations were sparse. Family units and demes of a few interbreeding families were widely scattered and comparatively isolated. Even with occasional interbreeding among all intervening demes, passage of a gene by inheritance from a deme in, say, South Africa to one in China would take a great many generations. It might well not occur at all, especially if, as would be likely, the gene had less selective value elsewhere than in South Africa. Under such conditions genetic differentiation of populations in different regions would be sure to occur, and there is no doubt that the human races did arise in that way.

European (Portugal)

African (Kenya)

Asiatic (China)

27-1 Some races of living man. (Above, left photo from Socony Mobil Oil Company; center, Kenya Information Office; right, AMNH; lower left, AMNH; right, Australian Information Office)

American Indian (Assiniboin)

Australian aborigine

Differentiation of subspecies is sometimes (but not always or even usually) a prelude to the rise of distinct species. It becomes so if a barrier to interbreeding arises between two subspecies and persists until interbreeding ceases entirely and finally becomes impossible (p. 429). If mankind had continued to live under the primitive conditions of race differentiation, it is entirely possible that speciation would have occurred and that there would have been, for instance, separate African and European species of men. That did not happen, and now it cannot happen. The partial isolation and regional divergence among groups of primitive men that *might* have made them separate species came to an end. Expanding populations reduced isolation. Human mobility, constantly increasing, practically wiped out any effectiveness of geographic barriers. There is now no place on earth where the population consists entirely of a race, or any other subdivision of the species, originally differentiated there. Effects of the prehistoric subspecies are still apparent enough, but biologically the subspecies really

no longer exist as such. There is no chance at all that the same sort of geographic divergence will continue or will be resumed.

There are still barriers to interbreeding, but now they are mainly cultural or social and only secondarily or in minor degree geographic. In part they follow the lines of the old geographic subspecies, as in the case of the cultural barrier in some countries between interbreeding of descendants of the prehistoric African and European subspecies. Many of the cultural barriers, however, follow quite different lines. Just now there is little interbreeding between Communists and non-Communists, and there has long been comparatively little between members of conflicting religions. In some European countries generations passed with almost no interbreeding between the hereditarily (but not genetically!) wealthy and the hereditarily poor, but that barrier is fast dissolving. If such cultural barriers were strong enough and continued long enough, they could lead to biological subspeciation, or even speciation, along wholly new lines. It would be entirely possible for a Communist race or a Catholic race to evolve. The chance is slim, however, for the barriers are not clear-cut, and cultural change is much more rapid than biological evolution. All we can say now is that racial divergence along the lines of the prehistoric subspecies has ceased. It seems impossible to predict whether racial differences will eventually disappear, whether renewed subspeciation on a cultural rather than geographic basis will happen, or whether there may be some other, unforeseen outcome.

RACIAL CHARACTERS

"How many races are there?" is a question that does not make biological sense. In order to answer that, races would have to be fixed or sharply definable units, and they are not. There is authority for classifying mankind into three to thirty or more races. No two family groups are quite alike (nor yet wholly different), nor are any two demes or groups of demes. (And "family group" and "deme," although useful terms, are also definable only vaguely and not absolutely.) It is purely a matter of convenience how many and what groups of men are to be called "races." A well-considered recent classification[2] recognizes European (Caucasoid), African (Negroid), Asiatic (Mongoloid), American Indian, and Australoid races, and that is probably as convenient an arrangement as any. Its author recognizes that it is arbitrary and that many smaller groups cannot with assurance be placed in one or another of those races.

A concept involved in earlier attempts to specify or identify the races of mankind is that of the "pure race." That, too, is nonsense biologically, a fact more pertinent here than the further fact that it has been connected with some of the most vicious notions ever to enter the human mind. A race or subspecies is a biological, systematic group and can be defined sensibly only in terms of populations and their heredity, hence of frequencies of genes and their effects. Presumably a "pure" race would be a group of individuals

all with the same genes or, at least, all free of some "impure" genes from their neighbors. No such group within a species exists in nature or can ever have existed in mankind. Adjacent demes, whether or not we classify them in different subspecies, exchange genes, and any continuing difference is merely a matter of how frequent various genes may be. Here and there, to be sure, a deme might exist with a frequent or universal gene (more strictly allele) quite lacking in some other deme, but still over the generations genes in both would fluctuate and would be exchanged with other demes. It is not biologically possible for a deme, a race, or a subspecies to be "pure" in any meaningful sense. The idea that there were a few pure primitive races, whose mixed-up descendants we are, or that there is now such thing as a pure Nordic, Anglo-Saxon,[3] or any other race is a fairy tale, and not always a pretty one.

Adaptation is so universal in nature and is so clearly involved in differences between subspecies that it is a reasonable conclusion that many differences between human races were originally adaptive. (This does not exclude the probability that some arose from random fluctuations of gene frequencies in small groups of primitive men.) That has been hard to check, however, one way or another. There is good, but inconclusive, evidence that differences in skin color were adaptive when and where they arose. The color of the earliest men, doubtless variable as color is in all races, probably ranged through shades of brown. Darker or black skin was apparently an adaptation in regions of damaging ultraviolet solar radiation, and lighter or white skin an adaptation to regions where that radiation (which is beneficial in *small* amounts) was deficient. Such genetic changes under the influence of selection take long periods of time. Whites have not been in Africa or Negroes in America nearly long enough for selection to have made a perceptible difference in their skin color. Is white or black skin more "primitive"? Which is "better"?

2 By W. C. Boyd, "Genetics and the Races of Man," 1950. He also lists a hypothetical "early European" race, perhaps now represented by the Basques.

3 Anglo-Saxons, or their descendants, are not a race, anyhow, or any other even arbitrarily definable biological population. Neither, incidentally, are Jews, although some groups Jewish in religion have tended to become so, as have some other religious groups.

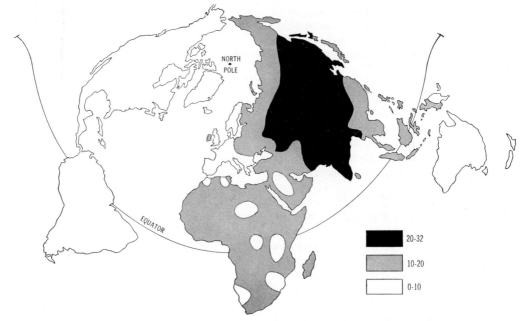

27-2 Distribution of the L^B blood group gene in world populations. The three intensities of shading refer to the percentage frequency of the L^B allele. It is clear that the gene controlling the B blood group is not uniformly distributed among human populations: it is relatively abundant in Asiatic populations and virtually absent in American Indians. (Note that the data apply to *original* populations in the areas concerned; B blood groups are now common in North and South America among populations that have come from Eurasia.) Of course, the same inhomogeneous distribution applies to the other blood group alleles: L^O is relatively abundant in the Western Hemisphere, less common in Eurasia. See also Fig. 17-5, which illustrates in more detail the blood group differences between adjacent races, in this case three Indian tribes in Montana.

Skin color is so obvious that we are inclined to think of it as the main indication of race. It is, however, superficial, both literally and figuratively. It would be more interesting and more important if we could measure hereditary differences in intelligence and personality between races, but so far all attempts have failed. The difficulty is that what can be measured under the names of "intelligence" and "personality" is so strongly influenced by learning that genetic differences (although they surely exist) are obscured. Groups of American Negroes usually average lower than whites from the same region on the scoring of standard intelligence tests. It is, however, known that these tests are strongly influenced by education and cultural background and that on an average Negroes do not now have equal educational and cultural opportunities with whites of the same region anywhere in the United States. The suspicion

that it is *that* difference, and not a genetic difference, which is being measured is confirmed by the fact that Negroes do test higher than whites in comparisons where they do have a cultural advantage, for instance in comparing urban northern Negroes with rural southern whites.

About all that can be said now is that if there are genetic racial differences in average intelligence and personality, these are so small in comparison with cultural differences and with genetic variation *within* each race as to have no apparent importance. There is also a theoretical biological reason for expecting this result when measuring intelligence, at least. During the prehistoric period of racial differentiation, it is inconceivable that intelligence was not at a premium everywhere. It would, then, be expected that natural selection would favor intelligence in all races, although the response might not be precisely the same everywhere. (This selective trend may be another that no longer operates in some modern societies.)

Recently a more direct approach to the study of genetic racial differences has been begun. Study is made particularly of the blood groups (p. 327), the genetics of which are known and simple and which can easily be determined in individuals. The best-known groups (O, A, B, AB) are dependent on three alleles, the frequencies of which have been determined in many populations (Fig. 27-2). In combination with similar studies of other known human genes, they may provide a more rational and meaningful basis for the biological classification of mankind than many of the older studies based on such things as skin color or head shape.

UNITY AND DIVERSITY

Man exemplifies in high degree the interplay of unity and diversity evident in the whole realm of life. Living men constitute a single species, *Homo sapiens*, by all criteria of modern definitions of species. They share a rich genetical heritage, and all are parts of an interbreeding, world-wide population. Specific unity makes it possible for desirable hereditary traits to be combined and spread, whatever their source. It makes all men fundamentally alike, with incomparably more biological resemblances than differences. The cultural apparatus has stopped or reversed primitive trends toward divergence. Mobility and communication are cultural reinforcements of the unity rooted in biological facts.

On the other hand, within the species there are innumerable differences among individuals and between groups, and both biological and cultural factors maintain diversity. Extensive variation within the bounds of one species is biologically favorable both because it extends the immediate range of adaptation and because it is the indispensable material for any progressive change. There is absolutely no evidence that any race or other group is inherently, biologically, better than another. Originally racial differences probably made *each* race better fitted biologically to the particular place where it lived, but cultural changes have largely or wholly eliminated even this local superiority of any race over any other.

The Basic Ecology of Homo sapiens

The diversity of human demes and races was originally related to the diversity of the natural communities in which men live. It still is to some extent, but with great changes involved in man's cultural evolution, an evolution arising from and interacting closely with his biological evolution.

Man everywhere lives in interspecific animal and plant communities, and he depends on his environment no less than any other organism. It is part of his cultural development that he reacts on the environment more widely and more strongly than any other species—a fact that would require special attention to this particular species in any textbook of general biology, even if it were written by a squirrel or an oyster.

PRIMITIVE MAN AND ENVIRONMENTS

Man's primitive position in natural communities was that of a particularly large, vicious land animal with an unusually wide range of foods. We are *omnivorous* ("eating everything") structurally, physiologically, and psychologically. That does not mean that men do or can eat literally everything, but that they eat almost any kind of animal food large enough to be worth the trouble and also a great variety of concentrated plant foods, especially fruits, seeds, and tubers or starchy roots. Biological consequences of this breadth of adaptation were that man could find food in almost any of the endlessly diverse natural communities of the earth and that in each community his status was complex. He became part of almost all food chains that could include a large animal.

Even before the clear establishment of civilization,[4] the human species had spread

4 The distinction between culture and civilization is important but not entirely clear. "Culture" includes social organization, learned activities, and constructions or manufactures of any human group. "Civilization" is simply a complex degree of culture, usually including a fixed form of government, communication beyond the face-to-face level, specialized agriculture and industry, and construction of at least semipermanent dwelling and business centers. All humans have a culture. Nowadays most of their cultures are civilizations.

into almost all land communities. Spread into the Americas was slowest (p. 798), but it occurred thousands of years ago and before the rise of civilizations anywhere. Noncivilized man lived practically everywhere on land except on the highest mountains, on some of the smallest and most barren islands, and in Antarctica. Civilization has greatly increased the density but has not appreciably changed the extension of man's distribution. Noncivilized cultures coped with a tremendous variety of environments, and they now survive (although everywhere with some impingement of civilization) precisely in the environments most difficult for man, those that are very cold, very dry, or very warm and humid. Early, slow biological adaptation was soon accompanied by and finally almost replaced by more rapid cultural adaptation. The two were and are intricately compensatory, and degrees and forms of each have varied greatly. The Alacalufs (now-extinct natives of Tierra del Fuego) devised practically no nonbiological protection against their severe climate, while the Eskimo culture includes excellent protection by shelters and clothing.

Man's biological reaction range (p. 334) is exceptionally wide. In addition to that came cultural evolution which enables a man of any biological constitution to make a cultural adaptation to almost any human environment. Thus are explained why biological differentiation, speciation, did not proceed far and why man's spread over the earth did not await the slow process of biological adaptation to each radically different environment.

Primitive culture was in large part, or at least it included, adaptation to environment. Environment was thus a decisive determinant in the diverse cultures evolved among primitive men. Civilized cultures are actually no less conditioned by environments, but the conditioning is less local and there is to far greater degree a reciprocal conditioning of the environment by culture. The most primitive men were surely food gatherers. Like an ameba, a tree, or a lizard, they accepted nature as they found it and fitted themselves into a natural community as another species among many, differing only in their increas-

ing ability for cultural as well as biological adaptation.

The immediate factors to which primitive man became adapted in each community are, by and large, the same environmental factors that affect all natural communities (see pp. 608 ff.). They are still important, although the interactions are profoundly modified in modern civilized human communities. Climate, soils, water supply, and the biotic environment consisting of protists, plants, and animals still strongly affect your own life, and you can see how much more direct and decisive the effect was on primitive man. Climate and soils determined, and still do to large extent, the growth of green plants on which the whole community depends. Animals interacted, and still interact, with man as foods, as competitors, and as antagonists (parasites and predators on man, for instance). Although he is decisively a land animal, man also early developed shore communities that derived most of their food from the sea and its shore. Fishing in inland waters was also among the earliest sources of human food.

Civilization brought other environmental relationships not found in primitive cultures or in organisms other than man, and yet with an element of primitive, direct environment-organism reaction. Industry requires power and raw materials (other than food), and this has environmental relations of no significance to nonindustrial organisms. The distribution and nature of human communities is influenced by the natural distribution of water power, mineral fuels, ores, and other industrial resources. In this, however, as in all his relationships with nature, civilized man has greatly modified the directness of his interaction with the environment.

CULTURAL MODIFICATION OF HUMAN ECOLOGY

Biological adaptation to direct effects of climate involves flexibility of reaction range, evolution of a new reaction range, or both. Cultural modification of the relationship, up to the present, has been almost entirely by protection against climates: clothing and shelter. Air-conditioned homes and other buildings represent a climax of that cultural trend. It is, by the way, an interesting example of the complexity and imperfections of cultural adaptation that even now in many places men (generic, of course, including women) wear clothing demonstrably and radically inappropriate as adaptation to the existing climate. Reciprocal influence of man on climate is as yet unimportant. Men have begun to tinker with the weather by cloud seeding, but no real effect on climate is yet evident. Other human activities, such as large drainage and irrigation projects, really have inadvertently changed local climates to some degree, but not widely or markedly.

Cultural changes have probably been greatest as regards food. The gathering of wild foods, sole resource of the earliest men and of almost all other organisms,[5] has become comparatively unimportant. It affects civilized communities on a large scale only in the form of commercial sea fishing, which is an enormous industry but yet accounts for only a small fraction of the food of mankind. Even among wild species of aquatic foods, many are now deliberately propagated by man and not simply gathered: oysters, trout, and pond fishes, for example. Gathering of wild land foods, such as wild rice, wild berries, piñon nuts, wild rabbits, deer, or antelope, persists for variety and recreation but plays no essential part in the food supply of civilized man.

Food gathering has, as everyone knows, been almost entirely supplanted by agriculture and animal husbandry, both of which go far back in history to the dim days even before the definitive rise of early civilizations. This is one of the two most radical changes of man's relationships with environments. It is decidedly a reciprocal interaction. On the side of the organism, the food supply of *Homo sapiens* has been enormously increased and made more dependable. On the side of the environment, everywhere that cultivated plants

[5] There is hardly any respect in which human activities are unique in kind, although most of them are unique in extent and complexity. Some ants grow cultivated plants (fungi) and do not gather wild food; some could claim to have invented animal husbandry, as they tolerate, indeed cultivate, aphids from which they gather a sugary fluid much as we gather milk from cows.

are grown or domestic animals are raised the biotic environment has been profoundly changed. There have also been repercussions in the physical environment, for instance in the composition of soils or the localization of erosion.

The other of the two most radical cultural changes in the organism-environment relationship of *Homo sapiens* has been decreased dependence on the immediate environment of here and now. Other organisms interact with an environment with which they are in actual physiological or sensory contact at each moment. That immediate environment is of course influenced by more distant happenings, and one cannot draw a circle anywhere around any natural community and say, "Here environmental effects on the community definitely end." Nevertheless it is true that nonhuman communities interact with their environments on a highly localized basis. That must also have been true of early *Homo sapiens*, but it decidedly is not true of modern man. He mines iron ore in Venezuela, smelts it in eastern United States, manufactures it into machinery in the Midwest, and uses the machinery in Australia. In Australia he grows sheep which are eaten in Great Britain, where wool from the sheep is also manufactured into cloth, which is worn in South Africa. He pipes water over the mountains to Los Angeles and there lives by the millions in a desert that might support a scant dozen families living on the actual capacity of their own immediate environment.

The world-wide interlocking of human supply, commerce, and industry is thoroughly familiar to you, perhaps so familiar that you do not think about it enough. We need not belabor the point beyond emphasizing that this is a biological phenomenon. Local environmental interactions have by no means been eradicated and are as important as ever; but they are caught up into a world-wide network of interactions. It is becoming increasingly true that a reaction anywhere affects the human environment in some way and degree everywhere. *Homo sapiens* is rapidly becoming a species (the only one) in which an individual's environment is not only his own surroundings but the whole earth.

Modification of the Environment

The results of man's cultural changes in his relationship to the environment have not affected man alone. They have reverberated through the whole world of life and have affected the environments of countless other organisms. If a state of nature is defined as one uninfluenced, directly or indirectly, by man, then you would search far to find a state of nature anywhere on earth today. It is certainly not to be found anywhere that man lives or travels, not in the remotest Amazonian jungle or the most barren desert. Perhaps it still exists on some unscaled Himalayan height or unplumbed oceanic deep, but even there some remote effect of human activity is likely to be felt.

All organisms influence their environments, and many have some small measure of active control over parts of their environments. The fact is obvious when a beaver builds a dam, and no less true when a tree sheds its leaves. Man, however, controls and modifies environments more extensively than any other organism.

LAND USE

Here in the United States and in many other of the most intensely developed parts of the world the most obvious widespread changes have been produced by man's destruction of natural communities to convert them and the space they occupied to his own uses. Indians had already considerably modified their environments in North America, but the changes they made were insignificant in comparison with what has happened since Europeans settled here. In 1492 almost the whole eastern half of North America was covered with vast forests. About 300 million acres of forests have since been destroyed. Most of the early clearing was for farmland; that is to say, biologically its purpose was to remove native communities with low supporting capacity for *Homo sapiens* and to replace them with controlled communities more productive of human food. Clearing has now become a negligible activity, simply because most of the good agricultural land was long ago cleared. Forests now remain mainly where they are themselves more productive for human use than would be farm-

ing where they stand. They are now cut for forest products, mostly lumber. Destruction of forests still goes on, although in the national forests and those controlled by the more enlightened private owners the cutting is so managed as to crop surplus growth and keep the forest healthy. Even in that situation, the controlled crop forest is a community unlike that of virgin forest. The same is true of extensive tracts early cut for farmland and now gone back to forest by natural succession or deliberate reforestation. We are not, at this point, concerned with whether this is a "good thing" or a "bad thing" but only making the biological observation that the natural communities have been destroyed or profoundly altered. It should be added that destruction of forests still goes on extensively by fires, most of which are of human origin.

Eradication of natural communities has been at least as profound in the vast zone of former grassland between the Mississippi and the Rocky Mountains. Here almost the whole of the climax vegetation has been plowed under and all the communities associated with it profoundly affected. Even where bits of sod have been spared, spreading effects have reached. It is now literally impossible to find anywhere a natural prairie community such as those that occupied thousands of square miles only a century ago.

Besides replacing native vegetation with introduced plants, man has also drained environments too wet for his crops and put water on those too dry. In the United States enormous areas have been drained, mostly in Florida, the Mississippi Valley, and the North Central states. The mere fact of draining radically changes the environment, and of course its usual purpose is to introduce new communities. Other immense areas, mostly west of the 100th meridian, have been irrigated and their native vegetation (for practically none of the reclaimed "desert" land was bare) again replaced by cultivated plants and introduced weeds.

Much American farmland is used to produce food for domestic animals (of which only the turkey is native to America). Such grassland as remains has also been converted almost entirely to that human use. Introduction of exotic animals on the grasslands and man's incessant efforts to protect them from competitors and real or fancied enemies have also changed the natural communities almost beyond recognition.

Land not used to produce food or raw materials is still not free from human disturbance. Cities, industrial plants, airfields, roads, and other such constructions wipe out the natural environment wherever they are built, and in the aggregate they cover a considerable fraction of the surface of the land. Even areas not permanently inhabited, such as the high mountain country, or those deliberately kept "natural," such as the national parks and parts of the national forests, are intensively used by man for recreation, if nothing else. No biologically minded person who joins the traffic jam in, say, Yellowstone Park can imagine for a minute that he is seeing a community natural in the sense of absence of radical human disturbance.

Even now—and intensity of use increases yearly—it is unlikely that there is an acre of land in the United States that is not sometimes and in some way used by man for his specific purposes and that has not been changed by that use. The same is true almost everywhere on earth, true to even greater extent where man's occupation has been longer, as in Europe, and true to less extent where exploitation has been less intense, as in the Amazon Basin, but nevertheless true. If you would like to return to nature, you were born too late.

DISTURBANCE OF COMMUNITIES

Let us now consider briefly but more explicitly some of the things that happen to communities as a result of human activities. The most radical thing that happens is, of course, that a community is destroyed as such and another put in its place. This is by no means a simple occurrence. When grassland is plowed up and planted in corn, the result is not simply that we have corn instead of grass. The grass and other associated green plants were, as you know, only a first link in innumerable food chains and one element in a populous community. Some of the food chains are cut off at the bottom when the grass is destroyed. The organisms in those chains die out or move elsewhere. It is man's intention that corn shall start food chains leading only to himself, but with all his controls he is unable to carry out those intentions. Some members of the destroyed community happily switch to corn, and some of the old food chains continue. Other organisms that eat corn (any part of the plant) move in, and their populations increase. New food chains develop. A whole community organization is rapidly resumed on the new basis.

Wherever man breaks the soil, drains it, waters it, or otherwise changes local conditions, he creates a new environment that is quickly exploited. Everyone who has lived in the West knows that tumbleweed (Russian thistle, *Salsola pestifer*) has the greatest difficulty in breaking into an established community. It almost never grows anywhere but along roads, on plowed or abandoned fields, and on range so badly overgrazed that much of the native vegetation has been destroyed. Under those conditions of human disturbance it rapidly spreads everywhere. There are many other plants, including some that are natives (such as bee plant, a species of *Cleome*), that spread rapidly along the sides of roads and on other disturbed soil. It is a general observation that cleared land is rapidly invaded by some plants and not at all by others, and that there is intense selection and rapid evolution in adaptation to what is always a new biotic environment and often also a changed physical environment. Thus not only new kinds of communities arise where man has passed, but also new successions and new climaxes. Seldom are things ever again quite the same.

It seems a fairly obvious fact that interference in a food chain or in a predator-prey balance is going to react on the whole chain or on both sides of the balance. Yet men have often deliberately interfered in such situations without foreseeing the results. The destruction of predators in the Kaibab forest is a good example (p. 655). Another along the same lines happens when coyotes are eliminated because they occasionally prey on sheep. The main food supply of the coyotes is rabbits, which may increase so in numbers when the coyotes are removed that the sheep are starved by competition with the rabbits for food. Or again, widespread use of DDT to control mosquitoes in some areas has led to death of desirable fishes and birds that feed on insects. And that suggests still another unforeseen result of human interference which has a tinge of ironic justice: use of insecticides, including DDT, sometimes merely has the result of evolving, by rapid selection, a strain of insects immune to the insecticides. Experimentation with the "wonder drugs" has also developed strains of bacteria immune to the drug, and even some that require the drug in order to thrive!

To revert to the tumbleweed or Russian thistle, this is, like a great many of our weeds, an unwitting introduction by man into North America (the Hopi Indians call it "white man's plant"). All over the world man has introduced plants and animals from elsewhere, sometimes unintentionally but often deliberately. So widespread are such introductions that there is now no place on earth where all the plants and animals are natives. If the introductions become established, they are bound to disturb the native communities, and they frequently lead to the extinction of native species. A policy of bringing in plants and birds considered more desirable than the native has decimated the beautiful native flora and fauna of the Hawaiian Islands and has effectively destroyed what was a unique biological community. Mongooses were also introduced and have had a large share in exterminating less harmful native species, as also happened in the West Indies. In Australia cacti and rabbits, also deliberately introduced, expanded explosively and almost ruined the economy of the country before they were brought under tenuous control.

Man has also wiped out numerous species single-handedly, such as the passenger pigeon and the dodo, and he reduced others, such as our bison and pronghorn antelope, to the verge of extinction before deciding to save a few for his own pleasure. On the other hand he has greatly increased the populations of some species, even aside from his domestic animals. House rats should be grateful to man who, although unwillingly, made possible their world-wide expansion. More pleasantly, some native quail find cultivated fields a fine addition to their environment and thrive in community with man.

Depletion and Conservation

All organisms derive materials and energy from their environments. All tend to increase in population and to spread in areas as greatly as is permitted by the capacity of the environment and their capacity to utilize the environment (including, of course, the biotic environment). All are checked, ultimately, by limitations of the environment and by such factors as competition and predation, which do not, as a rule, reduce the utilization of the environment but only determine the proportions of its resources that go to support each of the various species present. There is a tendency for each species to monopolize as much as possible of the supporting capacity of the environment. Man is no exception to any of these biological principles. Quite the contrary, it is precisely these principles that underlie and explain man's spread over the earth and the consequent disturbance of natural communities everywhere. That the disturbance is so incomparably greater than results of the same tendencies in any other species is merely a measure of the complexities of man's demands on the environment and of his success in enforcing them.

No organism other than man faces the environment with such a variety of needs and wants (the word is appropriate for man, but only questionably so for other organisms). Man's mental development and the cultural developments arising from it have made him eminently successful in satisfying even his extreme needs and wants. He wrests from other species what both could use, and also has uses for things that have little significance for any other species. Man is in these respects the most successful of species. His capacity is greatest, but he still is acting like any species of organism in a biologically natural way. Yet it is increasingly apparent that some of man's activities in successful exploitation of his environment are reducing the capacity of that environment to support man himself. To that extent he is living beyond his income, and any species that lives beyond its biological income eventually faces decimation or extinction. Man has the advantage in that he can foresee the possibility of disaster and may find means to avoid it.

UTILIZATION VS. PRESERVATION

A first reaction to the widespread destruction of natural communities is often a wish that they could be preserved. Many sentimentalists understand "conservation" as opposition to any disturbance of nature. Certainly biologists, above all people, are sensitive to the interest and beauty of nature, but they must recognize that the attitude of purely sentimental conservation—that is, a desire for the preservation of untrammeled nature—is as unsound biologically as it is impossible politically or socially. As a practical matter, and regardless of whether such action would be desirable, it would now be absolutely impossible to find a natural community of any great extent completely uninfluenced by man and to keep it so. If it could be done, what benefit would arise? Any visit to such a refuge or any study of it would immediately end its pristine nature.

Man is an organism, and all organisms utilize their environments. Man will do so no matter what anyone says or does. Even his destruction of nature is biologically natural. His utilization of the whole of his environment is biologically inevitable and is desirable from the viewpoint of his own species. Surely for a human being to take any other viewpoint would be monstrous. It is, however, evident that such utilization may be either wise or foolish. Wisdom in this sense also has a biological significance. Utilization is wise if it does really, both immediately and in the long run, produce maximum benefit for our species. That is the practically and biologically sound definition of conservation.

Wise utilization for production is that which increases or at any rate does not decrease the capacity of the environment to meet human needs. Increase in capacity, although it can be spectacular, is inherently limited. It has, indeed, been found that rapid increase may actually lead to ultimate decrease, as has happened in agricultural areas too intensively farmed. The ideal would be to put production on a cyclic basis, turning to the use of man such cycles as have kept all life going continuously for well over a billion years (Chapter 30). That involves a thorough understanding of biological cycles, with emphasis on the facts that you cannot get more out of a cycle than goes into it and that disturbance of any part upsets the whole.

Resources that can be operated in cycles are *renewable*. The possible rate of use is limited by the rate of the cycle as a whole and by the rate of input of energy, a resource that is *not* renewable because of the Second Law (p. 619). To the extent that energy is available and that its use is limited to the capacity of the cycle and the cycle is kept in operation, such resources are inexhaustible. This *possibility* applies particularly to biological resources, to food and to raw materials derived from plants and animals. Man need never lack food or organic raw materials if his consumption of them is kept to the rate of their production by continuously balanced cycles. Unfortunately, consumption does have a tendency to run ahead of the capacity of the cycles, and some efforts to increase their capacity have actually ended in decreasing it.

Other resources are *nonrenewable*. Their production cannot be made cyclic, not, at least, as man produces them and at rates even modestly sufficient for his demands. Our major sources of power, fuel, and light are nonrenewable. Petroleum (and its products, such as gasoline), natural gas, and coal are organic in origin, and hence theoretically renewable, but we are rapidly using up the accumulations of several hundred million years, and the rate of renewal is so extremely slow as to have no practical significance. Naturally fissionable elements, such as uranium, are hailed as a future source of power, but they are also strictly limited in amount and are decisively nonrenewable. Most of our intensively used mineral products, notably the metals such as iron, copper, and many others, are nonrenewable. Their atoms are not destroyed by use, but they are eventually so scattered as to be unrecoverable by any process economically possible now or foreseeable. An economy dependent on nonrenewable environmental resources, as ours surely is, cannot be permanent. Wise utilization of nonrenewable resources is evidently the slowest possible utilization with the least possible waste. When such resources will run out is not primarily a biological problem. It does concern biology that the best chance of an indefinite future for civilization seems to be the eventual substitution of nonrenewable by renewable materials, that is, in the main, of mineral by organic production.

Here (as on p. 653) it is possible to foresee consequences of continuous increase in the world population, consequences that few will consider pleasant. The absolute limit to otherwise unchecked population increase would be imposed (as it already has been in some countries) by food production. Since each link in a food chain dissipates energy and some materials, a maximum population would have to live as near the beginning of a food chain as possible: human food would consist solely of green plants. Because non-green plants and all animals compete with man for food, all would be exterminated as far as possible. Pressure for food production would be such that renewable production for any other use would be minimized. Nonrenewable resources would soon be gone, and industry, along with all the products of civilization as we know it, would be reduced to a minimum. What steps will be necessary to obviate this dismal prospect?

Even on a basis of greatest production, it can be shown that wise utilization often involves as little disturbance of natural communities as is practically feasible. The natural cycles may be as productive as any that man can substitute for them. That is probably particularly true of forests, of much semiarid and arid land, and of the seas. Forests over wide areas of poor soils and hilly or mountainous country in the Temperate Zone are more productive of useful organic materials than any method yet devised for farming the same land. That is also true of the vast tropical forests, the productivity of which is probably the largest natural resource not yet extensively utilized by man. Cutting down those forests to clear farmland, in the way traditional to us in the Temperate Zone, has so far almost invariably failed. The hopeful new trend is the devising of techniques for cropping the exuberant production of the forests themselves. As for regions with too little rainfall for farming, irrigation is not the full answer to their utilization. There is not enough available water to irrigate them all. Many of the desert and semidesert soils do not repay irrigation even when water can be put on them. In fact, where soils were good they have sometimes been ruined by irrigation through accumulation of salts from the evaporating water. But the natural communities of such areas, adapted to their low water supply, are as productive as the environment permits. In the sea the natural communities are extremely productive, and cropping of the natural food cycles by man is more effective than any other utilization in prospect.

Hitherto we have spoken of utilization in terms of material production. If the human population does reach the maximum capacity of the environment, no other utilization will have much significance. That point is not yet reached, and some may well hope it never is. In the meantime, we can afford and profit by nonproductive utilization of some of the surface of the earth. Space for recreation, or a silent place in which to think, or simply room to draw a clear breath—most of us think that, too, is good utilization of part of our environment. It is also of value, and practical in the fullest sense, to reserve what space we can for natural communities as little disturbed as possible, where biologists and everyone else can observe and learn more about the processes of nature by which we live and of which we are a part.

MAN AND SOIL

Conservationists have recently been greatly concerned with soil utilization, and for good reasons. We depend on natural soils for most of our food, whether more directly as plant food or less directly as animal food. It is possible to make excellent artificial soils or soil substitutes, but so far, at least, that is so expensive that it has little promise as a possible source of the bulk of human food. It is also unlikely that the aquatic environments, rich as they are, could economically be made the main source of plants and animals usable for human food; they are not so now, at any rate. The soil, then, is the basic factor in supplying man's most basic need, a double "basic" that makes soil fundamental indeed.

It has been carefully estimated that the United States has had 1517 million acres of economically usable farm and grazing land.

27-3   Erosion. *Left,* gully erosion in Guilford County, North Carolina. *Right,* wind erosion on a farm in Cimarron County, Oklahoma, April 1936.

By the same estimate, 282 million acres had been ruined by use up to 1947 and had become essentially unusable for the predictable future. It was estimated that continued use by traditional methods would soon ruin 775 million acres more. Only 460 million acres were considered in reasonably good shape and not seriously threatened. Some parts of the world are better off, and some are worse. In North Africa, for instance, an Arab historian wrote that it was once possible to ride from Egypt to Morocco under a continuous green canopy. The statement is almost incredible, for much of the ride today is over bare sand and rock; the soil, if soil there was, is gone. That the historian may not have exaggerated widely is attested by the presence of many ruined cities, once populous and now deserted and surrounded by desolation.

Soil is theoretically a renewable resource. All soils were formed, at some time, from bare rock, sands, silts, or barren clays, and soils are continuously being formed now (pp. 613 and 664). The process is slow. Under the best of conditions formation of a good agricultural soil takes centuries, and it may take thousands of years. Agricultural practices that result in loss of soil are therefore essentially mining it, using it up as a nonrenewable resource.[6]

When a farmer removes a crop from a field he also removes material that came from the soil and that would, under natural conditions, have returned to it. The process cuts

[6] These statements are only partly modified by the fact that silts spread by floods may be immediately highly fertile and have their fertility renewed each year, as in the Nile Valley. The fertile silts are soils eroded from areas upstream, so the process robs Peter to pay Paul.

Soil Conservation Service from Monkmeyer

27-4 Contour farming in the Elm Creek watershed, Bell County, Texas. By running his plowing and planting lines along the contours of the land, the farmer can minimize water, and therefore topsoil, runoff. The practice must often, as in this case, be a co-operative venture between adjacent landowners.

off part of the cycle of materials and depletes the soil. The cycle can be kept going by interspersing harvested crops with planting that does enrich the soil and by making good the losses by adding fertilizers. More serious and practically impossible to replace is actual physical loss of the soil by wind and water erosion after the protective natural plant cover is removed. A wind storm on May 12, 1934, swept up 300 million tons of soil from the plains east of the Rockies and began the "dust bowl" devastation that brought on an economic crisis and the migration of thousands of homeless "Okies," farmers whose farms had blown away (Fig. 27-3). In 1900 drip from a barn in Georgia started a gully in surrounding bare soil that has since spread to 3000 acres and washed away whole farms. The millions of acres of soil now lost in such ways (Fig. 27-3) cannot be recovered, but further losses are being slowed down, at least, by contour plowing, terracing, and more care in maintaining a vegetation cover (Fig. 27-4). On grazing land, heavy overgrazing has also laid bare the soil and promoted erosion, besides damaging the grass

community and permitting invasion of undesirable weeds (p. 680). The remedy is obvious although not easy: replanting of hardy grasses and reduced grazing (Fig. 27-5).

Erosion of soil is so real and serious a problem that those combating it may be excused some exaggeration. One of them says flatly that erosion is man-made. Another publishes a picture of a scrawny cow in front of badlands, with the implication that cow and friends are responsible for the badlands. The fact is that erosion is a natural process which went on for two billion years before man appeared, and that produced our badlands long before there were any cows in North America. Wherever erosion has taken the soil from farmland and grassland, it would sooner or later have done so without human help. That does not alter the fact that man has greatly hastened erosion and often localized it exactly where and when it does him the most damage. Recognition that erosion is an intermittent but inevitable and natural process everywhere on land puts the matter in truer perspective and should assist

Soil Conservation Service

27-5 Overgrazing on Texas range. To the left of the fence, where cattle have been kept out, there is still a good growth of grasses; to the right the land has been reduced to a minimum cover of sagebrush.

in planning to minimize the damage done by a process that cannot really be stopped.

FLOODS AND FLOOD CONTROL

Soil kept porous and covered with vegetation absorbs much rainfall. On cleared land the soil tends to pack, and more rain runs off over the surface. This is of course the immediate cause of accelerated erosion on cleared land, and it is also an interference with the water cycle which has extensive repercussions on living communities. Uplands from which forests have been cleared no longer retain water effectively, and the ground water below them is also less steadily maintained. Organic productivity is thus decreased by lack of steady water supply. The runoff also tends to produce floods more severe than those that would occur without human disturbance. Return to natural water conditions is generally desirable and can be obtained only by restoring vegetation on the uplands. Even natural flooding, without intensification by human activity, is a serious problem to those who live and farm along such rivers as the Mississippi and its main tributaries.

Flood control projects represent one of the most heroic efforts of man to control the natural environment and the intensification of natural forces resulting from man's own activities. Some attempt is made to control floods where they come from, in the runoff

in the uplands, but most of the effort goes into delaying the floodwaters downstream by holding them behind storage dams. The water so impounded may also be used for generating power and for irrigation. The geologist notes that the expedient is temporary, for all the storage reservoirs will fill up with silt in a few generations at most and then be useless. (Some have filled in a dozen years. See Fig. 27-6.) Extension of their usefulness demands that silting be reduced by controlling erosion above them. The biologist may add that adjustment of human utilization to the natural cycles of earth and life is the only *permanent* solution.

RENEWING RENEWABLE RESOURCES

When the whole situation is reviewed, it seems that man's troubles in the utilization of his environment have one general cause, and that the cause is rooted in biological principles. Life has kept going throughout its tremendously long history by the inpouring of energy from the sun and by interlocking inorganic and organic cycles and sequences of materials and energy on the earth. Man's manipulation of his environment has resulted in its deterioration, from his point of view, whenever he has ignored those natural processes instead of utilizing them. He accelerates the water cycle and the cycle of erosion, both of which are going to continue, man willing

U.S. Forest Service

27-6 Dams are a temporary solution to flood control problems. Mono Dam and Reservoir filled with silt, Los Padres National Forest, California.

or not. Then he becomes alarmed, but instead of recognizing the nature of the cycles and working with them, he tries to stop them. Intensifying floods by clearing the uplands, and then trying to stop them by dams is rather like whipping a horse and then shooting it when it runs away.

Similarly, man ignores food chains and then tries to control them by removing the one link that seems to him, often erroneously, to be responsible for the whole trouble, as when he kills coyotes only to have the more damaging rabbits increase. He may try to get out of a cycle more than goes into it, as in the many projects that are pumping down the water table without concern for the fact that no more water is continuously available from the ground than comes into it from rainfall. Also, he nets fish without remembering that next year's population depends on the reproductive capacity of those he leaves this year.

Man's intelligence is so great that he can do a great deal of damage to himself (and everything else) when he uses it unwisely.

Is his intelligence great enough for him to learn to use it wisely? To a biologist it looks as if man would be wise to live on and within his income—in other words, to use the *renewable* resources of the environment and to see to it that they *are* renewed.

Chapter Summary

Man in nature: the human environment in modern Western world—mechanization, communication, interdependence of communities—contrasted with that of primitive peoples; mankind one species with diverse local cultures; interaction between man and his environment.

Homo sapiens; systematics of man:

Man as chordate, mammal, primate, hominid, the single species in the genus *Homo;* unusually wide distribution; local differentiation, of both biological and cultural characters.

Origin and nature of human races: population evolution in man as in other animals; existence of subspecies, usually designated "races"; political and emotional overtones of word "race"; impermanence of subspecies as units; their intergradation; human subspecies breaking down because of human mobility; cultural and social factors only remaining barriers to subspecies breakdown and intermixing.

Racial characters; no unique answer to "How many races?" useful to distinguish five: Australoid, American Indian, Asiatic, Negroid, Caucasoid; concept of "pure" race as biological nonsense; skin color and other racial differences as adaptive, at least in part; no evidence for racial differences in intelligence; use of blood group frequencies as objective characterization of races; no race inherently "better" in any biological sense.

Basic ecology of *Homo sapiens:*

Primitive man and environments: man as omnivorous; as part of all food chains open to large animals, thus permitting success and wide dispersal of human culture; culture as, in part, adaptive; hence environmental impact on human culture.

Cultural modification of primitive human ecology: clothing, shelter; human influence on climate, on soils and drainage systems; transition from food gathering to agriculture, including animal husbandry; complex interdependence of modern communities in commerce.

Modification of the environment: land use and disturbance of natural communities; in North America, removal of forests and development of arable land; includes eradication of natural communities of animals; introduction of foreign plants and animals; dangers in disturbing community balance (exemplified by Kaibab deer, by DDT programs, and by introductions into Hawaii and Australia).

Depletion and conservation:

Severity of man's demands on environment; problems raised; possibility of solving them with foresight.

Utilization *vs.* preservation: "conservationism": its sentimental form; its wise form, as planned exploitation of environment to maximum *long-term* benefit of human species; renewable and nonrenewable resources; problems posed by the latter (exemplified by fuel and mineral resources).

Soils, erosion, flooding: prime significance of soils in food production; destruction of soils by present practices; soils theoretically renewable, but in practice nonrenewable; factors involved in soil destruction: overfarming, wind erosion, gully erosion, etc.; erosion a natural process seriously accelerated by man, especially by clearing of forests and other practices that increase flooding; flood control; the need for understanding ecologic processes; above all, the need to exploit principally renewable resources and to conserve nonrenewable resources.

The Geography
of Life

INTRODUCTION TO PART EIGHT

The llamas (above) and the camels (below) in our photograph are closely re lated animals; they had common ancestors in the not-too-distant past. We have used them to introduce Part 8 because they typify a class of problems that have long fasci nated and puzzled biologists. The problem arises from their present geographic dis tributions: the camel is Asian, and the llama is restricted to the Andean highlands of South America. How is it that such certainly related forms occur in such widely isolated areas with no contact whatsoever? Or, similarly, why is it that tapirs occur only in tropical America and Malaya? But, outstanding as these curious cases are, they do not represent the only class of problem that confronts the observer of geographic distribu tions. Why do cacti occur mostly in deserts in America—and why only in American, not in African, deserts? As soon as we begin to realize that there are some striking regulari ties to the distribution of organisms over the surface of the earth, it becomes clear that the subject is a large one with distinct problems of its own meriting special study.

The geography of life is open to two distinct lines of explanation, which are developed separately in Chapters 28 and 29.

First (Chapter 28), the distribution of any species of organism is ultimately limited by the distribution of suitable environments. The distribution of cacti is ulti mately limited by the distribution of deserts; the absence of cacti from the wet ground of American rain forests is explained by the ecological principle that they are not adapted to conditions of high moisture. The principle applies to all species, although the limiting environmental conditions are rarely so extremely or clearly defined as they are for cacti. Moreover, the limiting conditions are often other organisms, which, as we stressed throughout Part 7, are major constituents of any organism's environment.

Second (Chapter 29), the distributions of organisms are, however, rarely ex plained fully by the limited distribution of their appropriate environment: deserts occur in Africa but cacti do not. Full explanation of such cases demands introduction of strictly historical principles. Species arise in a particular locality and in the course of time they disperse, expanding their distribution into suitable environments elsewhere. Their dispersal is, however, contingent on some continuity of suitable habitats; the spread of cacti (originating in America) into African deserts has been blocked by the barrier of the Atlantic Ocean.

The distribution of camels and llamas points up fully the nature of the his torical principles involved in the analysis of distributions. Some millions of years ago the camel family did have a continuously suitable environment from Asia to South America—and this was occupied. But changing conditions of world climate and faunas have subsequently constricted this ecologically suitable range to the now widely separated areas of the Andes and Asia.

The distribution of the saguaro cactus within the Western Hemisphere is determined almost entirely by ecological factors, the topic of this chapter. The saguaro's distribution in the world as a whole involves additional purely historical causes, treated in Chapter 29. (Photo from National Park Service)

CHAPTER 28

Ecological Biogeography

THE BASES OF BIOGEOGRAPHY

A visit to the country is a pleasure that most of us seek periodically. The pleasure is greatly increased by an understanding of biological principles. One thing that cannot have failed to impress you in the countryside is that different associations of plants and animals occur even quite near each other. The living things in a stream or lake are decidedly different from those on land along the shore. Farther back on a hillside or a drier meadow other local communities will appear, plainly unlike those of the shore.

Thus at one locality a walk of a few feet can take you from one community into another. If you take a longer trip you will soon see that there are broader regional differences in communities. Suppose you take a vacation drive from New York to Tucson. For the first couple of days you will be in regions where

the predominant natural regional community, among the many different more localized communities, is usually a deciduous [1] forest. In the flatter areas most of the forest has been artificially replaced by farmland, but it is still evident that the deciduous forest represents the usual natural climax (p. 665). Farther along, west of the Mississippi, you will be in a region also extensively plowed into fields but with a natural predominance of open grassland communities. That extends onto the high plains of eastern Colorado and New Mexico, with a change in species of grass if you examine the communities more closely and with a botanist's eye. Then you may, depending on your route, have an interlude in mountain forests. Eventually, however, you will see the grassland grading into brush communities, dominated by such plants as sagebrush and greasewood. Finally those communities will grade into others, typical of the true desert, in which cactuses, mesquite, and ocotillo are most conspicuous.

If now you have the fortune to travel more widely, say to South America, you will encounter still other regional differences in natural communities. Some, such as rain forest or "jungle," live in conditions that you did not encounter on your travels in the United States. It is not surprising that all the species present are unfamiliar to you. Elsewhere,

[1] Deciduous trees are those that shed their leaves all at once, usually in the autumn. In the Temperate Zone most trees other than the coniferous evergreens are deciduous.

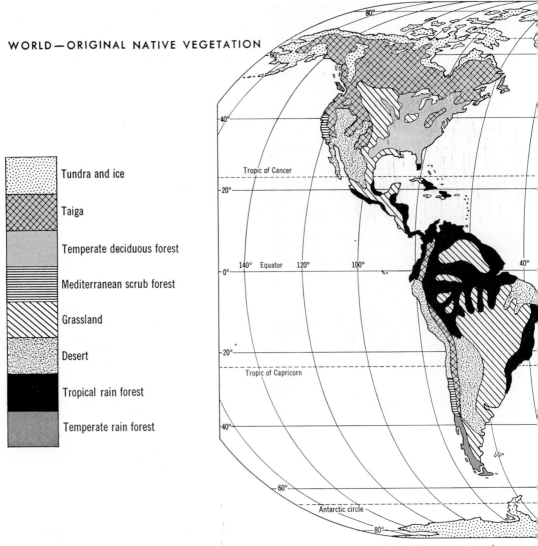

Tundra and ice

Taiga

Temperate deciduous forest

Mediterranean scrub forest

Grassland

Desert

Tropical rain forest

Temperate rain forest

28-1 The distribution of the original native vegetation of the world. The categories of vegetation on a map of this scale are necessarily broadly conceived. Thus, many of them—like taiga, temperate deciduous forest, and tropical rain forest—include within them a diversity of recognizably distinct subtypes.

however, the communities may look almost like some you saw back home. The pampas of Argentina are like the grasslands of the United States, and much of Patagonia looks like our southwestern thornbush deserts. Here in these superficially familiar surroundings it is surprising to find that the species present are just as distinctive from ours as those in the rain forest.

We have mentioned only plants by way of example because they are fundamental in all

communities and are easy to observe. The animals in the communities tend to have similar resemblances and differences on local, regional, and intercontinental scales. Many of their geographic distinctions are common knowledge. Everyone knows that you have to go up north to see a polar bear or out west to see a grizzly bear in their native haunts. You must go to Asia to see a wild tiger and to Australia to see a wild kangaroo.

These common observations show that

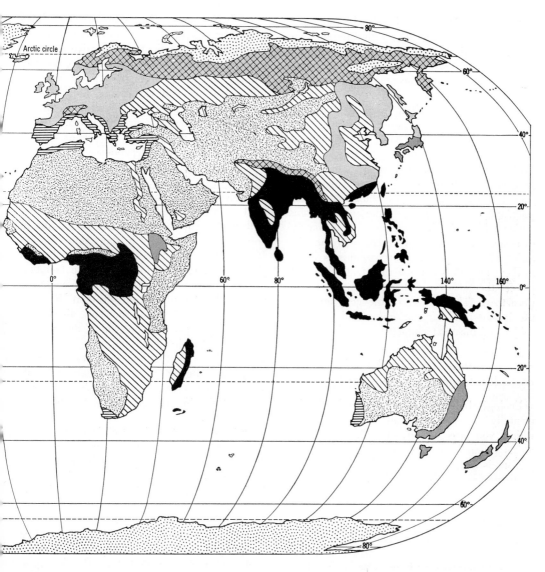

communities are not everywhere the same. Living things have a geography of their own, which, because it relates to life, is called *biogeography*. The observations further show that biogeographic relationships require the use of an expanding scale. Some involve a few square meters, others large regions, others whole continents, and others the entire earth. At the narrow end of the scale it is obvious that the geographic positions of living things depend primarily on the environment. The fish is in the stream; the squirrel is on the hillside. As the scale broadens, that factor continues to be evident. A deciduous forest

community in Pennsylvania and one in Missouri are similar because the climate, soil, and other environmental conditions are similar. They differ to the extent that the environments are not exactly the same. Further west on the high plains the climate is different, particularly in having less average annual rainfall. In the drier climate the forest community gives way to the grasslands community, and in the still drier Southwest the grasslands give way to the desert communities.

Such resemblances and differences in communities are ecological, and their study is *ecological biogeography*. In this aspect, the distribution of plants and animals and their associations in communities with different geographic positions are functional. They are adaptive. The present chapter is devoted to that subject. Before proceeding with it, however, we should note that there is more to biogeography than that. Ecological conditions in an Australian desert can be closely matched with one in Africa, or those in a Malayan jungle with one in South America. Ecology always and everywhere affects the geography of living things, but evidently it cannot provide the whole explanation of that geography. The puzzling differences among regional biotas [2] which are not due primarily to ecology are due to differences in the histories of the regions. Their organisms came to them at different times and from different places; they also evolved differently once they were there. That aspect of the geography of life is *historical biogeography*, and it is the subject of the next chapter.

Some Principles of Ecological Biogeography

Ecological biogeography depends fundamentally on some broad principles with which you are already familiar. Environments differ from place to place. Every organism is adapted to the environment at the particular place where it lives. Every organism is also a member of a community and is adapted to living with other members of the community, which are, in fact, part of the organism's environment. Interrelations in the community as a whole are, further, adaptive among themselves and are also such as to adapt the whole community to the conditions prevailing in its geographic position. You have been familiarized with these principles and with examples of their operation in previous chapters.

IMPORTANCE OF PLANTS IN BIOGEOGRAPHY

Plants play a predominant role in the geography of biotas, especially of those on the land. Green plants are at the beginning of all food chains. Their nature in a given place

strongly influences the nature of later links in the chains and therefore of the whole biota. Plants are also particularly sensitive to variations in the physical environment, especially climate and soil. Although animals are also influenced by such variations, their dependence on a given set of physical factors is usually less narrowly circumscribed.

Apparent dependence of animals on climate may in reality be a dependence on a given vegetation type, which is in turn primarily dependent on climate. Grazing animals are as a rule most abundant in areas with mean annual rainfall about 12 to 30 inches, and with that precipitation irregular or tending to concentrate in a relatively short rainy season. It is unlikely that grazing animals do best in that sort of climate, in spite of the fact that they are most common there. On the contrary, they suffer heavily from drought in such regions of moderate and unevenly distributed rainfall. But grasses, on which the grazers feed, do well in that kind of climate and are rarely the predominant vegetation in other situations. Many groups of animals are similarly restricted by the distribution of plant communities in which they find suitable food and shelter.

It is no less true in aquatic communities that plants are basic to the whole ecology. Nevertheless, as a rule and particularly in the sea, the more uniform aquatic environments have less sharply distinguished distribution of various kinds of plant communities. There other factors may be more important for biogeography. On land the kinds of plant communities are so varied, so well defined, and so basic for the whole biota that a map of vegetative provinces generally serves to indicate the ecological differentiation of biotas as a whole. A map of the main broad types of plant communities [3] is given in Fig. 28-1. The ecologically determined distribution of animals tends, by and large, to follow the same pattern.

HORIZONTAL AND VERTICAL CONTROLS

Temperature, solar radiation, and precipitation are the main controls of the plant communities. Each of these factors affects the

---

[2] A biota is the totality of organisms of a given place or region, its flora plus its fauna.

[3] These major communities are sometimes called "plant formations" by botanists.

vegetation directly or indirectly through effect on soil. Important for each of them is not only average intensity but also distribution through the year. Temperature and radiation have a familiar north-south gradient the effects of which are evident on the vegetation map of North America (Fig. 28-2). The tropics are without frost; daily variation of temperature is greater than seasonal variation; and sunshine is intense and of about equal duration throughout the year. Northward, seasonal variation of temperature becomes greater; as we proceed northward, frost is common through a longer and longer

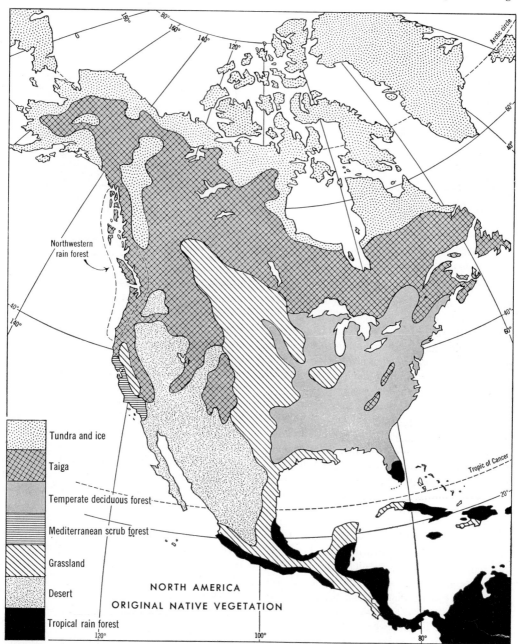

28-2 The distribution of original native vegetation in North America.

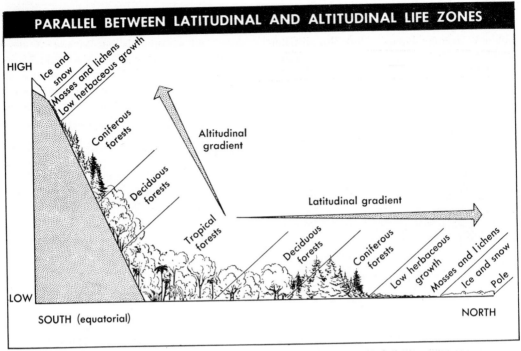

28-3 The parallel between the horizontal and vertical distributions of life zones.

part of the year; summers may be no cooler than in the tropics and are often hotter, but such periods of heat decrease in length to northward; radiation is not so intense as in the tropics, and its distribution through the year is increasingly uneven until the far north has months of continuous daylight and other months of continuous darkness.

There is also on the vegetation map of North America, especially through the Temperate Zone, an east-west differentiation. That is due mainly to changes in precipitation and subsequent evaporation. Rainfall follows a somewhat erratic pattern influenced by usual air movements, by distance from the coast, and by topography, among other usually less important factors. Precipitation is high on our northwest coast and in the mountains of California. Air moving eastward from there has lost moisture, and the result is an arid belt of deserts and semideserts. The Rocky Mountains again catch moisture, and the plains immediately eastward are semideserts of high, dry grassland. From there on to the Atlantic coast the general tendency, with many local irregularities, is for increase in rainfall,

largely because of moist air that periodically moves northeastward from the Gulf of Mexico. Similar irregular zoning of rainfall occurs on all the continents and in all of the north-south climatic zones of temperature and radiation. Deserts as well as lush rain forests occur in the tropics, and indeed one may occur right next to the other.

Besides these horizontal zonings of climates and of biotas along with them, there is a vertical zoning. If you climb any mountain of considerable height, the climate and the life perceptibly change as you go up. The most obvious climatic change is that it gets colder. That change is similar to one that occurs if you do not climb but simply travel north or south from the equator. Conditions on a mountain are similar to those at sea level farther north. The tops of mountains on the equator have considerable ecological resemblance to arctic lowlands. Timberline, above which trees do not grow, becomes lower from the southern Rockies into Alaska and finally reaches sea level at the northern tree line. These relationships between horizontal and vertical climatic zones are shown diagram-

696   THE GEOGRAPHY OF LIFE

TABLE 28-1 *Altitudinal life zones in New Mexico*

Altitude, feet *	Name of zone	Some characteristic plants	Some characteristic animals
2500- 4500	Lower Sonoran	Creosote bush, mesquite, ocotillo	Antelope squirrel, desert fox, road. runner, diamondback rattlesnake
4500- 7000	Upper Sonoran	Piñon pine, tree juniper ("cedar"), sagebrush, cottonwood, cholla cactus	Prairie dog, coyote, mourning dove, meadow lark, plains rattlesnake
7000- 8000	Transition	Ponderosa pine, narrow-leaf cottonwood, scrub oak, wild rose	Mule deer, Abert squirrel, mountain bobcat, black bear, wild turkey
8000-11,500	Canadian	Spruce, fir, aspen, cinquefoil, gentian	Elk, spruce squirrel, marmot, lemming mouse, Steller's jay, junco
11,500-12,500	Hudsonian	Foxtail pine	Cony, mountain jay
12,000-13,500	Arctic-Alpine	No trees. Alpine forget-me-not, spring beauty	Mountain sheep, ptarmigan

* The stated altitudes are approximate averages. In different parts of the state and on different exposures on valley and mountain slopes. the elevation of a given zone may be as much as 1000 feet above or below the stated figure, but the sequence remains the same.

matically in Fig. 28-3. The correspondence of an "arctic zone" on a high southern mountain and in the actual arctic is not, however, exact. Other factors than average temperature may be quite different in the two and may have a distinct ecological effect. How would sunshine, for instance, compare in the two?

Vertical zoning of biotas is particularly clear in our Southwest, from which a brief example, Table 28-1, may be drawn. Here the climatic control is precipitation rather than temperature, although that is important too. The higher the altitude, the greater the precipitation, as a rule.

The zones are so evident that a naturalist familiar with the region can generally tell his altitude within a few hundred feet just by looking at the vegetation. Nevertheless the zones follow each other gradually and not with a sharp line at a fixed elevation. Animals particularly, and also plants to some extent, may also spread into zones above and below those in which they are most abundant and characteristic.

Terrestrial Communities

Ecological geographic consideration of communities is something like those nested Chinese boxes or wooden eggs that some of us played with in childhood; when you opened one there was always a smaller one inside. The biggest box is the whole of life on earth. Next smaller are the whole of the land communities on one hand, and of the aquatic communities on the other. So it goes on down until we are considering the life of one thicket, one meadow, or one pool. What we are now going to consider, by way of example and to bring out further biogeographic principles, is something between the extremes of the series. It concerns broadly regional kinds of communities, each of which is of course quite variable and includes many different, more local communities.[4] The most important and widespread of them will be reviewed, but the list is not exhaustive. There are, for instance, highly distinctive kinds of geographically definable communities in salt lakes, marshes, or subterranean environments, but they are not considered here. You might consider them on your own. In each community you should especially try to answer two questions, as we shall do in the examples we discuss. The questions are: What are the special conditions of life here? How are they met by adaptations of and within the community?

[4] Major regional community types of the sort we are going to review are often called "biomes" by ecologists.

28-4 Tundra. *Left*, general view of tundra at Dumb Bell Bay on Ellesmere Island, Canada. *Right*, reindeer moss (a lichen) and other tundra vegetation, Finland.

TUNDRA AND ALPINE COMMUNITIES

In North America, Europe, and Asia a vast northern zone encircling the Arctic Ocean is known as the *tundra,* a word borrowed from the Russians. No similar extensive zone occurs in the Southern Hemisphere, because the south has little land in corresponding latitudes. The tundra (Fig. 28-4) of course has the arctic climate, cold on an average, with a long, dark winter and long or even continuous summer daylight. Frost may occur at any time of the year, and the ground is permanently frozen a few feet below the surface. During summer thaws the region is extremely wet, with saturated soils and innumerable bogs, ponds, and streams.

There are no upstanding trees in the tundra, but dwarf, shrubby alders, birches, willows, and conifers are common. Mosses, especially sphagnum, and lichens, especially "reindeer moss" (not a true moss), cover large areas. Herbs with large, brilliantly colored flowers are conspicuous and beautiful during the brief growing season. Temperatures for growth are minimal, and surviving plants must mature without becoming large. They must resist frequent frost. Many of them can be frozen solid at any phase of life, even when in flower, and survive to resume activity when another thaw

comes along. Tundra plants spend most of their lives in a state of suspended animation, active only in brief periods of warming sunshine.

Vast hordes of birds, especially waterfowl, nest in the tundra in summer, but most of them desert it in winter. Permanent residents include a few birds and mammals, warm-blooded and well protected by feathers or fur. Some of the resident birds, like the ptarmigan, and mammals, like the snowshoe hare, turn white in winter. White is protective coloration in a snowy environment and also minimizes heat loss by radiation. Musk oxen and caribou (wild reindeer) are large herbivores, dependent mainly on the abundant moss and lichens. Arctic hares and lemmings (small, ratlike rodents) are numerous and are preyed on by arctic foxes. Polar bears are amphibious; they frequent coasts and ice floes, but also wander inland on the tundra. Insects, especially flies, are so numerous as to be one of the major drawbacks of the tundra from the human point of view. Their eggs and larvae are particularly cold-resistant, and the adults appear by the billions on warmer summer days. There is no lack of life on a warm day in the tundra, but the numbers of species permanently resident there are smaller than in almost any other sort of community, even the deserts.

Conditions on high mountains, above timberline, resemble those of the tundra. The vegetation is similar in general appearance and may consist of species related to those in the arctic. Ptarmigan (an arctic grouselike bird) and varying hares, related to arctic hares and also turning white in winter, extend far south of the tundra in alpine environments. Alpine insects are often of arctic species or closely related to them.

TAIGA

The *taiga* (another word we owe to the Russians) occurs in a still broader zone just south of the tundra across northern North America, Europe, and Asia (Figs. 28-1 and 28-5). Like the tundra and for the same reason, it is practically absent in the Southern Hemisphere. Winter temperatures may be as severe as in the tundra, but there is a well-defined summer growing season of three to six months. That suffices for a heavy growth of hardy trees, and the taiga as a whole is a tremendous forest. In the typical taiga the forests are coniferous, especially spruce, although several other species of conifers occur. Alder, birch, and juniper thickets are also common. Burned areas of the coniferous forest are invaded by aspens and birches, which later are succeeded by conifers again.

The moose (called an "elk" in Eurasia) occurs throughout the whole taiga where not exterminated by man and is its most conspicuous animal. Smaller mammals are much more varied than in the tundra. Black bears, wolves, and martens are more common in this zone than elsewhere. Fishers, wolverines, and lynxes are practically confined to it. So are some rodents, such as the northern vole, although most of the abundant rodents are races or subspecies of groups also occurring farther south. Squirrels thrive in these rich coniferous forests. So do many birds, most of which, however, are here summer breeders and migrate southward in the fall. The many insects and other invertebrates are of species that lie dormant during the severe winters.

The coniferous forests of our western mountains have some distinctive characters of their own but are essentially extensions of the taiga, occurring at increasingly high altitudes the farther south they are. Many of their species, both of plants and animals, are the same as in the typical taiga. The hemlock-hardwood forest of southern Canada and down into the Appalachians is also an extension of the taiga.

National Film Board of Canada

28-5 Taiga. A Northern spruce forest along the Alaska Highway in Canada.

28-6 **Temperate deciduous forest.**

TEMPERATE DECIDUOUS FORESTS

Regions with moderate, well-distributed precipitation, with cold winters and warm summers, tend to develop regional communities in which deciduous trees dominate or climax the natural succession. Those conditions occur in the Temperate Zones where the average annual precipitation is somewhere around 40 inches, without very well-defined dry and rainy seasons. In the United States, most of the eastern half of the country has such a climate and was formerly covered by deciduous forest (Fig. 28-6). Northward it graded into the taiga, through the hemlock-hardwood forest, and southward into the southeastern pine forests, a special local group of communities conditioned by peculiarities of soils and drainage. The British Isles and practically all of central Europe were also formerly occupied by temperate deciduous forests, and so was a large region in China and southeastern Siberia. There are similar forests in the Temperate Zone of South America, but they are not so widespread there because the precipitation is not suitable over such large regions.

The word "deciduous" implies the most obvious characteristic of this climate and the most obvious adaptation to it. Half the year or somewhat more is the growing season, when perennial plants put on their leaves and are active, while annual plants go through the whole cycle from seed to seed. The rest of the year is a period of nearly suspended animation, with trees and fields bare.

Common trees of the deciduous forest are beech, tulip, sycamore, maple, oak, hickory, elm, poplar, and birch. Chestnut trees were formerly common but now have been almost eradicated in the United States by blight. The taiga and other coniferous forests include fewer species of trees, and locally a coniferous forest tends to be dominated by a single species. The deciduous forests have more varied local groupings, each of which commonly includes two or more species, as in the beech-maple climax (see p. 667) and oak-hickory, elm-ash-maple, or willow-cottonwood-sycamore communities. The complex distribution of these and other communities within the broader deciduous forest zone is governed by local conditions of climate, soil, and drainage.

The most striking herbivores of the deciduous forests are the browsing deer, mainly the white-tailed or Virginia deer in North America and other species in Eurasia and South America. In Eurasia wild pigs (or boars) are also characteristic of this group of communities, but they do not occur native in America. The principal predators on the larger herbivores are large cats. Our variously named puma, mountain lion, cougar, or panther (all the same species, *Felis concolor*) ranges into most of the environments of North and South America. It is now extinct in the eastern forests but was originally their commonest large carnivore. Wolves, although more characteristic of the taiga, also formerly ranged widely into these forests, both in Eurasia and in North America. Foxes are still common in them. The arboreal martens are locally as common here as in the taiga, and the raccoon (absent in Eurasia) is especially abundant in our deciduous forests. These forests throughout the world are also especially rich in tree squirrels. Among mammals of the North American deciduous forests, over a third of the species are mainly arboreal. Tree-nesting birds are also abundant, and woodpeckers have the most obvious connection with the forest environment. The leaf- and mold-covered forest floor is a world in itself, swarming with fungi and invertebrates.

RAIN FORESTS

The lushest and most complex forest communities develop where there is an abundant and continuous water supply and a long growing season, which may be continuous through the whole year. Such *rain forests* occur in the Temperate Zone, for instance on our northwest Pacific coast, where they have their own special characteristics and species. They are, however, most widespread and impressive in the tropics (Fig. 28-7) and subtropics. They cover most of Central America and northern South America, central Africa, southern Asia from India eastwards, the East Indies and South Pacific islands from Sumatra through New Guinea, and parts of northeastern Australia.

Nowhere is life more exuberant than in the tropical rain forests. A temperate or cold climate forest frequently consists of one species of trees and rarely has a dozen. A tropical rain forest generally includes a hundred or more species of trees, and as many

as five hundred have been counted in one such forest. Two trees of the same species seldom stand near each other. Having noted a tree of a given species, you may have to travel for miles through the jungle before you find another. The actual species present may be totally different in different rain forests, and are sure to be if the forests compared are in widely separated regions of the earth. Always, however, there is this peculiar abundance of species in each forest, and the general aspect or structure, the ecological make-up, of a tropical rain forest is remarkably uniform wherever it may be and whatever species may compose it.

All forests and, indeed, all communities have some degree of *vertical stratification* (Fig. 24-3). The conditions of life, the microenvironments (p. 612) are different at different elevations (or depths in soil or water). Many of the organisms are adapted accordingly to those vertical differences and zones. This is particularly striking in a tropical rain forest. The main trees all grow to about the same height, generally from 20 to 40 meters in various situations. Their spreading, leafy branches there form a canopy, continuous throughout the year, which intercepts almost all the direct sunlight. Here photosynthesis is most active and flowers and fruits are abundant, but in some respects the canopy is a difficult microenvironment. Water is at a premium, for no outside supply is available except when rain is actually falling. Variation in temperature and in humidity is considerable.

Microenvironmental conditions change continuously and radically through various levels below the canopy, down to and into the forest floor. The floor is dark even at noon, and among green plants only a few with the most modest photosynthetic requirements manage to grow there. Direct rain is cut off by the umbrella of the canopy, but the lower levels have constantly high humidity and are commonly dripping wet even when no rain is falling. The temperature is also nearly constant near the forest floor throughout the day and throughout the year. It is usually around 25° C., and in different regions seldom falls below 20° or rises above 30°. All over the United States (except on high mountains)

28-7 Tropical rain forest, Kenya, Africa. (From Fuller and Tippo, *College Botany*. © Henry Holt and Co.) Note the epiphytes (see p. 703) growing on the larger branches.

maximum summer temperatures are much higher than in the tropical jungle. The sustained warmth of the rain forest floor, however, and the constantly saturated atmosphere make a natural hothouse that is likely to be very trying to anyone accustomed to climates of the Temperate Zone.

Apart from the forest trees themselves, two habits of vegetation are especially characteristic of tropical rain forests: lianas and epiphytes. *Lianas* (a word of French origin) are climbing vines. Rooted in the dark forest floor, they use the standing trees as supports up which they climb toward the canopy, where they spread their leaves in the light. The rain forest is a tangle of lianas, slender or big and strong as bridge cables, looped and festooned around and among the trunks and branches of the trees.

Epiphytes[5] are plants that grow on other plants without parasitizing them or deriving from them anything but a base on which to grow. Growing especially in the upper levels and canopy of the rain forest, they are well above the dark floor and are bathed in light, even though their own height is small. Orchids, ferns, and many other epiphytes form veritable aerial gardens among the high branches of the trees of the rain forests. Without roots reaching to a water supply in the soil, the epiphytes of a rain forest are paradoxically adapted to a dry climate. They include cactuses, which store water in their pulpy tissues. The spread of cactuses from desert soils to the rain forests, which are wet but not for them, is a remarkable example of what is technically called *preadaptation*, that is, an adaptation to one environment that turns out to be equally advantageous in another, apparently quite different environment. Other rain forest epiphytes, notably the bromeliads[6] in South America, have the leaf bases so arranged that they catch rain and store it as in a tank against future need (Fig. 28-8). Those little tanks form a remarkable microenvironment of their own, in which insects, frogs, and other organisms develop. Like the cactuses, bromeliads have suc-

ceeded as canopy epiphytes in rain forest largely because of adaptations to a poor water supply which they acquired early in their history as desert plants.

28-8 Epiphytic bromeliads in Trinidad, West Indies. *Top*, a large clump of *Gravisia aquilega*. A group of plants this size holds many gallons of water and supports a pond fauna high in the trees. *Bottom*, part of the same clump brought to ground and with the leaves cut away to show how the leaf bases overlap to form the cups in which water collects (the water has spilled out from this specimen). Note the humus (dead leaves, etc.) that has accumulated; it is the plant's substitute for a soil.

5 See note 4 on p. 631.
6 Named for a Swedish botanist, Olaf Bromel. Incidentally, and peculiarly, this family of plants includes the Spanish "moss" (not moss at all) of our South, and also the pineapple.

Most of us think of the jungle, which is simply an overpopularized name for rain forest,[7] as teeming with animals. A first visit to a rain forest is disappointing in that respect, for animals are rarely seen there. Closer study reveals that animals are indeed common in those forests, although probably no more so than in our familiar Temperate Zone forests and grasslands. They are inconspicuous in the rain forest because many are nocturnal and most of those active during the day live high up in the canopy, where they are practically invisible from the ground. During the day the forest is oppressively silent, a silence likely to be broken only by the chattering or howling of monkeys (most of which are diurnal) or the squawking of parrots overhead. At dusk an ear-shattering chorus breaks out. Birds, mainly diurnal but foraging more quietly during the day, sound off as they settle for the night. Grasshoppers and allied insects make a din. They are joined most vociferously by tree frogs.

Ants, termites, flies, butterflies, beetles, and other insects are abundant in rain forest and are especially numerous in species there. Frogs also reach a sort of climax in this environment. Snakes are present but are rather rare, contrary to accounts written more to astonish than to instruct. Mammals are less abundant in the forest than in adjacent (or, for that matter, Temperate Zone) grasslands, but they are still quite numerous. Aboreal forms include monkeys and rodents, especially squirrels. In the Old World rain forests, ground-dwelling herbivores include musk deer, small forest antelopes, and forest pigs. In South America similar ways of life are represented mainly by terrestrial rodents and peccaries. In both hemispheres the ground herbivores are stalked by partly arboreal carnivores, especially cats, such as the Old World leopard and the New World jaguar. Here is an illustration of the fact that the same ecological roles exist in geographically widely separated environments, but that the roles may be filled by distinct species or even by animals of different families, orders, or classes in different regions.

GRASSLANDS

In drier parts of the tropics, forests may still extend in narrow zones along watercourses where there is a good underground supply of water. These are the *gallery forests*.[8] A similar forest formation can be seen in the United States and elsewhere in the Temperate Zone, where galleries of trees may border a stream far out into a region otherwise treeless. Away from the stream galleries are vast areas in both Tropical and Temperate zones where water supply does not suffice for tree growth but does permit a heavy growth of grasses and other small herbs. These areas are variously called prairies, steppes, savannas, pampas, or velds in different parts of the earth. All are ecologically similar and may be classed as *grasslands*.

The major North American grassland was the region of the high plains east of the Rocky Mountains. Most of it has now been plowed under to make way for crops. It has, however, been discovered that the drier parts of the region are more permanently productive as they were than as we have made them, and an effort is being made to return some of them to grass. Grasslands are even more extensive on other continents (Fig. 28-9).

The dominant environmental restriction of the grasslands is a low, intermittent water supply. Rainfall may be only 12-20 inches per year. Rainfall is more than that, even up to 40 inches or thereabouts, on some grasslands, but is unevenly distributed through the year. The irregularity of rain, porosity and drainage of the soil, or both factors together prevent a continuous or ample supply of water to plant roots. Other environmental conditions vary greatly in grasslands and help to give each its special characteristics. A savanna in the midst of Vene-

---

[7] The word "jungle," which is of Sanskrit derivation, originally meant a desert! It came to be applied to any wilderness. European travelers picked up the word in India and used it for the wilderness, as they considered it, of the rain forests there. Lately it has been so misused by explorers of the "Oh, how I suffered!" school that scientific explorers shy away from the word.

[8] The third main type of tropical forest, which we will not further characterize here, is sometimes called a winter forest. It occurs in areas of strongly defined rainy and dry seasons. The trees here are deciduous, shedding their leaves in the dry season and growing them again in the rainy season, the "winter" of dwellers in the tropics.

zuelan rain forest and the high prairie of Alberta have little in common except this: the water supply for plants is unreliable in both places. In both that one common feature has led to dominance of grasses, adapted to survival through unpredictable alternations of drought and downpour.

Within the grasslands different species and habits of grasses are adapted to special conditions of soil, precipitation, evaporation, and other environmental factors. The eastern, wetter parts of our North American grasslands had tall grasses, attaining heights up to three meters: bluestems, Indian grasses, slough grasses. The tall-grass prairie did repay plowing under; it is now our richest agricultural area, including the corn belt. In the arid western prairies short grasses predominated, especially grama and buffalo grasses, often growing among sagebrush. Between the extremes were mixed grasses, sod and bunch grasses, including needle grass, little bluestem, and wheat grass.

The grasslands swarm with animals, which are certainly more conspicuous and probably really more numerous in these communities than in any others on land. Primary consumers are the large grazing mammals especially. Countless millions of bisons and pronghorns [9] roamed our prairies. Even now the African grasslands support tremendous herds of zebras and of several species of grazing antelopes. Living in open country, these grassland ungulates are all fleet of foot; they are *cursorial*. Rodents, too, are extremely common primary consumers in the grasslands. Some, like the hares, are likewise cursorial. Many others, like the prairie dogs and other ground squirrels or the pocket gophers, are *burrowing* or *fossorial* animals. Australian grasslands have herbivores very different in appearance and relationships, but ecologically similar: large, grazing, cursorial kangaroos and small, burrowing, rodentlike pouched "mice." Predators are adapted to the herbivore prey: wild dogs, lions, and the like preying on the ungulates; weasels, snakes, and others on the smaller herbivores. Herbivorous insects, such as locusts and grasshop-

[9] Usually called buffalo and antelope, respectively, but they are quite distinct from the Old World animals to which those names were first and are still properly applied.

U.S. Fish and Wildlife Service

28-9   Grasslands, in National Bison Range, Moiese, Montana.

pers, are also incredibly numerous. So are birds. What are some of our characteristic herbivorous and predaceous birds in the grasslands?

DESERTS

With increasing aridity, grasslands grade into deserts (Fig. 28-10) without any sharp line of demarcation. Deserts are marked by low precipitation, generally 10 inches per year or less, which is likely to fall during a few heavy showers at erratic intervals. Deserts are also characterized by intense sunshine and very hot days, 35° or 40° C. and upwards, at least during summers; and the evaporation rate is very high. Nights are generally cold, even in summer, and variations in temperature reach extremes found in no other environment.

Most annual plants in the desert are small. When a shower falls, they grow rapidly, bloom, and produce seed all within a few

Trans World Airlines

28-10   Desert, in the Cerbat Mountain Range, Arizona. Joshua trees dominate the scene.

days. Among the most astonishing and beautiful sights on earth is one of our southwestern deserts carpeted with brilliant and many-hued flowers a few days after a spring rain. After another few days the desert is drab again, but scattered in it are millions of seeds waiting to perform the miracle again.

Perennial desert plants have small leaves or none at all, characters that decrease loss of water. Some have tremendously long roots, reaching deeply buried water. Others, notably the cactuses in our deserts, absorb water rapidly after a rain and store it in spongy internal tissues. Can you think of any adaptive or selective explanation for the fact that most of the desert perennials are spiny or thorny?

Animals of deserts are also adapted to the scarcity of water and extremes of temperature. Large mammals are rare in the deserts, although some Old World antelopes are adapted to extreme desert conditions. Small rodents are numerous. Almost all are burrowers, and many in different parts of the world have independently evolved bipedal, leaping locomotion. The kangaroo rat is an example in our deserts. Snakes and lizards are common in deserts, which nevertheless put sharp limitations on their activities. They are sluggish in the cold desert nights and yet they quickly

die of heat prostration in the sun. Consequently they are usually active only for short periods in the morning and evening and spend the rest of the time in burrows or crannies.

We have mentioned some other characteristics and scenes of desert life elsewhere in this book. They should be reviewed at this point.

Fresh-Water Communities

Land and aquatic habitats are about as different as they can be, and yet they do intergrade along shores, in coastal lagoons, and in swamps. Some plants and animals live habitually in such transitional zones. Many plants are rooted in water but rise from it into the air. Many animals spend part of the life cycle in water and part on land, and others alternate at will between the two. What are some of the plants and animals that do not belong fully either to the water or to the land?

Among strictly aquatic environments, those of fresh water are less varied than those on the land but more varied than those in the sea. A primary but not sharp distinction is between the flowing water of streams and the still water of lakes. Deep lakes may have fairly complex vertical stratification, depending especially on gradients of temperature and of light penetration below the surface.

There are a good many flowering plants in fresh-water communities: water lilies, duckweeds, water hyacinths, pickerel weeds, pondweeds, and others. Almost all, however, are only semiaquatic. They float on the surface or extend above it into the air. Algae are the predominant plants of fresh water, as of all aquatic environments. Most common in fresh water are diatoms and blue-green and green algae. They are the mainstay for photosynthesis in lakes and streams and may occur in such enormous numbers near the surface, where the light is strongest, as to form a scum of pea-soup consistency.

Fresh-water faunas are rich in phyla and classes, more so than any land communities. Only three animal phyla (p. 545) have members completely adapted to life in the open air, but almost all phyla have fresh-water representatives. What are the exceptions? (See Chapter 22.) Among the commonest of fresh-water organisms, in addition to algae, are protists (especially bacteria and ciliates), flatworms and several other groups of worms, rotifers, arthropods such as water "fleas," crayfishes, and insects (not as adults but as aquatic larvae), snails, and, of course, fishes.

Wherever you live, there is almost sure to be a fresh-water community near you. Even a mud puddle becomes such a community if it lasts a few days. Where do its organisms come from? What food chains and other ecological factors are prominent in other fresh-water communities known to you?

Although we cannot discuss other fresh-water communities further in the space available, we shall mention one extreme as an illustration of a peculiar environmental hazard and of adaptation related to it. Torrential mountain streams would soon be swept free of organisms if their inhabitants did not have some means of staying there in spite of the swift current. For some of the fishes of such streams, notably trout, that is fairly simple. They can manage to stand still by swimming hard. (Some biologists think that this was a factor in the origin of the vertebrates, see p. 559.) Flatworms, leeches, snails, and many insect larvae in swift streams are flattened, streamlined, or limpetlike. They can cling to the bottom or to stones while the water flows by. Some caddis-fly larvae live in cases to which they attach pebbles. The weight holds them on the bottom. Some fishes in that environment lack swim bladders, and some salamanders lack lungs; both losses make the animals heavier and better able to cling to the bottom. Other fishes and many tadpoles of swift water have sucking mouths with which they cling to rocks. This adaptation has arisen several times independently in tadpoles of quite different ancestry. Some clams, snails, and insect larvae moor themselves against the current with spun fibers. Floating larvae, so very common in the ocean, are unknown in fresh-water habitats.

The evolutionary origin of land vertebrates was dependent on another major ecological characteristic of some fresh-water environments: they are often only transitory, or at least dry up to such an extent that they stagnate, becoming low in dissolved oxygen. Lungs evolved in early fresh-water fishes in relation to this characteristic of their environment. And the only insects which have evolved special respiratory pigments are those inhabiting oxygen-poor fresh waters.

Marine Environments and Communities

The ocean covers more than two-thirds of the face of the earth.[10] Most of the main groups of organisms among protists, plants, and animals, all three, arose in the sea and are still abundant there. Among phyla, only the Bryophyta and Tracheophyta are basically nonmarine. Even among classes, the vast majority is predominantly marine, and nearly all have at least a few representatives in the seas. The only classes of animals that probably originated on land are those of the centipedes, millepedes, insects, and the amphibians and their descendants the reptiles, birds, and mammals. There are a few secondarily marine insects, reptiles, birds, and mammals. Some of the other classes may have arisen in fresh water, but most are of marine origin and all

[10] The area of the ocean is about 361 million square kilometers, that of the land about 149 million.

but one (the Onychophora, p. 570) now have marine representatives.

The ocean, then, is the largest abode of life, and the organisms that swarm in it are more fundamentally diverse than those of fresh water or of land. The small space allotted to marine communities (Fig. 1-2) in this chapter is out of proportion with their overwhelming extent and richness. There are three reasons for this disproportion in emphasis. First, we have already said a good deal about marine life in other chapters. Second, for all their vastness and diversity, marine communities do not represent as radically divergent and sharply distinct ecological types as do those of the land. Third, the communities of the land, our own environment, are more accessible for study and are of more immediate, practical importance to humans.

MARINE ENVIRONMENTS

The part of the sea most freely open to our investigation is the shore, the *littoral* [11] zone between high and low tides. It is only a narrow band around continents and islands, and the conditions of life there are peculiar. It is, nevertheless, as crowded with living things as any part of the earth. Its outstanding environmental characteristic is of course the rhythmical ebb and flow of the tides, now covering the littoral zone completely and now leaving it exposed to air except for the many shallow tidal pools. Radiation from the sun here strikes intensely, and variations of temperature and of saltiness of the water are much more pronounced than elsewhere in the sea.

Away from the littoral zone, out beyond low tide, the most important single factor affecting marine environments is the penetration of radiation from the surface. Near the surface radiation is strongest. Here must occur most of the photosynthesis in the ocean. Temperatures here vary with the seasons, as on land. The difference between summer and winter temperature may be as much as 25° C. or even a little more, although it is less than 5° C. over most of the ocean surface. Temperatures are also zoned like the climates of

the land, with a fairly constant surface temperature around 25° C. in the tropics grading off to temperatures rarely far from 0° C. near the poles. Daily, seasonal, and climatic differences of temperature in the sea are less than on land, because large bodies of water warm up and cool off far more slowly than do air and land surfaces.

There is no sharp point where radiation stops with increase in depth in the sea. Light becomes dimmer and dimmer until finally there is none. The penetration of radiation varies with the clearness of the water and with latitude. It is greatest in the tropics and least in the Arctic and Antarctic. Why? Photosynthesis is of course confined to the illuminated zone and therefore occurs through a greater depth in tropical than in arctic regions.

Below the illuminated zone eternal darkness reigns, broken only by the glow of such organisms as create their own light. There is no daily and very little seasonal or latitudinal variation in temperature, which is usually around 10°-15° C. at the top of the dark zone and grades down to near 0° C. in the great depths of the ocean.[12]

In the deepest parts of the ocean pressure due to the overlying water reaches nearly a thousand times the atmospheric pressure at the surface, and many kinds of organisms are known to live under pressures more than 600 times that of the atmosphere. It used to be assumed that pressure made life in the greater depths difficult or impossible. Now, however, it has been discovered that pressure makes little difference to most marine organisms. How can that be so? Pressure is equal inside and out. As long as it remains constant, it is not felt any more than we feel the nearly 15 pounds per square inch of atmospheric pressure in which we normally live. Food supply and temperature are the most decisive factors in determining how many and what kinds of organisms occur at various depths below the lighted zone. The life of the oceanic deeps is still poorly known, but there are some living things at all depths, even the greatest.

11 Some marine ecologists apply the term "littoral" to the ocean bottom as far out as light reaches it, but that is not in accord with the usual understanding of the word.

12 Fresh water freezes at 0° C., and becomes lighter and tends to rise as cooling drops below 4° C. Sea water continues to become denser down to its freezing point, which is more than a degree below 0° C.

The organization of communities in the ocean depends not only on depth and associated factors of light, temperature, and so on, but also on a special relationship between organisms and their surroundings. Many marine organisms simply float in the water, carried hither and yon by currents and often sinking or rising with changes in radiation and temperature. Those organisms are *planktonic* and all together make up the *plankton*.[13] Other organisms, especially fishes, swim freely in the water, actively seeking what they may devour or evading what may devour them. They are *nektonic* and make up the *nekton*.[14] Still others live on the bottom, where they may be attached or may crawl about to a usually quite limited extent. They are *benthonic* and are the *benthos*.[15]

A combination of these ways of life and of the physical zoning of the sea determines the major life zones and kinds of communities. There is the *littoral* zone, as already noted, where most organisms are benthonic. Some plankton and nekton exist in the tidal pools or come in with the tide. Beyond the littoral zone is the *neritic*[16] zone, shallow waters in which light penetrates to the bottom. Plankton, nekton, and benthos are all abundant, and photosynthesis goes on throughout. Still farther out are the *bathyal*[17] and *abyssal*[18] zones, vertically divided into three major environments and kinds of communities. Above is the lighted open water swarming with plankton, including all the photosynthetic organisms of these zones, and with nekton. Below are the dark waters in which nearly all life is nektonic. At the bottom is the benthos, consisting of scavengers and organisms of decay, mostly bacteria.

OVER-ALL ECOLOGY OF THE OCEAN

Beyond the littoral zone, with its special features, the beginning of marine food chains is in the photosynthetic plankton. It consists mostly of microscopic diatoms (p. 497) and

[13] From a Greek root meaning "wanderers."
[14] Greek for "swimming."
[15] Greek for "depth," meaning by implication "living at the bottom."
[16] From a Greek root referring to the sea, or to sea gods and nymphs.
[17] "Deep."
[18] "Bottomless" (which of course is not literally true).

dinoflagellates (Fig. 20-9), although more conspicuous green or brown algae, such as the famous Sargasso weed, also occur. Grazing, so to speak, on that grass of the sea are the many herbivores, especially various protists and crustaceans. Especially abundant and important are the crustaceans called copepods, little more than microscopic in size but so enormously numerous that they are the chief food of the largest animals that have ever lived, the whalebone whales.

The nektonic animals are for the most part carnivores. The whalebone whales and many fishes are among the carnivores that prey on the small herbivores. Toothed whales, sharks, squids, and many other nektonic animals prey mostly on other carnivores. There are many long food chains of the "dog eat dog" variety in the nekton.

Below the illuminated zone there are no living photosynthetic organisms. The community intake of food necessarily descends from above: sinking plankton, mostly dead when it reaches these levels, and both living and dead nektonic animals. Here, too, within the community every animal is potential prey for some other. Some of the deep sea fishes are among the most grotesque of all living things. Some can swallow whole fishes larger than themselves. Many are luminescent in this dark environment. Each light-producing species has characteristic colors and patterns of lights. The function of these animal lights is much disputed. What possibilities can you think of? It is pertinent that most deep sea fishes have functional eyes in spite of the fact that there is no light in their environment except that produced by themselves and other animals.

Finally, on the dark sea bottom the rain of dead organic matter from above comes to rest. Here are many scavengers and here, as on land, the many food chains come to an end with bacteria that break down complex organic compounds into simpler molecules. On land the products of bacterial decay are for the most part available to green plants and so start through the complex of cycles and food chains once more. On the sea bottom beyond the lighted zone, where most organic materials of the sea eventually lie, there are no photosynthetic organisms. This looks like a dead end. The total metabolism of the sea would seem to be a one-way process and not a self-renewing cycle. If that were so, life on earth would tend to run down, would indeed probably have run down by now, for even the most inland communities lose some organic material to the sea.

Fortunately the total ecology of the sea is cyclical, but the cycle is completed in an odd way. At many places near coasts winds and currents tend to move the surface water away. Its place is taken by an upwelling of water from the deeps, and with this water come the dissolved products of bacterial decay on the ocean floor. The upwelling of deep, cold water with its dissolved nutrients is periodic in some places, in others almost constant. Wherever it occurs it has the effect of fertilizing the sea. Diatoms and other photosynthetic organisms increase enormously, and thus a cycle is completed and another begins.

The main features of the entire cycle are shown in Fig. 24-9.

Chapter Summary

The bases of biogeography: diversity of vegetation types in the world; associated diverse faunas; their regional distribution the subject matter of biogeography; ecological *vs.* historical biogeography.

Principles of ecological biogeography:

Importance of plants in biogeography; plant distribution especially sensitive to physical environment; its role in determining animal distributions.

Horizontal and vertical controls: temperature, solar radiation, and precipitation as dominant factors controlling plant distribution; the consequent parallelism between altitudinal and latitudinal distribution of plant communities (exemplified by North American communities).

Terrestrial communities; major types exemplified and discussed: tundra and alpine communities, taiga, temperate deciduous forests, rain forests with vertical stratification, grasslands and gallery forests, deserts.

Fresh-water communities: still- and flowing-water communities; examples of adaptation to fresh-water life.

Marine environments and communities:

Ocean as largest habitat of life; marine faunas include all phyla but two.

Various marine ways of life and zones: planktonic, nektonic, and benthonic ways of life; the littoral, neritic, bathyal, and abyssal zones; over-all ecology of the ocean: the key roles of the illuminated surface zone and the accumulation of organic debris on the ocean floor; cycles in the sea.

The koala "bear" (Phascolarctos) *is a marsupial. Its distribution, sharply restricted to the Australian faunal region, is typical of many whose full explanation demands historical, as well as ecological analysis.* (Photo from Australian Travel Bureau)

CHAPTER 29

Historical Biogeography

Ecological biogeography, studied in the preceding chapter, goes far toward explaining why plants and animals live where they do. That explanation, however, is clearly incomplete. Ecology gives a satisfactory answer to such questions as why monkeys occur in the forests of South and Central America but not in the desert and grassland regions of our West and Southwest. It gives a similarly satisfactory explanation of the distribution of monkeys through Africa and southern Asia. It does not explain why monkeys in apparently identical ecological situations in South America and Africa belong to different species, genera, and families. Still less does it explain why forests in eastern Australia, ecologically similar to those occupied by monkeys in South America, Africa, and Asia, harbor no monkeys at all. Australia does have animals similar to monkeys in habits and habitat, with

nearly the same ecological roles, but they are not monkeys and the phylogenetic relationship is distant.

There are innumerable problems of that kind in all habitats. Oysters lead similar lives in the sea on the two sides of the Atlantic, but they are distinct species (according to some authorities, distinct genera). Lungfishes live in a few rivers of South America, Africa, and Australia, but they are of different genera on the three continents and they are completely absent in many other rivers apparently equally suitable for them. Large, spotted semi-arboreal cats occur in both South America and Africa, but the South American jaguar is specifically distinct from the African leopard.

The explanations of all these and many similar problems of biogeography are *historical* in nature. The earth has changed during its long history, and its floras and faunas have changed with it. They have changed not only in evolving into new species, genera, and so on but also geographically, in their distribution over the face of the earth.

Many facts like those exemplified above really present a double problem and require dual historical explanations. Take the jaguar and the leopard, for instance. There is no land connection between South America and Africa today, apparently no way in which the big cats could possibly travel from one to the other. Yet the two species are closely related. At some time not long ago, geologically speak-

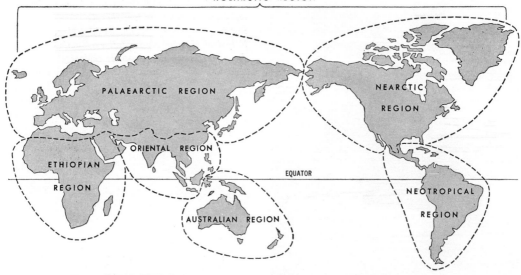

29-1 The faunal regions of the world.

ing, they had common ancestors in the same place, and those ancestors must have spread to both continents over practicable routes that no longer exist. That is one aspect of the problem. On the other hand, the jaguar and the leopard are different species, and the communities in which they live are radically different in taxonomic composition. We know that there must have been a way for land animals and plants to spread to the two continents, but how did their differences arise? That is the second aspect of the problem.

Biogeographic Regions

We have referred (p. 693) to the varying scale involved in biogeography. Ecological explanations of the distribution of plants and animals refer, for the most part, to the smaller end of the scale. They explain why a certain kind of community lives in one place, and another kind a mile away, why one lives at the foot of a mountain and another on top, or one in northern Canada and another in southern United States. Ecological and historical aspects interact and overlap all along the scale, but on the whole the historical side becomes predominant or most evident at the larger end of the scale. The most purely historical explanations apply to the resemblances and differences of the faunas of large areas, such as whole continents or seas.

FAUNAL REGIONS ON LAND

The first approach to any scientific problem is to recognize that a problem exists. Existing facts must be observed, relationships among them must be inferred, and then an explanation must be sought. The observations from which the science of biogeography arose began in antiquity. They bore on the familiar and even obvious fact that different plants and animals live in different places. With the wide exploration of the earth from the fifteenth century onward, the nature and magnitude of the problems became more evident. Facts of the distribution of organisms over the whole earth were gathered, and broadly regional interrelationships began to appear.

In the nineteenth century it became increasingly clear that there are regional patterns of floras and faunas that cannot be wholly, at least, explained by ecological factors. Such patterns occur in the sea as well as on land, but they are not, as a rule, so clear-cut in the sea, nor are the marine patterns as yet so well known. On land, regional patterns of plants are well marked, and so are those of all groups of animals that have been suffi-

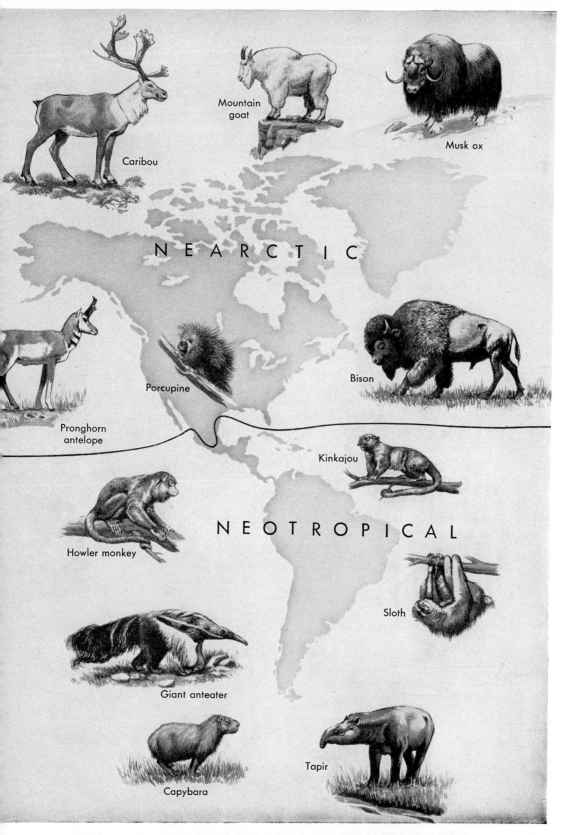

Caribou

Mountain goat

Musk ox

NEARCTIC

Pronghorn antelope

Porcupine

Bison

Kinkajou

NEOTROPICAL

Howler monkey

Sloth

Giant anteater

Tapir

Capybara

29-2 Mammals diagnostic, or characteristic, of the worlds' faunal regions: the New World.

Reindeer

Bison

Hedgehog

P A L A E

Polecat

Bintur

E T H I O P I A N

Aardvark

Gorilla

African
elephant

Zebra

Gnu

Giraffe

29-2 (continued)   Mammals of the world's faunal regions: the Old World.

Wild ass

Marco Polo sheep

A R C T I C

Indian elephant

Indian tiger

IENTAL

Malay tapir

Water buffalo

Gibbon

A U S T R A L I A N

Flying phalanger

Native cat

Bandicoot

Koala

Wombat

Kangaroo

ciently studied from this point of view. Best known, in the combination of present condition and historical explanation, is the biogeography of land mammals. We shall therefore stress the mammals as an example of facts, problems, and derived principles. You should, however, bear in mind that the problems are similar and the principles the same for all groups of organisms.

By the beginning of the twentieth century the essential facts about the over-all distribution of land mammals were known. When those facts were arranged and generalized, there emerged a pattern of *land faunal regions*. Each region has some measure of general faunal resemblance throughout, and each has distinctions from any other region. Several arrangements differing in detail have been proposed, but the one shown in Fig. 29-1 is as widely accepted as any.

Faunas intergrade everywhere, and there are no such sharp lines in nature as on the map. Note, too, that this particular pattern is based on mammals and birds; [1] its application to other groups of animals and to plants is also generally valid but less clear. Even for mammals and birds, its application to islands other than those recently connected to continents is misleading. With these provisos the pattern has a real validity that may be briefly demonstrated.

The *Holarctic* [2] region has such animals as the timber wolf, hares, moose (called "elk" in Europe), and stag (called "elk" in America) that range through most of it and only marginally, if at all, elsewhere. The New World and Old World parts are distinctive in a lesser way. For instance, our commonest deer are of a genus (*Odocoileus*) absent in Eurasia, and the wild boar of Eurasia Holarctic is absent here. The Holarctic is often separated into the *Nearctic* ["new (world) northern"] region or subregion and the Eurasian *Palaearctic* ["old (world) northern"].

The *Oriental region* is the haunt of the tiger, Indian elephant (a different genus from the African elephant), gibbons (p. 792), and many other mammals nearly or quite confined to this region. The *Ethiopian region* is

especially characterized by giraffes, zebras, African elephants, and a great abundance of antelopes, some related to Oriental species and others sharply distinct.

The *Neotropical* [3] *region* is more distinctive than any of those already mentioned. Among the many mammals nearly or entirely confined to this region are the guinea pigs and many related rodents, New World monkeys (ceboids, p. 601), sloths, true anteaters, and armadillos. The *Australian region* is even more distinctive. Its mammalian fauna consists mostly of marsupials, and all belong to families that occur nowhere else. [4] The peculiar monotremes (p. 597) are also confined to this region. There are some native placental mammals—bats, rats, and a dog—but most of them are also of distinct species or genera.

SOME PROBLEMS

A biogeographic map like that of Fig. 29-1 or 29-2 sums up many facts, but it is still only a generalized description. A description of things is not much use and indeed is not truly a part of science unless it helps to go further, to require explanations and to find them. The descriptive data of mammalian geographic distribution do require many explanations.

There are problems here of resemblances and differences. The fauna of North America north of Mexico (that is, of the Nearctic subregion) resembles that of northern Asia much more than that of South America. Yet the Nearctic is connected to South America and not to Asia. Northern Africa, although not connected directly to Europe, has an essentially European fauna. Central and southern Africa are farther from Asia than from northern Africa, but the fauna is considerably more like that of southern Asia.

Then there are problems of apparently conflicting resemblances and origins. One animal abundant throughout the taiga of North America, the porcupine, has its closest relatives in South America. Most of the other animals of

[3] "New (world) tropical." The name is somewhat misleading. An enormous part of this region, in southern South America, is outside the tropics.

[4] There are two families of living marsupials in North and South America, one of them including the familiar opossum, but these families are not present in Australia.

[1] The original proposal, in nearly this form (by Wallace, p. 807), was based on both mammals and birds.

[2] "Whole northern."

the taiga have their closest relatives in Asia. There are a few exceptions. Mule deer and whitetail deer, which do range into the taiga but are somewhat marginal there, are more closely related to some South American deer than to any in Asia. The geographic relationships seem anomalous in themselves, and they also suggest further questions as to places of origin. Did the taiga fauna as a whole come from Asia and a few members, such as porcupines and deer, spread into South America? Or are the forms with South American affinities, the porcupine and the deer, of South American origin? (We will give you the answer. Historical evidence proves that the first explanation is correct for the deer and the second for the porcupine.)

Many of the classic problems of biogeography, including some that have never been satisfactorily solved, arise from what are called *disjunctive* (that is, unconnected) *distributions*. It rather frequently happens that two closely related groups of organisms occur in widely separated regions, but that there are no equally closely related forms in between. Because the disjunctive groups are closely related, they must have had a common ancestry not long ago. Therefore ancestors of the existing groups must have spread from one region to the other, or to both regions from a third. The problem is to determine what route they followed and how. Famous examples among mammals are the tapirs, which live only in Central and South America and in southeastern Asia, and the camels, which live (as wild animals) only in South America and Asia. (Both those problems have been solved, as you will see later.) Still more puzzling examples occur among other groups of animals and among plants.

Such problems can be solved only by historical methods. Yet historical study soon raises other problems of its own. It sometimes shows that earlier faunal relationships were quite different from those of today. Thus further explanations are required. The fauna of Honduras (Central America, north of the Panama constriction) now is South American in predominant affinities. But we know from fossils that a few million years ago the mammals of Honduras had nothing to do with those of South America and were all of northern affinities. They were, in fact, more nearly related to mammals of Eurasia, even of Africa, than to those of next-door South America. At about the same time southern Europe, now part of the Holarctic region, had a fauna more closely related to that of the present Oriental region.

FAUNAL CHANGE AND EARTH CHANGE

Evidently faunas and faunal regions have not stayed put. A biogeographical map of the present world may be true enough as of now, but it is a static picture and does not convey anything of dynamic, historical processes. Those processes are the real story of biogeography. Confining attention to the static map is like looking at one frame of a motion picture instead of running through the whole film.

Organisms have developed on a constantly changing earth. Climates have changed. Mountains have arisen and been worn down. Shallow seas have advanced and retreated where now is land. Most important of all, from our present point of view, seas now separated by land have been united, lands now separated have also been united, and both seas and lands now united have at times been separated. During the latter part of geological history at least, the last hundred million years or more, major seas and lands, the oceans and continents, have had substantially their present identity.[5] Their outlines and detailed features have changed considerably, but they have existed continuously as geographic units. The connections among them have changed, however. That has had most profound effects on the distribution of organisms seen on such a large scale as in the biogeographic regions (Fig. 29-3).

Historical changes in any given biotic region and indeed within any community are of four kinds. (1) Evolutionary change takes place within each of the species present in region or community. (2) The proportionate numbers of individuals of the various species change; some become more and some less abundant. (3) Some species disappear, either locally or by total extinction; this is a special case of (2), the reduction of proportionate

5 Some disagree with this, but it is the consensus (see pp. 723 and 753).

numbers to zero. (4) New species spread into the region or community from elsewhere.

The last-mentioned kind of change is the one that is directly geographical. Historical biogeography is concerned primarily with the spread of species and of whole biotas—their dispersal. It is this that is so intimately bound up with the earth changes we have mentioned, because the earth changes open and close routes of dispersal. The geographic changes cannot, however, be wholly separate from the other kinds of change in regions and communities. Geographic spread of species is a cause of numerical changes, including extinction, in invaded communities. Such spread is generally accompanied by adaptive change in the species involved, because as they reach new environments selection tends to modify adaptation accordingly. Evolution may also be speeded up within the invaded communities, by an intensification of selection and change in its trend.

Basic to all these aspects of biogeography are the means of dispersal and the things that facilitate, hinder, or prevent it.

Dispersal and Isolation

MEANS OF DISPERSAL

All organisms have some means of dispersal. That is a necessity for living things. Can you imagine an organism that did not have any way of getting from one place to another? What would the consequences be for such a species?

The means of dispersal are most obvious in the many animals that go places under their own power. They fly, walk, crawl, or swim and so constantly change their precise geographic localities. Included in this category are most of the vertebrates, insects and other arthropods, many worms, some mollusks (such as the squids), and some coelenterates (in the medusa form, p. 525, although their locomotion is not so directive as in the other groups named). Most land animals above microscopic size and the actively swimming, nektonic aquatic animals belong to these groups.

Even among actively and directively motile organisms dispersal is not a simple matter of packing up and going somewhere else. It is to be distinguished from migrations, in which a whole population moves periodically to another region. That is a geographic movement, but only among regions already occupied on occasion and hence not an actual spread or dispersal of the species. Most animals have a strong attachment to the community into which they are born, whether that community is fixed at a single geographic locality or is mobile or migratory. Dispersal usually takes place through a sequence of generations. As the population becomes more dense, marginal individuals have a better chance if some of them move out from the center of density. Any one individual may move only a few centimeters, meters, or kilometers from where he was born. Continued over many generations, the sum of such movements may spread the species, or others derived from it, over a whole continent or ocean, or more than one.

The dispersal of protists, plants, and many animals is passive as far as the organisms themselves are concerned. Planktonic organisms are dispersed by currents in which they float. Sessile animals, such as corals, have floating larvae which are in effect temporarily planktonic and are similarly dispersed. (All sessile animals are aquatic.) Most plants have spores or seeds that are air-borne or are dispersed by animals and in other ways. Plant dispersal involves many intricate adaptations, some of which have already been mentioned (p. 378).

Insects, spiders, and other light animals are often blown for long distances by wind, and this may facilitate their dispersal. Fallen trees and mats of vegetation and debris are often floated long distances down rivers or carried for hundreds, even thousands, of kilometers by ocean currents. With them may go not only _etc._ seeds but also eggs and adult animals. Violent winds, especially tornadoes, occasionally pick up salamanders, toads, frogs, and even fishes and drop them elsewhere, still living. Flying birds frequently carry live seeds for great distances. Eggs and larvae of many small aquatic animals become attached to the feet or feathers of swimming and wading birds and are carried away and deposited elsewhere in the aerial wanderings of the birds.

In the world as we see it today and not as it was in a true state of nature, man is one of the most effective agencies of dispersal. He has purposely taken domesticated animals and cultivated plants wherever he himself dispersed. He has also purposely introduced many wild animals and plants in regions where they are not native. Mice, rats, and other small animals, especially insects, have hitchhiked with man, against his own intention, in boats, wagons, automobiles, and now airplanes. As a result, there is now probably no place on earth where all the plants and animals are native, none introduced purposely or accidentally by man.

ROUTES OF DISPERSAL

There are so many means of dispersal for kinds of organisms that it is somewhat surprising that there are few world-wide species. For a group with highly effective dispersal the final control would, after all, be purely ecological. That is, the group would soon occur wherever the environment provided an ecological role for which it was well adapted. That is true of man and of some of his commensals and parasites, but man and the organisms most closely associated with him are special cases. Few other species have literally world-wide suitable environments.

Dispersal depends not only on means but also on route. An analogy is that where you drive depends not only on having an automobile, the means, but also on where a road goes, the route. Nature has many routes, from broad turnpikes to bumpy back roads. It also has many barriers, roads that are closed for one species or another and regions where, for a given species, no roads exist.

For many nektonic animals of the open sea the whole ocean is a highway. They do tend to spread widely, until they encounter an environmental or ecological barrier. Distribution of plankton is most strongly affected by the great ocean currents. The over-all pattern of those currents is fairly constant now, although it must have had some radical regional changes in earlier geological times. A current from the Gulf of Mexico once flowed through what is now Central America into the Pacific, instead of doubling back into the Atlantic as the Gulf Stream. Thus routes may change in the sea as on land, but wherever they go the ocean currents are main dispersal routes for plankton spreading downstream. Dispersal of plankton against the current is unlikely.

The winds, turbulent and erratic as they are locally, have an over-all pattern of air movement that has probably changed little through geological time. For plants and animals with an air-borne dispersal phase, the zones of prevailing westerly winds, for instance, are and long have been major routes for dispersal from west to east.

Physical and climatic maps of Eurasia show that there is a pathway from western Europe clear across to northern China which could readily be traversed in all its parts by many land plants and animals (Fig. 29-3). That dispersal route has been extensively followed, as is evident from the fact that some natural communities in Europe are remarkably like others in China, thousands of kilometers away. Yet they are not exactly the same in the two regions. A dispersal route, no matter how open it may be, like the Eurasian corridor or the Atlantic equatorial current, is never 100 per cent effective.

For any given group of organisms there are dispersal routes that differ in the probability of dispersal. The scale of probabilities is continuous. At one extreme are routes along which dispersal is prompt and nearly certain. At the other extreme are routes so unsuitable that dispersal along them is so unlikely as to be effectively impossible. Of course for the group in question such an extremely low-probability route is more likely to be a barrier to spread than a dispersal route.

For whole biotas there is also a continuous scale of probabilities of dispersal or of migration. If chances are good for the spread of many or most species of a biota (although chances may still be poor or practically nil for some species), the route is a *corridor*. The Eurasian route previously mentioned has been a corridor for Holarctic floras and faunas. Other routes are more and more selective. Some species migrate readily along them, while others do not. The route may then be considered a *filter*, because it passes parts of biotas and holds others back. There is no sharp distinction between a corridor, which is still a filter for some individual species, and a filter, which is still a corridor for certain

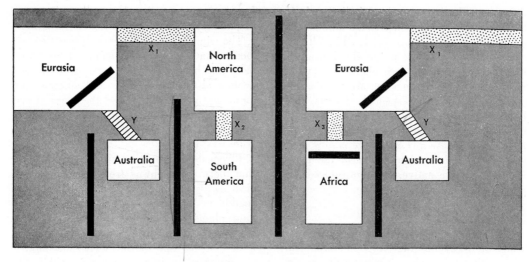

X_1, X_2, X_3 = the variable major filter bridges and corridors

Y = variable sweepstakes route

▮ = constant barriers during Cenozoic

29-3 World dispersal routes: barriers, filters, and corridors. Major features of the geographic history of faunas, especially mammals, are best accounted for by considering the continental blocks and the main sea barriers as constants, and the three main filter bridges and one main sweepstakes route as variables.

species. It is merely a matter of what percentage of a whole biota follows the route.

A good example of a filter route is the Middle American connection between North and South America. It is a continuous land bridge (except for the recent and narrow separation by the Panama Canal), and so is a potential pathway of migration for land plants and animals. In fact North and South American floras and faunas have become extensively mixed by dispersal on this route. (The example is more fully discussed later in this chapter, p. 725.) They are nevertheless still sharply distinct because most of the old native plants and animals of South America and many of those of North America were not able to migrate across the bridge. It filtered them out (Fig. 29-4).

BARRIERS

In a sense a barrier can be thought of as a dispersal route looked at from the other end of the scale of probability. Probabilities of dispersal for a given species along a given route may be anything from near 100 per cent to near 0. (Whether the chances are ever

exactly 100 per cent or 0 is a moot point.) If the chances are low, the route is a barrier. In consideration of whole biotas, almost any route may be a corridor for some species and a barrier for others. A filter route is of course a barrier for the species that are filtered out.

A barrier is any zone physically or ecologically unsuited for the organisms impeded by it. A mountain range is a barrier to species better adapted to lowland conditions on each side of it, and the lowlands are barriers between mountain ranges. Grassland is a barrier for forest animals, and forests are barriers for plains animals. A cold ocean current is a barrier for warm-water species.

Faunal regions are delimited by major barriers. The change from the Nearctic to the Neotropical across middle America is gradual, but it tends to center along the barrier formed by the change from temperate grassland and desert to tropical forests in Mexico. The Sahara and other deserts separate the Palaearctic and Ethiopian regions in Africa. The Himalayas and other mountains are the barrier between Palaearctic and Oriental in Asia. These barriers are not absolute. They

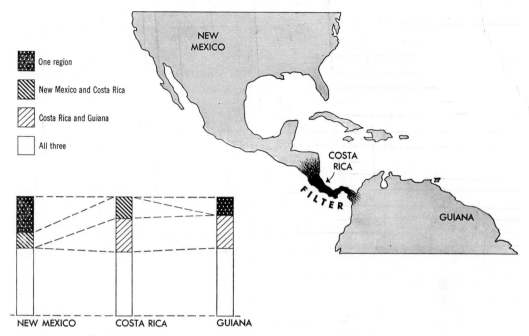

29-4 The Isthmus of Panama, a major filter route. The filter action of the isthmus is well illustrated by the graphs which show the high proportion of animals in both New Mexico and Guiana that either have failed entirely to cross the isthmus (black with white stipple) or have only got halfway across (crosshatches). The total height of the column for each of the three zones represents 100 per cent of the local mammalian fauna.

are filters, but strong ones. They have not always been there, and faunal regions have not always been delimited as they are now.

A special kind of barrier that is one of the strongest limitations on dispersal of organisms is purely ecological. Plant seeds may be wafted for hundreds of kilometers, perhaps even across an ocean. If they land on bare soil of suitable composition and in a suitable climate, the seeds will grow. Dispersal has occurred, and the species has spread geographically to a new region. But there is a catch in the word "bare." There is practically no environment that is not already occupied by plants adapted to it. There is little chance, indeed, that the new types of seeds will land on suitable bare soil. They will land in an established community where they must compete with species already fully established there, well adapted to the community's ecology and to the environment. Exceptional invaders can overcome this tremendous handicap, but the chances are usually slim.

There is reason to believe that the spores and seeds of innumerable species of plants have crossed the South Atlantic in both directions between Africa and South America. Carried especially by winds, birds, and currents, the number of such crossings in the last few million years of geological time must have been enormous. The African and South American floras do have some related species that were probably dispersed in this way.[6] On the whole, however, the floras are very different. The great majority of migrants failed to get a foothold in the foreign communities.

STRONG BARRIERS AND SWEEPSTAKES DISPERSAL

A plains animal is not likely to cross a mountain range, but it could do so in most instances and could find food and other necessities of life on the way. The animal might

[6] This is an expression of opinion. It is opposed by a few botanists who insist that there must have been a land connection across the South Atlantic in late geological times. The existence of such a connection late enough to be involved in dispersal of flowering plants, at least, is denied by a strong consensus of competent geologists and biogeographers.

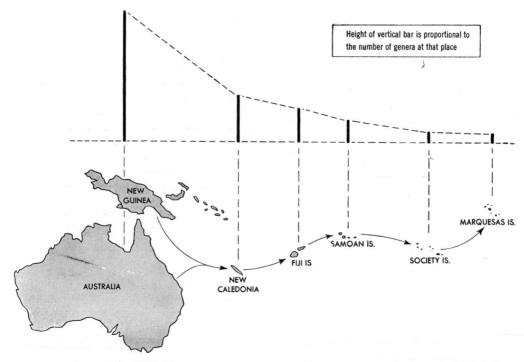

29-5 Dispersal along a sweepstakes route. A group of weevils (*Cryptorhynchinae*) has island-hopped from west to east. The vertical bars are proportional to the diversity (number of genera) of the group at each place. Clearly the group has been sifted out, fewer and fewer managing to follow each successive sweepstakes route. These insects are, even so, particularly good at sweepstakes dispersal.

be neither more nor less likely to cross an arm of the sea of equal width, but the character of the barrier is quite different. The sea is an environment in which a land animal cannot possibly carry on its normal activities. Similarly for seed plants, the sea is an area where they cannot possibly grow. As still another example, an isthmus is a barrier for marine animals where they cannot possibly colonize or sustain active life.

Barriers that represent not merely difficult but downright impossible habitats for the organisms in question are of the very strongest kind. Populations cannot spread across them by any normal processes of expansion or migration. If the barrier is crossed at all, it must be by individuals and in one jump, so to speak, not by the gradual expansion of a population. Even the strongest barriers of this kind can be crossed by many organisms and have been crossed repeatedly in the long history of life. That is *waif* or *sweepstakes dispersal*, "sweepstakes" because the individ-

ual chances of dispersal over such barriers are small, as are the chances of winning a sweepstakes, and yet the event does occur (Fig. 29-5).

A great natural experiment in sweepstakes dispersal occurred when the island volcano Krakatoa, near Java in the East Indies, blew up in 1883. Every trace of life on the island was destroyed.[7] The nearest island not destroyed by the eruption is over 18 kilometers distant, and yet in only three years there were 11 species of ferns and 15 of flowering plants on Krakatoa. Animals soon followed, and within 25 years there were 263 species of animals resident on the island. Most of them were insects, but there were 4 species of land snails, 2 of reptiles, and 16 of birds. In 1928, 45 years after the explosion, there were 47 species of vertebrates on the island, mostly flying forms (birds and bats), but including two kinds of rats.

[7] One species of earthworm may have pulled through the holocaust, but it probably did not.

The Hawaiian Islands are surrounded by a tremendous oceanic barrier and have never been connected to other land, but they have a luxuriant native land biota.[8] All the ancestors of the thousands of species of Hawaiian plants and animals reached there by sweepstakes dispersal.[9]

The possibility of sweepstakes dispersal exists for any group, but it is much higher for some than for others. It is highest for plants, especially those with wind-borne spores or seeds, and for small flying animals, especially insects but also birds and bats. That seems reasonable, and it is borne out by the data on Krakatoa and on the Pacific islands. Sweepstakes dispersal of strictly marine animals across a land barrier and of the strictly land (and nonflying) mammals across a sea barrier is least likely. There are no native land mammals on any of the Pacific islands beyond those immediately adjacent to Australia.[10]

One reason why the historical biogeography of land mammals has been studied more extensively than that of any other group is that they are little subject to sweepstakes dispersal. It can usually be assumed that their migration routes were on continuous land connections. Their geographic history thus is crucial in determining when and where variable earlier land connections existed. Nevertheless, it is practically certain that a few land mammals have had sweepstakes dispersal. Although exceptional, those instances have influenced mammalian biogeography markedly in some regions. Their recognition has cleared up some classic problems that seemed insoluble when it was supposed that land mammals *always* spread over continuous land.

Changing Biotas and Geography

THE WORLD CONTINENT

We noted above (p. 716) that the Neotropical and Australian regions are more dis-

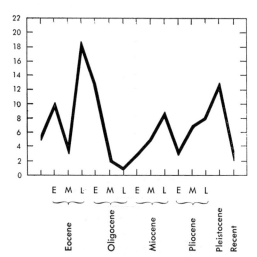

29-6 Interchange in the mammalian fauna of North America and Eurasia through the Cenozoic. (See Table 30-1.) The graph plots the numbers of items of evidence for interchange between Eurasia and North America through most of the Age of Mammals (Cenozoic). The intensity of *actual* interchange doubtless rather closely followed the ups and downs shown here. Evidence indicates that the land connection, when it existed, was between Alaska and northeastern Asia. E = early; M = middle; L = late.

tinctive than the Holarctic, Ethiopian, and Oriental regions. It was also mentioned that the fauna of northern North America is more like that of Asia, to which it is not connected by land, than that of South America, to which it is connected. The historical reasons for these facts may now be stated. Australia is now and has long been an island continent. South America is not now but was during most of the Age of Mammals, the last 75 million years or so, an island continent. Africa, Europe, Asia, and North America were separated from each other for various shorter times, but they were also connected periodically during the Age of Mammals.

As far as the mammals are concerned—and other groups of land organisms have also frequently tended to follow this pattern—Africa, Europe, Asia, and North America were long essentially one big land unit, a supercontinent or World Continent. There have been repeated regional isolation and differentiation from time to time, but by and large the history of land faunas has followed along the same broad lines on the World Continent. There

---

[8] Tragically overwhelmed now by the injudicious importation of nonnative plants and animals.
[9] Sweepstakes dispersal also explains the origin of the Galápagos Islands biota (p. 444).
[10] Some do have native rats, but these were probably introduced accidentally in Polynesian canoes.

has been frequent although always incomplete (filtered) intermigration of faunas among its different parts, the continents as we have them today.

With the aid of fossils it is possible to measure the relative intensities of intermigrations on the World Continent during the past 60 million years or so. The varying extent of dispersal of land mammals in either direction between Eurasia and North America is shown in Fig. 29-6. In general it is reasonable to conclude that when dispersal was comparatively high there was a land connection between the continents, and that when it was low there was a sea barrier. Other evidence indicates that the connection, when it existed, was between Alaska and northeastern Asia.[11]

The connection or connections within the Old World kept the World Continent faunas sufficiently mixed so that they retained a broad similarity. The connections were filters, however, and other filters developed within the continents. As might be expected, relatively few animals especially adapted to warm climates managed to cross the northern bridge between Asia and North America, in spite of the fact that Alaska was a good deal warmer during most of the Age of Mammals than it is now. (Contrary to some popularizations of the subject, it is not true that Alaska was ever tropical in climate.)

Regional differentiations of faunas thus could and did occur in spite of repeated mixing by intermigration. The World Continent did not develop a really uniform fauna, even where environmental conditions were closely similar. The alternating filter and barrier between Asia and North America gave a degree of isolation reflected now in considerable distinction of their faunas. In the Old World the east-west desert filter in Africa and the mountain filter in Asia developed during the Age of Mammals. Northern and southern faunas were more sharply separated than they otherwise would have been, or than they were earlier in the Age of Mammals. Narrowing of the land connection between Africa and Asia and extension of the desert filter in south-

western Asia also tended to isolate what had been more nearly uniform faunas, and finally resulted in the distinction we recognize now between the Ethiopian and Oriental regions.

ISLAND CONTINENTS

Similarities between the faunas of two regions naturally tend to be in proportion to the amount of intermigration that has occurred between them. Regions long connected by corridors have faunas of much the same composition, differentiated moderately on a local, ecological basis. Isolation, the interposition of barriers, leads to more radical differences on a regional, more historical than purely ecological, basis. The longer the period of isolation, the greater the differences. Australia and South America, long island continents, illustrate this principle, which explains the regional peculiarities of their floras and faunas.

In Australia most of the ecological roles (or ways of life) of land mammals are filled by marsupials. That is in itself a radical difference from the World Continent, where practically all such roles are filled by placentals.[12] If there had been a land migration route between the World Continent and Australia during the Age of Mammals, it seems certain that there would have been early mixture of placentals and marsupials there. Evidently Australia started the Age of Mammals with marsupials (and the now comparatively insignificant monotremes) only, and has been isolated by a strong barrier ever since.

Spreading over a whole continent with highly varied environments, the Australian marsupials early speciated profusely. Different lines rapidly became specialized in adaptation to the many possible ecological roles. They underwent, in short, an *adaptive radiation* on a grand scale. The roles assumed were generally similar to those of the phylogenetically distinct placentals of the World Continent. The result, as we have already mentioned in another connection (p. 470), was *convergence* between many Australian marsupials and World Continent placentals.

[11] There was probably also an earlier connection across Greenland to Europe, but it seems to have broken down permanently early in the Age of Mammals, if not before.

[12] Opossumlike marsupials were fairly common on the World Continent early in the Age of Mammals and are still present in North America, but they never developed any considerable diversity outside the island continents.

Later, rats, placental rodents that had evolved on the World Continent, also reached Australia. They are now numerous there and have evolved into many species and genera peculiar to that region. This is one of the facts of biogeography that can be explained only by sweepstakes dispersal. If the rats came in over a land connection, it is incredible that no other placentals accompanied them. Rats are also known on other evidence to be particularly good at oversea dispersal or island-hopping. The only other native placentals of Australia are bats, dispersed by flight and winds; a wild dog, probably introduced by the aborigines; and the aborigines themselves, who came by boat.

South America must have been connected with the World Continent, undoubtedly with its North American part, early in the Age of Mammals. It started out with a far more varied stock of land mammals than did Australia, including primitive marsupials and several groups of primitive placentals. Then the connection with North America was broken, and the mammals evolved in isolation in South America for tens of millions of years. Here, too, adaptive radiation occurred on a continental scale and here, too, there was extensive convergence toward World Continent mammals. Placentals, evolving into families and orders peculiar to South America, took over most roles. The marsupials, however, became much more diverse than they ever were on the World Continent and took over various roles. Most striking is the fact that all the predaceous carnivores of island South America were marsupials. Only placental mammals evolved into predators on the World Continent.

Later on, some 35 or 40 million years ago and thus just about the middle of the Age of Mammals, two new groups appeared in South America as the rats did in Australia. The most reasonable explanation is the same: the newcomers probably got there by sweepstakes dispersal, island-hopping down from Central America, which was not then attached to South America. The newcomers were New World monkeys and the rodents resembling guinea pigs; both types expanded greatly in South America and are still characteristic of that continent.

AN EXAMPLE OF FAUNAL INTERCHANGE

In the later part of the Age of Mammals, around 15 million years ago, the mammalian fauna of South America was far more distinctive than it is now. It had almost nothing in common with North America or the rest of the World Continent. Then movements of the earth's crust heaved up a land connection between the two continents. The result was first a trickle and later a flood of mammals from each continent onto the other. Such mixtures of faunas after disappearance of a barrier have often occurred, both on land and in the sea, but this is at present the clearest and most fully analyzed example (Fig. 29-4).

The filtering action of the connection was striking. From North America members of the racoon family reached South America first of all, probably even before the connection was complete. Wild dogs, cats, weasels, field mice, peccaries, deer, tapirs, and many others eventually passed the filter in great numbers. But other common North American mammals, such as beavers, pronghorns, and bison, did not. Why do you suppose these animals were filtered out? From South America into North America came porcupines, capybaras (large, amphibious rodents, extinct here now but still present in South America), armadillos, glyptodonts (large extinct relatives of the armadillos), giant sloths (large extinct relatives of the living tree sloths), and perhaps opossums, although they may have been in North America all along. Most of the South American mammals, however, failed to get completely through the filter. Among others, the peculiar native ungulates, the monkeys, and the marsupial predators did not.

Animals spread in both directions between North and South America, as is usual on most dispersal routes. North American animals were, however, more successful than those of South America in making their way into the communities of the other continent. Both continents became temporarily richer in land mammals than they had been. Before the interchange North America had 27 families of land mammals and South America 23. At the height of the interchange the figures were 34 and 36, respectively.

The increase in diversity involved some

duplication of ecological roles. Animals that had evolved convergently on the two separate continents now came into direct contact and competition. Such a situation cannot last indefinitely. Ultimately one of the competing forms wins out and one becomes extinct. The interchange was followed by widespread extinction of species, genera, and whole families. At present North America (north of Mexico) has only 23 families of land mammals—actually fewer than before the interchange—and South America has 30. Here, too, the mammals of North American origin were more successful; fewer of them became extinct. The only mammals of known or probable (the opossum) southern origin still present in our fauna are the porcupine, armadillo, and opossum, and none of them looms very large in the fauna. In present-day South America about half the mammals are descendants of comparatively recent invaders from North America. All its native hoofed mammals and all the marsupial predators became extinct.

The distinctiveness of the present Neotropical region involves three factors. Some oldtimers that evolved in South America when it was isolated still survive there and have not crossed the filter to North America: armadillos (one species only is north of the filter), sloths, anteaters, many rodents allied to the guinea pigs, and monkeys. Some mammals really of North American origin have become extinct in North but not in South America: the camels (the llama and others) and tapirs. Other groups are still common to the two continents, but in most instances they have diverged somewhat on the two sides of the filter. For example, the deer of South America are all of distinctive species, and several belong to distinctive genera that evolved there from North American ancestors but have never spread back to the north.

FAUNAL STRATIFICATION

Wide dispersal of plants and animals has been frequent through the geological past, but it has been scattered and episodic as new dispersal routes appeared or old ones disappeared. Moreover, it has seldom if ever happened that a *whole* biota, a complete and integrated community, was dispersed all at once. There is always some filtering. Thus it happens that the regional communities we have today consist of species whose ancestors spread into that region at different times. For example, in our now decimated grasslands fauna the bison (or "buffalo") and pronghorn (or "antelope") were the prominent large herbivores, both equally at home on the high plains. But the ancestors of the bison came here from Asia quite recently, geologically speaking—a matter of some 500,000 years. The ancestors of the pronghorn, on the other hand, have been here for tens of millions of years.

The division of a fauna into different *strata*, depending on how long the various groups have been in the region, is particularly clear among the land mammals of South America. There are three readily distinguished major faunal strata there. The oldest consists of descendants of animals dispersed to South America when it was connected with the World Continent around the beginning of the Age of Mammals. Armadillos, sloths, and anteaters are prominent surviving members of that stratum. The next stratum descends from animals that reached South America by sweepstakes dispersal around the middle of the Age of Mammals: monkeys and many native rodents such as the guinea pig. The youngest stratum consists of groups that invaded from North America when the continents were reunited toward the end of the Age of Mammals: field mice, dogs, cats, deer, and many others.

As a rule, with some exceptions, older faunal strata are more distinctive and peculiar to their region than younger strata. In other words, the longer a group has been in a particular region, the more likely it is to evolve along lines different from those of its relatives elsewhere. This is eminently true of the South American strata. There is nothing like a tree sloth anywhere else on earth. South American monkeys do resemble their relatives in Africa and Asia, but they belong to a distinct superfamily. South American field mice are, on the whole, barely distinguishable from their North American relatives (Fig. 29-7).

DISJUNCTION

We are now ready to review briefly the problems of disjunctive distribution men-

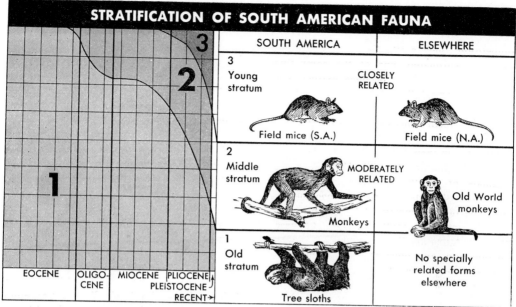

STRATIFICATION OF SOUTH AMERICAN FAUNA

	SOUTH AMERICA		ELSEWHERE
3 Young stratum	Field mice (S.A.)	CLOSELY RELATED	Field mice (N.A.)
2 Middle stratum	Monkeys	MODERATELY RELATED	Old World monkeys
1 Old stratum	Tree sloths		No specially related forms elsewhere

| EOCENE | OLIGO-
CENE | MIOCENE | PLIOCENE
PLEISTOCENE
RECENT→ | |

29-7 Stratification of the South American fauna. Three "strata" can be recognized: (1) ancient; in South America since the Eocene; no closely related forms elsewhere; sloths, anteaters, etc. (2) middle; in South America since late Eocene; New World monkeys, guinea pigs, etc.; arrived by sweepstakes dispersal; (3) youngest; arrived since the late Miocene and the reunion of North and South America; field mice, cats, dogs, deer, etc.

tioned earlier in this chapter (Fig. 29-8).

Some disjunctive distributions are simply explained by the fact that a climatic or other environmental change has restricted a formerly widespread group to scattered parts of its previous range. For instance pikas (small-eared, tailless relatives of the rabbit) occur disjunctively on various western mountain ranges and in the Yukon and adjacent parts of Alaska. They are cold-climate animals that became widely distributed during the Ice Age and now occur only where the climate is still like that of the Ice Age. *Glacial relicts,* as they are sometimes called, which are plants or animals widespread in the Ice Age and now scattered disjunctively in the far north and on mountains, are common in North America and Eurasia.

Pikas also occur on the cold northern steppes of Eurasia, which is not surprising for such a glacial relict. Disjunction between Old World and New World pikas is clearly accounted for by the sinking of the former land bridge between Asia and Alaska. It is not unusual for a barrier to arise where a migration route used to be, producing disjunc-

tion. Many closely related pairs of marine species are disjunctively distributed on the Atlantic and Pacific coasts of Central America. This at once suggests that there was a marine migration route across the region where the isthmian land barrier now stands. The suggestion is confirmed by geological studies. What connection do these facts have with the history of the South American land fauna?

The most striking and disputed instances of disjunctive distribution involved southern land areas. The examples of the tapirs and camels have already been mentioned (p. 717). Others include the marsupials in Australia and South America (absent in Eurasia), the southern beeches (*Nothofagus*) and pines (*Araucaria*) in Australia and adjacent islands and in South America (but not in Africa or the northern continents), and a group of strictly fresh-water fishes [13] in South America and Africa (and nowhere in the north). There are many others, among both plants and animals.

[13] The characins, frequently kept in tropical aquariums.

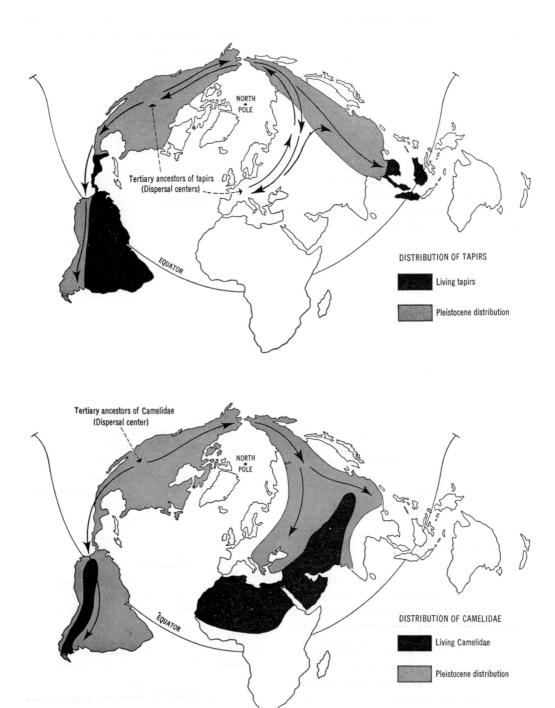

29-8 Disjunctive distributions. The strange disjunction in modern distributions like those of the tapirs (*above*, and see Fig. 29-2) and the camels (*below*, and see illus., p. 689) is explained by knowledge of their earlier distributions as revealed by fossils. Present-day disjunctive distributions are relicts of earlier continuous distributions.

We know from fossil evidence that many of these now disjunctive groups formerly occurred in northern lands. There is no reasonable doubt that they spread between the Old World and the New across the Asia-Alaska land connection. Change in climate reasonably explains their present survival only in the southern parts of the two hemispheres. It is known that the northern lands now have much more severe climates than they had during most of geological time. They are only now emerging from a severe Ice Age. That explanation clearly applies to the tapirs, which formerly ranged all over the Holarctic region and hence spread southward into the Oriental and Neotropical regions. It also applies to the camels, which lived only in North America during most of the Age of Mammals and hence finally spread to Asia and to South America. Among our other examples, this explanation also applies with more or less certainty to the marsupials and the southern, araucarian pines.

So many examples are established by the evidence of fossils that it can be stated as a general rule that land plants and animals now disjunctively distributed in the south were formerly northern and migrated between Asia and North America.[14] For many groups there is no adequate fossil evidence, but it is usually reasonable to assume that they followed the rule. It is, however, by no means established that *all* of them did and that the rule has no exceptions. It seems probable that some southern disjunctive groups of plants, and perhaps a few animals, were really dispersed across regions now oceanic, through the tropics and farther south.

There are two ways in which such dispersal might have happened: by former land connections across what are now tropical and southern areas, or by sweepstakes dispersal across those seas. The existence of former land connections variously placed among Africa, Australia, Antarctica, and South America was formerly a popular theory. It is still sustained, in one form or another, by some biogeographers. Most, however, now believe that that theory is neither necessary nor adequate to explain why the floras and faunas of the southern continents are most decidedly distinct in spite of the presence of some disjunctive groups on two or more of them. Probably whatever migration did take place directly between tropical and southern lands was by sweepstakes dispersal over sea barriers. It may have been facilitated by island chains no longer in existence and by milder climates, so that land plants may have been able to spread along Antarctica.

Chapter Summary

Biogeographic problems for which ecological explanation fails (exemplified by absence of monkeys in Australia); historical explanations needed.

Biogeographic regions:

Faunal regions of the land: Holarctic (Palaearctic and Nearctic), Oriental, Ethiopean, Neotropical, and Australian; typical animals listed.

Sample problems of historical biogeography, including: resemblances and differences between faunas; conflicting resemblances and origins; disjunctive distributions.

Faunal change and earth change: changing climates; changing connections between the land masses; and consequent (historical) change in faunal distributions; four categories of historical change in a biotic region, only one of which has direct geographic consequence—the movement of animals on a grand geographic scale, or dispersal.

Dispersal and isolation:

Means of dispersal: long-term nature of dispersal, involving several generations; distinguished from migrations; passive dispersal of protists and other small organisms; role of sea currents, winds, and severe storms; role of birds in dispersing seeds and other organisms; similar role of human migrations.

Routes of dispersal: open sea and currents for marine forms; prevailing westerly winds for air-borne organisms; easily traversed land routes; probability scale for dispersal of a biota; corridors, filters, and barriers.

[14] This rule was established by the great American paleontologist W. D. Matthew (see p. 807).

Barriers: obstacles to dispersal set up by physical or ecological conditions; physical barriers: mountain ranges, deserts, oceans; ecological barriers; chance crossings of nearly absolute barriers; idea of sweepstakes dispersal (exemplified by history of Krakatoa, the Hawaiian Islands, etc.).

Changing biotas and geography: The World Continent—Africa, Europe, Asia, and North America; a supercontinent with parts only intermittently isolated during Age of Mammals; relatively free dispersal within the World Continent as explanation of broad faunal similarities, especially of paradox provided by greater similarity between North American and Asian faunas than the similarity of North and South America; South America like Australia as an island continent during most of Age of Mammals; filters leading to development of regional differentiation within the World Continent: Palaearctic, Nearctic, Ethiopean, and Oriental.

The island continents, South America and Australia:

Marsupial fauna of Australia: absence of placentals in Australia at beginning of Age of Mammals; their subsequent exclusion by strong sea barrier; adaptive radiation of Australian marsupials; their convergence with placental adaptive types; Australian rats' arrival by sweepstakes dispersal; marsupials and primitive placentals in the early South American fauna; their isolation on the island continent; their adaptive radiation; late arrival of rodents and monkeys by sweepstakes dispersal.

Faunal interchange: an example provided by the faunas of South and North America; development of land connection 15 million years ago; interchange across it; success of North American forms in South America; relative failure of South American forms in North America; analysis of fauna before and after interchange.

Faunal stratification: exemplified by South America; occurrence of three strata in the fauna, each entering South America at a different time.

Disjunction: disjunctive distributions exemplified by certain animals and plants; two explanations: (1) some disjunctive distributions as relicts of formerly continuous distributions; (2) others as the result of true sweepstakes dispersal.

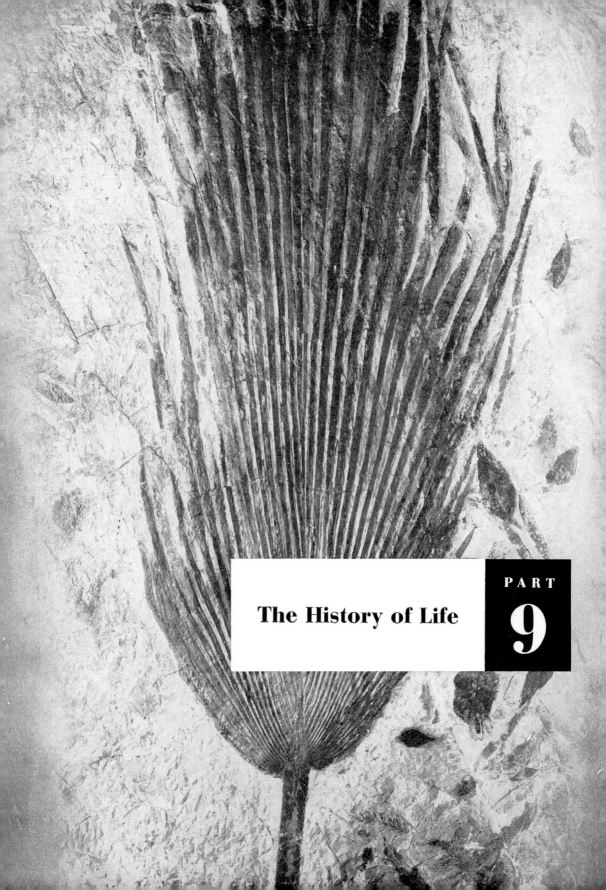

The History of Life

PART

9

INTRODUCTION TO PART NINE

In the seventeenth century the great French philosopher Descartes conjectured that we would reach a much deeper understanding of the world we live in if we could only know the processes by which the world had come into being. But it was not until the close of the eighteenth century and the early nineteenth that his conjecture was made a reality. Before this time—in Descartes' own day, for instance—science had concerned itself only with observation and inference about the workings of the contemporary world. In the social sciences the introduction of historical explanations came from French and Italian writers of the eighteenth century; in geology it came from Lyell in 1813; and in the life sciences it came from Darwin as late as 1859. Ever since, the scientist has perceived the world as something more than meets his eye; he has seen the present as a product of the past, and the past as something to be known and explained before the present can be understood.

In Part 9 we relate the actual history of life as a whole. The account begins with the young planet earth, sterile of life, and it ends with the rich diversity of living things that covers its surface today.

Chapter 30 is concerned largely with the principles of historical biology, with time scales and earth history, and with the nature of the historical record life has left. All history is a story of past events, and is knowable only where those events have left a record of themselves. For the later stages of evolution—for the past half-billion years!—life has left, in the rocks, a direct record of its history in the form of fossils like that of the ancient palm leaf which introduces Part 9. For the early stages of life's history a direct fossil record is lacking; but, as we argue later, these early stages of evolution are not on this account a book wholly closed to us.

Chapters 30, 31, and 32 describe the history of the living world in its certainly known later stages as documented in the rocks. The record reveals a long early phase in the ocean, where nearly all the major groups of organisms had their origin; and it shows how, some 250 million years ago, life eventually conquered the land. The history of terrestrial life focuses on the vertebrates which have dominated the scene and have left an excellent record of their past. For a very long period, about 130 million years, reptiles were masters of the available ways of life on land. Their spectacular downfall about 70 million years ago was followed by the equally spectacular radiation of long-insignificant forms, the mammals. The final stages in the history of terrestrial life concern the progress of the mammals toward their present modern aspect, and the ultimate emergence of man.

CHAPTER 30

Background, Beginnings, and Trends

"BEING" VERSUS "BECOMING"

There are many ways of looking at a tree or at a squirrel in the tree. There is the way of a poet, who projects into the scene a complex of associations with human experiences and emotions. There is a workaday way, which also sees tree and squirrel in human terms but in terms of utility, of board feet or of squirrel pie. Then there is the scientific way, which accepts the tree and the squirrel on their own terms as things existing in the natural world. Quite independently of our reactions to them they have form, composition, and activity of their own. The purpose of science is first to ascertain but then more especially to understand, in terms deeper than mere description, those properties of existing things. Scientific understanding may be sought along many lines, but it generally follows one of two broad approaches. One is

the avenue of *being*, and the other is that of *becoming*.

The law of gravitation, for instance, is something that *is*; it has not become something different since yesterday or a million years ago, and it will not become something different tomorrow or a million years hence. Most of the subject matter of the physical sciences is appropriately studied in terms of being rather than of becoming. That approach is also involved in much of biology. The processes of, say, photosynthesis in the tree or digestion in the squirrel exist and may be studied as *being* what they are and not as *becoming* something else. So may the whole tree and the whole squirrel be studied, but then it is evident that that approach alone is entirely inadequate for understanding living things. The tree and the squirrel have not always been what they are now. They have *become* so, and how they became so is essential to understanding what they are. The tree grew from a seed; the squirrel developed from a zygote in its mother's uterus. Understanding cannot stop there. It must follow the seed and the zygote back and back through the generations to times when there were no seeds or zygotes, no trees or squirrels. The long process of becoming that is evolution yields the most profound understanding of the organism that exists today.

You were introduced to that point of view in the first chapter of this book. It has been kept constantly in mind, and almost all that we have said about living things has been said in terms of becoming as well as of being. Now we propose to pay even more particular attention to the fact that life as manifested in all living organisms has a *history*. We shall review that history, with special attention to the peculiarly *historical principles* involved in it.

Time and the Earth

IN THE BEGINNING

History is what happens through a span of time. To follow it we need first of all a time scale on which to orient its events. Where should our scale start? Was there a beginning of time? That is a question that science cannot possibly answer. It is difficult, perhaps impossible, to imagine literally infinite time, but the problem must be left to religion or philosophy. There are good scientific reasons to believe that our solar system, at least, has not always existed in anything like its present form. Since life as we know it is absolutely conditioned by the solar system, the appropriate starting point for a biological time scale is the formation of the planets more or less in their present condition.

Unfortunately there is as yet no sure and accurate way of knowing how old the solar system is. We do know beyond any reasonable doubt that it is well over 2 billion years old; 3 billion is a probable lower limit. Certain astronomical considerations seem to place the probable upper limit somewhere around 10 billion years. That is not very precise, but it is a good deal better than the old guesses, which ranged from about 6000 years to untold trillions.

We know that the solar system is more than 2 billion years old because there are rocks exposed in the earth's crust that are over that age. The dating has been done by study of radioactive minerals. When a mineral containing a radioactive element, uranium for example, first crystallizes, it includes none of the products of radioactive transformation of that element. Such products then start to accumulate at a constant rate. A stable end product of the natural disintegration of uranium is one of the forms (isotopes) of lead, and that end product usually stays in the mineral along with what is left of the uranium. The rate of formation of lead from uranium is known, and therefore the age of a mineral can be determined from the ratio between the remaining uranium and the lead produced by disintegration of what was originally uranium. The formula is:

$$\frac{\text{Grams of lead}}{\text{Grams of uranium}} \times 7,600,000,000 =$$

$$\text{Age in years}$$

There are technical difficulties that introduce unavoidable uncertainties, but the best age determinations by this and related methods are reasonably accurate. They have dated numerous rocks at around 2 billion years. A few established dates are still older but not, as yet, more than about 3 billion. It is known that even those are not the oldest rocks exposed in the earth's crust. Radioactive minerals suitable for dating have not yet been found in rocks known to be still older (see next paragraph). It is also known that 2 billion years ago and more the earth had a solid, cool crust and that normal processes of rock oxidation, weathering, and erosion were going on. That means that there was already running and standing water on the surface and that the atmosphere cannot have been extremely different from what it is now. The significance to the biologist is that life on the earth was *possible* more than 2 billion years ago.

THE GEOLOGICAL TIME SCALE

The most accurate method of dating rocks in terms of years depends on finding a good, fresh crystal of a radioactive mineral that was formed at the same time as the rock. Unfortunately, such crystals are absent in most rocks. Still more unfortunately, they rarely occur in the rocks of most interest to a biologist—those that contain fossils. For these reasons the history of the earth and its life is most conveniently followed not by a time scale in years but by a different kind of scale, one that was developed long before the phenomenon of radioactivity was known. That geological time scale designates the *sequence* of events rather than the elapsed time between them. You can see that you could follow the history of the United States, for instance, perfectly well if you knew the order in which

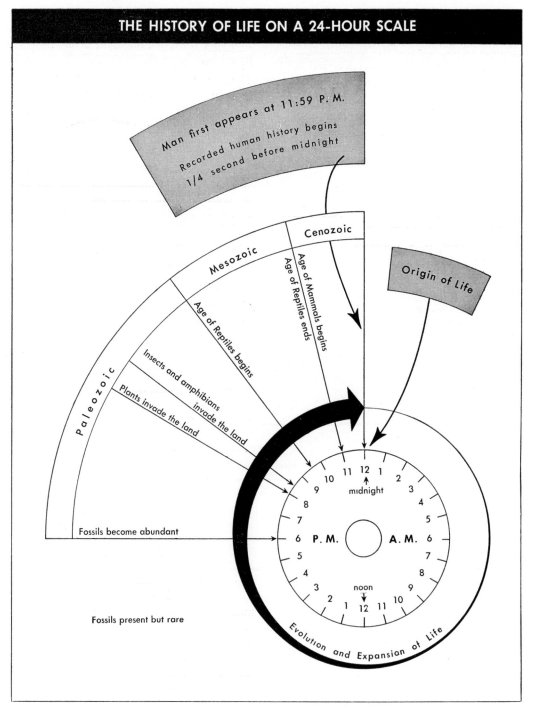

30-1 The history of life on a 24-hour scale.

all events occurred even if you did not know any dates. It would also be handy for discussion if you had names for successive periods. The periods might be named for presidents, or could be given arbitrary names.

The geological time scale now in general use is given in Table 30-1. Approximate times in years are also given, but in our discussion of the history of life the names of the eras and periods will be used rather than year dates. The year figures given are tied in with fairly well-established radioactivity dates at several points, but between those points they are not much better than shrewd guesses. For our purposes the whole time before the Paleozoic is lumped as Pre-Cambrian because there are few fossils in rocks of those ages, and their subdivisions have little biological significance.

We know much more about the later than about the earlier phases of the history of life and so use a more finely divided time scale as the recent is approached. It is hard to visualize the vast time span involved and the increasing tempo of the history as time went on. It may help to comprehend the relative

durations, at least, if we consider the history of life as if it had all occurred within the 24 hours from one midnight to the next. Let us arbitrarily set the beginning, the first midnight, at 2 billion years ago. On that scale fossils did not become abundant until 6 P.M. At 8 P.M. the invasion of the land by plants was under way, and by 8:30 insects and the first amphibians had joined them. The Age of Reptiles began about 9:30. It ended and the Age of Mammals began at about 11 P.M. Man appeared less than a minute before midnight, and the whole span of recorded human history occupies about the last ¼ second! (See Fig. 30-1.)

The Origin of Life

THE PROBLEMS

✔ Nothing is *directly* known about the origin of life. There could be only two kinds of direct evidence: fossils of the first organisms or the rise of similar organisms from nonliving matter today. No such fossils are known

TABLE 30-1   *The geological time scale*

Approximate time since the beginning of the periods, in millions of years	Eras	Periods or epochs *	Some important events in the history of life
.01 1		Recent Pleistocene	First men. Ice Age. Mixture and later thinning out of mammalian faunas
10 30 40 60 75	CENOZOIC (The Age of Mammals)	Pliocene Miocene Oligocene Eocene Paleocene	Culmination of mammals. Radiation of apes Modernization of mammalian faunas Expansion of mammals
135 165 205	MESOZOIC (The Age of Reptiles)	Cretaceous Jurassic Triassic	Last dinosaurs. Great expansion of angiosperms First mammals and birds First dinosaurs
230 280 325 360 425 500	PALEOZOIC	Permian Carboniferous † Devonian Silurian Ordovician Cambrian	Great expansion of primitive reptiles First reptiles. Great coal forests First amphibians. First insects First land plants Earliest known fishes Appearance of abundant marine invertebrates
3000+	PRE-CAMBRIAN	[Period names not well established and not needed for our purposes]	First known fossils

(Left margin: YOUNGER → ... OLDER)

* In technical geological use an epoch is a subdivision of a period, but the distinction is not important for our purposes. The names in this column for the Cenozoic are technically epochs and those for the Mesozoic and Paleozoic are periods.

† American geologists often call the early Carboniferous "Mississippian" and the late Carboniferous "Pennsylvanian."

or are ever likely to be. The first organisms were almost certainly extremely small and could hardly have become fossilized or be found and recognized if they had. It was formerly believed that life was, indeed, being generated all around us anew, but we now know that the supposed evidence for that opinion was false (p. 261). As far as is known no living things are now being generated from the nonliving. Certainly no one has yet created a living thing in a laboratory, although the *possibility* of doing so cannot be excluded on any strictly scientific grounds.

Scientific consideration of the origin of life must thus be based on indirect evidence. Nevertheless it need not be entirely speculative. The diverging paths that life has followed can be extrapolated backward into time and can give us some idea of what the most primitive organisms of all must have been like. Moreover, a great deal is known about the physical and chemical properties of the matter that enters into living things and about the processes that go on in the simplest existing or conceivable forms of life.

In the first place, most biologists agree that the earliest forms of life could and almost certainly did arise from nonliving matter by a natural process. On the basis of what is now known there is, at least, nothing improbable in that view.[1] That statement is in apparent opposition to widely held religious beliefs,

[1] Some popular writers and modern biologists have maintained the opposite. They claim to have demonstrated mathematically that the union of atoms into a living molecule or super-molecule "by accident," as some of them say, or by natural processes would be so extremely improbable as to be impossible. Their mathematics of probability is, however, demonstrably incorrect. They leave out of consideration some or all of three factors that tremendously increase the probability. First, atoms do not unite into molecules at random; some molecular configurations are incomparably more probable than others, and those basic for life (in the amino acids, for instance) were probable under conditions long ago when the event occurred. Second, an event extremely improbable in itself is almost certain to occur if there are enough possibilities of occurrence. The untold trillions of trillions of atoms and molecules in early seas, and time on the order of a billion years certainly gave possibility to even the most unlikely events. Furthermore, a single occurrence could suffice. Once an organic molecule reached the stage of reproduction and subsequent variation, selection would render probable the progression to a true organism. Third, the probability of formation of complex molecules is greatly increased by the template action of adsorption on such things as clay particles.

and we believe that the issue should be faced, even though it is generally avoided in textbooks. It is our own opinion that life arose naturally from nonliving matter and in accordance with the natural properties of the material universe. But we do not have the slightest idea, *as scientists*, where that nonliving matter came from in the first place or how the properties of the universe originated. If the whole universe was divinely created in the beginning, and no scientist can say on his own grounds that it was not, then that creation implied and included also the later origin of life without the necessary intervention of any second or subsidiary miracle. If, however, you prefer to have faith in a separate divine creation of life from the nonliving, then we still have no quarrel with you or, we trust, you with us. It is not a known fact that life arose naturally from the nonliving. That merely seems to us and to most biologists the more probable explanation, and you may accept it or not as you see fit.

A HYPOTHESIS ON THE FORERUNNERS OF LIFE

It seems to be a necessary prerequisite for the rise of life that complex organic molecules should first have arisen, especially amino acids and combinations of them into polypeptides (p. 109) and eventually proteins. Systems of such molecules may become capable of self-reproduction, at least in the sense that, if the environment supplies suitable materials and a source of energy, they can serve as patterns by which those materials are combined into likenesses of themselves. The likenesses would not always be perfect, and even at that extremely primitive level something akin to mutation would occur and variation would be present in the molecular population. Whether such molecular systems were themselves alive is a matter of definition. If the process really went along in anything like the way outlined by this hypothesis, then there was no exact point where the nonliving became alive. Acquisition of the full panoply of life was gradual.

Viruses almost certainly are not recent representatives of the first organisms or of their forerunners. Viruses do nevertheless show that giant organic molecules can be reproduced in a suitable medium. The medium for viruses is itself organic, a living cell. Obviously a living cell cannot have been the habitat of the first organisms, but it seems almost inescapable that life must have arisen in an environment that was *already* rich in organic compounds, some of complexity comparable at least to that of an amino acid. In the world as it is today the rise of such organic compounds by inorganic means must be a rare event indeed, but life did not arise in the world just as it is today. On other grounds [2]

[2] One item of that evidence is as follows: Atmospheres of other planets can be partially analyzed with the spectroscope. Jupiter's atmosphere consists largely of methane and ammonia, and the atmospheres of Saturn, Uranus, and Neptune are largely methane. The atmospheres of these planets have changed since the beginning of the solar system, but they have

it has been inferred that the original atmosphere of the earth contained little or no free oxygen or nitrogen but consisted largely of water vapor, ammonia (NH_3), and methane (CH_4), with minor but increasing amounts of carbon dioxide and free nitrogen, plus a variety of other minor constituents. It has further been inferred, and recently has been demonstrated experimentally, that the passage of a spark (as from lightning) or of strong ultraviolet radiation (as from the sun) through such a mixture can produce fairly complex organic compounds. Those compounds could well have become concentrated in pools, or even in primitive seas, where

almost certainly changed much less than earth's atmosphere.

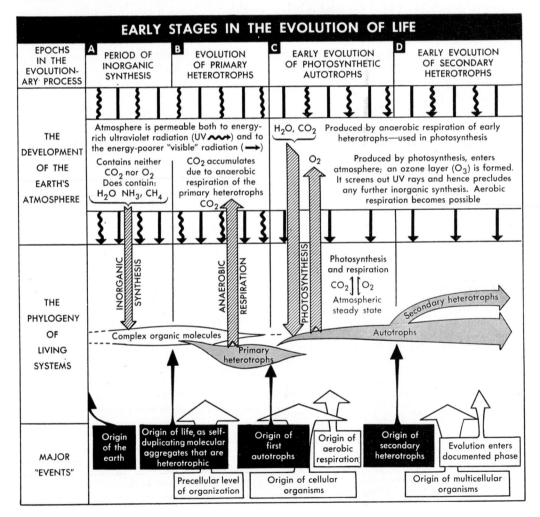

EARLY STAGES IN THE EVOLUTION OF LIFE

they could give rise to the giant molecules hypothesized as forerunners of life, and then would provide a suitable medium for the reproduction and the increasing variety of such molecules.

A next step would be the aggregation of molecules that interacted favorably with each other and with their environment. If, for instance, one kind of molecule reacted with the environment in such a way as to produce oxygen as a waste product and another kind used oxygen in an energy-producing reaction involved in respiration, their association could be favorable to both. Production and recombination of oxygen are used only as a simple example. It is unlikely that reactions of just that sort were involved in the earliest stages. The example shows, however, that different kinds of molecules can interact in such a way that their activities are more effective when they occur together than when each occurs alone. Probably even at the start the interactions were considerably more complex than mere interchange of oxygen by only two kinds of molecules.

Once such interacting aggregates began to form, they would tend to become more numerous and more distinctly and constantly organized in composition and pattern. A complex aggregate of favorably interacting molecules would have evident and great advantages over any remaining free-lance molecules. Given the existence of variation within molecules and within increasingly complex aggregates of molecules, natural selection would occur and would favor change in the direction of more effectively and constantly organized aggregates. The result would eventu-

---

30-2 The early stages of evolution. Four major stages are distinguished. *Stage One:* period of inorganic synthesis; the creation of conditions necessary for life's origin; the slow accumulation of (inorganically synthesized) complex molecules like amino acids, perhaps nucleic acids, and simple carbohydrates. Such inorganic synthesis and accumulation of organic compounds was possible at this unique stage in the evolution of earth because of three conditions then prevailing: (1) necessary precursor compounds (NH_3, CH_4) present in the atmosphere; (2) necessary energy available in the form of ultraviolet radiation penetrating the (ozone-free) atmosphere; (3) absence of life and, therefore, exclusion of decay. The first stage ends with the origin in the accumulated organic compounds of a molecular aggregate capable of self-duplication; such a system is alive. *Stage Two:* growth of populations of these "organisms." Their expansion and evolution took place at the expense of the reservoir of complex organic molecules accumulated in Stage One; this reservoir was the source not only of chemical building blocks but also of energy, which doubtless was mobilized for metabolic use through some form of anaerobic respiration that initiated the accumulation of CO_2 in the atmosphere. The first organisms were, in fact, heterotrophs ("other-feeders")—here termed primary heterotrophs to distinguish them from now-familiar heterotrophs that arose in an entirely different evolutionary context (Stage Four). Two important points about Stage Two: (1) its extent and duration were rigidly limited by the size of the reservoir of inorganically synthesized resources (Stage One) on which it was dependent; (2) the consumption of this reservoir by the first heterotrophs destroyed the conditions necessary for further "spontaneous" origins of living systems: from then on biogenesis became the only possible mode of origin of organisms. *Stage Three:* continuation of life beyond Stage Two was dependent on mutational origin of capacity to synthesize organic compounds from simple, renewable resources—dependent, in other words, on origin of autotrophy. Some chemosynthesis (p. 111) may originally have played a role, but the foundation of all later life and its evolution were dependent on development of the photosynthetic ability. Photosynthesis was possible in part because of atmospheric CO_2 accumulated in Stage Two; photosynthesis led to oxygenation of atmosphere, which had two major consequences: (1) an ozone (O_3) layer formed, screening out most of the sun's ultraviolet rays and excluding thereafter any further inorganic synthesis; (2) conditions were established for the evolution of aerobic respiration; thereafter photosynthesis and respiration maintained a steady state of CO_2 and O_2 in the atmosphere. *Stage Four:* the probably often-repeated origin and expansion of populations of secondary heterotrophs; they are mutational descendants of autotrophs (cf. Fig. 20-9); they have indefinitely renewable resources of energy and materials for their growth in the form of the now well-established autotrophs which mobilize solar energy for the whole world of life. Living systems had probably attained a cellular level of organization before the origin of secondary heterotrophs: all still-surviving heterotrophs (with the exception of viruses) have attained a cellular level, and probably have inherited it from a common ancestor. Viruses (and perhaps some bacteria) may represent surviving primary heterotrophs, but in our opinion this is improbable: they are more likely extremely degenerate secondary heterotrophs. One direction of heterotroph evolution—that set by parasitism—leads to degeneration of most systems except that of reproduction.

ally be a true multimolecular organism, a primitive protist, alive by any definition.

EARLY ORGANISMS

At first sight it might seem logical that the earliest true organisms must have been self-feeders, performing all their necessary organic syntheses from quite simple inorganic materials and using either other inorganic materials or solar radiation as a source of energy. It might even seem absurd to think that the first organisms could have been other-feeders when there were no other kinds of organisms to feed on. That opinion was formerly popular among students of the subject, but in recent years almost all biologists have come to an opposite conclusion.[3] Self-feeding requires more complex organization and metabolism than other-feeding (p. 112). It strains the scientific imagination too far to think that the very first organisms can have been so complex, and no one has succeeded in visualizing in convincing detail how such organisms could originate from molecular forerunners.

The whole process becomes simpler and easier to understand on the hypothesis that the earliest organisms were, in essence, other-feeders. Of course they could not (not all of them, anyway) feed on other organisms. They could, however, be other-feeders in the sense that they fed on carbohydrates, amino acids, and other fairly complicated organic compounds. Then their own syntheses and energy transformations would be comparatively simple. A requirement for this hypothesis is that the earliest organisms must have lived in an environment rich in organic compounds that had not been synthesized by living organisms. We have just seen that there is good reason to believe that such environments may well have existed in the earliest waters on the earth.

Such a state of affairs could not persist indefinitely. *As organisms multiplied, they would rapidly consume all the available organic materials.* Synthesis by inorganic processes would soon tend to lag behind consump-

tion. Moreover, conditions on the earth and especially in its atmosphere were changing. The organisms themselves would cause much of the change. They would, for instance, tend to lock up much of the carbon that formerly was in methane or more complex compounds, or to convert it into CO_2, from which more complex organic molecules are less likely to be formed by inorganic processes. Inorganic synthesis of foods must inevitably have fallen nearly to zero, as it is today and has been through the whole history of life except in the dimmest era of beginnings. If nothing else had happened, life would have become extinct after a brief flare-up that led no further than to a few primitive protists.

Imagine what would happen if, as some needed organic compound were becoming rare in the environment, there appeared a mutant organism that could synthesize that compound from simpler and more widely available materials. The mutant organism would have a tremendous advantage over the others, and its descendants would soon become the dominant, or even the only, remaining organisms. As other compounds became rarer, additional mutations for their synthesis would be favored by selection. Step by step the trend would be toward greater self-sufficiency, toward more complete self-feeding. The culmination of this stage of evolution would be in organisms that could use CO_2 as their sole external source of carbon and solar radiation as their sole external source of energy. Such organisms would of course be photosynthetic protists and eventually plants.

In the meantime environmental conditions on earth had changed radically and could never again be those under which life originated. The surface of the earth, once molten, must already have cooled well below the boiling point of water when life arose. (Why?) Early in the history it cooled still further, to approximately its present temperatures. The original ammonia and methane of the atmosphere were incorporated in the increasingly complex organic systems or were transformed (in part) into N_2 and CO_2, which probably constituted most of the atmosphere relatively soon after life arose. After the rise of photosynthesis, organisms

[3] It is interesting evidence of Darwin's genius that he held the view now considered most likely, although many biologists after him overlooked his opinion on this matter and the strong arguments in favor of it.

themselves made the most important change in the atmospheric composition. They must have reduced the percentage of CO_2 in the atmosphere and also—and especially—have increased the percentage of oxygen, previously rare or absent except in compounds. High in the atmosphere the oxygen then formed an ozone (O_3) layer, still present. That layer screens out much of the ultraviolet in the sun's radiation. The earlier influx of ultraviolet was, by this hypothesis, the principal energy source for the nonorganic synthesis of complex molecules. As ultraviolet was cut off from the surface of the earth, visible light (not significantly absorbed by the ozone layer) became the chief source of energy through organic pigments (now mostly the chlorophylls) in living systems. These changes, largely caused by the early living systems, made further spontaneous origin of such systems impossible and gave organisms a virtual monopoly on organic syntheses.

All of the preceding is hypothetical, but it is in accordance with what we do know of the properties of living things and their environments. Even if we consider it wholly fanciful, it does illustrate possible kinds of interactions and one possibility, at least, as to what went on in the remotest, dark, unrecorded stages of evolution. When we first begin to get a little real light on the scene, the physical conditions of earth and atmosphere were much as they are today and photosynthetic organisms already existed. Their existence made possible the concomitant and subsequent evolution of other organisms that fed on them and on the materials synthesized by them: plant-eaters, parasites, and organisms of decay. Then there could also evolve still another stage: meat-eaters that feed on plant-eaters. The possible sequence in these early stages of evolution is summarized diagrammatically in Fig. 30-2.

Fossils and the Historical Record

PRINCIPLES

The history of life ceases to be hypothesis and inference and becomes direct knowledge when fossils are available. A fossil is a fact: it is a visible trace of some organism that lived in the geological past. That is the fundamental basis of *paleontology*, the study of ancient life (the Greek roots mean exactly that). Science arises from the observation of isolated facts, but it does not become truly science until those facts are seen in relationship to others and are placed in an explanatory context. The paleontological deciphering of the history of life involves, among others, these observations and inferences:

A fossil, an organism with definite characteristics shown by its remains. Further inference concerns characteristics and activities not directly preserved.

The geographic locality at which the fossil was buried and near which it must have lived, another observed fact.

The age of the fossil, an inference based on a wide range of geological and paleontological data.

Association of the fossil with others of the same species, the basis of systematic study of the fossil population.

Association with fossils of other species, part of the basis for the study of the community and the environment (and also of the age).

Characteristics of the rocks in which the fossil occurs and of the position and mode of burial of the fossil in those rocks—further data for the study of environment and age.

Relationships of the fossil population to others, earlier, contemporaneous, and later; comparisons and inferences leading to phylogeny and to classification.

The broader generalizations and principles of the history of life, with which we must be mainly concerned in this summary of an intricate branch of the life sciences, are derived from a vast number of detailed observations and inferences mainly of these kinds.

UNIFORMITARIANISM

There is an important principle fundamental for paleontology, geology, or any science that has historical aspects: the present is a key to the past. That principle was the subject of bitter controversy a century or two ago, when it was endowed with the formidable name of *the doctrine of uniformi-*

tarianism. It is now accepted as true by virtually all scientists, and without it there could be no really scientific study of any kind of history.

The doctrine of uniformitarianism is that the fundamental properties of the universe, the nature and the modes of interaction of matter and energy, have not changed. They are independent of the passage of time. It is only the forms that they have taken and the status of the results of their past interactions that change through time. Liquid water on the earth always has run downhill (unless counteracted by some opposite physical force), and a certain amount of water running at a given velocity over a bed of defined coherence, grain size, and so on, always erodes that bed to a predictable degree. These facts are basic in the unchanging, uniformitarian properties of the universe. The amount of erosion that has occurred and the resultant size and shape of the eroded valley change. They have a history, although the *process* of erosion has none. Similarly we conclude that chromosomes of a given structure and composition under defined environmental conditions always did, do, and will have the same influence on a developing organism and that the same changes in the chromosomes are uniformly associated with the same changes in the organism. The changes that have, in fact, occurred in organisms have a history but, again, the processes do not.

Another way to put the principle is to recall the contrast between *being* and *becoming* made at the beginning of this chapter. The characteristics of nature that simply *are* are those inherent in the properties of matter and energy. Time is irrelevant to them; they have no history. The things that change and that *become* are configurations arising in accordance with the timelessly uniform processes. History is concerned with those "becoming" configurations.

By this principle the geologist is able to interpret past changes in the sculpturing of the face of the earth by processes that can be observed now in action and that can also be studied now experimentally. The biologist is similarly able to interpret the fossil record by processes still proceeding in living organisms and also subject to present experimentation. He can be sure that the processes were just the same in the past as they are now. Perhaps that seems obvious to you. If so, it is only because a hard-won scientific attitude now permeates much of our intellectual atmosphere. The timelessness of the properties and processes of the universe was by no means obvious to earlier thinkers. Establishment of that principle was one of the major triumphs in the history of human thought.

WHAT FOSSILS ARE

It is a wonderful thing that you can hold in your hand the remains of an organism that lived hundreds of millions of years ago. It is a common observation that dead organisms usually molder and become unrecognizable in a few years at most, sometimes even within hours. "Dust thou art, to dust returnest" is indeed the common lot of living things. The organisms of decay see to that, and it is good for the continuity of the communities of life that it is so. Yet there are millions upon millions of ancient organisms that have never wholly decayed.

Fossils are being formed today, but they are only a minutely small fraction of the organisms that die.[4] It has always been true that an exceedingly small fraction of organisms has fossilized. A still smaller fraction by far has been recovered and studied. Nevertheless, the numbers of organisms have been so countless and time so long that even so minute a fraction adds up to a respectable documentation of the history of life.

The usual first condition for preservation as a fossil is burial before decay is complete.[5] Natural burial occurs when a dead organism sinks into mud or sand or when those and other sediments are swept over its remains by waves or streams, occasionally by winds. Organisms may be buried whole, but frequently they are already dismembered to

[4] Moreover, they are being formed where you are most unlikely to see them, for reasons that you will be able to discern for yourself.

[5] A few relatively young fossils have not been buried. There are exceptions to many of our statements here, but we are concerned with what is usual. Exceptional fossils may be particularly interesting, but they have comparatively little importance in an over-all view of the history of life.

some extent when they are buried. The same agency that buries them may break them up. Once buried, any further decay must stop short of obliteration. Fossils available to us as documents must then stay buried down to, or nearly to, the present time. An early Cambrian shell can end up in the laboratory only if it remained buried for some 500 million years and never was washed out again by erosion in all the intervening upheavals and remodelings of the earth's crust.

Erosion cannot have touched for all those years the fossil now in the laboratory, but erosion must finally have come near it. As a rule, fossils cannot be found and collected unless they are again at or near the surface of the earth where the fossil hunter can find them.[6] Fortunately, rocks of all ages are now exposed at the surface, even though they may have been deep within the crust at some time in their history. The earth's crust has been continually rising in one place, sinking in another, buckling and breaking here and there. The higher parts are constantly being worn down by processes of erosion, and thus some among even the oldest rocks are now at the surface.

The processes of decay are highly effective and may continue even after burial, if that is not too deep and not in somewhat unusual naturally antiseptic conditions. Decay usually obliterates all the soft parts of an animal, leaving only the skeletal parts, which consist mainly of resistant inorganic materials. Fossil mollusks usually consist of the shells alone. Fossil vertebrates seldom preserve anything but bones, teeth, and hard scales, if any. Fossil insects are none too common because insects are unlikely to be buried, but those that do occur are often unusually complete because of the tough, over-all external skeleton. Fossil plants also usually have lost all the soft parts, the protoplasmic cell contents. Tough leaf coatings, cell walls, spore skins, and such decay-resistant parts are, however, frequently preserved. Even the soft parts of plants and more rarely those of animals may

6 The only important exceptions here are small fossils frequently recovered from deep drilled wells. They are useful in the petroleum industry, but do not bulk large in the documentation of the history of life.

also be preserved as a dark film of carbonaceous material.

It is a common misapprehension that fossils are petrified, that the organisms have "turned to rock." Such a thing rarely happens, at least in the usual understanding of the words. Preserved hard parts usually consist of the same material as when the organism was alive, perhaps with some recrystallization or slight chemical change. Spaces left by the decay of soft parts, for instance in the marrow of a bone or inside the cell walls of a tree trunk, are often filled with secondary deposits of a mineral, frequently silica (SiO_2 in various forms). After burial and hardening of the surrounding sediments, the hard parts of a fossil may be dissolved by percolating waters. Then a cavity, a mold, may be left, or else mineral-laden waters may precipitate silica or some other mineral in the space, producing a mineral replica of the original fossil. (See Figs. 30-3 and 30-4.)

PRE-CAMBRIAN FOSSILS

We have already noted (p. 736) that there is no fossil record of the beginnings of life. From inferences as to what the earliest organisms must have been like, it seems hardly possible that they could have been preserved as fossils or recovered and recognized even if they were preserved in some way. The disappointing possibilities of the earliest fossil records unfortunately apply to a long span of geological time. Life *may* have existed 2 billion years ago (p. 734), but fossils become varied and abundant only with the beginning of the Cambrian, a mere 500 million years past. Thus the reasonably good fossil record as now known may not cover more than about the last quarter of the history of life.

The whole span of the Pre-Cambrian is poor in fossils, but is not an absolute blank. The most conspicuous evidences of Pre-Cambrian life are extensive limestones (some of them in the Big Belt Mountains of Montana, for instance) that seem to be of organic origin. That is not absolutely certain, but the consensus now is that they were deposited around primitive algae, probably blue-greens (p. 496). Some of them are on the order of a billion years old, perhaps even more. Late Pre-Cambrian iron deposits contain micro-

30-3 Fossil hunting and preparation in the field and laboratory. *Left,* a paleontologist uncovering a fossil. *Below,* a fossil exposed in the field. It is a giant bony fish, *Portheus,* which lived more than 70 million years ago. *Below, left,* a fossil is covered with plaster of Paris for shipment to the laboratory. *Below, right,* the fossil is carefully removed from the plaster casing.

Below, left, cleaning a vertebra of the fossil reptile *Hesperosuchus.*
Below, right, a mounted skeleton in final stages of preparation.

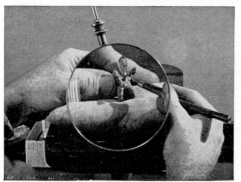

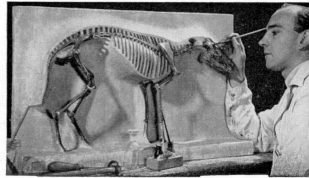

30-4 A diversity of fossils. Fragments of the plant *Otozamites* from the Petrified Forest of Arizona. This cycad (p. 516) lived about 200 million years ago. *Below*, an ammonite (p. 569) from the Jurassic; about 150 million years old.

Below, fossil dinosaur tracks in Texas.

Below, detail of the dinosaur *Corythosaurus*, showing muscle and skin on the tail vertebrae.

scopic structures interpreted as bacteria and blue-green algae. Some recent bacteria form similar iron deposits. In older Pre-Cambrian rocks are structures of carbon that are almost surely organic, although the sort of organism that may have made them cannot be determined. Still other Pre-Cambrian rocks have traces of what seem to be burrows of worm-like animals. Other Pre-Cambrian fossils have been reported, including even animals as advanced as arthropods, but there is good reason to doubt either that they are genuine fossils or that their age is really Pre-Cambrian.

Arthropods and some varieties of other animals do occur in earliest Cambrian rocks. The sudden contrast between the Pre-Cambrian rocks, in which animal fossils are rare or dubious, and the Cambrian, in which they are abundant, poses a serious problem. Why? A good scientist must be prepared to say, "I don't know," and that is at the present the correct answer here. But a scientist is not likely to stop at that. Even though we do not know the answer, what are the possibilities, and are some more likely than others? The principal possibilities seem to be:

1. The various groups of animals that appear in the early Cambrian did not exist earlier; they evolved then each in one enormous step (a mutation?) from protists.

2. They had existed in much the same form for a long time during the Pre-Cambrian, but earlier fossils just have not happened to be preserved or to be found.

3. They arose gradually but at an unusually high evolutionary rate during an immediately Pre-Cambrian span for which rocks that could contain their fossils are rare or absent on the surface at present.

4. Their Pre-Cambrian ancestors were soft-bodied and did not fossilize; their appearance in the fossil record approximately coincides with the evolution of hard parts.

Can you think of other possibilities? All of these have good arguments both pro and con, and each has been supported by competent students. To us the first seems most unlikely, because it is not in good agreement with our understanding of later evolutionary processes. The second is a distinct possibility, but is

unlikely to be the whole explanation. Both the third and fourth seem probable. They are not contradictory, and both could be true, as well as—to perhaps a lesser extent—the second.

THE OVER-ALL RECORD

With the Cambrian begins a rich, continuous record of the history of life in the form of fossils. There are some groups that we infer must have been present and important but are nevertheless rare, although not entirely absent, as fossils. Among these are bacteria and worms. (What basis is there for inferring that they were present and important even when not represented by fossils? Why would they tend to be underrepresented in the fossil record?) On the whole the record is amazingly good when we consider the infinitesimal chance that any one organism, or even a representative of any one species, has had of winding up on a paleontologist's desk.

The broad features of the record are given in Figs. 30-5 and 30-6, which show when main groups of plants and animals are definitely known, by fossils in hand, to have existed. The relative widths of the bands show roughly, but only very roughly, the comparative diversity of known fossils at various times.

Some Major Tendencies

In the next two chapters some of the events in the history of life since the beginning of the Cambrian will be examined in logical and chronological sequence. Attention will of course be given not merely to the events but also to the principles and processes underlying those events and illustrated by them. First we propose to take a quick look at the history as a whole, as it is schematically represented in Figs. 30-5 and 30-6. In this scheme and in the ever-changing panorama of plants and animals that it symbolizes, there are certain broad tendencies. Those tendencies tie in with much that you have already learned; they are understandable in the light of previous chapters. They also provide a background against which the drama of Chapters 31-32 will be played.

The first striking generalization about the total tendency of evolution is that life has expanded. The total number of living things has increased. The bulk of matter in living form has increased. The number of different kinds of organisms has increased. Their diversity, in the sense of the extent of differences among them and not only in the number of species, has increased. All of these increases may be viewed as aspects of the expansion of life, although they are quite distinct from each other.

If you think of the time when life was just getting under way and compare it with the present day, it is quite obvious that life must have expanded tremendously in every possible way. The record of the first and most radical phases of that expansion is unfortunately poor or wholly lost. Yet expansion is still clearly evident in the last quarter or so of the time, when we do have a fairly good record. Expansion is seen in Fig. 30-6, where it reflects especially the increase in number of kinds of organisms. It also shows increase in basic diversity with the increase in numbers of phyla, and this is still more evident when classes, for instance, are counted against a time scale. New structural extremes, new levels of organization, have continually arisen without an equal loss of the old. Divergence has continued. There is far more difference between an ameba, a maple tree, and a man living today than among any organisms that were alive in the Cambrian.

It is noteworthy from Fig. 30-6 and other data that expansion of that sort, at least, has not been constant. There have been times of especially great outbreaks, one might say, of multiplicity and diversity: one occurred in the Devonian for both plants and animals. There have even been times when in this respect evolution seemed to be losing ground: both plants and animals seem on the whole to have decreased in multiplicity and diversity between the Permian and the Triassic. Nevertheless, the general tendency for increase in these respects is plain.

Increase in numbers of individuals and in total bulk of living matter cannot be read directly from the fossil record. (Why not?) That there must have been tremendous ex-

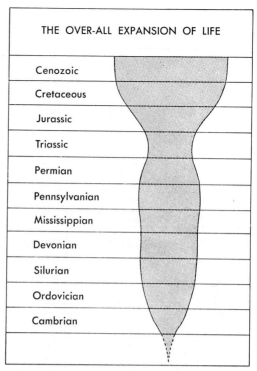

THE OVER-ALL EXPANSION OF LIFE

| Cenozoic |
| Cretaceous |
| Jurassic |
| Triassic |
| Permian |
| Pennsylvanian |
| Mississippian |
| Devonian |
| Silurian |
| Ordovician |
| Cambrian |

30-5 The expansion of life. The width of the pathway is approximately in proportion to the known diversity of organisms (plant and animal) at various times in the past. Note the constriction of the pathway during the late Permian and Triassic; this reflects the Permo-Triassic crisis (p. 767).

pansion in these respects, too, since life began is obvious. There is much uncertainty and room for differences of opinion as to the rates of increase at various times and as to whether these kinds of expansion continued into later phases of the history. Numbers of individuals tend to be in inverse ratio to their size (p. 623). The evolution of large plants may have involved a distinct decrease in the total number of photosynthetic organisms, at least.

Among the factors limiting the bulk of living matter, or its total turnover or metabolic activity, are input of solar energy and efficiency of photosynthesis. There is no reason to believe that either radiation input or photosynthetic efficiency has increased significantly since well back in the Pre-Cambrian. Even a few primitive species in the Pre-Cambrian might have filled their environment with as great a bulk of living matter and might have

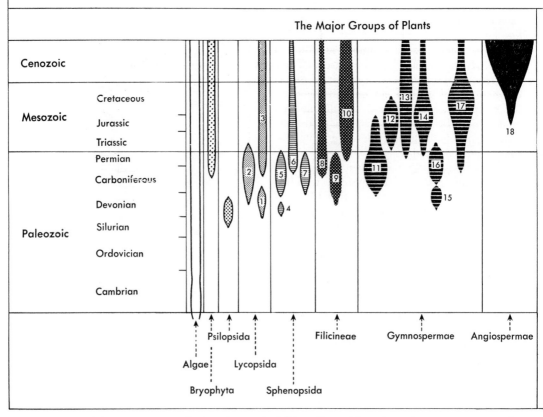

The Major Groups of Plants

30-6 Broad features of the fossil record of life. The width of the pathways is approximately in proportion to the known variety of organisms in each phylum through time. Note these general points: (1) Diversity increases through time (cf. the summary graph in Fig. 30-5). (2) Evidence of the Permo-Triassic crisis is striking: there is a constriction in virtually every animal phylum during the Triassic. (3) Within the plants, which are given here in greater detail than the animals, the generalization is clear that the more complex groups (e.g., gymnosperms and angiosperms) arise progressively later in the fossil record. (The same generalization is evident for vertebrate animals,

had as much metabolic turnover as was possible—and the possibility may not have increased much or at all since then in a particular environment, such as the sea. However, two other factors tend to increase both numbers and total bulk of organisms: invasion of new environments and lengthening of food chains (p. 620). Both those tendencies were plainly still active long after the Cambrian.

OCCUPATION OF ENVIRONMENTS

The expansion of life has been accompanied by both more extensive and more intensive occupation of the possible environments for

life on the earth. In fact the spread in environments has been, in a sense, one of the main reasons for the general expansion. The most spectacular example of extension in environment, spread into great areas hitherto unoccupied, was the invasion of the land by plants and animals. Until Silurian times life was confined to the water, as far as we know.[7] Then started a movement into land environments not completed until some hundreds of millions of years later.

[7] There may have been some protists, simple plants, and even a few wormlike animals earlier in moist soils. If so, they are unknown as fossils.

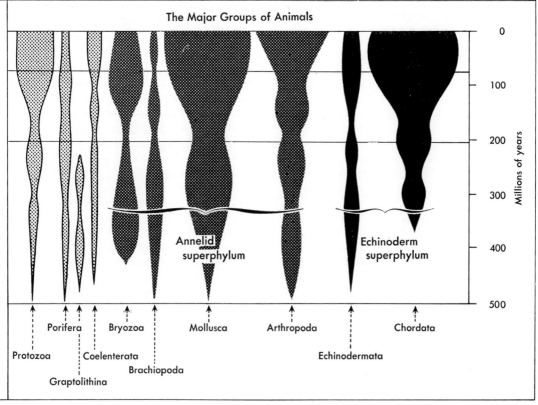

The Major Groups of Animals

for example, in Figs. 32-4 and 32-6.) The numbered subgroups among the plants are: *Lycopsida:* (*1*) Protolepidodendrales, (*2*) Lepidodendrales, (*3*) Lycopodiales; *Sphenopsida:* (*4*) Hyeniales, (*5*) Calamitales, (*6*) Equisetales, (*7*) Sphenophyllales; *Filicineae:* (*8*) Marattiales, (*9*) Coenopteridales, (*10*) Filicales; *Gymnospermae:* (*11*) Pteridospermae, (*12*) Cycadeoidales, (*13*) Cycadales; (*14*) Ginkgoales, (*15*) Pityeae, (*16*) Cordaiteae, (*17*) Coniferales; *Angiospermae:* (*18*) monocotyledons and dicotyledons. (From Arnold, *An Introduction to Paleobotany*, McGraw-Hill, 1947)

Increasingly intensive occupation of environments is also evident in the fossil record. This takes the form of increasingly fine subdivision of niches (p. 612). Along with it goes increasing specialization of the organisms in the niches. As a simple example, instead of one species of animal eating ten kinds of plants there may be ten species each eating one kind of plant.

Another factor in environmental expansion is the fact that the expansion in itself creates new environments that can be occupied in their turn. For instance the high "gardens" of epiphytes in the crowns of forest trees (p. 703) occupy an environment that did

not exist until the forest trees evolved. Lengthening of food chains also interlocks with expansion in general and occupation of environments and subdivision of niches in them. Increasingly large plants and animals give increasing opportunities for evolution of new links in food chains leading from them. Each new species of, say, mammals is a possible environment for a new species of parasite, which may itself link up a new food chain.

CHANGE: PERSISTENCE AND REPLACEMENT

Another evident over-all aspect of the whole of evolution is its constant state of flux. Nowhere in the fossil record is there any time of static equilibrium. Change has been slower at some times than at others and faster in some groups of organisms than in others, but some change has always been going on. There is not even any evidence that evolution tends to approach an equilibrium or that has, on an average, slowed down as if it ight eventually reach completion. There are, is true, some biologists who think that such a final state has now been essentially reached. To them we can only say that change has *always* occurred through the past and we see no reason why it should stop now. The next 10 million years should settle the point, but there may be no biologists around when it is decided.

Some other biologists hold that the rate of evolutionary change has tended to accelerate ever since life began and that flux is now at its greatest so far. That is a tricky point that we cannot discuss adequately here. It depends largely on just what is meant by the rate of evolution, which is not so simple to define as you might think. Part of the argument has to do with the expansion of life, which is clearly a fact but which has not shown constant acceleration and may not be going on at all right now. Unlike change in a more general sense, expansion has not been constant in the past and cannot continue indefinitely into the future. There are limits to the amounts and kinds of organisms that earth can accommodate at any one time.

How can there be change without expansion? The fossil record is replete with examples. Some groups of organisms have persisted for long times without notable change. They get into a comfortable rut, a persisting environment to which they are well adapted, and they remain there. However, there are more examples of the replacement of now extinct organisms by others better adapted to what are essentially the same environments. Environments suitable for seed ferns, cycadeoids, cordaites, and other early land plants exist today, but those plants do not. The flowering plants (and to less extent the conifers) have replaced them.

Expansion and replacement are two of the main factors in the constant change among living things, and, if expansion is limited, replacement has not so far appeared to be.

COMPLICATION AND IMPROVEMENT

Increasing complication and improvement of biological functioning are the changes most often mentioned in discussions of the over-all tendency of evolution. You may be surprised that we have left them till the last. We have done so purposely with the intention of de-emphasizing them, because we believe that they are overemphasized and somewhat misunderstood in much popular thought and teaching. The question of increasing complication has been considered previously (p. 747), probably at sufficient length. It has certainly been an important factor in various phases of the history of life, but it has been far from universal as an evolutionary tendency, and it has not been particularly noticeable in the last few hundred million years of history.

The most important point to stress about improvement, change for the better, or progress in evolution is that it is not inherent.[8] It is not built into the nature of the universe or of life. Improvement has occurred in the course of evolution, not because that is an inherent and general tendency, but where and when it had a natural, immediate cause: selection. That statement could fall into the fallacy of circular reasoning if it were taken for granted that what selection favors is improvement.

There can be many definitions of improvement, and selection does not necessarily favor improvement by a particular definition. Nor does evolution inevitably tend toward improvement by any definition. Nevertheless what may reasonably be called improvement has occurred so frequently that it may be considered a common, not universal, tendency in the history of life. It has taken many forms, but especially these three: (1) increasingly precise and effective adaptation to a particular

[8] A few biologists think that it is. This is of course an inference, not an observable fact, and therefore it is open to dispute. In such matters we have tried to follow the consensus of competent modern biologists. When the point is important and there is strong disagreement, we have played fair with you and said so. Biology, like all sciences, is not a finished structure with all doubts settled.

way of life; (2) marked change in structure and function, making possible ways of life, occupation of environments, and so on, increasingly far removed from the ancestral ways and environments; (3) increasing perception of the environment and increasing complexity, flexibility, and appropriateness of reactions to stimuli.

Tendency (1) is most widespread and least important in this over-all view of the history of life, although of great importance among the details of the history. You can supply plenty of examples from your own observations or reading, in previous chapters of this book or elsewhere. A good example of (2) is the rise of root-stem-leaf differentiation and of vascular tissue in plants, making possible true land life, or of the egg in reptiles, realizing the same possibility. Tendency (3) is peculiar to animals and is especially pertinent to the rise of man. In spite of considerable evidence to the contrary, we do have a right to consider ourselves an improvement over other organisms. To a lesser degree, improvement of a generally similar kind is evident among many other evolutionary lines of animals.

Chapter Summary

Being *vs.* becoming: two broad approaches to scientific explanation: the explanation of tree and squirrel as entities in being and as entities in the process of becoming; historical principles in the understanding of becoming.

Time and the earth:

Beginnings: estimates of age of planets: 2 to 3 billion years; radioactivity of rocks as tool for dating; possibility that life is more than 2 billion years old.

Geological time scale: primarily a scale of sequence only; approximation to absolute time scale by radioactivity datings; analogy of the history of life with a 24-hour day.

Origin of life:

Problems: fossil evidence unavailable; practical impossibility of experimental re-creation of processes involved; discussion therefore restricted to indirect evidence, but nevertheless fruitful; scientific belief in natural origin of life from non-living world; scientific and religious beliefs.

Forerunners of life, a hypothesis: inorganic synthesis of complex organic molecules from atmospheric constituents; energized by lightning and ultraviolet radiation; slow accumulation of such molecules on sterile earth; ultimate origin of aggregates of such molecules capable of self-duplication and, therefore, alive.

Early organisms: heterotrophic (other-feeding) status of first living systems: their utilization of accumulation of inorganically synthesized molecules, and thus ultimate destruction of conditions for further spontaneous origin of life; their production of CO_2 by anaerobic respiration; origin by mutation of photosynthetic autotrophs (self-feeding organisms) utilizing CO_2 and solar energy; subsequent origin of modern heterotrophs feeding on the autotrophs.

Fossils and the historical record:

Principles of paleontological method: fossils as facts; observations and inferences concerning fossils.

Uniformitarianism: an historical doctrine—the present as a key to the past; its wide application; physical laws as independent of the passage of time; but actual structures and organisms have a history—their present state a key to their past.

Definition of fossils; conditions (especially erosion) for preservation and ultimate recovery by man; fossils predominantly of former hard parts of organisms; fossils not usually petrified.

Pre-Cambrian fossils: their scarcity; possibility of some blue-green algae and bacteria; life's beginnings not recorded in the rocks; fossil record may span only last quarter of life's total history; problem posed by absence of Pre-Cambrian fossils; four possible interpretations.

The over-all fossil record.

Some major tendencies in the history of life:

Life's expansion: increase in total number and diversity of living organisms; rate of expansion not constant; periods of rapid diversification in Devonian, of rapid decrease in Permian-Triassic; factors involved in expansion of life: occupation of new environments and lengthening of food chains.

Occupation of environments: invasion of land by aquatic forms; further subdivision of niches; creation of new environments by organisms.

Evolution as change: continual flux—absence of static equilibrium; change as replacement of one group by another, as well as expansion, or the multiplication of groups.

Complication and improvement of organic structure; as aspect of evolution; usually overemphasized; evolutionary change never guaranteed to be progressive; problem of defining evolutionary progress; three interpretations of the term: (1) increasingly precise adaptations, (2) marked structural changes, making possible new ways of life, and (3) increasing perception.

Diplurus (top) *lived about 200 million years ago;* Latimeria (below) *is still in existence. Both are members of the crossopterygians, the group which conquered the land and gave rise to all later land vertebrates.* (Photo from American Museum of Natural History)

CHAPTER 31

Ancient Seas,

and Conquest

of the Land

If you had a time machine, set it for 500,-000,000 B.C., and took off, you would have a rude shock when you arrived. Even though you started from a mountaintop, you might find yourself floundering in a sea when you landed. That would be an unpleasant demonstration of the fact that the face of the earth has changed radically. The main ocean basins and continental masses probably already existed in the Cambrian,[1] but their outlines

---

[1] That statement is disputed among geologists and is still far from certain. Practically all agree that the Pacific basin already existed. One school thinks that the North Atlantic existed but that a continental mass extended from South America across where the South Atlantic now is to Africa and thence across where the Indian Ocean now is to southern Asia and Australia. Still another school, definitely a minority among American geologists, at least, holds that all the continental masses were then united or nearly so and that the only major ocean basin was the Pacific, then vastly larger than it is now. We are not concerned with the paleogeographers' disputes. That lands and seas were

were different. There were mountains, but not where our mountains now stand. Shallow seas, arms of the oceans, flooded far into the interior of the continental blocks, across what is now dry land.

If you had the luck to arrive on land, all would seem well at first. The air would be breathable. Clouds, winds, and rain would be familiar. The climate would probably be better than where, or we should say *when,* you now live—better, at least, if you like it to be rather warm throughout the year, without sharp alternation of hot summers and cold winters. At second glance, the land would seem completely alien to you. It would be alien, not so much because of the unfamiliar topography as because it would be completely bare. No grass, no shrubs, no trees, no buzzing insects, singing birds, or scurrying rodents—no life at all. You would quickly starve unless you could reach the seashore, and even there everything would be unfamiliar. There would be seaweeds, shellfish, and other marine life in some abundance, but all of kinds you never saw before. There would be no fishes. You might eke out a dreary existence by eating shellfish, if they proved not to be poisonous to you, but at best you would be deeply impressed with the fact that the earth has not always been the pleasant world you live in now.

---

then quite different from what they are now is certain, regardless of their exact shapes.

Cambrian and Ordovician Seas

APPEARANCE OF THE ANIMAL PHYLA

Fossil animals suddenly become abundant with the beginning of the Cambrian, and almost all the phyla appear as fossils during that period, a remarkable phenomenon that we have already discussed (p. 743). The suddenness of the change from the almost barren Pre-Cambrian rocks is real enough, but it is not true that all the phyla mysteriously show up at precisely the same time. The Cambrian was a very long period, on the order of 75 or 80 million years, and the various major groups of animals straggle into the fossil record throughout that long span. Some, notably the vertebrates, do not appear until some time in the Ordovician, also a long period of some 60 to 65 million years. Many major groups probably were actually originating during the long time represented by the Cambrian and Ordovician. We need not look for the origins of all of them in the Pre-Cambrian.

The straggling into the record of major groups of animals and the great expansion of life in the Cambrian and Ordovician can be told better in figures than in words. Table 31-1 shows the numbers of phyla and classes of animals (including animal-like protists) definitely known as fossils at the stated times or earlier.

Before the end of the Ordovician all the protistan and animal phyla that are at all likely to be preserved as fossils were definitely present. Most of them had already become highly diversified, as shown in classification by their subdivision into classes and lesser groups, including a great number of species. The land was still barren and there was probably little life in lakes and rivers, but the seas were full of organisms in great abundance and variety. Life in the sea has changed greatly since then, but its over-all ecology was already well established at that time, well over 350 million years ago. Later changes within the marine environments have been replacements rather than expansion.

Since the Ordovician innumerable groups have died out, but as they disappeared their places were simply taken over by other groups, generally of more recent origin. Among animals and animal-like protists that are at all likely to leave a fossil record, there are only 12 phyla and 31 classes in the present seas. That actually represents a slight decrease from the 13 phyla and 33 classes known for late Ordovician seas. The recent phyla are the same as those of the Ordovician.[2] Several of the classes are of later origin and have replaced extinct classes present in the Ordovician. Replacement has been more and more complete at lower levels of the hierarchy of classification. No species have survived from Ordovician to recent, and perhaps only one genus has: *Lingula*, a primitive brachiopod, has hung on, little changed, like an animal Methuselah. In terms of lack of essential difference from its present form, *Lingula* may be the oldest living thing on earth. Some of the protists and algae have probably changed as little since times still more remote, but their claims are not supported by the clear evidence of fossils.

THE LIFE OF THE LATE ORDOVICIAN

We cannot follow in even a summary way the life of the seas through all of the geological periods. A quick review of Ordovician life (Fig. 31-1) will, however, show a characteristic marine flora and fauna similar in a general way to all that followed it. Some of the most striking subsequent changes will be mentioned later. For characteristics of the

TABLE 31-1 *Numbers of major groups of animals surely known to have existed in subdivisions of Cambrian and Ordovician Time*

	Number of phyla	Number of classes
Cambrian		
Early	8	12
Middle	11	20
Late	12	22
Ordovician		
Early	12	27
Middle	12	32
Late	13	33

2 The additional phylum in the Ordovician was the Graptolithina, and their status as a distinct phylum is questionable (p. 523).

various groups refer to Chapters 22-23 and for their classification see pp. 477-81.

Flagellates, forams, and radiolarians are protists known as fossils by late Ordovician times. They seem then to have been rather similar to some living today. No other protists are at all likely to fossilize, but probably most or all of the other main groups were also in existence. It is reasonably certain that bacteria were abundant. Algae have left a poor record, but they are positively known to have existed in the Ordovician and they were probably highly abundant and quite varied. Diatoms, which do such a large proportion of the photosynthesis in present-day waters, are not known from the Ordovician or for long after. Since they are fairly common fossils once they do appear (in the Jurassic), it is probable that they had not yet evolved in earlier times and that the lack of fossil diatoms in the Ordovician is not just a failure of preservation or discovery. Fungi and bryophytes are unknown from the Ordovician, but fungi, at least, may well have occurred then. Their tissues are so soft that their fossil records consist of only a few chance discoveries. Vascular plants had not yet evolved in the Ordovician.

Sponges were present in Ordovician seas and do not seem to have undergone any really striking changes since then. Coelenterates were abundant, and some of them built large reefs, as they do today. Ordovician reefs were, however, formed mostly by groups more primitive than the true corals, now usually dominant on reefs. The true corals had just appeared (middle Ordovician). Floating graptolites occurred in enormous numbers and would have been the most unfamiliar of Ordovician organisms to a time-traveling zoologist. There is nothing like them today. Bryozoans were generally similar to those still living. Brachiopods were much more numerous than they are now, when they are almost down to relict status. Most of them had by late Ordovician developed heavy, ribbed, calcareous shells, but the really fancy ones were to come later in the Paleozoic.

The clamlike pelecypods, principal rivals of the brachiopods, which they have now almost entirely replaced, had appeared only in the early Ordovician and were just beginning to be common in the late Ordovician. The sea snails (gastropods) are an older group of mollusks (since early Cambrian) and were abundant in Ordovician seas. They looked much like some modern forms, but they have since become considerably more diverse and there has been almost complete replacement of earlier groups of low taxonomic scope (families, genera, and species). The most striking mollusks of the Ordovician, and perhaps of all time, were not clams or snails but cephalopods, nautiloids related to the now relict chambered nautilus. Some were coiled and somewhat resembled their surviving relative. Others were straight and reached great lengths, up to five meters or so. They were much the largest animals of their time. The ammonites, relatives of the nautiloids with more complex partitions between the chambers, had not yet appeared in the Ordovician. The squids and octopuses, now the only abundant cephalopods, were not to evolve until much later.

The dominant arthropods during most of the Paleozoic were the bizarre, now extinct trilobites, which reached their climax in the Ordovician. There were a few true crustaceans, but nothing like the crabs or lobsters, which represent a group that later completely replaced the trilobites, had yet appeared. Strangest of Ordovician arthropods, to our eyes, were the eurypterids, which look something like crustaceans but are really more nearly related to spiders and scorpions. Their remains are rare in Ordovician rocks and usually much broken. It has been suggested that they were originally a fresh-water group and that their Ordovician fossils had been washed down by rivers into the sea. No fossil insects are known from the Ordovician, and they almost certainly had not yet evolved. That event has to await the covering of the land with vegetation.

Echinoderms were another abundant group in late Ordovician seas. They included ancestors of all the living groups and were not very strikingly different from these. They also included a greater variety of extinct groups, some primitive and some peculiar divergent lines.

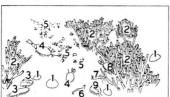

31-1 Some faunas of Early Paleozoic seas.
Middle Cambrian, western North America: (*1*) a jellyfish (*Scyphozoa*); (*2*) the spongelike organism *Archeocyathus*; (*3*) trilobites, *Ogygopsis*; (*4*) *Sidneyia*, an arachnid; (*5*) *Barrella*, a crustacean; (*6*) an annelid worm; (*7*) a holothurian (echinoderm); (*8*) a crustacean, *Hymenocaris*; (*9*) a trilobite, *Neolenus*.

Middle Ordovician, central North America: (*1*) straight-shelled ("orthoconic") nautiloid cephalopods; (*2*) a gastropod; (*3*) two small trilobites, *Calymene*; (*4*) a large trilobite, *Isotelus*; (*5*) massive coral; (*6*) branching coral; (*7*) two solitary corals.

Middle Silurian, Illinois—a coral-reef community: (1) stalked (sessile) cystoid echinoderms; (2) a cephalopod mollusk, *Phragmoceras*; (3) honeycomb coral, *Favosites*; (4) tube coral, *Syringopora*; (5) chain coral, *Halysites*; (6) a solitary coral; (7) a nautiloid cephalopod; (8) the trilobite, *Isotelus*; (9) another trilobite, *Actinurus*; (10) a group of brachiopods, *Pentamerus*; (11) three specimens of the brachiopod *Leptaena*; (12) a cephalopod mollusk, *Cyrtorizoceras*.

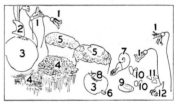

Late Silurian, New York State: (1) a eurypterid, *Pterygotus*; (2) a group of snails, *Pycnomphalus*; (3) a eurypterid, *Carcinosoma*; (4) eurypterids, *Hughmilleria*.

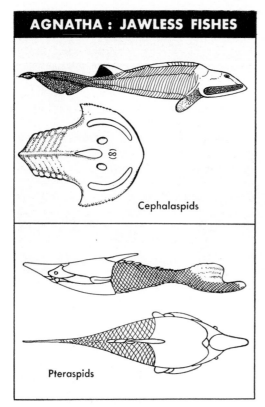

AGNATHA : JAWLESS FISHES

Cephalaspids

Pteraspids

31-2 Agnatha, earliest and jawless "fishes." *Top,* whole specimen of *Cephalaspis* in side view; and dorsal view of head and trunk region of *Kieraspis,* showing paired eye sockets (round), a median nostril, and the pair of crescent-shaped apertures supposed to be electric organs like those of the modern electric eel. *Bottom,* side and dorsal views of *Pteraspis.*

It is in the late Ordovician [3] that the first fossil vertebrates appear, completing the roster of the animal phyla as far as these can readily be preserved as fossils. Strange as it seems to think of a sea without fishes, that was the state of the seas before this time. It may, indeed, still have been true at this time. Few exposed rocks of Ordovician age were laid down in streams or lakes, but the scattered and fragmentary remains of the earliest known fishes are found in situations where they may well have been washed down by streams to a beach or sea. Some authorities also believe on theoretical grounds that the first fishes probably evolved in running fresh water. If so, and especially if the eurypterids

[3] Or possibly a little before, toward the end of middle Ordovician.

also arose in fresh water, plants (algae) must already have been abundant in those waters. Then there were probably also numerous fresh-water protists and a variety of invertebrates. Nevertheless, life in fresh water must have been far less common or diversified than in the sea then, or than in fresh waters today.

The first fishes were jawless agnaths (p. 582), primitive, few, and unimpressive. Their appearance is, however, one of the most dramatic events in the history of life. It marked the rise of the phylum that was to become dominant in every sphere that it invaded and that was eventually to produce the writers and the readers of this book.

The Age of Fishes

The Silurian, next period after the Ordovician, was no exception to the rule of ceaseless change in the history of life. Graptolites declined, corals expanded, species and genera arose and died out. It was, nevertheless, a period without any striking innovations among aquatic organisms. Its most important biological event was the still feeble beginning of the occupation of the land, an event to which we will return.

The next period, the Devonian, was a period of accelerated evolutionary activity in many groups of organisms. Most important (from the human point of view, at any rate) is the fact that fishes first became common in the Devonian and that their most basic differentiation occurred mainly in that period. For these reasons the Devonian is often called the Age of Fishes.

The scanty Ordovician and Silurian fossil vertebrates are all, or nearly all,[4] jawless fishes, agnaths. They were well represented in the early Devonian, including bottom-living forms with broad, flattened head shields (cephalaspids, Fig. 31-2) as well as more active swimmers (such as the pteraspids, Fig. 31-2). They declined rapidly thereafter, and by the end of the Devonian they were all extinct except for the unknown lines that led to the living lampreys and hagfishes (p. 582).

This is one of the most striking examples

[4] There is some not completely satisfactory evidence of placoderms in the late Silurian.

of the historical principle of *replacement*. The Devonian agnaths were plainly being erased from the ecological picture by another, more efficient group of fishes: the placoderms. The placoderms arose from agnaths, but not from those they replaced in the Devonian. They evolved from primitive Silurian agnaths by the transformation of a set of gill arches into movable jaws, among other changes (Fig. 18-12, p. 453). Throughout most of the Devonian the placoderms expanded as the agnaths contracted. Toward the end of the Devonian the placoderms themselves were being replaced by still other groups of fishes, the Chondrichthyes and Osteichthyes (p. 583). Most placoderms became extinct at the close of the Devonian, although a few struggled on into the Permian.

In their heyday the placoderms were highly diversified. Most normal in appearance, to eyes used to recent fishes, was a group of little, sharklike forms (acanthodians, Fig. 31-3). That group also happens to be the one that survived into the early Permian before it became extinct. Another abundant group included bottom-livers and mud-feeders (antiarchs, Fig. 31-3), evidently ecologically similar to the flattened agnaths and competing successfully with them. A third group of placoderms (arthrodires, Fig. 31-3) must have been violently predaceous. Most members of the group had powerful, gaping jaws with sharp shearing blades. They must have been the scourge of Devonian waters. They came in all sizes, suitable to prey on almost anything that moved. The largest of them were monsters 10 meters or so in length, quite as fearsome as any shark today.

The fishes destined to replace the later placoderms arose from early placoderms, just as the placoderms arose from early agnaths and then replaced the later agnaths. The replacing groups, finally successful in that they are the dominant fishes today, are the Chondrichthyes (see p. 584) and the Osteichthyes (p. 586). Both arose in the Devonian and were becoming abundant by the end of that period. The Devonian chondrichthyans included sharks not too unlike those of today, and several other divergent branches, most

of which have become extinct.[5] The flattened skates and rays, now quite common, evolved from sharks at a much later date, in the Jurassic. Their strong dorsoventral flattening is a distinctive adaptive type that has evolved several times in different groups. There were placoderms quite skatelike in body form and probably in habits.

It has previously been emphasized that the chondrichthyans were originally adapted to salt water and the osteichthyans to fresh water (p. 585). In the Devonian the osteichthyans were still mostly fresh-water fishes, although their eventually highly successful invasion of salt water was probably already under way. Even in the Devonian the osteichthyans were differentiated into three basic groups, not then very obviously or fundamentally distinct but with decidedly different prospects in the history of life. One group, that of the crossopterygians or crossopts (Fig. 31-4, see also p. 588), gave rise in the later Devonian to the amphibians and, through them, to all the vertebrates of the land and air. After the amphibians had appeared, other lines of crossopts lingered on in diminishing numbers. They are represented today by the single relict *Latimeria*.[6]

Another basic group of Devonian osteichthyans, that of the paleoniscoids (Fig. 31-3) gave rise to a great radiation of fishes in both salt and fresh waters. That radiation, beginning in the Permian and continuing through the Mesozoic, produced nearly all our present-day fishes plus a number of extinct Mesozoic groups later replaced by the teleosts (p. 587), which have been the dominant fishes since the Cretaceous. (The teleosts were also products of the Mesozoic radiation originally rooted in the paleoniscoids.)

The third basic group of Devonian osteichthyans was that of the lungfishes (Figs. 23-18 and 31-3). They were among the most common fishes in the later Devonian, but since then they have dwindled steadily until now they are represented by only three relict

5 One of those branches does live on in the comparatively uncommon chimaeras (p. 586).
6 A second living genus has been named, but at the time of this writing it seems probable that it is not validly distinct from **Latimeria.**

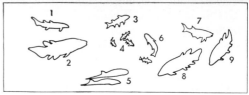

All photos American Museum of Natural History

31-3 Some Devonian fishes. Upper photograph, a Devonian "aquarium," the members of which are identified in the line drawing above: (*1*) *Osteolepis*, a crossopterygian (Osteichthyes); (*2*) *Holoptychius*, another crossopt; (*3* and *6*) *Climatius*, an acanthodian (Placodermi); (*4*) *Diplacanthus*, another acanthodian; (*5*) *Coccosteus*, a primitive arthrodiran (Placodermi); (*7*) *Cheirolepis*, a paleoniscoid (Osteichthyes) (see also figure in left center); (*8* and *9*) *Dipterus*, a primitive lungfish (Osteichthyes). *Left center, Cheirolepis*, a Devonian paleoniscoid. The paleoniscoids gave rise to nearly all our present-day fish, including the dominant teleosts (see p. 587). *Lower left, Dinichthys* (restoration), an arthrodire (Placodermi), which reached 30 feet in length.

genera. The lungfishes illustrate particularly well two phenomena that are widespread in the history of life: change of pace and stagnation. They were rather slowly differentiated from other osteichthyans during the early Devonian. Once the group was well established, it evolved with increasing rapidity, culminating around the transition from middle to late Devonian. This rapid change was, however, abortive. The lungfishes seem to have been squeezed, so to speak, between the two other groups that pre-empted the main possibilities for expansion: descendants of the paleoniscoids occupied most of the aquatic vertebrate niches, and descendants of the crossopts moved onto the land and eventually occupied its vertebrate niches. By the end of the Paleozoic, lungfish evolution had slowed almost to a standstill. The species became stereotyped and confined essentially to one narrow niche in which they have remained ever since without any further important changes.

Apart from the fishes, the most important event in Devonian seas was probably the rise of the ammonites (p. 778), cephalopods that were to be the dominant marine mollusks of the Mesozoic. Their ancestral group, that of the nautiloids, continued but was dwindling rapidly in the Devonian: another of the innumerable instances of replacement. Most important of all, however, is the fact that the movement of life onto the land was in full swing during the Devonian and was an accomplished fact by the end of that period.

Occupation of the Land

THE DIFFICULTIES

We have previously had occasion to refer to the difficulties of life on land and to some of the adaptations of plants and animals to terrestrial environments (pp. 504, 590). The outstanding difficulty is that land organisms are no longer surrounded by water, as their ancestors all were. Water must still be obtained from somewhere: by root absorption from the soil, by breathing water vapor from air (a scanty resource in most situations), by drinking liquid water on the surface, by eating plants and animals (which contain water), or by metabolism of carbohydrates and fats in such a way as to release water. Once acquired, water must be conserved against evaporation. All the fully terrestrial plants and animals have external coverings of one sort or another by which evaporation is controlled and limited. In spite of this needed protection against desiccating air, it is necessary to obtain CO_2 (in the case of plants) and O_2 from the air, and also to discharge waste gases into the air. Land plants have stomates (p. 85) and associated structures. Land animals have lungs, tracheae (p. 133), or pouches or modified gills that function as lungs. Gravity, no special problem to an organism buoyed up by water, becomes serious for all but the smallest land organisms. The great majority of land animals, excluding only small and wormlike forms, have strong skeletons, external or internal. All true land plants

have supportive tissues, especially in the stems, and all of any great size are woody. Extremes of temperature from season to season outside the tropics and from day to night everywhere (including the tropics) are far greater on land than in the water. Land plants and animals have numerous adaptations to those fluctuations. Some have been noted in previous pages, and you can probably think of others.

All life arose in the water, and most of the phyla of protists, plants, and animals became differentiated there. There are still far more aquatic than terrestrial major groups of organisms. That there are more *species* of organisms on land than in the water is due to the greater diversity of land environments and to the success of two groups in particular, flowering plants and insects, in occupying and subdividing the innumerable terrestrial niches. Life in the soil has become extremely diverse, but most of the organisms living there cannot be considered terrestrial in the fullest sense of the word. They can stand exposure to air briefly or at some special phases of the life cycle, but they must be surrounded by water at other crucial phases, at least, and so must be considered partly if not entirely aquatic.

Only four phyla include organisms that can be considered fully adapted to land life: Tracheophyta among plants; Mollusca, Arthropoda, and Chordata (Vertebrata) among animals.

EARLIEST LAND PLANTS AND ANIMALS

In the historical sequence of occupation of the land, it seems necessary that plants should have led the way. Animals require accessible plant material at the beginning of their food chains. This is borne out by the fossil record, in which land plants begin to appear before any land animals. The first fossils of land plants appear in the middle Silurian, and they are for the most part small psilopsids (p. 507). At least one may be a forerunner of the lycopods or transitional between the psilopsids and that group. Basic divergence of the subphyla of vascular plants may have been already under way, but if so it had certainly not yet gone far.

The earliest known possible land animal is

31-4 The vertebrates conquer the land. *Upper left*, restoration of the Devonian lobe-fin fish, *Eusthenopteron*, crawling out of the water. *Lower left*, the skeleton of *Eusthenopteron*. *Upper right*, the primitive Carboniferous-Permian labyrinthodont (p. 764) amphibian, *Diplovertebron*. *Lower right*, skeleton of *Diplovertebron*. Note that the limb bones of *Diplovertebron* show the same pattern, now familiar, as all higher vertebrates (Fig. 19-2); this pattern is still not clear in *Eusthenopteron*.

a scorpion from the late Silurian. It is enough like the modern scorpions, which are fully terrestrial, to suggest that it had the same habits. It is, however, also similar to its aquatic forerunners, so the question is not entirely settled.

During the Devonian, land plants became common. Some of them reached the size of trees, and the first forests grew on the earth. Psilopsids continued, but they had become scarce by late Devonian. The incoming, replacing groups were the lycopsids (p. 507), sphenopsids (p. 508), and ferns, all of which were abundant by late Devonian. A few primitive gymnosperms (cordaites, p. 516) had also appeared. Those groups continued to expand greatly in the Carboniferous, when they formed the great coal forests along with the newly evolved seed ferns (p. 512).[7]

In the Devonian are found a few animals that were certainly terrestrial. All are arthropods: a mite, several forerunners of the spiders probably not yet advanced enough to be definitely classified as spiders, and a creature that may similarly have been a forerunner of the insects.

By the end of the Devonian some of the crossopts had developed legs and had become amphibians (p. 588).[8] They still had fishlike tails and were probably still almost as aquatic as fishes. Nevertheless, they were the first vertebrates to walk on land, and their de-

---

[7] Most textbooks say that seed ferns appeared in the middle Devonian, on the evidence of a

fossil forest found near Gilboa, New York. It has, however, been found that the supposed "seeds" of those trees are really spore cases. Of course this does not exclude the possibility or even the probability that seed ferns will eventually be found in the Devonian.

[8] There is some dispute whether the earliest surely identified amphibians are from the latest Devonian or earliest Carboniferous. In geological perspective the difference is not great and does not matter to us.

Chicago Natural History Museum

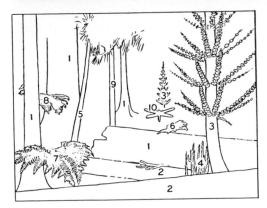

31-5 A Carboniferous forest. Lycopsids: (*1*) various species of *Sigillaria*; (*2*) two species of *Lepidodendron*. Sphenopsids: (*3*) *Calamites*; (*4*) *Sphenophyllum*. Ferns: (*5*) *Caulopteris*; (*6*) *Mariopteris*. Gymnosperms: (*7* and *8*) two species of the seed-fern genus *Neuropteris*; (*9*) *Cordaites*. Insects: (*10*) a primitive dragonfly, *Meganeura monyi*.

scendants were to rise to dominance in the new environment (Fig. 31-4).

The Permo-Carboniferous

The Permian and Carboniferous, last two periods of the Paleozoic following the Devonian, had much in common and may be considered together.

COAL FORESTS

The Carboniferous, "carbon-bearing," is so called because many extensive coal deposits are of that age, including our Appalachian coal fields in Pennsylvania and adjacent states.[9] The coal is the compressed remains of plants that grew in widespread, swampy forests. Deep burial for long periods of time has driven out the more volatile constituents of the plant tissues, and the compacted residue has a higher percentage of carbon than the original plants. It still retains traces of the original structure, however, and associated

[9] There are, however, many rich coal deposits of younger ages in the United States and elsewhere.

shales and sandstones are often rich in well-preserved fossil plants. Thus we are well acquainted with the composition of the forests and the structure of their plants. You are already acquainted with the main groups represented: lycopsids such as *Lepidodendron* and *Sigillaria;* seed ferns, including *Neuropteris; Cordaites* and its relatives; and the conifers, which did not, however, become distinct until the late Carboniferous, when *Walchia* and other genera appeared. In the late Permian and early Triassic cycadeoids, cycads, and ginkgos appeared, but they had no part in the earlier coal forests (Fig. 31-5).

LAND INVERTEBRATES

Animal life, so rare hitherto, swarmed in Carboniferous forests. Here appear the first land snails, the only mollusks to complete the great transition from water to air. Undoubted terrestrial scorpions are common, and so are relatives and ancestors of the spiders. Centipedes are present. Most striking and most important of the land invertebrates are insects. The majority of them in the Carboniferous belonged to orders unfamiliar in aspect and now extinct, but cockroaches were already there, and so were forerunners of the dragonflies. Several other recent orders appeared in the Permian, among them the May flies, thrips, bugs, lacewings, and beetles. Most of the modern orders (16 out of 24) are known from the Jurassic or earlier. The Carboniferous insects were remarkable for their large size. The average body length of known species is about 5 centimeters, and a length of 20 centimeters was not uncommon. One dragonflylike giant had a wingspread of nearly 75 centi-

Peabody Museum of Natural History, Yale U.

31-6   A giant dragonfly (*Dunbaria*) from the Permian.

meters (Fig. 31-6). No later insect even approaches such dimensions. It is noticeable that the groups of insects now particularly associated with flowers were absent in these early faunas. They begin to appear in the fossil record in the Jurassic and spread greatly during the Cretaceous and early Cenozoic, in close parallel with the fossil record of the flowering plants.

AMPHIBIANS

Amphibians were particularly common during the Carboniferous and scarcely less so in the Permian. The Permo-Carboniferous is sometimes called the Age of Amphibians, although as a matter of fact amphibians were already much outnumbered by reptiles in the Permian. None of the modern groups had yet evolved. Most Permo-Carboniferous amphibians were labyrinthodonts (Fig. 31-4).[10] Typically they were clumsy brutes with four short, sprawling legs, big, flattened heads, and stubby tails. *Eryops* (Fig. 31-7), an early Permian labyrinthodont about 1½ meters long, is an example of that common type. There were, however, many other kinds, sizes, and shapes. Among the most bizarre were some that were long and snakelike, or others with extraordinary triangular heads.

REPTILES

The transition of the vertebrates to land life was completed when the reptiles arose. Since the change was gradual, it is difficult to point to an exact time and say, "Here the reptiles appear," but some of the latest Carboniferous fossils seem to represent true reptiles. Certainly reptiles were abundant in the Permian. Most of the Permian reptiles belonged to only two main groups, neither of which was at all like any reptiles living today. The *root reptiles,*[11] cotylosaurs, were most primitive (Fig. 31-9). They intergraded with the earlier labyrinthodont amphibians and often looked not unlike those ancestors, although they did develop some more bizarre later forms. Even more common then were the *mammal-like reptiles.* The earliest of them,

10 "Labyrinth-toothed," so called because the tissues of the teeth seen in cross-section have an intricate, mazelike pattern.
11 So called because they are the stock from which most or all of the higher land vertebrates were derived.

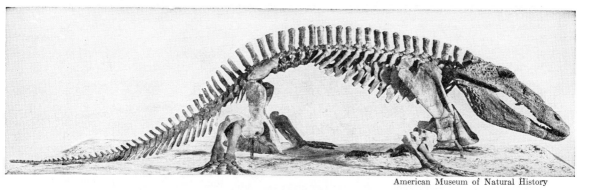

31-7 *Eryops*, an early Permian labyrinthodont amphibian.

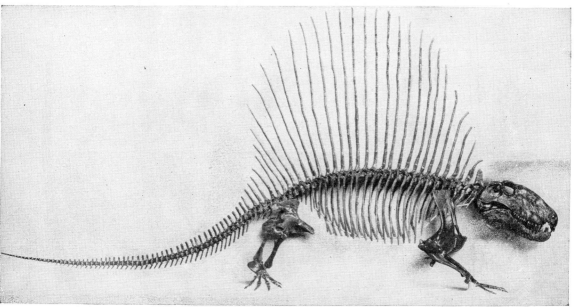

31-8 *Dimetrodon*, an early mammal-like reptile.

the pelycosaurs [12] included the ancestry of the whole group (hence also of the mammals) and also some divergent, extinct lines of creatures like *Dimetrodon* (Fig. 31-8), with a fantastic fin on the back, supported by the elongated spines of the vertebral column. The somewhat later and eventually more varied therapsids [13] were the dominant land animals of the late Permian and early Triassic and were the immediate ancestors of the mammals. They are best known from South Africa,

where they have been found in almost incredible numbers, but some have been found in Russia, China, Brazil, the United States, and elsewhere. They doubtless occurred on all the continental land areas of the Permian and Triassic. (See also Fig. 31-9.)

One of the oddest features of the history of life is that reptiles had hardly completed the transition from water to land before some of them took to the water again. Among the earliest known reptiles is a little group of aquatic (probably fresh-water) fish-eaters. The group became extinct almost at once, but several other, later groups of reptiles also became aquatic.

[12] "Basin reptiles," so called because of the basinlike pelvis.
[13] "Mammal-arched," because the cheekbone or zygomatic arch was constructed as in the mammals and not as in other reptiles.

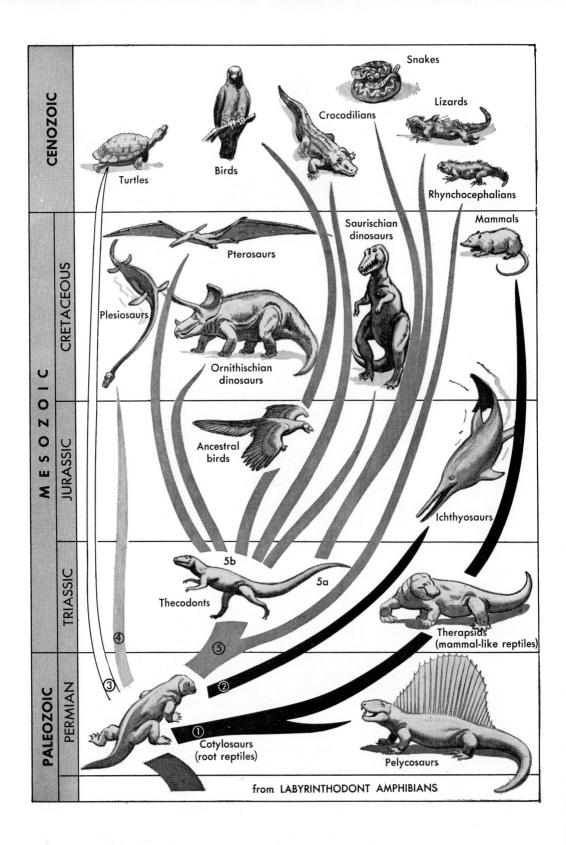

CENOZOIC

MESOZOIC

PALEOZOIC

CRETACEOUS

JURASSIC

TRIASSIC

PERMIAN

Snakes

Lizards

Crocodilians

Birds

Turtles

Rhynchocephalians

Mammals

Saurischian
dinosaurs

Pterosaurs

Plesiosaurs

Ornithischian
dinosaurs

Ancestral
birds

Ichthyosaurs

5b

5a

Thecodonts

Therapsids
(mammal-like reptiles)

④

⑤

③

②

① Cotylosaurs
(root reptiles)

Pelycosaurs

from LABYRINTHODONT AMPHIBIANS

The Age of Reptiles

The Permian was already an age of reptiles, but the term is usually applied to the next three periods, the Triassic, Jurassic, and Cretaceous, composing the Mesozoic era.

PERMO-TRIASSIC CRISIS

The later Permian and early Triassic were times of crisis in the history of life. Evolution in many groups was exceptionally rapid. Decline or extinction of once-flourishing kinds of organisms was accompanied by sudden expansion of others. The ammonites (cephalopod mollusks) were one of the rapidly changing, expanding groups of the Permian, and they became extremely abundant and varied in the Triassic. On the other hand the brachiopods declined greatly, and many of their groups became extinct in the Permian. They were never again the common marine shells that they had been through most of the Paleozoic. Trilobites, which had been slowly declining since the Ordovician, finally became extinct in the Permian. So did several old groups of echinoderms and of corals. More modern groups of mollusks, echinoderms, and crustaceans appeared in the Triassic and expanded rather steadily thereafter.

The fishes, too, changed markedly. The last placoderms disappeared. Most of the archaic chondrichthyans and osteichthyans declined, their places taken by more progressive offshoots that evolved and expanded steadily through the Mesozoic and on to now.

On land most of the great coal-forest trees became extinct, while the cycadeoids, cycads, ginkgos, and conifers expanded. The flowering plants probably originated in the Triassic, although the early fossil evidence is obscure.

31-9 The radiation of reptiles. The "root reptiles," or cotylosaurs, derived from the labyrinthodont Amphibia. From the cotylosaurs five major lines of reptilian evolution can be traced: (1) to the mammal-like reptiles and mammals; (2) to the ichthyosaurs; (3) to the turtles; (4) to the plesiosaurs; and (5) to the thecodonts (5b; see p. 769) and from the snakes, lizards, and rhynchocephalians (5a). From the Triassic thecodonts another major radiation took place: the crocodiles, birds, and flying reptiles (pterosaurs), as well as the great dinosaur orders, the Ornithischia and the Saurischia.

A likely hypothesis is that they originated in upland environments, poorly represented in the fossil record. Flowering plants were still rare, even questionable, in lowlands in the Jurassic. In the Cretaceous, however, they began their remarkable expansion. By the end of that period they had replaced the great majority of other land plants and already had the dominance that they retain today.

Most of the Paleozoic groups of amphibians were victims of the Permo-Triassic crisis. One circumscribed group of labyrinthodonts was fairly common (highly so in some particularly favorable localities) in the Triassic, but even it disappeared at the end of that period. Thereafter, as far as is known, only the immediate ancestors of the comparatively few modern amphibians continued.

Changes among the reptiles were not less dramatic. The two main groups of late Permian reptiles did survive and, for a time, thrive in the Triassic, but they were nearly extinct at the end of that period. Only a few very advanced mammal-like reptiles continued into the Jurassic, although others of their lineages were then represented by the mammals themselves.

In the Triassic there was a great radiation of new reptilian orders. It set the pattern for the great diversity and dominance of reptiles that continued throughout the Mesozoic. Most impressive and famous of the innumerable mesozoic reptiles were the many kinds of dinosaurs.

DINOSAURS [14]

To generations of schoolchildren *the* dinosaur has been the *Brontosaurus* ("thunder reptile"). *Brontosaurus* was, indeed, a Dinosaur of Distinction, some 20 meters in length (with close relatives probably reaching 25) and weighing about 25 metric tons. No larger animals ever walked on land.[15] But *Brontosaurus* was only one among many. Dinosaurs came in a wide selection of shapes and sizes. Some would have made suitable lap pets as far as size is concerned. Some walked on their hind legs, some on all fours. Some ate meat, some plants. They well illustrate the

[14] "Terrible reptiles."
[15] But some did and do swim the seas. The largest animal of all is not a dinosaur but the still-surviving sulfur-bottom whale.

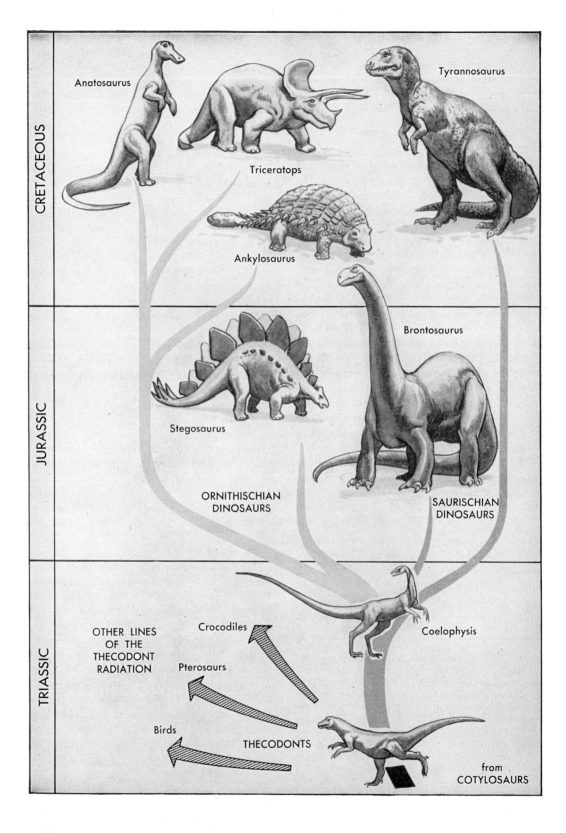

CRETACEOUS

Anatosaurus

Triceratops

Tyrannosaurus

Ankylosaurus

JURASSIC

Brontosaurus

Stegosaurus

ORNITHISCHIAN
DINOSAURS

SAURISCHIAN
DINOSAURS

TRIASSIC

OTHER LINES
OF THE
THECODONT
RADIATION

Crocodiles

Pterosaurs

Coelophysis

Birds

THECODONTS

from
COTYLOSAURS

31-10 The history of the dinosaurs. The earliest (late Triassic) dinosaurs were saurischian and are well represented by the small *Coelophysis;* they were part of the radiation of thecodonts. The ornithischian dinosaurs early diverged as a distinct order.

---

potentialities of life on land and an evolutionary adaptive radiation that produced animals following up many of the potentialities (Figs. 31-9 and 31-10).

In the early Triassic dinosaurs did not exist as such. Their ancestry was represented by a primitive group, the thecodonts, that radiated even more widely than the dinosaurs. One line led to the flying reptiles (p. 772), another to the crocodiles. Two divergent lines from the early Triassic radiation led to animals collectively called dinosaurs. The extent of their diversity can be best shown by citing well-known examples of some of the main groups of dinosaurs:

Coelophysis [16] of the late Triassic was one of the first dinosaurs (Fig. 31-10). It was lightly built, reaching about 3 meters in length, with most of the length in the slender tail and neck. It ran on its long hind legs, but its fore legs were also well developed. The head was of moderate size. It was a meat-eater but not, by all appearances, an especially ferocious one.

Tyrannosaurus ("tyrant reptile,") Figs. 31-10 and 31-11) of the late Cretaceous represents a culmination of the dinosaurian carnivores, the carnosaurs ["flesh (-eating) reptiles"] which evolved steadily through the Jurassic and Cretaceous. It was a tremendous brute, some 14 meters long and 5½ meters high in standing pose. The great head was armed with saberlike teeth. It walked on its hind legs, balanced by a heavy tail. The front legs were proportionately tiny and must have been almost useless.

Brontosaurus you already know (Fig. 31-10). It represents the group of the sauropods,[17] largest of dinosaurs, with four stocky, elephantine limbs and long necks and tails. The heads were comparatively small, and the feeble teeth can have served only for gathering

16 "Hollow process," in reference to the light, hollowed-out nature of processes on some of the bones.
17 "Reptile-footed," in contrast with dinosaurs that had feet suggestive of birds.

succulent, probably mainly aquatic, vegetation.

Anatosaurus [18] is a late Cretaceous representative of the duck-billed dinosaurs, numerous throughout Jurassic and Cretaceous (Fig. 31-10). The front ends of upper and lower jaws were toothless, flattened, and broadened, something like the bill of a duck. Farther back in the jaws was a large battery of shearing teeth, adapted to chopping up harsh vegetation. The animals were bipedal on land, but the later species, at least, were amphibious and swam with webbed feet and a powerful, laterally compressed tail. Some of the later duck-bills developed fantastic crests and projections on the head, the function of which is much disputed.

Stegosaurus [19] was four-footed, with a double row of plates down the back and of sharp spikes on the tail (Fig. 31-10). The small head contained absurdly feeble teeth,[20] and the animal probably ate soft vegetation. *Stegosaurus* is late Jurassic in age. Nothing quite like it occurs later, but the Cretaceous group of armored dinosaurs exemplified by *Ankylosaurus* [21] was somewhat similar in general build and probably in habits (Fig. 31-10). Instead of separate plates, however, they had a bony armor that almost completely encased the body. Survival of herbivores under heavy attack from carnivores usually depends on either speed, hiding, weapons, or armor. These reptilian tanks had the last-mentioned defense. Can you think of examples of the various ways of defense in other groups of animals?

Triceratops ("three-horn face"), another herbivore, combined partial armor with weapons (Fig. 31-10). A strong, bony frill protected its otherwise vulnerable neck, and it had three sharp horns, one on the nose and a pair above the eyes. It exemplifies the horned dinosaurs, which are confined to the

18 "Duck reptile." The name **Trachodon** ("rough tooth") is more familiar for this creature and is usually found in texts, but it is unfortunately invalid under the rules of nomenclature.
19 "Roof reptile," because the plates down the back suggested roofing tiles to the namer.
20 Some dinosaurs had no teeth at all, and the most popular theory is that they ate eggs. However, recent birds have no teeth and yet many of them can eat practically anything.
21 "Fused, or stiffened, reptile," so called because of the fusion of plates in its armor.

31-11 *Tyrannosaurus rex.*

late Cretaceous and there evolved rapidly. In spite of the name, the most primitive "horned dinosaurs" had no horns; they did have neck armor. The horns are varied in advanced forms, which may have one, two, three, or five horns.

SOME OTHER MESOZOIC REPTILES

The dinosaurs were the dominant medium-sized to large terrestrial vertebrates of the Mesozoic, but they did not occupy all possible reptilian niches. Along with them lived a great variety of other reptiles with different habits and habitats. Land reptiles mostly below dinosaur size included, even in the Triassic, the *Rhynchocephalia* (see p. 591). *Lizards* (p. 591) appeared in the Jurassic, and *snakes* (p. 591) in the Cretaceous. The amphibious to fully aquatic *crocodiles* (p. 591) evolved at the end of the Triassic and have been quite

31-12 Aquatic reptiles of the Mesozoic. *Top*, plesiosaurs (one of which holds a fish in its mouth) and ichthyosaurs (jumping). *Bottom, Ichthyosaurus quadricissus*, fossil skeletons, including those of young, which were evidently born alive in a manner analogous to that of mammals.

abundant ever since, although recently somewhat reduced. *Turtles*, apparently at first amphibious in fresh water but later spreading widely from the high seas to the deserts, appeared in the Triassic. They have been expanding quite steadily ever since. The groups mentioned in this paragraph are the only ones of all the Mesozoic reptilian hordes that still survive. They have undergone no really essential changes since the Cretaceous, although of course many new species have arisen and there has been much change in detail (Fig. 31-9).

Several groups of reptiles became fully aquatic and marine in the Mesozoic. The *plesiosaurs* [22] had a broad, flattened body, four paddles, and a long neck or tail, or both (Fig. 31-12). Someone has likened them to a snake threaded through a turtle. (But they

had no turtle-like external armor.) They appeared in the Triassic and were abundant in the Jurassic and through the Cretaceous. The *ichthyosaurs* [23] looked something like sharks and even more like porpoises or dolphins (Fig. 31-9 and 31-12). They also appeared in the Triassic and were most numerous in the Jurassic. Only a few survived into the Cretaceous, and they died out well before the end of that period. Both these groups of marine reptiles ate fish, and the ichthyosaurs, at least, also relished active cephalopods. Food habits of extinct animals usually have to be inferred from the tooth and jaw apparatus, but for the ichthyosaurs stomach contents have been found in the fossil skeletons.

In the late Cretaceous, another group of large, marine, fish-eating reptiles evolved and had a brief but lively career: the *mosasaurs*.[24]

[22] "Nearly reptiles." We are not sure what the namer had in mind when he applied that name to a group completely reptilian, however queer in appearance and habits.

[23] "Fish reptiles," from the fishlike external appearance.

[24] "Reptiles of the River Meuse" (in Belgium). They were first found in that region, although now best known from Kansas.

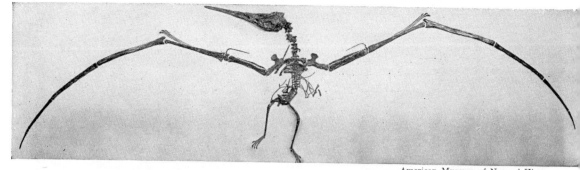

31-13 A pterosaur, or flying reptile. The fossil skeleton of *Nyctosaurus*.

They were overgrown lizards that went to a marine existence. There are no fully aquatic lizards today, but the Galápagos lizard swims out to sea in search of food. With appropriate variation, that is a situation in which natural selection could produce a new race of mosasaurlike lizards.

INTO THE AIR

Once the land was occupied, there remained only one great unoccupied sphere accessible to life on the earth: the atmosphere. Even now there are no completely aerial organisms; none live their whole lives suspended in air. Fully terrestrial animals are, however, already aerial in physiological adaptation. They do live surrounded by air, derive oxygen directly from that medium, and are adequately protected from the perils that air has for animals of aquatic ancestry. To be launched fully into the atmosphere for longer or shorter periods, they require only an additional mechanical adaptation, some structure that can sustain them in air against the pull of gravity.

Flight was already completely achieved by insects in the Carboniferous and has remained an insect specialty ever since, although there are, of course, a good many nonflying insects.

The only other organisms that evolved sustained, directed flight [25] were two related lineages of late Triassic or early Jurassic

[25] This excludes the many organisms that float passively in air at some time in their lives: plant spores and seeds, spiders with silken "parachutes," and so on. It also excludes a number of animals that make directed glides but not sustained flights: "flying" fishes, "flying" squirrels, and a few others.

reptiles. They arose, independently of each other, from the ancestral group that also independently gave rise to the dinosaurs. One enjoyed considerable but transient success: the pterosaurs ("wing reptiles," Figs. 31-13 and 31-14). The other lineage, after a slow start, went on to become so distinctive and so exuberantly widespread and diverse that it is no longer considered reptilian but a new, higher class: the birds (Fig. 31-14).

The pterosaurs flew by means of a thin membrane of skin, stretched between body, forearm, and the enormously elongated fourth finger. (The fifth finger was lost.) The mechanism was similar to a bat's wing, but apparently less efficient (Fig. 19-3). In bats, several fingers support the wing. Some pterosaurs were as small as sparrows. Others were giants with wingspread up to eight meters, the largest animals that ever flew. The known pterosaurs are believed to have skimmed over the Mesozoic seas catching fish, much as terns do today. Whether there were inland species with different habits is a moot point.

The first known bird is *Archaeopteryx* ("ancient wing") from the middle Jurassic of Germany (Fig. 31-14). It had teeth, a long, jointed tail, and so many other reptilian characters that it might well be considered a reptile if only the bones were known. By an extremely rare and fortunate chance, impressions of feathers, which generally do not fossilize, were preserved. They show that *Archaeopteryx* did have a feathered wing attached to its otherwise reptilian forearm and hand. (See Figs. 2-4 and 23-26.)

31-14 A Jurassic scene. On the ground is the small dinosaur *Ornitholestes;* in the air are pterosaurs and the ancestral bird *Archaeopteryx.* The trees are cycadeoids.

That rare discovery has a bearing on general theories of evolution. It has been maintained that really radical adaptive changes must have taken place all at once, in one mutational leap or *saltation.* A living, workable intermediate between, say, a reptile and a bird, a fish and an amphibian, or a land mammal and a whale is considered unthinkable by followers of that school. But *Archaeopteryx* is about as completely intermediate between a reptile and a bird as one can imagine. Furthermore, some likewise rare latest Devonian or earliest Carboniferous animals have recently turned out to be almost perfectly midway between fishes and amphibians. The

intermediates between land mammals and whales have not yet been found, but in the face of these other discoveries who can reasonably claim that they never existed?

RISE OF MAMMALS

The once great group of the mammal-like reptiles became steadily more and more mammal-like through the Permian and the Triassic. In the latest Triassic and early Jurassic a few fragmentary fossils suggest that some of them may then have become mammals by definition. The process was gradual, and the distinction is necessarily arbitrary at first. Remains of unquestionable mammals appear in the middle Jurassic and at intervals thereafter. The mammal-like reptiles, those that did not make the grade and become mammals, declined greatly toward the end of the Triassic and became extinct in the Jurassic.

The history of mammals will be summarized in Chapter 32. Here it suffices to record that they did appear during the Mesozoic, but that they remained obscure, overshadowed by the reptiles, until the end of that era.

THE GREAT DYING

The late Cretaceous was a time of widespread extinction. Among the many invertebrate groups that declined or died then, the ammonites are most striking. They are extremely abundant in most Cretaceous marine rocks, but near the end of that period they disappeared completely and for good. It is interesting that they had *almost* become extinct long before, at the end of the Triassic, when only one small group, probably only a single genus, survived. From it, however, a tremendous new radiation occurred in the Jurassic and into the Cretaceous. The failure of even one genus to pull through the similar crisis at the end of the Cretaceous and to restock Cenozoic seas may have been due to competition from then abundant squidlike cephalopods—but that is speculative.

The great marine reptiles, plesiosaurs, ichthyosaurs, and mosasaurs, also became extinct in the Cretaceous. Yet, oddly enough, nothing radical happened to the fishes living along with them and on which they fed. There was some extinction and replacement, but the dominant modern teleost families were becoming established in the late Cretaceous, and for the most part they continued their expansion through what was for many animals the time of the great dying.

On land, all the dinosaurs became extinct. Of all the hordes of Mesozoic reptiles, only four orders survived (p. 591), and one of those (Rhynchocephalia) dwindled to relict status.

Innumerable attempts have been made to explain the great dying, and especially the extinction of the dinosaurs, but none is satisfactory. It is agreed that there was some widespread environmental change, but no one has come up with a really plausible and well-supported theory as to just what the change was. In any attempt to explain this mystery certain facts should be kept in mind:

Groups that became extinct were of many wholly different kinds living in entirely different environments.

Other groups living along with them and in the same general environments did not become extinct, and some did not even undergo evident change.

It is not logically necessary or probable that any *one* factor caused the extinction.

The extinction was not sudden, although it has often been said to be. It really went on over millions and tens of millions of years. Many kinds of dinosaurs gradually disappeared, and only a few were left at the very end. Ichthyosaurs were already rare in the early Cretaceous, and they disappeared long before the end of the period.

Whatever may have been its exact causes and sequences, the great dying did occur. It closed an era, and it opened the world to a new era: the Age of Mammals.

Chapter Summary

Cambrian and Ordovician seas: appearance of some major groups and great expansion of life generally in the Cambrian and Ordovician; life still marine; the land barren; few or no fresh-water faunas; replacements in the post-Ordovician marine faunas.

Life of the late Ordovician: most protist groups present; diatoms did not arise until Jurassic; no bryophytes, or vascular plants; sponges and coelenterates, graptolites, bryozoans, and brachiopods, the latter much more abundant than later; pelecypods and gastropods common; nautiloid cephalopods dominant among mollusks; trilobites abundant as dominant arthropods; eurypterids; echinoderms abundant; first appearance of fishes, the agnaths.

The Age of Fishes: faunal changes in the Silurian: the Devonian as the Age of Fishes; replacement of agnaths by placoderms; placoderm types: acanthodians, antiarchs, and arthrodires; replacement of placoderms by Chondrichthyes and Osteichthyes; three basic osteichthyan groups: crossopterygians, paleoniscoids, and lungfishes; evolutionary derivatives of the three groups.

Occupation of the land: difficulties facing organisms on land; overcome by only four phyla: Tracheophyta, Mollusca, Arthropoda, and Chordata; earliest land plants and animals: Silurian psilopsids and scorpions; Devonian land plants abundant: psilopsids, lycopsids, sphenopsids, ferns, and some primitive gymnosperms; Devonian land animals: arthropods; first appearance of amphibians.

The Permo-Carboniferous, close of the Paleozoic: coal forests; nature of coal; the principal genera: *Lepidodendron, Sigillaria, Neuropteris, Cordaites, Walchia;* land invertebrates: land snails, scorpions, centipedes, cockroaches, and dragonflies; amphibians: labyrinthodonts, like *Eryops;* reptiles abundant by the Permian: cotylosaurs, mammal-like reptiles, and others.

Mesozoic, the Age of Reptiles: Permo-Triassic crisis; widespread extinctions; replacements in marine faunas; replacement of coal forests by cycadeoids, cycads, ginkgos, and conifers; emergence of angiosperms; decline of amphibians; major changes in the reptilian fauna.

Dinosaurs: as one line of descent from thecodonts; typical genera: *Coelophysis, Tyrannosaurus, Brontosaurus, Anatosaurus, Stegosaurus, Ankylosaurus, Triceratops.*

Of the other Mesozoic reptiles, a few still surviving: rhynchocephalians, lizards, snakes, crocodiles, turtles; plesiosaurs; ichthyosaurs; mosasaurs.

Into the air: pterosaurs, the flying reptiles; birds; bearing of *Archaeopteryx* on theories of evolution.

Rise of the mammals: mammal-like reptiles; their slow evolution through Permo-Triassic times; fully mammals by late Triassic and early Jurassic.

The great dying: widespread extinctions in the Cretaceous (ammonites as a spectacular case); also plesiosaurs, ichthyosaurs, and mosasaurs; but survival of all major fish groups; extinction of all the dinosaurs; the problem of explaining the great dying; cautions in its interpretation.

Highly evolved mammals like the horse typify that modernization of the living world which is the story of the Cenozoic era.
(Photo by Massie from Missouri Resources Division)

CHAPTER 32

Modernization
of the Living World

By the end of the Cretaceous we are far along in the history of life, with a mere 75 million years or so to go. What remains chronologically is the Cenozoic era, often popularly designated as the Age of Mammals. Its brief last part is the Age of Man, who is a mammal, too. From our vantage point at the time called *now*, the greatest interest of the last 75 million years is that they did eventuate in the modern world. The origin of what is now, the modernization of the earth and its life, thus becomes a main theme in this chapter. Before we concentrate on the mammals and man, the theme involves some considerations of principle and of the more wide-ranging modernization of other groups of organisms.

The history of life is not the sort of thing we could imagine if there were no fossil record to set us right. On the evidence of present-day organisms alone, attempted reconstruc-

tion of the history would probably postulate a relatively simple divergence and successive rise of the various living phyla, classes, orders, and so on, and the steadily progressive advance of each toward its present condition. Such was the postulate, expressed or unexpressed, of most of the early thinkers about evolution, before a substantial historical record had been recovered. Even now, that hypothetical picture of the history of life is sometimes taken for granted in expositions of evolution. It may, too, unconsciously affect the views of students who really know better.

A sequence of origins of progressively "higher" groups and the subsequent modernization of each have, indeed, occurred in the course of evolution. The actual history, however, is not only more complicated but also more fitful and seemingly erratic. It includes many and important episodes that would never have been predicted in the absence of fossils. Who would have imagined, for instance, that early forests were not simply composed of primitive ancestors of our present trees but, in largest part, of groups now either totally extinct or represented by a few insignificant herbs? The whole drama of the rise and fall of the dinosaurs would be unimaginable. How could one possibly infer from present conditions that the environments now dominated by mammals were long occupied not by earlier mammals or their reptilian ancestors but by hordes of other reptiles with neither descendants nor similar substitutes in the present world?

It is still more strange that, after mammals had arisen, a very long time passed before they began to assume their present roles. The modernization of floras and faunas has been neither steady nor straightforward. It has often advanced in, geologically speaking, short spurts, now in one group, now in another. It has also involved innumerable detours when dominance and seeming progress were by groups of organisms that were, in fact, to have little or no part in the modern world of life.

Modernization in Aquatic Environments

Aquatic environments were the first to be occupied by living things. It might be expected and is on the whole correct that they would have approached their present aspect at earlier times than the land environments. You have seen (p. 755) that even in the late Ordovician, more than 350 million years ago, the seas, at least, swarmed with plants and animals about as diverse as those now living in the same environments. The aquatic phyla were the same then as now. Yet in detail the modernization of these biotas [1] has not involved the progressive change of most of the lesser groups, the classes, orders, families, and so on, then dominant. Instead, most of these groups have been extinguished without issue and replaced by others whose direct ancestors were few and obscure in the Ordovician.

AQUATIC PLANTS

The fossil record of aquatic plants is inadequate. Most of them are soft-bodied and usually fossilize as a structureless smear of carbon or not at all. Nevertheless we do know that algae were already common far back in the Pre-Cambrian. It is probable that most of the main groups of algae were present in the Paleozoic. They have never lost their dominance in all aquatic environments. Certainly many new species have evolved more recently, but on the whole the aspect and general composition of aquatic floras seems already to have been modern several hundred million

[1] A biota is the flora plus the fauna; the totality of living things in a given environment or place.

years ago. The most recent important change for which there is good evidence was the appearance of the diatoms, first found as fossils in the Jurassic and increasingly common since then. Now they account for a good fraction of the photosynthesis in most aquatic environments.

INVERTEBRATES

Some modern groups of aquatic invertebrates date back without really profound change from the early Paleozoic. Most of them, however, have had extensive replacement since then within groups and adaptive niches. Corals, bryozoans, and clams, for instance, had much the same roles in Paleozoic seas as they do now and did not look very different superficially. Nevertheless, there has been almost complete replacement in these groups, not only of species and genera but of families and superfamilies, even, in some instances, of orders. Without going into detail, it may be said that for these groups and for most other aquatic invertebrates the beginning of the definitive replacement tended to be most evident during the Permo-Triassic crisis.

Modernization of aquatic invertebrates proceeded apace during the Mesozoic, and in most respects it was essentially complete in the late Cretaceous. In only one respect would the fauna of late Cretaceous seas have seemed particularly strange to anyone familiar with modern seas: the now extinct ammonites were still abundant (Fig. 32-1). When they disappeared at the beginning of the Cenozoic, the aquatic invertebrate faunas were almost thoroughly modern. Changes during the Cenozoic have their own fascination, but they were matters of detail, of not very distinctive changes among species and genera and their precise geographic distributions.

FISHES

Although they got started so much later, the fishes rather closely paralleled the aquatic invertebrates in their modernization. As already noted (p. 767), the archaic groups of fishes dominant in the Paleozoic dwindled during or before the Permo-Triassic crisis. The beginning of dominance of higher bony fishes was evident in the Triassic. The most progressive main group, that of the teleosts,

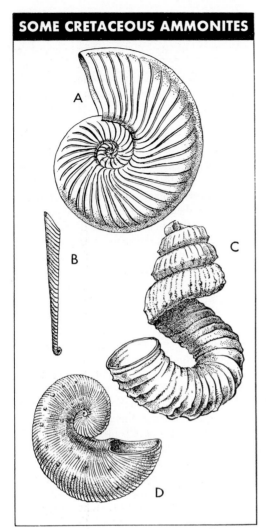

32-1 Some Cretaceous ammonites. *A. Oxytropidoceras acutocarinatum* ($\times\frac{2}{3}$ natural size). *B. Baculites compressus* ($\times\frac{5}{6}$). *C. Heteroceras* sp. ($\times\frac{2}{3}$). *D. Scaphites nodosus* ($\times\frac{2}{3}$).

had appeared and was spreading in the Jurassic. By the end of the Cretaceous it was fully dominant and modern in aspect. Changes during the Age of Mammals have, again, been matters of detail.

OTHER AQUATIC AND AMPHIBIOUS VERTEBRATES

The archaic amphibians also mostly disappeared in the Permo-Triassic crisis. None are known after the Triassic. The rise of the modern groups is poorly documented by fossils, for some unknown reason, but frogs and salamanders thoroughly modern in build were present by Cretaceous times, at latest.

The rise of several groups of aquatic reptiles in the latest Paleozoic and during the Mesozoic introduced a bizarre and unmodern note in the aquatic faunas of those times. The extinction of most of them in the Cretaceous left the turtles and crocodiles (with their allies the alligators) as the common amphibious or aquatic reptiles. Neither group has changed essentially during the Cenozoic.

The most striking change in aquatic environments during the Cenozoic, practically the only change of really deep significance, was the rise and spread of aquatic mammals, whales, seals, sea cows, and their relatives (Fig. 23-28). They began to appear in the Eocene and were common and essentially modernized in the Miocene.

Modernization in Land Environments

PLANTS

As you already know, the dominant, archaic vegetation of the Carboniferous vanished, for the most part, during the Permo-Triassic crisis. In the Triassic and Jurassic there was a sort of interim dominant floral type composed mainly of ferns, cycadeoids, cycads, ginkgos, and conifers. Most of those groups do survive now, but in greatly diminished numbers. Their dominance and the near absence of flowering plants gave the plant life of the Triassic and Jurassic a decidedly nonmodern aspect (Fig. 31-14). By late Cretaceous time, however, the aspect was fully modern. No distinctive groups of plants are known from the late Cretaceous that do not survive today. The flowering plants were then already decidedly dominant, and almost all their modern groups date from then or from quite early in the Cenozoic. Changes during the middle and late Cenozoic involved little more than the shifting of established floras as climates changed.

INSECTS

Modernization of insects also began during the Permo-Triassic crisis, when most of the archaic groups that had appeared in the Carboniferous became extinct. No important groups (for instance, no orders) that are now extinct evolved after the Permian. The whole picture of insect evolution during the Mesozoic was one of steady expansion by the evolution of new groups that were to continue onward into the modern world. Expansion in detail went on also through the Cenozoic and is perhaps still going on, but most if not all of the main groups of insects were already present and modern in form in the late Cretaceous. Furthermore, no important known groups of Cretaceous insects have become extinct. As far as we can judge from a spotty fossil record, the insects come closer than any other group to the simple historical sequence discussed as a postulate at the beginning of this chapter.

REPTILES

As we said earlier, the modernization of land reptiles was essentially only a matter of extinction of the dinosaurs. That left the lizards, snakes, and tortoises, all of which had nearly reached their modern form while the dinosaurs still lived. A good deal of expansion in detail and sometimes intricate speciation have occurred among lizards and snakes during the Cenozoic.

BIRDS

Birds rarely fossilize except under unusual circumstances, so that their fossil record is spotty. Patient accumulation has, however, revealed the essentials of their history. They arose in the Jurassic (p. 772) and became fully birdlike, essentially modern in structure, by the end of the Cretaceous. Some of them then still had teeth, but their scanty remains suffice to show that their skeletons were no longer semireptilian but completely avian. They had, moreover, undergone some sharp divergence or adaptive radiation, for, along with normal flying birds, there were large,

American Museum of Natural History

32-2 The great toothed diver (*Hesperornis regalis*). A large, wingless, swimming bird of the Cretaceous. Note that it "still" possesses teeth.

wingless, swimming birds at that time (Fig. 32-2).

Expansion and subdivision of the birds, their main adaptive radiation, apparently oc-

American Museum of Natural History

32-3 *Diatryma*, a large flightless bird of the Eocene.

curred early in the Cenozoic. Most of the orders of birds were already present in the Eocene. Miocene birds generally differ hardly at all from their recent descendants. Despite the comparatively thin fossil record, birds surely flitted throughout the Cenozoic in great numbers, and it would be as true to call that the Age of Birds as to call it the Age of Mammals.

Large, flightless birds (Fig. 32-3) evolved on all the larger land areas of the Cenozoic. Three groups have survived: ostriches in Africa and Arabia (and formerly over most of Eurasia); rheas in South America; and cassowaries and the closely related emus in Australia and New Guinea. More have become extinct: *Diatryma* in North America, with relatives in Europe; moas in New Zealand; "elephant birds" (*Aepyornis* and relatives) in Madagascar; and several extinct kinds in South America along with the rheas. It is an oddity of evolution that the birds, after acquiring flight and dominating a new environment, repeatedly gave rise to lines in which flight was lost. The large running birds have

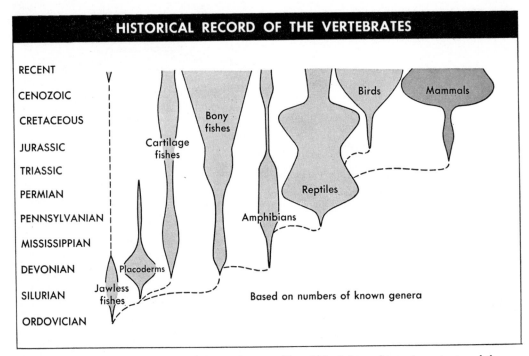

32-4 The historical record of the vertebrates. The width of the pathways is a measure of the relative abundance of the several classes. The mammals emerge in the late Triassic-early Jurassic.

competed, on the whole quite successfully, with mammals on their own terms.[2]

The History of the Mammals

MESOZOIC MAMMALS

You recall that the mammals evolved from mammal-like reptiles in the late Triassic or earliest Jurassic (Fig. 32-4). They are about as old as flowering plants, turtles, or crocodiles, and probably older than teleost fishes, lizards, snakes, or birds. They are by and large the most progressive, by most definitions the very "highest," of all organisms. Yet their modernization and their rise to dominance in their own environments was slower than for most other groups dominant in one environment or another at various times in the history of life. For at least 75 and perhaps as much as 90 million years after they first appeared, mammals cut a small figure in the world. That duration is at least as long as the whole era of their later dominance, the Age of Mammals. By the late Jurassic they had some diversity, but even up to the end of the Cretaceous they remained small, mostly about mouse-sized, and rare.[3] (See Fig. 32-5.)

The mammals of the Jurassic (Fig. 32-6) fall into only three quite circumscribed adaptive types: one group probably ate seeds and small fruits; another comprised carnivores predaceous in a small way; most of them (the third group) were what is commonly called "insectivorous," which means that they ate almost any small food bits, mostly of animal

2 A widely held theory has it that the running birds held their own because they evolved where mammalian carnivores were absent (New Zealand) or supposedly ineffective (Madagascar, Australia, ancient but not modern South America). But they also evolved in North America, Eurasia, and Africa along with admittedly highly effective mammalian carnivores. Here is an evolutionary problem that evidently has not been solved as yet.

3 The Mesozoic mammals were not mice, which evolved much later, but most of them were of about that size. The largest may have been about the size of a house cat. It is of course possible that larger and more varied mammals evolved during the Mesozoic in places where no fossils have been preserved or found. Yet it seems almost impossible that larger mammals can have existed for very long before the Paleocene or can have become very diversified and abundant without leaving any trace at all in the record we do have.

MESOZOIC MAMMALS

Deltatheridium

Zalambdalestes

Photo from American Museum of Natural History

32-5 Mesozoic mammals. *Above,* skulls (part of them restored) of two small Cretaceous mammals, *Deltatheridium* (skull 1¾ inches long) and *Zalambdalestes* (skull 2 inches long). *Below,* photograph of the skull of a Mesozoic mammal.

origin. By the end of the Cretaceous, 30 or more million years later, their evolutionary change was considerable. Yet as far as the record shows, mammals were if anything even more circumscribed ecologically. The seed-eaters were still there, relatively little changed, and there were somewhat more progressive and varied insectivorous forms. The little predators were gone and were not replaced.

Why were the mammals so obscure for so

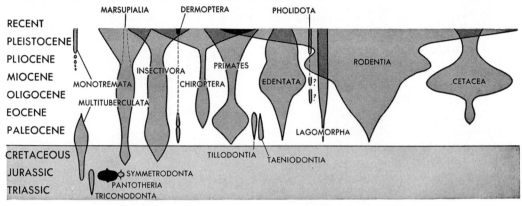

RECENT
PLEISTOCENE
PLIOCENE
MIOCENE
OLIGOCENE
EOCENE
PALEOCENE

CRETACEOUS
JURASSIC
TRIASSIC

MARSUPIALIA   DERMOPTERA   PHOLIDOTA

MONOTREMATA   INSECTIVORA   PRIMATES   RODENTIA
MULTITUBERCULATA   CHIROPTERA   EDENTATA   CETACEA

LAGOMORPHA

TILLODONTIA   TAENIODONTIA

SYMMETRODONTA
PANTOTHERIA
TRICONODONTA

32-6 The historical record of the orders of mammals. For each of the orders of mammals the width of the pathway is proportional to its known variety in each of the geological periods in which it lived. The Mesozoic-Cenozoic boundary (Cretaceous-Paleocene) is indicated. The mammals as a class had emerged from their reptilian ancestry by the Jurassic, in which period four distinct orders are present. Of these the Pantotheria probably gave rise to all later orders. Note the great variety in the histories of the different orders: some reach great diversity and maintain this for a long time before slowly declining to extinction (Notungulata) or to near extinction (Proboscidea); some rapidly reach a maximum and subsequently decline rapidly (Condylarthra) or slowly (Perissodactyla). A striking generalization about the history of individual orders is that none expands slowly to a climax and then declines rapidly. Only the rodents seem to have main-

long? We do not know, but we can offer a hypothesis. When amphibians arose, they had a new way of life with no competitors. Expansion was rapid, geologically speaking, as you would expect. Early reptiles had to still greater extent access to new ways of life and new environments empty of any possible competitors. They not only expanded rapidly but also eventually all but wiped out the amphibians, whose environments overlapped theirs. When mammals arose, the situation was quite different. Niches or adaptive types accessible to the mammals, where they would much later become dominant, were already almost fully occupied by well-adapted reptiles.

In the over-all picture of the ecology of the Mesozoic lands, mammals appear as if they were merely a few specialized reptilian offshoots, occupying a few narrow niches to which they were confined by the pressure of other, temporarily successful specialized reptilian lineages. That mammals did survive through the Jurassic and Cretaceous and managed to hang onto some, at least, of their small niches is a tribute to their inherently more efficient physiology and reproduction

(p. 597). Brains probably did not help at this stage of the game, for what evidence we have strongly suggests that Mesozoic mammals were not significantly brighter than their reptilian neighbors.

THE BEGINNING OF
THE AGE OF MAMMALS

The Cenozoic (Table 30-1) began at an unfortunate time from the fossil-hunters' point of view. In the long seesaw between the uplift and the wearing down of the continents it was a time of predominant, widespread uplift. A result was that erosion was likewise widespread. Most of the eroded material was reworked and eventually deposited beyond the margins of what is now dry land. Few deposits of sediments were made and left where we can now get at them. Consequently there are few available deposits of the beginning of the Cenozoic, the early Paleocene, where fossils of land animals can be found. In spite of intensive search, early Paleocene mammals have been found in only one part of the earth: in and near the Rocky Mountains in the United States. Later Paleocene

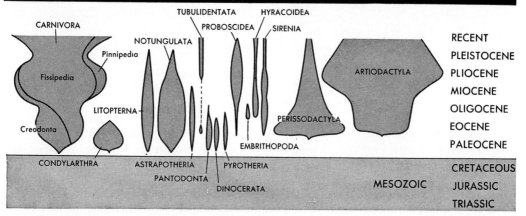

HISTORICAL RECORD OF THE ORDERS OF MAMMALS

tained anything like a steady increase throughout their history. Some internal detail is given for the carnivores to show what is generally typical of the history of an order. The early expansion of the carnivores was almost entirely due to the now long-extinct group, the Creodonta, which underwent a quite diverse adaptive radiation. One product of this radiation was a basic new carnivore type, the Fissipedia (dogs, raccoons, bears, cats, etc.). The fissipede carnivores themselves underwent a strong adaptive radiation and in so doing gradually replaced the creodonts. At a still later time a third distinct group of carnivores, the Pinnipedia (seals, walruses) arose as a product of fissipede radiation. The pinnipedes, invading a wholly new adaptive zone (the sea), have never threatened to replace the fissipedes from which they arose.

mammals are known from Europe, Asia, and South America, and probably early Paleocene mammals will be found elsewhere eventually. In the meantime we can follow the detailed change from Age of Reptiles to Age of Mammals only in the Rocky Mountain region. Obviously a good deal that we do not know about must have been going on elsewhere.

In the Rocky Mountain region the latest Cretaceous rocks contain dinosaurs in some numbers and also tiny mammals. The mammals included one holdover group from the Jurassic, the old seedeaters,[4] which were to become extinct in the early Eocene. The "insectivorous" forms were mostly marsupials (p. 599), closely similar to our modern opossums, which are still thriving in spite of the fact that they have hardly changed at all since that remote date. With them were a few true insectivores, that is, placental mammals classified in the order Insectivora (Fig. 32-6).

In the earliest Paleocene rocks the dinosaurs are completely absent; they seem to have disappeared with startling suddenness. The fauna is already dominated by mam-

[4] Multituberculates, so called from the many tubercles or cusps on their grinding teeth.

mals, although as yet these are of only a few kinds. Opossumlike marsupials and placental insectivores are still present and will continue to be, in one place or another, throughout the Cenozoic, but they are now in a small minority. The common mammals now are somewhat larger. The largest in the early Paleocene was about the size of a not-too-robust collie. Most of these moderate-sized early mammals were much alike. Strong differentiation among placental mammals had not yet occurred. They were long, rather short-legged, running (probably not very swiftly) on feet with five toes. Tails were long, heavy at the base, and heads were small in proportion. The teeth suggest that most of these animals were omnivorous, some with a tendency to rely more on plant and some more on animal food (Fig. 32-7). Distinct separation of hoofed herbivores and clawed carnivores had not evolved.

Later faunas in the American Paleocene show marked and relatively rapid expansion and divergence of the placental mammals. By late Paleocene there are many kinds: numerous hoofed herbivores, some of them now well over a meter in height; fairly specialized

American Museum of Natural History

32-7 *Ectoconus*, a Paleocene mammal.

predaceous carnivores of many sizes and kinds; small forerunners of the monkeys; the first, still very rare, rodents; and others. The later Paleocene faunas from Europe and Asia suggest that much the same sort of expansion had been going on there. It was probably shared by the whole World Continent (p. 723), the intermittently united land masses of Africa, Eurasia, and North America. In South America a great expansion was at least well under way in the late Paleocene, although it was already peculiar to that island continent (p. 725).

What had happened is fairly clear: the mammals were finally inheriting the earth. Extinction of most of the Mesozoic land reptiles left empty environments which were occupied by the mammals in a world-wide adaptive radiation most active during the Paleocene. The mammals, more efficient and more capable of divergent adaptation, eventually went farther than the reptiles ever had in occupation and subdivision of the environmental niches. All this only makes more mysterious and more exasperating the problem of *why* the Mesozoic reptiles became extinct and left the environmental opportunity to the mammals. The record seems to make it clear that the dinosaurs did not become extinct because the mammals had expanded, but on the contrary that the mammals expanded because the dinosaurs previously had become extinct.

MODERNIZATION OF MAMMALS

Eocene and Oligocene mammals. For reasons with which you are already familiar (p. 725), modernization of the South American mammalian faunas was long delayed. It did not occur until the late Pliocene and Pleistocene. Elsewhere, on the World Conti-

nent, basic modernization occurred most prominently in the Eocene, with a filling in of detail in the Oligocene and later. Probably all the main groups, the orders (p. 473), of living placental mammals were already in existence in the Eocene.[5] Most of the living families were present by the end of the Oligocene, at latest. It is significant that no family of placental mammals still living dates from before the Eocene, but that most of them do date from before the Miocene.

There were more orders of placental mammals in the early Eocene than there have ever been since. The modern orders were arising, and the older, Paleocene orders were not yet extinct. Expansion of the modern groups at the expense of the older ones, which were for the most part entirely replaced, is very evident through the Eocene (Fig. 32-8). By the middle of the Oligocene the number of orders was almost down to the present level.

Eocene and Oligocene faunas do look strange to us in spite of the rapid moderniza-

[5] There are sixteen living orders of placental mammals, of which thirteen are definitely known by fossils in the Eocene. The other three orders (scaly anteaters, aardvarks, and hyraxes) do not appear in the fossil record until later. They are, however, all small groups that originated in the Old World tropics, from which few Eocene fossils are known. Their apparent absence in the Eocene is almost surely due only to lack of discovery.

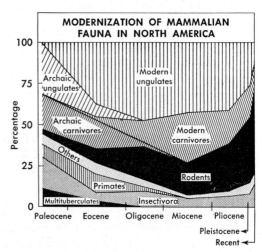

32-8 The modernization of the mammalian fauna of North America. Note the extensive replacement that took place in the Eocene and Oligocene.

Eohippus

Uintathere

Titanothere

Camel

Oreodont

Oligocene
sabertooth

32-9 Some Eocene and Oligocene mammals.

Moeritherium

Gomphotherium

Woolly
mammoth

tion that was going on then. There are three main reasons for their exotic look: some of the striking and peculiar ancient groups were not yet extinct; some modern groups then had a different geographic distribution and occurred in unexpected places; and, as a point of detail, the direct ancestors of our present mammals had not yet reached just their present forms.

Ancient and now extinct groups of mammals prominent in the Eocene and Oligocene include, among the herbivores, the uintatheres (Fig. 32-9), the titanotheres (Fig. 32-9), and, in North America only, the oreodonts (Fig. 32-9), extremely abundant in the Oligocene. Among striking extinct carnivores, the sabertooths [6] appeared in earliest Oligocene and were prominent throughout the World Continent until the Pleistocene, when they became extinct. Startling later changes in geographic distribution are illustrated by the presence of abundant camels and horses in North America through much of the Cenozoic, in spite of the fact that there are no native camels or horses here now. (To what parts of the world are camels and horses now native?)

Equally striking, especially at later dates, are the changes in areas occupied by the bulky proboscidians, the elephants and their allies. Mastodons (Fig. 32-10), the more primitive

[6] Frequently called "saber-toothed tigers," but they were not tigers.

32-10 The proboscidians. *Moeritherium,* the earliest known proboscidian (Eocene of Egypt) was apparently amphibious in habit, and about the size of a pig. There is no evidence in its structure to suggest the striking morphological change in the faces of its later descendants. *Trilophodon,* from the Miocene of North America, looks somewhat more familiar to us as a member of the elephant lineage: it has short tusks (upper incisor teeth enormously developed) and a trunk (nose and upper lip enormously developed). The trilophodons were, however, also characterized by a feature that disappeared in later forms: they had a greatly elongate lower jaw complete with tusks (lower incisor teeth) which were formed like a shovel and doubtless served for digging in vegetation. All the proboscidians are herbivores (cf. Fig. 23-28). *Mammuthus primigenius,* the woolly mammoth of the Pleistocene, was a fully evolved elephant. Note the huge upper tusks and the trunk; the lower jaw has shortened, and there are no lower tusks.

members of the group, enter the fossil record in Egypt in the Oligocene. In the Miocene they spread everywhere on the World Continent and were, for instance, common in North America from late Miocene through the Pleistocene. In the Pleistocene the mammoths or elephants (mammoths are simply the extinct species of elephants) arose and also spread abundantly everywhere on the World Continent, including North America. Now they occur, as natives, only in southeastern Asia and central and southern Africa.

The horse family. Changes in modern groups from the Eocene onward are well illustrated by that classic example of evolution, the horse family (Figs. 2-5 and 32-11). Its earliest known member is eohippus, in the early Eocene. "Little eohippus, no bigger than a fox," generally stood about 45 to 60 centimeters high. It had four toes on the front feet and three on the hind, each toe ending in a tiny hoof. The small head lacked the heavy muzzle of modern horses and had comparatively large eyes set near the middle, not far back as in our horse. The teeth were simple, not fit for grazing but only for browsing on soft vegetation.

The contrast between little eohippus and the large horses of today is great. Yet almost all the intermediate stages are known, a powerful demonstration not only that evolution is a fact but also of how it has occurred. This group, at least, convincingly demonstrates that progressive change is a process of spread of small mutations and new combinations of genes and chromosomes in variable populations. Other examples, and there are now many about as good as that of the horse family, suggest that that is the rule in evolutionary sequences, although not necessarily a rule with no exceptions.

It is to be emphasized that the picture of steady, gradual change from eohippus to *Equus,* the modern horses, still commonly given in popular discussions is quite incorrect. The true history of the horse family does not show a lineage that gradually increased in size, reduced the number of toes, and developed higher, more complex teeth from eohippus to *Equus.* In the first place, there was not *a* lineage but, at times, dozens of

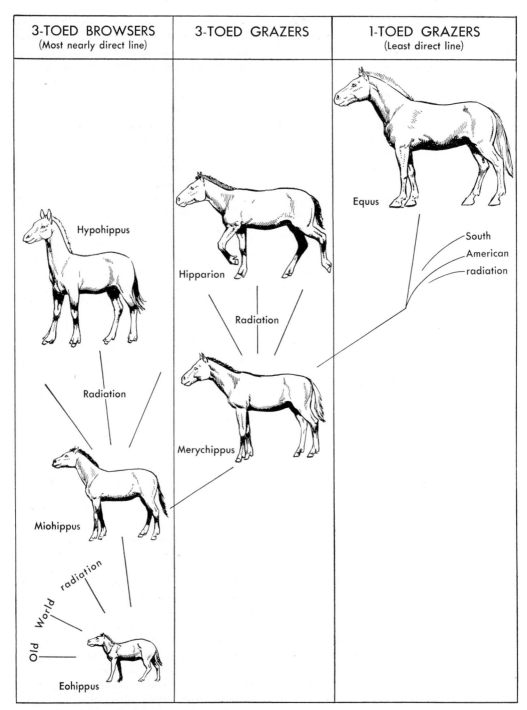

3-TOED BROWSERS (Most nearly direct line)	3-TOED GRAZERS	1-TOED GRAZERS (Least direct line)

Equus

South American radiation

Hypohippus

Hipparion

Radiation

Radiation

Merychippus

Miohippus

Old World radiation

Eohippus

32-11 History of the horses. *Miohippus* was only one product of an early radiation from eohippus. It was still three-toed and browsed on trees and bushes. From *Miohippus* many forms arose, most of which remained three-toed browsers; but one of them, *Merychippus*, made the major step to the grazing habit; it began exploiting the extensive grasslands of the Miocene period. The line eventually leading to the one-toed *Equus* from *Merychippus* was, again, only one of several in the adaptive radiation of the three-toed grazers. Thus the lineage from eohippus to *Equus* is the least direct of those that might be traced through the succession of adaptive radiations.

them. The phylogeny is intricately branched, although all but a few of the branches have now become extinct. Increase in size and change in the feet were not constant but sporadic. There was no significant increase in average size for the first 15 million years or the last 5 or more. Between times, increase was usual but not constant. After the Eocene (when there was no noticeable change in the feet), horses developed three mechanically and functionally different kinds of feet. Each type arose comparatively rapidly, and once it had arisen each tended to remain constant in most lineages, not to change steadily toward another type. All three were common in different groups of late Cenozoic horses, although only one type has survived today. The change from eohippus to *Equus* did occur, of course, but it occurred irregularly through the complex phylogeny shown in greatly oversimplified fashion in Fig. 32-11.

Forerunners of Man

We may forgive ourselves for being more interested in the evolution of man and his relatives than in horses or other nonhuman groups. The fossil record of human origin and of the order Primates (p. 601) in general is now quite extensive. It does still have gaps, which of course we would like to fill in. Many of them will doubtless be filled as larger gaps in the past have been filled by new finds of fossils. Some gaps may always remain, because the fossils are simply not preserved or where we can find them, but the main features of the history are already clear.

That the primates have not left as complete a fossil record as, for instance, the horses is readily understandable. The greater part of the history of the horse family—its most central and progressive part, at least—took place in one region, a region rich in fossils and well explored by bone diggers: central North America. The history of the primates was more far-flung, with crucial episodes in several different regions. Moreover, central parts of the history evidently occurred in tropical areas, which are, as a rule, neither very rich in fossil deposits nor as yet thoroughly explored for them. The primate way of life also militates against a good fossil record. Most primates are and have been arboreal, and tree dwellers are comparatively unlikely to be buried and to fossilize. It has further been suggested that higher primates were too bright to be fossilized with any great frequency. A shrewd animal has a better chance to avoid being mired down or swept away in a flood, or suffering other accidents that could readily lead to burial and fossilization.

EARLY PROSIMIANS

The main groups of primates were briefly mentioned on p. 601. The history starts with the most primitive of these groups, that of the prosimians or pre-monkeys (Fig. 32-12). Their oldest known fossils are found in the middle Paleocene of the Rocky Mountain region. Prosimians were abundant through the Eocene, not only in North America but also in Eurasia and probably in Africa, where the Eocene fossil record is extremely poor as far as yet discovered. They are absent from the known North American record after the early Oligocene, but they lived on in parts of the Old World. They now live only in tropical Asia and adjacent islands, in Africa, and in the large island of Madagascar. The continental forms are mostly rare and comprise only a few species. One group of prosimians, that of the lemurs (Fig. 32-13), is, however, common and diversified in Madagascar, where they are the only primates (except man). This abundant survival of so primitive a group is an interesting evolutionary phenomenon. Their ancestors gained access to the island early in the Cenozoic, before higher primates arose. The lemurs then underwent an adaptive radiation on the large island and have been protected from effective competition. Later primates did not cross the sea barrier between Africa and Madagascar, so that the island became an asylum for prosimians.

Primates were probably more widespread and included more species in the Eocene than at any later time. Those primitive early primates had evolved from still more primitive Insectivora (p. 599). It is, indeed, impossible to draw a sharp line between the orders Insectivora and Primates. Prosimians, even now, have poorly developed brains. Most of them have rather long, pointed snouts,

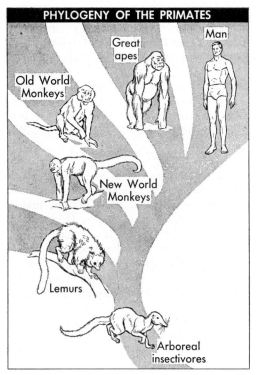

PHYLOGENY OF THE PRIMATES

Man

Great apes

Old World Monkeys

New World Monkeys

Lemurs

Arboreal insectivores

32-12 The phylogeny of the primates. The figure is not scaled either to size of animal or to time.

markedly unlike the flattened faces and more localized noses of monkeys, apes, and men. The eyes usually look more to the side than to the front. A basic characteristic of primates present in early prosimians is the retention and further evolution of grasping hands and, often, feet, with apposable thumb and big toe. In connection with this adaptation, the insectivore claws early began to evolve into nails.

There were innumerable divergent lines among Paleocene and Eocene primates and primatelike insectivores. Many of them became specialized in peculiar ways and have become extinct. The ones most significant for further evolution retained simple, primitive teeth and had a tendency toward enlargement of the cranium, reduction of the snout, and enlargement of the eyes, which also tended toward a more anterior than lateral outlook.

MONKEYS

The Old World monkeys, cercopithecoids, and New World monkeys, ceboids (p. 601),

are fully distinct phylogenetic units (Fig. 23-29). They have always had approximately the same geographic distribution that they have now: cercopithecoids in the warmer parts of Africa, Asia, and Europe,[7] and ceboids in South and Central America. Both groups evolved from prosimians, probably from closely related prosimians, but they arose separately, on different continents. (Why did not these warm-climate animals migrate in either direction between Eurasia and North America?)

Both groups first appeared in the Oligocene. They differ from prosimians in similar ways. They have larger, more effective brains, with expansion especially of the upper part of the cortex (see p. 213). The brain case correspondingly forms a larger proportion of the head. The snout is reduced, and the flattened monkey face is characteristic. The eyes are pointed more nearly forward, and the fields of vision of the two eyes overlap widely. The shortened muzzle involves a shortening of upper and lower jaws, and the number of teeth is reduced. The molars are squared, but remain simple. Hands and feet are grasping, but no more so than in some prosimians.

Differences between cercopithecoids and ceboids are not profound or important. They suffice merely as indexes to the fact that the two were of somewhat different ancestry. Ceboids have retained some primitive features lost in cercopithecoids, but they are more advanced in some respects. They are not a lower group, but just a different one. They have no bearing on the ancestry of the cercopithecoids, apes, or man.

APES

The name "ape" is sometimes applied to monkeys, but strictly it means a member of one particular family of the Primates: the Pongidae (Fig. 32-14). Sometimes they are called *anthropoid*[8] *apes* to make the distinction clear. The living apes are the *gorilla* and

[7] The only European monkeys now are the famous "apes" (really monkeys, not apes) of the Rock of Gibraltar, but monkeys used to occur more widely in southern Europe.

[8] "Manlike." Some of the confusion may have arisen from German usage, in which "Affen" correctly applies to what we call "monkeys," and our "apes," strictly speaking, are "Menschenaffen," "men-monkeys."

American Museum of Natural History and
New York Zoological Society

32-13 Lemurs. *Left*, reconstruction of the Eocene lemur *Notharctus*. Note the grasping hands and feet; the thumb closes over the branch in the opposite direction to the fingers (cf. p. 794). *Right*, a living lemuroid, *Loris tardigradus* ("the slender Loris"). Note the thumb of the left hand, and the manner in which both eyes are directed forward, permitting stereoscopic vision (cf. p. 794).

chimpanzee of central Africa, the *orangutan* [9] of Sumatra and Borneo, and the *gibbons* of southeastern Asia. All are above average size for primates, and gorillas are big brutes, the males becoming heavier and stronger than any men. All lack tails.[10] They have relatively larger brains and brain cases than the monkeys and are in general more intelligent.

All recent apes except the gorilla are strictly arboreal, spending almost their whole lives in trees. Gibbons, smallest of the apes, have tremendously long arms and are astonishing acrobats. They swing (*brachiate*) and jump for great distances between branches. When they do come to the ground, they walk on their hind legs, holding up the long arms as balancers. The other apes habitually walk on all fours unless they have been taught to walk clumsily on the hind legs as a circus

9 A Malay name meaning "forest man."
10 A few monkeys are also tailless. Incidentally, ability to hang by the tail, sometimes considered typical of all monkeys, is confined to a few South American monkeys.

or vaudeville trick. Gorillas sometimes climb trees, and their immediate ancestors were evidently arboreal, but now they spend most of their time on the ground. Chimpanzees and orangutangs do not swing from limb to limb with the abandon of gibbons, but they are agile four-handed climbers and spend most of their time in trees.

Apes have always been confined to the warmer parts of the Old World. The earliest known fossils occur in the Oligocene, along with the first Old World monkeys. Apes and cercopithecoids share some characters present neither in the ceboids nor in the prosimians. The earliest forms are hard to tell apart. It is apparent that apes either were derived from a branch of the earliest cercopithecoids or that they and the cercopithecoids had an immediate common ancestry among the prosimians. The distinction is more one of terminology than of significant difference in the phylogeny.

In the Miocene, apes became much more

32-14 The great apes, *Pongidae*. Note hands and eyes. The gibbon is brachiating.

varied than they are today. Their remains are not common, but diligent search has turned up fragments of many species in the Miocene of eastern Africa and the Pliocene of India, and a few in the Miocene and Pliocene of Europe. There was a great expansion of the family starting at about the beginning of the Miocene. Some of the members of that late Cenozoic complex were aberrant and became extinct. Others were ancestral to the modern apes and were already becoming specialized in similar ways. Still others, especially in the early Miocene, were comparatively light, agile forms not yet strongly specialized for arboreal life and lacking other characters peculiar to the surviving apes. *Proconsul* (Fig. 32-15), from the early Miocene of Kenya, is the most completely known and is among the less specialized.

32-15 *Proconsul*, fossil ape from the Miocene of Africa (Kenya).

THE AUSTRALOPITHECINES

In 1925 was discovered the first of a remarkable group of fossil primates known as the *australopithecines* ["southern monkeys (or apes)"]. Since then, numerous tooth and jaw fragments, several nearly complete skulls, and some fragments of the pelvis and limbs have been collected. They are definitely known only from South Africa, although some fragments from southern Asia and Europe may belong to the same group (Fig. 32-16).

The australopithecine brain is comparable in size and complexity with that of the larger living apes. It is decidedly smaller than in any normal human. The skull as a whole is apelike in appearance, but it has a number of more manlike anatomical details. Among these is evidence that it was set squarely on top of the backbone, not thrust forward as in the apes. The teeth are decidedly more manlike than apelike. The pelvis and limb fragments suggest that the australopithecines walked upright, or nearly so, a posture decidedly human in contrast with the apes.

The australopithecines form a group distinct from either apes or men. They resemble both about equally, but in different ways. The combination of what is essentially an ape's brain with nearly human dentition and posture is remarkable and was not anticipated in earlier speculation about intermediates between apes and men.

There is nothing in their anatomy that would exclude the australopithecines from a phylogenetically intermediate position between primitive Miocene (not recent) apes and early man. They could, however, be an extinct, separate branch from the Miocene or Pliocene expansion of the ape family. Even in that case it would be a fact that they are more manlike than other apes, living or extinct. They do tend to link apes and man. Beyond that fact, their precise relationships are disputed. Much depends on their geological age, which has not been precisely established. If they (or some of them) prove to be distinctly older than any fossil men, the possibility that they include our actual ancestors will be enhanced. At present it seems somewhat more likely that the known forms are little if at all older than some fossil men. In that case they obviously cannot be ancestors of man, although the possibility would remain that they are late survivors of a group from which man earlier arose.

Man's Place in Nature

HUMAN ORIGINS

Even the pre-evolutionary biologists recognized that man is an animal, fundamentally like other animals but distinguished as a species by higher and different development of intelligence. Linnaeus (p. 462), an anti-evolutionist, classified man, *Homo sapiens*, in the order Primates with the prosimians, monkeys, and apes. That classification is still accepted by virtually all biologists. Knowledge of evolution makes it evident that man's distinctive characteristics arose in the same way as those of other species of animals, by more or less gradual change in varying populations. That man's material being evolved from other and (in intelligence, at least) lower animals is about as certain as a scientific conclusion can be. That man has an immortal soul and that other animals do not is a proposition that scientific investigation can neither affirm nor deny. You are free to reach your own conclusions about that, or to accept whatever religious tenet seems worthy of your faith.

Man's classification as a primate is now accepted as valid on a phylogenetic basis. His physical ancestry was, at some time in the past, the same as that of all the other primates. His more precise relationships among the primates are disputed. Even scientists cannot always avoid being swayed by emotion and prejudice when they deal with their own origins. There is, nevertheless, a clear consensus as to the most important points in the light of modern knowledge.

It is obvious to the most casual visitor to zoo or circus that the apes are the most manlike of living nonhumans. This has been confirmed by intensive investigation of structure, physiology, and behavior. It is, however, impossible that any living ape represents the human ancestry or is even very closely similar to it. Obviously no animal now living can be literally ancestral to animals of any other living species. Moreover, all the living apes have specializations that pretty surely did not occur in our ancestry. The apes undoubtedly had a common ancestry with us, but since then they have diverged definitely from the line of our later ancestors. It is not impossible and is in fact probable that some of the primitive Miocene members of the ape family were our ancestors. Whatever the precise degree of their relationships to man, the australopithecines add greatly to the weight of evidence favoring that conclusion.

Man's most distinctive, most truly human characteristic is his brain. But the origin of man and, indeed, of his brain was dependent on older features, passed on from a prehuman ancestry and reflecting early primate adaptations. Three of the most important of those prehuman acquisitions, in the order in which they evolved, are: grasping hands; binocular, stereoscopic vision; and upright posture.

The earliest primates were arboreal, as so many still are. A fundamental adaptation to arboreal life was the apposable thumb, already present in the oldest known fossil prosimians. With it, the hand was able to *grasp* the branches of trees. That ancient adaptation now makes possible for us all our most complex *manipulations,* and hence all the tools we make and use as *our* most powerful adaptive equipment.

In the earliest primates and the most primitive of those still surviving, the eyes are directed more laterally, somewhat as in a long-nosed dog. The two fields of vision overlap only slightly, and an object is ordinarily seen with only one eye at a time. In various lines of descent there was an early trend for the eyes to point more forward, so that the fields overlapped more widely. Then an object was generally seen with both eyes at once, with *binocular* ("two-eyed") vision. That, in turn, laid the basis for an actual fusion of the images from both eyes as perceived in the brain, giving *stereoscopic* ["solid (three-dimensional) viewing"] vision. These developments were also probably adaptations to arboreal life, in which acute vision and depth perception have special importance. On the ground there is always *something* under foot, but an animal moving from branch to branch *must* know precisely where the next branch is. In man, more than in most other vertebrates, vision has become the dominant sense, source of our most valuable information about the world around us. And this priceless stereoscopic vision has combined with the earlier grasping hand in *hand-eye co-ordination,* the basis of tool use.

Primates are basically four-footed in locomotion and posture. In the larger arboreal monkeys and in the apes there was a trend toward brachiation (p. 791), swinging from tree branches by the forearms instead of

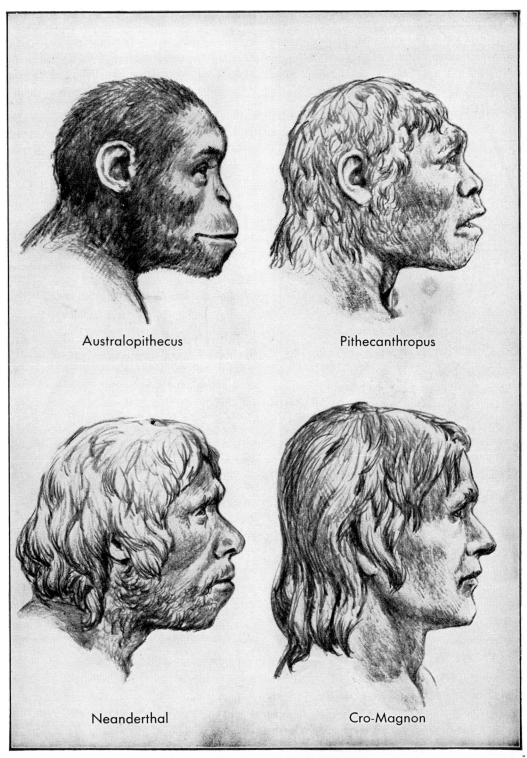

Australopithecus

Pithecanthropus

Neanderthal

Cro-Magnon

32-16 *Australopithecus* and fossil men.

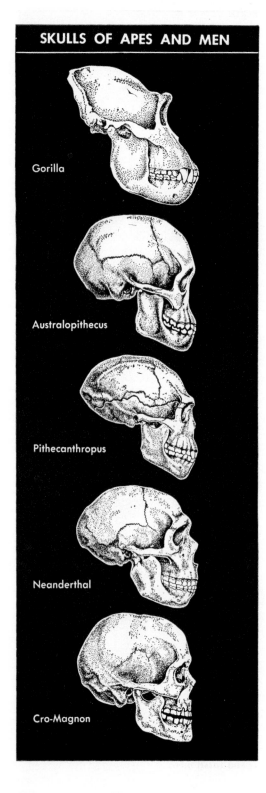

Gorilla

Australopithecus

Pithecanthropus

Neanderthal

Cro-Magnon

walking along the branches on four feet. That involves a straightening of the trunk of the body and an adaptive elongation of the arms. Our own ancestors never became extremely specialized brachiators like the modern apes (especially the gibbons), but some advance along that trend facilitated the upright posture when our ancestors came down to walk and live on the ground. That posture freed the hands from use in locomotion and permitted efficient specialization of fore and hind limbs: fore (now upper) limbs for manipulation only, hind (now lower) limbs for locomotion only.

Thus our ancient arboreal primate ancestors supplied the basis for becoming human. The australopithecines had grasping hands, stereoscopic vision, and erect posture. After that stage came the final great expansion of the brain—and we were men!

FOSSIL MEN

Just when man arose and what fossils should be called human are matters of definition. Not one but many "missing links" are now known, and it is arbitrary which of them we choose to call "men." Some would confine the designation to populations of *Homo sapiens* just like those now living. Others insist that even the australopithecines should be called "men." Our decision, which follows the most usual present practice, is to exclude the australopithecines but to include all the more manlike fossil groups. All are confined to the Pleistocene, as far as is known. That means that none of them is at all likely to be more than a million years old, and most of

32-17 Skulls of apes and men. In considering apes and men as a group, it is useful to recognize two sets of skull features: one set (technically called paleanthropic) characterizes apes and earlier men; the other set (called neanthropic) characterizes modern men. Paleanthropic skull characters include: (1) small brain case volume; (2) brain case shallow relative to length; (3) heavy bony brow ridges over the eyes; (4) jaws protrude forward in front of a vertical dropped from the eye; (5) large canine teeth; (6) receding lower jaw—no chin. Neanthropic characters of the skull are the opposite. Thus: (1) large brain case volume; (2) brain case deep relative to length; (3) no brow ridges; (4) jaws do not extend in front of eyes; (5) small canine teeth; (6) chin protrudes forward.

them must be under 500,000. Dating is still inexact in this range. In any event, man has a respectable antiquity from the viewpoint of human history, but he is a newcomer, a Johnny-come-lately, in comparison with almost all other kinds of animals.

If the australopithecines are considered non-human, the most primitive fossil men are represented by a group of skulls, jaws, and other fragments found in Java and another found near Peking in China. The most primitive Java men (Figs. 32-16 and 32-17) have been called *Pithecanthropus* ["monkey (or ape) men"], and the Peking men *Sinanthropus* ("China men"). They are, however, so similar that they probably represent merely different demes, or at most different subspecies, of a single specific population. A few fragments found in Africa and elsewhere suggest that archaic men of this general kind may have occurred throughout most of the Old World. Apparently none of them ever discovered America.

Skulls of this archaic group retained apelike characters which are reduced or lost in all living men. The brain case was small. Brain size varied greatly, from about 775 cubic centimeters to about 1300. The average was about 1000, which is neatly intermediate between living apes and men.[11] There were heavy ridges above the eyes. The jaws and teeth protruded markedly in front, and the chin retreated as in apes. All in all, these archaic fossils nearly split the difference between apes and men, although the weight of resemblances is a little on the human side.

NEANDERTHAL [12] MEN

Later than the archaic group just described there lived another large and varied population, distinctly more advanced but still more primitive than modern man (Fig. 32-16). They have been found at many places in Europe, Asia, and Africa. The scattered finds show individual and probably racial differences, but they are enough alike for all to be considered as one variable population, the Neanderthals or Neanderthaloids (that is, Neanderthal-like).

The Neanderthaloids were short, stocky, powerful people with large, heavy-boned heads. Brow ridges were still present and the chin was still retreating, but neither character was as extreme as in the older Java and Peking men. The forehead was retreating and the brain low, but surprisingly enough the total size of the brain was as great as in modern men. We do not know how we would stack up with Neanderthaloids in an intelligence test, but we do know that their intelligence was considerable in amount and human in quality. They constructed a large variety of beautifully made tools and were successful hunters. They sometimes buried their dead and put offerings or sacrifices in the grave, which implies that they had a religion and rituals.

EARLY "HOMO SAPIENS"

Several fossil skulls have been discovered that are somewhat older than the typical Neanderthals but that show greater resemblance to modern man. Among these are the Swanscombe (England) skull, unfortunately only a few fragments, and the more nearly complete Steinheim and Ehringsdorf (Germany) skulls.[13] They are not fully modern in appearance and do have some primitive and Neanderthaloid traits, but they are more like *Homo sapiens* than are the most fully developed later Neanderthals (Fig. 32-16). They indicate that the history of man in the Pleistocene was not a simple line that could be symbolized by Java man → Neanderthal man → modern man.

There are two main possibilities. One is that Pleistocene man constituted a single species but was split up into highly varying demes, some more *Homo sapiens*-like, even at an early date, and others retaining or even accentuating more archaic characters. Selection within the species eventually eliminated archaic variants. That seems the more probable explanation, especially as some fossil men do represent contemporaneous intermediates between the Neanderthaloid and the more extreme modern types. The other

11 The average cranial capacity is about 500 cubic centimeters for recent gorillas and about 1350 cubic centimeters for modern man. Both vary considerably.
12 From the Neander Valley ("Thal" in German), where the first described remains were found near Düsseldorf, Germany.
13 All these discoveries are named for the places where they were found.

main possibility is that the Neanderthaloids were a separate branch of mankind, a species that became extinct and was replaced in competition with forerunners of *Homo sapiens.* The contrast between these two theories is not absolutely clear-cut.

True *Homo sapiens,* indistinguishable from modern man, is first known in the last glacial stage of the Pleistocene. Cro-Magnon men, first found in France, lived at least 20,000 and probably not over 50,000 years ago (Fig. 32-16). All discoveries of younger fossil men are also true *Homo sapiens,* with no more variation or regional differentiation than still occurs.

In spite of inevitable doubts as to certain details, the increasing modernization of human populations during the Pleistocene is a fact, and it bears eloquent witness to the rise of *Homo sapiens* by natural evolutionary processes.

EARLY MAN IN AMERICA

No men truly primitive in a biological sense ever reached the Americas as far as is yet known. America was peopled by repeated invasions from Asia, mainly although perhaps not exclusively by way of Alaska. The oldest reasonably well-dated traces of man in America are only about 10,000 years old. It is quite likely that somewhat older remains will eventually be found. It seems fairly certain, however, that man did not reach America until the closing stage of the Pleistocene. By then *Homo sapiens,* with various racial and lesser distinctions, was universal in the Old World. Only *Homo sapiens,* mainly or entirely mongoloid in origin, ever reached the New World before the European discovery.

And What of the Future?

That brings the biological aspects of the history of life up to date. *Homo sapiens* has evolved and has expanded to nearly all the lands of the earth. He dominates the land environments as no other species or larger group of organisms ever has. He is, so far, the culmination of the whole incredibly long and complex evolutionary process.

It is natural to sit back at this point and to speculate on the future history of life. The simplest assumption would be that past trends would continue indefinitely. It is, however, one of the lessons of history that trends do not continue indefinitely. They eventually change direction or stop. There is reason to believe that the trend of physical evolution by which man arose has now stopped. Under present conditions man's future biological evolution is more likely to be degenerative than progressive. But man himself is a new factor in the history of life and one that seems just now to be highly unpredictable.

The being and the becoming of the universe, its rules and its history, will always limit and condition what can occur. Man, for the first time ever, has conscious knowledge of many of the rules and much of the history. He can use that knowledge to modify and guide his own destiny and the destinies of other organisms. How he will in fact use that awesome power is hidden in the darkness of the future. Perhaps the only safe prediction is that you and your descendants, whether you want to or not, whether indeed you know it or not, will have the most decisive influence on the future history of life.

Chapter Summary

The Cenozoic era: Age of Mammals; 75 million years' duration; man's appearance at very end of Cenozoic; the vicissitudes and complexity of life's history as revealed by fossils.

Modernization of aquatic environments: a process of replacement of lesser groups (classes, orders, families) within the same ancient phyla.

Aquatic plants: very little change; Jurassic appearance of diatoms only major event.

Invertebrates: extinction of ammonites by early Cenozoic the outstanding event.

Fishes: by end of Cretaceous, full emergence of teleosts as dominant fish group.

Other aquatic vertebrates: extinction of archaic amphibians (Triassic); rise of aquatic reptiles in Mesozoic, of aquatic mammals in Cenozoic.

Modernization of land environments:

Plants: disappearance of the predominantly lycopsid-sphenopsid forests during Permo-Triassic; forests of Triassic-

Jurassic mostly ferns and gymnosperms (cycadeoids, cycads, ginkgos, and conifers); by late Cretaceous forests are of modern aspect—predominantly angiosperms.

Insects: their modernization during Mesozoic, essentially complete by late Cretaceous.

Reptiles: extinction of dinosaurs, leaving lizards, snakes, and tortoises.

Birds: poor fossil record; their Jurassic origin; modernization complete by end of Cretaceous; adaptive radiation in the Cenozoic, including origin of large flightless forms.

History of the mammals:

Mesozoic mammals: Triassic-Jurassic origin of mammals; their early evolution slow; small size and scarcity at end of Cretaceous; the three groups of Jurassic mammals; effect of reptilian competition on history of Mesozoic mammals.

Beginning of the Age of Mammals: geological factors responsible for poor early Cenozoic fossil record; faunal changes from Cretaceous to Paleocene; generalized character of early Paleocene mammals; diversification of mammals by late Paleocene; their adaptive radiation, made possible by evacuation of niches by reptilian extinctions.

Modernization of mammals: their post-Paleocene history; modernization of South American faunas delayed to Pliocene; on World Continent most of modernization occurred in Eocene and Oligocene; typical Eocene and Oligocene groups: uintatheres, titanotheres, oreodonts, sabertooths; history of the elephants and of the horses; complexity of the eohippus-*Equus* lineage.

Forerunners of man: the fossil record of primates; effect of their arboreal way of life on quality of the record.

Early prosimians: lemurs; their early distribution, and more recent radiation in Madagascar; insectivore-primate relationships; primate characteristics.

Monkeys: Old World and New World types.

Apes: anthropoids; the four living types; large size and predominantly arboreal habit; restriction to warm climate, and other characteristics; close relationship to Old World monkeys; Miocene expansion; *Proconsul.*

Australopithecus: a late group of fossil anthropoids from South Africa; their manlike features; possibility that they are human ancestors.

Man's place in nature:

Human origins: man as primate; evolution from lower forms; probability of ancestors among Miocene apes; distinctive biological attributes of man: brains, grasping hand, binocular-stereoscopic vision, upright posture; the early evolution of these characters as adaptations to aboreal life.

Fossil men: all less than a million years old; most younger than a half-million; *Pithecanthropus* and *Sinanthropus* skull characters; Neanderthal man: his wide distribution, size, skull characters, tools, and other cultural relicts.

Early *Homo sapiens:* the Swanscombe, Steinheim, and Ehringsdorf skulls; the relation of Neanderthal to modern man; Cro-Magnon man, first true *sapiens* of about 20,000 to 50,000 years ago.

Early man in America: mongoloid immigration from Asia; oldest remains 10,000 years old.

The future: man's current dominant biological role; the human evolutionary future: little expected in physical structure, but social and cultural evolution potentially in human power to control.

The History of Biology

Man made his first appearance on the biological scene about a million years ago; but on a time scale which measures in the billions that period is as nothing. On a 24-hour-scale for the whole history of life we found *Homo sapiens* emerging just a moment—one minute—ago. The whole of recorded human history fills only the final quarter-second before the midnight that is now.

Capacity for thought and analysis is the key adaptation whose evolution accounts for the incredible rate of human progress in this last "quarter-second" of life's history. Man uses his mind to greater biological effect than any organism ever used its bodily adaptation; his unparalleled mastery over the physical environment is due entirely to the technology and social systems produced by the evolution of knowledge. The advent of thinking man was, in fact, a great turning point in life's history: it set off a wholly new trend and tempo in evolutionary progress; it initiated *cultural* evolution. The *biological* evolution of man is, to be sure, still proceeding as rapidly as ever; but the rate of change in the human gene pool is dwarfed by the pace at which our social and intellectual adaptation—our culture—is evolving.

Our task as biologists is essentially complete because the study of cultural evolution is the traditional domain of the human historian. Knowledge of its historical growth is, however, essential to the proper understanding of a science, and we have devoted Part 10 to a brief outline of the history of biology. This history, like that of all culture, has been a complex evolution subject to many influences. Its full analysis would show how the progress of biological insight has interacted with other aspects of cultural evolution; how it has usually depended on, and sometimes led, the growth of the other sciences; how the invention of tools and techniques has played a role; how social forces in general have shaped its course, and how society in turn has been profoundly influenced by that ultimate self-consciousness of life which biology represents. The culture of man, no less than his body, is an integrated whole; it has evolved as a whole and should be studied as a whole.

Part 10 is too brief to allow a full study of the history of biology; it is a summary of major trends, events, and persons that are central to the fuller story. As to the influence of society, and of thought in other sciences, we let our earlier discussion in Chapter 2 suffice. But however one tells the story—in full or, as here, in brief—two features always stand out: one is the astonishing youth of the science of life; and the other is the towering influence of Charles Darwin, whose portrait introduces Part 10. If we must count the whole of human history as a minute, how shall we count the century since publication (1859) of *The Origin of Species?* Darwin's book marks the entry of biology into the mainstream of scientific thought, which was largely shaped by the earlier growth of physics; his concepts of evolution and natural selection are still the general principles that bring order into the diverse facts of life.

CHAPTER 33

The Long Search

Man has been trying to learn the secrets of life for centuries and millennia. The methods and knowledge that constitute biology today are an accumulation that began among our prehistoric ancestors. The search has continued with sometimes wavering but generally accelerating pace and success up to the present minute. It still has far to go, and it continues unabated. Already it is one of the great achievements of mankind. The history of the search is something we can all be proud of, unlike the shabby histories of dynasties and conquests. Even though summarized in irreducibly small compass, that history is also one of the best ways to review what the science of biology is—its scope, aims, and subdivisions. We have chosen the historical approach to give a final over-all view of the science that you have now studied.

One point is likely to be obscured in so brief a review of the history of a science and must be strongly emphasized now. The acquisition of biological knowledge has been the work of tens of thousands of devoted students. Some, of course, have been more brilliant or (what is not necessarily at all the same thing) have turned out to be historically more important than others. We shall name a few. The men we name were all great, although the list cannot begin to include all of the great nor can it be claimed to designate the very greatest of them. The men named typify an epoch, mark a culmination of achievement, or were involved in a turning point in biological research. Even in these respects they did not stand alone, but were surrounded and upheld by innumerable others who cannot be named here.

No scientist ever made a discovery of his own. Every one had many predecessors and contemporaries whose work was just as essential to his discovery as anything that he did. The idea of evolution and also that of natural selection were already old when Darwin wrote *The Origin of Species.* That does not belittle Darwin's position among the greatest of all biologists. It does put the matter in better perspective. Science is a cumulative, social product. It includes but does not wholly consist of the work of individuals who can be labeled "great."

We will not name any living biologists in this historical review. There are now more biologists than ever before. Many of them are certainly as brilliant as any in the past, and some of them will surely be adjudged great by future historians. So many are brilliant that to select a few in this brief space would be unfair and misleading. Selection of the greatest must be left to posterity.

Natural History

Biology began as a branch of natural history. Natural history began as an attempt to observe and describe the physical universe. The expression "natural history" is still used in almost that sense as a broad and popular term to refer to all the natural sciences collectively, as in the names of our many museums of natural history. Research and study in the natural sciences are, however, now carried on under the names of the innumerable special sciences into which the old, almost all-embracing subject of natural history has inevitably been split.

In the ancient world, natural history, and particularly that part of it dealing with animals, reached a culmination among the Greeks and in the person of Aristotle (384-322 B.C.). He compiled descriptions, excellent on the whole, of most of the phenomena of animal life known in his day and culture. Neither he nor any of the other ancients advanced deeply and correctly into an *understanding* of the principles beneath the observed phenomena. With a few lucky exceptions they were unable to formulate the right questions because they held philosophies that were fundamentally not scientific, in the modern definition of the word. Beyond the level of simple observation, and sometimes even at that level, they tended to ask and to answer questions about nature in terms of their nonscientific philosophies rather than in terms of nature itself.

Many centuries passed before it was usual for the students of nature to approach the subject in an actually naturalistic way, to rely on nature itself to suggest the questions and to supply the answers. Among the landmarks in this change of attitude were the discoveries that the earth is not the center of the universe (Copernicus, 1473-1543) and that hitherto mysterious activities in this universe can be reduced to mathematical law (Newton, 1642-1727). The gradual and often painful liberation of inquiry from philosophical, authoritarian, and dogmatic preconceptions gave rise to science in the full, modern sense.

CLASSIFICATION AND SYSTEMATICS

The period in which scientific attitude and method were coming into form was also the great period of navigations and explorations. Europeans discovered the rest of the world. Strange plants and animals were among the most striking of the discoveries. Natural history, which had degenerated after Aristotle, sometimes into sheer fantasy, was revived on a broader and more objective basis. Collections were formed and compendia written. Agricola (1490-1555), although more famous for his work on mining and mineralogy, also made systematic biological collections. Gesner (1516-1565) and Fuchs (1501-1566), among the first who may be called biologists in a nearly modern sense, also collected. They used the new arts of printing from type and illustrating with woodcuts to publish huge works on natural history. Cesalpino (1519-1603) first attempted a really serious classification, in the modern spirit, of the whole plant kingdom.

The more orderly approach to natural history and the flood of new discoveries increased the desire and the need to classify organisms. Efforts were made to establish classifications on a natural system, rather than on superficial resemblances or fancied properties. Ray (1627-1705), an English botanist, classified both plants and animals and was one of the greatest forces in production of a truly systematic science of systematics. The pre-eminent place of the Swedish botanist Linnaeus (1707-1778) has been mentioned elsewhere (p. 462). He formalized the consistent use of the hierarchy and system of nomenclature still in use. Modern classification is conventionally dated from him, although it has changed much since his day, and in some ways the earlier Ray seems more modern in retrospect.

The climax of description and classification for their own sake was reached by Linnaeus, his contemporaries, and his early successors. Buffon (1707-1788) produced a voluminous natural history so complete and so well written that it is still a household work in France. Cuvier (1769-1832) also advanced the systematics of animals and was among the first to insert extinct animals into the system.

The pre-Darwinian systematists, those we have named and many others, were largely concerned with developing a "natural classification." From our vantage point, with all their work and all that done since then available, it appears that they never achieved a *natural* definition of a "natural classification." Their criteria as to what was natural in classification was merely intuitive, occasionally acute and occasionally absurd, or it was based on philosophical considerations with no evident connection with the material facts of nature. A workable connection appeared only when the truth of evolution was generally recognized. Phylogeny is a material fact of nature (even when, like many other such facts, it is incompletely known to us),[1] and it does provide a possible basis for natural classification.

Phylogenetic classification is mainly, although not entirely, post-Darwinian. Its great expansion, even in Darwin's lifetime, is exemplified in the sometimes overoptimistic work of the German zoologist Haeckel (1834-1919). He produced elaborate phylogenetic trees and corresponding classifications. They have not all stood up well in detail, but they pointed to one of the directions in which the science of systematics was to develop.

To this day the identification and classification of organisms, one of the earliest activities in the field of natural history, is a main preoccupation of most botanists and zoologists. After the first excitement of applying evolutionary concepts to classification had worn off, it seemed for a time to be settling into dull routine. Recently, however, this science of *systematics* has been rejuvenated, and it is now unusually active and interesting. The revival is due largely to two related factors. First is the change in point of view from classifying individuals to classifying populations (p. 463). Second is a broader concept of the basis and significance of systematics. The science is no longer merely classification in the sense of pigeonholing and labeling. It is the study of the diversity of organisms and of their relationships among themselves. As such it ramifies into most other branches of biology, notably biogeography, ecology, and genetics.

The science of systematics has become so vast and so complex that no one now attempts to do original research in more than a small part of the whole field. The primary division is into *botany* and *zoology*, with *protistology* (study of protists) often lately added as a third. Even a systematic zoologist, for instance, does not work on the whole animal kingdom. Among many other specialties, he may be an *entomologist* (student of insects), a *malacologist* (student of mollusks), an *ichthyologist* (student of fishes), a *herpetologist* (student of amphibians and reptiles), an *ornithologist* (student of birds), or a *mammalogist* (student of mammals).

LIFE SCIENCES AND
THE SCOPE OF BIOLOGY

The fractionation of systematics into many different specialties illustrates a trend in all the sciences, necessary as the bulk of knowledge has increased and the skills required have become so different. What our forebears were content to call "natural history" has become a score of major sciences comprising hundreds of specialties. Among the sciences having to do with life or, briefly, the *life sciences*, systematics probably most nearly retains the approach and interests of the earlier natural historians. It is, of course, part of the broader science or superscience of *biology*.

Biology, literally "the study of life," should logically include any study of living (or formerly living) things. In usual practice it does not. Several sciences just as much concerned with living things are not generally considered parts of biology and have not been so considered in this book. They have become so complex in themselves and have developed such different materials, methods, and aims that they are most conveniently, if not logically, excluded from the general study of life. Among the more important of these life sciences apart from biology are *agriculture*,

---

[1] The reconstructed phylogenies in books are theoretical and may possibly be proved wrong by later discoveries, but phylogeny as it actually occurred by descent from parent to offspring was real and factual.

the study of cultivated plants and domesticated animals; *medicine*, the study of disturbances of functions and their correction; *anthropology*, the study of man; *psychology*, the study of behavior; and *sociology*, the study of human communities.

It is of course impossible to draw a sharp line between biology and the other life sciences. General biology is a necessary basis for the understanding not only of the various sciences, such as systematics, included in biology itself, but also of all the other life sciences. There is overlap all along the line. The student of animal behavior is, as we have noted (p. 229), simultaneously biologist and psychologist. Bacteriology, physiology, and anatomy, among other subjects, belong equally to biology and to medicine. Subdivision is necessary, but it must be remembered that any subdivision of the whole subject "natural history" or "science" or, grandly, "knowledge" is arbitrary.

The Organism in Its Environment

The great explorations of the fifteenth, sixteenth, and seventeenth centuries were seldom carried out by scientists. The explorers sought booty, empire, trade, and also, to be sure, geographic information but with aims seldom directly scientific. They incidentally revealed new worlds for science, as well, and we have seen that they stimulated the study of natural history. Later on, expeditions were sent out with the primary purpose of obtaining scientific data. Some scientific exploration was done in the eighteenth century or even earlier, and innumerable expeditions are now sent out as a matter of routine by museums and other scientific institutions. The golden age of scientific exploration was, however, the nineteenth century.

Many of the great naturalists of the nineteenth century served an apprenticeship in science on long voyages, and many based their major contributions on that experience. Darwin (1809-1882) went around the world on the *Beagle* as a young man and made observations that were to lead to his theory of evolution. T. H. Huxley (1825-1895), champion of Darwin and a great biologist in his own right, cruised on the *Rattlesnake*.

Many oceanographic expeditions studied marine life, and brought back specimens for the work of innumerable specialists. The British *Challenger* expedition (1872-1876) is among the most famous.

As a result of expeditions and of individual travels by naturalists, organisms were being studied more intensively and over wider areas in the field, out where they live all over the earth. Attention was turning increasingly not only to the classification of animals and their anatomy and physiology but also to their distribution and to their lives in their natural environments. Thus from the broad stream of natural history two more special sciences came to be distinguished: *biogeography* and *ecology*.

BIOGEOGRAPHY

Some ideas about the distribution of plants and animals date back to antiquity, indeed to prehistory. The compendious natural histories of the seventeenth and later centuries customarily designated the habitat of each organism described. Such designation has always been an accepted and necessary part of systematics. The clear development of a scientific biogeography, involving enlightening generalization and explanatory theory as well as flat descriptive statement, was nevertheless a rather late development in biology.

The earlier status of attempts at scientific biogeography is amusingly illustrated by the polemic between the eminent French naturalist Buffon and the eminent American president and amateur naturalist Jefferson. Buffon stated that American animals are smaller than their European relatives because the climate is wetter. Jefferson reasonably pointed out, with evidence, first, that American animals are not smaller and, second, that the American climate is not wetter. There that particular hypothesis rests up to now.

Humboldt (1769-1859) spent five years in South America in his thirties and then returned to Germany to make fundamental contributions not only to biology but also to geology and meteorology. When he died he was well along with a work that was, quite simply, to include everything known about the universe, scientific, historical, and artistic! Before that, he produced a study of the geography of plants that was the modern starting point for both biogeography and ecology.

The English naturalist Wallace (1823-1913) was another of the great field biologists, with a year in Brazil and several in the East Indies. He is most famous because he worked out the theory of natural selection independently of Darwin and, thanks to Darwin's integrity, published it at the same time. His greatest contribution, however, was a book on the geographical distribution of animals (1876) in which he firmly established biogeography as a science. In fact, very little of fundamental importance has been since added to his main subject, the present regional distribution of land birds and mammals.

Wallace saw and stressed the fact that regional distributions must be explained on a historical basis (p. 711). He tried to develop historical principles in the light of knowledge of his day, but the knowledge was insufficient for more than a bare start. Historical biogeography must necessarily rest on a synthesis of information from fossils and from living organisms. The most fundamental contribution in this respect was probably that by the American paleontologist W. D. Matthew (1871-1930). In 1915 he published an unpretentious paper on the subject which has stimulated and oriented most of the progress made since then.

Today many biologists, especially ecologists, systematists, and paleontologists, are actively working on problems of biogeography, but there are few biogeographers primarily as such. The division of the subject into ecological and historical aspects has been mentioned (p. 694). Ecological marine biogeography has lagged behind and is one of the promising fields for future research.

ECOLOGY

Humboldt's pioneering work was, in modern terms, as much ecological as biogeographical. Much earlier natural history presaged the science of ecology, and so did much of the biogeographic and marine biological work that grew out of it in the nineteenth century. It was not, however, until the last quarter of that century that more explicitly ecological concepts came to the fore and that a distinct science of ecology began to develop. The first general works specifically devoted to this subject were by the Danish biologist Warming (1841-1924) in 1895 and the Swiss Schimper (1856-1901) in 1898. Both were botanists writing on plant ecology.

Main themes of animal ecology also emerged from the earlier studies of less specialized naturalists. Such themes are prominent in Darwin's works. Animal ecology, as such, nevertheless was slow to develop, slower than plant ecology. That side of the science is mainly a product of the twentieth century, and some of its pioneers are still working.

At present ecology is among the most active and most fascinating of the biological sciences. It seems that a really general ecology is still in the formative stage, and here is one of the enticing fronts of advancing knowledge. Most field studies of living organisms now have an ecological orientation. Basic attitudes and principles of ecology have also permeated most of the biological sciences, and some other sciences as well. Considerable sections of this book have been devoted to exposition of those principles, and we now need only recall a few of the most essential of them: the universality and nature of adaptation; the concept of populations as dynamic groups (remember, too, what a revolution this concept has worked in systematics and genetics as well as in ecology proper); the principle that all organisms are parts of multispecific communities, which are organized and interacting units.

Related to these ecological principles is the broader biological principle of levels of organization: molecular, cellular, individual, population (or intraspecific society), and community (or interspecific aggregation), each level including and to some extent analogous with all lower levels but each with phenomena and principles peculiar to it. Ecology also illustrates the broad contacts of biology with other sciences, in this case particularly with sociology.

The Organism in the Laboratory

What may still be called the naturalist's approach to biology is particularly evident in the biological sciences whose rise has now been briefly scanned: systematics, biogeography, and ecology. There were other approaches, even in the earliest formative times for science. One of these was what we would now call the laboratory approach. Organisms were dissected or experiments were made with them. The distinction is far from sharp; all biological sciences are so interlocked and overlapping that none can be absolutely distinguished from the others. Experiments are an integral part of ecology, for instance, and animal behavior is frequently studied outside the laboratory. Nevertheless, in origin and in dominant techniques ecology has been a field science, and animal behavior a laboratory science.

HUMAN AND COMPARATIVE ANATOMY

The study of human anatomy is and has always been more an adjunct to medicine than a part of biology in the usual sense, but of course the connection between medicine and biology is intimate, and the separation more or less arbitrary. In ancient and medieval times dissection of human cadavers was generally considered impious and was often illegal. Such anatomical knowledge as existed came mostly from dissection of monkeys, pigs, and a few other animals. Yet that dissection was done as an adjunct to human medicine. Doctors who would have been shocked by any suggestion of evolutionary relationships between men and monkeys nevertheless treated their patients as if they were monkeys! In the fourteenth century dissection of humans was legally authorized in Bologna, then one of the few world centers of learning. Slowly through the next two or three centuries dissection became a recognized part of the medical curriculum.[2]

The modern study of human anatomy dates from 1543, as nearly as a fixed date can be assigned. That year Vesalius (1514-1564) published a book based on his own dissections and describing objectively what he had seen in the human body. The book was not popular at the time, because most doctors still preferred the confused and often absurd anatomical notions inherited from the Romans (especially Galen, about 130-200 A.D.). Nevertheless Vesalius' work did slowly persuade anatomists that the way to learn about the human body was to look at it, rather than read Galen—just as the naturalists were beginning to look at nature instead of reading Aristotle.

More definitely biological is the study of *comparative anatomy*. The dissection of a pig in order to find out what the human body is like was, in a sense, comparative anatomy—except that comparison was rarely made. By the late sixteenth century followers of Vesalius were extending their observations to various animals and actually making comparisons. As early as 1555 the French zoologist Belon (1517-1564) [3] pointed out correspondences—what we would call "homologies"—between the bones of a bird and of a man.

Human anatomy as usually studied has always been purely descriptive, and so has been much comparative anatomy. To attain stature as a true science, interpretive principle and explanatory theory must be added. There was already a hint of these in Belon, but a truly theoretical comparative anatomy was first consistently developed by Goethe (1749-1832), Oken (1779-1851), and others in their period. Its theoretical basis was typological, embodying the principle of the archetype (see p. 462). Most modern biologists reject that principle, and yet it laid a firm basis for the evolutionary comparative anatomy that was to follow. It was the English zoologist Richard Owen (1804-1892) who anachronistically carried typological (but not evolutionary) anatomy to its highest point, although he lived well into the Darwinian period.

Since 1859 (the date of publication of *The Origin of Species*) the theoretical basis of comparative anatomy has become evolutionary. Resemblances and differences are traced in terms of ancestry and changing adaptation. The fundamental principle of homology,

2 Even so, dissection was rarely performed either by students or professors. A flunky did the dirty work while, from his podium, the professor read to the students what Galen had written about the various organs more than a thousand years earlier.

3 You have perhaps noticed that most great biologists had longer lives than was usual in their times. Belon's 47 years of life were not short for the sixteenth century, but they would have been longer if he had not been murdered. Most biologists, even the explorers, have died in bed.

intuitively recognized by Belon and other pre-evolutionary biologists, has become evolutionary. No one landmark stands out clearly in this general change, but perhaps the work of Wiedersheim (1848-1923) is as good an example as any. His great handbook of comparative vertebrate anatomy is a painstaking compilation of facts presented in the new spirit.

Human anatomy and comparative anatomy today are generally taught as descriptive subjects technologically prerequisite for a medical career. As such they have little scientific biological interest. Interpretive, evolutionary comparative anatomy has passed largely into the hands of the paleontologists, among whom it continues to be a lively and progressive subject for research. Another sort of interpretive anatomy is functional, and that too is lively and perhaps undergoing a renaissance. It connects anatomy with physiology, from which, indeed, anatomy has never been and could not be wholly divorced.

PHYSIOLOGY

Up until the seventeenth century physiology, philosophy, and theology assigned the greatest importance to the circulatory system, without any idea that it is a circulatory system. The Greeks thought that the arteries contained air. Galen corrected that, but taught that blood ebbs and flows in the veins. Centuries later it was still believed that the heart, liver, and blood were the seats and nutrients of the soul and of the various "spirits" of the body. Among the theologians who made mystical studies of the circulatory system was Servetus (1511-1553), whose views on this and other subjects so annoyed the Calvinists that he was burned at the stake.

It was Harvey (1578-1657) who demonstrated in a small work published in 1628 that the blood does circulate and that its movement is purely mechanical, produced by the heart, which is simply a pump. The discovery was so revolutionary in bringing the very seat of the soul into the realm of material science that the origin of scientific biology is commonly dated from 1628. Yet Harvey never freed himself from other mistakes of the Aristotelian system and never

fully envisioned a purely scientific approach to biology. That the old concepts died hard is exemplified by the fact that Swedenborg (1688-1772) made really important advances in physiology, but did so in terms of a mystical theology so that he is remembered now as a theologian rather than a physiologist.

In the meantime workers who were primarily anatomists and physicians made great strides toward a purely naturalistic physiology. It can, however, hardly be said that a physiology entirely scientific, as we now consider science, was achieved until the nineteenth century. Here the name of Bernard (1813-1878) stands out. In a series of brilliantly planned and executed experiments he demonstrated most of the basic features of animal metabolism and showed how its processes tend to maintain equilibrium in a constantly changing system (p. 159).

Since Bernard fundamental progress has been made in physiology, for the most part along special lines and often in relationship to other branches of the life sciences. *General* or *cellular physiology* has developed, a study not of organ systems in the complex vertebrate body but of physical and chemical conditions and events within single cells and their protoplasm. That is, indeed, in the last analysis the basis of functioning of the organ systems as well. It leads in turn to the sciences of *biophysics* and *biochemistry*, so characteristic of present-day biology. Research in *medical physiology*, including such topics as the action of endocrines and of drugs, continues to be extremely active and also to follow, in part, biochemical lines. *Sensory and nerve physiology* is basic to the study of behavior and through the latter to psychology. This general field of biological study deserves brief separate notice.

NERVE AND SENSORY PHYSIOLOGY

The early physiological anatomists were frequently concerned with the nervous system. That was the main physiological preoccupation of Swedenborg, who localized the activities of the "soul" (consciousness and related phenomena) in the cerebral cortex and believed that various parts of the cortex were connected by nerves to various other parts of the body. A contemporaneous universal genius, Haller (1708-1777), studied the "irritability" and "sensibility" of tissues and organs and connected these phenomena with the nervous system. The works of Swedenborg and Haller now seem primitive in many respects, but between them they pointed the way to most of the fundamentals of nerve and sensory physiology.

It is in this sphere that the long and still not entirely conclusive philosophical struggle between the vitalists and the materialists in biology comes especially to the fore. The vitalists maintain that life is or involves something nonmaterial, forever outside possible observation or scientific explanation. The materialists believe that the phenomena peculiar to living things arise from the nature and complexity of their organization and do not involve either materials or processes absent in the nonliving world. One of the important lessons of the history of science is that the materialistic approach is a *necessary* part of scientific method. Most vitalists accept that as an essential restriction in research, but they insist that when all the resources of science have been exhausted there still will remain a vital element in life beyond the reach of scientific method.

It is impossible, at least at present, to *prove* either the vitalist or the materialist position. It is, nevertheless, a fact that a main trend in the history of biology has been that more and more phenomena earlier ascribed to the mysterious "vital force" have been explained by purely material processes. The crucial and as yet not completely conclusive test comes in dealing with the incomparably complex phenomena of the nervous system, with its mysteries of sensation, perception, consciousness, and mind.

The point is well illustrated by two of the founders of modern nerve physiology. J. P. Müller (1801-1858) was one of the last investigators who successfully ranged over almost the whole field of biology. He studied, among many things, the actions of sensory and motor nerves in animals. In his own work and that of his many famous students he laid a firm foundation for modern nerve physiology, even though his own philosophical conclusions were vitalistic. In 1840 Müller assigned to one of his students, Du Bois-

Reymond (1818-1896), the study of electrical phenomena in nerves and muscles. Du Bois-Reymond soon saw that these material phenomena provide a possible explanation, at least, for the supposedly vitalistic operation of the nervous system. He refuted the whole vitalistic philosophy in a way thoroughly convincing to most, but not all, later biologists.

Most subsequent work on nerve physiology, still a highly active field, has followed and expanded the sort of experimental approach taken by Müller and Du Bois-Reymond. Even more important, they were pioneers in the application of the physical to the biological sciences, a movement that is now at a most active and productive phase.[4]

ANIMAL BEHAVIOR

Approaching a related field from a different direction, the work of nineteenth-century and earlier naturalists abounds in descriptions of animal behavior. With few exceptions the observations were anecdotal, and their interpretation was anthropomorphic (see p. 230). They smacked as much of folklore as of science. Nevertheless there were exceptions, and in this connection the work of Fabre (1823-1915) is outstanding. Although he is sometimes dismissed as a "mere" popularizer (his name does not even appear in some voluminous histories of biology), he made extensive, careful, firsthand observations on insect behavior. Furthermore, he reported the observations accurately and objectively, and he strenuously rejected anthropomorphic interpretations.[5]

4 The importance of Müller and more especially of Du Bois-Reymond in the history of biology has generally been underestimated. Du Bois-Reymond is barely mentioned in some books on the subject, probably because his original research was confined to a single and narrow field. Nevertheless, his methods and views mark a turning point in biology. It is worth noting that he did not subscribe to the extreme mechanism that became popular among nineteenth-century scientists, the view that all the phenomena of the universe are in principle mechanical and completely predictable. He held that, although the phenomena of life are nonvitalistic and can be reduced to those of the physical sciences, the basic concepts of the physical sciences are themselves abstractions not open to ultimate explanation. That reservation makes his work seem all the more modern.
5 In one of the fascinating passages of his "Entomological Memoirs" he gave Erasmus Darwin (Charles' grandfather) a lambasting for daring to suggest that wasps reason.

We have earlier (p. 230) noted the influence of Lloyd Morgan (1852-1936) and Jacques Loeb (1859-1924) on the rise of animal behavior as a distinct science. Its growth was marked by the introduction of controlled experimental methods and by the correlation of behavior with nerve physiology. Here the work of Pavlov (1849-1936) is also of major historical importance. Its scope and applicability are decidedly limited in the field of animal behavior as a whole (see p. 245), but his work marked and accelerated the rise of careful experimentation and physiological interpretation.

The ramifications of the science of animal behavior into other life sciences are many and crucial. Relationships with anatomy and physiology are obviously particularly intimate. The ecology of animals cannot be disentangled from their behavior. Comparative psychology is simply animal behavior as studied by psychologists. Experimental psychology is largely concerned with the physiological basis of animal behavior, especially of the species *Homo sapiens* and *Rattus rattus*. All such studies are now very active, and we seem to be on the threshold of developing a more meaningful, evolutionary science of comparative behavior.

Within the Organism

SCIENCE AND TECHNIQUE

The history of a science is greatly influenced by the development of new instruments and techniques. Major advances in science often depend on technological improvements: the invention of the telescope in astronomy, the invention of air pumps in the physics of an earlier day or of particle accelerators in our own time, the manufacture of delicate scales in chemistry, and many others. This aspect of history is important, but it can be overemphasized. Scientific advances do not necessarily demand new apparatus, nor does technological progress inevitably advance science. It is noteworthy that recognition of evolution, the most revolutionary single event in the history of biology, involved no instrumentation and no techniques that had not been used for centuries. It is a grave and fairly common mistake to confuse gadgetry with science.

The biological sciences we have so far considered started out as naked-eye sciences and are so to a large extent even today. It is true that elaborate apparatus is now sometimes used in them in physiological and behavioral experiments, for example, but much of their content is accessible to anyone with his unaided senses, his hands, and such simple instruments as have been available since early civilizations: a few knives, dishes, and the like. We now turn to several biological sciences that have more decisively depended on special apparatus and advanced laboratory techniques. We can more definitely say that progress in them would not have gotten beyond a primitive level if it had not been accompanied by invention.

In the first rank among inventions important in the history of biology are instruments for enlarging visible things: simple lenses, then compound microscopes of increasing complexity in structure and operation, and finally the electron microscope. They have other uses as well, but their greatest impact in biology has come from seeing more deeply into the fine structure within the organism. Then there has been increasing application to biology of apparatus, methods, and concepts primarily developed in the sciences of physics and chemistry. This is a motley group, from the simplest application of pressure or of a chemical reagent to an organism on to the use of electrophoresis, tracer isotopes, and many other methods in modern biology. With these methods, too, one of the most important of their many results is the ability to get down farther and farther into the organism, down to the processes that go on at the molecular level.

MICROORGANISMS

In the seventeenth century simple lenses with great magnifying power (superior to the power of the early compound microscopes) began to be constructed. Biologists soon applied the lenses to everything they could think of. Among the most enthusiastic were two Dutch naturalists, Swammerdam (1637-1680), who first saw red blood corpuscles and made anatomical studies of small insects, and Leeuwenhoek (1632-1723), who first saw bacteria, other protists, and sperms. Their observations and those of other early enthusiasts were unsystematic but so wide-ranging that most of what can be seen under moderate magnifications had been described well before the nineteenth century.

The most stunning of the early discoveries under the microscope was the whole world of otherwise invisible microorganisms, mostly protists, the existence of which had hardly been suspected. It was found, too, that many visible and known organisms had unsuspected microscopic phases in their life cycles, such as spores or small eggs. These discoveries had a bearing on the then generally accepted doctrine of spontaneous generation. We have already mentioned the parts played at an early date by Redi (1621-1697) and much later by Pasteur (1822-1895) in disproving that doctrine.

Even before microorganisms had been seen it had been speculated that infection was caused by invisible "seeds of disease." With increased acquaintance with bacteria and other protists, the speculation became a conviction. Koch (1843-1910) was among those who demonstrated beyond question that some, at least, of the infectious diseases are caused by "germs." Koch also invented a technique for obtaining and growing cultures, as they are called, of microorganisms in the laboratory. That invention, extremely simple once it was thought of, made possible the science of *bacteriology*, which is fundamental to modern medicine. More broadly, with modifications and additions Koch's technique has made possible physiological and other experiments on all kinds of living microorganisms and has been instrumental in the rise of the more strictly biological science of *microbiology*. In this one case a whole science has been borne of a technique!

Just to show how broadly such inventions can ramify, the techniques of culturing microorganisms are now extensively used in population and physiological genetics and also in the commercial growing of orchids (which have microscopic seeds) for corsages.

CELLS AND TISSUES

The microscope made it possible to carry anatomy to greater depths, to study not only the organs and tissues visible to the naked eye but also their microscopic make-up. Here, too, a great surprise lay in wait, for it soon appeared that skin, muscles, and so on are not continuous structures but are made up of minute, discrete units, the cells.

Cells, at first the hollow spaces among the walls of dead plant tissues (Hooke, 1635-1703) and later living protoplasmic cells, were among the first things seen by the earliest microscopists. Tissues in the modern sense, as distinct from the organs made up of various tissues, were first clearly described and named at the end of the eighteenth century by Bichat (1771-1802). It took longer to bring the two observations together and to realize that tissues are made up of cells. Bichat failed to do so because from some quirk of human nature he did not take microscopic observations seriously.[6]

The idea that all tissues develop from and are composed of cells and cell secretions was first clearly expressed by Schwann (1810-1882). Although Schwann, himself, did not successfully carry the idea much further, that is the basis for one of the most important of all biological principles: the fundamental similarity of developmental units and of intracellular processes in all living organisms. The modern concept of protoplasm as the essential medium of life in the cell and of the cell as the structural unit of life was essentially reached in the 1860's by Schultze (1825-1874). By 1858 Virchow realized (p. 39) that all cells are the offspring of other cells, and paved the way for union of the cell theory with that of evolution.

The study of tissues, frequently from the medical point of view, has become the science of *histology*. The study of cells is *cytology*. The discovery that heredity is carried and development controlled (for the most part, at least) by structures that can be made visible within the cells has greatly stimulated twentieth-century research in cytology. This field

6 Bichat was one of the shortest-lived of great biologists, and a genius of his caliber might well have taken the next step if he had lived longer.

is sometimes now considered a separate science, *cytogenetics.*

EMBRYOLOGY

The development of some plants and animals from seeds and eggs was known to primitive man and was considered by philosophers and scientists from the Greeks on. The part of this process most easily visible to the naked eye is, however, simple growth. The far more fundamental processes of differentiation were the subject of speculation by Aristotle and many later students, but a scientific approach to them was hardly possible until the invention of the microscope.

Swammerdam (p. 258) and other early microscopists started embryology off on a false track and began a long controversy that seems, in retrospect, to have been futile and unnecessary. It is, however, a futile thing in itself to apply that adjective to mistakes that were inevitable in the historical setting of their own times. Such faltering has occurred in all of man's intellectual pursuits, not to mention his social or political ones. Other important examples in biology are: the doctrine of special creation; belief in spontaneous generation; and the theory of the inheritance of acquired characteristics.

The false track in embryology was *preformation,* the theory that the seed or sperm contains a miniature of the adult and all its organs so that embryological development is considered as nothing but growth (p. 259). The preformationists did not boggle at the idea that Adam's body contained in miniature the bodies of all the humans that ever have lived or ever will live on earth. They produced drawings of human sperm with a "homunculus," a little man, crouching inside.

There were opponents of preformation from the start, but before the nineteenth century most of them were, in their own ways, equally wide of the mark. Modern embryology may be said to take form in the work of Von Baer (1792-1876). He discovered the microscopic mammalian egg and traced it through fertilization to final form. He showed that differentiation is gradual and occurs in the course of repeated cellular division. He systematized the principle of embryonic cell layers (which had been seen before). He also made comparative studies, showed the value of embryology in the study of homologies and relationships among mammals, and noted that the embryos of different vertebrates resemble each other more than do the adults.

Since Von Baer an enormous amount of descriptive work on embryology has been done. Von Baer's theoretical interpretations have in large part stood up and have been put on an evolutionary basis. Haeckel's reinterpretation in evolutionary terms of "recapitulation" (p. 352) went too far and has required modification, returning actually more nearly to Von Baer's original statements. A brilliant statement of evolutionary comparative embryology was produced by Balfour (1851-1882) as a young man (an accident ended his life in its prime).

In the present century embryology has become almost entirely experimental and is mainly focused on seeking biochemical and biophysical explanations for organization and differentiation in the developing individual. Much progress has been made, but the connection between the genetic system of the zygote and the structure of the developed organism is still full of profound mysteries. Here are some of the most important unsolved problems of biology.

BIOCHEMISTRY AND BIOPHYSICS

The modern sciences of biochemistry and biophysics have developed from the field of physiology in general and are hardly distinguishable from some phases of physiology. The tendency now is for physiology to be restricted to studies with a more directly biological approach, in terms of organs and organisms. Biochemistry and biophysics study related phenomena less in terms of the organism than in terms of specific chemical reactions and physical changes. The physiologist may study chemical input and output in the anatomical system of a leaf or the speed, force, and continuity of contraction in a given muscle. The biochemist may study the sequence of special reactions involved in photosynthesis, wherever that occurs, and the biophysicist may concern himself with internal changes of state in muscle fibers generally. The instrumentation of biochemistry and biophysics is particularly elaborate and is adapted, for the most part, from chemistry and physics.

A leader in the application of physical and chemical methods to physiology was J. P. Müller (1801-1858), who has already been mentioned. Besides his own important work, he turned into these fields a host of his students, including Schwann and Du Bois-Reymond, also previously mentioned, as well as Helmholtz and other eminent biologists. Helmholtz (1821-1894) was a surgeon who did important work in both pure physics and pure biology and, along with Du Bois-Reymond, was a pioneer in combining the two. He was ingenious in devising apparatus and he used physical methods in the study of vision and hearing.

Liebig (1803-1873) was at first a pure chemist and then turned to the chemical aspects of physiology. Through his writing and teaching he led a group of nineteenth-century biochemists who attacked, and in their major aspects solved, such basic problems as the oxygen, carbon, and nitrogen cycles in plants and animals and the chemistry of digestion. Among the numerous later biologists who ushered in the modern science of biochemistry Emil Fischer (1852-1919) may be mentioned. With new reagents and methods, he made great strides in deciphering the molecular structure of complex organic compounds, still an active field of research.

Great stress on biochemistry and to only slightly less extent on biophysics is characteristic of biology at the present time. These are probably now the most intensely cultivated and rapidly advancing of the biological sciences. Although other fields are not neglected, some biologists feel that these may even be unduly stressed at present. After all, understanding of the *organism* as such is the primary object of the biological sciences; many of the answers are within the scope of biochemistry or biophysics—but many are not!

Organisms Through Time

Naturalists at first had a nearly static view of nature. They studied it as it is, and few of them saw any reason to envision any radical changes in the past or future. In fact, until well into the nineteenth century many biolo-gists accepted the then current theological opinion that the world is less than 6000 years old, a time so short as practically to exclude a historical view of nature. All the biological sciences reviewed up to this point were originally unconcerned with periods of time longer than the life cycles of individual organisms. Some of them have since been revolutionized by the introduction of historical concepts, notably systematics, biogeography, ecology, and comparative anatomy, and all have been influenced by those concepts, but that was not and in some instances still is not their primary concern.

The principal biological sciences that are necessarily, inherently concerned with changes through time longer than a generation are paleontology and genetics.

PALEONTOLOGY

Paleontology is one of the sciences that belongs equally to the physical and the biological sciences. It is as much a part of geology as it is of biology, just as biochemistry is as much chemistry as biology. Fossils, the principal objects of paleontological study, occur in sedimentary rocks, the study of which is part of the science of geology. Many of the principles basic for paleontology are more geological than biological.

Fossils were known to the ancient philosophers, some of whom recognized them as the remains of ancient organisms. Later that correct opinion was often discarded, and it was not until around the beginning of the nineteenth century that the basic principles necessary for a science of paleontology were generally accepted. The most essential of these principles are: fossils are traces of once living organisms and can be studied and classified as such; most of them belong to species and larger groups no longer living; they occur in a definite historical sequence of extinct floras and faunas, living organisms being simply the latest members of that sequence.

The final essential step for the foundation of the science of paleontology was recognition of rock sequences containing characteristic sequences of extinct organisms. As usual, many students contributed to that result and several reached it at about the same time, but among them the English professional civil engineer and amateur geologist W. Smith (1769-1839) is worthy of special mention.

It was the French zoologist Cuvier (1769-1832), as much as any one man, who made paleontology a distinct biological science. He published systematic descriptions of many extinct species and recognized major features of their sequence, although necessarily in a crude and incomplete way. His accomplishment was brilliant, but it must be added that there were then in geology and paleontology two of the important wrong turns that checker the history of science (see p. 813), and Cuvier took them both. He believed in catastrophism rather than uniformitarianism (see p. 742) and in special creation rather than evolution. So great was Cuvier's authority that most paleontologists followed his false lead. Their progress was greatly impeded by the fact that they had to be slowly persuaded to uniformitarianism by the geologists and to evolution by the biologists, although, now that they have been persuaded, it is obvious that their science pre-eminently reflects both principles. Uniformitarianism was established especially by the British geologists Hutton (1726-1797) and Lyell (1797-1875). Some remarks on the rise of evolution are made later in this chapter.

Modern paleontology, uniformitarian and evolutionary, was a product of the late nineteenth century. The paleobotanists, micropaleontologists (students of microscopic fossils, mostly protists), and invertebrate paleontologists have contributed greatly. The more biological approach and integration with other biological sciences have, however, been due in greater measure to the vertebrate paleontologists. Among the most important figures in this respect are the Russian Kovalevsky [7] (1842-1883) and the Americans Cope (1840-1897) and Osborn (1857-1935).

The discovery of new species of fossils continues today at an accelerated pace, and descriptive, systematic paleontology has never been more active. Most significant in paleontology at present, however, is a broadening of the base and aims of the science. Its data, and also its methods, are being

[7] As with many Russian names, this one has been transliterated into our alphabet in several different ways.

combined with those of all the other biological sciences to produce a historical view of all aspects of biology. Paleontology, strictly speaking, is the principal parent of what seems to be emerging as a new biological science, *historical biology*.

GENETICS

Genetics was not, in origin, historical to the same extent or in the same sense as paleontology. Some aspects of it have, however, become so, and genetics has always and necessarily been concerned with time, with changes through generations and less with events in single life cycles.

Notions of heredity, some correct and some fantastic (p. 278), have doubtless been current since man became articulate. As a distinct science worthy of the name, however, genetics is the youngest of all the main biological sciences. Attempts to study heredity before 1900 were marked by a whole series of wrong turnings. You are already familiar with some of these: inheritance by blood and the more sophisticated but equally wrong idea of inheritance by the assemblage of particles from all over the body; blending inheritance; the inheritance (as such) of acquired characters. Variations of these incorrect theories dominated biological thought about heredity right up until the twentieth century.

You are also familiar (from Chapter 12) with the importance of the methods and results of Mendel (1822-1884) and with their rediscovery by De Vries (1848-1935) and others. The elaboration of formal or, strictly speaking, Mendelian genetics was largely due to Morgan (1867-1945) and his students and followers. That branch of genetics is concerned principally with tracing the heredity of single, readily separable gene mutations, the recombinations of such mutations, and their association and sequence in the chromosomes.

Such work is still basic for genetics, but at present the main interests of geneticists have followed other lines of what has become a vast and increasingly ramifying science. Interactions between genes and effects of the whole genetic apparatus have assumed greater importance than the study of single genes. Joint study of chromosomes and genes—

cytogenetics—has become a subscience of its own, with essential contributions to systematics and other biological sciences. Direct studies of the physiological effects of genes are made with the mold *Neurospora* (p. 325) and an increasing number of other organisms. The nature and action of genes and chromosomes are being intensively investigated with biochemical and biophysical methods. There is increasing interest in extranuclear inheritance, through the cytoplasm or particles in it, and its relationship to the primary, chromosomal genetical mechanism. The relationship between the genetical apparatus and differentiation of the developing organism is a vital and difficult subject, as was mentioned in discussing embryology.

Among all these divergent recent developments of genetics, few have had greater interest or wider implications than *population genetics*. Random and selective changes in the genetic composition of populations, isolating mechanisms, breeding patterns, and many other population phenomena are studied in the field, in the laboratory, and by mathematical models. The greatest importance of these studies is their bearing on the universal and intricate fact of evolution.

EVOLUTION

We have been following the subdivision of biology into the various biological sciences in the framework of the history of the subject. Evolution is not a science, nor is it a discovery or a principle that has emerged from one of the biological sciences. It is a fact that is true of the subject matter of all of biology in general, and of all of the life sciences. Also, our knowledge and theories of how it operates do not come from any one of the life sciences but in varying degrees from all of them. Thus evolution requires separate mention here, and, since it is the most pervasive of all the principles you have learned about life, this final mention of it may fittingly close your introduction to biology.

The ancients and the theological philosophers who were the principal persons to carry Western intellectual thought up to the dawning of the scientific age had little or no inkling of evolution in the modern sense. They saw a certain unity in nature; they spoke of affinities or relationships among organisms; and they discerned a (highly irregular and imperfect) sequence of living things, the "ladder of life" (p. 539). It is easy to read our evolutionary interpretation into what they said, and what they said was capable of logical development into evolutionary theory. But they never clearly said and evidently did not believe that the unity, affinities, and sequence of living things are material facts, due to modifications of physical descent, and not only philosophical or metaphysical ideas.

The concept of evolution as a material fact of life began to appear, at first hesitantly and vaguely, when biology was just beginning to be a science, back in the sixteenth and seventeenth centuries. By the end of the eighteenth century evolution was a definitely stated and widely known concept, but a concept that was rejected by the majority of the biologists of that period. Its eventual acceptance depended in part on further accumulation of facts that finally could not reasonably be interpreted in any other way.

General acceptance also awaited the development of underlying and still more basic principles about nature. There had to be recognition that the age of the earth is to be counted not in thousands of years but in millions, at least. There also had to be a choice between catastrophism and uniformitarianism, for although catastrophism does not logically exclude evolution it produced a cast of mind far less favorable to the idea of evolution than did uniformitarianism. Those preliminaries for acceptance of evolution were gifts from geology to biology. It is highly significant that Darwin was strongly influenced by Lyell, who assigned great antiquity to the earth and who figured largely in the triumph of uniformitarianism.

On the biological side, acceptance of evolution awaited the slowly growing conviction that there are similarities throughout the whole realm of life and that they have a physical and not only a metaphysical basis. The cell theory was developing along with the concept of evolution, and it was no coincidence that the universality of protoplasm and of evolution reached full recognition at almost the same time. Finally, acceptance of evolution had to await proposal of some plausible theory as to how it operates.

He had many more hesitant and speculative predecessors, but the French zoologist Lamarck (1744-1829) was the first really thoroughgoing evolutionist. He proclaimed that all species are the related products of evolution, and he proposed an explanatory theory that was plausible, in the state of biology at the time, even though we now consider it incorrect. He believed that organisms had followed a pattern of increasing perfection (the old "ladder of nature") and had also become divergent from that pattern through local adaptation. Adaptation was claimed to be the cumulative, inherited effect of responses to environmental stimuli.

After Lamarck evolutionary views were inceasingly held by other biologists, but, as everyone knows, their final acceptance came after the publication in 1859 of *The Origin of Species* by Darwin. Darwin, a great and wide-ranging naturalist even aside from his work on evolution, marshaled evidence from the whole field of the biology of his day. He demonstrated that the present state of the living world can be reasonably explained only as the result of evolution. As the major, but in his opinion not the only, cause of evolution he proposed natural selection. Darwin's explanation of evolution, truly brilliant as far as it went, was inevitably incomplete, principally because so little was then known about heredity.

After Darwin there was long dispute between the adherents of natural selection and those, called neo-Lamarckians, who believed in more direct environmental influences on heredity. The dispute was settled as far as most biologists are concerned by the study of genetics, especially population genetics, in the twentieth century. Genetics has rehabilitated Darwin's natural selection as the cause of adaptation, giving it a broader, somewhat different, but not contradictory meaning. Genetics has also supplied the principal elements lacking in Darwin's own theory.

We do not need to discuss how the modern theory of evolution has permeated all the biological sciences, nor how all of them in synthesis have supported the truth of evolution and deepened our knowledge of its processes.

This whole book is a demonstration of those results.

A textbook of biology might close with a statement of the importance and fascination of biology and of how it enriches your understanding of life. For this, too, we let the whole book speak. If we have not conveyed this message by now, no final word will do it.

Chapter Summary

The long search for the "secrets of life": the work of many; science as a historical growth of ideas and insights.

Natural history: original broad meaning of term; transition from philosophical, authoritarian, dogmatic approach to the naturalistic attitude: Copernicus and Newton.

Classification and systematics: collections and compendia: Agricola, Gesner, Fuchs; first serious classifications: Cesalpino, Ray, Linnaeus; Buffon and Cuvier; phylogenetic or natural classification as post-Darwinian; the systematic subsciences.

Life sciences and the scope of biology: growth of biology from natural history into many and diverse special sciences.

The organism and its environment: the great naturalistic explorers of the nineteenth century, especially Darwin and Huxley.

Biogeography: Humboldt; Wallace; W. D. Matthew.

Ecology: the pioneers Warming and Schimper; ecology fully developed only in twentieth century.

The organism in the laboratory; the laboratory, as against naturalist's, approach to biology.

Human and comparative anatomy: history of human dissection; Vesalius and the birth of modern anatomy; Belon and the beginnings of comparative anatomy; Goethe, Oken, and Owen; typological anatomy; evolutionary basis to modern comparative anatomy: Wiedersheim.

Physiology: ancient ideas on the workings of the body: Galen and Servetus; Harvey and the beginnings of modern physiology; Claude Bernard; emergence of general and cellular physiology, of biophysics and biochemistry.

Nerve and sensory physiology: Sweden-borg's mystical views; Haller and J. P. Müller and Du Bois-Reymond as co-founders of modern nerve physiology; refutation of vitalism; electrical phenomena of nerves as basis of the nervous system's activity.

Animal behavior: nineteenth-century work anecdotal and anthropomorphic; Fabre as exception; origins of modern work on behavior: Lloyd Morgan and Jacques Loeb; the correlation of behavior and nerve physiology: Pavlov.

Within the organism:

Science and technique: influence of techniques and instruments on advance of science; in biology, the importance of the microscope; and more modern techniques of physics and chemistry.

Microorganisms: influence of microscope; Swammerdam and Leeuwenhoek; the "spontaneous generation" problem: Redi and Pasteur; bacteria and disease: Koch; modern microbiology.

Cells and tissues: impact of microscope again; beginnings of histology: Hooke, Bichat; the cell theory: Schwann, Schultze, Virchow; cytology and cytogenetics.

Embryology: preformationism as a blind alley; the beginnings of modern embryology; Von Baer; Balfour and evolutionary comparative embryology; modern experimental embryology; its relation to genetics.

Biochemistry and biophysics: as derivative studies from physiology; J. P. Müller's students, Du Bois-Reymond, Schwann, and Helmholtz, the latter as student of vision and hearing; Liebig; Fischer; modern biochemistry and biophysics.

Organisms through time:

Paleontology: as both geology and biology; beginnings of the modern science in early nineteenth century; paleontological principles: W. Smith and the sequence of strata; Cuvier's great contributions, and two false steps; Hutton, Lyell, and uniformitarianism; beginnings of vertebrate paleontology: Kovalevsky, Cope, and Osborn; emergence of a historical biology.

Genetics: early ideas; beginnings of modern formal genetics: Mendel, De Vries, Morgan; recent trend to study of gene action; gene and cytoplasm; gene and embryo; population genetics.

Evolution: first glimmerings in the post-Renaissance period; full statement of theory by close of eighteenth century; factors influencing its ultimate scientific acceptance; Lamarck as first thorough-going evolutionist; Darwin and natural selection; post-Darwinian debate between neo-Lamarckians and selectionists; recent influence of genetics, especially in settling the Lamarckian-Darwinian debate in favor of Darwin.

SUGGESTIONS FOR FURTHER READING

PART 1: INTRODUCTION

TEXTBOOKS AND REFERENCE WORKS

Dampier, W. C., *A History of Science*, 3rd Edition, Macmillan, 1942.

Nordenskiöld, E., *The History of Biology*, Tudor, 1928.

Singer, C., *A History of Biology*, Revised Edition, Schuman, 1950.

GENERAL DISCUSSIONS

Bates, M., *The Nature of Natural History*, Scribner's, 1950.

Conant, J. B., *On Understanding Science*, Mentor, 1947.

Yonge, C. M., *A Year on the Great Barrier Reef*, Putnam, 1930.

Yonge, C. M., *The Seas*, Warne, London, 1936.

Young, J. Z., *Doubt and Certainty in Science*, Oxford Univ. Press, 1951.

PART 2: THE UNIT OF LIVING ORGANIZATION

REFERENCE AND ADVANCED TEXTBOOKS

Baldwin, E., *Dynamic Aspects of Biochemistry*, 2nd Edition, Cambridge Univ. Press, 1952.

Cowdry, E. V., *A Textbook of Histology*, 4th Edition, Saunders, 1952.

Greep, R. O. (Ed.), *Histology*, Blakiston, 1954.

Heilbrunn, L. V., *An Outline of General Physiology*, 2nd Edition, Saunders, 1943.

Wilson, E. B., *The Cell in Development and Heredity*, 3rd Edition, Macmillan, reprinted 1947.

INTERMEDIATE TEXTBOOKS

De Robertis, E. D. P., W. W. Nowinski, and F. A. Saez, *General Cytology*, 2nd Edition, Saunders, 1954.

Smith, G. M., E. M. Gilbert, G. S. Bryan, R. I. Evans, and J. T. Stauffer, *A Textbook of General Botany*, 5th Edition, Macmillan, 1953.

Transeau, E. N., H. C. Sampson, and L. H. Tiffany, *Textbook of Botany*, 2nd Edition, Harper, 1952.

GENERAL DISCUSSIONS

Baldwin, E., *An Introduction to Comparative Biochemistry*, 3rd Edition, Cambridge Univ. Press, 1948.

Dixon, M., *Multi-Enzyme Systems*, Cambridge Univ Press, 1951.

Hill, R., *Photosynthesis*, Wiley, 1955.

Tracey, M. V., *Principles of Biochemistry*, Pitman, 1954.

PART 3: MAINTENANCE AND INTEGRATION OF THE ORGANISM

REFERENCE AND ADVANCED TEXTBOOKS

Ariëns Kappers, C. U., *The Evolution of the Nervous System*, Bohn, Haarlem, Holland, 1929.

Best, C. H., and N. B. Taylor, *The Physiological Basis of Medical Practice*, 5th Edition, Williams & Wilkins, 1950.

Prosser, C. L. (Ed.), *Comparative Animal Physiology*, Saunders, 1950.

INTERMEDIATE TEXTBOOKS

Bonner, James, and A. W. Galston, *Principles of Plant Physiology*, Freeman, 1952.

Carlson, A. J., and V. Johnson, *The Machinery of the Body*, 3rd Edition, Univ. of Chicago Press, 1948.

Heilbrunn, L. V., *An Outline of General Physiology*, 2nd Edition, Saunders, 1943.

Romer, A. S., *The Vertebrate Body*, Saunders, 1949.

Scheer, B. T., *Comparative Physiology*, Wiley, 1918.

GENERAL DISCUSSIONS

Adrian, E. D., *The Mechanism of Nervous Action*, Oxford Univ. Press, 1935.

Cannon, W. B., *The Wisdom of the Body*, 2nd Edition, Norton, 1939.

Carter, G. S., *A General Zoology of the Invertebrates*, 3rd Edition, Sidgwick & Jackson, London, 1918.

Cassirer, E., *Essay on Man*, Anchor Books, 1955.

Herrick, C. J., *Neurological Foundations of Animal Behavior*, Holt, 1924.

Jennings, H. S., *The Behavior of the Lower Organisms*, Columbia Univ. Press, 1906.

Leopold, A. C., "Photoperiodism in Plants," *Quart. Rev. Biol.* 26:247-63, 1951.

Lorenz, K. Z., *King Solomon's Ring*, Crowell, 1952.

Smith, H. W., *Studies in the Physiology of the Kidney*, Univ. of Kansas Press, 1939.

Smith, H. W., *From Fish to Philosopher*, Little, Brown, 1953.

Thorpe, W. H., *Learning and Instinct in Animals*, Harvard Univ. Press, 1956.

Tinbergen, N., *Social Behavior in Animals*, Wiley, 1953.

Von Frisch, K., *The Dancing Bees*, Harcourt, Brace, 1955.

Young, J. Z., in *Evolution, Essays Presented to E. S. Goodrich*, Oxford Univ. Press, 1936, pp. 179-204, "The Evolution of the Nervous System and of the Relationship of Organism and Environment."

PART 4: REPRODUCTION: THE CONTINUITY OF LIFE

REFERENCE AND ADVANCED TEXTBOOKS

Stern, C., *Human Genetics*, Freeman, 1950.

Wilson, E. B., *The Cell in Development and Heredity*, 3rd Edition, Macmillan, reprinted 1947.

INTERMEDIATE TEXTBOOKS

Barth, L. G., *Embryology*, Revised Edition, Dryden, 1953.

Huettner, A. F., *Fundamentals of Comparative Embryology of the Vertebrates*, Revised Edition, Macmillan, 1949.

Sinnott, E. W., L. C. Dunn, and Th. Dobzhansky, *Principles of Genetics*, 4th Edition, McGraw-Hill, 1950.

Smith, G. M., E. M. Gilbert, G. S. Bryan, R. I. Evans, and J. F. Stauffer, *A Textbook of General Botany*, 5th Edition, Macmillan, 1953.

Srb, A., and R. D. Owen, *General Genetics*, Freeman, 1955.

Waddington, C. H., *An Introduction to Modern Genetics*, Allen & Unwin, London, 1939.

GENERAL DISCUSSIONS

Berrill, N. J., *Sex and the Nature of Things*, Dodd, Mead, 1953.

Bonner, J. T., *Morphogenesis*, Princeton Univ. Press, 1952.

Clark, W. E. Le G., and P. B. Medawar (Eds.), *Essays on Growth and Form*, Oxford Univ. Press, 1945.

Corner, G. W., *Ourselves Unborn*, Yale Univ. Press, 1944.

Corner, G. W., *The Hormones in Human Reproduction*, Revised Edition, Princeton Univ. Press, 1947.

Darwin, C. R., *The Various Contrivances by Which Orchids Are Fertilized by Insects*, 2nd Edition, Revised, Appleton, 1877.

PART 5: THE MECHANISM OF EVOLUTION

REFERENCE AND ADVANCED TEXTBOOKS

Dobzhansky, Th., *Genetics and the Origin of Species*, 2nd Edition, 1941; and 3rd Edition, 1951, Columbia Univ. Press.

Huxley, J. S., *Evolution: the Modern Synthesis*, Harper, 1943.

Mayr, E., *Systematics and the Origin of Species*, Columbia Univ. Press, 1942.

Simpson, G. G., *The Major Features of Evolution*, Columbia Univ. Press, 1953.

Stebbins, G. L., *Variation and Evolution in Plants*, Columbia Univ. Press, 1950.

INTERMEDIATE TEXTBOOKS

Carter, G. S., *Animal Evolution*, Sidgwick & Jackson, London, 1951.

Dobzhansky, Th., *Evolution, Genetics, and Man*, Wiley, 1955.

Moody, P. A., *Introduction to Evolution*, Harper, 1953.

GENERAL DISCUSSIONS

Darwin, C. R., *The Origin of Species; and the Descent of Man*, Modern Library, 1948.

Lack, D., *Darwin's Finches*, Cambridge Univ. Press, Cambridge, 1947.

Simpson, G. G., *The Meaning of Evolution*, Yale Univ. Press, 1949.

PART 6: THE DIVERSITY OF LIFE

REFERENCE AND ADVANCED TEXTBOOKS

Arnold, C. A., *An Introduction to Paleobotany*, McGraw-Hill, 1947.

Borradaile, L. A., and F. A. Potts, *The Invertebrata*, 2nd Edition, Macmillan, 1935.

Gregory, W. K., *Evolution Emerging*, Vols. 1-2, Macmillan, 1951.

Hyman, L. H., *The Invertebrates*, Vols. 1-3, McGraw-Hill, 1940-51.

Imms, A. D., *A General Textbook of Entomology*, 4th Edition, Methuen, London, 1938.

Mayr, E., E. B. Lindsley, and R. L. Usinger, *Methods and Principles of Systematic Zoology*, McGraw-Hill, 1953.

Parker, T. J., and W. A. Haswell, *A Textbook of Zoology*, 2 vols., 6th Edition, Macmillan, 1940.

Romer, A. S., *Vertebrate Paleontology*, 2nd Edition, Univ. of Chicago Press, 1945.

Smith, G. M., *Cryptogamic Botany*, Vols. 1-2, 2nd Edition, McGraw-Hill, 1955.

Young, J. Z., *The Life of Vertebrates*, Oxford Univ. Press, 1950.

INTERMEDIATE TEXTBOOKS

Brown, W. H., *The Plant Kingdom*, Ginn, 1935.

Buchsbaum, R., *Animals Without Backbones*, Univ. of Chicago Press, 1938.

Frost, S. W., *General Entomology*, McGraw-Hill, 1942.

Romer, A. S., *Man and the Vertebrates*, 3rd Edition, Univ. of Chicago Press, 1941.

Romer, A. S., *The Vertebrate Body*, Saunders, 1950.

Smith, G. M., E. M. Gilbert, G. S. Bryan, R. I. Evans, and J. T. Stauffer, *A Textbook of General Botany*, 5th Edition, Macmillan, 1953.

Storer, T. I., *General Zoology*, 2nd Edition, McGraw-Hill, 1951.

GENERAL DISCUSSIONS, FIELD GUIDES, AND NATURAL HISTORIES

Anderson, E. A., *Plants, Life and Man*, Little, Brown, 1952.

Beddard, F. E., *Mammalia, Cambridge Natural History*, Vol. 10, Macmillan, 1920.

Berrill, N. J., *The Origin of Vertebrates*, Oxford Univ. Press, 1955.

Boulière, F., *The Natural History of Mammals*, Knopf, 1954.

Clark, W. E. Le G., *History of the Primates*, 4th Edition, British Museum, 1954.

Fisher, J., *Birds as Animals*, Heinemann, London, 1939.

Gregory, W. K., and F. LaMonte, *The World of Fishes*, American Museum of Natural History, 1947.

Imms, A. D., *Insect Natural History*, Blakiston, 1951.

Palmer, R. S., *The Mammal Guide*, Doubleday, 1954.

Pough, R. H., *Audubon Bird Guide*, 2 vols., Doubleday, 1946-51.

Sporne, K. R., "The Phylogenetic Classification of Angiosperms," *Biol. Rev.*, 31:1-29, 1956.

Swain, R. B., *The Insect Guide*, Doubleday, 1949.

Teale, E. W., *Near Horizons*, Dodd, Mead, 1942.

PART 7: THE LIFE OF POPULATIONS AND COMMUNITIES

REFERENCE AND ADVANCED TEXTBOOKS

Allee, W. C., A. E. Emerson, O. Park, T. Park, and K. P. Schmidt, *Principles of Animal Ecology*, Saunders, 1949.

Andrewartha, H. G., and L. C. Birch, *The Distribution and Abundance of Animals*, Univ. of Chicago Press, 1954.

Clements, F. E., and V. E. Shelford, *Bio-ecology*, Wiley, 1939.

Kroeber, A. L., *Anthropology*, Harcourt, Brace, 1948.

U. S. Department of Agriculture, *Food and Life*, U. S. Government Printing Office, 1939.

Weaver, J. E., and F. E. Clements, *Plant Ecology*, McGraw-Hill, 1938.

INTERMEDIATE TEXTBOOKS

Braun-Blanquet, J., *Plant Sociology: the Study of Communities*, McGraw-Hill, 1932.

Clarke, G. L., *Elements of Ecology*, Wiley, 1954.

Daubenmire, P. F., *Plants and Environment*, Wiley, 1947.

Davis, D. H., *The Earth and Man*, Macmillan, 1942.

Odum, E. P., *Fundamentals of Ecology*, Saunders, 1953.

Oosting, H. J., *The Study of Plant Communities*, Freeman, 1948.

Transeau, E. N., H. C. Sampson, and L. H. Tiffany, *Textbook of Botany*, Harper, 1940.

GENERAL DISCUSSIONS

Allee, W. C., *The Social Life of Animals*, Norton, 1951.

Alverdes, F., *Social Life in the Animal World*, Harcourt, Brace, 1927.

Bates, M., *The Nature of Natural History*, Scribner's, 1950.

Benedict, R., *Patterns of Culture*, Mentor, 1946.

Blum, H. F., *Time's Arrow and Evolution*, Princeton Univ. Press, 1951.

Boyd, W. C., *Genetics and the Races of Man*, Little Brown, 1950.

Burnet, F. M., *Virus as Organism*, Harvard Univ. Press, 1945.

Coon, C. S., *The Story of Man*, Knopf, 1954.

Dunn, L. C., and Th. Dobzhansky, *Heredity, Race, and Society*, Mentor, 1946.

Elton, C. S., *The Ecology of Animals*, 2nd Edition, Wiley, 1946.

Graham, E. H., *Natural Principles of Land Use*, Oxford Univ. Press, 1944.

Haskins, C. P., *Of Societies and Men*, Norton, 1951.

Kluckhohn, C., *Mirror for Man*, McGraw-Hill (Whittlesey House), 1949.

Michener, C. D., and M. H. Michener, *American Social Insects*, Van Nostrand, 1951.

Osborn, F., *Our Plundered Planet*, Grosset, 1951.

Pearl, R., *The Natural History of Populations*, Oxford Univ. Press, 1939.

Smith, T., *Parasitism and Disease*, Princeton Univ. Press, 1934.

Wheeler, W. M., *Social Life Among the Insects*, Harcourt, Brace, 1923.

Zinsser, H., *Rats, Lice and History*, Little, Brown, 1945.

PART 8: THE GEOGRAPHY OF LIFE

TEXTBOOKS AND REFERENCE WORKS

Allee, W. C., A. E. Emerson, O. Park, T. Park, and K. P. Schmidt, *Principles of Animal Ecology*, Saunders, 1949.

Beaufort, L. F., *Zoogeography of the Land and Inland Waters*, Sidgwick & Jackson, London, 1951.

Ekman, S. P., *Zoogeography of the Sea*, Sidgwick & Jackson, London, 1953.

Hesse, R., W. C. Allee, and K. P. Schmidt, *Ecological Animal Geography*, Revised Edition, Wiley, 1951.

Schimper, A. F. W., *Plant Geography upon an Ecological Basis*, Oxford Univ. Press, 1903.

GENERAL DISCUSSIONS

Bates, W., *The Naturalist on the River Amazons*, Dent, London, 1940.

Darwin, C. R., *The Voyage of the Beagle*, Dent, London, 1950.

Huxley, T. H., *Diary of the Voyage of H.M.S. Rattlesnake*, Chatto, London, 1935.

Matthew, W. D., *Climate and Evolution*, 2nd Edition, New York Academy of Sciences, 1939.

Simpson, G. G., *Evolution and Geography*, Oregon State Board of Education, 1953.

Wallace, A. R., *Travels on the Amazon and Rio Negro*, Ward Lock, London, 1889.

PART 9: THE HISTORY OF LIFE

TEXTBOOKS AND REFERENCE WORKS

Arnold, C. A., *An Introduction to Paleobotany*, McGraw-Hill, 1947.

Clark, W. E. Le G., *The Fossil Evidence for Human Evolution*, Univ. of Chicago Press, 1935.

Colbert, E. H., *Evolution of the Vertebrates*, Wiley, 1955.

Dunbar, C. O., *Historical Geology*, Wiley, 1949.

Gregory, W. K., *Evolution Emerging*, 2 vols., Macmillan, 1951.

Moore, R. C., C. G. Lalicker, and A. G. Fischer, *Invertebrate Fossils*, McGraw-Hill, 1952.

Romer, A. S., *Vertebrate Paleontology*, Univ. of Chicago Press, 1945.

GENERAL DISCUSSIONS

Andrews, H. N., *Ancient Plants and the World They Lived In*, Comstock, 1947.

Colbert, E. H., *The Dinosaur Book*, American Museum of Natural History, 1954.

Moore, R., *Man, Time and Fossils*, Knopf, 1953.

Simpson, G. G., *Horses*, Oxford Univ. Press, 1951.

Simpson, G. G., *Life of the Past*, Yale Univ. Press, 1953.

PART 10: THE HISTORY OF BIOLOGY

TEXTBOOKS AND REFERENCE WORKS

Dampier, W. C., *A History of Science*, 3rd Edition, Macmillan, 1942.

Gabriel, M. L., and S. Fogel, *Great Experiments in Biology*, Prentice-Hall, 1955.

Hall, T. S., *A Source Book of Animal Biology*, McGraw-Hill, 1951.

Nordenskiöld, E., *The History of Biology*, Tudor, 1928.

Singer, C., *A History of Biology*, Revised Edition, Schuman, 1950.

GENERAL DISCUSSIONS

Dubos, R. T., *Louis Pasteur, Free Lance of Science*, Little, Brown, 1950.

Irvine, W., *Apes, Angels and Victorians*, McGraw-Hill, 1955.

ACKNOWLEDGMENTS FOR ILLUSTRATION SOURCES

Cover photo, Carl Strüwe.

Opening to Part 1 : photo by Hugh Spencer.

1-3 After Buchsbaum, R., *Animals Without Backbones*, Rev. Edition, Univ. of Chicago Press, 1948.
1-4 After Buchsbaum.
1-5 In part after Pauli, W. F., *The World of Life*, Houghton Mifflin, 1949.
2-5 Modified from Simpson, G. G., *Horses*, Oxford Univ. Press, 1951.

Opening to Part 2 : photo by Carl Strüwe.

3-1 Redrawn from Wilson, E. B., *The Cell in Development and Heredity*, 3rd Edition, Macmillan, reprinted 1947.
3-2 Redrawn from Wilson.
3-4 Redrawn from several figures in Greep, R. O. (Ed.), *Histology*, Blakiston, 1954.
3-8 Redrawn from Greep.
3-9 Redrawn from Rogers, J. S., T. H. Hubbell, and C. F. Byers, *Man and the Biological World*, 2nd Edition, McGraw-Hill, 1952.
3-10 Redrawn from Weisz, P. B., *Biology*, McGraw-Hill, 1954.
3-13 Redrawn from Storer, T. I., *General Zoology*, McGraw-Hill, 1943.
3-14 In part after Hyman, L. H., *The Invertebrates: Protozoa Through Ctenophora*, McGraw-Hill, 1940 ; in part redrawn from Kenoyer, L. A., H. N. Goddard, and D. D. Miller, *General Biology*, 3rd Edition, Harper, 1953.
3-15 Redrawn from Smith, G. M., E. M. Gilbert, G. S. Bryan, R. I. Evans, and J. T. Stauffer, *A Textbook of General Botany*, 5th Edition, Macmillan, 1953.
3-16 In part redrawn from Smith, Gilbert, *et al.*; in part redrawn from Sinnott, E. W., and K. S. Wilson, *Botany: Principles and Problems*, 5th Edition, McGraw-Hill, 1955.
3-17 Redrawn from Brown, W. H., *The Plant Kingdom: A Textbook of General Botany*, Ginn (Athenaeum Press), 1935.
3-18 Redrawn from figures in Smith, Gilbert, *et al.*
3-23 Redrawn from Hardin, G., *Biology: Its Human Implications*, 2nd Edition, Freeman, 1952.
3-26 Redrawn from several figures in Greep.
3-27 In part redrawn from Neal, H. V., and H. W. Rand, *Chordate Anatomy*, Blakiston, 1939 ; after Bremer.
3-28 Redrawn from figures in Greep ; Storer ; Neal and Rand ; and Smith, P. E. (Ed.), *Bailey's Textbook of Histology*, 10th Edition, Williams & Wilkins, 1940.
4-1 Redrawn from Amberson, W. R., and D. C. Smith, *Outline of Physiology*, 1948. By permission of the artist. Norris Jones, and the Williams & Wilkins Company.
4-4 Redrawn with modification from Prosser, C. L. (Ed.), *Comparative Animal Physiology*, Saunders, 1950.
4-8 Based on a figure by Baldwin, E., *An Introduction to Comparative Biochemistry*, Cambridge Univ. Press, 1948.
5-1 Redrawn from Oginsky, E. L., and W. W. Umbreit, *An Introduction to Bacterial Physiology*, Freeman, 1954.

Opening to Part 3 : photo by Carl Strüwe.

6-1 Redrawn from figures in Hardin and in Storer.
6-2 In part after Storer.
6-4 Based on a figure in Thomas, M., *Plant Physiology*, J. & A. Churchill, London, 1940.
6-5 In part after a figure in Hardin.
6-6 In part after Buchsbaum.
6-10 Based on a figure in Storer.
6-12 Redrawn with modifications from Storer.
6-13, 6-14 Redrawn from Storer.
7-1 Slightly modified from a figure in Weisz.
7-2 Based on a figure in Thomas.
7-3 In part based on a figure in Bonner, J., and A. W. Galston, *Principles of Plant Physiology*, Freeman, 1952.
7-5 Parts based on figures in Hardin ; Borradaile, L. A., and F. A. Potts, *The Invertebrata*, Cambridge Univ. Press, 1938 ; and Hall, T. S., and F. Moog, *Life Science*, Wiley, 1955.
7-6 Redrawn from Storer.
7-7 In part based on a figure in Pauli ; in part redrawn from Hall and Moog.
7-9 Redrawn from Rogers, Hubbell, and Byers and from Hardin.
7-10 Redrawn with modification from many sources.
7-11 Redrawn from Storer.
7-13 In part based on a figure in Kudo, R. R., *Protozoology*, 3rd Edition, C C Thomas, 1946.
8-1 Based on a figure in Carter, G. S., *A General Zoology of the Invertebrates*, 3rd Edition, Sidgwick & Jackson, 1948.
8-2 In part based on a figure in Hall and Moog.
8-3 In part based on a figure in Villee, C. A., *Biology*, 2nd Edition, Saunders, 1954.
8-6 Drawn from photographs in Villee.
8-7 Redrawn with modification from Turner, C. D., *General Endocrinology*, Saunders, 1948 ; and Carlson, A. J., and V. Johnson, *The Machinery of the Body*, 3rd Edition, Univ. of Chicago Press ; and Patten, B. M., *Human Embryology*, Blakiston Div., McGraw-Hill, 1946.
8-8 Drawn from a photograph in Turner.
8-9 Redrawn from Bonner and Galston.

Opening to Chapter 9 : photo from J. Z. Young, *Doubt and Certainty in Science*, Oxford Univ. Press, London, 1951. With permission.

9-1 After Jennings, H. S., *Behavior of the Lower Organisms*, Columbia Univ. Press, 1906.
9-3 Based on figures in Pace, D. M., and B. W. McCashland, *College Physiology*, Crowell, 1955 ; and Romer, A. S., *The Vertebrate Body*, Saunders, 1950.
9-4 Redrawn from several figures in Plate, L., *Allgemeine Zoologie und Abstammungslehre*, Fischer, Jena, 1924.
9-5 In part redrawn from Rogers, Hubbell, and Byers ; in part redrawn from Pace and McCashland ; in part redrawn from Von Frisch, K., *The Dancing Bees*, Harcourt, Brace, 1955.
9-6 In part redrawn from Von Frisch ; in part redrawn from Prosser.
9-7 Redrawn from Parker, T. J., and W. A. Haswell, *A Textbook of Zoology*, 6th Edition, Macmillan, 1940.
9-8 Redrawn from Carter.
9-9 Redrawn with modification from figures in Storer ; Weisz ; and Pace and McCashland.
9-10 Redrawn with modification from Storer.
9-11 Based on figures in Hardin.

9-12 Redrawn from figures in Parker and Haswell, and in Storer.
9-13 *A* redrawn with modification and permission from Demerec, M. (Ed.), *Biology of Drosophila,* Wiley, 1950.
9-14 Redrawn from Romer, A. S., *The Vertebrate Body,* Saunders, 1950.
9-15 Redrawn from figures in Romer.
9-16 Redrawn from figures in Romer.
9-17 Redrawn from a figure in Hardin.
9-18 Redrawn with permission from Penfield, W., and T. Rasmussen, *The Cerebral Cortex of Man,* Macmillan, 1950.
9-19 Redrawn from Storer, T. I., and R. L. Usinger, *Elements of Zoology,* McGraw-Hill, 1955.
10-3 Redrawn from figures in Prosser.
10-4 In part based on figures in Storer.
10-5 *B* after Gray and Lissmann, *J. Exp. Biol.,* Vol. 15, 1938 (with permission) from a figure in Carter.
10-8, 10-9, 10-10, 10-11 Redrawn from figures in Jennings.
10-12 Redrawn from a figure in Hall and Moog.
10-13 Redrawn from a figure in Tinbergen, N., *Social Behavior in Animals,* Methuen, London ; Wiley, New York, 1953.
10-14 Based on a figure in Young, J. Z., *Doubt and Certainty in Science.*
10-15 Redrawn from Hardin.
10-17 After Schneirla in Roeder, K. D. (Ed.), *Insect Physiology,* Wiley, 1953.
10-18 Redrawn from Roeder.
10-19 Redrawn from several figures in Von Frisch.

Opening to Part 4 : photo by Dr. L. B. Shettles.

Opening to Chapter 11 : photo by Dr. Shinya Inoué from *Chromosoma,* Bd. 5, 1953 ; with permission.

Opening to Chapter 12 : drawing from *General Genetics* by Adrian M. Srb and Ray D. Owen, Freeman, 1952. Originally after Sturtevant and Beadle, *An Introduction to Genetics,* Saunders, 1939.

13-5 Redrawn from a figure in Crick, F. H. C., "The Structure of the Hereditary Material" in *The Physics and Chemistry of Life,* Simon & Schuster, 1955.
13-8 Redrawn from a figure in Crick.
13-13 Redrawn from Storer.
13-15 Redrawn from a figure in Srb and Owen.
13-16 Drawn from photographs in Sinnott, E. W., L. C. Dunn, and Th. Dobzhansky, *Principles of Genetics,* 4th Edition, McGraw-Hill, 1950.
13-17 In part after Reidel, H., in *Arch. F. Entwicklungsmechanik,* Vol. 132, 1935, Springer-Verlag (with permission).
14-1 Redrawn from Huettner, A. F., *Fundamentals of Comparative Embryology of the Vertebrates,* Revised Edition, Macmillan, 1949.
14-2 Redrawn from Wilson.
14-3 Redrawn from figures in Barth, L. G., *Embryology,* Revised Edition, Dryden, 1953.
14-4 Redrawn from figures in Huettner.
14-5 Redrawn from a figure in Young, J. Z., *The Life of Vertebrates,* Oxford Univ. Press, London, 1950.
14-6 Redrawn from figures in Huettner and in Storer.
14-7 Redrawn from Barth.
14-8 Redrawn from figures in Barth.
14-9 Redrawn from a figure in Winchester, A. M., *Genetics,* Houghton Mifflin, 1951.
14-11 Redrawn from a figure in Wigglesworth, V. B., *The Principles of Insect Physiology,* 3rd Edition, Methuen, London, 1947.
14-12 Redrawn from a figure in Minot, C. S., *The Problem of Age, Growth, and Death,* Putnam, 1908.
14-13 Redrawn with modification from Etkin, W., *College Biology,* Crowell, 1950.
14-14 In part after Parker and Haswell ; in part redrawn from Storer.

14-16 Redrawn from figures in Thompson, D'A., *On Growth and Form,* Cambridge Univ. Press, 1942.
15-1 Redrawn from figures in Strasburger, E., *Textbook of Botany,* 6th English Edition, Macmillan, London, 1930.
15-4, 15-5, 15-6, 15-7, 15-8, 15-9, 15-11 The detail of plant structure in these figures redrawn from Smith, Gilbert, *et al.*
15-12 Detail for this figure from Sinnott and Wilson.
15-13 *A* redrawn from Knuth, P., *Handbook of Flower Pollination,* Oxford Univ. Press, London, 1906 : *B* and *C* redrawn from Strasburger ; *D* and *E* redrawn, with permission, from Ames, O., "Pollination of Orchids Through Pseudocopulation," *Botanical Museum Leaflets,* Vol. 5, No. 1, 1937, Harvard Univ. Press.
15-17 Detail from Buchsbaum.
15-18 Redrawn from Storer.
15-19 Redrawn from Young J. Z., *The Life of Vertebrates,* after Huxley, J. S., in *Proc. Zool. Soc. Lond.,* 1914, with permission.
15-23 Redrawn from Romer, A. S., *Man and the Vertebrates,* 3rd Edition, Univ. of Chicago Press, 1941.
15-26 Redrawn from figures in Pauli and in Storer.

Opening to Part 5 : photo © Fouke Fur Company, 1946.

16-4 Redrawn with permission from Reed, S. C., and E. W. Reed, "Natural Selection in Laboratory Populations of Drosophila." *Evolution,* Vol. 4, 1950.
16-5 Top right photo from Tinbergen, N., *Social Behavior in Animals,* Methuen, London, with permission.
17-3 Redrawn from Srb and Owen.
17-5 Based on data given by Boyd, W. C., *Genetics and the Races of Man,* Little, Brown, 1950 ; with permission.
17-6, 17-7 Redrawn with permission from figures in Mayr, E., *Systematics and the Origin of Species,* Columbia Univ. Press, 1942.
17-8 Redrawn with permission from figures in Miller, A. H., "Speciation in the Avian Genus Junco," *Univ. Calif. Publ. Zool.,* Vol. 44, No. 3, 1941.
17-9 Redrawn with permission from a figure in Clausen, J., *Stages in the Evolution of Plant Species,* Cornell Univ. Press, 1951.
17-10 In part redrawn from Hesse, R., W. C. Allee, and K. P. Schmidt, *Ecological Animal Geography,* Wiley, 1951.
18-1 Redrawn with modification from Parker and Haswell ; Storer, Borradaile and Potts ; Imms, A. D., *Insect Natural History,* Blakiston, 1951 ; Hesse, R., and F. Doflein, *Tierbau und Tierleben,* B. G. Teubner. Leipzig and Berlin, 1914.
18-5 Redrawn from a figure in Cornes, J. J. S., "Attitude and Concealing Coloration," *Nature,* 140:684, 1937.
18-6 After Hesse and Doflein.
18-8 Based, with permission, on the figures and data of Lack, D., *Darwin's Finches,* Cambridge Univ. Press, Cambridge, 1947.
18-9 Redrawn, with permission, from a figure in Lack.
18-11 Based, with permission, on data and figures in Lack.
18-12 Redrawn with modifications from many sources, including Pauli ; Romer, *Man and the Vertebrates ;* and *Columbia University Laboratory Manual in General Zoology,* 1945.

Opening to Part 6 : photo © Douglas P. Wilson.

Opening to Chapter 19 : redrawn from figures in Scott, W. B., *A History of Land Mammals in the Western Hemisphere,* Rev. Edition, Macmillan, 1937.

19-3 In part redrawn from figures in Storer and in Romer, *Man and the Vertebrates.*
19-4 Modified from a figure in Kyle, H. M., *The Biology of Fishes,* Macmillan, 1930.
19-5 Redrawn with modification from Storer.
19-7 Based on figures in Brehms, A. E., *Brehms Tierleben Allgemeine Kunde des Tierreichs,* 4th Edition, Leipzig und Wien Bibliographisches Institut, 1912.
20-2 Redrawn from figures in Smith, Gilbert, *et al.*
20-4 Redrawn from figures in Kudo and in Borradaile and Potts.
20-6 Redrawn from figures in Kudo and in Borradaile and Potts.
20-8 Redrawn from Buchsbaum.
20-9 Redrawn from figures in Kudo; and Smith, G. M., *Cryptogamic Botany,* Vol. I, McGraw-Hill, 1938.
20-13 Redrawn from Smith, Gilbert, *et al.*
22-1 Redrawn from figures in Hall and Moog.
22-3 Redrawn from figures in Parker and Haswell.
22-4 Redrawn from figures in Buchsbaum.
22-5 Redrawn from figures in Borradaile and Potts.
22-7 In part after Parker and Haswell; in part after Bullough, W. S., *Practical Invertebrate Anatomy,* Macmillan, 1950.
22-8 Redrawn from figures in Hegner, R. W., *College Zoology,* Macmillan.
22-9 In part redrawn from Buchsbaum; in part redrawn, with permission, from Pennak, R. W., *Fresh-Water Invertebrates of the United States.* Copyright, 1953, The Ronald Press Company.
22-10 Redrawn from figures in Buchsbaum and in Borradaile and Potts.
22-11 The drawing of *Chaetopterus* after F. A. Potts in Borradaile and Potts, with permission. Photos: above, left, Ralph Buchsbaum; above, right, © Douglas P. Wilson; below, right, American Museum of Natural History.
22-12 In part after Borradaile and Potts; and Buchsbaum.
22-14 In part after Storer; in part after Hall and Moog.
22-16 Redrawn with modification from Storer.
22-17 Redrawn from Storer.
22-18 Figures of the individual animals from Kudo and from Borradaile and Potts.
22-19 Redrawn from figures in Hyman.
22-23 *A* redrawn from Hardin; *B* redrawn from figures in Storer and in Hesse and Doflein.
23-1 Based on Storer.
23-3 Above, Hugh Spencer; center left, Willis T. Hammond; center right, both © Douglas P. Wilson; lower left, © Douglas P. Wilson; lower right, American Museum of Natural History.
23-6 Based on a figure in Borradaile and Potts.
23-7 Redrawn from figures in Storer.
23-8 All photos © Douglas P. Wilson, except crab, U.S. Fish and Wildlife Service, and sow bug, U.S. Department of Agriculture.
23-11 All photos Hugh Spencer, except king crab, American Museum of Natural History.
23-12 Redrawn from figures in Storer.
23-13 Luna moth and ants, Hugh Spencer; stinkbug and fly, American Museum of Natural History; dragonfly, louse, and boll weevil, U.S. Department of Agriculture; mosquitoes, wasp, and bumblebee, Lynwood Chace from National Audubon Society; grasshopper, John R. Clawson from National Audubon Society.
23-14 Modified from Romer, *Man and the Vertebrates.*
23-15 Redrawn from J. Z. Young, *The Life of Vertebrates.*
23-17 Redrawn from Storer.
23-19 In part after Norman, J. R., *A History of Fishes,* A. A. Wyn, New York, 1951.
23-21 Above, left, U.S. Fish and Wildlife Service; all others American Museum of Natural History except center right, Charles Halgren.
23-22 Redrawn, with permission, from Colbert, E. H., *Evolution of the Vertebrates,* Wiley, 1955.

23-23 Redrawn from figures in Storer.
23-25 Terns, Australian Information Service; jay and heron, American Museum of Natural History; kiwi, New Zealand Consulate; goose, U.S. Fish and Wildlife Service; hawk, Charles Halgren.
23-26 Modified from Colbert.
23-28 Leopard, Charles Halgren; mouse and mole, American Museum of Natural History; anteater, Ewing Galloway; elephant, Sabena; porpoise, Miami News Bureau; bat, H. E. Edgerton from National Audubon Society.

Opening to Part 7: photo from Chamber of Commerce, San Jose, California.

24-1 Redrawn from figures in Wigglesworth.
24-3 Based on a figure in Pittendrigh, C. S., *Evolution,* Vol. 2, 1948.
24-7 Redrawn from a figure in Allee, W. C., A. E. Emerson, O. Park, T. Park, and K. P. Schmidt, *Principles of Animal Ecology,* Saunders, 1949; after Sverdrup, H. U., M. W. Johnson, and R. H. Fleming, *The Oceans,* Prentice-Hall, 1942 (with permission).
24-8 Redrawn from figures in Odum, E. P., *Fundamentals of Ecology,* Saunders, 1953.
24-9 Redrawn from a figure in Allee, *et al.,* after Park, O., W. C. Allee, and V. E. Shelford, *A Laboratory Introduction to Animal Ecology and Taxonomy,* Univ. of Chicago Press, 1939 (with permission).
25-1 Based, with permission, on data and figures given in Lack.
25-2 Parts 1 and 2 redrawn from Turtox Key Card, courtesy General Biological Supply House, Inc., Chicago; part 3 after Emerson in Allee *et al.,* with permission.
25-3 Redrawn from figures in Storer and in Parker and Haswell.
25-4 In part after a figure in Buchsbaum.
26-1 Based on a figure in Odum.
26-2 Redrawn from figures in Allee *et al.;* after Pearl, R., *The Biology of Population Growth,* Knopf, 1930, with permission; and after Davidson, *J. Trans. Roy. Soc. South Australia,* Vol. 62, 1938.
26-3 Redrawn from figures in Allee *et al.;* after Gause.
26-4 Redrawn from a figure in Allee *et al.;* after Leopold, A., *Wisc. Conserv. Dept. Publ.,* 321, 1943, with permission.
26-5 Redrawn from a figure in Allee *et al.;* after Gause.
26-6 Redrawn from a figure in Allee *et al.;* after Park, T., "Studies in Population Physiology," *J. Exp. Zool.,* Vol. 65, 1933, with permission.
26-7 Redrawn from a figure in Allee *et al.;* after Russell, E. S., and C. M. Yonge, *The Seas,* Warne, London, 1928, with permission.
26-8 Upper figure reproduced with the permission of Dr. Boyd W. Walker, Univ. of California at Los Angeles.
26-9 Redrawn from a figure in Clarke, G. L., *Elements of Ecology,* Wiley, 1954; after Baker, J. R., "Latitude and Egg Seasons in Old World Birds," *Proc. Zool. Soc. Lond.,* 1938, with permission.
26-10 Redrawn from a figure in J. Z. Young, *The Life of Vertebrates.*
26-11 Redrawn from a figure in Allee *et al.;* after MacLulich, D. A., "Fluctuations in the Numbers of the Varying Hare," *Univ. Toronto Stud. Biol. Series* 43, 1937, with permission of University of Toronto Press.
26-12 Modified from a figure in Lobeck, A. K., *Geomorphology,* McGraw-Hill, 1939; after Dachnowski.
27-2 Based on data given by Sinnott, Dunn, and Dobzhansky.

Opening to Part 8: photo from Standard Oil Company of New Jersey.

28-3 Modified from a figure in Allee *et al.*; after Wolcott.
28-8 After Pittendrigh.
29-3, 29-4, 29-5, 29-6, 29-7 Redrawn from Simpson, G. G., *Evolution and Geography*, Oregon State Board of Education, 1953.
29-8 Redrawn with modification from Matthew, W. D., *Climate and Evolution*, 2nd Edition, Spec. Publ. N. Y. Acad. Sci., Vol. 1, 1939; with permission.

Opening to Part 9: photo from American Museum of Natural History.

30-5 Redrawn from Simpson, *Evolution and Geography*.
30-6 Data for plants redrawn (with change in time scale) by permission from *An Introduction to Paleobotany* by C. A. Arnold. Copyright, 1947. McGraw-Hill Book Company, Inc. Data for animals from Simpson, G. G., *Life of the Past*, Yale Univ. Press, 1953.
31-2 Redrawn from figures in Romer, A. S., *Vertebrate Paleontology*, Univ. of Chicago Press, 2nd Edition, 1945; and Young, J. Z., *The Life of Vertebrates*.
31-9, 31-10 Modified, with permission, from *The Dinosaur Book*, by Edwin H. Colbert, published by McGraw-Hill Book Company, Inc. Copyright, 1954, by the American Museum of Natural History.
32-1 Redrawn from figures in Dunbar, C. O., *Historical Geology*, Wiley, 1949.
32-4 Redrawn from a figure in Simpson, G. G., *The Meaning of Evolution*, Yale Univ. Press, 1949.
32-5 Redrawn from Romer, *Vertebrate Paleontology*; after Simpson.
32-6 Redrawn from figures in Simpson, *The Meaning of Evolution*.
32-8 Simplified from Simpson, *Geography and Evolution*.
32-9 Redrawn from figures in Scott.
32-11 Redrawn from a figure in Simpson, *Horses*.
32-12 Modified after Romer, *Man and the Vertebrates*.
32-17 Redrawn from figures in Romer, *Vertebrate Paleontology*.

Opening to Part 10: photo from American Museum of Natural History.

INDEX

(Page numbers in italics refer to figures.)

Cell theory, 39; chemical version of, 90; history of, 39, 40

Cells, 39, 43, 812; animal, *40;* characterization of, 39; diversity of, *40;* environment of, 70; generalized, *39;* how materials are acquired by, 79; living, *44;* materials and processes in, 70; membranes of, 46; metabolic machinery of, 90; muscle, 64; nerve, 67, 191; of the blood, 144; organization of, 44; plant, *40, 47;* reproduction of, 51; shape of, *46;* size and shape of, 44; vacuoles of, *47;* walls of, 46

Cellular physiology, 809

Cellular respiration, 129

Cellularity, 259

Cellulose, 46, 71, 76-77, 106; digestion of, 123, 632

Cenozoic era, 736; life of, 776; mammals of, 782

Centipedes, 479, 570; in Carboniferous, 764

Central nervous system, 210-11

Centriole, *44,* 47, 225, 267; necessary for movement, 269

Centromeres, 267, 273, 276

Centrosomes, *39, 44,* 47; in mitosis, 51

Centurus uropygialis, 627

Cephalaspids, 758, *758*

Cephalochordata, 480, 538, *542,* 557, 559

Cephalopoda, 479, 563, *565, 566, 569;* in Ordovician, 755; locomotion of, *570*

Ceratium tripos, 495

Ceratodinium asymmetricum, 494

Cercopithecoids, 601, 790

Cercopithecus, 601

Cereals, 518

Cerebellum, 213

Cerebral cortex, 213; homunculus of, *217*

Cerebral hemispheres, 213

Cerebrum, 213; evolution of, 213

Cereus giganteus, 627

Certhidia, 446

Cesalpino, Andrea, 804

Cestodes, 479, *530;* adaptations to parasitism, *634*

Cetaceans, 481, 601

Chaetognatha, 479, 528, 544

Chaetopterus pergamentaceous, 536

Chain behavior, 249

Chain reaction, in behavior, 239

Challenger, the, 806

Chance, effects of, in evolution, 402

Characins, disjunctive distribution of, 727

Characteristics, supposed inheritance of, 279

Characters in common, 463

Charadriiformes, 593, *596*

Charophyceae, 477

Checkerboard, for study of gene combination, 285

Cheirolepis, 760, 762

Chelonia, 591

Chemical composition, as stimulus, 188

Chemical co-ordination, 173

Chemical energy, 91

Chemical senses, 203

Chemical work, 91

Chemistry, elements of, 71

Chemoreceptors, 195

Chestnuts, 700

Chicken, development of the, 341

Chicken pox, 638

Chilipods, 479, 570, *573*

Chilomonas paramœcium, 494

Chimaeras, 586, 759

Chimpanzees, 601, 791

Chiroptera, 599

Chitons, 479, 563

Chlamydomonas, 363

Chlamydomonas monadina, 494

Chlamydomonas-Polytoma pair, 112

Chlamys, 568

Chlorine, 75

Chlorophyceae, 477

Chlorophyll, 98, *99; a* and *b* forms of, 99; place of, in cell, 47; similarity of, to hemoglobin, 71

Chlorophyta, 477, 497

Chloroplasts, 47, 58, 60-61, 99

Cholera, 639

Cholesterol, 143

Chondrichthyans, 480, 584, *585,* 759

Chorda, mesoderm, 345

Chordates, 480, 530, 537, 545-46; adaptation of, to land life, 761; origin of, 557; tabular comparison of, 549

Chorion, 385

Chromomeres, 313

Chromosome theory, 277; historical origin of, 277; tests of, 292

Chromosomes, 47, 267; basis of segregation of, *289;* chemical composition of, 315; crossing over of, *303;* diploid number of, *271;* duplication of, 270; helical structure of, *269;* in *Drosophila, 293, 312;* in gynandromorphs, *299;* in meiotic divisions, *274;* in mitosis, 51; in mitotic divisions, *274;* in sex determination, *293;* independent assortment of, *275, 291;* linkage maps, *305;* movement of, in mitosis, 269; mutations of, 322; nondisjunction of, *298;* numbers of, 270, 311; protein in, 78; random assortment of, 275; rearrangements of, 323; reproduction of, 318; size of, 311

Chrysalis, *386*

Chrysaora, 529

Chrysophyceae, 477

Chrysophyta, 477, 497

Ciconiiformes, 593, *596*

Cilia, 225, 491

Ciliary motion, 225

Ciliates, 477, 491, 550, 552, 707; neurofibrillar system of, *493;* size of, *552;* types of, *491*

Ciliophora, 477, 488

Circulation, 137, 142

Circulatory mechanism, 146

Circulatory systems, comparison of, in main animal phyla, 546; of earthworm, *141;* of snail, *141;* of squid, *141;* open and closed, *141;* tabular comparison of, 549

Cirripeds, 479; parasitism by, 637

Citric acid, 103

Civilization, 675

Cladonia, 499

Clams, 479, 563, 566, 707; chemical receptors of, 203; circulation in, 142; modernization of, 777; mutualism among, 632; on coral reef, 10; reproduction of, 381; skeletons of, 67

Clans, 646

Claspers, 586

Class, in the systematic hierarchy, 473; statistical, 417

Classification, 804; of organisms, 477; practice of, 473; principles of, 459

Clay, 613

Cleavage, 339, *339;* effect of yolk in, *341*

Cleome, 679

Climate, 609

Climatius, 760

Climax, 665; changes of, 665

Clines, 425; altitudinal, *426*

Clocks, internal, 208, 659

Clonorchis sinensis, 636

Clostridium botulinum, 488

Clothes moth, 123

Clothing, 676

Clotting of blood, 144

Clover, 488

Club mosses, 507

Coagulation of proteins, 144

Coal, 615, 763

Coal forests, 507-08, 512, 516, 763

Cobalt, 75

Coccophagus scutellaris, 633

Coccosteus, 760

Cockroaches, commensalism in, 630; in Carboniferous, 764; nocturnalism in, 658; wood-eating, 632

Coconuts, dispersal of, 378

Cocoons, 385

Coelenterates, 478, 525, 545-46; active dispersal of, 718; behavior of, 238, 241; excretion in, 155; gastrulation of, 342; general organization of, *526;* in Ordovician, 755; life cycles of, *527;* life span of, 650; mutualism among, 632; nervous system of, 209; relationship of, to flatworms, 553; reproductive cycles of, 379; siphonophores, *528;* special effectors in, 229; tabular comparison of, 549

Coelom, 344; comparison in main animal phyla, 545; development of, in annelid superphylum, 555; development of, in echinoderm superphylum, 558; origin of, *555;* tabular comparison of, 549

Coelophysis, 769

Coelosphaerium, 496

Cohort, in the systematic hierarchy, 474

Colaptes chrysoides, 627

Cold, receptors of, 195

Cold-blooded animals, 172

Coleoptile, 183, *184*

Colias, 581

Collagen, 110

Collenchyma, 58; fibers of, *59*

Collip, James Bertram, 178

Colloidal systems, 49

Colloids, 49, *50;* protein, 50; protein solutions as, 79

Colon bacillus, 316

Colonies, analogy with societies, 643; coral, 7; protistan, 55

Color, genetic determination of, 330; relationship of, to wave length and to photosynthesis, 100; variable, in skin, 181-82

Color vision, 199

Coloration, adaptive, 408; protective and warning, *409;* warning, 411

Comets, 13

Commensalism, 630

Communist Party, views on heredity, 280

Communities, 607; development of, 649; disturbance of, by man,

679; human, 669; interaction of, 626; terrestrial, 697
Community succession, 664
Compensation point, 132
Competition, 627, 640; as limitation on populations, 655; nature of, 628; relationship of, to evolution, 629
Complication, as trend in history of life, 750
Compound, 71
Concentration, chemical, effects of, on reactions, 92
Concepts, 250
Conceptual scheme, 24
Condensation, 77, 106; forming of proteins by, 78
Conditioned reflexes, 243; simple, 244
Conditioned response, 245
Conduction, 186
Conductive tissues, 59
Conductors, 187
Condylarths, 31, 481
Cones, 517; in retina, 201
Coniferales, 517
Conifers, 478, *516*, 517, 698, 764, 778; in Triassic, 767; white pine, *517*
Conjugated proteins, 78
Conjugation, 359, 492; in *Paramecium, 492*
Conks, 500
Connective tissues, 67, *68;* origin of, from mesoderm, 344
Conocephalum conicum, 506
Conservation, 680
Continuity, of germ plasm, 336; of life, 257
Contour farming, *684*
Contractile vacuoles, 48, 154, *154*
Convergence, 470; among Australian marsupials, 724; among South American mammals, 725; in communities, 665
Convergent evolution, of hummingbird and hummingmoth, *470;* of placental and marsupial mammals, *471*
Convolutions of brain, 215
Co-operation, 641
Co-ordination, chemical, 173; relationship of, to rise of multicellular animals, 552
Cope, Edward Drinker, 815
Copepods, 479, 571, 709
Copernicus, Nikolaus, 23, 804
Copper, 75
Copulation, 258, 383
Coral reef, community succession on, 664
Corals, 7, *8*, 478, 526; cell environments of, 161; digestive system of, 124; excretion in, 155; extinction among, 767; in Ordovician, 755; in Silurian, 758; larvae of, 385; modernization of, 777; mutualism among, 632; nervous system of, 209; passive dispersal of, 718; skeletons of, *10;* special effectors in, 229; transport within, 141
Cordaitales, 516
Cordaites, 478, *515*, 516, *763*, 764; in Devonian, 762
Cordianthus ampullaceus, 515
Cords, nerve, 210
Cork, 58, 61
Corn, 371, 520; inheritance of ear size in, 307; linkage in, 300
Corpora quadrigemina, 213

Corpus luteum, 175
Correns, Karl Erich, 282, 289
Corridor, 719
Cortex, cerebral, 213
Cottonwoods, 5, 700
Cotyledons, 520
Cotylosaurs, 480, 764
Cougar, 701
Courtship, 382; as isolating mechanism, 431; as related to natural selection, 406; of the great crested grebe, *382*
Cowries, 10
Cows, 481, 601; digestion of cellulose by, 123; digestive system of, 126; intestinal bacteria in, 632
Coyotes, 5; and human disturbance of ecology, 679; effect of, on prey populations, 655
Crabs, 479, 571; blood of, 146; digestion of cellulose in, 123; king, 479; regeneration in, 160
Crayfishes, 571, 707; blood of, 146
Creatine phosphate, 130
Creation, special, 26
Creodonts, 480
Crepuscular animals, 658
Cretaceous period, 736; extinction in, 774; mammals of, 781
Cretinism, 175-76
Crinoids, 480, 537, *538*
Crocodiles, 480, 591, 770; modernization of, 778
Crocodilus palustris, 592
Cro-Magnon man, 798
Crossing over, 300, 302
Crossopterygians, 451, 480, 588, 759
Cross-pollination, 374
Crows, 593
Crustaceans, 479, 571, *572*, 630, 709; blood of, 146; color vision in, 199; hormones of, 182; in Ordovician, 755; in Triassic, 767; life span of, 650; parasitism among, 633, 637
Cryptomonas ovata, 494
Cryptomonas-Chilomonas pair, 112
Ctenophores, 478, 523, 528, 544, 554
Cuckoos, 633
Cucumaria frondosa, 540
Cucumbers, sea, *9,* 10, 480, 537, *540*
Cultigens, 520
Cultural adaptation, 676
Culture, human, 675; modification of human ecology by, 676
Currents, 611; as means of dispersal, 719
Cursorial ungulates, 705
Cutin, 60
Cuttings, 358
Cuttlefish, hormones of, 182
Cutworms, 530
Cuvier, Georges, 566, 805, 815
Cycadales, 516
Cycadeoidales, 515
Cycadeoids, 478, *514*, 515, 764, *773*, 778; in Triassic, 767
Cycads, 478, 514-15, 764, 778; in Triassic, 767
Cycle, carbon, 614; nitrogen, 615; of breeding activity in sparrow, *661;* rock, 618; water, 618
Cycles, annual, 659; daily, 657; lunar, 659; of materials, 614; of minerals, 617; relationship of, to conservation, 681
Cycloposthium bipalmatum, 491
Cypresses, 517

Cystoids, 480
Cytochrome, 103
Cytogenetics, 813, 815
Cytokinesis, 267
Cytology, 812
Cytoplasm, 45; structure of, 47

D, vitamin, 128
Daddy longlegs, 573
Dahlia, 529
Daily cycles, 657
Dandelions, 520; dispersal of, 378
Dandruff, 64
Daphnia, 571
Darwin, Charles Robert, 23, 25, 27, 32-33, 42, 90, 233, 278, 407, 412, 429, 433, 443-45, 463, 535, 652, 740, 803, 806-07, 816-17; on inheritance of acquired characters, 280
Darwin, Erasmus, 27, 810
Darwinism, social, 412
Darwin's finches, *445, 629*
Dasycercus, 471
Dasyurus, 471
DeVries, Hugo, 282, 289, 429, 815
Death, 166, 257
Death rates, 650
Decapods, 571
Decay, 487, 615; caused by fungi, 501; flagellates involved in, 493
Deciduous forest, 700
Deciduous trees, 517, 691
Deer, 5, 481, 654-55, 700, 716-17, 725; in Neotropical region, 726; in South American faunal strata, 726
Deer mice, distribution of tail length in, 418
Defense of territory, 640
Defibrinated blood, 142
Deficiency diseases, 127
Deficiency of genes, 323
Degeneration, 112; of parasites, 635
Dehydration, in synthesis of fats, 108; in synthesis of proteins, 110
Dehydration synthesis, 77, 106; forming proteins, 78
Dehydrogenation, 96
Demes, 396, 464; differences between, 422
Democritus, 278, 280
Demospongiae, 478
Dendrites, 191
Denitrifying bacteria, 617
Density, as limitation on populations, 655
Depletion of resources, 680
Dermacentor, 575
Descent, interpretation of, in systematics, 464
Deserts, 627, 705, *706;* natural selection in, 408; productivity of, 682
Desoxyribose nucleic acid, 315. *See also* DNA
Development, 259, 335; closed, 336; control of, 263; control of, by genes, 330; determination in, *346;* evolution of, 352; genetic control of, 346; of the embryo, 259; open, 336; phases of, 337; presumptive fate in, *346*
Deviation, 354
Devonian period, 736; life of, 758; plants of, 762
Diabetes, 175, 177
Diabetes mellitus, 177, 333
Diaphragm, 168, 597; action of, *169*

Diastole, 146
Diatoms, **477, 497, *498*, 707, 709-10,** 777 ; influence of, on aquatic communities, 624
Diatryma, 780, *780*
Dicotyledons, 62, 478, 519
Dietary requirements, 112
Differentiation, 336 ; in protistan colonies, 56 ; of roles, 642
Difflugia urceolata, 489
Diffusion, 80 ; in air, 81 ; in water, 81 ; through membranes, 82
Diffusion rate, *81*
Digestion, 77, 121 ; extracellular, 124, *124 ;* intracellular, 124
Digestive system, 124 ; comparison of, in main animal phyla, 545 ; of chicken, *126 ;* of clam, *119 ;* of coelenterates, *125 ;* of earthworms, *125 ;* of flatworms, *125 ;* of man, *118 ;* of protozoa, *125 ;* tabular comparison of, 549
Dimetrodon, 765, *765*
Dinichthys, 760
Dinoflagellates, 112, 477, 709
Dinosaurs, 480, 767 ; chances of survival of, to recent, 588 ; duckbilled, 769 ; extinction of, 774 ; horned, 769 ; radiation of, *768*
Dionne quintuplets, 340
Dioon edule, 514
Diphtheria, 639
Diplacanthus, 760
Diploid chromosome number, 271
Diploidy, 270, *271,* 276
Diplophase, 362
Diplopods, 479, 570, *573*
Diplovertebron, 762
Diptera, *578,* 580
Dipterus, 760
Disaccharase, 123
Discrimination, in sensory receptors, 201
Diseases, bacterial, 488 ; caused by flagellates, 493 ; caused by fungi, 501 ; caused by parasites, 637 ; caused by protists, 483 ; caused by sporozoans, 490 ; deficiency, 127
Disjunction, 726
Disjunctive distributions, 717
Dispersal, 718 ; across Isthmus of Panama, *721 ;* interchange between continents, *723 ;* of conifers, 518 ; of plants, 377 ; routes and barriers, 719, *720 ;* sweepstake, 722
Distribution, disjunctive, *728 ;* of *Clematis, 398 ;* of variation in demes, 417
Diurnal animals, 657
Divergence, 472
Diversity, caused by natural selection, 405
Divisions, in the systematic hierarchy, 473 ; of roles, 642
DNA (desoxyribose nucleic acid) 315, 327 ; duplication of, *320 ;* reproduction of, 320 ; structure of, *318*
Dodo, 680
Dogfishes, 586 ; as example of vertebrate evolution, 539
Dogs, 601, 630, 725 ; Australian, 725 ; behavioral conditioning of, 244 ; color vision in, 199 ; homologies of limbs of, 465 ; in South American faunal strata, 726 ; interpretation of behavior of, 231 ; sense of smell in, 203 ; temperature regulation in, 173

Dollo, Louis, 469
Dollo's law, 469
Dominance, 642 ; among groups of plants and animals, 518 ; relationship of, to gene action, 327
Dominant alleles, 284
Dragonflies, 580 ; in Carboniferous, 764 ; larvae of, 385
Drainage, 678
Drive, biological, 247
Drosophila, experimental natural selection in, 405 ; sexual isolating mechanisms in, 431
Drosophilia melanogaster, 292 ; chromosome number in, 311
Du Bois-Reymond, Emil, 810, 814
Duck-billed dinosaurs, 769
Ducks, 593
Duckweeds, 707
Dunbaria, 764
Duodenum, digestion in, 123 ; hormone production in, 176
Duplication, of ecological roles, 726 ; of genes, 323
Dust bowl, 684
Dwarfism, 180
Dysentery, 638

E, vitamin, 128
Ear ossicles, *452 ;* Weberian, *468*
Eardrums, 202
Ears, 195, 202 ; evolution of, in vertebrates, 451 ; human, *204*
Earth, 14 ; age of the, 734 ; evolution of the, 28
Earthworms, 479, 535 ; behavior of, 240-41, 243 ; digestive system of, 126 ; feeding of, 118 ; hearts of, 142 ; muscular system of, 227
East, E. N., 307
Echinoderm superphylum, 557
Echinoderms, 480, 530, 537, 544, 546-47 ; behavior of, 240 ; excretion in, 155 ; extinction among, 767 ; general organization of, *538 ;* in Ordovician, 755 ; in Triassic, 767 ; larvae of, *558 ;* tabular comparison of, 549
Echinoidea, 480, *538*
Echinus, 266
Echinus esculentus, 540
Ecological biogeography, 691
Ecological incompatibility, 627
Ecology, 807
Ectocarpus, 364
Ectoconus, 784
Ectoderm, 342
Ectoprocta, 479, 533
Edentata, 599
Edrioasteroidea, 480
Effectiveness of stimuli, 189
Effectors, 187, 222 ; in plants, 222 ; in protists, 223 ; muscular, 227
Efferent nerves, 211
Egg cell, differentiation of, *340 ;* human, *41 ;* maturation of, 337 ; production of, 337
Eggs, 359 ; floating and sinking, 611 ; human, 258 ; of animals, 380 ; of birds, as cells, 44 ; of mammals, 387 ; of reptiles, 590 ; of terrestrial vertebrates, *386 ;* of vertebrates, 384
Egypt, 23
Ehringsdorf skull, 797
Ejaculation, 387
Élan vital, 22, 35-36
Electrical properties of environment, as stimulus, 188
Electricity, as energy, 91
Electromagnetic spectrum, *189*

Electron transfer, as oxidation-reduction process, 96
Elements, 71
Elephant bird, 780
Elephants, 481, 601, 716 ; changes in distribution of, 787 ; life span of, 650 ; pulse rate of, 166 ; reproductive rate of, 651
Elk, 699, **716**
Ellobiophyra donacis, 491
Elms, 700
Embolism, 144
Embolus, 144
Embryo sac, of plants, 370
Embryology, 813
Embryos, human, *260 ;* development of human, 259
Emotions, 253
Empirical chemical formulas, 77
Emu, 780
Emulsion, 49
Endergonic reactions, 95, 619
Endocrine glands, 174, *174*
Endocrine tissues, 174
Endocrines, 174
Endoderm, 342
Endoprocta, 479, 533
Endosperm, 371
Energy, 91 ; activation, *93 ;* capture of, 5, 96 ; chemical, 91 ; conversions of, *14 ;* exchange of, 95 ; expenditure of, 454 ; flow of, 607 ; in chemical reactions, 72 ; kinetic, 91, *92,* 618 ; limitations on populations, 653 ; mechanical, 91 ; of activation, 93 ; of chemical reactions, 93 ; of the reaction, 95 ; potential, 91, *92,* 618 ; potential, of chemical structure, 93 ; reaction, *93 ;* release and expenditure of, 100 ; release of, in organisms, 74, 96, 101 ; resources of, in cells, 110 ; solar, expenditure of, 609 ; sources of, 93 ; traffic in, in coral reef, 11 ; traffic in, in forest, 6 ; transfers of, 618
Entomologists, 580, 805
Environment, 608 ; biotic, 614 ; chemical, 613 ; control of internal, 164 ; effect of, on gene action, 333 ; influence of, on survival, 408 ; internal, 161-62 ; modification of, by man, 678 ; physical, 608
Environmental gradients, 426
Environments, capacity of, for population, 652 ; historical occupation of, 748 ; inter- and intraspecific, 627 ; occupation of, 443
Enzyme specificity, 101
Enzymes, 93 ; action of, *95 ;* digestive, 122 ; in cellular release of energy, 101 ; relationship to genes, 325
Eocene epoch, 736 ; mammals in, 784
Ephedra, 511
Epidemic, 663
Epidermis, 58, 60 ; of anus, origin from ectoderm, 344 ; of leaves, role played in osmosis, 85 ; of mouth, origin from ectoderm, 344 ; of nostril, origin from ectoderm, 344
Epididymis, 386
Epidinium, 54, 56
Epinephrin, 178
Epiphytes, 510, 631, 703
Epithalamus, 213
Epithelia, 63 ; origin of, from mesoderm, 344 ; types of, *64*

Epizootic, 663
Equilibration, organ of, 195
Equilibrium, genetic, 399; in diffusion, 81; in osmosis, 82; organs of, 202; osmotic, in aquatic animals, 86; sense of, 203
Equisetum sylvaticum, 508
Equisetums, 508; summary of characteristics of, 520
Equus, 787
Erosion, *683*
Eryops, 764, 765
Erythrocytes, 144
Escherichia coli, 316
Essential oils, 110
Estrogen, 175
Ethiopian region, 716
Eucalyptocrinus crassus, 540
Euglena, 493
Euglena-Astasia pair, 112
Euglena pisciformis, 494
Euphausia, 571
Euphausids, 479
Euphorbias, 408, 460, 470, 472
Euplotes, 493
Eurasia, connection of, to North America, 724; faunal regions of, 716
Eurasian corridor, 719
Europe, as part of World Continent, 723
European race, 673
Eurypterids, 479, 574; in Ordovician, 755
Eustachian tubes, 451
Eusthenopteron, 762
Evergreen trees, 517
Evolution, 816; and human thought, 433; as change in the genetic equilibrium, 402; causes of, 405; change of pace in, 760; early stages of, *738;* elementary processes of, 395; indeterminate, 402; irreversibility of, 469; irrevocability of, 469; of development, 352; over-all fossil record of, 746; proofs of, 28; relationship of, to cell theory, 90; social, 28; theory of, 25; theory of, historical rise of, 26
Evolutionary descent, taxonomic grouping according to, *475*
Evolutionary progress, 451
Excretion, 154; function of liver in, 165
Exergonic reactions, 95, 619
Exophthalmia, 175, *177*
Expansion of forms of life, 747
Experimentation on animals, 181
Expiration, 129
Explanation, in biology, 35; in science, 20
Extinction, 450, 629; following human introductions, 680; "the great dying," 774
Eyes, 188, 195, 197; camera, image formation by, *198;* compound, 197; compound, image formation by, *200;* of planarians, 211; role of, in evolution of man, 794; variety of, *196*

F_1 generation, 283
F_2 generation, 283
Fabre, Jean Henri, 810
Facilitation of nerve impulses, 194
Falconiformes, 593, *596*
Family, as basis of insect societies, 644; in the systematic hierarchy, 473; role of, in human societies. 646

Fatigue, 130
Fat-soluble vitamins, 128
Fats, 48, 77, 90; as energy sources, 96; as vitamins, 128; digestion of, 122; digestive enzymes in, 123; energy storage in, 101; function of, 108; in plasma, 143; synthesis of, 107; transport of, 153; water from, 72
Fatty acids, 77, 107; as products of digestion, 123
Faunal change, 717
Faunal interchange, 725
Faunal regions, 712, *712;* barriers separating, 720; characteristic mammals of, *713-15*
Faunal stratification, 726
Faunas, division of, into strata, 726
Feathers, 173, 591; structure of, *594*
Feces, 155
Fecundity, nonrandom, 406
Felis, 471
Felis concolor, 701
Felis pardus, 600
Fermentation, 130, *502*
Ferns, 478, 506, 508, *509-10,* 778; dispersal of, 377; epiphytic, 703; gametophytes, *370;* in Devonian, 762; reproductive cycle of, 367; seed, 512; sporangia, *370;* summary of characteristics of, 520
Fertilization, 258, *271,* 339, 359; in animals, 380; in flowering plants, 370; in reproductive cycle, 361
Fibers, protein, 50
Fibrin, 144
Fibrinogen, 144
Field of organization, 161
Field orientation, 160
Figs, adaptations of, for pollination, 376
Filicineae, 478, 508
Filter, 719
Filter feeders, 118; clams as, *119*
Finches, Darwin's, 445
Fins, homologies in, 466
Firs, 517
Fischer, Emil, 814
Fisheries, periodism in, 662
Fishers, 699
Fishes, 31, 707, 709; age of, 758; bony, 480; circulation in, 142; color vision in, 199; commensalism among, 630-31; density effects on populations of, 657; disjunctive distribution of, 727; electrical, 229; excretion in, 155; fresh-water, osmotic control in, 87; growth regulation in, 181; hearing of, 468; hearts of, 146; homologies of fins in, 466; in Devonian, 758; in Ordovician, 758; in Permo-Triassic crisis, 767; isolating mechanisms in, 431; jawless, 480, 582; marine, osmotic control in, 86; modernization of, 777; passive dispersal of, 718; possible parasitism among, 633; pressure receptors in, 202; proofs of position in evolutionary sequence, 30; reproduction of, 381, 385; respiratory system of, 135; schooling of, 641; sense of smell in, 203; special sense organs of, 188
Fission, 379
Flagella, 225, 269, 493
Flagellary motion, *225*
Flagellates, 112, 477, 492, 548, 550; behavior of, 236; colonial, *56;*

green, 55; in Ordovician, 755; in termites, 632; mutualism among, 632; types of, *494*
Flatworms, 479, 530, 544, 556, 707; behavior of, 236, 240-41; digestive system of, 124; evolutionary limitations of, 450; mutualism among, 632; nervous systems of, 209; parasitism among, 633; regeneration in, 160; relationship of, to coelenterates, 553; transport within, 141
Flavoprotein, 103
Fleas, 580, 630; parasitism among, 634; water, 479
Flickers, 627
Flies, 5, 580; behavior of, 236; density effects on populations of, 656
Flight, adaptations to, 772
Flightless birds, 780
Flippers, 470
Flood control, 685, *686*
Flowering, influence of light on, 88; timing of, 377
Flowering plants, 478; dominance of, 778; mutualism among, 632; origin and expansion of, 767; reproductive cycle of, *373*
Flowers, 369, 518; biological significance of, 374
Fluid tissues, 69
Flukes, 479, 530, 636
Fluorine, 75
Flycatchers, 628
Follicles, 337, 387
Fomes, 500
Food, 71; and human culture, 677
Food chains, 620; as limitation on populations, 653; interference in, by man, 679
Food vacuole, 48, 119
Food webs, 620; of ocean community, *620*
Foraminifera, 490, *490,* 550; in Ordovician, 755
Forebrain, 212; function of, 215
Forelimbs, evolution of, in horse family, *31;* in vertebrates, 27, *465*
Forests, coal, 763; community succession in, 664; description of southwestern, 3; destruction and utilization of, 678; earliest, 762; of Carboniferous, *763;* ponderosa pine, *4;* productivity of, 682; temperate deciduous, *700;* tropical rain, *702*
Form, interpretation of, in systematics, 464
Formed elements of the blood, 142, 144
Fossil record, broad features of, *748-49*
Fossils, 29, 741-42; collection and preparation of, *744;* of Grand Canyon, *28;* types of, *745;* use of, in seeking petroleum, 490
Fossorial animals, 705
Foxes, 701; population cycles of, 663
Fraternal twins, 340
Frequency distribution, 417, *418*
Fresh water, as environment, 162; temperatures in, 171
Fresh-water communities, 706
Frogs, 590, 704; as example of vertebrate evolution, 539-40; hormones of, 181; modernization of, 778; passive dispersal of, 718; respiration of, 133

598; control of internal environment in, 164; ear of, 202; eggs of, 384; evolution of aquatic, 778; excretion in, 156; fertilization in, 383; growth in, 349; hearts of, 146; history of, 781, 782-83; in hierarchy of classification, 460; marsupial, 471; modernization of, 784; mutualism among, 632; nocturnal habits of, 657; of Eocene and Oligocene, 785; of Mesozoic, 781; placental, 471; proofs of position in evolutionary sequence, 30; reproduction of, 386; respiratory system of, 135; rise of, 773; sense of smell in, 203; societies of, 646; visceral nervous system of, 218

Mammary glands, 386

Mammoths, changes in distribution of, 787

Mammuthus primigenius, 786

Man, adaptability of, 440; adaptation of races of, 673; Age of, 776; amino acid needs of, 78; among mammals, 601; archaic, 797; as agent of dispersal, 718-19; as environment for parasites, 633; barriers to interbreeding in, 672; basic ecology of, 675; behavioral and mental characteristics of, 250; blood cells of, 145; blood groups of, 327; body temperature of, 172; brain of, 212; cerebrum of, 215; chromosome number of, 271, 311; circulatory mechanism of, 146; classification of, 473; communities of, 669; composition of protoplasm of, 48; control of internal environment of, 164; cranial nerves of, 213; digestive system of, 126; diurnal nature of, 657; ear bones of, 468; ear of, 202; egg cells of, 337; embryo, characteristics of, 352; embryo, development of, 259; eyes and vision of, 199; factors in evolutionary progress of, 451; field of organization of, 161; first appearances of, in America, 798; forebrain function in, 216; forerunners of, 789; fossil, 796; growth in, 349; heart motion in, 166; heart of, 146; homologies of limbs of, 465; hormones of, 174; infectious diseases of, 638; innate vs. learned behavior in, 241; kidneys of, 156; language of, 252; life span of, 650; localization of function in brain of, 217; loss of ability to synthesize in, 113; lymphatic system of, 153; modification of environment of, 678; motivation of learning in, 247; muscular respiration in, 129; muscular tissues of, 64; mutation rates in, 324; mutualism in, 632; natural selection in, 413; neoteny in, 354; nutrition of, 127; oestrus cycle in, 389; origin and relationships of, 793; pituitary gland in, 178; plant food supply of, 518; plasma of, 163; pleiotropic mutation in, 332; polymorphism in, 421; primitive, ecology of, 675; pulse rate of, 166; races and subspecies of, 671; rate of nerve impulses in, 192; reflexes in, 242; regeneration in, 160; relative growth in, 352; reproduction of, 257;

respiratory rates of, 132; responses of, to radiation, 188; sense of smell in, 203; senses of, 195; size of cells in, 44; size of egg of, 44; skin of, 64; societies of, 646; survivorship in, 651; symbiosis in, 631; systematics of, 670; tapeworms of, 636; territoriality in, 641

Mandrills, 601

Mandrillus sphinx, 602

Manganese, 75; in synthesis of chlorophyll, 100

Mangroves, dispersal of, 378

Mantle, 563

Maples, 700

Maps of genes, 304

Marine environments and communities, 707

Mariopteris, 763

Marmosets, 601

Marmota, 471

Marrow, as source of blood cells, 145

Mars, 15

Marsupials, 465, 470, 480, 598, 599, 716, 724; disjunctive distribution of, 727; in Cretaceous and early Cenozoic, 783

Martens, 699, 701

Mastigamoeba, 550

Mastigophora, 477, 488, 492

Mastodons, changes in distribution of, 787

Materials, as limitation on populations, 653; flow of, 607; inorganic, 72; of living things, 71; organic, 75

Mating, nonrandom, 405

Matrix of connective tissues, 67

Matter, living and nonliving, 35

Matthew, W. D., 729, 807

Maturation, 348; of behavior, 253

May flies, 580; in Permian, 764

Mazes, 246

McAtee, Waldo Lee, 410

McLeod, John James Richard, 178

Mechanical energy, 91

Medawar, P. B., 351

Medicine, 806; effects of, on natural selection, 414

Medulla oblongata, 168, 213

Medusas, 379, 525; active dispersal of, 718

Megaceros, 355

Meganeura monyi, 763

Megaspores, 370

Meiosis, 272, 337; and crossing over, 302; compared with mitosis, 274; in reproductive cycle, 361; mechanism of segregation in, 290; mutation during, 322; significance of, 275

Membranes, body, of protists, 118; diffusion through, 80; nuclear, in mitosis, 51; of cells, 39, 46; permeable, 82; semipermeable, 82, 83

Mendel, Gregor, 281, 422, 815

Mendelian population, 397

Mendelian ratios, 282, 290

Menhaden, 631

Menstruation, 390

Merismopedia, 496

Meristematic tissue, 58, 58

Meristems, 58, 58, 160, 336

Mesa Verde, 62

Mesoderm, 342; origin of, 555

Mesozoans, 479, 523, 528, 544

Mesozoic era, 736; mammals of, 781

Mesquite, 628

Mesquite climax, 665

Metabolism, 90; as essential attribute of living things, 16; basic processes of, in cells, 100; comparison of, in animals and plants, 522; oxygen and carbon dioxide involved in, 74; rates and temperatures of, 610

Metamorphosis, 385; hormonal control of, in insects, 182; induced by thyroxin, 181

Metaphase, 267

Metasequoia, 518

Metazoa, 552

Meteors, 13

Methane, in earth's orginal atmosphere, 738

Metridium sessile, 529

Mice, 599, 725; adaptability in, 440; genetics of color in, 330; in South American faunal strata, 726; respiratory rate of, 132

Microbes, 637

Microbiology, 812

Microclimates, 611; in forest, 612

Microorganisms, 811

Micropaleontologists, 815

Micropaleontology, 490

Micropallas whitneyi, 627

Microscopes, 45

Microspores, 369, 508

Midbrain, 212; function of, 215

Midgets, 180

Migration, 171, 718; relationship of, to light, 88

Mildews, 477, 501

Milk, 386, 597; hormonal stimulation of, 181

Milkweed bugs, warning coloration in, 411

Millepedes, 479, 570

Mimicry, 411

Mimosa, 223, 235

Mineral cycles, 617, 617

Mineral salts, 75

Minot, C., 351

Mints, 520

Miocene epoch, 736

"Missing links," 796

Mississippian period, 736

Mites, 5, 573; forerunners of, in Devonian, 762; parasitism among, 633

Mitochondria, 39, 41, 44, 48; function of, in energy release, 105

Mitosis, 51, 266; compared with meiosis, 274; events and stages in, 268; in protozoans, 489; in trillium, 53; in whitefish, 52; mutation during, 322; significance of, 275

Moas, 780

Mobility, comparison of, in animals and plants, 522

Mode, 417

Modernization, 776; in aquatic environments, 777; in land environments, 778; of mammals, 784

Modifiers, 330

Moeritherium, 786

Molds, 6, 477-78, 500; digestion in, 124; slime, 477, 494

Molecular movement, 80

Molecules, 71; sizes of, in solutions and colloids, 50

Moles, 599

Mollusks, 479, 528, 535, 544, 546, 554, 557, 563; active dispersal of, 718; adaptation of, to land life, 761; chemical receptors in, 203; circulation in, 142; classes of, 565; eyes of, 197; foot

Mollusks (Cont.)
of, 563; general organization of, *564;* hormones of, 182; in Carboniferous, 764; in Triassic, 767; mutualism among, 632; tabular comparison of, 549
Mongoloid race, 673
Mongooses, disturbance of native ecology by, 680
Monkey puzzle tree, 518
Monkeys, 601, 704, 716; color vision in, 199; concept formation by, 251; geographic distribution of, 711; history of, 790; in Neotropical region, 726; in South American faunal strata, 726; South American, 725; territoriality in, 641
Monocotyledons, 62, 478, 519
Monotremes, 597, *599,* 716, 724
Moose, 699, 716
Morgan, Conway Lloyd, 230, 233, 811
Morgan, Thomas Hunt, 292, 302, 815
Morgan's canon, 230, 234, 244, 252
"Mormon tea," 511
Morning glories, 520
Morphogenesis, 336
Morphology, adaptive, 435
Morphotypes, 463
Morula, 339
Mosaic disease, 316
Mosasaurs, 771; extinction of, 774
Mosquitoes, and human disturbance of ecology, 680; and malaria, 490; differing food of male and female, 642
Moss animals, 532
Mosses, 162, 478, 505; reproductive cycle of, 366
Moths, 408, 435, 580; daily cycles of, 658; flights of male to female, 207; pollination of yuccas by, 376; protective coloration in, 410
Motion, ameboid, 223
Motivation, 247
Motor nerves, 211
Motor neurons, 193
Mountain lions, 5, 101
Mouth, 195; adaptive diversity of, in insects, 435; epidermis of, origin from ectoderm, 344
Movement, autonomous, as essential attribute of living things, 17; forced, 234; molecular, 80; nontropistic, 235; of organisms, 222; of plants, 222; of water or air, 611; reflex, 232
Mules, 432
Muller, H. J., 324
Müller, J. P., 810, 814
Multicellular animals, origin of, 554
Multicellular organisms, 55; origin of, 493
Multiple alleles, 327
Multiple-factor inheritance, *306, 308*
Multiple factors, 304
Multituberculates, in Cretaceous and early Cenozoic, 783
Mus, 471
Musci, 478
Muscle, 227; heart, 166; intracellular respiration of, *131;* origin of, from mesoderm, 344; respiration in, 129; types of, *66*
Muscle fibers, 110, 228
Muscle-skeleton mechanisms, *226*
Muscle tissues, 64

Muscular motion, 227
Mushrooms, 478, 500
Musk deer, 704
Musk oxen, 698
Mussels, 479, 566
Mustards, 520
Mutants, 321
Mutation, 321; effects of, on genetic equilibrium, 402; experimental production of, 324; rates of, 324; relationship of, to parallelism, 472; role of, in speciation, 429
Mutualism, 630-31
Mya, 566
Mycelium, 499
Mycophyta, 477
Myelin sheath, *66*
Myiarchus tyrannulus, 628
Myrmecobius, 471
Myrmecophaga, 471, 600
Mytilus, 568
Myxedema, 175, 176
Myxomycetes, 477, 494
Myxophyta, 477, 494, 497

Nails, origin of, from ectoderm, 344
Names, technical, of organisms, 476
Ñata cattle, 321
Natural gas, 615
Natural history, 804
Natural selection, 403, 405, 454; action of gene frequency in, *404;* and competition, 640; as historical process, 443; changing concepts of, 412; creative aspects of, 412; effect of, on population variation, *420;* experimental demonstration of, *406;* relationship of, to convergence, 472; theory of, 26; theory of, Darwin's development of, 32
Nature and nurture, 333
Nautiloids, 569; in Devonian, 761; in Ordovician, 755
Nautilus, 479, 563, 566
Nautilus pompilius, 569
Navigation, by bees, 207-08; by birds, 207-08
Neanderthal man, 797
Neanderthaloids, 797
Nearctic region, 716
Nectar, 374
Nectaries, 154
Necturus maculosus, 589
Needle grass, 705
Negroes, 673-74
Negroid race, 673
Nekton, 709
Nematocysts, *526*
Nematodes, 479, 528, 531, *532,* 544-46, 557; diseases caused by, 639; parasitism among, 633; tabular comparison of, 549
Nematomorpha, 531, 544
Nemertea, 479, 528
Neocortex, 213
Neo-Lamarckians, 817
Neopallium, 213
Neoteny, 354
Neotropical region, 716
Nephridia, 563
Neptune, atmosphere of, 738
Nereis, 536
Neritic zone, 709
Nerve cells, *66;* size of, 44
Nerve conduction, rates and strength of, 192
Nerve cord, of vertebrates, 211
Nerve net, 209; behavior of, 238
Nerves, 67, 70, 191; connections be-

tween, 192; parasympathetic, 219; patterns and responses of, 194; sympathetic, 219
Nervous system, autonomic, 218, *218;* basic features of, in vertebrates, 211; history of, 208; interaction of, with endocrines, 183; origin of, 209; reflexes, *243;* regulation of internal environment by, 217; relationship of, to behavior, 238; types of, 210, 212; visceral, 218
Nervous tissues, 66; origin of, from ectoderm, 344
Neural folds, 345
Neural plate, 345
Neurons, 191; human, *41*
Neuropteris, 763, 764
Neurospora, genetics of, 325; mutations in, *326*
New Mexico, life zones in, 697
Newton, Sir Isaac, 24, 804
Niacin, 128
Niches, 611, 627; and intraspecific competition, 640; regulation of, by competition, 629
Nicotinic acid, 128
Nightshades, 520
Nitella, 499
Nitrates, 74, 487, 616; in synthesis of amino acids, 110
Nitrifying bacteria, 617
Nitrites, 74, 487
Nitrogen, 72; as product of decay, 487; entrance of, into organic synthesis, 105; excretion of, in various animals, 156; fixation of, 487; in earth's original atmosphere, 738; source of, 74
Nitrogen cycle, 615, *616*
Nitrogen-fixing bacteria, 487, 616
Noctiluca, 493
Noctiluca scintillans, 495
Nocturnal animals, 657
Nodes, lymph, 153
Nomenclature, in systematics, 475
Nongreen plants, as agents of decay, 487; digestion in, 124
Nonrandom fecundity, 406
Nonrandom mating, 405
Nonrandom reproduction, 403
Nonvascular plants, 137, 497
Nordics, 673
Normal curve of probability, 418
North America, as part of World Continent, 723; connection of, to Eurasia, 724; faunal interchange of, with South America, 725; faunal regions of, 716
Norway, human communities in, 669
Nose, 195, 203
Nostoc, 496
Nostrils, 205; epidermis of, origin from ectoderm, 344
Notharctus, 791
Nothofagus, 650; disjunctive distribution of, 727
Notochord, 537, 559, 582
Notoryctes, 471
Ntemigonus crysolleucas, 642
Nucleic acid, 79, 315; duplication of, *320;* structure of, *318*
Nucleolus, 47, 267
Nucleoplasm, 45
Nucleoproteins, 79, 315
Nucleus, 39, 47, 267; control by, in *Acetabularia,* 265; control by, in sea urchins, *266;* control of development by, 264; in mitosis,